CW00703990

Acute p.

Boris Alexeev

Acute problems of theoretical physics

Dark Matter, Dark Energy, Physical Vacuum, High Temperature Super-conductivity, Ball Lightning

LAP LAMBERT Academic Publishing

Imprint

Any brand names and product names mentioned in this book are subject to trademark, brand or patent protection and are trademarks or registered trademarks of their respective holders. The use of brand names, product names, common names, trade names, product descriptions etc. even without a particular marking in this work is in no way to be construed to mean that such names may be regarded as unrestricted in respect of trademark and brand protection legislation and could thus be used by anyone.

Cover image: Provided by the author

Publisher:
LAP LAMBERT Academic Publishing
is a trademark of
International Book Market Service Ltd., member of OmniScriptum Publishing Group
17 Meldrum Street, Beau Bassin 71504, Mauritius
Printed at: see last page
ISBN: 978-620-2-51530-6

Copyright © Boris Alexeev
Copyright © 2020 International Book Market Service Ltd., member of OmniScriptum Publishing Group

ACUTE PROBLEMS OF THEORETICAL PHYSICS

Dedicated to Professor Alexander A. Kobzarev

PREFACE

About 130 years Boltzmann equation belongs to the fundamental equations of physics. The destiny of this equation is as dramatic as destiny of its great creator. Even in Boltzmann's days there was a complete awareness that his equation acquires a fundamental importance for physics and that its range of validity stretches from transport processes and hydrodynamics all the way to cosmology – thus fully justifying the keen attention it attracted and debates it provoked. Both sides of the dispute have exhausted their arguments. Thus, the development of Boltzmann kinetic theory has turned out to be typical for any revolutionary physical theory – from rejection to recognition and further to a kind of "canonization".

About forty years ago it was shown by the author of this book, that taking into account the variation of the distribution function over times of the order of the collision time leads to additional terms in Boltzmann equation, which are proportional to mean time *between* collisions of particles and therefore to Knudsen number and viscosity in hydrodynamic limit of the theory. Moreover it turns out that these terms – which influence grows with increase of Knudsen number – cannot be omitted in the case of small Knudsen numbers because these terms contain small parameters in front of senior derivatives. Then these terms should be conserved in the theory in all diapason of evolution of Knudsen numbers. I am working in kinetic theory more than 40 years and this conclusion was dramatic first and foremost for me.

Therefore the case in point is of unprecedented situation in physics, when the fundamental physical equation is revised. During my stay in Marseille as Invited Professor A.J.A. Favre remind me Henri Poincaré' phrase after death of great Austrian physicist - "Boltzmann was wrong, but his mistake is equal to zero". It's a pity but the situation in kinetic theory is more serious. Obviously changing of fundamental equation leads - to the some extent - to possible changes of known results in modern transport theory in physics. This book reflects the scales of these alterations. One is safe to say – as main result of the generalized Boltzmann kinetic theory – this theory has showed it to be a highly effective tool for solving many physical problems in areas where the classical theory runs into difficulties.

Author is deeply indebted to Academicians A P Alexandrov, A A Dorodnitsin, V L Ginzburg, A A Samarskii, L I Sedov for their interest in this work and in the subject in general.

"Alles Vergängliche
ist nur ein Gleichniss!"
Boltzmann's epigraph
for his "Vorlesungen über Gastheorie"
(all the past is only a legend);
Non-local physics is the soliton kingdom

CHAPTER 1. MAIN PRINCIPLES OF NONLOCAL PHYSICS

1.1. Some historical remarks and the problem formulation.

In 1872 L Boltzmann, then a mere 28 years old, published his famous kinetic equation for the one-particle distribution function $f(\mathbf{r},\mathbf{v},t)$ [1]. He expressed the equation in the form

$$\frac{Df}{Dt} = J^{st}(f) \tag{1.1.1}$$

where J^{st} is the collision ("stoß") integral, and

$$\frac{D}{Dt} = \frac{\partial}{\partial t} + \mathbf{v}\cdot\frac{\partial}{\partial \mathbf{r}} + \mathbf{F}\cdot\frac{\partial}{\partial \mathbf{v}} \tag{1.1.2}$$

is the substantial (particle) derivative, $\mathbf{v}$ and $\mathbf{r}$ being the velocity and radius-vector of the particle, respectively.

It was postulated that equation (1.1.1) governs the transport processes in a one-component gas which is sufficiently rarefied that only binary collisions between particles are of importance. While we are not concerned here with the explicit form of the collision integral (which determines the change of the distribution function f in binary collisions), note that it should satisfy conservation laws. For the simplest case of elastic collisions in a one-component gas we have

$$\int J^{st}\psi_i d\mathbf{v} = 0\,, (i = 1,2,3)\,, d\mathbf{v} = dv_x dv_y dv_z\,, \tag{1.1.3}$$

where ψ_i are the collision invariants ($\psi_1 = m$, $\psi_2 = m\mathbf{v}$, $\psi_3 = mv^2/2$, m is the mass of the particle) related to the laws of conservation of mass, momentum, and energy.

Integrals of the distribution function (i.e. its moments) determine the macroscopic hydrodynamic characteristics of the system, in particular the number density of particles

$$n = \int f d\mathbf{v} \tag{1.1.4}$$

and the temperature T:

$$\frac{3}{2}k_B T n = \frac{1}{2} m \int f(\mathbf{v} - \mathbf{v}_0)^2 d\mathbf{v}. \quad (1.1.5)$$

Here k_B is the Boltzmann constant, and $\mathbf{v}_0$ the hydrodynamic flow velocity. It follows then that multiplying the Boltzmann integro-differential equation term by term by collisional invariants ψ_i, integrating over all particle velocities, and using the conservation laws (1.1.3) we arrive at the differential equations of fluid dynamics, whose general form is known as the hydrodynamic Enskog equations.

The Boltzmann equation (BE) is not of course as simple as its symbolic form above might suggest, and it is in only a few special cases that it is amenable to a solution. One example is that of a Maxwellian distribution in a locally, thermodynamically equilibrium gas in the event when no external forces are present. In this case the equality

$$J^{st} = 0 \quad (1.1.6)$$

is met, giving the Maxwellian distribution function

$$f^{(0)} = n\left(\frac{m}{2\pi k_B T}\right)^{\frac{3}{2}} \cdot \exp\left(-\frac{mV^2}{2k_B T}\right), \quad (1.1.7)$$

where $\mathbf{V} = \mathbf{v} - \mathbf{v}_0$ is the thermal velocity. Since 1866, Boltzmann has published articles in the Sitzungs Berichte Keiserliche Akademie von Wissenschaften (reports of the Royal Vienna Academy of Sciences). In 1872 an article appeared: "Weitere Studien über das Wärmegleichgewicht unter Gasmolekulen", 1872, 66(2), S. 275. It is believed that in 1872 the Boltzmann physical kinetics began. In 1873, at the world exhibition in Vienna, a memorable conversation took place with Prof. Vroblevsky, who recommended Boltzmann to write an accessible course of lectures on kinetic theory. Boltzmann replied that he was unlikely to be able to do it – he has very bad eyes. An excellent answer followed: "Ein Grund mehr sich zu beeilen" (One more reason to hurry). The first edition of this book appeared only in 1896 (Preface dated September 1895). Second edition (exact reprint with no changes came in 1910 after the death of Boltzmann). The book appeared with an epigraph: "Alles Vergängliche ist nur ein Gleichniss".

It was much later, years after Boltzmann's death in 1906, that an analytic method for solving the Boltzmann equation was developed for the purpose of calculating transport coefficients. This method, developed in 1916 - 1917 by Chapman and Enskog [2-5], led to explicit expressions for the coefficients of viscosity, thermal conductivity, diffusion, and later thermal diffusion in a system with a small parameter (which for Chapman and Enskog's particular problem of a non-reacting gas was the Knudsen number, the ratio of the particle's mean free path to a characteristic hydrodynamic dimension).

However, even in Boltzmann's days there was a complete awareness that his equation acquires a fundamental importance for physics and that its range of validity stretches from transport processes and hydrodynamics all the way to cosmology — thus fully justifying the keen attention it attracted and debates it provoked. Of the many results L Boltzmann derived from his kinetic equation, one of the most impressive is the molecular-kinetic interpretation of the second principle of thermodynamics and in particular of the statistical meaning of the concept of entropy. It turned out that it is possible to define the function

$$H = \int f \ln f d\mathbf{v}, \tag{1.1.8}$$

(H is the first letter in the English word *heat* and German word *Heizung*) which behaves monotonically in a closed system. If the relation between S, the entropy per unit volume of an ideal gas, and the H-function is written in the form

$$S = -k_B H + const\,, \tag{1.1.9}$$

then one can prove the inequality

$$\partial S / \partial t \geq 0 \tag{1.1.10}$$

The laconic formula

$$S = k \log W\,, \tag{1.11.11}$$

connecting the entropy S and the thermodynamic probability W, is inscribed on Boltzmann's tombstone.

Boltzmann's grave in the cemetery of Vienna

Ever since their creation, Boltzmann's physical kinetics and the Boltzmann equation have received severe criticism, much of which remains of interest even today. Let us elaborate on this.

To begin with, Boltzmann's contemporaries were very much in the dark regarding the relation between the Boltzmann equation and classical mechanics — in particular, with the Newton equation. The Boltzmann equation was obtained in a phenomenological manner based on convincing physical arguments and reflects the fact that the distribution function does not change along the particle's trajectory between collisions but rather changes as a result of an "instantaneous" interaction between colliding particles.

J Loschmidt noted in 1876 that the Boltzmann equation underlying the H-theorem includes only the first time derivative whereas the Newton equation contains the second ('square of time') and hence the equations of motion are reversible in time. This means that if a system of hard-sphere particles starts a "backward" motion due to the particles reversing their direction of motion at some instant of time, it passes through all its preceding states up to the initial one, and this will increase the H-function whose variation is originally governed by reversible equations of motion. The essential point to be made here is that the observer cannot prefer one of the situations under study, the "forward" motion of the system in time, in favor of the second situation, its 'backward' motion. In other words, the problem of the reversibility of time arises here.

Although somewhat differently formulated, essentially the same objection was made in 1896 by Planck's student E Zermelo, who noted that the H-theorem is inconsistent with Poincare's "recurrence" theorem proved in 1890 and stated that any physical system, even with irreversible thermodynamic processes operating in it, has a nonzero probability of returning to its original state. Boltzmann, himself fully aware of this possibility, wrote in the second part of his Lectures on the Theory of Gases (see Ref. [6], p. 251): "As a result of the motion of gas molecules, the *H*-function always decreases. The unidirectional nature of this process does not follow from the equations of motion, which the molecules obey. Indeed, these equations do not change if time changes sign."

There is a well-known example from probability theory, which Boltzmann employed as an argument in his discussions — sometimes very heated ones — with Zermelo, Planck and Ostwald. If a six-sided die is thrown 6000 times, one expects each side to turn up about 1000 times. The probability of, say, a six turning up 6000 times in a succession has a vanishing small value of $(1/6)^{6000}$. This example does not clear up the matter, however. Nor do the two papers which Boltzmann's student P Ehrenfest wrote in co-authorship with T Afanas'eva-Ehrenfest after the death of the great Austrian physicist.

Their first model, reported by Afanas'eva-Ehrenfest at the February 12, 1908 meeting of the Russian Physic-Chemical Society, involved the application of the H-theorem to the "plane" motion of a gas [7]. Suppose P-molecules, nontransparent to one another, start moving normally to axis y and travel with the same velocity in the direction of axis x. Suppose further that in doing so they undergo elastic collisions with Q-particles, squares with sides at an angle of 45° to axis y, which are nontransparent to the molecules and are all at rest.

It is readily shown that shortly after, all the molecules will divide themselves into four groups, and it is a simple matter to write down the change in the number of molecules P in each group in a certain time Δt and then to define a "planar-gas" H-function

$$H = \sum_{i=1}^{4} f_i \ln f_i , \qquad (1.1.12)$$

where f_i is the number of molecules of the i-th kind, i.e. of those moving in one of the four possible directions. If all the velocities reverse their direction, the H-function starts to increase and reverts to the value it had when the P-molecules started their motion from the y axis. While this simple model confirms the Poincare-Zermelo theorem, it does not at all guarantee that the H-function will decrease when the far more complicated Boltzmann model is used.

P and T Ehrenfest's second model [8], known as the lottery's model, features two boxes, A and B, and N numbered balls to which there correspond "lottery tickets" placed in a certain box and which are all in box A initially. The balls are then taken one by one from A and transferred to B according to the number of a lottery ticket, drawn randomly. Importantly, the ticket is not eliminated after that but rather is returned to the box. In the event that the newly drawn ticket corresponds to a ball contained in B, the ball is returned to A. As a result, there will be approximately $N/2$ balls in either box.

Now suppose one of the boxes contains n balls — and the other accordingly $N - n$ balls — at a certain step s in the drawing process. We can then define Δ, a function, which determines the difference in the number of balls between the two boxes: $\Delta = n - (N - n) = 2n - N$. In 'statistical' equilibrium, $\Delta = 0$ and $n = N/2$, The dependence $\Delta(s)$ will imitate the behavior of the H-function in a Boltzmann gas.

This example is also not convincing enough because this "lottery" game will necessarily lead to a fluctuation in the Δ function, whereas Boltzmann kinetic theory excludes completely fluctuations in the H-function. By the end of his life Boltzmann went over to fluctuation theory, in which the decrease of the H-function in time is only treated as the process the system is most likely to follow. This interpretation, however, is not substantiated by his kinetic theory since the origin of the primary fluctuation remains unclear (the galactic scale of such fluctuation included).

One of the first physicists to see that Boltzmann equation must be modified in order to remove the existing contradictions was J Maxwell. Maxwell thought highly of the results of Boltzmann, who in his turn did much to promote Maxwell electrodynamics and its experimental verification.

We may summarize Maxwell's ideas [9] as follows. The equations of fluid dynamics are a consequence of the Boltzmann equation. From the energy equation, limiting ourselves to one dimension for the sake of simplicity and neglecting some energy transfer mechanisms (in particular, convective heat transfer), we obtain the well-known heat conduction equation

$$\frac{\partial T}{\partial t} = a^2 \frac{\partial^2 T}{\partial x^2} \tag{1.1.13}$$

The fundamental solution of equation (1.1.13) up to the dimensional constant is

$$T(x,t) = \frac{1}{2\sqrt{(\pi a^2 t)}} \exp\left(-\frac{x^2}{4a^2 t}\right) \tag{1.1.14}$$

and represents the temperature at point x at instant t provided at time $t=0$ an amount of heat cp, with p the density and a the thermal diffusivity of the medium, is evolved at the origin of coordinates. Defining an argument of a function T as $\theta = a^2 t$ with the dimension of a coordinate squared we obtain

$$T = \frac{1}{2\sqrt{\pi\theta}} \exp\left(-\frac{x^2}{4\theta}\right) \tag{1.1.15}$$

The temperature distribution given by this equation is unsatisfactory physically. For small values of θ, the temperature at the heat evolution point $x=0$ is indefinitely large. On the other hand, at any arbitrarily distant point x the temperature produced by an instantaneous heat source will be different from zero for arbitrarily small times. While this difference may be small, it is a point of principal importance that it has a finite value.

As Landau and Lifshitz noted in their classical *Course of Theoretical Physics* ([10], p. 283), "The heat conduction process described by the equations obtained here has the property that any thermal perturbation becomes instantaneously felt over all space". This implies an infinitely fast propagation of heat, which is absurd from the point of view of molecular-kinetic theory. In the courses of mathematical physics this result is usually attributed to the fact that the heat conduction equation is derived phenomenological, neglecting the molecular-kinetic mechanism of heat propagation. However, as has been already noted, the parabolic equation (1.1.13) follows from the Boltzmann equation.

Major difficulties arose when the question of existence and uniqueness of solutions of the Navier - Stokes equations was addressed. O A Ladyzhenskaya has shown for three-dimensional flows that under smooth initial conditions a unique solution is only possible over a finite time interval. Ladyzhenskaya even introduced a "correction" into the Navier - Stokes equations in order that its unique solvability could be proved (see discussion in [11]). It turned out that in this case the viscosity coefficient should be dependent on transverse flow-velocity gradients - with the result that the very idea of introducing kinetic coefficients should be overhauled.

In the early nineties, I worked for a long time in France in Marseille in the Laboratory of none-equilibrium media at Aix-en-Provence University. The laboratory actively collaborated with the Institute of turbulence (l'Institut de mécanique statistique de la turbulence (IMST)). I made a report on the strict theory of turbulence at the seminar of this Institute at the invitation of the Director of the Institute academician Favre (Alexandre Favre). The report was highly appreciated by Favre, who said after the report, "I have been waiting for this report all my life." After one of our subsequent meetings, he recalled the words of A. Poincaré: "Boltzmann was wrong, but his mistake was zero." I said Boltzmann was wrong, and his mistake was not zero.

Academician Mikhail Alexandrovich Leontovich (b. 1903, known for saying that he reads nothing but his works): "I know why Boltzmann hanged himself. He realized that his equation was wrong." The phrase uttered in the Physics-Uspekhy editorial office.

1.2. Shortcomings of the Boltzmann physical kinetics

A breakthrough period in the history of kinetic theory occurred in the late 1930s and early 1940s, when it was shown through efforts of many scientists — of which Bogolyubov certainly tops the list — how, based on the Liouville equation for the multi-particle distribution function f_N of a system of N interacting particles, one can obtain a one-particle representation by introducing a small parameter $\varepsilon = nv_{in}$, where n is the number of particles per unit volume and v_{in} is the interaction volume [12 - 17]. This hierarchy of equations is usually referred to as the Bogolyubov or BBGKY (Bogolyubov - Born - Green - Kirkwood - Yvon) chain.

We do not present the technical details but refer the reader to the classical works cited above or, for example, to Ref. [17]. Some fundamental points of the problem are worth mentioning here, however.

(1) Integrating the Liouville equation

$$\frac{\partial f_N}{\partial t}+\sum_{i=1}^{N}\mathbf{v}_i\cdot\frac{\partial f_N}{\partial \mathbf{r}_i}+\sum_{i=1}^{N}\mathbf{F}_i\cdot\frac{\partial f_N}{\partial \mathbf{v}_i}=0 \quad (1.2.1)$$

subsequently over phase volumes $d\Omega_{s+1},...,d\Omega_N$ $\left(d\Omega_j \equiv d\mathbf{r}_j d\mathbf{v}_j\right)$, one obtains a kinetic equation for the s-particle distribution function, with the distribution function f_{s+1} in the integral part of the corresponding equation.

In other words, the set of integro-differential equations turns out to be a linked one, so that in the lowest-order approximation the distribution function f_1 depends on f_2. This means formally that, strictly speaking, the solution procedure for such a set should be as follows. First find the distribution function f_N and then solve the set of BBGKY equations subsequently for decreasingly lower-order distributions. But if we know the function f_N, there is no need at all to solve the equations for f_s and it actually suffices to employ the definition of the function

$$f_s=\int f_N\left(t,\Omega_1,...,\Omega_N\right)d\Omega_{s+1}...d\Omega_N \quad (1.2.2)$$

We thus conclude that the rigorous solution to the set of BBGKY equations is again equivalent to solving Liouville equations. On the other hand, the seemingly illogical solution procedure involving a search for the distribution function f_1 is of great significance in kinetic theory and in non-equilibrium statistical mechanics. This approach involves breaking the BBGKY chain by introducing certain additional assumptions (which have a clear physical meaning, though). These assumptions are discussed in detail below.

(2) For a non-reacting gas, the Boltzmann equation is valid for two time scales of distribution functions: one of the order of the mean free time of the particles, and the other the hydrodynamic flow time. The Boltzmann equation is invalid for time lengths of the order of the collision times. Notice that a change from the time scale to the length scale can of course be made if desired.

(3) After the BBGKY chain is broken and f_2 represented as a product of one-particle distribution functions (which is quite reasonable for a rarefied gas), the Boltzmann equation cannot be written in a classical form with only one

small parameter ε and it reduces instead to the Vlasov equation in a self-consistent field.

(4) Because the Boltzmann equation does not work at distances of the order of the particle interaction radius (or at the r_{in} scale), Boltzmann particles are point like and structureless, and it is one of the inconsistencies of the Boltzmann theory that the resulting collision cross sections of the particles enter the theory by the collision integral.

(5) Usually the one-particle distribution function is normalized to the number of particles per unit volume. For Boltzmann particles the distribution function is “automatically” normalized to an integer because a point-like particle may only be either inside or outside a trial contour in a gas — unlike finite-diameter particles which of course may overlap the boundary of the contour at some instant of time. Another noteworthy point is that the mean free path in Boltzmann kinetic theory is only meaningful for particles modeled by hard elastic spheres. Other models face difficulties related, though, to the level of one-particle description employed. The requirement for the transition to a one-particle model is that molecular chaos should exist prior to a particle collision.

The advent of the BBGKY chain led to the recognition that whatever generalization of Boltzmann kinetic theory is to be made, the logic to be followed should involve all the elements of the chain, i.e. the Liouville equation, the kinetic equations for *s*-particle distribution functions f_s, and the hydrodynamic equations. This logical construction was not generally adhered to.

For understanding these shortcomings of the Boltzmann physical kinetics we don't even need to write equations (at the first stage). I begin with the short reminding of basic principles of the generalized Boltzmann physical kinetics, non-local statistical physics delivered in monographs [18-22], my lectures on YouTube [23] and some main papers [24-31].

Boltzmann physical kinetics is based on a reduced description of dissipative processes and the principle of local thermodynamic equilibrium (LTE). It is assumed that the distribution function (DF) does not change within a physically infinitesimal volume (say, **PhSV**) containing, nevertheless, enough particles to introduce macroscopic parameters (such as temperature and concentration), unchanged within the **PhSV**.

But **PhSV** is an *open* thermodynamic system that reacts to the environment only after its interaction with "foreign" particles that have penetrated into the considered **PhSV** from neighboring $\mathbf{PhSV}_n$. These particles will be able to transmit information only after the collision with the **PhSV** particles, in other words, after the residence time in the **PhSV** of the order of the average time between collisions.

Nonlocal effects can be demonstrated by animating the motion of particles — solid spheres in a neutral gas. Let in a certain volume contains a single-component rarefied gas, in which basically there are pair collisions. With the help of a spatial grid, we divide a non-equilibrium physical system into open subsystems — a set of physically infinitely small volumes. We will highlight one of these small volumes. To observe the evolution of particles in the selected volume and adjacent small volumes, color the particles and follow their movement. In the selected volume, the particles are colored blue; there are a lot of them to talk about the possibility of local statistical description at the level of single-particle distribution function DF f. In adjacent small volumes particles are painted in different colors corresponding to different distribution functions f. Particles of neighboring volumes are carriers of information about other DFs and, penetrating into the "blue" volume, adjust to the "blue" DF (if we are talking about relaxation on translational degrees of freedom) after several collisions. Let, for simplicity, the relaxation process requires only one collision

In other words, the particle that penetrated the "blue" volume changes its color to blue after the first collision with the "blue" particle. It is possible in animation to observe how in the allocated physically infinitely small volume ("blue" volume) appears a border of the "multi-colored" area, the characteristic size of which is the order of the average free path. It is clear that this boundary effect will always exist in the chosen method of diagnosis; regardless of the method of partitioning the system set of physically infinitely small open subsystems (see animations in [23]).

This fact reflects the existence of nonlocal effects proportional to the mean free path, the number of Knudsen or the mean time between collisions of particles. The Boltzmann equation (BE) fully ignores non-local effects and contains only the local collision integral J^B. But these nonlocal effects are irrelevant only in equilibrium systems, where the kinetic approach goes into methods of statistical mechanics. As a result the difficulties of classical Boltzmann physical kinetics arise.

Result:

1) kinetic theory should be non-local,

2) the effect is of the order of Knudsen number,

3) the effect is due to the reduced description and is not related to the specific division of the physical system by the **PhSV** grid,

4) accurate derivation of the kinetic equation with respect to the one-particle DF should lead to corrections of the order of the Knudsen number before uncoupling the Bogolyubov chain,

5) this means that in the Boltzmann equation the terms of the order of the Knudsen number are lost, significant for both large and small Knudsen numbers,

6) the Boltzmann equation does not even belong to the class of minimal models, being only a "plausible" equation,

7) Boltzmann equation in this sense — the wrong equation.

Boltzmann, who wrote his famous kinetic equation, did not understand the root of the problems; the very problems that led Boltzmann to suicide in 1906.

It is clear that this is a revolution in the theory of dissipative processes, in particular – in hydrodynamics. In the hydrodynamic Navier–Stokes equation, which is a direct consequence of the Boltzmann equation, one-order (in the Knudsen number) terms are lost, which in the classical Navier–Stokes equation contain viscosity. As a result we have the problems with turbulence, the problems of existence and uniqueness of the solution of the Navier–Stokes equations. These Boltzmann error problems led to the (incorrect) assertion that 96% of matter and energy are of unknown origin.

A weak point of the classical Boltzmann kinetic theory also is the way it treats the dynamic properties of interacting particles. On the one hand, as the so-called "physical" derivation of the BE suggests, Boltzmann particles are treated as material points; on the other hand, the collision integral in the BE brings into existence the cross sections for collisions between particles.

A rigorous approach to the derivation of the kinetic equation for the distribution function (DF) f_1 (KE_{f_1}) is based on the hierarchy of the Bogolyubov - Born - Green - Kirkwood - Yvon (BBGKY) equations.

A KE_{f_1} obtained by the multi-scale method turns into the BE if one ignores the change of DF over a time of the order of the collision time (or, equivalently, over a length of the order of the particle interaction radius). It is important to note [17] that accounting for the third of the scales mentioned above has the consequence that, prior to introducing any approximations destined to break the Bogolyubov chain, additional terms, generally of the same order of magnitude, appear in the BE. If the method of correlation functions is used to derive KE_{f_1} from the BBGKY equations, then a passage to the BE implies the neglect of non-local and time delay effects. Given the above difficulties of the Boltzmann kinetic theory (BKT), the following clearly interrelated questions arise.

First, what is a physically infinitesimal volume and how does its introduction (and, as a consequence, the unavoidable smoothing out of the DF) affect the kinetic equation?

And second, how does a systematic account for the proper diameter of the particle in the derivation of the KE_{f_1} affect the Boltzmann equation? In the theory we develop here, we will refer to the corresponding KE_{f_1} as the generalized nonlocal kinetic equation, or GNKE.

Accordingly, our purpose in this introduction is first to explain the essence of the physical generalization of the BE and then to take a look at the specifics of the derivation of the GNE, when (as is the case in plasma physics) the self-consistent field of forces must of necessity be introduced. As the Boltzmann equation is the centerpiece of the theory of transport processes (TTP), the introduction of an alternative KE_{f_1} leads in fact to an overhaul of the entire theory, including its macroscopic (for example, hydrodynamic) aspects. Conversely, a change in the macroscopic description will inevitably affect the kinetic level of description. Because of the complexity of the problem, this interrelation is not always easy to trace when solving a particular TTP problem. The important point to emphasize is that at issue here is not how to modify the classical equations of physical kinetics and hydrodynamics to include additional transport mechanisms (in reacting media, for example); rather we face a situation in which, those involved believe, we must go beyond the classical picture if we wish the revised theory to describe experiment adequately. The alternative TTPs can be grouped conventionally into the following categories:

(1) theories that modify the mac copic (hydrodynamic) description and neglect the possible changes of the kinetic description;

(2) hose changing the kinetic description at the KE_{f_1} level without bothering much whether these changes are consistent with the structure of the entire BBGKY chain, and

(3) kin c and hydrodynamic alternative theories consistent with the BBGKY hierarchy.

It should be recognized that after the intense debates of the early 20th century, the search for an alternative kinetic equation for a one-particle distribution function has gradually leveled off or, perhaps more precisely, has become of marginal physical importance. Both sides of the dispute have exhausted their arguments. On the other hand, the Boltzmann equation has proven to be successful in solving a variety of problems, particularly in the calculation of kinetic coefficients. Thus, the development of Boltzmann kinetic theory has turned out to be typical for any revolutionary physical theory — from rejection to recognition and further to a kind of "canonization"

As it is shown [17-31] the theory of transport processes (including quantum mechanics) can be considered in the frame of unified theory based on the non-local physical description. In particular the generalized hydrodynamic equations represent an effective tool for solving problems in the very vast area of physical problems including turbulence. For simplicity in introduction, we will consider fundamental methodic aspects from the qualitative standpoint of view avoiding excessively cumbersome formulas. A rigorous description is found, for example, in the monographs [17-22].

Transport processes in open dissipative systems are considered in physical kinetics. Therefore, the kinetic description is inevitably related to the system diagnostics. Such an element of diagnostics in the case of theoretical description in physical kinetics is the concept of the physically infinitely small volume$(\mathbf{PhSV})$. The correlation between theoretical description and system diagnostics is well-known in physics. Suffice it to recall the part played by test charge in electrostatics or by test circuit in the physics of magnetic phenomena. The traditional definition of **PhSV** contains the statement to the effect that the **PhSV** contains a sufficient number of particles for introducing a statistical description; however, at the same time, the **PhSV** is much smaller than the volume V of the physical system under consideration; in a first approximation, this leads to local approach in investigating the transport processes. It is assumed in classical hydrodynamics that local thermodynamic equilibrium is first established within the **PhSV**, and only after that the transition occurs to global thermodynamic equilibrium if it is at all possible for the system under study. Let us consider the hydrodynamic description in more detail from this point of view. Assume that we have two neighboring physically infinitely small volumes $\mathbf{PhSV}_1$ and $\mathbf{PhSV}_2$ in a non-equilibrium system. The one-particle distribution function (DF) $f_{sm,1}(\mathbf{r}_1,\mathbf{v},t)$ corresponds to the volume $\mathbf{PhSV}_1$, and the function $f_{sm,2}(\mathbf{r}_2,\mathbf{v},t)$ — to the volume $\mathbf{PhSV}_2$. It is assumed in a first approximation that $f_{sm,1}(\mathbf{r}_1,\mathbf{v},t)$ does not vary within $\mathbf{PhSV}_1$, same as $f_{sm,2}(\mathbf{r}_2,\mathbf{v},t)$ does not vary within the neighboring volume $\mathbf{PhSV}_2$. It is this assumption of locality that is implicitly contained in the Boltzmann equation (BE) [17 - 22]. However, the assumption is too crude. Indeed, a particle on the boundary between two volumes, which experienced the last collision in $\mathbf{PhSV}_1$ and moves toward $\mathbf{PhSV}_2$, introduces information about the $f_{sm,1}(\mathbf{r}_1, \mathbf{v}, t)$ into the neighboring volume $\mathbf{PhSV}_2$. Similarly, a particle on the boundary between two volumes, which experienced the last collision in $\mathbf{PhSV}_2$ and moves toward $\mathbf{PhSV}_1$, introduces information about the DF $f_{sm,2}(\mathbf{r}_2, \mathbf{v}, t)$ into the neighboring volume $\mathbf{PhSV}_1$. The relaxation over translational degrees of freedom of particles of like masses occurs during several collisions. As a result, "Knudsen layers" are formed on the boundary between neighboring physically infinitely small volumes, the characteristic dimension of which is of the order of path length. Therefore, a correction must be introduced into the DF in the **PhSV**, which is proportional to the mean time between collisions and to the substantive derivative of the DF.

Let a particle of finite radius be characterized as before by the position $\mathbf{r}$ at the instant of time t of its center of mass moving at velocity $\mathbf{v}$. Then, the situation is possible where, at some instant of time t, the particle is located on the interface between two volumes. In so doing, the lead effect is possible (say, for $\mathbf{PhSV}_2$), when the center of mass of particle moving to the neighboring volume $\mathbf{PhSV}_2$ is still in $\mathbf{PhSV}_1$. However, the delay effect takes place as well, when the center of mass of particle moving to the neighboring volume (say, $\mathbf{PhSV}_2$) is already located in $\mathbf{PhSV}_2$ but a part of the particle still belongs to $\mathbf{PhSV}_1$.

Moreover, even the point-like particles (starting after the last collision near the boundary between two mentioned volumes) can change the distribution functions in the neighboring volume. The adjusting of the particles dynamic characteristics for translational degrees of freedom takes several collisions. As result, we have in the definite sense "the Knudsen layer" between these volumes. This fact unavoidably leads to fluctuations in mass and hence in other hydrodynamic quantities. Existence of such "Knudsen layers" is not connected with the choice of space nets and fully defined by the reduced description for ensemble of particles of finite diameters in the conceptual frame of open physically small volumes, therefore – with the chosen method of measurement.

This entire complex of effects defines non-local effects in space and time. The corresponding situation is typical for the theoretical physics – we could remind about the role of probe charge in electrostatics or probe circuit in the physics of magnetic effects.

The physically infinitely small volume (**PhSV**) is an *open* thermodynamic system *for any division of macroscopic system by a set of PhSVs.* However, the BE

$$Df/Dt = J^B, \tag{1.2.3}$$

where J^B is the Boltzmann collision integral and D/Dt is a substantive derivative, fully ignores non-local effects and contains only the local collision integral J^B. The foregoing nonlocal effects are insignificant only in equilibrium systems, where the kinetic approach changes to methods of statistical mechanics.

This is what the difficulties of classical Boltzmann physical kinetics arise from.

Suppose that DF f corresponds to $\mathbf{PhSV}_1$ and DF $f-\Delta f$ is connected with $\mathbf{PhSV}_2$ for Boltzmann particles. In the boundary area in the first approximation, fluctuations will be proportional to the mean free path (or, equivalently, to the mean time between the collisions). Then for **PhSV** the correction for DF should be introduced as

$$f^a = f - \tau Df/Dt \tag{1.2.4}$$

in the left hand side of classical BE describing the translation of DF in phase space. As the result

$$Df^a/Dt = J^B, \tag{1.2.5}$$

where J^B is the Boltzmann local collision integral. Important to notice that it is only qualitative explanation of GBE derivation obtained earlier (see for example [17-22]) by different strict methods from the BBGKY – chain of kinetic equations. The structure of the KE_f is generally as follows

$$\frac{Df}{Dt} = J^B + J^{nl}, \tag{1.2.6}$$

where J^{nl} is the non-local integral term incorporating in particular the time delay effect. The generalized Boltzmann physical kinetics, in essence, involves a local approximation

$$J^{nl} = \frac{D}{Dt}\left(\tau\frac{Df}{Dt}\right) \tag{1.2.7}$$

for the second collision integral, here τ being proportional to the mean time *between* the particle collisions. All of the known methods of deriving kinetic equation relative to one-particle DF lead to approximation (1.2.7), including the method of many scales, the method of correlation functions, and the iteration method. We can draw here an analogy with the Bhatnagar - Gross - Krook (BGK) approximation for J^B,

$$J^B = \frac{f_0 - f}{\tau}, \tag{1.2.8}$$

which popularity as a means to represent the Boltzmann collision integral is due to the huge simplifications it offers. In other words – the local Boltzmann collision integral admits approximation via the BGK algebraic expression, but more complicated non-local integral can be expressed as differential form (1.2.7). The ratio of the second to the first term on the right-hand side of Eq. (1.2.6) is given to an order of magnitude as $J^{nl}/J^B \approx O(Kn^2)$ and at large Knudsen numbers (defining as ratio of mean free path of particles to the character hydrodynamic length) these terms become of the same order of magnitude. It would seem that at small Knudsen numbers answering to hydrodynamic description the contribution from the second term on the right-hand side of Eq. (1.2.6) is negligible.

This is not the case, however. When one goes over to the hydrodynamic approximation (by multiplying the kinetic equation by collision invariants and then integrating over velocities), the Boltzmann integral part vanishes, and the second term on the right-hand side of Eq. (1.2.5) gives a single-order contribution in the generalized Navier - Stokes description. Mathematically, we cannot neglect a term with a small parameter in front of the higher derivative. Physically, the appearing additional terms are due to viscosity and they correspond to the small-scale Kolmogorov turbulence [17-24].

The integral term J^{nl} turns out to be important both at small and large Knudsen numbers in the theory of transport processes.

Thus, $\tau Df/Dt$ is the distribution function fluctuation, and writing Eq. (1.2.5) without taking into account Eq. (1.2.4) makes the BE non-closed. From viewpoint of the fluctuation theory, Boltzmann employed the simplest possible closure procedure $f^a = f$. Then, the additional GBE terms (as compared to the BE) are significant for any *Kn*, and the order of magnitude of the difference between the BE and GBE solutions is impossible to tell beforehand. For GBE the generalized *H*-theorem is proven [17]. The rigorous approach to derivation of kinetic equation relative to one-particle DF f (KE_{f_1}) is based on employing the hierarchy of Bogolyubov equations [17-24]

$$\frac{D}{Dt}\left(f - \tau\frac{Df}{Dt}\right) = J^B. \tag{1.2.9}$$

Clearly, approaches to the modification of the KE_{f_1} must be based on certain principles, and it is appropriate to outline these in brief here. There are general requirements to which the generalized KE_{f_1} must satisfy.

(1) Because the artificial breaking of the BBGKY hierarchy is unavoidable in changing to a one-particle description, the generalized KE_{f_1} should be obtainable with the known methods of the theory of kinetic equations, such as the multi-scale approach, correlation function method, iterative methods, and so forth, or combinations of them. In each of these, some specific features of the particular alternative KE_{f_1} are highlighted.

(2) There must be an explicit link between the KE_{f_1} and the way we introduce the physically infinitesimal volume - and hence with the way the moments in the reference contour with transparent boundaries fluctuate due to the finite size of the particles.

(3) In the non-relativistic case, the KE_{f_1} must satisfy the Galileo transformation.

(4) The KE_{f_1} must ensure a connection with the classical H - theorem and its generalizations.

(5) The KE_{f_1} should not lead to unreasonable complexities in the theory.

The last requirement needs some commentary. The integral collision terms - in particular, the Boltzmann local integral, and especially the non-local integral with time delay - have a very complex structure.

The "caricature" the BGK approximation makes of the Boltzmann collision integral (to use Yu L Klimontovich's expressive word) has turned out to be a very successful approach, and this algebraically approximated Boltzmann collision integral is widely used in the kinetic theory of neutral and ionized gases.

The generalized Boltzmann equation introduces a local differential approximation for the non-local collision integral with time delay. Here, we are faced in fact with the "price – quality" problem familiar from economics. That is, what price - in terms of the increased complexity of the kinetic equation - are we ready to pay for the improved quality of the theory? An answer to this question is possible only through experience with practical problems.

Obviously the generalized hydrodynamic equations (GHE) will explicitly involve fluctuations proportional to τ. In the hydrodynamic approximation, the mean time τ between the collisions is related to the dynamic viscosity μ by

$$\tau p = \Pi \mu , \qquad (1.2.10)$$

where the factor Π is defined by the model of collision of particles: for neutral hard-sphere gas, $\Pi = 0.8$, [32, 33].

For example, the continuity equation changes its form and will contain terms proportional to viscosity. On the other hand, if the reference volume extends over the whole cavity with the hard walls, then the classical conservation laws should be obeyed, and this is exactly what the monograph [18] proves.

Suppose we have a gas of hard spheres kept in a hard-wall cavity as shown in Fig. 1.1. Consider a reference contour drawn at a distance of the order of a particle diameter from the cavity wall. The mathematical expectation of the number of particles moving through the reference surface strictly perpendicular to the hard wall is zero. Therefore, in the first approximation, fluctuations will be proportional to the mean free path (or, equivalently, to the mean time between the collisions). As a result, the hydrodynamic equations will explicitly involve fluctuations proportional to τ. For example, the continuity equation changes its form and will contain terms proportional to viscosity. However, we will here attempt to "guess" the structure of the generalized continuity equation using the arguments outlined above.

Neglecting fluctuations, the continuity equation should have the classical form with

$$\rho^a = \rho - \tau A, \tag{1.2.11}$$

$$(\rho \mathbf{v}_0)^a = \rho \mathbf{v}_0 - \tau \mathbf{B}. \tag{1.2.12}$$

Strictly speaking, the factors A and $\mathbf{B}$ can be obtained from the generalized kinetic equation, in our case, from the GBE. Still, we can guess their form without appeal to the KE_{f_1}.

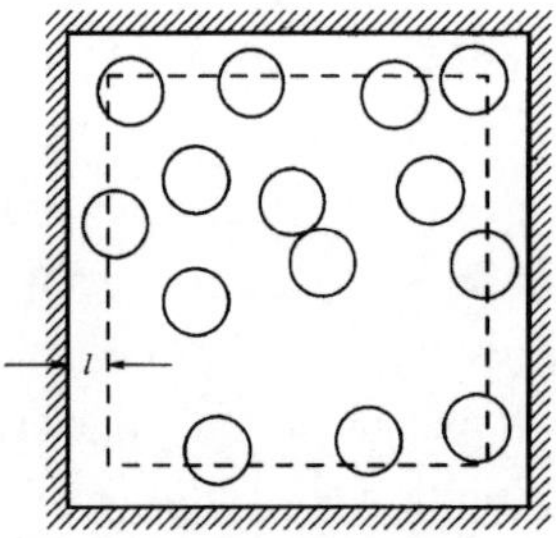

Fig. 1.1. Closed cavity and the reference contour containing particles of a finite diameter.

Indeed, let us write the generalized continuity equation

$$\frac{\partial}{\partial t}(\rho - \tau A) + \frac{\partial}{\partial \mathbf{r}} \cdot (\rho \mathbf{v}_0 - \tau \mathbf{B}) = 0 \qquad (1.2.13)$$

in the dimensionless form using l, the distance from the reference contour to the hard wall (see Fig. 1.1) as a length scale. Then, instead of τ, the (already dimensionless) quantities A and $\mathbf{B}$ will have the Knudsen number $Kn_l = \lambda / l$ as a coefficient. In the limit $l \to 0, \mathrm{Kn}_l \to \infty$ the contour embraces the entire cavity contained within hard walls, and there are no fluctuations on the walls. In other words, the classical equations of continuity and motion must be satisfied at the wall. Using hydrodynamic terminology, we note that the conditions

$$A = 0, \mathbf{B} = 0 \qquad (1.2.14)$$

correspond to a laminar sub-layer in a turbulent flow. Now if a local Maxwellian distribution is assumed, then the generalized equation of continuity in the Euler approximation is written as

$$\frac{\partial}{\partial t}\left\{\rho - \tau\left[\frac{\partial \rho}{\partial t} + \frac{\partial}{\partial \mathbf{r}} \cdot (\rho \mathbf{v}_0)\right]\right\} + \frac{\partial}{\partial \mathbf{r}} \cdot \left\{\rho \mathbf{v}_0 - \tau\left[\frac{\partial}{\partial t}(\rho \mathbf{v}_0) + \frac{\partial}{\partial \mathbf{r}} \cdot \rho \mathbf{v}_0 \mathbf{v}_0 + \vec{I} \cdot \frac{\partial p}{\partial \mathbf{r}} - \rho \mathbf{a}\right]\right\} = 0,$$

(1.2.15)

where $\vec{I}$ is the unit tensor.

Fluctuation effects occur in any open thermodynamic system bounded by a control surface transparent to particles. The generalized nonlocal kinetic equation (GNKE) (1.2.9) leads to generalized hydrodynamic equations (GHE) [17 - 22] as the local approximation of non local effects, for example, to the continuity equation

$$\frac{\partial \rho^a}{\partial t} + \frac{\partial}{\partial \mathbf{r}} \cdot (\rho \mathbf{v}_0)^a = 0, \qquad (1.2.16)$$

where ρ^a, $\mathbf{v}_0{}^a$, $(\rho \mathbf{v}_0)^a$ are calculated in view of non-locality effect in terms of gas density ρ, hydrodynamic velocity of flow $\mathbf{v}_0$, and density of momentum flux $\rho \mathbf{v}_0$; for locally Maxwellian distribution, ρ^a, $(\rho \mathbf{v}_0)^a$ are defined by the relations

$$(\rho - \rho^a)/\tau = \frac{\partial \rho}{\partial t} + \frac{\partial}{\partial \mathbf{r}} \cdot (\rho \mathbf{v}_0), \qquad (1.2.17)$$

$$(\rho \mathbf{v}_0 - (\rho \mathbf{v}_0)^a)/\tau = \frac{\partial}{\partial t}(\rho \mathbf{v}_0) + \frac{\partial}{\partial \mathbf{r}} \cdot \rho \mathbf{v}_0 \mathbf{v}_0 + \vec{I} \cdot \frac{\partial p}{\partial \mathbf{r}} - \rho \mathbf{a}. \qquad (1.2.18)$$

where $\vec{I}$ is a unit tensor, and $\mathbf{a}$ is the acceleration due to the effect of mass forces.

In the general case, the parameter τ is the non-locality parameter; in quantum hydrodynamics, its magnitude is defined by the "time-energy" uncertainty relation. The violation of Bell's inequalities is found for local statistical theories, and the transition to non-local description is inevitable.

G Uhlenbeck, in his review of the fundamental problems of statistical mechanics [34], examines in particular the Kramers equation [35] derived as a consequence of the Fokker - Planck equation

$$\frac{\partial f}{\partial t}+\mathbf{v}\cdot\frac{\partial f}{\partial \mathbf{r}}+\mathbf{a}\cdot\frac{\partial f}{\partial \mathbf{v}}=\beta\left[\frac{\partial}{\partial \mathbf{v}}\cdot(\mathbf{v}f)+\frac{k_B T}{m}\frac{\partial}{\partial \mathbf{v}}\cdot\frac{\partial f}{\partial \mathbf{v}}\right] \qquad (1.2.19)$$

where $f(\mathbf{r},\mathbf{v},t)$ is the distribution function of Brownian particles, $\mathbf{a}$ is the acceleration due to an external field of forces, and $m\beta$ is the coefficient of friction for the motion of a colloid particle in the medium. What intrigues Uhlenbeck is how Kramers goes over from the Fokker - Planck equation (1.2.19) to the Einstein - Smoluchowski equation

$$\frac{\partial \rho}{\partial t}+\frac{\partial}{\partial \mathbf{r}}\cdot\left(\frac{\mathbf{a}}{\beta}\rho-\frac{k_B T}{m\beta}\frac{\partial \rho}{\partial \mathbf{r}}\right)=0, \qquad (1.2.20)$$

(ρ is the density) which has the character of the hydrodynamic continuity equation. In Uhlenbeck's words, “the proof of this change-over is very interesting, it is a typical Kramers-style proof. It is in fact very simple but at the same time some tricks and subtleties it involves make it very hard to discuss”. The velocity distribution of colloid particles is assumed to be Maxwellian. The “trick”, however, is that Kramers integrated along the line

$$\mathbf{r}+\frac{\mathbf{v}}{\beta}=\mathbf{r}_0, \qquad (1.2.21)$$

and the number density of particles turned out to be given by the formula

$$n(\mathbf{r}_0,t)=\int f\left(\mathbf{r}_0-\frac{\mathbf{v}}{\beta},\mathbf{v},t\right)d\mathbf{v}. \qquad (1.2.22)$$

So what exactly did H Kramers do? Let us consider this change from the point of view of the generalized Boltzmann kinetic theory (GBKT) using, wherever possible, qualitative arguments to see things more clearly. Now, having in mind the Kramers method, let us compare the generalized continuity equation (1.2.15) and the Einstein - Smoluchowski equation (1.2.20). Equation (1.2.15) reduces to equation (1.2.20) if

(a) the convective transfer corresponding to the hydrodynamic velocity $\mathbf{v}_0$ is neglected;

(b) the temperature gradient is less important than the gradient of the number density of particles, $n\frac{\partial T}{\partial \bar{r}} << T\frac{\partial n}{\partial \bar{r}}$, and

(c) the temporal part of the density fluctuations is left out of account.

By integrating with respect to velocity v from $-\infty$ to $+\infty$ along the line

$$\mathbf{r}+\frac{\mathbf{v}}{\beta}=\mathbf{r}_0, \qquad (1.2.23)$$

Kramers introduced non-local collisions without accounting for the time delay effect. In our theory, the coefficient of friction $\beta=\tau^{-1}$, which corresponds to the binary collision approximation. If the simultaneous interaction with many particles is important and must be accounted for, additional difficulties associated with the definition of the coefficient of friction β arise, and Einstein - Smoluchowski theory becomes semi-phenomenological.

Notice that the application of the above principles also leads to the modification of the system of Maxwell equations. While the traditional formulation of this system does not involve the continuity equation, its derivation explicitly employs the equation

$$\frac{\partial \rho^a}{\partial t}+\frac{\partial}{\partial \mathbf{r}}\cdot\mathbf{j}^a=0, \qquad (1.2.24)$$

where ρ^a is the charge per unit volume, and $\mathbf{j}^a$ a the current density, both calculated without accounting for the fluctuations. As a result, the system of Maxwell equations written in the standard notation, namely

$$\frac{\partial}{\partial \mathbf{r}}\cdot\mathbf{B}=0,\ \frac{\partial}{\partial \mathbf{r}}\cdot\mathbf{D}=\rho^a,\ \frac{\partial}{\partial \mathbf{r}}\times\mathbf{E}=-\frac{\partial \mathbf{B}}{\partial t},\ \frac{\partial}{\partial \mathbf{r}}\times\mathbf{H}=\mathbf{j}^a+\frac{\partial \mathbf{D}}{\partial t} \qquad (1.2.25)$$

contains

$$\rho^a=\rho-\rho^{fl},\mathbf{j}^a=\mathbf{j}-\mathbf{j}^{fl}. \qquad (1.2.26)$$

The ρ^{fl}, $\mathbf{j}^{fl}$ fluctuations calculated using the GBE are given, for example, in Ref. [18]. In rarefied media both effects lead to Johnson's flicker noise observed in 1925 for the first time by J.B. Johnson by the measurement of current fluctuations of thermo-electron emission. For plasma τ is the mean time between "close" collisions of charged particles.

Now several remarks of principal significance:

1. All fluctuations are found from the strict kinetic considerations and tabulated [18-22]. The appearing additional terms in GHE are due to viscosity and they correspond to the small-scale Kolmogorov turbulence. The neglect of formally small terms is equivalent, in particular, to dropping the (small-scale) Kolmogorov turbulence from consideration and is the origin of all principal difficulties in usual turbulent theory. Fluctuations on the wall are equal to zero, from the physical point of view this fact corresponds to the laminar sub-layer. Mathematically it leads to additional boundary conditions for GHE. Major difficulties arose when the question of existence and uniqueness of solutions of

the Navier - Stokes equations was addressed. O A Ladyzhenskaya has shown for three-dimensional flows that under smooth initial conditions a unique solution is only possible over a finite time interval. Ladyzhenskaya even introduced a "correction" into the Navier - Stokes equations in order that its unique solvability could be proved. GHE do not lead to these difficulties.

2. It would appear that in continuum mechanics the idea of discreteness can be abandoned altogether and the medium under study be considered as a continuum in the literal sense of the word. Such an approach is of course possible and indeed leads to the Euler equations in hydrodynamics. However, when the viscosity and thermal conductivity effects are to be included, a totally different situation arises. As is well known, the dynamical viscosity is proportional to the mean time τ between the particle collisions, and a continuum medium in the Euler model with $\tau = 0$ implies that neither viscosity nor thermal conductivity is possible.

3. The non-local kinetic effects listed above will always be relevant to a kinetic theory using one particle description – including, in particular, applications to liquids or plasmas, where self-consistent forces with appropriately cut-off radius of their action are introduced to expand the capability of GBE [27].

4. Introduction of open control volume by the reduced description for ensemble of particles of finite diameters leads to fluctuations (proportional to Knudsen number) of velocity moments in the volume. This fact leads to the significant reconstruction of the theory of transport processes. Obviously the mentioned non-local effects can be discussed from viewpoint of breaking of the Bell's inequalities [36] because in the non-local theory the measurement (realized in $\mathbf{PhSV}_1$) has influence on the measurement realized in the adjoining space-time point in $\mathbf{PhSV}_2$ and verse versa.

5. Madelung's quantum hydrodynamics is equivalent to the Schrödinger equation (SE) and furnishes the description of the quantum particle evolution in the form of Euler equation and continuity equation. Madelung's interpretation of SE (connected with wave function $\psi = \alpha \exp(i\beta)$) leads the probability density $\rho = \alpha^2$ and velocity $\mathbf{v} = \frac{\partial}{\partial \mathbf{r}}(\beta\hbar / m)$. Madelung quantum hydrodynamics does not lead to the energy equation on principal; the corresponding dependent variable p in the energy equation of the generalized quantum hydrodynamics developed by me can be titled as the rest quantum pressure or simply quantum pressure.

6. Generalized Boltzmann physical kinetics brings the strict approximation of non-local effects in space and time and after transfer to the local approximation

leads to parameter τ, which on the quantum level corresponds to the uncertainty principle “time-energy”.
7. GHE produce SE as a deep particular case of the generalized Boltzmann physical kinetics and therefore of non-local hydrodynamics.
8. The appearance of the nonlocal τ parameter is consistent with the Heisenberg uncertainty relation.

But in principle GNE (and therefore GHE) needn’t in using of the “time-energy” uncertainty relation for estimation of the value of the non-locality parameter τ. Moreover the “time-energy” uncertainty relation does not produce the exact relations and from position of non-local physics is only the simplest estimation of the non-local effects. Really, let us consider two neighboring physically infinitely small volumes $\mathbf{PhSV_1}$ and $\mathbf{PhSV_2}$ in a non-equilibrium system. Obviously the time τ should tends to diminish with increasing of the velocities u of particles invading in the nearest neighboring physically infinitely small volume ($\mathbf{PhSV_1}$ or $\mathbf{PhSV_2}$):

$$\tau = H_\tau / u^n . \qquad (1.2.27)$$

But the value τ cannot depend on the velocity direction and naturally to tie τ with the particle kinetic energy, then

$$\tau = H_\tau \big/ mu^2 , \qquad (1.2.28)$$

where H_τ is a coefficient of proportionality, which reflects the state of physical system. In the simplest case H_τ is equal to Plank constant $\hbar$ and relation (1.2.28) became compatible with the Heisenberg relation. The non-locality parameter τ plays the same role as the transport coefficients in local hydrodynamics. The different models can be introduced for the τ definition, but the corresponding results not much different like in local kinetic theory for different models of the particles interaction.

In the general case, the parameter τ is the non-locality parameter; in quantum hydrodynamics, its magnitude is correlated with the “time-energy” uncertainty relation [18 - 23].

It is known that Ehrenfest adiabatic theorem is one of the most important and widely studied theorems in Schrödinger quantum mechanics. It states that if we have a slowly changing Hamiltonian that depends on time, and the system is prepared in one of the instantaneous eigenstates of the Hamiltonian then the state of the system at any time is given by an the instantaneous eigenfunction of the Hamiltonian up to multiplicative phase factors.

The adiabatic theory can be naturally incorporated in generalized quantum hydrodynamics based on local approximations of non-local terms. In the simplest case if ΔQ is the elementary heat quantity delivered for a system executing the transfer from one state (the corresponding time moment is t_{in}) to the next one (the time moment t_e) then

$$\Delta Q = \frac{1}{\tau} 2\delta(\overline{T}\tau), \tag{1.2.29}$$

where $\tau = t_e - t_{in}$ and $\overline{T}$ is the average kinetic energy. For adiabatic case Ehrenfest supposes that

$$2\overline{T}\tau = \Omega_1, \Omega_2, ... \tag{1.2.30}$$

where $\Omega_1, \Omega_2, ...$ are adiabatic invariants. Obviously for Plank's oscillator

$$2\overline{T}\tau = nh. \tag{1.2.31}$$

Then the adiabatic theorem and consequences of this theory deliver the general quantization conditions for non-local quantum hydrodynamics.

Now we can turn our attention to the quantum hydrodynamic description of individual particles. The abstract of the classical Madelung's paper [37] contains only one phrase: "It is shown that the Schrödinger equation for one-electron problems can be transformed into the form of hydrodynamic equations". The following conclusion of principal significance can be done from the previous consideration [18 - 23]:

1. Madelung's quantum hydrodynamics is equivalent to the Schrödinger equation (SE) and leads to the description of the quantum particle evolution in the form of Euler equation and continuity equation. Quantum Euler equation contains additional potential of non-local origin which can be written for example in the Bohm form. SE is consequence of the Liouville equation as result of the local approximation of non-local equations.
2. Generalized Boltzmann physical kinetics leads to the strict approximation of non-local effects in space and time and *in the local limit* leads to parameter τ, which on the quantum level corresponds to the uncertainty principle "time-energy".
3. Generalized hydrodynamic equations (GHE) lead to SE as a deep particular case of the generalized Boltzmann physical kinetics and therefore of non-local hydrodynamics.

As an additional explanation we place the structure of the generalized transport theory.

The Structure of the Generalized Transport Theory

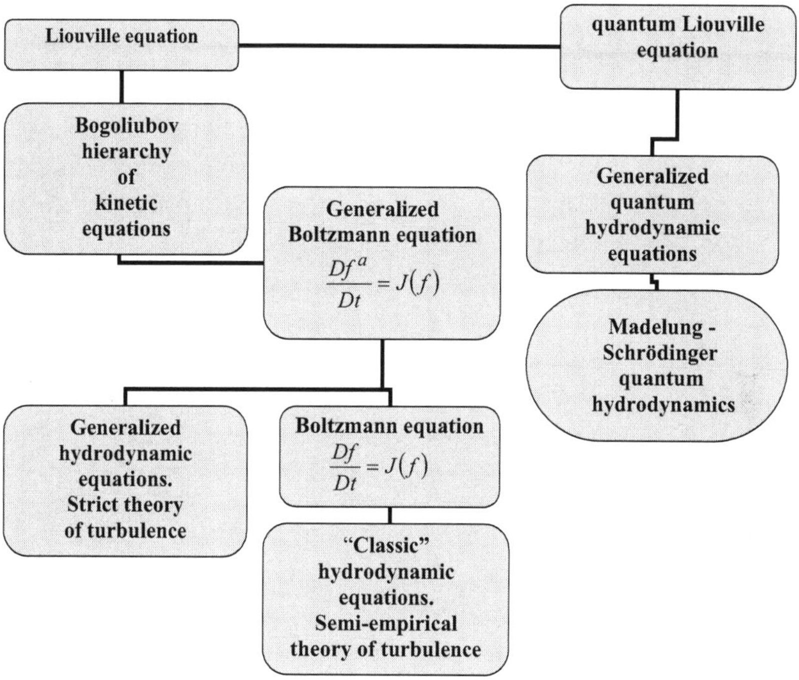

Finally we can state that introduction of control volume by the reduced description for ensemble of particles of finite diameters leads to fluctuations (proportional to Knudsen number) of velocity moments in the volume. This fact leads to the significant reconstruction of the theory of transport processes. The violation of Bell's inequalities [36] is found for local statistical theories, and the transition to non-local description is inevitable.

Violation of the Bell inequalities is established and the transition to a non-local description is inevitable.

Twenty-first century physics is nonlocal physics.

CHAPTER 2. BASIC NONLOCAL EQUATIONS

2.1. Basic nonlocal equations in Cartesian coordinate system

The generalized nonlocal kinetic equation (GNKE) inevitably leads to formulation of new hydrodynamic equations, which is titled as generalized hydrodynamic equations (GHE). Classical hydrodynamic equations of Enskog, Euler and Navier-Stokes are particular cases of these equations. For the purpose of derivation of GHE let us transform GBE to the form convenient for further application. Write down the second term in the left of GBE

$$\frac{Df_\alpha}{Dt}-\frac{D}{Dt}\left(\tau_\alpha\frac{Df_\alpha}{Dt}\right)=J_\alpha^{st,el}+J_\alpha^{st,inel} \tag{2.1.1}$$

in the explicit form

$$\frac{D}{Dt}\left(\tau_\alpha\frac{Df_\alpha}{Dt}\right)=\frac{D\tau_\alpha}{Dt}\frac{Df_\alpha}{Dt}+\tau_\alpha\frac{D}{Dt}\frac{Df_\alpha}{Dt} \tag{2.1.2}$$

where

$$\frac{D}{Dt}=\frac{\partial}{\partial t}+\mathbf{v}_\alpha\cdot\frac{\partial}{\partial\mathbf{r}}+\mathbf{F}_\alpha\cdot\frac{\partial}{\partial\mathbf{v}_\alpha}, \tag{2.1.3}$$

$$\begin{aligned}\frac{D}{Dt}\frac{Df_\alpha}{Dt}&=\frac{\partial^2 f_\alpha}{\partial t^2}+2\mathbf{v}_\alpha\cdot\frac{\partial^2 f_\alpha}{\partial\mathbf{r}\,\partial t}+2\mathbf{F}_\alpha\cdot\frac{\partial^2 f_\alpha}{\partial\mathbf{v}_\alpha\partial t}+\\&+\mathbf{v}_\alpha\cdot\frac{\partial}{\partial\mathbf{r}}\left[\mathbf{v}_\alpha\cdot\frac{\partial f_\alpha}{\partial\mathbf{r}}\right]+\mathbf{F}_\alpha\cdot\frac{\partial}{\partial\mathbf{v}_\alpha}\left(\mathbf{v}_\alpha\cdot\frac{\partial f_\alpha}{\partial\mathbf{r}}\right)+\\&+\frac{\partial\mathbf{F}_\alpha}{\partial t}\cdot\frac{\partial f_\alpha}{\partial\mathbf{v}_\alpha}+\mathbf{v}_\alpha\cdot\frac{\partial}{\partial\mathbf{r}}\left(\mathbf{F}_\alpha\cdot\frac{\partial f_\alpha}{\partial\mathbf{v}_\alpha}\right)+\mathbf{F}_\alpha\cdot\frac{\partial}{\partial\mathbf{v}_\alpha}\left(\mathbf{F}_\alpha\cdot\frac{\partial f_\alpha}{\partial\mathbf{v}_\alpha}\right),\end{aligned} \tag{2.1.4}$$

In doing so we should keep in mind that mean time between collisions of α-particles does not depend on velocity. If parameter τ is connected with the relaxation time, then

$$\frac{D\tau_\alpha}{Dt}=\frac{\partial\tau_\alpha}{\partial t}+\mathbf{v}_\alpha\cdot\frac{\partial\tau_\alpha}{\partial\mathbf{r}}. \tag{2.1.5}$$

The terms in (2.1.4) can be transformed. For example:

$$\mathbf{v}_\alpha\cdot\frac{\partial}{\partial\mathbf{r}}\left(\mathbf{v}_\alpha\cdot\frac{\partial f_\alpha}{\partial\mathbf{r}}\right)=\mathbf{v}_\alpha\mathbf{v}_\alpha:\frac{\partial^2 f_\alpha}{\partial\mathbf{r}\,\partial\mathbf{r}}, \tag{2.1.6}$$

$$\mathbf{F}_\alpha\cdot\frac{\partial}{\partial\mathbf{v}_\alpha}\left(\mathbf{v}_\alpha\cdot\frac{\partial f_\alpha}{\partial\mathbf{r}}\right)=\mathbf{F}_\alpha\mathbf{v}_\alpha:\frac{\partial^2 f_\alpha}{\partial\mathbf{r}\,\partial\mathbf{v}_\alpha}+\mathbf{F}_\alpha\cdot\frac{\partial f_\alpha}{\partial\mathbf{r}}, \tag{2.1.7}$$

$$\mathbf{v}_\alpha\cdot\frac{\partial}{\partial\mathbf{r}}\left(\mathbf{F}_\alpha\cdot\frac{\partial f_\alpha}{\partial\mathbf{v}_\alpha}\right)=\mathbf{v}_\alpha\mathbf{F}_\alpha:\frac{\partial^2 f_\alpha}{\partial\mathbf{v}_\alpha\partial\mathbf{r}}+\frac{\partial f_\alpha}{\partial\mathbf{v}_\alpha}\mathbf{v}_\alpha:\frac{\partial}{\partial\mathbf{r}}\mathbf{F}_\alpha, \tag{2.1.8}$$

$$\mathbf{F}_\alpha\cdot\frac{\partial}{\partial\mathbf{v}_\alpha}\left(\mathbf{F}_\alpha\cdot\frac{\partial f_\alpha}{\partial\mathbf{v}_\alpha}\right)=\mathbf{F}_\alpha\mathbf{F}_\alpha:\frac{\partial^2 f_\alpha}{\partial\mathbf{v}_\alpha\partial\mathbf{v}_\alpha}+\frac{\partial f_\alpha}{\partial\mathbf{v}_\alpha}\mathbf{F}_\alpha:\frac{\partial}{\partial\mathbf{v}_\alpha}\mathbf{F}_\alpha. \tag{2.1.9}$$

The sign ":" in (2.1.6) - (2.1.9) denotes as usual, the double tensor production. For example in (2.1.7)

$$\mathbf{F}_\alpha \mathbf{v}_\alpha : \frac{\partial^2 f_\alpha}{\partial \mathbf{r} \partial \mathbf{v}_\alpha} = \sum_{ij=1}^{3} F_{\alpha i} v_{\alpha j} \frac{\partial^2 f_\alpha}{\partial r_j \partial v_{\alpha i}}. \tag{2.1.10}$$

The derivative of external forces $\mathbf{F}_\alpha$ ($\alpha = 1,...,\eta$) with respect to velocity appears in the right side of (2.1.10); force $\mathbf{F}_\alpha$ - acting on the particle of species α - is related to the unit of mass of this particle. If $\mathbf{F}_\alpha$ does not depend on velocity, this derivative is naturally turns into zero. In the following notation for the force independent of velocity is $\mathbf{F}_\alpha^{(1)}$. If $\mathbf{F}_\alpha$ includes Lorentz force, noted as $\mathbf{F}_\alpha^B$ ($\mathbf{B}$ - magnetic induction), then

$$\mathbf{F}_\alpha = \mathbf{F}_\alpha^{(1)} + \mathbf{F}_\alpha^B \tag{2.1.11}$$

the subsequent transformations of (2.1.9) can be realized:

$$\begin{aligned} &\frac{\partial f_\alpha}{\partial \mathbf{v}_\alpha} \mathbf{F}_\alpha : \frac{\partial}{\partial \mathbf{v}_\alpha} \mathbf{F}_\alpha = \frac{\partial f_\alpha}{\partial \mathbf{v}_\alpha} \mathbf{F}_\alpha^{(1)} : \frac{\partial}{\partial \mathbf{v}_\alpha} \mathbf{F}_\alpha^B + \frac{\partial f_\alpha}{\partial \mathbf{v}_\alpha} \mathbf{F}_\alpha^B : \frac{\partial}{\partial \mathbf{v}_\alpha} \mathbf{F}_\alpha^B = \\ &= \left(\frac{q_\alpha}{m_\alpha}\right)^2 \frac{\partial f_\alpha}{\partial \mathbf{v}_\alpha} \cdot \left\{\mathbf{B}(\mathbf{v}_\alpha \cdot \mathbf{B}) - B^2 \mathbf{v}_\alpha\right\} + \frac{\partial f_\alpha}{\partial \mathbf{v}_\alpha} \mathbf{F}_\alpha^{(1)} : \frac{\partial}{\partial \mathbf{v}_\alpha} \mathbf{F}_\alpha^B, \end{aligned} \tag{2.1.12}$$

because

$$\mathbf{F}_\alpha^B = \frac{q_\alpha}{m_\alpha} [\mathbf{v}_\alpha \times \mathbf{B}], \tag{2.1.13}$$

where q_α is charge of the particle of species α.

The last term in the right side of relation (2.1.12) is written as:

$$\frac{\partial f_\alpha}{\partial \mathbf{v}_\alpha} \mathbf{F}_\alpha^{(1)} : \frac{\partial}{\partial \mathbf{v}_\alpha} \mathbf{F}_\alpha^B = \frac{q_\alpha}{m_\alpha} \frac{\partial f_\alpha}{\partial \mathbf{v}_\alpha} \cdot \left(\mathbf{F}_\alpha^{(1)} \times \mathbf{B}\right). \tag{2.3.14}$$

Sign "×" corresponds to vector product. GBE can contain Umov-Pointing vector $\mathbf{S} \sim [\mathbf{E}, \mathbf{H}]$ ($\mathbf{H}$ is magnetic intensity) in explicit form because the force of non-magnetic origin $\mathbf{F}_\alpha^{(1)}$ can be connected with electric intensity $\mathbf{E}$. As a result

$$\begin{aligned} &\frac{\partial f_\alpha}{\partial \mathbf{v}_\alpha} \mathbf{F}_\alpha : \frac{\partial}{\partial \mathbf{v}_\alpha} \mathbf{F}_\alpha = \left(\frac{q_\alpha}{m_\alpha}\right)^2 \frac{\partial f_\alpha}{\partial \mathbf{v}_\alpha} \cdot \left\{\mathbf{B}(\mathbf{v}_\alpha \cdot \mathbf{B}) - B^2 \mathbf{v}_\alpha\right\} + \\ &+ \frac{q_\alpha}{m_\alpha} \frac{\partial f_\alpha}{\partial \mathbf{v}_\alpha} \cdot \left(\mathbf{F}_\alpha^{(1)} \times \mathbf{B}\right) \end{aligned} \tag{2.1.15}$$

We reach the generalized nonlocal kinetic equation in the form

$$\left(\frac{\partial f_\alpha}{\partial t}+\mathbf{v}_\alpha\cdot\frac{\partial f_\alpha}{\partial \mathbf{r}}+\mathbf{F}_\alpha\cdot\frac{\partial f_\alpha}{\partial \mathbf{v}_\alpha}\right)\left[1-\left(\frac{\partial \tau_\alpha}{\partial t}+\mathbf{v}_\alpha\cdot\frac{\partial \tau_\alpha}{\partial \mathbf{r}}\right)\right]-$$
$$-\tau_\alpha\left[\frac{\partial^2 f_\alpha}{\partial t^2}+2\frac{\partial^2 f_\alpha}{\partial \mathbf{r}\partial t}\cdot\mathbf{v}_\alpha+\frac{\partial^2 f_\alpha}{\partial \mathbf{r}\partial \mathbf{r}}:\mathbf{v}_\alpha\mathbf{v}_\alpha+2\frac{\partial^2 f_\alpha}{\partial \mathbf{v}_\alpha\partial t}\cdot\mathbf{F}_\alpha+\right.$$
$$+\frac{\partial \mathbf{F}_\alpha}{\partial t}\cdot\frac{\partial f_\alpha}{\partial \mathbf{v}_\alpha}+\mathbf{F}_\alpha\cdot\frac{\partial f_\alpha}{\partial \mathbf{r}}+\frac{q_\alpha}{m_\alpha}\frac{\partial f_\alpha}{\partial \mathbf{v}_\alpha}\cdot\left(\mathbf{F}_\alpha^{(1)}\times\mathbf{B}\right)+ \qquad (2.1.16)$$
$$+\left(\frac{q_\alpha}{m_\alpha}\right)^2\frac{\partial f_\alpha}{\partial \mathbf{v}_\alpha}\cdot\left[\mathbf{B}(\mathbf{v}_\alpha\cdot\mathbf{B})-B^2\mathbf{v}_\alpha\right]+\frac{\partial f_\alpha}{\partial \mathbf{v}_\alpha}\mathbf{v}_\alpha:\frac{\partial}{\partial \mathbf{r}}\mathbf{F}_\alpha+$$
$$\left.+\frac{\partial^2 f_\alpha}{\partial \mathbf{v}_\alpha\partial \mathbf{v}_\alpha}:\mathbf{F}_\alpha\mathbf{F}_\alpha+2\frac{\partial^2 f_\alpha}{\partial \mathbf{v}_\alpha\partial \mathbf{r}}:\mathbf{v}_\alpha\mathbf{F}_\alpha\right]=J_\alpha^{st,el}+J_\alpha^{st,inel}.$$

As is seen the explicit form of differential part of GNKE is much more complicated in comparison with Boltzmann equation. As result the transition to generalized hydrodynamic equations (GHE) requires more efforts, but this work following the standard procedure of obtaining of the hydrodynamic description: multiplication GNKE by the particle collision invariants $\psi_\alpha^{(i)}$ (i=1,2,3) and integration over all $\mathbf{v}_\alpha$. Result of this procedure leads to the generalized Enskog equations of continuity, momentum and energy.

Strict consideration leads to the following system of the generalized hydrodynamic equations (GHE) [18, 38-40] written in the generalized Euler form:

Continuity equation for species α:

$$\frac{\partial}{\partial t}\left\{\rho_\alpha-\tau_\alpha^{(0)}\left[\frac{\partial \rho_\alpha}{\partial t}+\frac{\partial}{\partial \mathbf{r}}\cdot(\rho_\alpha\mathbf{v}_0)\right]\right\}+$$
$$+\frac{\partial}{\partial \mathbf{r}}\cdot\left\{\rho_\alpha\mathbf{v}_0-\tau_\alpha^{(0)}\left[\frac{\partial}{\partial t}(\rho_\alpha\mathbf{v}_0)+\frac{\partial}{\partial \mathbf{r}}\cdot(\rho_\alpha\mathbf{v}_0\mathbf{v}_0)+\overset{\leftrightarrow}{\mathrm{I}}\cdot\frac{\partial p_\alpha}{\partial \mathbf{r}}-\rho_\alpha\mathbf{F}_\alpha^{(1)}-\frac{q_\alpha}{m_\alpha}\rho_\alpha\mathbf{v}_0\times\mathbf{B}\right]\right\}=R_\alpha,$$
(2.1.17)

Continuity equation for mixture:

$$\frac{\partial}{\partial t}\left\{\rho-\sum_\alpha\tau_\alpha^{(0)}\left[\frac{\partial \rho_\alpha}{\partial t}+\frac{\partial}{\partial \mathbf{r}}\cdot(\rho_\alpha\mathbf{v}_0)\right]\right\}+$$
$$+\frac{\partial}{\partial \mathbf{r}}\cdot\left\{\rho\mathbf{v}_0-\sum_\alpha\tau_\alpha^{(0)}\left[\frac{\partial}{\partial t}(\rho_\alpha\mathbf{v}_0)+\frac{\partial}{\partial \mathbf{r}}\cdot(\rho_\alpha\mathbf{v}_0\mathbf{v}_0)+\overset{\leftrightarrow}{\mathrm{I}}\cdot\frac{\partial p_\alpha}{\partial \mathbf{r}}-\right.\right. \qquad (2.1.18)$$
$$\left.\left.-\rho_\alpha\mathbf{F}_\alpha^{(1)}-\frac{q_\alpha}{m_\alpha}\rho_\alpha\mathbf{v}_0\times\mathbf{B}\right]\right\}=0,$$

Momentum equation

$$\frac{\partial}{\partial t}\left\{\rho_\alpha \mathbf{v}_0 - \tau_\alpha^{(0)}\left[\frac{\partial}{\partial t}(\rho_\alpha \mathbf{v}_0)+\frac{\partial}{\partial \mathbf{r}}\cdot \rho_\alpha \mathbf{v}_0 \mathbf{v}_0 + \frac{\partial p_\alpha}{\partial \mathbf{r}} - \rho_\alpha \mathbf{F}_\alpha^{(1)} - \right.\right.$$
$$\left.\left. -\left(\frac{q_\alpha}{m_\alpha}\right)\rho_\alpha \mathbf{v}_0 \times \mathbf{B}\right]\right\} - \mathbf{F}_\alpha^{(1)}\left[\rho_\alpha - \tau_\alpha^{(0)}\left(\frac{\partial \rho_\alpha}{\partial t} + \frac{\partial}{\partial \mathbf{r}}\cdot(\rho_\alpha \mathbf{v}_0)\right)\right] -$$
$$-\frac{q_\alpha}{m_\alpha}\left\{\rho_\alpha \mathbf{v}_0 - \tau_\alpha^{(0)}\left[\frac{\partial}{\partial t}(\rho_\alpha \mathbf{v}_0)+\frac{\partial}{\partial \mathbf{r}}\cdot \rho_\alpha \mathbf{v}_0 \mathbf{v}_0 + \frac{\partial p_\alpha}{\partial \mathbf{r}} - \rho_\alpha \mathbf{F}_\alpha^{(1)} - \right.\right.$$
$$\left.\left. -\frac{q_\alpha}{m_\alpha}\rho_\alpha \mathbf{v}_0 \times \mathbf{B}\right]\right\} \times \mathbf{B} + \frac{\partial}{\partial \mathbf{r}}\cdot\left\{\rho_\alpha \mathbf{v}_0\mathbf{v}_0 + p_\alpha \ddot{\mathbf{I}} - \tau_\alpha^{(0)}\left[\frac{\partial}{\partial t}(\rho_\alpha \mathbf{v}_0 \mathbf{v}_0 + \right.\right.$$
$$+ p_\alpha \ddot{\mathbf{I}}) + \frac{\partial}{\partial \mathbf{r}}\cdot\left(\rho_\alpha(\mathbf{v}_0\mathbf{v}_0)\mathbf{v}_0 + \rho_\alpha\overline{(\mathbf{v}_0 \mathbf{V}_\alpha)\mathbf{V}_\alpha} + \rho_\alpha \overline{(\mathbf{V}_\alpha \mathbf{v}_0)\mathbf{V}_\alpha} + \right.$$
$$\left. + \rho_\alpha \overline{(\mathbf{V}_\alpha \mathbf{V}_\alpha)}\mathbf{v}_0\right) - \mathbf{F}_\alpha^{(1)}\rho_\alpha \mathbf{v}_0 - \rho_\alpha \mathbf{v}_0 \mathbf{F}_\alpha^{(1)} -$$
$$-\frac{q_\alpha}{m_\alpha}\rho_\alpha[\mathbf{v}_0 \times \mathbf{B}]\mathbf{v}_0 - \frac{q_\alpha}{m_\alpha}\rho_\alpha \overline{[\mathbf{V}_\alpha \times \mathbf{B}]\mathbf{V}_\alpha} -$$
$$\left.\left.-\frac{q_\alpha}{m_\alpha}\rho_\alpha \mathbf{v}_0[\mathbf{v}_0 \times \mathbf{B}] - \frac{q_\alpha}{m_\alpha}\rho_\alpha \overline{\mathbf{V}_\alpha[\mathbf{V}_\alpha \times \mathbf{B}]}\right]\right\} =$$
$$= \int m_\alpha \mathrm{v}_\alpha J_\alpha^{st,el} d\mathbf{v}_\alpha + \int m_\alpha \mathrm{v}_\alpha J_\alpha^{st,inel} d\mathbf{v}_\alpha. \quad (2.1.19)$$

Energy equation for mixture:

$$\frac{\partial}{\partial t}\left\{\frac{\rho v_0^2}{2} + \frac{3}{2}p + \sum_\alpha \varepsilon_\alpha n_\alpha - \sum_\alpha \tau_\alpha^{(0)}\left[\frac{\partial}{\partial t}\left(\frac{\rho_\alpha v_0^2}{2} + \frac{3}{2}p_\alpha + \varepsilon_\alpha n_\alpha\right) + \right.\right.$$
$$\left.\left. + \frac{\partial}{\partial \mathbf{r}}\cdot\left(\frac{1}{2}\rho_\alpha v_0^2 \mathbf{v}_0 + \frac{5}{2}p_\alpha \mathbf{v}_0 + \varepsilon_\alpha n_\alpha \mathbf{v}_0\right) - \mathbf{F}_\alpha^{(1)}\cdot\rho_\alpha \mathbf{v}_0\right]\right\} +$$
$$+\frac{\partial}{\partial \mathbf{r}}\cdot\left\{\frac{1}{2}\rho v_0^2 \mathbf{v}_0 + \frac{5}{2}p\mathbf{v}_0 + \mathbf{v}_0\sum_\alpha \varepsilon_\alpha n_\alpha - \sum_\alpha \tau_\alpha^{(0)}\left[\frac{\partial}{\partial t}\left(\frac{1}{2}\rho_\alpha v_0^2 \mathbf{v}_0 + \right.\right.\right.$$
$$\left. + \frac{5}{2}p_\alpha \mathbf{v}_0 + \varepsilon_\alpha n_\alpha \mathbf{v}_0\right) + \frac{\partial}{\partial \mathbf{r}}\cdot\left(\frac{1}{2}\rho_\alpha v_0^2 \mathbf{v}_0 \mathbf{v}_0 + \frac{7}{2}p_\alpha \mathbf{v}_0 \mathbf{v}_0 + \frac{1}{2}p_\alpha v_0^2 \ddot{\mathbf{I}} + \right.$$
$$\left. + \frac{5}{2}\frac{p_\alpha^2}{\rho_\alpha}\ddot{\mathbf{I}} + \varepsilon_\alpha n_\alpha \mathbf{v}_0 \mathbf{v}_0 + \varepsilon_\alpha \frac{p_\alpha}{m_\alpha}\ddot{\mathbf{I}}\right) - \rho_\alpha \mathbf{F}_\alpha^{(1)}\cdot \mathbf{v}_0 \mathbf{v}_0 - p_\alpha \mathbf{F}_\alpha^{(1)}\cdot\ddot{\mathbf{I}} -$$
$$-\frac{1}{2}\rho_\alpha v_0^2 \mathbf{F}_\alpha^{(1)} - \frac{3}{2}\mathbf{F}_\alpha^{(1)}p_\alpha - \frac{\rho_\alpha v_0^2}{2}\frac{q_\alpha}{m_\alpha}[\mathbf{v}_0 \times \mathbf{B}] - \frac{5}{2}p_\alpha \frac{q_\alpha}{m_\alpha}[\mathbf{v}_0 \times \mathbf{B}] -$$
$$\left.\left. - \varepsilon_\alpha n_\alpha \frac{q_\alpha}{m_\alpha}[\mathbf{v}_0 \times \mathbf{B}] - \varepsilon_\alpha n_\alpha \mathbf{F}_\alpha^{(1)}\right]\right\} - \left\{\mathbf{v}_0 \cdot \sum_\alpha \rho_\alpha \mathbf{F}_\alpha^{(1)} - \right.$$
$$\left. -\sum_\alpha \tau_\alpha^{(0)}\left[\mathbf{F}_\alpha^{(1)}\cdot\left(\frac{\partial}{\partial t}(\rho_\alpha \mathbf{v}_0) + \frac{\partial}{\partial \mathbf{r}}\cdot\rho_\alpha \mathbf{v}_0 \mathbf{v}_0 + \frac{\partial}{\partial \mathbf{r}}\cdot p_\alpha \ddot{\mathbf{I}} - \rho_\alpha \mathbf{F}_\alpha^{(1)} - q_\alpha n_\alpha [\mathbf{v}_0 \times \mathbf{B}]\right)\right]\right\} = 0.$$

(2.1.20)

Here $\mathbf{F}_\alpha^{(1)}$ are the forces of the non-magnetic origin, $\mathbf{B}$ - magnetic induction, $\ddot{\mathbf{I}}$ - unit tensor, q_α - charge of the α-component particle, p_α - static pressure for α-

component, $\mathbf{V}_\alpha$ - thermal velocity, ε_α - internal energy for the particles of α-component, $\mathbf{v}_0$ - hydrodynamic velocity for mixture.

Poisson equation for the gravitational field

$$\frac{\partial}{\partial \mathbf{r}}\cdot\mathbf{g}=-4\pi\gamma_N\left[\rho-\tau\left(\frac{\partial\rho}{\partial t}+\frac{\partial}{\partial \mathbf{r}}\cdot\rho\mathbf{v}_0\right)\right]. \tag{2.1.21}$$

2.2. Generalized nonlocal kinetic equation in spherical coordinate system

In the following we intend to derivate generalized nonlocal kinetic equation spherical coordinate system shown as figure 2.2.1. Find the necessary derivatives in the spherical coordinate system. Thus we will consider that

$$r^2=x^2+y^2+z^2, \tag{2.2.1}$$

$$\sin\theta=\frac{\sqrt{x^2+y^2}}{r}, \tag{2.2.2}$$

$$\mathrm{tg}\varphi=\frac{y}{x}. \tag{2.2.3}$$

Then from (2.2.1) we have

$$\frac{\partial r}{\partial x}=\frac{1}{2}\left(x^2+y^2+z^2\right)^{-1/2}2x=\frac{x}{r}=\sin\theta\cos\varphi, \tag{2.2.4}$$

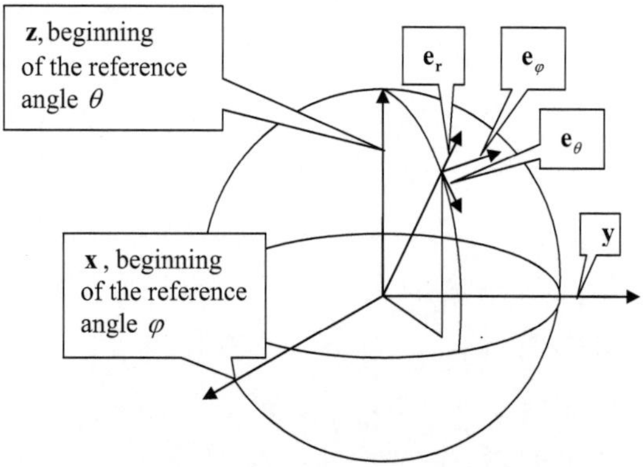

Figure 2.2.1. Spherical coordinate system

From equation (2.2.2) we find

$$\cos\theta\frac{\partial\theta}{\partial x}=\frac{1}{2r}\left(x^2+y^2\right)^{-1/2}2x-\frac{\left(x^2+y^2\right)^{1/2}}{r^2}\sin\theta\cos\varphi=$$
$$=\frac{1}{r^2\sin\theta}x-\frac{1}{r}\sin^2\theta\cos\varphi=\sin\theta\cos\varphi\frac{1}{r\sin\theta}-\frac{1}{r}\sin^2\theta\cos\varphi= \tag{2.2.5}$$
$$=\cos\varphi\frac{1}{r}-\frac{1}{r}\sin^2\theta\cos\varphi=\frac{1}{r}\cos\varphi\left(1-\sin^2\theta\right)=\frac{\cos^2\theta\cos\varphi}{r}$$

and from (2.2.5)

$$\frac{\partial\theta}{\partial x}=\frac{\cos\theta\cos\varphi}{r}. \tag{2.2.6}$$

Correspondingly from (2.2.3)

$$\frac{1}{\cos^2\varphi}\frac{\partial\varphi}{\partial x}=-\frac{y}{x^2}=-\frac{r\sin\theta\sin\varphi}{r^2\sin^2\theta\cos^2\varphi}=-\frac{\sin\varphi}{r\sin\theta\cos^2\varphi}, \tag{2.2.7}$$

or

$$\frac{\partial\varphi}{\partial x}=-\frac{\sin\varphi}{r\sin\theta}. \tag{2.2.8}$$

Analogically

$$\frac{\partial r}{\partial y}=\frac{1}{2}\left(x^2+y^2+z^2\right)^{-1/2}2y=\frac{y}{r}=\sin\theta\sin\varphi, \tag{2.2.9}$$

$$\frac{\partial r}{\partial y}=\sin\theta\sin\varphi, \tag{2.2.10}$$

$$\frac{\partial r}{\partial z}=\frac{1}{2}\left(x^2+y^2+z^2\right)^{-1/2}2z=\frac{z}{r}=\cos\theta \tag{2.2.11}$$

$$\cos\theta\frac{\partial\theta}{\partial y}=\frac{1}{2r}\left(x^2+y^2\right)^{-1/2}2y-\frac{\left(x^2+y^2\right)^{1/2}}{r^2}\sin\theta\sin\varphi=$$
$$=\frac{1}{r^2\sin\theta}y-\frac{1}{r}\sin^2\theta\sin\varphi=\sin\theta\sin\varphi\frac{1}{r\sin\theta}-\frac{1}{r}\sin^2\theta\sin\varphi \tag{2.2.12}$$

or

$$\cos\theta\frac{\partial\theta}{\partial y}=\sin\varphi\frac{1}{r}-\frac{1}{r}\sin^2\theta\sin\varphi==\frac{1}{r}\sin\varphi\left(1-\sin^2\theta\right)=\frac{\cos^2\theta\sin\varphi}{r}, \tag{2.2.13}$$

or

$$\frac{\partial\theta}{\partial y}=\frac{\cos\theta\sin\varphi}{r}. \tag{2.2.14}$$

Analogically

$$\cos\theta\frac{\partial\theta}{\partial z}=-\frac{\left(x^2+y^2\right)^{1/2}}{r^2}\cos\theta=-\frac{1}{r}\sin\theta\cos\theta, \tag{2.2.15}$$

or

$$\frac{\partial\theta}{\partial z}=-\frac{1}{r}\sin\theta. \tag{2.2.16}$$

From (2.2.3) follows

$$\frac{1}{\cos^2\varphi}\frac{\partial\varphi}{\partial y}=\frac{1}{x}=\frac{1}{r\sin\theta\cos\varphi}, \tag{2.2.17}$$

or

$$\frac{\partial\varphi}{\partial y}=\frac{\cos\varphi}{r\sin\theta} \tag{2.2.18}$$

and

$$\frac{\partial\varphi}{\partial z}=0. \tag{2.2.19}$$

Expressing the derivative $\frac{\partial}{\partial x}$ in spherical coordinates, we obtain

$$\begin{gathered}\frac{\partial}{\partial x}=\left(\frac{\partial r}{\partial x}\right)\frac{\partial}{\partial r}+\left(\frac{\partial\theta}{\partial x}\right)\frac{\partial}{\partial\theta}+\left(\frac{\partial\varphi}{\partial x}\right)\frac{\partial}{\partial\varphi}=\\ =\sin\theta\cos\varphi\frac{\partial}{\partial r}+\frac{\cos\theta\cos\varphi}{r}\frac{\partial}{\partial\theta}-\frac{\sin\varphi}{r\sin\theta}\frac{\partial}{\partial\varphi}\end{gathered}, \tag{2.2.20}$$

Similar expressions can be obtained for two other operators:

$$\begin{gathered}\frac{\partial}{\partial y}=\left(\frac{\partial r}{\partial y}\right)\frac{\partial}{\partial r}+\left(\frac{\partial\theta}{\partial y}\right)\frac{\partial}{\partial\theta}+\left(\frac{\partial\varphi}{\partial y}\right)\frac{\partial}{\partial\varphi}=\\ =\sin\theta\sin\varphi\frac{\partial}{\partial r}+\frac{\cos\theta\sin\varphi}{r}\frac{\partial}{\partial\theta}+\frac{\cos\varphi}{r\sin\theta}\frac{\partial}{\partial\varphi}\end{gathered}, \tag{2.2.21}$$

$$\begin{gathered}\frac{\partial}{\partial z}=\left(\frac{\partial r}{\partial z}\right)\frac{\partial}{\partial r}+\left(\frac{\partial\theta}{\partial z}\right)\frac{\partial}{\partial\theta}+\left(\frac{\partial\varphi}{\partial z}\right)\frac{\partial}{\partial\varphi}=\\ =\cos\theta\frac{\partial}{\partial r}-\frac{\sin\theta}{r}\frac{\partial}{\partial\theta}\end{gathered}, \tag{2.2.22}$$

We write a summary of the formulas for the first derivatives:

$$\frac{\partial}{\partial x}=\sin\theta\cos\varphi\frac{\partial}{\partial r}+\frac{\cos\theta\cos\varphi}{r}\frac{\partial}{\partial\theta}-\frac{\sin\varphi}{r\sin\theta}\frac{\partial}{\partial\varphi}, \tag{2.2.23}$$

$$\frac{\partial}{\partial y}=\sin\theta\sin\varphi\frac{\partial}{\partial r}+\frac{\cos\theta\sin\varphi}{r}\frac{\partial}{\partial\theta}+\frac{\cos\varphi}{r\sin\theta}\frac{\partial}{\partial\varphi}, \tag{2.2.24}$$

$$\frac{\partial}{\partial z}=\cos\theta\frac{\partial}{\partial r}-\frac{\sin\theta}{r}\frac{\partial}{\partial\theta}, \tag{2.2.25}$$

where

$$x=r\sin\theta\cos\varphi,\ y=r\sin\theta\sin\varphi,\ z=r\cos\theta. \tag{2.2.26}$$

A vector $\mathbf{p}$ can be written in the alternative forms

$$\mathbf{p}=P_r\mathbf{e}_r+P_\varphi\mathbf{e}_\varphi+P_\theta\mathbf{e}_\theta=P\mathbf{i}+Q\mathbf{j}+R\mathbf{k}. \tag{2.2.27}$$

Multiply both parts of the equation (2.2.27) scalar on $\mathbf{i}$, get

$$P=P_r(\mathbf{e}_r\cdot\mathbf{i})+P_\varphi(\mathbf{e}_\varphi\cdot\mathbf{i})+P_\theta(\mathbf{e}_\theta\cdot\mathbf{i}), \tag{2.2.28}$$

or, using (2.2.26),

$$P=P_r\sin\theta\cos\varphi-P_\varphi\sin\varphi+P_\theta\cos\theta\cos\varphi. \tag{2.2.29}$$

$$Q = P_r \sin\theta \sin\varphi + P_\varphi \cos\varphi + P_\theta \cos\theta \sin\varphi, \tag{2.2.30}$$

$$R = P_r \cos\theta - P_\theta \sin\theta. \tag{2.2.31}$$

In particular for vector $\mathbf{v}$ we find

$$\begin{aligned}\mathbf{v} &= (v_r \sin\theta\cos\varphi - v_\varphi \sin\varphi + v_\theta \cos\theta\cos\varphi)\mathbf{i} + \\ &+ (v_r \sin\theta\sin\varphi + v_\varphi \cos\varphi + v_\theta \cos\theta\sin\varphi)\mathbf{j} + (v_r\cos\theta - v_\theta \sin\theta)\mathbf{k}\end{aligned} \tag{2.2.32}$$

Taking into account the relations (see (2.2.23) – (2.2.25))

$$\frac{\partial f}{\partial x} = \sin\theta\cos\varphi\frac{\partial f}{\partial r} + \frac{\cos\theta\cos\varphi}{r}\frac{\partial f}{\partial \theta} - \frac{\sin\varphi}{r\sin\theta}\frac{\partial f}{\partial \varphi}, \tag{2.2.33}$$

$$\frac{\partial f}{\partial y} = \sin\theta\sin\varphi\frac{\partial f}{\partial r} + \frac{\cos\theta\sin\varphi}{r}\frac{\partial f}{\partial \theta} + \frac{\cos\varphi}{r\sin\theta}\frac{\partial f}{\partial \varphi}, \tag{2.2.34}$$

$$\frac{\partial f}{\partial z} = \cos\theta\frac{\partial f}{\partial r} - \frac{\sin\theta}{r}\frac{\partial f}{\partial \theta}. \tag{2.2.35}$$

we have

$$\begin{aligned}\mathbf{v}\cdot\frac{\partial f}{\partial \mathbf{r}} &= (v_r \sin\theta\cos\varphi - v_\varphi\sin\varphi + v_\theta\cos\theta\cos\varphi)(\sin\theta\cos\varphi\frac{\partial f}{\partial r} + \frac{\cos\theta\cos\varphi}{r}\frac{\partial f}{\partial\theta} - \frac{\sin\varphi}{r\sin\theta}\frac{\partial f}{\partial\varphi}) + \\ &+ (v_r\sin\theta\sin\varphi + v_\varphi\cos\varphi + v_\theta\cos\theta\sin\varphi)(\sin\theta\sin\varphi\frac{\partial f}{\partial r} + \frac{\cos\theta\sin\varphi}{r}\frac{\partial f}{\partial\theta} + \frac{\cos\varphi}{r\sin\theta}\frac{\partial f}{\partial\varphi}) + \\ &+ (v_r\cos\theta - v_\theta\sin\theta)(\cos\theta\frac{\partial f}{\partial r} - \frac{\sin\theta}{r}\frac{\partial f}{\partial\theta}).\end{aligned} \tag{2.2.36}$$

Let us transform (2.2.36).

$$\begin{aligned}\mathbf{v}\cdot\frac{\partial f}{\partial \mathbf{r}} &= v_r(\frac{\partial f}{\partial r} - \frac{\sin\varphi\cos\varphi}{r}\frac{\partial f}{\partial\varphi}) + v_r(\frac{\sin\theta\cos\theta\cos^2\varphi}{r}\frac{\partial f}{\partial\theta}) + \\ &(-v_\varphi\sin\varphi + v_\theta\cos\theta\cos\varphi)(\sin\theta\cos\varphi\frac{\partial f}{\partial r} + \frac{\cos\theta\cos\varphi}{r}\frac{\partial f}{\partial\theta} - \frac{\sin\varphi}{r\sin\theta}\frac{\partial f}{\partial\varphi}) + \\ &+ v_r(\frac{\sin\theta\cos\theta\sin^2\varphi}{r}\frac{\partial f}{\partial\theta}) + v_r(\frac{\sin\varphi\cos\varphi}{r}\frac{\partial f}{\partial\varphi}) + \\ &+ (v_\varphi\cos\varphi + v_\theta\cos\theta\sin\varphi)(\sin\theta\sin\varphi\frac{\partial f}{\partial r} + \frac{\cos\theta\sin\varphi}{r}\frac{\partial f}{\partial\theta} + \frac{\cos\varphi}{r\sin\theta}\frac{\partial f}{\partial\varphi}) + \\ &+ v_r(-\frac{\sin\theta\cos\theta}{r}\frac{\partial f}{\partial\theta}) + (-v_\theta\sin\theta)(\cos\theta\frac{\partial f}{\partial r} - \frac{\sin\theta}{r}\frac{\partial f}{\partial\theta})\end{aligned} \tag{2.2.37}$$

or

$$\begin{aligned}\mathbf{v}\cdot\frac{\partial f}{\partial \mathbf{r}} &= v_r\frac{\partial f}{\partial r} + \\ &+ (-v_\varphi\sin\varphi + v_\theta\cos\theta\cos\varphi)(\sin\theta\cos\varphi\frac{\partial f}{\partial r} + \frac{\cos\theta\cos\varphi}{r}\frac{\partial f}{\partial\theta} - \frac{\sin\varphi}{r\sin\theta}\frac{\partial f}{\partial\varphi}) \\ &+ (v_\varphi\cos\varphi + v_\theta\cos\theta\sin\varphi)(\sin\theta\sin\varphi\frac{\partial f}{\partial r} + \frac{\cos\theta\sin\varphi}{r}\frac{\partial f}{\partial\theta} + \frac{\cos\varphi}{r\sin\theta}\frac{\partial f}{\partial\varphi}) + \\ &+ (-v_\theta\sin\theta)(\cos\theta\frac{\partial f}{\partial r} - \frac{\sin\theta}{r}\frac{\partial f}{\partial\theta})\end{aligned} \tag{2.2.38}$$

or

$$\mathbf{v}\cdot\frac{\partial f}{\partial \mathbf{r}} = v_r\frac{\partial f}{\partial r} +$$
$$+ v_\theta(\cos\theta\sin\theta\frac{\partial f}{\partial r} + \frac{\cos^2\theta\cos^2\varphi}{r}\frac{\partial f}{\partial \theta} - \frac{\cos\theta\cos\varphi\sin\varphi}{r\sin\theta}\frac{\partial f}{\partial \varphi})$$
$$+ v_\varphi\frac{1}{r\sin\theta}\frac{\partial f}{\partial \varphi} + v_\theta(\frac{\cos\theta\cos\theta\sin^2\varphi}{r}\frac{\partial f}{\partial \theta} + \frac{\cos\theta\sin\varphi\cos\varphi}{r\sin\theta}\frac{\partial f}{\partial \varphi}) + \tag{2.2.39}$$
$$+(-v_\theta)(\sin\theta\cos\theta\frac{\partial f}{\partial r} - \frac{\sin^2\theta}{r}\frac{\partial f}{\partial \theta})$$

or

$$\mathbf{v}\cdot\frac{\partial f}{\partial \mathbf{r}} = v_r\frac{\partial f}{\partial r} + v_\theta(\frac{\cos^2\theta\cos^2\varphi}{r}\frac{\partial f}{\partial \theta} - \frac{\cos\theta\cos\varphi\sin\varphi}{r\sin\theta}\frac{\partial f}{\partial \varphi}) +$$
$$+ v_\varphi\frac{1}{r\sin\theta}\frac{\partial f}{\partial \varphi} + v_\theta(\frac{\cos^2\theta\sin^2\varphi}{r}\frac{\partial f}{\partial \theta} + \frac{\cos\theta\sin\varphi\cos\varphi}{r\sin\theta}\frac{\partial f}{\partial \varphi}) + \tag{2.2.40}$$
$$+(-v_\theta)(-\frac{\sin^2\theta}{r}\frac{\partial f}{\partial \theta})$$

and finally

$$\mathbf{v}\cdot\frac{\partial f}{\partial \mathbf{r}} = v_r\frac{\partial f}{\partial r} + v_\theta\frac{1}{r}\frac{\partial f}{\partial \theta} + v_\varphi\frac{1}{r\sin\theta}\frac{\partial f}{\partial \varphi} \tag{2.2.41}$$

Let us derivate now $\dot{\mathbf{v}}\cdot\frac{\partial f}{\partial \mathbf{v}}$ in spherical coordinate system. With this aim we should find $\dot{\mathbf{e}}_r$, $\dot{\mathbf{e}}_\theta$, $\dot{\mathbf{e}}_\varphi$ (see also figure 2.2.1).

$$\dot{\mathbf{e}}_r = \frac{d}{dt}\mathbf{e}_r = \frac{d\theta}{dt}\mathbf{e}_\theta + \sin\theta\frac{d\varphi}{dt}\mathbf{e}_\varphi = \dot{\theta}\mathbf{e}_\theta + \sin\theta\dot{\varphi}\mathbf{e}_\varphi, \tag{2.2.42}$$

$$\dot{\mathbf{e}}_\theta = \frac{d}{dt}\mathbf{e}_\theta = \frac{d\mathbf{e}_\theta}{d\theta}\frac{d\theta}{dt} + \frac{d\mathbf{e}_\theta}{d\varphi}\frac{d\varphi}{dt} = \frac{d\mathbf{e}_\theta}{d\theta}\frac{d\theta}{dt} + \cos\theta\frac{d\varphi}{dt}\mathbf{e}_\varphi =$$
$$= -\mathbf{e}_r\frac{d\theta}{dt} + \cos\theta\frac{d\varphi}{dt}\mathbf{e}_\varphi, \tag{2.2.43}$$

$$\dot{\mathbf{e}}_\varphi = \frac{d}{dt}\mathbf{e}_\varphi = \frac{d\mathbf{e}_\varphi}{d\theta}\frac{d\theta}{dt} + \frac{d\mathbf{e}_\theta}{d\varphi}\frac{d\varphi}{dt} =$$
$$= -\sin\theta\frac{d\varphi}{dt}\mathbf{e}_r - \cos\theta\frac{d\varphi}{dt}\mathbf{e}_\theta. \tag{2.2.44}$$

Comments to the base relations (2.2.42) – (2.2.44);

1. The change $\dot{\mathbf{e}}_\theta$ and $\dot{\mathbf{e}}_\varphi$ in (2.2.43), (2.2.44) won't happen if you increase just r. This is taken into account when calculating derivatives.
2. Since we calculate scalar products (of type $\mathbf{v}\cdot\frac{\partial f}{\partial \mathbf{r}}$) it is not important whether the right-hand or left-hand coordinate system is used.

3. When calculating changes, for example, $\frac{d\mathbf{e}_\theta}{d\theta}\frac{d\theta}{dt}+\frac{d\mathbf{e}_\theta}{d\varphi}\frac{d\varphi}{dt}=\frac{d\mathbf{e}_\theta}{d\theta}\dot{\theta}+\frac{d\mathbf{e}_\theta}{d\varphi}\dot{\varphi}$ it is convenient to fix (for example φ, in this case $\dot{\varphi}=0$) and consider the change $\frac{d\mathbf{e}_\theta}{d\theta}$ of the unit vector $\mathbf{e}_\theta$. Then

$$\begin{aligned}\mathbf{v}&=\frac{d\mathbf{r}}{dt}=\frac{d}{dt}(r\mathbf{e}_r)=r\frac{d\mathbf{e}_r}{dt}+\mathbf{e}_r\frac{dr}{dt}=r(\frac{d\theta}{dt}\mathbf{e}_\theta+\sin\theta\frac{d\varphi}{dt}\mathbf{e}_\varphi)+\frac{dr}{dt}\mathbf{e}_r=\\&=\dot{r}\mathbf{e}_r+r\dot{\theta}\mathbf{e}_\theta+r\sin\theta\dot{\varphi}\mathbf{e}_\varphi\end{aligned}\tag{2.2.45}$$

and

$$\begin{aligned}\dot{\mathbf{v}}&=\frac{d\mathbf{v}}{dt}=\frac{d^2\mathbf{r}}{dt^2}=\frac{d}{dt}(\dot{r}\mathbf{e}_r+r\dot{\theta}\mathbf{e}_\theta+r\sin\theta\dot{\varphi}\mathbf{e}_\varphi)=\dot{r}\dot{\mathbf{e}}_r+\ddot{r}\mathbf{e}_r+\dot{r}\dot{\theta}\mathbf{e}_\theta+r\ddot{\theta}\mathbf{e}_\theta+\\&+r\dot{\theta}\dot{\mathbf{e}}_\theta+\dot{r}\sin\theta\dot{\varphi}\mathbf{e}_\varphi+r\dot{\theta}\cos\theta\dot{\varphi}\mathbf{e}_\varphi+r\sin\theta\dot{\varphi}\dot{\mathbf{e}}_\varphi+r\sin\theta\ddot{\varphi}\mathbf{e}_\varphi\end{aligned}\tag{2.2.46}$$

As a summary we write down (2.2.47):

$$\begin{aligned}&x=r\sin\theta\cos\varphi,\ y=r\sin\theta\sin\varphi,\ z=r\cos\theta;\\&v_x=v\sin\theta\cos\varphi,\ v_y=v\sin\theta\sin\varphi,\ v_z=v\cos\theta;\\&v_r=\dot{r},\ v_\theta=r\dot{\theta},\ v_\varphi=r\sin\theta\dot{\varphi};\\&\dot{\mathbf{e}}_r=\frac{d\theta}{dt}\mathbf{e}_\theta+\sin\theta\frac{d\varphi}{dt}\mathbf{e}_\varphi,\ \dot{\mathbf{e}}_\theta=-\mathbf{e}_r\frac{d\theta}{dt}+\cos\theta\frac{d\varphi}{dt}\mathbf{e}_\varphi,\ \dot{\mathbf{e}}_\varphi=-\sin\theta\frac{d\varphi}{dt}\mathbf{e}_r-\cos\theta\frac{d\varphi}{dt}\mathbf{e}_\theta.\end{aligned}\tag{2.2.47}$$

After substituting $\dot{\mathbf{e}}_r$, $\dot{\mathbf{e}}_\theta$, $\dot{\mathbf{e}}_\varphi$ in the explicit form one obtains

$$\begin{aligned}\dot{\mathbf{v}}&=\ddot{r}\mathbf{e}_r+\dot{r}(\dot{\theta}\mathbf{e}_\theta+\sin\theta\dot{\varphi}\mathbf{e}_\varphi)+(r\ddot{\theta}+\dot{r}\dot{\theta})\mathbf{e}_\theta+\\&+r\dot{\theta}(-\mathbf{e}_r\dot{\theta}+\cos\theta\dot{\varphi}\mathbf{e}_\varphi)+\mathbf{e}_\varphi(\dot{r}\sin\theta\dot{\varphi}+r\cos\theta\dot{\theta}\dot{\varphi})+\\&+r\sin\theta\dot{\varphi}(-\sin\theta\dot{\varphi}\mathbf{e}_r-\cos\theta\dot{\varphi}\mathbf{e}_\theta)+r\sin\theta\ddot{\varphi}\mathbf{e}_\varphi\end{aligned}\tag{2.2.48}$$

or

$$\begin{aligned}\dot{\mathbf{v}}&=(\ddot{r}-r\dot{\theta}^2-r\sin^2\theta\dot{\varphi}^2)\mathbf{e}_r+(r\ddot{\theta}+\dot{r}\dot{\theta})\mathbf{e}_\theta+\\&+\mathbf{e}_\varphi(\dot{r}\sin\theta\dot{\varphi}+r\cos\theta\dot{\theta}\dot{\varphi})-r\sin\theta\cos\theta\dot{\varphi}^2\mathbf{e}_\theta+\\&+r\dot{\theta}\cos\theta\dot{\varphi}\mathbf{e}_\varphi+\dot{r}(\dot{\theta}\mathbf{e}_\theta+\sin\theta\dot{\varphi}\mathbf{e}_\varphi)+r\sin\theta\ddot{\varphi}\mathbf{e}_\varphi,\end{aligned}\tag{2.2.49}$$

or

$$\begin{aligned}\dot{\mathbf{v}}&=(\ddot{r}-r\dot{\theta}^2-r\sin^2\theta\dot{\varphi}^2)\mathbf{e}_r+(r\ddot{\theta}+2\dot{r}\dot{\theta}-r\sin\theta\cos\theta\dot{\varphi}^2)\mathbf{e}_\theta+\\&+\mathbf{e}_\varphi(r\sin\theta\ddot{\varphi}+2\dot{r}\sin\theta\dot{\varphi}+2r\cos\theta\dot{\theta}\dot{\varphi})\end{aligned}\tag{2.2.50}$$

Then we formulate a summary (2.2.51)

$$\begin{aligned}&v_r=\dot{r},\ v_\theta=r\dot{\theta},\ v_\varphi=r\sin\theta\dot{\varphi};\\&\dot{\mathbf{v}}_r=(\ddot{r}-r\dot{\theta}^2-r\sin^2\theta\dot{\varphi}^2)\mathbf{e}_r,\ \dot{\mathbf{v}}_\theta=(r\ddot{\theta}+2\dot{r}\dot{\theta}-r\sin\theta\cos\theta\dot{\varphi}^2)\mathbf{e}_\theta,\\&\dot{\mathbf{v}}_\varphi=(r\sin\theta\ddot{\varphi}+2\dot{r}\sin\theta\dot{\varphi}+2r\cos\theta\dot{\theta}\dot{\varphi})\mathbf{e}_\varphi;\end{aligned}\tag{2.2.51}$$

and

$$\dot{\mathbf{v}}\cdot\frac{\partial f}{\partial \mathbf{v}}=(\ddot{r}-r\dot{\theta}^2-r\sin^2\theta\dot{\varphi}^2)\frac{\partial f}{\partial v_r}+(r\ddot{\theta}+2\dot{r}\dot{\theta}-r\sin\theta\cos\theta\dot{\varphi}^2)\frac{\partial f}{\partial v_\theta}+$$
$$+(r\sin\theta\ddot{\varphi}+2\dot{r}\sin\theta\dot{\varphi}+2r\cos\theta\dot{\theta}\dot{\varphi})\frac{\partial f}{\partial v_\varphi} \tag{2.2.52}$$

Using (2.2.51) we can rewrite (2.2.52) in the form

$$\dot{\mathbf{v}}\cdot\frac{\partial f}{\partial \mathbf{v}}=\left[\ddot{r}-\frac{v_\theta^2}{r}-\frac{v_\varphi^2}{r}\right]\frac{\partial f}{\partial v_r}+\left[r\ddot{\theta}+2\frac{v_r v_\theta}{r}-\frac{v_\varphi^2}{r}\cot\theta\right]\frac{\partial f}{\partial v_\theta}+$$
$$+\left[r\sin\theta\ddot{\varphi}+2\frac{v_r v_\varphi}{r}+2\frac{v_\theta v_\varphi}{r}\cot\theta\right]\frac{\partial f}{\partial v_\varphi} \tag{2.2.53}$$

In the presence of external or self-consistent forces $\mathbf{F}$ acting on the mass unit, the relation (2.2.53) is written in the form:

$$\dot{\mathbf{v}}\cdot\frac{\partial f}{\partial \mathbf{v}}=\left[F_r-\frac{v_\theta^2}{r}-\frac{v_\varphi^2}{r}\right]\frac{\partial f}{\partial v_r}+\left[F_\theta+2\frac{v_r v_\theta}{r}-\frac{v_\varphi^2}{r}\cot\theta\right]\frac{\partial f}{\partial v_\theta}+$$
$$+\left[F_\varphi+2\frac{v_r v_\varphi}{r}+2\frac{v_\theta v_\varphi}{r}\cot\theta\right]\frac{\partial f}{\partial v_\varphi}. \tag{2.2.54}$$

Vlasov equation in the spherical coordinate system in the case of potential forces

$$\frac{\partial f}{\partial t}+v_r\frac{\partial f}{\partial r}+v_\theta\frac{1}{r}\frac{\partial f}{\partial \theta}+v_\varphi\frac{1}{r\sin\theta}\frac{\partial f}{\partial \varphi}+\left[-\frac{v_\theta^2}{r}-\frac{v_\varphi^2}{r}-\frac{\partial \Phi}{\partial r}\right]\frac{\partial f}{\partial v_r}+$$
$$+\left[2\frac{v_r v_\theta}{r}-\frac{v_\varphi^2}{r}\cot\theta-\frac{1}{r}\frac{\partial \Phi}{\partial \theta}\right]\frac{\partial f}{\partial v_\theta}+\left[2\frac{v_r v_\varphi}{r}+2\frac{v_\theta v_\varphi}{r}\cot\theta-\frac{1}{r}\frac{\partial \Phi}{\partial \varphi}\right]\frac{\partial f}{\partial v_\varphi}=0. \tag{2.2.55}$$

Alexeev equation in the spherical coordinate system

$$\frac{\partial f}{\partial t}+v_r\frac{\partial f}{\partial r}+v_\theta\frac{1}{r}\frac{\partial f}{\partial \theta}+v_\varphi\frac{1}{r\sin\theta}\frac{\partial f}{\partial \varphi}-\left[\frac{v_\theta^2+v_\varphi^2}{r}+\frac{\partial \Phi}{\partial r}\right]\frac{\partial f}{\partial v_r}+\left[2\frac{v_r v_\theta}{r}-\frac{v_\varphi^2}{r}\cot\theta-\frac{1}{r}\frac{\partial \Phi}{\partial \theta}\right]\frac{\partial f}{\partial v_\theta}+$$
$$+\left[2\frac{v_r v_\varphi}{r}+2\frac{v_\theta v_\varphi}{r}\cot\theta-\frac{1}{r}\frac{\partial \Phi}{\partial \varphi}\right]\frac{\partial f}{\partial v_\varphi}-$$
$$\left\{\begin{array}{l}\frac{\partial}{\partial t}+v_r\frac{\partial}{\partial r}+v_\theta\frac{1}{r}\frac{\partial}{\partial \theta}+v_\varphi\frac{1}{r\sin\theta}\frac{\partial}{\partial \varphi}+\left[-\frac{v_\theta^2}{r}-\frac{v_\varphi^2}{r}-\frac{\partial \Phi}{\partial r}\right]\frac{\partial}{\partial v_r}+\left[2\frac{v_r v_\theta}{r}-\frac{v_\varphi^2}{r}\cot\theta-\frac{1}{r}\frac{\partial \Phi}{\partial \theta}\right]\frac{\partial}{\partial v_\theta}+\\ +\left[2\frac{v_r v_\varphi}{r}+2\frac{v_\theta v_\varphi}{r}\cot\theta-\frac{1}{r}\frac{\partial \Phi}{\partial \varphi}\right]\frac{\partial}{\partial v_\varphi}\end{array}\right\}$$
$$\tau\left\{\begin{array}{l}\frac{\partial f}{\partial t}+v_r\frac{\partial f}{\partial r}+v_\theta\frac{1}{r}\frac{\partial f}{\partial \theta}+v_\varphi\frac{1}{r\sin\theta}\frac{\partial f}{\partial \varphi}-\left[\frac{v_\theta^2+v_\varphi^2}{r}+\frac{\partial \Phi}{\partial r}\right]\frac{\partial f}{\partial v_r}+\left[2\frac{v_r v_\theta}{r}-\frac{v_\varphi^2}{r}\cot\theta-\frac{1}{r}\frac{\partial \Phi}{\partial \theta}\right]\frac{\partial f}{\partial v_\theta}+\\ +\left[2\frac{v_r v_\varphi}{r}+2\frac{v_\theta v_\varphi}{r}\cot\theta-\frac{1}{r}\frac{\partial \Phi}{\partial \varphi}\right]\frac{\partial f}{\partial v_\varphi}=J^B.\end{array}\right\}$$

(2.2.56)

2.3. Basic nonlocal hydrodynamic equations in spherical coordinate system.

Nonlocal physical kinetics leads to the strict approximation of non-local effects in space and time [18-23] and after transmission to the local approximation leads to parameter τ, which on the quantum level corresponds to the uncertainty principle "time-energy". In the general case, the parameter τ is the non-locality parameter; in quantum hydrodynamics, its magnitude is defined by the "time-energy" uncertainty relation.

Strict consideration leads to the system of the generalized hydrodynamic equations (GHE) [19] written here for a one species physical system. We begin with the formulation of the nonlocal continuity equation in the spherical coordinate system with the independent variables r,θ,φ (radial distance r, polar angle θ and azimuth angle φ):

Continuity equation

$$\frac{\partial}{\partial t}\left\{\rho-\tau\left[\frac{\partial\rho}{\partial t}+\frac{1}{r^2}\frac{\partial(r^2\rho v_{0r})}{\partial r}+\frac{1}{r\sin\theta}\frac{\partial(\rho v_{0\varphi})}{\partial\varphi}+\frac{1}{r\sin\theta}\frac{\partial(\rho v_{0\theta}\sin\theta)}{\partial\theta}\right]\right\}$$

$$+\frac{1}{r^2}\frac{\partial}{\partial r}\left\{r^2\left\{\rho v_{0r}-\tau\left[\frac{\partial}{\partial t}(\rho v_{0r})+\frac{1}{r^2}\frac{\partial(r^2\rho v_{0r}^2)}{\partial r}+\frac{1}{r\sin\theta}\frac{\partial(\rho v_{0\varphi}v_{0r})}{\partial\varphi}+\frac{1}{r\sin\theta}\frac{\partial(\rho v_{0\theta}v_{0r}\sin\theta)}{\partial\theta}-\rho g_r\right]\right\}\right\}$$

$$+\frac{1}{r\sin\theta}\frac{\partial}{\partial\varphi}\left\{\rho v_{0\varphi}-\tau\left[\frac{\partial}{\partial t}(\rho v_{0\varphi})+\frac{1}{r^2}\frac{\partial(r^2\rho v_{0r}v_{0\varphi})}{\partial r}+\frac{1}{r\sin\theta}\frac{\partial(\rho v_{0\varphi}^2)}{\partial\varphi}+\right.\right.$$

$$\left.\left.\frac{1}{r\sin\theta}\frac{\partial(\rho v_{0\theta}v_{0\varphi}\sin\theta)}{\partial\theta}-\rho g_\varphi\right]\right\}+\frac{1}{r\sin\theta}\frac{\partial}{\partial\theta}\left\{\sin\theta\left\{\rho v_{0\theta}-\tau\left[\frac{\partial}{\partial t}(\rho v_{0\theta})+\frac{1}{r^2}\frac{\partial(r^2\rho v_{0r}v_{0\theta})}{\partial r}+\right.\right.\right.$$

$$\left.\left.\left.\frac{1}{r\sin\theta}\frac{\partial(\rho v_{0\varphi}v_{0\theta})}{\partial\varphi}+\frac{1}{r\sin\theta}\frac{\partial(\rho v_{0\theta}^2\sin\theta)}{\partial\theta}-\rho g_\theta\right]\right\}\right\}$$

$$-\frac{1}{r^2}\frac{\partial}{\partial r}\left(\tau r^2\frac{\partial p}{\partial r}\right)-\frac{1}{r^2\sin\theta}\frac{\partial}{\partial\theta}\left(\tau\sin\theta\frac{\partial p}{\partial\theta}\right)-\frac{1}{r^2\sin^2\theta}\frac{\partial}{\partial\varphi}\left(\tau\frac{\partial p}{\partial\varphi}\right)=0, \qquad (2.3.1)$$

where p - static pressure, ρ - mass density, $\mathbf{v}_0$ - hydrodynamic velocity.

Motion equation for the $\mathbf{e}_r$ direction

$$\frac{\partial}{\partial t}\left\{\rho v_{0r}-\tau\left[\frac{\partial}{\partial t}(\rho v_{0r})+\frac{1}{r^2}\frac{\partial(r^2\rho v_{0r}^2)}{\partial r}+\frac{1}{r\sin\theta}\frac{\partial(\rho v_{0\varphi}v_{0r})}{\partial\varphi}+\frac{1}{r\sin\theta}\frac{\partial(\rho v_{0\theta}v_{0r}\sin\theta)}{\partial\theta}\right.\right.$$

$$\left.\left.+\frac{\partial p}{\partial r}-\rho g_r\right]\right\}-g_r\left[\rho-\tau\left(\frac{\partial\rho}{\partial t}+\frac{1}{r^2}\frac{\partial(r^2\rho v_{0r})}{\partial r}+\frac{1}{r\sin\theta}\frac{\partial(\rho v_{0\varphi})}{\partial\varphi}+\frac{1}{r\sin\theta}\frac{\partial(\rho v_{0\theta}\sin\theta)}{\partial\theta}\right)\right]$$

$$+\frac{1}{r^2}\frac{\partial}{\partial r}\left\{r^2\left\{\rho v_{0r}^2-\tau\left[\begin{array}{l}\frac{\partial}{\partial t}\left(\rho v_{0r}^2\right)+\frac{1}{r^2}\frac{\partial\left(r^2\rho v_{0r}^3\right)}{\partial r}+\frac{1}{r\sin\theta}\frac{\partial\left(\rho v_{0\varphi}v_{0r}^2\right)}{\partial\varphi}\\+\frac{1}{r\sin\theta}\frac{\partial\left(\rho v_{0\theta}v_{0r}^2\sin\theta\right)}{\partial\theta}-2g_r\rho v_{0r}\end{array}\right]\right\}\right\}$$

$$+\frac{1}{r\sin\theta}\frac{\partial}{\partial\varphi}\left\{\rho v_{0\varphi}v_{0r}-\tau\left[\frac{\partial}{\partial t}\left(\rho v_{0\varphi}v_{0r}\right)+\frac{1}{r^2}\frac{\partial\left(r^2\rho v_{0\varphi}v_{0r}^2\right)}{\partial r}+\frac{1}{r\sin\theta}\frac{\partial\left(\rho v_{0\varphi}^2 v_{0r}\right)}{\partial\varphi}\right.\right.$$

$$\left.\left.+\frac{1}{r\sin\theta}\frac{\partial\left(\rho v_{0\theta}v_{0\varphi}v_{0r}\sin\theta\right)}{\partial\theta}-g_\varphi\rho v_{0r}-g_r\rho v_{0\varphi}\right]\right\}$$

$$+\frac{1}{r\sin\theta}\frac{\partial}{\partial\theta}\left\{\sin\theta\left\{\rho v_{0\theta}v_{0r}-\tau\left[\begin{array}{l}\frac{\partial}{\partial t}\left(\rho v_{0\theta}v_{0r}\right)+\frac{1}{r^2}\frac{\partial\left(r^2\rho v_{0\theta}v_{0r}^2\right)}{\partial r}+\frac{1}{r\sin\theta}\frac{\partial\left(\rho v_{0\varphi}v_{0\theta}v_{0r}\right)}{\partial r}\\+\frac{1}{r\sin\theta}\frac{\partial\left(\rho v_{0\theta}^2 v_{0r}\right)}{\partial r}-g_\theta\rho v_{0r}-v_{0\theta}\rho g_r\end{array}\right]\right\}\right\}$$

$$+\frac{\partial p}{\partial r}-\frac{\partial}{\partial r}\left(\tau\frac{\partial p}{\partial t}\right)-2\frac{\partial}{\partial r}\left(\tau\left(\frac{1}{r^2}\frac{\partial\left(r^2 p v_{0r}\right)}{\partial r}+\frac{1}{r\sin\theta}\frac{\partial\left(p v_{0\varphi}\right)}{\partial\varphi}+\frac{1}{r\sin\theta}\frac{\partial\left(p v_{0\theta}\sin\theta\right)}{\partial\theta}\right)\right)$$

$$-\frac{1}{r^2}\frac{\partial}{\partial r}\left(\tau r^2\frac{\partial\left(p v_{0r}\right)}{\partial r}\right)-\frac{1}{r^2\sin\theta}\frac{\partial}{\partial\theta}\left(\tau\sin\theta\frac{\partial\left(p v_{0r}\right)}{\partial\theta}\right)-\frac{1}{r^2\sin^2\theta}\frac{\partial}{\partial\varphi}\left(\tau\frac{\partial\left(p v_{0r}\right)}{\partial\varphi}\right)=0. \quad (2.3.2)$$

Write down motion equation onto $\mathbf{e}_\theta$- direction for the spherical coordinate system:

$$\frac{\partial}{\partial t}\left\{\rho v_{0\theta}-\tau\left[\frac{\partial}{\partial t}\left(\rho v_{0\theta}\right)+\frac{1}{r^2}\frac{\partial\left(r^2\rho v_{0r}v_{0\theta}\right)}{\partial r}+\frac{1}{r\sin\theta}\frac{\partial\left(\rho v_{0\varphi}v_{0\theta}\right)}{\partial\varphi}+\frac{1}{r\sin\theta}\frac{\partial\left(\rho v_{0\theta}^2\sin\theta\right)}{\partial\theta}+\right.\right.$$

$$\left.\left.+\frac{1}{r}\frac{\partial p}{\partial\theta}-\rho g_\theta\right]\right\}-g_\theta\left[\rho-\tau\left(\frac{\partial\rho}{\partial t}+\frac{1}{r^2}\frac{\partial\left(r^2\rho v_{0r}\right)}{\partial r}+\frac{1}{r\sin\theta}\frac{\partial\left(\rho v_{0\varphi}\right)}{\partial\varphi}+\frac{1}{r\sin\theta}\frac{\partial\left(\rho v_{0\theta}\sin\theta\right)}{\partial\theta}\right)\right]+$$

$$+\frac{1}{r^2}\frac{\partial}{\partial r}\left\{r^2\left\{\rho v_{0r}v_{0\theta}-\tau\left[\frac{\partial}{\partial t}\left(\rho v_{0r}v_{0\theta}\right)+\frac{1}{r^2}\frac{\partial\left(r^2\rho v_{0r}^2 v_{0\theta}\right)}{\partial r}+\frac{1}{r\sin\theta}\frac{\partial\left(\rho v_{0\varphi}v_{0r}v_{0\theta}\right)}{\partial\varphi}+\right.\right.\right.$$

$$\left.\left.\left.+\frac{1}{r\sin\theta}\frac{\partial\left(\rho v_{0\theta}^2 v_{or}\sin\theta\right)}{\partial\theta}-g_r\rho v_{0\theta}-v_{0r}\rho g_\theta\right]\right\}\right\}+\frac{1}{r\sin\theta}\frac{\partial}{\partial\varphi}\left\{\rho v_{0\varphi}v_{0\theta}-\tau\left[\frac{\partial}{\partial t}\left(\rho v_{0\varphi}v_{0\theta}\right)+\right.\right.$$

$$\left.\left.+\frac{1}{r^2}\frac{\partial\left(r^2\rho v_{0r}v_{0\varphi}v_{0\theta}\right)}{\partial r}+\frac{1}{r\sin\theta}\frac{\partial\left(\rho v_{0\varphi}^2 v_{0\theta}\right)}{\partial\varphi}+\frac{1}{r\sin\theta}\frac{\partial\left(\rho v_{0\theta}^2 v_{0\varphi}\sin\theta\right)}{\partial\theta}-g_\varphi\rho v_{0\theta}-v_{0\varphi}\rho g_\theta\right]\right\}+$$

$$+\frac{1}{r\sin\theta}\frac{\partial}{\partial\theta}\left\{\sin\theta\left\{\rho v_{0\theta}^2-\tau\left[\frac{\partial}{\partial t}\left(\rho v_{0\theta}^2\right)+\frac{1}{r^2}\frac{\partial\left(r^2\rho v_{0r}v_{0\theta}^2\right)}{\partial r}+\frac{1}{r\sin\theta}\frac{\partial\left(\rho v_{0\varphi}v_{0\theta}^2\right)}{\partial\varphi}+\right.\right.\right.$$

$$\left.\left.\left.+\frac{1}{r\sin\theta}\frac{\partial\left(\rho v_{0\theta}^3\sin\theta\right)}{\partial\theta}-2g_\theta\rho v_{0\theta}\right]\right\}\right\}+\frac{1}{r}\frac{\partial p}{\partial\theta}-\frac{1}{r}\frac{\partial}{\partial\theta}\left(\tau\frac{\partial p}{\partial t}\right)-$$

$$-\frac{2}{r}\frac{\partial}{\partial\theta}\left(\tau\left(\frac{1}{r^2}\frac{\partial\left(r^2 p v_{0r}\right)}{\partial r}+\frac{1}{r\sin\theta}\frac{\partial\left(p v_{0\varphi}\right)}{\partial\varphi}+\frac{1}{r\sin\theta}\frac{\partial\left(p v_{0\theta}\sin\theta\right)}{\partial\theta}\right)\right)-$$

$$-\frac{1}{r^2}\frac{\partial}{\partial r}\left(\tau r^2\frac{\partial\left(p v_{0\theta}\right)}{\partial r}\right)-\frac{1}{r^2\sin\theta}\frac{\partial}{\partial\theta}\left(\tau\sin\theta\frac{\partial\left(p v_{0\theta}\right)}{\partial\theta}\right)-\frac{1}{r^2\sin^2\theta}\frac{\partial}{\partial\varphi}\left(\tau\frac{\partial\left(p v_{0\theta}\right)}{\partial\varphi}\right)=0.$$

(2.3.3)

Now we write down motion equation onto $\mathbf{e}_\varphi$- direction for the spherical coordinate system:

$$\frac{\partial}{\partial t}\left\{\rho v_{0\varphi}-\tau\left[\frac{\partial}{\partial t}\left(\rho v_{0\varphi}\right)+\frac{1}{r^2}\frac{\partial\left(r^2\rho v_{0r}v_{0\varphi}\right)}{\partial r}+\frac{1}{r\sin\theta}\frac{\partial\left(\rho v_{0\varphi}^2\right)}{\partial\varphi}+\frac{1}{r\sin\theta}\frac{\partial\left(\rho v_{0\theta}v_{0\varphi}\sin\theta\right)}{\partial\theta}\right.\right.$$

$$\left.\left.+\frac{1}{r\sin\theta}\frac{\partial p}{\partial\varphi}-\rho g_\varphi\right]\right\}-g_\varphi\left[\rho-\tau\left(\frac{\partial\rho}{\partial t}+\frac{1}{r^2}\frac{\partial\left(r^2\rho v_{0r}\right)}{\partial r}+\frac{1}{r\sin\theta}\frac{\partial\left(\rho v_{0\varphi}\right)}{\partial\varphi}+\frac{1}{r\sin\theta}\frac{\partial\left(\rho v_{0\theta}\sin\theta\right)}{\partial\theta}\right)\right]$$

$$+\frac{1}{r^2}\frac{\partial}{\partial r}\left\{r^2\left\{\rho v_{0r}v_{0\varphi}-\tau\left[\frac{\partial}{\partial t}\left(\rho v_{0r}v_{0\varphi}\right)+\frac{1}{r^2}\frac{\partial\left(r^2\rho v_{0r}^2 v_{0\varphi}\right)}{\partial r}+\frac{1}{r\sin\theta}\frac{\partial\left(\rho v_{0\varphi}^2 v_{0r}\right)}{\partial\varphi}\right.\right.\right.$$

$$\left.\left.\left.+\frac{1}{r\sin\theta}\frac{\partial\left(\rho v_{0\theta}v_{or}v_{0\varphi}\sin\theta\right)}{\partial\theta}-g_r\rho v_{0\varphi}-v_{0r}\rho g_\varphi\right]\right\}\right\}+\frac{1}{r\sin\theta}\frac{\partial}{\partial\varphi}\left\{\rho v_{0\varphi}^2-\tau\left[\frac{\partial}{\partial t}\left(\rho v_{0\varphi}^2\right)\right.\right.$$

$$\left.\left.+\frac{1}{r^2}\frac{\partial\left(r^2\rho v_{0r}v_{0\varphi}^2\right)}{\partial r}+\frac{1}{r\sin\theta}\frac{\partial\left(\rho v_{0\varphi}^3\right)}{\partial\varphi}+\frac{1}{r\sin\theta}\frac{\partial\left(\rho v_{0\theta}v_{0\varphi}^2\sin\theta\right)}{\partial\theta}-2g_\varphi\rho v_{0\varphi}\right]\right\}$$

$$+\frac{1}{r\sin\theta}\frac{\partial}{\partial\theta}\left\{\sin\theta\left\{\rho v_{0\theta}v_{0\varphi}-\tau\left[\frac{\partial}{\partial t}\left(\rho v_{0\theta}v_{0\varphi}\right)+\frac{1}{r^2}\frac{\partial\left(r^2\rho v_{0r}v_{0\theta}v_{0\varphi}\right)}{\partial r}+\frac{1}{r\sin\theta}\frac{\partial\left(\rho v_{0\varphi}^2 v_{0\theta}\right)}{\partial\varphi}\right.\right.\right.$$

$$\left.\left.\left.+\frac{1}{r\sin\theta}\frac{\partial\left(\rho v_{0\theta}^2 v_{0\varphi}\sin\theta\right)}{\partial\theta}-g_\theta\rho v_{0\varphi}-v_{0\theta}\rho g_\varphi\right]\right\}\right\}+\frac{1}{r\sin\theta}\frac{\partial p}{\partial\varphi}-\frac{1}{r\sin\theta}\frac{\partial}{\partial\varphi}\left(\tau\frac{\partial p}{\partial t}\right)$$

$$-\frac{2}{r\sin\theta}\frac{\partial}{\partial\varphi}\left(\tau\left(\frac{1}{r^2}\frac{\partial\left(r^2 p v_{0r}\right)}{\partial r}+\frac{1}{r\sin\theta}\frac{\partial\left(p v_{0\varphi}\right)}{\partial\varphi}+\frac{1}{r\sin\theta}\frac{\partial\left(p v_{0\theta}\sin\theta\right)}{\partial\theta}\right)\right)$$

$$-\frac{1}{r^2}\frac{\partial}{\partial r}\left(\tau r^2\frac{\partial\left(p v_{0\varphi}\right)}{\partial r}\right)-\frac{1}{r^2\sin\theta}\frac{\partial}{\partial\theta}\left(\tau\sin\theta\frac{\partial\left(p v_{0\varphi}\right)}{\partial\theta}\right)-\frac{1}{r^2\sin^2\theta}\frac{\partial}{\partial\varphi}\left(\tau\frac{\partial\left(p v_{0\varphi}\right)}{\partial\varphi}\right)=0.$$

(2.3.4)

Energy equation in the gravitational field (see also (2.1.20)):

$$\frac{\partial}{\partial t}\left\{\frac{1}{2}\rho v_0^2+\varepsilon n+\frac{3}{2}p-\tau\left[\frac{\partial}{\partial t}\left(\frac{1}{2}\rho v_0^2+\varepsilon n+\frac{3}{2}p\right)+\frac{1}{r^2}\frac{\partial}{\partial r}\left(r^2 v_{0r}\left(\frac{1}{2}\rho v_0^2+\varepsilon n+\frac{5}{2}p\right)\right)\right.\right.$$

$$+\frac{1}{r\sin\theta}\frac{\partial}{\partial\varphi}\left(v_{0\varphi}\left(\frac{1}{2}\rho v_0^2+\varepsilon n+\frac{5}{2}p\right)\right)+\frac{1}{r\sin\theta}\frac{\partial}{\partial\theta}\left(\sin\theta v_{0\theta}\left(\frac{1}{2}\rho v_0^2+\varepsilon n+\frac{5}{2}p\right)\right)$$

$$\left.\left.-\rho\left(g_r v_{0r}+g_\varphi v_{0\varphi}+g_\theta v_{0\theta}\right)\right]\right\}+\frac{1}{r^2}\frac{\partial}{\partial r}\left\{r^2\left\{\left(\frac{1}{2}\rho v_0^2+\varepsilon n+\frac{5}{2}p\right)v_{0r}-\tau\left[\frac{\partial}{\partial t}\left(\left(\frac{1}{2}\rho v_0^2+\varepsilon n+\frac{5}{2}p\right)v_{0r}\right)\right.\right.\right.$$

$$+\frac{1}{r^2}\frac{\partial}{\partial r}\left(r^2\left(\frac{1}{2}\rho v_0^2+\varepsilon n+\frac{7}{2}p\right)v_{0r}^2\right)+\frac{1}{r\sin\theta}\frac{\partial}{\partial\varphi}\left(\left(\frac{1}{2}\rho v_0^2+\varepsilon n+\frac{7}{2}p\right)v_{0\varphi}v_{0r}\right)$$

$$+\frac{1}{r\sin\theta}\frac{\partial}{\partial\theta}\left(\sin\theta\left(\frac{1}{2}\rho v_0^2+\varepsilon n+\frac{7}{2}p\right)v_{0\theta}v_{0r}\right)$$

$$-\rho\left(g_r v_{0r}+g_\varphi v_{0\varphi}+g_\theta v_{0\theta}\right)v_{0r}-\left(\frac{1}{2}\rho v_0^2+\varepsilon n+\frac{3}{2}p\right)g_r\Bigg]\Bigg\}\Bigg\}+\frac{1}{r\sin\theta}\frac{\partial}{\partial\varphi}\left\{\left(\frac{1}{2}\rho v_0^2+\varepsilon n+\frac{5}{2}p\right)v_{0\varphi}\right.$$

$$-\tau\left[\frac{\partial}{\partial t}\left(\left(\frac{1}{2}\rho v_0^2+\varepsilon n+\frac{5}{2}p\right)v_{0\varphi}\right)+\frac{1}{r^2}\frac{\partial}{\partial r}\left(r^2\left(\frac{1}{2}\rho v_0^2+\varepsilon n+\frac{7}{2}p\right)v_{0r}v_{0\varphi}\right)\right.$$

$$+\frac{1}{r\sin\theta}\frac{\partial}{\partial\varphi}\left(\left(\frac{1}{2}\rho v_0^2+\varepsilon n+\frac{7}{2}p\right)v_{0\varphi}^2\right)+\frac{1}{r\sin\theta}\frac{\partial}{\partial\theta}\left(\sin\theta\left(\frac{1}{2}\rho v_0^2+\varepsilon n+\frac{7}{2}p\right)v_{0\theta}v_{0\varphi}\right)$$

$$-\rho\left(g_r v_{0r}+g_\varphi v_{0\varphi}+g_\theta v_{0\theta}\right)v_{0\varphi}-\left(\frac{1}{2}\rho v_0^2+\varepsilon n+\frac{3}{2}p\right)g_\varphi\Bigg]\Bigg\}+$$

$$+\frac{1}{r\sin\theta}\frac{\partial}{\partial\theta}\left\{\sin\theta\left\{\left(\frac{1}{2}\rho v_0^2+\varepsilon n+\frac{5}{2}p\right)v_{0\theta}-\tau\left[\frac{\partial}{\partial t}\left(\left(\frac{1}{2}\rho v_0^2+\varepsilon n+\frac{5}{2}p\right)v_{0\theta}\right)+\right.\right.\right.$$

$$+\frac{1}{r^2}\frac{\partial}{\partial r}\left(r^2\left(\frac{1}{2}\rho v_0^2+\varepsilon n+\frac{7}{2}p\right)v_{0r}v_{0\theta}\right)+\frac{1}{r\sin\theta}\frac{\partial}{\partial\varphi}\left(\left(\frac{1}{2}\rho v_0^2+\varepsilon n+\frac{7}{2}p\right)v_{0\varphi}v_{0\theta}\right)+$$

$$+\frac{1}{r\sin\theta}\frac{\partial}{\partial\theta}\left(\sin\theta\left(\frac{1}{2}\rho v_0^2+\varepsilon n+\frac{7}{2}p\right)v_{0\theta}^2\right)-\rho\left(g_r v_{0r}+g_\varphi v_{0\varphi}+g_\theta v_{0\theta}\right)v_{0\theta}-\left(\frac{1}{2}\rho v_0^2+\varepsilon n+\frac{3}{2}p\right)g_\theta\Bigg]\Bigg\}\Bigg\}$$

$$-\left\{\rho\left(g_r v_{0r}+g_\varphi v_{0\varphi}+g_\theta v_{0\theta}\right)-\tau\left[g_r\left(\frac{\partial}{\partial t}(\rho v_{0r})+\frac{1}{r^2}\frac{\partial}{\partial r}\left(r^2\rho v_{0r}^2\right)+\frac{1}{r\sin\theta}\frac{\partial}{\partial\varphi}(\rho v_{0\varphi}v_{0r})+\right.\right.\right.$$

$$\left.+\frac{1}{r\sin\theta}\frac{\partial}{\partial\theta}(\rho v_{0\theta}v_{0r}\sin\theta)+\frac{\partial p}{\partial r}-\rho g_r\right)$$

$$+g_\varphi\left(\frac{\partial}{\partial t}(\rho v_{0\varphi})+\frac{1}{r^2}\frac{\partial}{\partial r}\left(r^2\rho v_{0r}v_{0\varphi}\right)+\frac{1}{r\sin\theta}\frac{\partial}{\partial\varphi}\left(\rho v_{0\varphi}^2\right)+\frac{1}{r\sin\theta}\frac{\partial}{\partial\theta}(\rho v_{0\theta}v_{0\varphi}\sin\theta)\right.$$

$$\left.+\frac{1}{r\sin\theta}\frac{\partial p}{\partial\varphi}-\rho g_\varphi\right)+g_\theta\left(\frac{\partial}{\partial t}(\rho v_{0\theta})+\frac{1}{r^2}\frac{\partial}{\partial r}\left(r^2\rho v_{0r}v_{0\theta}\right)+\frac{1}{r\sin\theta}\frac{\partial}{\partial\varphi}(\rho v_{0\varphi}v_{0\theta})\right.$$

$$\left.+\frac{1}{r\sin\theta}\frac{\partial}{\partial\theta}\left(\rho v_{0\theta}^2\sin\theta\right)+\frac{1}{r}\frac{\partial p}{\partial\theta}-\rho g_\theta\right)\Bigg]\Bigg\}-\frac{1}{r^2}\frac{\partial}{\partial r}\left(\tau r^2\frac{\partial}{\partial r}\left(\frac{1}{2}p v_0^2+\varepsilon n v_0^2+\frac{5}{2}\frac{p^2}{\rho}\right)\right)$$

$$-\frac{1}{r^2\sin\theta}\frac{\partial}{\partial\theta}\left(\tau\sin\theta\frac{\partial}{\partial\theta}\left(\frac{1}{2}p v_0^2+\varepsilon n v_0^2+\frac{5}{2}\frac{p^2}{\rho}\right)\right)-\frac{1}{r^2\sin^2\theta}\frac{\partial}{\partial\varphi}\left(\tau\frac{\partial}{\partial\varphi}\left(\frac{1}{2}p v_0^2+\varepsilon n v_0^2+\frac{5}{2}\frac{p^2}{\rho}\right)\right)$$

$$+\frac{1}{r^2}\frac{\partial}{\partial r}\left(r^2\tau p g_r\right)+\frac{1}{r\sin\theta}\frac{\partial}{\partial\varphi}(\tau p g_\varphi)+\frac{1}{r\sin\theta}\frac{\partial}{\partial\theta}(\tau p g_\theta\sin\theta)=0, \qquad (2.3.5)$$

where ε is the internal energy, $v_0^2=v_{0r}^2+v_{0\varphi}^2+v_{0\theta}^2$.

2.4. Generalized nonlocal kinetic equation in cylindrical coordinate system

As usual the three coordinates (r,φ,z) of a point P are defined as:

- The axial distance or radial distance r is the Euclidian distance from the z-axis to the point P.

- The azimuth φ is the angle between the reference direction on the chosen plane and the line from the origin to the projection of P on the plane.
- The axial coordinate or height z is the signed distance from the chosen plane to the point P.
- In concrete situations, and in many mathematical illustrations, a positive angular coordinate is measured counterclockwise as seen from any point with positive height (see figure 2.4.1)

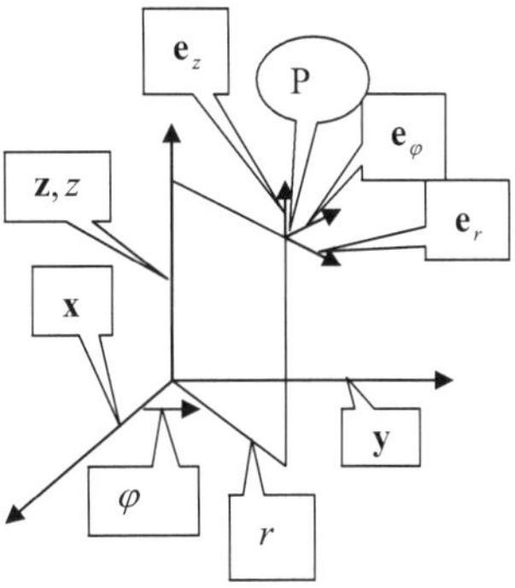

Figure 2.4.1. Cylindrical coordinate system

We follow the same method of GNKE derivation in the cylindrical coordinate system as it was done above for spherical coordinate system. Analog of (2.2.27)

$$\mathbf{v} = v_r\mathbf{e}_r + v_\varphi\mathbf{e}_\varphi + v_z\mathbf{e}_z = \dot{r}\mathbf{e}_r + r\dot{\varphi}\mathbf{e}_\varphi + \dot{z}\mathbf{e}_z . \qquad (2.4.1)$$

Analog of (2.2.48)

$$\mathbf{a} = \frac{d\mathbf{v}}{dt} = \ddot{r}\mathbf{e}_r + \dot{r}\dot{\mathbf{e}}_r + \dot{r}\dot{\varphi}\mathbf{e}_\varphi + r\ddot{\varphi}\mathbf{e}_\varphi + r\dot{\varphi}\dot{\mathbf{e}}_\varphi + \ddot{z}\mathbf{e}_z + \dot{z}\dot{\mathbf{e}}_z . \qquad (2.4.2)$$

Analog of relations (2.2.42) – (2.2.44)

$$\dot{\mathbf{e}}_r = \dot{\varphi}\mathbf{e}_\varphi ,\ \dot{\mathbf{e}}_\varphi = -\dot{\varphi}\mathbf{e}_r ,\ \dot{\mathbf{e}}_z = 0 . \qquad (2.4.3)$$

Using (2.4.3) we find from (2.4.2)

$$\mathbf{a} = \frac{d\mathbf{v}}{dt} = (\ddot{r} - r\dot{\varphi}^2)\mathbf{e}_r + (2\dot{r}\dot{\varphi} + r\ddot{\varphi})\mathbf{e}_\varphi + \ddot{z}\mathbf{e}_z , \qquad (2.4.4)$$

Analog of (2.2.51)

$$v_r = \dot{r} \rightarrow \dot{v}_r = \ddot{r} , \qquad (2.4.5)$$

$$v_\varphi = r\dot{\varphi} \rightarrow \dot{v}_\varphi = \dot{r}\dot{\varphi} + r\ddot{\varphi} , \qquad (2.4.6)$$

$$v_z = \dot{z} \rightarrow \dot{v}_z = \ddot{z} . \qquad (2.4.7)$$

From (2.4.4) – (2.4.7) follow

$$\mathbf{a}=\frac{d\mathbf{v}}{dt}=(\dot v_r-\frac{v_\varphi^2}{r})\mathbf{e}_r+(\frac{v_r v_\varphi}{r}+\dot v_\varphi)\mathbf{e}_\varphi+\dot v_z\mathbf{e}_z\,. \tag{2.4.8}$$

In the presence of external or self-consistent forces $\mathbf{F}$

$$\mathbf{F}=\dot v_r\mathbf{e}_r+\dot v_\varphi\mathbf{e}_\varphi+\dot v_z\mathbf{e}_z \tag{2.4.9}$$

acting on the mass unit, the relation (2.4.8) is written in the form:

$$\mathbf{a}=\frac{d\mathbf{v}}{dt}=(F_r-\frac{v_\varphi^2}{r})\mathbf{e}_r+(\frac{v_r v_\varphi}{r}+F_\varphi)\mathbf{e}_\varphi+F_z\mathbf{e}_z\,. \tag{2.4.10}$$

One obtains for the potential field of forces

$$\mathbf{a}_{pot}=-\frac{\partial\Phi}{\partial\mathbf{r}}=-\frac{\partial\Phi}{\partial r}\mathbf{e}_r-\frac{1}{r}\frac{\partial\Phi}{\partial\varphi}\mathbf{e}_\varphi-\frac{\partial\Phi}{\partial z}\mathbf{e}_z \tag{2.4.11}$$

and (2.4.10) transforms into

$$\mathbf{a}=\frac{d\mathbf{v}}{dt}=(-\frac{v_\varphi^2}{r}-\frac{\partial\Phi}{\partial r})\mathbf{e}_r+(\frac{v_r v_\varphi}{r}-\frac{1}{r}\frac{\partial\Phi}{\partial\varphi})\mathbf{e}_\varphi-\frac{\partial\Phi}{\partial z}\mathbf{e}_z\,. \tag{2.4.12}$$

The Vlasov equation in cylindrical coordinates

$$\frac{Df}{Dt}=\frac{\partial f}{\partial t}+\dot r\frac{\partial f}{\partial r}+\dot\varphi\frac{\partial f}{\partial\varphi}+\dot z\frac{\partial f}{\partial z}+\dot v_r\frac{\partial f}{\partial v_r}+\dot v_\varphi\frac{\partial f}{\partial v_\varphi}+\dot v_z\frac{\partial f}{\partial v_z}=0\,. \tag{2.4.13}$$

But

$$v_\varphi=r\dot\varphi \tag{2.4.14}$$

then

$$\frac{Df}{Dt}=\frac{\partial f}{\partial t}+v_r\frac{\partial f}{\partial r}+\frac{v_\varphi}{r}\frac{\partial f}{\partial\varphi}+v_z\frac{\partial f}{\partial z}+\dot v_r\frac{\partial f}{\partial v_r}+\dot v_\varphi\frac{\partial f}{\partial v_\varphi}+\dot v_z\frac{\partial f}{\partial v_z}=0 \tag{2.4.15}$$

Two variants of the Vlasov equation can be written:

$$\begin{aligned}&\frac{Df}{Dt}=\frac{\partial f}{\partial t}+v_r\frac{\partial f}{\partial r}+\frac{v_\varphi}{r}\frac{\partial f}{\partial\varphi}+v_z\frac{\partial f}{\partial z}+\\&+\left(F_r-\frac{v_\varphi^2}{r}\right)\frac{\partial f}{\partial v_r}+\left(F_\varphi+\frac{v_r v_\varphi}{r}\right)\frac{\partial f}{\partial v_\varphi}+F_z\frac{\partial f}{\partial v_z}=0\end{aligned}, \tag{2.4.16}$$

and

$$\begin{aligned}&\frac{Df}{Dt}=\frac{\partial f}{\partial t}+v_r\frac{\partial f}{\partial r}+\frac{v_\varphi}{r}\frac{\partial f}{\partial\varphi}+v_z\frac{\partial f}{\partial z}-\\&-\left(\frac{v_\varphi^2}{r}+\frac{\partial\Phi}{\partial r}\right)\frac{\partial f}{\partial v_r}+\frac{1}{r}\left(v_r v_\varphi-\frac{\partial\Phi}{\partial\varphi}\right)\frac{\partial f}{\partial v_\varphi}-\frac{\partial\Phi}{\partial z}\frac{\partial f}{\partial v_z}=0\end{aligned} \tag{2.4.17}$$

Two forms (2.4.16), (2.4.17) are coincided with the WOLFRAM information. Alexeev equation can be written in the cylindrical coordinate system as follows

$$\frac{Df}{Dt}-\frac{D}{Dt}\left(\tau\frac{Df}{Dt}\right)=J^B, \tag{2.4.18}$$

where

$$\frac{D}{Dt}=\left[\frac{D}{Dt}\right]_{cyl}=\frac{\partial}{\partial t}+v_r\frac{\partial}{\partial r}+\frac{v_\varphi}{r}\frac{\partial}{\partial\varphi}+v_z\frac{\partial}{\partial z}+$$
$$+\left(F_r-\frac{v_\varphi^2}{r}\right)\frac{\partial}{\partial v_r}+\left(F_\varphi+\frac{v_r v_\varphi}{r}\right)\frac{\partial}{\partial v_\varphi}+F_z\frac{\partial}{\partial v_z} \tag{2.4.19}$$

or

$$\frac{D}{Dt}=\left[\frac{D}{Dt}\right]_{cyl}=\frac{\partial}{\partial t}+v_r\frac{\partial}{\partial r}+\frac{v_\varphi}{r}\frac{\partial}{\partial\varphi}+v_z\frac{\partial}{\partial z}-$$
$$-\left(\frac{v_\varphi^2}{r}+\frac{\partial\Phi}{\partial r}\right)\frac{\partial}{\partial v_r}+\frac{1}{r}\left(v_r v_\varphi-\frac{\partial\Phi}{\partial\varphi}\right)\frac{\partial}{\partial v_\varphi}-\frac{\partial\Phi}{\partial z}{}_z\frac{\partial}{\partial v_z} \tag{2.4.20}$$

2.5. Generalized Boltzmann H-theorem and problems of irreversibility of time, inflation and the Hubble expansion

Boltzmann's *H*-theorem is of principal importance for kinetic theory and provides, in fact, the kinetic substantiation of the theory. The generalized *H*-theorem was proven in 1992 (see, for example, [18, 19]); we present below the main fragments of the derivation. Consider first a simple gas; external forces are absent. Then, the GNKE-equation is reduced to the form

$$\frac{\partial f}{\partial t}-\frac{\partial}{\partial t}\left(\tau\frac{\partial f}{\partial t}\right)=J^B \tag{2.5.1}$$

We will introduce Boltzmann's *H*-function,

$$H=\int f\ln f d\mathbf{v}. \tag{2.5.2}$$

We indicate auxiliary relations

$$\frac{\partial f}{\partial t}\ln f=\frac{\partial}{\partial t}(f\ln f)-\frac{\partial f}{\partial t}, \tag{2.5.3}$$

$$\frac{\partial^2 f}{\partial t^2}\ln f=\frac{\partial^2}{\partial t^2}(f\ln f)-\frac{1}{f}\left(\frac{\partial f}{\partial t}\right)^2-\frac{\partial^2 f}{\partial t^2}. \tag{2.5.4}$$

Let us multiply both parts of equation (2.5.1) by $\ln f$, and transform the equation to the form (2.5.5) using equations (2.5.3), (2.5.4):

$$\frac{\partial}{\partial t}(f\ln f)-\frac{\partial f}{\partial t}-\tau\frac{\partial^2}{\partial t^2}(f\ln f)+\tau\frac{1}{f}\left(\frac{\partial f}{\partial t}\right)^2+\tau\frac{\partial^2 f}{\partial t^2}-$$
$$-\ln f\frac{\partial\tau}{\partial t}\frac{\partial f}{\partial t}=J^B\ln f \tag{2.5.5}$$

or

$$\frac{\partial}{\partial t}(f\ln f)-\tau\frac{\partial^2}{\partial t^2}(f\ln f)+\tau\frac{1}{f}\left(\frac{\partial f}{\partial t}\right)^2-\frac{\partial\tau}{\partial t}\frac{\partial}{\partial t}(f\ln f)= \\ =J^B\ln f+\frac{\partial f}{\partial t}-\tau\frac{\partial^2 f}{\partial t^2}-\frac{\partial\tau}{\partial t}\frac{\partial f}{\partial t} \tag{2.5.6}$$

Using once more (2.5.1) we find

$$\frac{\partial}{\partial t}(f\ln f)-\tau\frac{\partial^2}{\partial t^2}(f\ln f)+\tau\frac{1}{f}\left(\frac{\partial f}{\partial t}\right)^2-\frac{\partial\tau}{\partial t}\frac{\partial}{\partial t}(f\ln f)= \\ =(1+\ln f)J^B \tag{2.5.7}$$

We will now integrate equation (2.5.7) term-by-term with respect to all values of velocities and use the definition of the *H*-function,

$$\frac{dH}{dt}-\tau\frac{d^2H}{dt^2}-\frac{d\tau}{dt}\frac{dH}{dt}=-\tau\int\frac{1}{f}\left(\frac{\partial f}{\partial t}\right)^2 d\mathbf{v}+\int(1+\ln f)J^B d\mathbf{v}\,. \tag{2.5.8}$$

But the following inequalities is valid

$$-\tau\int\frac{1}{f}\left(\frac{\partial f}{\partial t}\right)^2 d\mathbf{v}+\int(1+\ln f)J^B d\mathbf{v}\le 0\,. \tag{2.5.9}$$

Really the first integral in (1.4.9) obviously is not positive, for the second integral Boltzmann's transformation can be applied

$$\int(1+\ln f)J^B d\mathbf{v}=\int(1+\ln f)(f'f_1'-ff_1)gbdbd\varphi d\mathbf{v}d\mathbf{v}_1= \\ =\frac{1}{4}\int(1+\ln f+1+\ln f_1-1-\ln f'-1-\ln f_1')(f'f_1'-ff_1)gbdbd\varphi d\mathbf{v}d\mathbf{v}_1= \\ =\frac{1}{4}\int\ln\frac{ff_1}{f'f_1'}(f'f_1'-ff_1)gbdbd\varphi d\mathbf{v}d\mathbf{v}_1. \tag{2.5.10}$$

The second relation in the chain of equalities (2.5.10) is obtained by formal re-notation of forward and backward collisions with using of the principle of microscopic reversibility which can be written for this case in the form

$$d\mathbf{v}d\mathbf{v}_1=d\mathbf{v}'d\mathbf{v}_1'\,. \tag{2.5.11}$$

Following Boltzmann we notice that the value $\ln\frac{ff_1}{f'f_1'}$ is positive or negative depending on whether ff_1 more than $f'f_1'$ or less. In either case, the sign of $\ln\frac{ff_1}{f'f_1'}$ is opposite of sign of the difference $f'f_1'-ff_1$.

Then one obtains

$$\frac{d}{dt}\left(H-\tau\frac{dH}{dt}\right)\le 0\,. \tag{2.5.12}$$

We will introduce the H^a- function in accordance with the definition

$$H^a=H-\tau\frac{dH}{dt}\,. \tag{2.5.13}$$

Then the inequality is valid that makes up the conclusion of the generalized H-theorem,

$$\frac{dH^a}{dt} \le 0. \tag{2.5.14}$$

If suppose that τ is constant not depending on time, inequality (2.5.14) can be considered as combination of two principles – Boltzmann's principle

$$\frac{dH}{dt} \le 0 \tag{2.5.15}$$

and Prigogine's principle [41, 42]

$$\frac{d^2H}{dt^2} \ge 0. \tag{2.5.16}$$

For closed physical systems H-function is limited function, in particular this function will be restricted from below. In other words integral $\int f \ln f d\mathbf{v}$ does not tends to -∞ if $v \to \infty$, i.e. integral converges.

For this aim consider integral

$$\int f \frac{1}{2} m v^2 d\mathbf{v} = \frac{1}{2} \rho \overline{v^2}, \tag{2.5.17}$$

where ρ is density and upper line connected with averaging of corresponding value.

Integral (2.5.17) is the value of kinetic energy for unit volume and therefore is finite. Suppose that function f decreases with $v \to \infty$ faster than $e^{-\frac{mv^2}{2k_BT}}$, i.e.

$$f < e^{-\frac{mv^2}{2k_BT}} \tag{2.5.18}$$

and

$$\ln f < -\frac{mv^2}{2k_BT}. \tag{2.5.19}$$

Then $\int f \ln f d\mathbf{v} > -\infty$.

If f decreases with $v \to \infty$ slower, than $e^{-\frac{mv^2}{2k_BT}}$, i.e.

$$-\ln f < \frac{mv^2}{2k_BT}, \tag{2.5.20}$$

the convergence of integral $\int f \ln f d\mathbf{v} > -\infty$ is defines with help of (2.5.17). Really, in this case $-f \ln f < \frac{1}{2k_BT} mv^2 f$ and integral of this value should be limited by virtue of (2.5.14), because the kinetic energy of physical system is limited. In all cases integral in (2.5.17) – connected with kinetic energy of closed system - is limited function. During time evolution the decreasing H-function – and therefore H^a- function - is limited when $v \to \infty$.

On this stage of investigation we can state that generalized H-function (H^a) is not increasing function for all hypothetical manners of the H-function behavior.

The possibility of appearance in equilibrium state (if $H^a = 0$) of the exponentially increasing in time H-function (and infinite growth of energy of closed system) on the first glance can be excluded by turning into zero of the constant of integrating. In this case the model of the space homogeneous physical system is not correct. But appearance of growing fluctuations in the local equilibrium state is the extremely important feature of physical statistical systems.

Now what happens to the fluctuations that develop in the system? To see this, consider the generalized equation of continuity, which was "guessed" in Chapter 1 and which is direct consequence of GNKE in hydrodynamic limit

$$\frac{\partial}{\partial t}\left\{\rho - \tau\left[\frac{\partial\rho}{\partial t} + \frac{\partial}{\partial \mathbf{r}} \cdot (\rho\mathbf{v}_0)\right]\right\} +$$
$$+ \frac{\partial}{\partial \mathbf{r}} \cdot \left\{\rho\mathbf{v}_0 - \tau\left[\frac{\partial}{\partial t}(\rho\mathbf{v}_0) + \frac{\partial}{\partial \mathbf{r}} \cdot \rho\mathbf{v}_0\mathbf{v}_0 + \bar{\bar{\mathbf{I}}} \cdot \frac{\partial p}{\partial \mathbf{r}} - \rho\mathbf{a}\right]\right\} = 0, \qquad (2.5.21)$$

This equation we write down here in the generalized Eulerian formulation under the assumption of no external forces and for the one-dimensional unsteady case:

$$\frac{\partial}{\partial t}\left\{\rho - \tau^{(0)}\left[\frac{\partial\rho}{\partial t} + \frac{\partial}{\partial x}(\rho v_0)\right]\right\} + \frac{\partial}{\partial x}(\rho v_0) = \frac{\partial}{\partial x}\left\{\tau^{(0)}\left[\frac{\partial}{\partial t}(\rho v_0) + \frac{\partial}{\partial x}(p + \rho v_0^2)\right]\right\} . (2.5.22)$$

where $\tau^{(0)}$ is the mean time between collisions calculated in the locally Maxwellian approximation: $\tau^{(0)}p = \Pi\mu$ (as was indicated, the factor Π being of order unity; for the hard-sphere model, $\Pi = 0.8$ to first-order approximation in Sonine polynomials [32, 33]).

We shall assume that except for shock-wave-type regions hydrodynamic quantities vary not too rapidly on the scale of the order of the mean time between collisions:

$$\frac{\rho}{\tau^{(0)}} \gg \frac{\partial\rho}{\partial t}, \quad \frac{\rho}{\tau^{(0)}} \gg \frac{\partial}{\partial x}(\rho v_0), \qquad (2.5.23)$$

the temperature variations are small, the convective transfer is negligible, and the chaotic motion is highly energetic as compared to the kinetic energy of the flow, i.e. $\overline{V^2}/v_0^2 \gg 1$ (for example, for hydrogen at normal pressures and temperatures, we have $v_0 = 10cms^{-1}$, giving 3.4 x 10^8 for this ratio). Consequently, equation (2.5.22) becomes

$$\frac{\partial \rho}{\partial t} = \frac{\partial}{\partial x}\left(\frac{\tau^{(0)} p}{\rho}\frac{\partial \rho}{\partial x}\right) \tag{2.5.24}$$

or

$$\frac{\partial \rho}{\partial t} = \frac{\partial}{\partial x}\left(D\frac{\partial \rho}{\partial x}\right), \tag{2.5.25}$$

where $D = \Pi\mu/\rho$ is the self-diffusion coefficient [32, 33]. Equation (2.5.25) is the diffusion equation, with the implication that

(a) A locally increasing density fluctuation immediately activates the diffusion mechanism which smoothes it out, and

(b) The generalized Boltzmann H-theorem proved above ensures that the smoothed fluctuations come to equilibrium.

Relation (2.5.8) can be rewritten as:

$$\frac{dH^a}{dt} = -\tau\int\frac{1}{f}\left(\frac{\partial f}{\partial t}\right)^2 d\mathbf{v} + \frac{1}{4}\int \ln\frac{ff_1}{f'f_1'}(f'f_1' - ff_1)gbdbd\varphi d\mathbf{v}d\mathbf{v}_1. \tag{2.5.26}$$

The second integral in the right-side of equation (2.5.26) is less or equal to zero because of obvious inequality

$$(b-a)\ln\frac{a}{b} \le 0, \tag{2.5.27}$$

where $b = f'f_1', a = ff_1$. Then in stationary state the equality is valid

$$f_1'f' = ff_1, \tag{2.5.28}$$

which leads to the Maxwellian distribution function.

If the Boltzmann *H*-function defined with help of distribution function f obtained from GNKE, in hydrodynamic limit the value $\tau\frac{dH}{dt}$ should be considered as fluctuation of *H*-function on the Kolmogorov's level of the turbulence description; then H^a in relation

$$H^a = H - \tau\frac{dH}{dt} \tag{2.5.29}$$

is averaged value of *H*-function.

For multi-component gas, the analog of equation (2.5.1) has the form

$$\frac{\partial f_\alpha}{\partial t} - \frac{\partial}{\partial t}\left(\tau_\alpha\frac{\partial f_\alpha}{\partial t}\right) = J_\alpha^{B,el}, \quad (\alpha = 1,\ldots,\eta) \tag{2.5.30}$$

As a result, the *H*-function for the component a is written as

$$H_\alpha = \int f_\alpha \ln f_\alpha d\mathbf{v}_\alpha. \tag{2.5.31}$$

Subsequent mathematics is analogous, and therefore, the inequality assumes the following form:

$$\frac{d}{dt}\left(H_\alpha - \tau_\alpha \frac{dH_\alpha}{dt}\right) \le 0 \tag{2.5.32}$$

or

$$\frac{dH_\alpha^a}{dt} \le 0 \tag{2.5.33}$$

The summation over all components leads to the H-function for the mixture,

$$H = \sum_\alpha \int f_\alpha \ln f_\alpha d\mathbf{v}_\alpha, \tag{2.5.34}$$

$$H^a = \sum_\alpha \left(H_\alpha - \tau_\alpha \frac{dH_\alpha}{dt}\right) = H - \sum_{\alpha=1}^{\eta} \tau_\alpha \frac{dH_\alpha}{dt} \tag{2.5.35}$$

and inequality

$$\frac{dH^a}{dt} \le 0, \tag{2.5.36}$$

which results from (2.5.33).

Let chemical reactions proceed in a multi-component gas mixture, for which the integral of bimolecular collisions has the form [17-19] ($\beta, \gamma, \delta = 1,\ldots,\eta$)

$$J_\alpha^{st,nel} = \frac{1}{2}\sum_r \sum_{\beta\gamma\delta} \int \left[\frac{s_\alpha s_\beta}{s_\gamma s_\delta}\left(\frac{m_\alpha m_\beta}{m_\gamma m_\delta}\right)^3 f_\gamma' f_\delta' - f_\alpha f_\beta\right] g_{\alpha\beta} d\overset{r}{\sigma}{}_{\alpha\beta}^{\gamma\delta} d\mathbf{v}_\beta, \tag{2.5.37}$$

where $d\overset{r}{\sigma}{}_{\alpha\beta}^{\gamma\delta}$ is the differential cross section of inelastic collision in the rth reaction

$$A_\alpha + A_\beta \to A_\gamma + A_\delta, \tag{2.5.38}$$

and $s_\alpha, s_\beta, s_\gamma, s_\delta$ are the statistical weights of the energy state of particles $A_\alpha, A_\beta, A_\gamma, A_\delta$, [43]. In this case GNKE has the form:

$$\frac{\partial f_\alpha}{\partial t} - \frac{\partial}{\partial t}\left(\tau_\alpha \frac{\partial f_\alpha}{\partial t}\right) = \sum_j \int \left[f_\alpha' f_j' - f_\alpha f_j\right] g_{\alpha j} d\sigma_{\alpha j}^{\alpha j} d\mathbf{v}_j + \tag{2.5.39}$$
$$+ \frac{1}{2}\sum_r \sum_{\beta\gamma\delta} \int \left[\xi_{\alpha\beta}^{\gamma\delta} f_\gamma' f_\delta' - f_\alpha f_\beta\right] g_{\alpha\beta} d\overset{r}{\sigma}{}_{\alpha\beta}^{\gamma\delta} d\mathbf{v}_\beta.$$

Now, the analog of (2.5.8) after summation over α is written as

$$\sum_\alpha \left[\frac{dH_\alpha}{dt} - \tau_\alpha \frac{d^2 H_\alpha}{dt^2} - \frac{d\tau_\alpha}{dt}\frac{dH_\alpha}{dt}\right] = -\sum_\alpha \tau_\alpha \int \frac{1}{f_\alpha}\left(\frac{\partial f_\alpha}{\partial t}\right)^2 d\mathbf{v}_\alpha +$$
$$+ \sum_\alpha \int (1 + \ln f_\alpha) J_\alpha^{st,el} d\mathbf{v}_\alpha + \frac{1}{2}\sum_{r,\beta,\gamma,\delta,\alpha} \int (1 + \ln f_\alpha)\left(\xi_{\alpha\beta}^{\gamma\delta} f_\gamma' f_\delta' - \right. \tag{2.5.40}$$
$$\left. - f_\alpha f_\beta\right) g_{\alpha\beta} d\overset{r}{\sigma}{}_{\alpha\beta}^{\gamma\delta} d\mathbf{v}_\alpha d\mathbf{v}_\beta.$$

Obviously in integral sum in the write-side of (2.5.40) indexes $\alpha,\beta,\gamma,\delta$ are dummy and the transformation is valid:

$$\sum_r \sum_{\alpha\beta\gamma\delta} \int (1+\ln f_\alpha)\left(\xi_{\alpha\beta}^{\gamma\delta} f'_\gamma f'_\delta - f_\alpha f_\beta\right) g_{\alpha\beta}\, d\overset{r}{\sigma}{}_{\alpha\beta}^{\gamma\delta}\, d\mathbf{v}_\alpha d\mathbf{v}_\beta =$$
$$= \tfrac{1}{4}\sum_r \sum_{\alpha\beta\gamma\delta} \int \ln \frac{f_\alpha f_\beta}{f_\gamma f_\delta}\left(\xi_{\alpha\beta}^{\gamma\delta} f'_\gamma f'_\delta - f_\alpha f_\beta\right) g_{\alpha\beta}\, d\overset{r}{\sigma}{}_{\alpha\beta}^{\gamma\delta}\, d\mathbf{v}_\alpha d\mathbf{v}_\beta, \tag{2.5.41}$$

We use the principle of microscopic reversibility [17]

$$\xi_{\alpha\beta}^{\gamma\delta} g_{\alpha\beta}\, d\overset{r}{\sigma}{}_{\alpha\beta}^{\gamma\delta}\, d\mathbf{v}_\alpha d\mathbf{v}_\beta = g'_{\gamma\sigma}\, d\overset{r}{\sigma}{}_{\gamma\delta}^{\alpha\beta\,\prime}\, d\mathbf{v}'_\gamma d\mathbf{v}'_\delta . \tag{2.5.42}$$

and once again arrive at the formulation of the *H*-theorem

$$\frac{dH^a}{dt} \le 0, \quad H^a = H - \sum_{\alpha=1}^{\eta} \tau_\alpha \frac{dH_\alpha}{dt}, \tag{2.5.43}$$

although, as we can see, inequality (2.5.33) may prove invalid in the presence of chemical reactions.

We will now investigate the thermodynamic inequality (2.5.36) from the standpoint of the existing causal relations and direction of time.

This effect is a direct result of approximation (1.2.7), into which the motion in the direction opposite to the "time arrow" was introduced, so that the state of the system at the given moment of time is defined in a determinate manner by collisions that occurred in the past.

We will introduce the physical principle of causality as some operator which "cuts out," from all events possible at the present moment of time, only the certain event whose causes exist in the past, and which transfers the certain event under consideration in the present into the class of causal relations for some possible event in the future. Thereby, the irreversibility of time is introduced as well. In other words, one cannot speak of the principle of causality without using the concept of irreversibility of time.

What may be the result of formal rejection of the principle of causality in this particular case? If one abandons the additional statement that the cause precedes the effect, τ in relation (2.5.8) may be replaced by $(-\tau)$,

$$\frac{dH^{a'}}{dt} - \tau \int \frac{1}{f}\left(\frac{\partial f}{\partial t}\right)^2 d\mathbf{v} = \frac{1}{4}\int \ln \frac{ff_1}{f'f'_1}\left(f'f'_1 - ff_1\right) g b\, db\, d\varphi\, d\mathbf{v}\, d\mathbf{v}_1 . \tag{2.5.44}$$

where

$$H^{a'} = H + \tau \frac{dH}{dt} \tag{2.5.45}$$

or, to put it differently,

$$\frac{dH^{a'}}{dt} - \tau \int \frac{1}{f} \left(\frac{\partial f}{\partial t} \right)^2 d\mathbf{v} \le 0 . \qquad (2.5.46)$$

Nothing can now be said about the sign of derivative $dH^{a'}/dt$ in (2.5.46). Inequality (2.5.46) may also bold in case $dH^{a'}/dt > 0$, because from this value the nonnegative integral

$\tau \int \frac{1}{f} \left(\frac{\partial f}{\partial t} \right)^2 d\mathbf{v}$ is subtracted, which does not vary when *t* is replaced by (-*t*).

Therefore, the principle of entropy increase follows directly from the principle of irreversibility of time.

Let us return to the relations (2.5.14), (2.5.29) written for the equilibrium state.

$$\frac{dH^{a}}{dt} = \frac{d}{dt} \left(H - \tau \frac{dH}{dt} \right) = 0 , \qquad (2.5.47)$$

or

$$H - \tau \frac{dH}{dt} = C = const . \qquad (2.5.48)$$

Taking into account that the energy reference level can be chosen arbitrarily we write down (2.5.48) in the form

$$H = \tau \frac{dH}{dt} . \qquad (2.5.49)$$

Let us suppose now that nonlocal parameter τ is constant, then after integration

$$H = \exp(t / \tau) . \qquad (2.5.50)$$

Remarks:

1. Relation (2.5.50) defines the exponential grows energy H in the physical systems in which there are no relaxation mechanisms similar to diffusion (see (2.5.25)).
2. Relation (2.5.50) is introduced as a postulate in so called inflation theory. In cosmology inflation is a theory of exponential expansion of space expansion in the early universe. One supposes that the inflation epoch lasted from 10^{-36} seconds after the conjectured Big Bang singularity to some time between 10^{-33} and 10^{-32} seconds after the singularity. Following the inflationary period, the universe continues to expand, but at a less rapid rate.
3. As we see inflation theory cannot be applied to the early Plank period of Big Bang; inflation theory has no Cauchy conditions and practically needs in the matter existing without relaxation mechanisms.

H-function is proportional to the square of velocity v^2 of the expansion. From (2.5.49) follows

$$v^2 = 2v\tau \frac{dv}{dt} \qquad (2.5.51)$$

or

$$\frac{dv}{dt} = \frac{1}{2\tau} v . \qquad (2.5.52)$$

After integration the both parts of (2.5.52) by time variable we find

$$v = \frac{1}{2} \int_0^t \frac{v}{\tau} dt . \qquad (2.5.53)$$

If nonlocal parameter τ is constant, then

$$v = \frac{1}{2\tau} r , \qquad (2.5.54)$$

where r is radius of the expanding physical system including Universe.

We conclude that Hubble relation (Hu is the Hubble constant)

$$v = \mathrm{Hu}\ r \qquad (2.5.55)$$

is

1. The deep particular case of nonlocal physics.
2. Hubble relation cannot be obtained by the methods of local physics.
3. Hubble relation corresponds to the constant nonlocal parameter $\mathrm{Hu} = \frac{1}{2\tau}$.
4. Hubble regime corresponds to the Universe expansion with acceleration even if Hu=const, namely after differentiating (2.5.55) by time we find

$$\frac{dv}{dt} = \mathrm{Hu}^2 r . \qquad (2.5.56)$$

5. Usually so called the regime of the Universe expansion with acceleration corresponds to the dependence $\tau = \tau(t)$ and to the deviation of (2.5.53) to the direction of the addition acceleration or deceleration of the physical process of the expanding.
6. Moreover the dependences $\tau = \tau(t)$ can exist leading to the backward motion of Universe.

2.6. Fundamental nonlocal parameter τ.

In principle GHE needn't in using of the "time-energy" uncertainty relation for estimation of the value of the non-locality parameter τ. Moreover the "time-energy" uncertainty relation does not lead to the exact relations and from position of non-local physics is only the simplest estimation of the non-local effects. Really (see also Chapter 1), let us consider two neighboring physically infinitely small volumes $\mathbf{PhSV}_1$ and $\mathbf{PhSV}_2$ in a non-equilibrium system. Obviously the time τ should tend to diminishing with increasing of the velocities u of particles invading in the nearest neighboring physically infinitely small volume (**PhSV**$_1$ or **PhSV**$_2$):

$$\tau = H_\tau / u^n . \tag{2.6.1}$$

But the value τ cannot depend on the velocity direction and naturally to tie τ with the particle kinetic energy, then

$$\tau = H_\tau / \left(mu^2\right), \tag{2.6.2}$$

where H_τ is a coefficient of proportionality, which reflects the state of physical system. In the simplest case H_τ is equal to Plank constant $\hbar$ and relation (2.6.2) becomes compatible with the Heisenberg relation. Possible approximations of τ - parameter in details in the monographs [18 - 22] are considered. But some remarks of the principal significance should be done.

It is known that Ehrenfest adiabatic theorem is one of the most important and widely studied theorems in Schrödinger quantum mechanics. It states that if we have a slowly changing Hamiltonian that depends on time, and the system is prepared in one of the instantaneous eigenstates of the Hamiltonian then the state of the system at any time is given by an the instantaneous eigenfunction of the Hamiltonian up to multiplicative phase factors.

The adiabatic theory can be naturally incorporated in generalized quantum hydrodynamics based on local approximations of non-local terms. In the simplest case if ΔQ is the elementary heat quantity delivered for a system executing the transfer from one state (the corresponding time moment is t_{in}) to the next one (the time moment t_e) then

$$\Delta Q = \frac{1}{\tau} 2\delta\left(\overline{T}\tau\right), \tag{2.6.3}$$

where $\tau = t_e - t_{in}$ and $\overline{T}$ is the average kinetic energy. For adiabatic case Ehrenfest supposes that

$$2\overline{T}\tau = \Omega_1, \Omega_2, ... \tag{2.6.4}$$

where $\Omega_1, \Omega_2, ...$ are adiabatic invariants. Obviously for Plank's oscillator

$$2\overline{T}\tau = nh . \tag{2.6.5}$$

Then the adiabatic theorem and consequences of this theory deliver the general quantization conditions for non-local quantum hydrodynamics.

In the important problem of nonlocal plasma physics we intend to obtain the soliton solutions of the generalized hydrodynamic equations (GHE) in the self-consistent electric field. In this case, all the elements of a possible plasma formation of the soliton type must move with the same translational velocity.

Consequently, the GHE system consists of the generalized Poisson equation (reflecting the effects of charge fluctuations and density flux of charge), two equations of continuity for positively and negatively charged components (in particular, for electrons and ions), equation of motion and two equations of energy for positive and negatively charged components. This system of six *non-stationary one-dimensional* equations can be written in the form ([18-22]):

(Poisson's Equation)

$$\frac{\partial^2\psi}{\partial x^2} = -4\pi e\left\{\left[n_i - \tau_i\left(\frac{\partial n_i}{\partial t} + \frac{\partial}{\partial x}(n_i u)\right)\right] - \left[n_e - \tau_e\left(\frac{\partial n_e}{\partial t} + \frac{\partial}{\partial x}(n_e u)\right)\right]\right\}, \qquad (2.6.6)$$

(Continuity equation for a positively charged component),

$$\frac{\partial}{\partial t}\left\{\rho_i - \tau_i\left[\frac{\partial \rho_i}{\partial t} + \frac{\partial}{\partial x}(\rho_i u)\right]\right\} + \frac{\partial}{\partial x}\left\{\rho_i u - \tau_i\left[\frac{\partial}{\partial t}(\rho_i u) + \frac{\partial}{\partial x}(\rho_i u^2) + \frac{\partial p_i}{\partial x} - \rho_i F_i\right]\right\} = 0, \qquad (2.6.7)$$

(The equation of continuity for the negatively charged component),

$$\frac{\partial}{\partial t}\left\{\rho_e - \tau_e\left[\frac{\partial \rho_e}{\partial t} + \frac{\partial}{\partial x}(\rho_e u)\right]\right\} + \frac{\partial}{\partial x}\left\{\rho_e u - \tau_e\left[\frac{\partial}{\partial t}(\rho_e u) + \frac{\partial}{\partial x}(\rho_e u^2) + \frac{\partial p_e}{\partial x} - \rho_e F_e\right]\right\} = 0,$$

(2.6.8)

(Equation of motion)

$$\frac{\partial}{\partial t}\left\{\rho u - \tau_i\left[\frac{\partial}{\partial t}(\rho_i u) + \frac{\partial}{\partial x}(p_i + \rho_i u^2) - \rho_i F_i\right] - \tau_e\left[\frac{\partial}{\partial t}(\rho_e u) + \frac{\partial}{\partial x}(p_e + \rho_e u^2) - \rho_e F_e\right]\right\}$$

$$-\rho_i F_i - \rho_e F_e + F_i \tau_i\left(\frac{\partial \rho_i}{\partial t} + \frac{\partial}{\partial x}(\rho_i u)\right) + F_e \tau_e\left(\frac{\partial \rho_e}{\partial t} + \frac{\partial}{\partial x}(\rho_e u)\right) \qquad (2.6.9)$$

$$+\frac{\partial}{\partial x}\left\{\begin{array}{l}\rho u^2 + p - \tau_i\left[\frac{\partial}{\partial t}(\rho_i u^2 + p_i) + \frac{\partial}{\partial x}(\rho_i u^3 + 3 p_i u) - 2\rho_i u F_i\right] - \\ - \tau_e\left[\frac{\partial}{\partial t}(\rho_e u^2 + p_e) + \frac{\partial}{\partial x}(\rho_e u^3 + 3 p_e u)\right] - 2\rho_e u F_e\end{array}\right\} = 0,$$

(The energy equation for a positively charged component)

$$\frac{\partial}{\partial t}\left\{\rho_i u^2 + 3p_i - \tau_i\left[\frac{\partial}{\partial t}(\rho_i u^2 + 3p_i) + \frac{\partial}{\partial x}(\rho_i u^3 + 5p_i u) - 2\rho_i F_i u\right]\right\}$$

$$+\frac{\partial}{\partial x}\left\{\rho_i u^3 + 5p_i u - \tau_i\left[\frac{\partial}{\partial t}(\rho_i u^3 + 5p_i u) + \frac{\partial}{\partial x}\left(\rho_i u^4 + 8p_i u^2 + 5\frac{p_i^2}{\rho_i}\right) - F_i(3\rho_i u^2 + 5p_i)\right]\right\}$$

$$-2u\rho_i F_i + 2\tau_i F_i\left[\frac{\partial}{\partial t}(\rho_i u) + \frac{\partial}{\partial x}(\rho_i u^2 + p_i) - \rho_i F_i\right] = -\frac{p_i - p_e}{\tau_{ei}},$$

(2.6.10)

(The energy equation for the negatively charged component)

$$\frac{\partial}{\partial t}\left\{\rho_e u^2+3p_e-\tau_e\left[\frac{\partial}{\partial t}\left(\rho_e u^2+3p_e\right)+\frac{\partial}{\partial x}\left(\rho_e u^3+5p_e u\right)-2\rho_e F_e u\right]\right\}$$
$$+\frac{\partial}{\partial x}\left\{\rho_e u^3+5p_e u-\tau_e\left[\frac{\partial}{\partial t}\left(\rho_e u^3+5p_e u\right)+\frac{\partial}{\partial x}\left(\rho_e u^4+8p_e u^2+5\frac{p_e^2}{\rho_e}\right)-F_e\left(3\rho_e u^2+5p_e\right)\right]\right\}$$
$$-2u\rho_e F_e+2\tau_e F_e\left[\frac{\partial}{\partial t}\left(\rho_e u\right)+\frac{\partial}{\partial x}\left(\rho_e u^2+p_e\right)-\rho_e F_e\right]=-\frac{p_e-p_i}{\tau_{ei}},$$

(2.6.11)

where u is the translational velocity of the quantum object, ψ - the scalar potential, n_i and n_e are the numerical density of charged components, and F_i and F_e are the forces acting on the unit mass of positively and negatively charged particles.

Approximations for a nonlocal parameters τ_i, τ_e and τ_{ei}, need an additional explanation. The following approximations for τ_i and τ_e

$$\tau_i = H_\tau / m_i u^2, \quad \tau_e = H_\tau / m_e u^2. \tag{2.6.12}$$

correspond to the (2.6.2). For non-local interaction parameter of positive and negative particles (in particular, the electron – ion interaction) τ_{ei} is applicable the ratio

$$\frac{1}{\tau_{ei}}=\frac{1}{\tau_e}+\frac{1}{\tau_i} \tag{2.6.13}$$

In this case, the parameter τ_{ei} corresponds to the relaxation time of different species in the process of interaction. Conversion (2.6.13) is consistent with the Heisenberg's uncertainty principle if $H=\hbar$. From (2.6.13) follows

$$\frac{1}{\tau_{ei}}=\frac{\tau_e+\tau_i}{\tau_e\tau_i}=\frac{\dfrac{\hbar}{m_e u^2}+\dfrac{\hbar}{m_i u^2}}{\dfrac{\hbar^2}{u^4}\dfrac{1}{m_e m_i}}=\frac{u^2}{\hbar}\left(m_e+m_i\right). \tag{2.6.14}$$

Then

$$u^2\left(m_e+m_i\right)\tau_{ei}=\hbar. \tag{2.6.15}$$

Equation (2.6.15) is an obvious consequence of the uncertainty relation for the combined particle which mass is equal to m_i+m_e.

Under the differencing scheme is usually understood a system of differential equations, (with additional conditions) chosen for description a particular problem of mathematical physics. Let some linear non-stationary problem of mathematical physics be considered. It can be interpreted as an abstract Cauchy problem

$$B(t)\frac{du(t)}{dt}+A(t)u(t)=f(t),\ 0<t\leq T,\ u(0)=u_0; \qquad (2.6.16)$$

here operators $A(t)$ and $B(t)$ defined on everywhere dense set of Banach spaces S_B. When the initial problem is approximated by a finite difference scheme, the space S_B is replaced by a family of finite-dimensional spaces S_f. The segment [0, T] is replaced by the grid

$$t_n = n\tau;\ n=0,1,...K;\ K\tau = T.$$

The operators $A(t)$ and $B(t)$ are replaced by difference operators acting in space S_f, and derivative $\frac{du(t)}{dt}$ - by a difference relation $\frac{u(t_{n+1})-u(t_n)}{\tau}$. As a result, we obtain the operator-difference equation

$$By_t + Ay = \varphi,\ y(t=0)=y_0. \qquad (2.6.17)$$

Equation (2.6.17) is a two-layer finite-difference scheme, because it binds the values of the unknown value $y(t)$ on two time layers $t=t_n$ and $t=t_{n+1}$. The record of a two-layer difference scheme in the form of (2.6.17) is known as a canonical form. Along with (2.6.17) we consider the equation with zero the right-hand side

$$By_t + Ay = 0,\ y(t=0)=y_0. \qquad (2.6.18)$$

A two-layer difference scheme (1.3.18) defined in the linear space S_f. Suppose that in S_f the norms $\|y(t)\|$ is introduced, which measure the solution of problem (1.3.18).

Definition 1. Scheme (2.6.18) is called stable if there exist constant M, independent of the numerical steps in space and time such that for any y_0 the solution of the problem (2.6.18)) can be estimated as

$$\|y(t_{n+1})\| \leq M\|y(0)\|. \qquad (2.6.19)$$

It means that in this case scheme (1.3.18) is stable on initial data. Let in Gibert space H be given a self-adjoint positive operator D.

Definition 2. The *energy* space H_D is the linear space H in which the scalar product $(y,v)_D = (Dy,v)$ and the norm $\|y\|_D = \sqrt{(Dy,y)}$ are introduced.

Definition 3. The difference scheme (2.6.18) is called a stable in H_D space, if any $y_n \in H_D$ and all $n=0,1,...$ for the solution of y_{n+1} of problem (1.3.18) the estimation

$$\|y_{n+1}\|_D \leq \|y_n\|_D \qquad (2.6.20)$$

is valid.

Thus, stability in this sense is uniform stability according to initial data, and the constant M is equal to one (see definition (2.6.19)). We consider scheme (2.6.18) with operators A and B acting in Hilbert space H. We formulate a basic theorem that proves the stability of the scheme (2.6.18) in the energetic space H_A constructed by the operator A of the scheme (1.3.18).

Theorem (A. A. Samarskii, [44]):

Let the operator A is self-adjoint and positive operator and does not depend on n. If exists the operator B^{-1} then for stability of the scheme (2.6.18) in H_A it is necessary and sufficient the implementation of operator non-equality

$$B_0 \geq \frac{1}{2}\tau A \tag{2.6.21}$$

where

$$B_0 = \frac{1}{2}\left(B + B^*\right). \tag{2.6.22}$$

We give an interpretation of this inequality (2.6.21) from a physical point of view. The relation (2.6.22) can be written in other form supposing that B is a real operator

$$\frac{1}{2}\tau A \leq B. \tag{2.6.23}$$

Let $\frac{1}{2}A = E$ correspond to the energy of a physical system and $B = \hbar$ is Planck constant in the limit case. We reach the relation

$$\tau_s E \leq \hbar, \tag{2.6.24}$$

where τ_s is a time step in the difference scheme. In particular

$$\frac{1}{2}\tau_s u^2 \leq \frac{\hbar}{m_e}, \tag{2.6.25}$$

where

$$\nu_{e,qu} = \frac{\hbar}{m_e} = 1.1577 \frac{cm^2}{s} \tag{2.6.26}$$

is the quantum kinematic viscosity for electron component. Let us denote

$$\nu_{mesh} = \frac{1}{2}\tau_s u^2 \tag{2.6.27}$$

as a mesh kinematic viscosity. Then in this case it should be

$$\nu_{mesh} \leq \nu_{e,qu}. \tag{2.6.28}$$

The well-known Heisenberg's uncertainty principle can be written in the form "energy - time" (compare with (2.6.2)).

$$\tau_H E \geq \hbar. \tag{2.6.29}$$

Let us denote also

$$v_H = \frac{1}{2}\tau_H u^2 \qquad (2.6.30)$$

Then the choice of the approximations in the form (2.6.12) is reasonable also from the position of the numerical calculations on the quantum level and for the electron species corresponds to relation

$$v_{mesh} = v_{e,qu} = v_{e,H} \,. \qquad (2.6.31)$$

More details in the theory of the τ approximation can be found in [18 - 23].

Generalized hydrodynamic equations (GHE) should contain Schrödinger equation (SE) as a deep special case. This affirmation was proved in articles [28, 29]. In other words, we formulated in explicit form all assumptions (all steps) that should be implemented to obtain SE from the GNKE and GHE. At the final stage, for simplicity, a non – stationary 1D model of the Madelung-Schrödinger was obtained without taking into account external forces.

So, we can state that SE is a deep special case of generalized hydrodynamic equations. This means that a new quantum mechanics of dissipative processes has been created.

Note that the Schrödinger equation and its equivalent hydrodynamic form of Madelung do not describe dissipative processes and therefore cannot be effectively used in nanotechnology. The Boltzmann equation essentially "does not work" at the distances of the order of the radius of interaction of particles and, therefore, can not be effectively used in the theoretical study of nanotechnology even in the framework of "plausible" models.

GHE have extremely important for astrophysics special cases when density $\rho \to 0$ (the initial stage of evolution of the Universe, the Big Bang) and when density $\rho \to \infty$ (evolution of the black hole). Both limiting cases have no physical or mathematical meaning in "classical" hydrodynamics. Thus, we have a unified statistical theory of dissipative structures, which has a hydrodynamic shape. We will, as already mentioned, refer to the corresponding system of equations as the fundamental equations of the unified theory (UT)

A rhetorical question arises - why does the Schrödinger equation work at all?

2.7. Fluctuations of hydrodynamic quantities. Nonlocal Maxwell equations.

From position of kinetic theory the appearance of τ-terms can be considered as fluctuations in the strict theory of turbulence, [19, 20]. Consequently, this system of equations contains more unknowns (namely, averaged values $\rho^a, (\rho\mathbf{v}_0)^a, p^a, (\rho\mathbf{v}_0\mathbf{v}_0)^a$, and $\left[\mathbf{v}_0\left(\rho v_0^2+5p\right)\right]^a$) than equations, thus presenting the typical problem of the classical theory of turbulence, which consists in closing the moment equations.

In our theory the solution of this problem consists simply in returning to equations written for real, genuine hydrodynamic values. And only in situation when micro-scale turbulent fluctuations are absent we reach classical Euler equations.

Table 2.7.1. Fluctuations of hydrodynamic quantities on the Kolmogorov scale in the framework of the generalized Euler equations.

№	Hydrodynamic value A	Fluctuation A^f
1	ρ	$\tau\left[\frac{\partial\rho}{\partial t}+\frac{\partial}{\partial\mathbf{r}}\cdot(\rho\mathbf{v}_0)\right]$
2	$\rho\mathbf{v}_0$	$\tau\left[\frac{\partial}{\partial t}(\rho\mathbf{v}_0)+\frac{\partial}{\partial\mathbf{r}}\cdot(\rho\mathbf{v}_0\mathbf{v}_0)+\frac{\partial p}{\partial\mathbf{r}}-\rho\mathbf{g}\right]$
3	$\mathbf{v}_0$	$\tau\left[\frac{\partial\mathbf{v}_0}{\partial t}+\left(\mathbf{v}_0\cdot\frac{\partial}{\partial\mathbf{r}}\right)\mathbf{v}_0+\frac{1}{\rho}\frac{\partial p}{\partial\mathbf{r}}-\mathbf{g}\right]$
4	$p\delta_{\alpha\beta}+\rho v_{0\alpha}v_{0\beta}$	$\tau\left[\frac{\partial}{\partial t}(p\delta_{\alpha\beta}+\rho v_{0\alpha}v_{0\beta})+\frac{\partial}{\partial r_\gamma}(p v_{0\alpha}\delta_{\beta\gamma}+\right.$ $+p v_{0\beta}\delta_{\alpha\gamma}+p v_{0\gamma}\delta_{\alpha\beta}+\rho v_{0\alpha}v_{0\beta}v_{0\gamma})$ $\left.-g_\beta\rho v_{0\alpha}-g_\alpha\rho v_{0\beta}\right]$
5	$3p+\rho v_0^2$	$\tau\left[\frac{\partial}{\partial t}(3p+\rho v_0^2)+\right.$ $\left.+\frac{\partial}{\partial\mathbf{r}}\cdot\left(\mathbf{v}_0\left(\rho v_0^2+5p\right)\right)-2\mathbf{g}\cdot\rho\mathbf{v}_0\right]$
6	p	$\tau\left[\frac{\partial p}{\partial t}+\frac{\partial}{\partial\mathbf{r}}\cdot(p\mathbf{v}_0)+\frac{2}{3}p\frac{\partial}{\partial\mathbf{r}}\cdot\mathbf{v}_0\right]$
7	$\mathbf{v}_0\left(\rho v_0^2+5p\right)$	$\tau\left\{\frac{\partial}{\partial t}\left[\mathbf{v}_0\left(\rho v_0^2+5p\right)\right]+\frac{\partial}{\partial\mathbf{r}}\cdot\left[\rho v_0^2\mathbf{v}_0\mathbf{v}_0++\ddot{\mathrm{I}}p v_0^2+7p\mathbf{v}_0\mathbf{v}_0+5\ddot{\mathrm{I}}\frac{p^2}{\rho}\right]\right.$ $-2\rho\mathbf{v}_0\mathbf{v}_0\cdot\mathbf{g}-5p\ddot{\mathrm{I}}\cdot\mathbf{g}-\rho v_0^2\ddot{\mathrm{I}}\cdot\mathbf{g}-p\left[\frac{\partial}{\partial\mathbf{r}}\left(5\frac{p}{\rho}+v_0^2\right)+\right.$ $\left.\left.+2\left(\mathbf{v}_0\cdot\frac{\partial}{\partial\mathbf{r}}\right)\mathbf{v}_0-\frac{4}{3}\mathbf{v}_0\left(\frac{\partial}{\partial\mathbf{r}}\cdot\mathbf{v}_0\right)\right]\right\}$

Maxwell electro dynamical equations also should contain the corresponding fluctuations. Really let us write down the classical Maxwell equations in the usual notations.

$$\frac{\partial}{\partial \mathbf{r}} \cdot \mathbf{D} = \rho , \tag{2.7.1}$$

$$\frac{\partial}{\partial \mathbf{r}} \cdot \mathbf{B} = 0 , \tag{2.7.2}$$

$$\frac{\partial}{\partial \mathbf{r}} \times \mathbf{E} = -\frac{\partial \mathbf{B}}{\partial t} , \tag{2.7.3}$$

$$\frac{\partial}{\partial \mathbf{r}} \times \mathbf{H} = \frac{\partial \mathbf{D}}{\partial t} + \mathbf{j} , \tag{2.7.4}$$

where ρ and $\mathbf{j}$ are the charge and current densities respectively. In the general case

$$\mathbf{D} = \varepsilon\varepsilon_0 \mathbf{E} , \tag{2.7.5}$$

$$\mathbf{B} = \mu\mu_0 \mathbf{H} . \tag{2.7.6}$$

Taking into account fluctuations we find

$$\varepsilon_0 \frac{\partial}{\partial \mathbf{r}} \cdot \left[\left(\varepsilon^0 + \varepsilon^{fl} \right) \mathbf{E} \right] = \rho^a + \rho^{fl} , \tag{2.7.7}$$

$$\mu_0 \frac{\partial}{\partial \mathbf{r}} \cdot \left[\left(\mu^a + \mu^{fl} \right) \mathbf{H} \right] = 0 , \tag{2.7.8}$$

$$\frac{\partial}{\partial \mathbf{r}} \times \mathbf{E} = -\mu_0 \frac{\partial}{\partial t} \left[\left(\mu^a + \mu^{fl} \right) \mathbf{H} \right] , \tag{2.7.9}$$

$$\frac{\partial}{\partial \mathbf{r}} \times \mathbf{H} = \varepsilon_0 \frac{\partial}{\partial t} \left[\left(\varepsilon^0 + \varepsilon^{fl} \right) \mathbf{E} \right] + \mathbf{j}^a + \mathbf{j}^{fl} , \tag{2.7.10}$$

2.8. The nonlocal theory of longitudinal electromagnetic waves.

We use generalized nonlocal Maxwell equations to prove the existence of longitudinal electromagnetic waves. To this end let's differentiate in time both parts of the equation (2.7.8).

$$\frac{\partial}{\partial t} \left[\frac{\partial}{\partial \mathbf{r}} \times \mathbf{H} \right] = \frac{\partial^2 \mathbf{D}}{\partial t^2} + \frac{\partial}{\partial t} \mathbf{j}^c , \tag{2.8.1}$$

where $\mathbf{j}^c = \mathbf{j}^a + \mathbf{j}^{fl}$, or

$$\frac{\partial}{\partial \mathbf{r}} \times \frac{\partial}{\partial t} \left(\mu\mu_0 \mathbf{H} \frac{1}{\mu\mu_0} \right) = \frac{\partial^2 \mathbf{D}}{\partial t^2} + \frac{\partial}{\partial t} \mathbf{j}^c \tag{2.8.2}$$

or

$$\frac{\partial}{\partial \mathbf{r}} \times \left[\frac{1}{\mu\mu_0} \frac{\partial}{\partial t} [\mu\mu_0 \mathbf{H}] + \mu \mathbf{H} \frac{\partial}{\partial t} \frac{1}{\mu} \right] = \frac{\partial^2 \mathbf{D}}{\partial t^2} + \frac{\partial}{\partial t} \mathbf{j}^c \tag{2.8.3}$$

or

$$\frac{\partial}{\partial \mathbf{r}}\times\left[\frac{1}{\mu\mu_0}\frac{\partial}{\partial t}[\mu\mu_0\mathbf{H}]-\mathbf{H}\frac{\partial \ln\mu}{\partial t}\right]=\frac{\partial^2\mathbf{D}}{\partial t^2}+\frac{\partial}{\partial t}\mathbf{j}^c. \tag{2.8.4}$$

Obviously the second term in the square bracket can be omitted with the good accuracy, we find

$$\frac{\partial}{\partial \mathbf{r}}\times\left[\frac{1}{\mu\mu_0}\frac{\partial}{\partial t}[\mu\mu_0\mathbf{H}]\right]=\frac{\partial^2\mathbf{D}}{\partial t^2}+\frac{\partial}{\partial t}\mathbf{j}^c \tag{2.8.5}$$

and using (2.7.7)

$$\frac{\partial}{\partial \mathbf{r}}\times\left[\frac{1}{\mu\mu_0}\frac{\partial}{\partial \mathbf{r}}\times\mathbf{E}\right]=-\frac{\partial^2\mathbf{D}}{\partial t^2}-\frac{\partial}{\partial t}\mathbf{j}^c, \tag{2.8.6}$$

It is known that the double vector product is

$$\mathbf{a}\times\mathbf{b}\times\mathbf{c}=\mathbf{b}(\mathbf{a}\cdot\mathbf{c})-\mathbf{c}(\mathbf{a}\cdot\mathbf{b}). \tag{2.8.7}$$

Then the formal application the identity (2.8.7) containing the vector differential operators $\frac{\partial}{\partial \mathbf{r}}$ leads to relation

$$\frac{\partial}{\partial \mathbf{r}}\times\left[\frac{1}{\mu\mu_0}\frac{\partial}{\partial \mathbf{r}}\times\mathbf{E}\right]=\frac{1}{\mu\mu_0}\frac{\partial}{\partial \mathbf{r}}\left[\frac{\partial}{\partial \mathbf{r}}\cdot\mathbf{E}\right]-\frac{1}{\mu\mu_0}\left(\frac{\partial}{\partial \mathbf{r}}\cdot\frac{\partial}{\partial \mathbf{r}}\right)\mathbf{E}. \tag{2.8.8}$$

or in another notations

$$\frac{\partial}{\partial \mathbf{r}}\times\left[\frac{1}{\mu\mu_0}\frac{\partial}{\partial \mathbf{r}}\times\mathbf{E}\right]=\frac{1}{\mu\mu_0}\frac{\partial}{\partial \mathbf{r}}\left[\frac{\partial}{\partial \mathbf{r}}\cdot\mathbf{E}\right]-\frac{1}{\mu\mu_0}\Delta\mathbf{E}. \tag{2.8.9}$$

Let us show by the direct calculation that the relation (2.8.7) is valid also for this case with some restrictions. Really we have for the vector products

$$\frac{\partial}{\partial \mathbf{r}}\times\mathbf{E}=\left(\frac{\partial}{\partial y}E_z-\frac{\partial}{\partial z}E_y\right)\mathbf{i}+\left(\frac{\partial}{\partial z}E_x-\frac{\partial}{\partial x}E_z\right)\mathbf{j}+\left(\frac{\partial}{\partial x}E_y-\frac{\partial}{\partial y}E_x\right)\mathbf{k} \tag{2.8.10}$$

and

$$\frac{\partial}{\partial \mathbf{r}}\times\frac{1}{\mu\mu_0}\left[\left(\frac{\partial}{\partial y}E_z-\frac{\partial}{\partial z}E_y\right)\mathbf{i}+\left(\frac{\partial}{\partial z}E_x-\frac{\partial}{\partial x}E_z\right)\mathbf{j}+\left(\frac{\partial}{\partial x}E_y-\frac{\partial}{\partial y}E_x\right)\mathbf{k}\right]=$$
$$=\frac{\partial}{\partial \mathbf{r}}\times\left[\frac{1}{\mu\mu_0}\left(\frac{\partial}{\partial y}E_z-\frac{\partial}{\partial z}E_y\right)\mathbf{i}\right]+\frac{\partial}{\partial \mathbf{r}}\times\left[\frac{1}{\mu\mu_0}\left(\frac{\partial}{\partial z}E_x-\frac{\partial}{\partial x}E_z\right)\mathbf{j}\right]+\frac{\partial}{\partial \mathbf{r}}\times\left[\frac{1}{\mu\mu_0}\left(\frac{\partial}{\partial x}E_y-\frac{\partial}{\partial y}E_x\right)\mathbf{k}\right] \tag{2.8.11}$$

$$\frac{\partial}{\partial \mathbf{r}}\times\left[\frac{1}{\mu\mu_0}\left(\frac{\partial}{\partial y}E_z-\frac{\partial}{\partial z}E_y\right)\mathbf{i}\right]=\frac{\partial}{\partial z}\left[\frac{1}{\mu\mu_0}\left(\frac{\partial}{\partial y}E_z-\frac{\partial}{\partial z}E_y\right)\right]\mathbf{j}-\frac{\partial}{\partial y}\left[\frac{1}{\mu\mu_0}\left(\frac{\partial}{\partial y}E_z-\frac{\partial}{\partial z}E_y\right)\right]\mathbf{k}, \tag{2.8.12}$$

$$\frac{\partial}{\partial \mathbf{r}}\times\left[\frac{1}{\mu\mu_0}\left(\frac{\partial}{\partial z}E_x-\frac{\partial}{\partial x}E_z\right)\mathbf{j}\right]=-\frac{\partial}{\partial z}\left[\frac{1}{\mu\mu_0}\left(\frac{\partial}{\partial z}E_x-\frac{\partial}{\partial x}E_z\right)\right]\mathbf{i}+\frac{\partial}{\partial x}\left[\frac{1}{\mu\mu_0}\left(\frac{\partial}{\partial z}E_x-\frac{\partial}{\partial x}E_z\right)\right]\mathbf{k}, \tag{2.8.13}$$

$$\frac{\partial}{\partial \mathbf{r}}\times\left[\frac{1}{\mu\mu_0}\left(\frac{\partial}{\partial x}E_y-\frac{\partial}{\partial y}E_x\right)\mathbf{k}\right]=\frac{\partial}{\partial y}\left[\frac{1}{\mu\mu_0}\left(\frac{\partial}{\partial x}E_y-\frac{\partial}{\partial y}E_x\right)\right]\mathbf{i}-\frac{\partial}{\partial x}\left[\frac{1}{\mu\mu_0}\left(\frac{\partial}{\partial x}E_y-\frac{\partial}{\partial y}E_x\right)\right]\mathbf{j} \tag{2.8.14}$$

Let us transform (2.8.12)

$$\begin{aligned}&\frac{\partial}{\partial z}\left[\frac{1}{\mu\mu_0}\left(\frac{\partial}{\partial y}E_z-\frac{\partial}{\partial z}E_y\right)\right]\mathbf{j}-\frac{\partial}{\partial y}\left[\frac{1}{\mu\mu_0}\left(\frac{\partial}{\partial y}E_z-\frac{\partial}{\partial z}E_y\right)\right]\mathbf{k}=\\&=\frac{1}{\mu\mu_0}\frac{\partial}{\partial z}\left(\frac{\partial}{\partial y}E_z-\frac{\partial}{\partial z}E_y\right)\mathbf{j}-\left(\frac{\partial}{\partial y}E_z-\frac{\partial}{\partial z}E_y\right)\frac{1}{\mu_0\mu^2}\frac{\partial\mu}{\partial z}\mathbf{j}-\\&-\frac{1}{\mu\mu_0}\frac{\partial}{\partial y}\left(\frac{\partial}{\partial y}E_z-\frac{\partial}{\partial z}E_y\right)\mathbf{k}+\left(\frac{\partial}{\partial y}E_z-\frac{\partial}{\partial z}E_y\right)\frac{1}{\mu_0\mu^2}\frac{\partial\mu}{\partial z}\mathbf{k}=\\&=\frac{1}{\mu\mu_0}\frac{\partial}{\partial z}\left(\frac{\partial}{\partial y}E_z-\frac{\partial}{\partial z}E_y\right)\mathbf{j}-\left(\frac{\partial}{\partial y}E_z-\frac{\partial}{\partial z}E_y\right)\frac{1}{\mu_0\mu}\frac{\partial\ln\mu}{\partial z}\mathbf{j}-\\&-\frac{1}{\mu\mu_0}\frac{\partial}{\partial y}\left(\frac{\partial}{\partial y}E_z-\frac{\partial}{\partial z}E_y\right)\mathbf{k}+\left(\frac{\partial}{\partial y}E_z-\frac{\partial}{\partial z}E_y\right)\frac{1}{\mu_0\mu}\frac{\partial\ln\mu}{\partial z}\mathbf{k}\end{aligned} \tag{2.8.15}$$

Let us omit now not only time derivatives of the logarithmic terms of the magnet permeability but also space derivatives of the logarithmic terms of the magnet permeability. We find

$$\begin{aligned}&\frac{\partial}{\partial z}\left[\frac{1}{\mu\mu_0}\left(\frac{\partial}{\partial y}E_z-\frac{\partial}{\partial z}E_y\right)\right]\mathbf{j}-\frac{\partial}{\partial y}\left[\frac{1}{\mu\mu_0}\left(\frac{\partial}{\partial y}E_z-\frac{\partial}{\partial z}E_y\right)\right]\mathbf{k}=\\&=\frac{1}{\mu\mu_0}\frac{\partial}{\partial z}\left(\frac{\partial}{\partial y}E_z-\frac{\partial}{\partial z}E_y\right)\mathbf{j}-\frac{1}{\mu\mu_0}\frac{\partial}{\partial y}\left(\frac{\partial}{\partial y}E_z-\frac{\partial}{\partial z}E_y\right)\mathbf{k}=\end{aligned} \tag{2.8.16}$$

Analogical transformations are applied to relations (2.8.13) and (2.8.14):

$$\frac{\partial}{\partial \mathbf{r}}\times\left[\frac{1}{\mu\mu_0}\left(\frac{\partial}{\partial z}E_x-\frac{\partial}{\partial x}E_z\right)\mathbf{j}\right]=-\frac{1}{\mu\mu_0}\frac{\partial}{\partial z}\left(\frac{\partial}{\partial z}E_x-\frac{\partial}{\partial x}E_z\right)\mathbf{i}+\frac{1}{\mu\mu_0}\frac{\partial}{\partial x}\left(\frac{\partial}{\partial z}E_x-\frac{\partial}{\partial x}E_z\right)\mathbf{k}, \tag{2.8.17}$$

$$\frac{\partial}{\partial \mathbf{r}}\times\left[\frac{1}{\mu\mu_0}\left(\frac{\partial}{\partial x}E_y-\frac{\partial}{\partial y}E_x\right)\mathbf{k}\right]=\frac{1}{\mu\mu_0}\frac{\partial}{\partial y}\left(\frac{\partial}{\partial x}E_y-\frac{\partial}{\partial y}E_x\right)\mathbf{i}-\frac{1}{\mu\mu_0}\frac{\partial}{\partial x}\left(\frac{\partial}{\partial x}E_y-\frac{\partial}{\partial y}E_x\right)\mathbf{j}. \tag{2.8.18}$$

After summation one obtains after using the formulated conditions

$$\frac{\partial}{\partial z}\left[\frac{1}{\mu\mu_0}\left(\frac{\partial}{\partial y}E_z-\frac{\partial}{\partial z}E_y\right)\right]\mathbf{j}-\frac{\partial}{\partial y}\left[\frac{1}{\mu\mu_0}\left(\frac{\partial}{\partial y}E_z-\frac{\partial}{\partial z}E_y\right)\right]\mathbf{k}-$$
$$-\frac{\partial}{\partial z}\left[\frac{1}{\mu\mu_0}\left(\frac{\partial}{\partial z}E_x-\frac{\partial}{\partial x}E_z\right)\right]\mathbf{i}+\frac{\partial}{\partial x}\left[\frac{1}{\mu\mu_0}\left(\frac{\partial}{\partial z}E_x-\frac{\partial}{\partial x}E_z\right)\right]\mathbf{k}+$$
$$+\frac{\partial}{\partial y}\left[\frac{1}{\mu\mu_0}\left(\frac{\partial}{\partial x}E_y-\frac{\partial}{\partial y}E_x\right)\right]\mathbf{i}-\frac{\partial}{\partial x}\left[\frac{1}{\mu\mu_0}\left(\frac{\partial}{\partial x}E_y-\frac{\partial}{\partial y}E_x\right)\right]\mathbf{j}=$$
$$=\left[\frac{\partial}{\partial y}\left[\frac{1}{\mu\mu_0}\left(\frac{\partial}{\partial x}E_y-\frac{\partial}{\partial y}E_x\right)\right]-\frac{\partial}{\partial z}\left[\frac{1}{\mu\mu_0}\left(\frac{\partial}{\partial z}E_x-\frac{\partial}{\partial x}E_z\right)\right]\right]\mathbf{i}+$$
$$+\left[\frac{\partial}{\partial z}\left[\frac{1}{\mu\mu_0}\left(\frac{\partial}{\partial y}E_z-\frac{\partial}{\partial z}E_y\right)\right]-\frac{\partial}{\partial x}\left[\frac{1}{\mu\mu_0}\left(\frac{\partial}{\partial x}E_y-\frac{\partial}{\partial y}E_x\right)\right]\right]\mathbf{j}+$$
$$+\left[\frac{\partial}{\partial x}\left[\frac{1}{\mu\mu_0}\left(\frac{\partial}{\partial z}E_x-\frac{\partial}{\partial x}E_z\right)\right]-\frac{\partial}{\partial y}\left[\frac{1}{\mu\mu_0}\left(\frac{\partial}{\partial y}E_z-\frac{\partial}{\partial z}E_y\right)\right]\right]\mathbf{k}=$$
$$=\frac{1}{\mu\mu_0}\left[\frac{\partial}{\partial y}\frac{\partial}{\partial x}E_y-\Delta E_x+\frac{\partial^2 E_x}{\partial x^2}+\frac{\partial}{\partial z}\frac{\partial}{\partial x}E_z\right]\mathbf{i}+$$
$$+\frac{1}{\mu\mu_0}\left[\frac{\partial}{\partial z}\frac{\partial}{\partial y}E_z-\Delta E_y+\frac{\partial^2 E_y}{\partial y^2}+\frac{\partial}{\partial x}\frac{\partial}{\partial y}E_x\right]\mathbf{j}+$$
$$+\frac{1}{\mu\mu_0}\left[\frac{\partial}{\partial x}\frac{\partial}{\partial z}E_x-\Delta E_z+\frac{\partial^2 E_z}{\partial z^2}+\frac{\partial}{\partial y}\frac{\partial}{\partial z}E_y\right]\mathbf{k}=$$
$$=\frac{1}{\mu\mu_0}\left[\frac{\partial}{\partial y}\frac{\partial}{\partial x}E_y+\frac{\partial^2 E_x}{\partial x^2}+\frac{\partial}{\partial z}\frac{\partial}{\partial x}E_z\right]\mathbf{i}+ \qquad (2.8.19)$$
$$+\frac{1}{\mu\mu_0}\left[\frac{\partial}{\partial z}\frac{\partial}{\partial y}E_z+\frac{\partial^2 E_y}{\partial y^2}+\frac{\partial}{\partial x}\frac{\partial}{\partial y}E_x\right]\mathbf{j}+$$
$$+\frac{1}{\mu\mu_0}\left[\frac{\partial}{\partial x}\frac{\partial}{\partial z}E_x+\frac{\partial^2 E_z}{\partial z^2}+\frac{\partial}{\partial y}\frac{\partial}{\partial z}E_y\right]\mathbf{k}-\frac{1}{\mu\mu_0}\Delta\mathbf{E}$$

Let us use the identity

$$\frac{\partial}{\partial\mathbf{r}}\left[\frac{\partial}{\partial\mathbf{r}}\cdot\mathbf{E}\right]=\frac{\partial}{\partial x}\left[\frac{\partial E_x}{\partial x}+\frac{\partial E_y}{\partial y}+\frac{\partial E_z}{\partial z}\right]\mathbf{i}+\frac{\partial}{\partial y}\left[\frac{\partial E_x}{\partial x}+\frac{\partial E_y}{\partial y}+\frac{\partial E_z}{\partial z}\right]\mathbf{j}+\frac{\partial}{\partial z}\left[\frac{\partial E_x}{\partial x}+\frac{\partial E_y}{\partial y}+\frac{\partial E_z}{\partial z}\right]\mathbf{k} \qquad (2.8.20)$$

Then

$$\left[\frac{\partial}{\partial y}\frac{\partial}{\partial x}E_y+\frac{\partial^2 E_x}{\partial x^2}+\frac{\partial}{\partial z}\frac{\partial}{\partial x}E_z\right]\mathbf{i}+\left[\frac{\partial}{\partial z}\frac{\partial}{\partial y}E_z+\frac{\partial^2 E_y}{\partial y^2}+\frac{\partial}{\partial x}\frac{\partial}{\partial y}E_x\right]\mathbf{j}+$$
$$+\left[\frac{\partial}{\partial x}\frac{\partial}{\partial z}E_x+\frac{\partial^2 E_z}{\partial z^2}+\frac{\partial}{\partial y}\frac{\partial}{\partial z}E_y\right]\mathbf{k}=\frac{\partial}{\partial\mathbf{r}}\left[\frac{\partial}{\partial\mathbf{r}}\cdot\mathbf{E}\right] \qquad (2.8.21)$$

Finally

$$\frac{\partial}{\partial\mathbf{r}}\times\left[\frac{1}{\mu\mu_0}\frac{\partial}{\partial\mathbf{r}}\times\mathbf{E}\right]=\frac{1}{\mu\mu_0}\frac{\partial}{\partial\mathbf{r}}\left[\frac{\partial}{\partial\mathbf{r}}\cdot\mathbf{E}\right]-\frac{1}{\mu\mu_0}\Delta\mathbf{E}\,. \qquad (2.8.22)$$

Then the equation (2.8.5) is written as follows

$$\frac{\partial^2 \mathbf{D}}{\partial t^2}+\frac{\partial}{\partial t}\mathbf{j}^c=\frac{1}{\mu\mu_0}\Delta\mathbf{E}-\frac{1}{\mu\mu_0}\frac{\partial}{\partial\mathbf{r}}\left[\frac{\partial}{\partial\mathbf{r}}\cdot\mathbf{E}\right] \tag{2.8.23}$$

or if the electric permeability does not depend on time we have

$$\varepsilon\varepsilon_0\frac{\partial^2 \mathbf{E}}{\partial t^2}+\frac{\partial}{\partial t}\mathbf{j}^c=\frac{1}{\mu\mu_0}\left\{\Delta\mathbf{E}-\frac{\partial}{\partial\mathbf{r}}\left[\frac{\partial}{\partial\mathbf{r}}\cdot\mathbf{E}\right]\right\} \tag{2.8.24}$$

or

$$\frac{1}{v_\phi^2}\frac{\partial^2 \mathbf{E}}{\partial t^2}+\mu\mu_0\frac{\partial}{\partial t}\mathbf{j}^c=\Delta\mathbf{E}-\frac{\partial}{\partial\mathbf{r}}\left[\frac{\partial}{\partial\mathbf{r}}\cdot\mathbf{E}\right] \tag{2.8.25}$$

or

$$\frac{1}{v_\phi^2}\frac{\partial^2 \mathbf{E}}{\partial t^2}+\mu\mu_0\frac{\partial}{\partial t}\mathbf{j}^a+\mu\mu_0\frac{\partial}{\partial t}\mathbf{j}^{fl}=\Delta\mathbf{E}-\frac{\partial}{\partial\mathbf{r}}\left[\frac{\partial}{\partial\mathbf{r}}\cdot\mathbf{E}\right], \tag{2.8.26}$$

where (see also Table 2.7.1)

$$\mathbf{j}^{fl}=\tau\left[\frac{\partial}{\partial t}(\rho\mathbf{v}_0)+\frac{\partial}{\partial\mathbf{r}}\cdot(\rho\mathbf{v}_0\mathbf{v}_0)+\frac{\partial p}{\partial\mathbf{r}}-\rho\mathbf{g}\right] \tag{2.8.27}$$

or

$$\mathbf{j}_E^{fl}=\tau\left[\frac{\partial}{\partial t}(nq\mathbf{v}_0)+\frac{\partial}{\partial\mathbf{r}}\cdot(nq\mathbf{v}_0\mathbf{v}_0)+\frac{q}{m}\frac{\partial}{\partial\mathbf{r}}(nk_BT)-nq\mathbf{g}\right]. \tag{2.8.28}$$

Then the nonlocal equation (2.8.26) takes the form

$$\begin{gathered}\frac{1}{v_\phi^2}\frac{\partial^2 \mathbf{E}}{\partial t^2}+\mu\mu_0\frac{\partial}{\partial t}\left\{\tau\frac{\partial}{\partial t}(nq\mathbf{v}_0)\right\}=\Delta\mathbf{E}-\frac{\partial}{\partial\mathbf{r}}\left[\frac{\partial}{\partial\mathbf{r}}\cdot\mathbf{E}\right]-\mu\mu_0\frac{\partial}{\partial t}\mathbf{j}^a-\\-\mu\mu_0\frac{\partial}{\partial t}\left\{\tau\left[\frac{\partial}{\partial\mathbf{r}}\cdot(nq\mathbf{v}_0\mathbf{v}_0)+\frac{q}{m}\frac{\partial}{\partial\mathbf{r}}(nk_BT)-nq\mathbf{g}\right]\right\}\end{gathered} \tag{2.8.29}$$

$$\begin{gathered}\frac{1}{v_\phi^2}\frac{\partial^2 \mathbf{E}}{\partial t^2}+\mu\mu_0\frac{\partial}{\partial t}\left\{\tau\frac{\partial}{\partial t}\mathbf{j}^a\right\}=\Delta\mathbf{E}-\frac{\partial}{\partial\mathbf{r}}\left[\frac{\partial}{\partial\mathbf{r}}\cdot\mathbf{E}\right]-\mu\mu_0\frac{\partial}{\partial t}\mathbf{j}^a-\\-\mu\mu_0\frac{\partial}{\partial t}\left\{\tau\left[\frac{\partial}{\partial\mathbf{r}}\cdot(\mathbf{j}^a\mathbf{v}_0)+\frac{q}{m}\frac{\partial}{\partial\mathbf{r}}(nk_BT)-nq\mathbf{g}\right]\right\}\end{gathered} \tag{2.8.30}$$

where

$\mu_0=1{,}25663706212(19)\cdot10^{-6}\,N\cdot A^{-2}$, $\varepsilon_0=8{,}8541878128(13)\cdot10^{-12}m^{-3}kg^{-1}s^4A^2$, $c=\dfrac{1}{\sqrt{\varepsilon_0\mu_0}}$,

$v_\phi=\dfrac{1}{\sqrt{\varepsilon_0\mu_0\varepsilon\mu}}$.

Let be

$$\mathbf{j}^a = \sigma\mathbf{E}, \tag{2.8.31}$$

where σ is the coefficient of conductivity. In the simplest Drude model

$$\sigma = \frac{ne^2}{2m^*}\tau_r, \tag{2.8.32}$$

where n is numerical electron density, m^* is effective mass, τ_r is the relaxation time, the dimension of the conductivity is s^{-1} If $\tau = const$ and the coefficient of conductivity $\sigma(x, y, z)$, we have

$$\left[1+\frac{\tau\sigma}{\varepsilon_0\varepsilon}\right]\frac{\partial^2\mathbf{E}}{\partial t^2} = v_\phi^2\left\{\Delta\mathbf{E} - \frac{\partial}{\partial\mathbf{r}}\left[\frac{\partial}{\partial\mathbf{r}}\cdot\mathbf{E}\right]\right\} - \frac{\sigma}{\varepsilon_0\varepsilon}\frac{\partial\mathbf{E}}{\partial t} - \frac{\tau}{\varepsilon_0\varepsilon}\frac{\partial}{\partial t}\left[\frac{\partial}{\partial\mathbf{r}}\cdot(\sigma\mathbf{E}\mathbf{v}_0)\right] - \\ - \frac{\tau}{\varepsilon_0\varepsilon}\frac{\partial}{\partial t}\left[\frac{q}{m}\frac{\partial}{\partial\mathbf{r}}(nk_BT) - nq\mathbf{g}\right] \tag{2.8.33}$$

For the 1D case (x - direction) we find

$$\left[1+\frac{\tau\sigma}{\varepsilon_0\varepsilon}\right]\frac{\partial^2 E_x}{\partial t^2} = -\frac{\sigma}{\varepsilon_0\varepsilon}\frac{\partial E_x}{\partial t} - \frac{\tau}{\varepsilon_0\varepsilon}\frac{\partial}{\partial t}\left[\frac{\partial}{\partial x}(\sigma E_x v_{0x})\right] - \frac{\tau}{\varepsilon_0\varepsilon}\frac{\partial}{\partial t}\left[\frac{q}{m}\frac{\partial}{\partial x}(nk_BT) - nqg_x\right]. \tag{2.8.34}$$

After integration we find

$$\left[1+\frac{\tau\sigma}{\varepsilon_0\varepsilon}\right]\frac{\partial E_x}{\partial t} = -\frac{\sigma}{\varepsilon_0\varepsilon}E_x - \frac{\tau}{\varepsilon_0\varepsilon}\frac{\partial}{\partial x}(\sigma E_x v_{0x}) - \frac{\tau}{\varepsilon_0\varepsilon}q\left[\frac{1}{m}\frac{\partial}{\partial x}(nk_BT) - ng_x\right] + f(x), \tag{2.8.35}$$

where the Boltzmann constant $k_B = 1{,}380649\cdot 10^{-23} J/K$.

Let us consider the main features of the solution of equation (2.8.35). With this aim we suppose that $v_{0x} = const$, $\sigma = const$ and the last terms can be omitted. The last terms in equation (2.8.35) can be omitted if the pressure gradient can compensate the influence of the gravitation force acting on the volume unit and $f(x) = 0$. We have

$$\left[1+\frac{\tau\sigma}{\varepsilon_0\varepsilon}\right]\frac{\partial E_x}{\partial t} + \frac{\tau\sigma v_{0x}}{\varepsilon_0\varepsilon}\frac{\partial E_x}{\partial x} = -\frac{\sigma}{\varepsilon_0\varepsilon}E_x. \tag{2.8.36}$$

The solution of this equation is a damping longitudinal E-wave. Really

$$E_x = \exp\left(-\frac{1}{\tau v_{0x}}x\right)\Phi\left[\left(1+\frac{\tau\sigma}{\varepsilon_0\varepsilon}\right)x - \frac{\tau\sigma v_{0x}}{\varepsilon_0\varepsilon}t\right]. \tag{2.8.37}$$

Conclusions:

1. The validity of the solution (2.8.37) could be verified by the direct substitution of this relation (2.8.37) into equation (2.8.36). Really

$$
\begin{aligned}
&\left[1+\frac{\tau\sigma}{\varepsilon_0\varepsilon}\right]\left\{\exp\left(-\frac{1}{\tau v_{0x}}x\right)\Phi'\left[\left(1+\frac{\tau\sigma}{\varepsilon_0\varepsilon}\right)x-\frac{\tau\sigma v_0}{\varepsilon_0\varepsilon}t\right]\left(-\frac{\tau\sigma v_{0x}}{\varepsilon_0\varepsilon}\right)\right\}+\\
&+\frac{\tau\sigma v_0}{\varepsilon_0\varepsilon}\exp\left(-\frac{1}{\tau v_{0x}}x\right)\Phi\left[\left(1+\frac{\tau\sigma}{\varepsilon_0\varepsilon}\right)x-\frac{\tau\sigma v_{0x}}{\varepsilon_0\varepsilon}t\right]\left(-\frac{1}{\tau v_{0x}}\right)+\\
&+\frac{\tau\sigma v_0}{\varepsilon_0\varepsilon}\exp\left(-\frac{1}{\tau v_{0x}}x\right)\Phi'\left[\left(1+\frac{\tau\sigma}{\varepsilon_0\varepsilon}\right)x-\frac{\tau\sigma v_{0x}}{\varepsilon_0\varepsilon}t\right]\left(1+\frac{\tau\sigma}{\varepsilon_0\varepsilon}\right)=\\
&=-\frac{\sigma}{\varepsilon_0\varepsilon}\exp\left(-\frac{1}{\tau v_{0x}}x\right)\Phi\left[\left(1+\frac{\tau\sigma}{\varepsilon_0\varepsilon}\right)x-\frac{\tau\sigma v_{0x}}{\varepsilon_0\varepsilon}t\right]
\end{aligned}
\tag{2.8.38}
$$

$$
\begin{aligned}
&\left[1+\frac{\tau\sigma}{\varepsilon_0\varepsilon}\right]\left\{\exp\left(-\frac{1}{\tau v_{0x}}x\right)\Phi'\left[\left(1+\frac{\tau\sigma}{\varepsilon_0\varepsilon}\right)x-\frac{\tau\sigma v_0}{\varepsilon_0\varepsilon}t\right]\left(-\frac{\tau\sigma v_{0x}}{\varepsilon_0\varepsilon}\right)\right\}+\\
&+\frac{\tau\sigma v_0}{\varepsilon_0\varepsilon}\exp\left(-\frac{1}{\tau v_{0x}}x\right)\Phi'\left[\left(1+\frac{\tau\sigma}{\varepsilon_0\varepsilon}\right)x-\frac{\tau\sigma v_{0x}}{\varepsilon_0\varepsilon}t\right]\left(1+\frac{\tau\sigma}{\varepsilon_0\varepsilon}\right)=0
\end{aligned}
\tag{2.8.39}
$$

2. If the non-locality parameter τ is equal to zero, the electric intensity for the longitudinal waves (EMLW) also turns into zero. It means that EMLW cannot exist in the frame of the classic Maxwell electrodynamics.

3. Equation (2.8.35) can be written in the form

$$\left[1+\frac{\tau\sigma}{\varepsilon_0\varepsilon}\right]\frac{\partial E_x}{\partial t}+\frac{\tau\sigma}{\varepsilon_0\varepsilon}v_{0x}\frac{\partial E_x}{\partial x}=-\frac{\sigma}{\varepsilon_0\varepsilon}E_x-\frac{\tau}{\varepsilon_0\varepsilon}\frac{q}{m}\left[\frac{\partial}{\partial x}(nk_BT)-\rho g_x\right]. \tag{2.8.40}$$

The last term in square bracket takes into account the influence of the pressure gradient and the gravitation force. If nonlocal parameter $\tau=0$, then

$$\frac{\partial E_x}{\partial t}=-\frac{\sigma}{\varepsilon_0\varepsilon}E_x \tag{2.8.41}$$

and we have in the local electrodynamics the exponential E_x attenuation (if $f(x)=0$ in (2.8.35)) without the wave creation

$$E_x=E_{x,t=0}\exp\left(-\frac{\sigma t}{\varepsilon\varepsilon_0}\right). \tag{2.8.42}$$

4. The existence of longitudinal electromagnetic waves does not contradict (nonlocal) electrodynamics if longitudinal waves are actually detected and the medium in which they are generated is known, then in this case the problem of substantiating such waves in electrodynamics is reduced to the search for

material equations characterizing the response of the medium to the influence of the field and the joint solution of these material equations and Maxwell's equations, with appropriate boundary conditions.

5. Let be

$$\left(1+\frac{\tau\sigma}{\varepsilon_0\varepsilon}\right)x-\frac{\tau\sigma v_0}{\varepsilon_0\varepsilon}t=const=C. \tag{2.8.43}$$

Then

$$\left(1+\frac{\tau\sigma}{\varepsilon_0\varepsilon}\right)\frac{dx}{dt}=\frac{\tau\sigma v_0}{\varepsilon_0\varepsilon} \tag{2.8.44}$$

or

$$v_{EMLW}=\frac{dx}{dt}=\frac{\tau\sigma v_0}{\varepsilon_0\varepsilon}\left[1+\frac{\tau\sigma}{\varepsilon_0\varepsilon}\right]^{-1}=\frac{\tau\sigma v_0}{\varepsilon_0\varepsilon}\frac{\varepsilon_0\varepsilon}{\varepsilon_0\varepsilon+\tau\sigma}=\frac{\tau\sigma}{\varepsilon_0\varepsilon+\tau\sigma}v_0=\frac{1}{1+\frac{\varepsilon_0\varepsilon}{\tau\sigma}}v_0. \tag{2.8.45}$$

Low permittivity (low epsilon) materials are now attracting wide attention due to potential novel applications in optics and radio communications. Surface plasmon polaritons (SPPs) are electromagnetic waves that travel along a metal-dielectric or metal–air interface, practically in the infrared or visible - frequency. The term "surface plasmon polariton" explains that the wave involves both charge motion in the metal ("surface plasmon") and electromagnetic waves in the air or dielectric ("polariton"). Application of SPPs enables subwavelength optics in microscopy and lithography beyond the diffraction limit. It also enables the first steady-state micro-mechanical measurement of a fundamental property of light itself: the momentum of a photon in a dielectric medium.

Longitudinal electromagnetic waves play important role in plasma, in surface plasmon polaritons in anisotropic materials, in space-charge waves in semiconductor materials. Then for so called that in Epsilon Near Zero (ENZ) materials the velocity $v_{EMLW}\cong v_0$ (the usual light velocity). For the following details of the wave process one needs the explicit form of the $\Phi(x,t)$ function and boundary and initial conditions.

6. As we see from (2.8.45) written here as

$$v_{EMLW}=\frac{1}{1+\frac{\varepsilon_0\varepsilon}{\tau\sigma}}v_0, \tag{2.8.46}$$

$$v_{EMLW}\to v_0 \text{ if } \varepsilon\to 0. \tag{2.8.47}$$

Obviously to overcome this velocity limit is possible only in the systems with negative conductivity where formally

$$v_{EMLW}\to\infty \text{ if } \sigma\to-\frac{\varepsilon_0\varepsilon}{\tau}. \tag{2.8.48}$$

The possibility of the appearance of negative conductivity in a non-equilibrium electron system, i.e., a situation in which the current flows opposite to the electric field, was apparently indicated for the first time by Krömer in the late 1950s [45]. The mechanism of absolute negative conductivity (ANC) in a two-dimensional electron system placed into magnetic and ac electric fields, which is associated with two-dimensional electron scattering by impurities, accompanied by ac field photon absorption, was proposed in [46]. The state with negative conductivity is unstable, the system decays into domains, and the measured macroscopic resistance becomes zero. The existence of this effect was experimentally confirmed in 2002 [47]. Particular attention of researchers has been recently attracted to a new carbon material, i.e., graphene, consisting of a single layer of carbon atoms and having a planar hexagonal structure. Electromagnetic waves propagating in carbon structures become highly nonlinear even at relatively weak fields, which results in possible propagation of electromagnetic solitary waves (which are soliton analogs, or even solitons) in carbon nanotubes and graphene (see review in [19]). The discussed properties of carbon structures have generated both increased theoretical interest and attempts at application in nonlinear optical devices.

Let us consider now the magnetic field evolution in the longitudinal EM wave. With this aim let us transform equation (2.8.33) written as follows

$$\left[1+\frac{\tau\sigma}{\varepsilon_0\varepsilon}\right]\frac{\partial^2\mathbf{E}}{\partial t^2}=v_\phi^2\left\{\frac{\partial^2\mathbf{E}}{\partial x^2}+\frac{\partial^2\mathbf{E}}{\partial y^2}+\frac{\partial^2\mathbf{E}}{\partial z^2}-\frac{\partial}{\partial\mathbf{r}}\left[\frac{\partial E_x}{\partial x}+\frac{\partial E_y}{\partial y}+\frac{\partial E_z}{\partial z}\right]\right\}- \\ -\frac{\sigma}{\varepsilon_0\varepsilon}\frac{\partial\mathbf{E}}{\partial t}-\frac{\tau\sigma}{\varepsilon_0\varepsilon}\frac{\partial}{\partial t}\left[\frac{\partial}{\partial\mathbf{r}}\cdot(\mathbf{E}\mathbf{v}_0)\right]-\frac{\tau}{\varepsilon_0\varepsilon}\frac{\partial}{\partial t}\left[\frac{q}{m}\frac{\partial}{\partial\mathbf{r}}(nk_BT)-nq\mathbf{g}\right] \qquad (2.8.49)$$

For the x – component we find

$$\left[1+\frac{\tau\sigma}{\varepsilon_0\varepsilon}\right]\frac{\partial^2E_x}{\partial t^2}=v_\phi^2\left\{\frac{\partial^2E_x}{\partial y^2}+\frac{\partial^2E_x}{\partial z^2}-\frac{\partial}{\partial x}\left[\frac{\partial E_y}{\partial y}+\frac{\partial E_z}{\partial z}\right]\right\}- \\ -\frac{\sigma}{\varepsilon_0\varepsilon}\frac{\partial E_x}{\partial t}-\frac{\tau\sigma}{\varepsilon_0\varepsilon}\frac{\partial}{\partial t}\left[\frac{\partial}{\partial\mathbf{r}}\cdot(\mathbf{E}v_{0x})\right]-\frac{\tau}{\varepsilon_0\varepsilon}\frac{\partial}{\partial t}\left[\frac{q}{m}\frac{\partial}{\partial x}(nk_BT)-nqg_x\right] \qquad (2.8.50)$$

or

$$\left[1+\frac{\tau\sigma}{\varepsilon_0\varepsilon}\right]\frac{\partial^2E_x}{\partial t^2}=v_\phi^2\left\{\frac{\partial}{\partial y}\left[\frac{\partial E_x}{\partial y}-\frac{\partial E_y}{\partial x}\right]+\frac{\partial}{\partial z}\left[\frac{\partial E_x}{\partial z}-\frac{\partial E_z}{\partial x}\right]\right\}- \\ -\frac{\sigma}{\varepsilon_0\varepsilon}\frac{\partial E_x}{\partial t}-\frac{\tau\sigma}{\varepsilon_0\varepsilon}\frac{\partial}{\partial t}\left[\frac{\partial}{\partial\mathbf{r}}\cdot(\mathbf{E}v_{0x})\right]-\frac{\tau}{\varepsilon_0\varepsilon}\frac{\partial}{\partial t}\left[\frac{q}{m}\frac{\partial}{\partial x}(nk_BT)-nqg_x\right] \qquad (2.8.51)$$

Taking into account (2.7.3) one obtains for the z – component

$$\frac{\partial E_x}{\partial y}-\frac{\partial E_y}{\partial x}=\frac{\partial B_z}{\partial t} \qquad (2.8.52)$$

and for the y – component

$$\frac{\partial E_z}{\partial x}-\frac{\partial E_x}{\partial z}=\frac{\partial B_y}{\partial t}. \tag{2.8.53}$$

Then from (2.8.51) – (2.8.53) follows

$$\left[1+\frac{\tau\sigma}{\varepsilon_0\varepsilon}\right]\frac{\partial^2 E_x}{\partial t^2}=v_\phi^2\left\{\frac{\partial}{\partial y}\frac{\partial B_z}{\partial t}-\frac{\partial}{\partial z}\frac{\partial B_y}{\partial t}\right\}-\frac{\sigma}{\varepsilon_0\varepsilon}\frac{\partial E_x}{\partial t}-\frac{\tau\sigma}{\varepsilon_0\varepsilon}\frac{\partial}{\partial t}\left[\frac{\partial}{\partial \mathbf{r}}\cdot\left(\mathbf{E}v_{0x}\right)\right]- \\ -\frac{\tau}{\varepsilon_0\varepsilon}\frac{\partial}{\partial t}\left[\frac{q}{m}\frac{\partial}{\partial x}\left(nk_BT\right)-nqg_x\right] \tag{2.8.54}$$

or

$$\left[1+\frac{\tau\sigma}{\varepsilon_0\varepsilon}\right]\frac{\partial^2 E_x}{\partial t^2}=v_\phi^2\frac{\partial}{\partial t}\left\{\frac{\partial B_z}{\partial y}-\frac{\partial B_y}{\partial z}\right\}-\frac{\sigma}{\varepsilon_0\varepsilon}\frac{\partial E_x}{\partial t}-\frac{\tau\sigma}{\varepsilon_0\varepsilon}\frac{\partial}{\partial t}\left[\frac{\partial}{\partial \mathbf{r}}\cdot\left(\mathbf{E}v_{0x}\right)\right]- \\ -\frac{\tau}{\varepsilon_0\varepsilon}\frac{\partial}{\partial t}\left[\frac{q}{m}\frac{\partial}{\partial x}\left(nk_BT\right)-nqg_x\right] \tag{2.8.55}$$

After integration we find

$$\left[1+\frac{\tau\sigma}{\varepsilon_0\varepsilon}\right]\frac{\partial E_x}{\partial t}=v_\phi^2\left\{\frac{\partial B_z}{\partial y}-\frac{\partial B_y}{\partial z}\right\}-\frac{\sigma}{\varepsilon_0\varepsilon}E_x-\frac{\tau\sigma}{\varepsilon_0\varepsilon}\left[\frac{\partial}{\partial \mathbf{r}}\cdot\left(\mathbf{E}v_{0x}\right)\right]- \\ -\frac{\tau}{\varepsilon_0\varepsilon}\left[\frac{q}{m}\frac{\partial}{\partial x}\left(nk_BT\right)-nqg_x\right]+f(x,y,z) \tag{2.8.56}$$

Compare this equation with the equation (2.8.35) written for 1D case

$$\left[1+\frac{\tau\sigma}{\varepsilon_0\varepsilon}\right]\frac{\partial E_x}{\partial t}=-\frac{\sigma}{\varepsilon_0\varepsilon}E_x-\frac{\tau\sigma}{\varepsilon_0\varepsilon}\frac{\partial}{\partial x}\left(E_xv_{0x}\right)-\frac{\tau}{\varepsilon_0\varepsilon}\left[\frac{q}{m}\frac{\partial}{\partial x}\left(nk_BT\right)-nqg_x\right] \tag{2.8.57}$$

Conclusion: if the propagation of the longitudinal electromagnetic wave differs little from the one-dimensional mode, then

$$v_\phi^2\left\{\frac{\partial B_z}{\partial y}-\frac{\partial B_y}{\partial z}\right\}=0 \tag{2.8.58}$$

or

$$\frac{\partial B_z}{\partial y}=\frac{\partial B_y}{\partial z}. \tag{2.8.59}$$

In local case for vacuum we have from (2.8.56)

$$\frac{\partial E_x}{\partial t}=v_\phi^2\left\{\frac{\partial B_z}{\partial y}-\frac{\partial B_y}{\partial z}\right\} \tag{2.8.60}$$

or

$$\frac{\partial E_x}{\partial t}=\frac{1}{\varepsilon_0\varepsilon\mu_0\mu}\left\{\frac{\partial B_z}{\partial y}-\frac{\partial B_y}{\partial z}\right\} \tag{2.8.61}$$

or

$$\frac{\partial H_z}{\partial y}-\frac{\partial H_y}{\partial z}=\frac{\partial D_x}{\partial t}. \tag{2.8.62}$$

This equation is well known local Maxwell equation written for vacuum

$$[\mathrm{curl}\mathbf{H}]_x = \left[\frac{\partial \mathbf{D}}{\partial t}\right]_x . \tag{2.8.63}$$

Writing down equation (2.8.56) in the general vector form we obtain

$$\begin{aligned}\left[1+\frac{\tau\sigma}{\varepsilon_0\varepsilon}\right]\frac{\partial \mathbf{E}}{\partial t} &= v_\phi^2 \mathrm{curl}\mathbf{B} - \frac{\sigma}{\varepsilon_0\varepsilon}\mathbf{E} - \frac{\tau\sigma}{\varepsilon_0\varepsilon}\left[\frac{\partial}{\partial \mathbf{r}}\cdot(\mathbf{E}\mathbf{v}_0)\right] - \\ &-\frac{\tau}{\varepsilon_0\varepsilon}\left[\frac{q}{m}\frac{\partial}{\partial \mathbf{r}}(nk_BT) - nq\mathbf{g}\right] + \left[\frac{\partial \mathbf{E}}{\partial t}\right]_{t=0}(x,y,z).\end{aligned} \tag{2.8.64}$$

Let us obtain now the generalized nonlocal formulation of the Pointing – Umov theorem. In other words we intend to obtain the law of the energy conservation for electro-magnetic processes. We use the vector identity

$$\mathrm{div}[\mathbf{E},\mathbf{H}] \equiv \mathbf{H}\cdot\mathrm{curl}\mathbf{E} - \mathbf{E}\cdot\mathrm{curl}\mathbf{H}, \tag{2.8.65}$$

or for the case under consideration

$$\mathbf{E}\cdot\mathrm{curl}\mathbf{B} = \mu_0\mu\mathbf{H}\cdot\mathrm{curl}\mathbf{E} - \mu_0\mu\,\mathrm{div}[\mathbf{E},\mathbf{H}]. \tag{2.8.66}$$

Using (2.8.64) and (2.8.66) one obtains after scalar multiplications by $\mathbf{E}$ the both sides of equation (2.8.64)

$$\begin{aligned}\left[1+\frac{\tau\sigma}{\varepsilon_0\varepsilon}\right]\mathbf{E}\cdot\frac{\partial \mathbf{E}}{\partial t} &= v_\phi^2(\mu_0\mu\mathbf{H}\cdot\mathrm{curl}\mathbf{E} - \mu_0\mu\,\mathrm{div}[\mathbf{E},\mathbf{H}]) - \frac{\sigma}{\varepsilon_0\varepsilon}E^2 - \frac{\tau\sigma}{\varepsilon_0\varepsilon}\mathbf{E}\cdot\left[\frac{\partial}{\partial \mathbf{r}}\cdot(\mathbf{E}\mathbf{v}_0)\right] - \\ &-\frac{\tau}{\varepsilon_0\varepsilon}\left[\frac{q}{m}\mathbf{E}\cdot\frac{\partial}{\partial \mathbf{r}}(nk_BT) - nq\mathbf{E}\cdot\mathbf{g}\right] + \mathbf{E}\cdot\left[\frac{\partial \mathbf{E}}{\partial t}\right]_{t=0}(x,y,z)\end{aligned} \tag{2.8.67}$$

or

$$\begin{aligned}\left[1+\frac{\tau\sigma}{\varepsilon_0\varepsilon}\right]\frac{\partial}{\partial t}\frac{\varepsilon\varepsilon_0 E^2}{2} &= -\mathbf{H}\cdot\frac{\partial \mathbf{B}}{\partial t} - \mathrm{div}[\mathbf{E},\mathbf{H}] - \sigma E^2 - \tau\sigma\mathbf{E}\cdot\left[\frac{\partial}{\partial \mathbf{r}}\cdot(\mathbf{E}\mathbf{v}_0)\right] - \\ &-\tau\left[\frac{q}{m}\mathbf{E}\cdot\frac{\partial}{\partial \mathbf{r}}(nk_BT) - nq\mathbf{E}\cdot\mathbf{g}\right] + \varepsilon_0\varepsilon\mathbf{E}\cdot\left[\frac{\partial \mathbf{E}}{\partial t}\right]_{t=0}(x,y,z)\end{aligned} \tag{2.8.68}$$

or

$$\begin{aligned}\sigma E^2 &= -\varepsilon_0\varepsilon\frac{\partial}{\partial t}\frac{E^2}{2} - \mu_0\mu\frac{\partial}{\partial t}\frac{H^2}{2} - \tau\sigma\frac{\partial}{\partial t}\frac{E^2}{2} - \mathrm{div}[\mathbf{E},\mathbf{H}] - \tau\sigma\mathbf{E}\cdot\left[\frac{\partial}{\partial \mathbf{r}}\cdot(\mathbf{E}\mathbf{v}_0)\right] - \\ &-\tau\left[\frac{q}{m}\mathbf{E}\cdot\frac{\partial}{\partial \mathbf{r}}(nk_BT) - nq\mathbf{E}\cdot\mathbf{g}\right] + \varepsilon_0\varepsilon\mathbf{E}\cdot\left[\frac{\partial \mathbf{E}}{\partial t}\right]_{t=0}(x,y,z)\end{aligned} \tag{2.8.69}$$

or

$$\begin{aligned}\sigma E^2 &= -\frac{\partial}{\partial t}\left[\frac{\varepsilon_0\varepsilon E^2 + \mu_0\mu H^2}{2}\right] - \mathrm{div}[\mathbf{E},\mathbf{H}] - \\ &-\tau\left\{\sigma\frac{\partial}{\partial t}\frac{E^2}{2} + \sigma\mathbf{E}\cdot\left[\frac{\partial}{\partial \mathbf{r}}\cdot(\mathbf{E}\mathbf{v}_0)\right] + \frac{q}{m}\mathbf{E}\cdot\frac{\partial}{\partial \mathbf{r}}(nk_BT) - nq\mathbf{E}\cdot\mathbf{g}\right\} + \varepsilon_0\varepsilon\mathbf{E}\cdot\left[\frac{\partial \mathbf{E}}{\partial t}\right]_{t=0}(x,y,z).\end{aligned} \tag{2.8.70}$$

In the local case we find

$$\sigma E^2 = -\frac{\partial}{\partial t}\left[\frac{\varepsilon_0 \varepsilon E^2 + \mu_0 \mu H^2}{2}\right] - \mathrm{div}[\mathbf{E},\mathbf{H}]. \tag{2.8.71}$$

This equation is well known local energy equation written for vacuum, where the left hand side of this equation corresponds to the Joule heating. Let us remind that in the coordinate notations we have

$$\left[\frac{\partial}{\partial \mathbf{r}}\cdot(\mathbf{E}\mathbf{v}_0)\right] = \frac{\partial}{\partial x}(E_x \mathbf{v}_0) + \frac{\partial}{\partial y}(E_y \mathbf{v}_0) + \frac{\partial}{\partial z}(E_z \mathbf{v}_0), \tag{2.8.72}$$

$$\begin{aligned}
\mathbf{E}\cdot\left[\frac{\partial}{\partial \mathbf{r}}\cdot(\mathbf{E}\mathbf{v}_0)\right] &= \mathbf{E}\cdot\left[\frac{\partial}{\partial x}(E_x \mathbf{v}_0) + \frac{\partial}{\partial y}(E_y \mathbf{v}_0) + \frac{\partial}{\partial z}(E_z \mathbf{v}_0)\right] = \\
&= E_x\left[\frac{\partial}{\partial x}(E_x v_{0x}) + \frac{\partial}{\partial y}(E_y v_{0x}) + \frac{\partial}{\partial z}(E_z v_{0x})\right] + \\
&+ E_y\left[\frac{\partial}{\partial x}(E_x v_{0y}) + \frac{\partial}{\partial y}(E_y v_{0y}) + \frac{\partial}{\partial z}(E_z v_{0y})\right] + \\
&+ E_z\left[\frac{\partial}{\partial x}(E_x v_{0z}) + \frac{\partial}{\partial y}(E_y v_{0z}) + \frac{\partial}{\partial z}(E_z v_{0z})\right].
\end{aligned} \tag{2.8.73}$$

Let us return now to the relation (2.6.2) for the τ estimation. For the photon gas we have

$$\tau = H_\tau/(h\upsilon), \tag{2.8.74}$$

where H_τ is a coefficient of proportionality, which reflects the state of physical system. In the simplest case H_τ is equal to Plank constant h and relation (2.6.2) becomes compatible with the Heisenberg relation. Then in the simplest case for the photon gas

$$\tau_{ph} = 1/\upsilon_{ph}. \tag{2.8.75}$$

There are many experimental investigations devoted to the study of the propagation of longitudinal electromagnetic waves. We will indicate the work of [48], which contains conclusions:

1. A centrally fed ball antenna, 6 cm diameter, producing a pulsating 433.59MHz spherical source charge, generated such a wave, that was detected by an identical ball antenna. The longitudinality of $\mathbf{E}$ was demonstrated by intervening a cubic array of 9 half-wavelength wires, that absorbed the wave when the wires were parallel (but not when perpendicular) to the direction of propagation.
2. Exponential loss of the signal with distance. – The observed signal beyond 100m decreases more rapidly with distance than the inverse square of the distance. This loss corresponds to an additional exponential loss with distance. (It could be noticed that for long distances from the sources the spherical wave front can be considered as a flat wave).

3. Longitudinal electro-dynamic waves can account for the huge signal observed from nuclear bomb explosions. – One of us (Wesley) was unable to explain the huge electro-dynamic signal produced by a nuclear-bomb explosion, when it was assumed that only transverse electro-dynamic waves are possible. It is now clear from the present demonstration of the actual existence of longitudinal waves, that the huge electro-dynamic signal produced by a nuclear-bomb explosion is a longitudinal signal or wave. The electrons ejected radially outward produce a radial transient oscillating charge separation that readily generates a huge longitudinal electro-dynamic signal. It may, thus, also be assumed that stellar novas and super novas will also be sources of extremely energetic transient longitudinal waves, which should be readily detectable on the Earth with the appropriate antenna to receive longitudinal waves.

2.9. About single wire energy transmission.

The nonlocal relativistic theory of transport processes is created (see [20, 21]) and applied to investigation of massless particles including photons. The problem of "single photon" is considered with aim to describe the boundary between the particle and field descriptions of photon gas. Analytical solutions of non-local non-stationary 2D equations are obtained for the physical system near the state of thermodynamic equilibrium.

The single wire transmission of energy was proposed by Nicola Tesla [49]. But this patent contains only the technical description of the device without theoretical comments. The developed theory in 2.10 is the basement of the single wire transmission of energy. We intend to deliver some following comments to the problem of the single wire transmission using the qualitative considerations.

Some significant remarks:

1. Current commonly accepted physical theories imply or assume the photon to be strictly massless. The great precision, which was reached in measuring of the photon charge, is equal to $\sim 5 \cdot 10^{-52}$ C; for the mass is $1.1 \cdot 10^{-52}$ kg, [50]. The photon also has no electric charge; it is stable and carries spin angular momentum that does not depend on its frequency.

2, Electron–positron annihilation occurs when an electron (e^-) and a positron (e^+ the electron's antiparticle) collide. At low energies, the result of the collision is the annihilation of the electron and positron, and the creation of energetic photons: $e^- + e^+ \rightarrow \gamma + \gamma$. There are only a very limited set of possibilities for the final state. The most probable is the creation of two or more photons. At high energies, other particles can be created. All processes must satisfy a number of conservation laws including conservation of electric charge. The net charge before and after is zero.

3. The theory is that the spin of the photon has only a longitudinal orientation, but such a view does not have unambiguous experimental confirmation. The full momentum of the photon J $J = s_{sp}\hbar,\ s_{sp} = \pm 1, \pm 2, ...$ takes integer values, starting at one: J = 1, 2, 3,.... The impossibility for a photon to have $J = 0$ was derived from the fact that the electromagnetic wave is transverse and therefore cannot be described by a spherically symmetric wave function in the Schrödinger theory. As we see this conclusion should be reconsidered. Photons with a certain value J are referred to as dipole photons (J = 1); quadrupole photon (J = 2); octupole photon (J = 3) etc.

4. Compton's experiment convinced physicists that light can behave as a stream of particles whose energy is proportional to the frequency. In 1924 Satyendra Nath Bose derived Planck's law for black-body radiation without using any electromagnetism, but rather a modification of coarse-grained counting of phase space. Einstein showed that this modification is equivalent to assuming that photons are rigorously identical and that it implied a "mysterious non-local interaction", [51, 52]. In the same papers, Einstein extended Bose's formalism to material particles (bosons) and predicted that they would condense into their lowest quantum state at low enough temperatures; this Bose-Einstein condensation was observed experimentally in 1995.

5. The photon is the gauge boson in electromagnetic theory and therefore all other quantum numbers of the photon (such as lepton and baryon numbers, flavor quantum numbers) are zero. The photon does not obey the Pauli Exclusion Principle.

6. Electron–positron annihilation occurs when an electron (e^-) and a positron (e^+ the electron's antiparticle) collide. At low energies, the result of the collision is the annihilation of the electron and positron, and the creation of energetic photons: $e^- + e^+ \rightarrow \gamma + \gamma$. There are only a very limited set of possibilities for the final state. The most probable is the creation of two or more photons. At high energies, other particles can be created. All processes must satisfy a number of conservation laws including conservation of electric charge. The net charge before and after is zero.

7. Obviously "a bridge" should exist between non-local "hydrodynamic" description of the massless particles and wave electromagnetism. The classical

formulae for the energy and momentum of electromagnetic field can be re-expressed in terms of photon events. For example, the pressure of electromagnetic radiation on an object derives from the transfer of photon momentum per unit time and unit area to that object.

As a result we are in front of so called "the single photon problem". The human eye was used as a very sensitive detector of singles photons in the thirties years of the previous century. It concerns of investigation of the Cherenkov radiation emitted when a charged particle (as an electron for example) passes through a dielectric media at a speed greater than the phase velocity of light in the media; (basic publication [53], 1958 Nobel Prize).

The energy of a single photon in the visible or near-infrared range is around 10^{-19} J. A single-photon detector now is an extremely sensitive device capable of registering these quantum objects. Single-photon detectors support applications at the frontiers of science and engineering. Conventional single-photon detectors are based on photomultipliers and avalanche photodiodes, and are used in a wide range of time-correlated single-photon counting applications.

Single-photon sources are developed now as light sources emitting light as single particles or photons. The Heisenberg uncertainty principle dictates that a state with an exact number of photons of a single frequency cannot be created. However, Fock states (or number states) can be studied for a system where the electric field amplitude is distributed over a narrow bandwidth. In this context, a single-photon source gives rise to an effectively one-photon number state. Photons from an ideal single-photon source exhibit quantum mechanical characteristics. These characteristics include photon anti-bunching, so that the time between two successive photons is never less than some minimum value.

Then the potential energy of the electron interaction must be correlated with photon energy by transmission from particle to wave description and vice versa.

The relativistic motion equation in [20, Chapter 9] contains the typical (unusual for the local description) cross-term "gravitational – electromagnetic forces". In particular, the propagation of photons along positive and negative directions of the y-axis is accompanied by the appearance of the self-consistent component of the magnetic induction along the z-axis and the self-consistent x-component of the electric and gravitational fields. The theory leads to the simplest "bridge" approximation:

$$\frac{e^2}{r_{\max}} = h\nu \qquad (2.9.1)$$

From (2.9.1) follows

$$e^2 = \frac{r_{\max}}{\lambda} hc \text{ or } e^2 = k_\phi hc, \tag{2.9.2}$$

where $k_\phi = \frac{r_{\max}}{\lambda}$. Coefficient k_ϕ has a transparent physical sense: the condition $r > r_{\max}$ leads to transmission from the particle to wave description. But from other side $k_\phi = \frac{e^2}{hc} = \frac{1}{2\pi}\frac{e^2}{\hbar c} = \frac{1}{2\pi}1/137.03600300 \approx 1.16 \cdot 10^{-3}$ is the fine-structure constant α divided by 2π. Then relation

$$e^2 = \alpha\hbar c. \tag{2.9.3}$$

can be considered as a "bridge" between corpuscular and wave descriptions. Relation (2.9.3) can be used also for a straightforward precision measurement of the fine-structure constant α or other values in this combination. Relations for pseudo dipole (2.9.1), (2.9.4)

$$e_{pch} = \pm\sqrt{\alpha\hbar c} \tag{2.9.4}$$

define the photon pseudo-charge permitting to investigate the transport processes of photon gas as a carrier of electro-magnetic field.

The design of a single-wire power transmission system involves the use of a very thin metal wire that is not directly involved in the transmission of energy and serves as a waveguide. Let us consider the role of the waveguide in more details. The simplest waveguide is arranged as follows. You are sitting in front of a computer monitor and looking at the screen with both eyes. Then hold a rolled-up sheet of paper (say the size A4) to one eye and look at the screen again. You will see a bright spot through the tube, as the photon flux density increases dramatically in the tube due to the reflection of photons from the tube wall.

The mentioned wire performs the same role. Indeed, the free electrons of the metal polarize the pseudo-dipoles of the photons, causing them:

1. To occupy the area near the wire (similar to the movement of dust particles to the charged surface of a cathode ray tube),
2. To move along the direction of the wire-waveguide.

CHAPTER 3 DARK MATTER PROBLEM

The dark matter problem is considered from positions of the Newtonian theory of gravitation and non-local kinetic theory. It is found that explanation of Hubble effect in the Universe and peculiar features of the rotational speeds of galaxies need not in introduction of new essence like dark matter and dark energy. The origin of difficulties consists in total Oversimplification following from principles of local physics and reflects the general shortcomings of the local kinetic transport theory.

3.1 Some preliminary remarks.

Let us remind the main conclusions from the previous consideration.

In the twentieth century local physics discovered that 96% of matter and energy in the Universe is of unknown origin. More exactly – the evidence for so called "dark matter" dates from the 1930s. So called "dark energy" is an unknown form of energy that seems to be the source of a repulsive force causing the expansion of the universe to accelerate. Evidence for its existence was found only ~10 years ago. Swiss astronomer Fritz Zwicky discovered dark matter existence from the standpoint of classical statistical mechanics of non equilibrium processes.

Vera Rubin conducted thorough astronomical observations. It turned out that the outer stars (rotating about the galactic center) were moving in orbits much faster than it followed from the theory of Kepler, and with the central mass greater than "visible" by astronomers.

A special place in astrophysics is the effect of Hubble — expanding groups of galaxies, accompanied by a proportional increase in the rate of expansion groups based on the distance from the main center of gravity. The proportionality factor is the Hubble constant (Hu, for Universe $\mathrm{Hu}=2.3\cdot 10^{-18}$ s^{-1}), which as it turns out, is not a constant value, $v = \mathrm{Hu}\, r$. We introduce the Hubble parameter notation using the first two letters of the surname (as in similarity theory) in order to avoid confusion with the Boltzmann H-function.

The main origin of the Hubble effect (including the matter expansion with acceleration) is self – catching of expanding matter by the self-consistent gravitational field in conditions of the weak influence of the central massive bodies, (see [18, 19] and Section 2.5).

It would seem that we are dealing with the well studied problem in classical gas dynamics of point explosion. Not at all, the classical dynamics of a point explosion has no a Hubble mode. The solution for the quasi-equilibrium state of the system, corresponding nonlocal fluctuation of the Boltzmann H function, is written as

$$H = H_{eq} \exp\left(\frac{t}{\tau}\right). \qquad (3.1.1)$$

This solution has a deep physical meaning. It turns out that even in the quasi-equilibrium state the H-function of Boltzmann experiences fluctuations. This fundamental fact can not be derived within the local theory of Boltzmann. In a cosmological aspect, the mentioned solution is the basis for the theory of inflation of the Universe.

Indeed, let us differentiate that both parts of the Hubble relation on time, we have $\frac{dv}{dt} = \mathrm{Hu}v$. For the rate of the expansion we find out $v = v_0 \exp(\mathrm{Hu}t)$ and for energy "fluctuations"

$$H_{en} = H_{en,0} \exp(t/\tau), \qquad (3.1.2)$$

where $\tau = (2\mathrm{Hu})^{-1}$, (see also (2.5.55)). Then one of the main relations of the inflation theory (including the Hubble effect) can be interpreted from the position of the generalized Boltzmann physical kinetics.

It is important to notice that the mentioned results of the inflation theory *cannot correspond to the beginning of the Big Bang* because of the absence of mass. The first moments of the Big Bang are connected with the explosion of primary physical vacuum (PV) as a result of Hadamard instability of physical system.

As usual in critical situations, a lot of money comes into play, since serious experiments at the micro level has always been of a costly nature.

What is the root of the problems? The Boltzmann equation works from the molecular to cosmological level, but has an amazing origin and equally obvious drawbacks. Regarding the origin, the equation is based on Newtonian mechanics, which contains in the equation the second derivative by time. But the Boltzmann kinetic equation has only the first temporal derivative. This fact leads to the irreversibility of the processes; hence the irreversible nature of the evolution of H-functions and the inevitable question: Where does the initial fluctuation appear from, if Boltzmann kinetic theory does not contain fluctuations in principle? You do not even need (initially) to write equations. Indeed, Boltzmann physical kinetics is based on a reduced description of dissipative processes and the principle of local thermodynamic equilibrium (LTE).

It is assumed that the distribution function (DF) is not changed within a physically infinitely small volume (say, a $\mathbf{PhSV_1}$) that contains, however, enough particles for the introduction of macroscopic parameters (such as temperature and concentration), which are constant within **PhSV**. But **PhSV** is an open thermodynamic system that responds to the environment only after its interaction with foreign particles, penetrated from a neighboring **PhSV**. These particles can transmit information only after collision with the particles $\mathbf{PhSV_1}$; in other words, after a time τ of order of the average time *between* collisions. Then in the simplest case of the gas objects nonlocal parameter τ can be considered as a corresponding relaxation time.

Results:

1) kinetic theory must be non-local in principle;

2) the effect is of the order of the Knudsen number;

3) the effect is due to reduced description and not associated with a specific division of a physical system by a net of **PhSV**;

4) accurate derivation of the kinetic equation relative to one-particle DF should lead to corrections of the order of the Knudsen number even before the decoupling of the Bogolyubov hierarchy;

5) this means that in the Boltzmann equation the terms of the order of the Knudsen number are lost; the terms of the order of the Knudsen number, important at large and at small Knudsen numbers;

6) the Boltzmann equation does not belong even to the class of minimal models as being the only plausible equation; and

7) the Boltzmann equation in this sense is the wrong equation.

It is clear that this is a revolution in the theory of dissipative processes, in particular in hydrodynamics. In the hydrodynamic Navier–Stokes equation, which is a direct consequence of the Boltzmann equation, the terms of the order proportional to a viscosity are partly lost. It leads to the problem of turbulence and the problems of existence and uniqueness of solutions of the Navier–Stokes equations.

We now turn to the logic of the development of the non-local theory:

A) In 1926 Madelung published a brilliant article [37] in which he transformed the quantum postulate (Schrödinger equation) in hydrodynamics. In other words, the evolution of a *single* bound electron was possible to interpret as some effective *flow*.

B) In 1964 John Stewart Bell [36] found that local statistical theory of dissipative processes is incorrect in principle.

C) In 2007 I found (see for example [19-23]) that the Schrödinger equation and hydrodynamic Madelung's form are a deep particular case of nonlocal kinetic equations as a result of the transition to the local limit of non-local equations.

This means that generalized physical kinetics (as created earlier by me) has been extended to quantum physics in the form of quantum hydrodynamics. I would even say such emotional words — the biggest secret of the Schrödinger equation (SE) is a strange thing — why, in fact, it generally works? Honestly, it starts to work when we go beyond the postulate that it is. Here just note again that:

1. SE is not able to give a self-consistent description of the nucleus - electron shell.

2. SE does not lead to an independent analogue of the hydrodynamic energy equation.

3. SE is not a dissipative equation and therefore cannot be applied to the description of dissipative processes in nanotechnology.

When the crisis erupted in theoretical physics, the opinion of many physicists was to claim that the resolution of contradictions is achievable only through a comprehensive theory, working from the structure of the electron to the cosmological scale.

The crisis has come from cosmological observations. Of course, I believed that the influence of non-locality in the physical models would be significant. But look at the scale of the effect! As I mentioned, 96% of matter and energy disappeared from consideration.

This theory includes a solution to the problem of the Hubble Universe expansion (including expansion with acceleration) and the emergence of a shelf on the graph of dependence of the orbital velocity from the center of gravity. But there is one very important circumstance to which I would like to draw attention. Unified theory (unified theory of dissipative structures) has the form of the hydrodynamic equations. This fact facilitates its use in applications.

However, some external similarity caused by the genesis of the equations, should not deceive. For example, these equations have solutions (in contrast to classical hydrodynamics), when the density tends to infinity (black hole in cosmology), or the density tends to zero (the birth of the Universe, when there is no substance and no electromagnetic field).

If the equations have non-trivial solutions for the birth of the Universe and its initial evolution, the problem of creation of the Universe goes from an abstract philosophical or religious problem to the task of finding and interpreting the solutions of specific equations.

About forty years after Zwicky's initial observations Vera Rubin [54, 55], astronomer at the Department of Terrestrial Magnetism at the Carnegie Institution of Washington presented findings based on a new sensitive spectrograph that could measure the velocity curve of edge-on spiral galaxies to a greater degree of accuracy than had ever before been achieved. Together with Kent Ford, Rubin announced at a 1975 meeting of the American Astronomical Society the astonishing discovery that most stars in spiral galaxies orbit at roughly the same speed reflected schematically on figure 3.1.1.

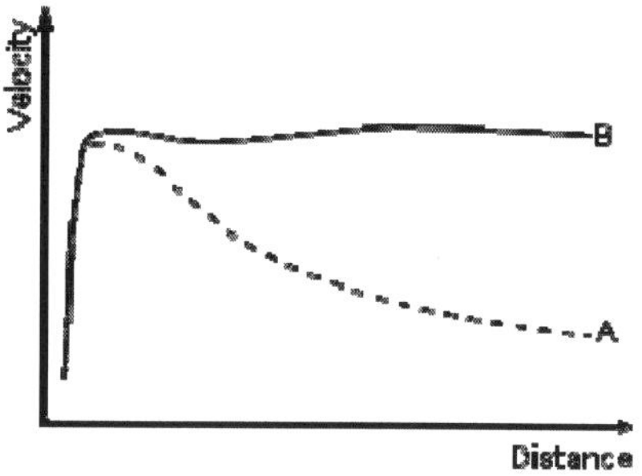

Fig. 3.1.1. Rotation curve of a typical spiral galaxy: predicted (**A**) and observed (**B**).

For example, the rotation curve of the type B corresponds to the galaxy NGC3198. The following extensive radio observations determined the detailed rotation curve of spiral disk galaxies to be flat (as the curve B), much beyond as seen in the optical band. Obviously the trivial balance between the gravitational and centrifugal forces ($\gamma_{N,LD} = 6.677 \cdot 10^{-8} \ cm^3/(g \cdot s^2)$)

$$\gamma_N \frac{mM}{r^2} = \frac{mV_{orb}^2}{r} \tag{3.1.3}$$

leads to the relation between orbital speed V_{orb} and galactocentric distance r as

$$V_{orb}^2 = \gamma_N M / r . \tag{3.1.4}$$

As a result for the galaxy of mass M we have the rotational curve like A. The obvious contradiction with the velocity curve B having a 'flat' appearance out to a large radius was explained by introduction of a new physical essence – dark matter (which increasing “visible” mass M). The result of this activity is known – undetectable dark matter which does not emit radiation, inferred solely from its gravitational effects. But it means that upwards of 50% of the mass of galaxies was contained in the dark galactic halo.

Therefore we have two hypothetical identities from *the position of local physics*:

Dark Matter

• An undetected form of mass that emits little or no light but whose existence we infer from its gravitational influence. Evidence for its existence dates from the 1930s and is very solid from the position of the local physics.

Dark Energy

• An unknown form of energy that seems to be the source of a repulsive force causing the expansion of the universe to accelerate.

• Evidence for its existence was found only ~10 years ago, and it is much less well-understood.

Although these have similar sounding names, they refer to two very different things, which have been identified by very different means.

We give the typical evaluations of these effects which can be found in Internet for unseen "Dark" influences in the Cosmos.

"Normal" Matter: ~ 4.4%

– Normal matter inside stars: ~ 0.6%

– Normal matter outside stars: ~ 3.8%

• Dark Matter: ~ 25%,

• Dark Energy ~ 71%.

We can measure an object's mass from the orbital period. This comes from Newton's form of Kepler's third law, which can be rewritten as (see (3.1.4)):

$$M_{enc} = V_{orb} r^2 / \gamma_N , \tag{3.1.5}$$

r is average orbital separation, M_{enc} is a mass enclosed by orbit. So by measuring the orbit velocity and separation, we can determine the total mass enclosed by the orbit. Any non luminous component of the Universe can only be detected indirectly, by its gravitational influence on the luminous (light-emitting) components.

It is estimated that there are approximately 10^{11} stars in the disk of the Milky Way galaxy in total, most of these stars have a slightly lesser mass than the Sun have. The Sun lies approximately 8.5 kiloparsecs (~27,7 10^3 light years) from the center of the Milky Way (1 parsec = $3{,}08568\times10^{16}$ m = 3,2616 light years).

The solar mass ($M_{\odot}$) is a standard unit of mass in astronomy, equal to approximately $1{,}99 \cdot 10^{30}$ kilograms.

It is impossible to believe that the Kepler's theory leads to so bad results in the absolutely analogical situation of the star rotation. In other words – is it possible to create the theory realizing the continuous transfer from "Kepler rotation" to "Rubin rotation" without artifact like "dark matter"? The corresponding theory will be constructed in this Chapter. The problems of "dark energy" will be solved from positions of nonlocal physics.

Galaxies are a massive ensemble of stars and other material orbiting about a common center. Its constituents held together by the mutual gravitational interaction. Galaxies usually classified into two major types: elliptical and disk galaxies. The primordial low-density diffuse clouds of light elements started to contract and collapsed into smaller fragments of the size of galaxies. During runaway gravitational collapse, where stars formed quickly in large numbers and started to shine at once before the gravitational collapse finished, an elliptical proto-galaxy was born. The energy of gravitational collapse was converted to the chaotic motion of stars. If the primordial gas was shrunken by the gravity more slowly, the gas have had enough time to start rotation and settled into a regular disk galaxy where it formed stars. This is known as the gravitational collapse theory of a galaxy formation. Elliptical galaxies are not flat ellipses, but they are three-dimensionally elliptical. Orbits of stars do not show a systematic rotation in such galaxies and are largely chaotic. Elliptical galaxies are smooth, featureless and almost spherical. Elliptical galaxies are slowly rotating objects supported by pressure, i.e. their dynamics is dominated by the irregular motion of stars.

Disk galaxies consist of relatively young stars, open clusters (loose clusters of stars), middle age stars like the Sun, gas and dust (interstellar matter or ISM). Observations of disk galaxies are showing that these galaxies have the very thin disk whose radius is of order 10 kilo parsecs and thickness is of order 100 parsecs.

The most of the stars in a disk galaxy travel on nearly circular orbits. Stars in disk galaxies usually rotate with a constant velocity in the range of $100\text{km} \cdot \text{s}^{-1}$ to $300\text{km} \cdot \text{s}^{-1}$ with only a low dispersion of the velocity of order $\sim 10\text{km} \cdot \text{s}^{-1}$. Therefore, the angular momentum must govern the structure of disk galaxies. Stars in the Milky Way galaxy usually rotate with a velocity of $\sim 220\text{km} \cdot \text{s}^{-1}$ and with a low velocity dispersion of about $40\text{km} \cdot \text{s}^{-1}$. Disk galaxies contain mainly blue stars that are very massive and are known to live shortly.

Because these young stars still exist in disk galaxies, these galaxies are referred to as young galaxies. These stars are born mainly in spiral arms. The spiral arms look like that they contain a more mass than their surroundings.

A roughly spherical halo of galaxy contains globular clusters (GCs), i.e. isolated dense stellar clusters of millions of stars, and other ISM. Like in elliptical galaxies, the motion of stars in globular clusters is chaotic. Globular clusters usually contain old red (giant) stars and are therefore very old. The stellar halo has a mass in the range of 15 to 30 percent of the mass of disk. The diameter of the halo is approximately the same as the diameter of the disk.

Local physics demonstrates the following lines of the dark matter evidence

– Orbits of stars in galaxies.

– Motions of galaxies in galaxy clusters including behavior of hot gas in galaxy clusters.

– Gravitational lensing.

Local physics is trying to explain "dark effects" introducing in consideration new massive particles, namely MACHOS or WIMPS. MACHOs – massive compact halo objects (dead or failed stars in the halos of galaxies, brown dwarfs, white dwarfs, small black holes). WIMPs –weakly interacting massive particles (mysterious neutrino-like particles). In our nonlocal theory we needn't to introduce new kinds of massive particles. All problems can be solved using the first principles of physics.

In conclusion of this item we should underline that the fate of the Universe depends on the theory of dark matter and dark energy.

3.2. History of the dark matter problem.

By the end of the twentieth century revealed from the position of local physics that 96% of matter and energy in the Universe is of unknown origin, appeared "dark matter" and "dark" energy. Swiss astronomer Fritz Zwicky discovered its existence from the standpoint of classical statistical mechanics of non-equilibrium processes. Here (Fig. 3.2.1) you can see the portrait of Fritz Zwicky and a plaque on the house in Varna (Bulgaria), where Fritz Zwicky was born.

Fig. 3.2.1. Fritz Zwicky, February 14, 1898 — February 8, 1974)

By the way, father of F. Zwicky (Fridolin) stayed in Varna until 1945, his mother died in Varna in 1927, and the sister married a Bulgarian and has lived all his life in Varna.

In 1933, Swiss astronomer Fritz Zwicky of CalTech decided to study a small group of seven galaxies in the Coma Cluster [56, 57]. Its objective was to calculate the total mass of this cluster by studying the dispersion speeds of these seven galaxies. The dispersion speeds characterize how the speed of these seen galaxies differed from each other. By using Newton laws, he calculated its "dynamic mass", then compared it with the "luminous mass", which is the mass calculated from the quantity of light emitted by the cluster. The luminous mass can be calculated taking into account the reasonable distribution of the star population in the galaxies.

The dispersion speeds are directly related to the cluster's mass. In fact, a star cluster can be compared with a gas, where the particles would be galaxies. If the gas is hot and light, the dispersion speed of the particles is high. If the gas is cold and heavy, the dispersion speed is weak.

Zwicky discovered that the speeds observed in the Coma Cluster were very high. The dynamic mass was 400 times larger than the luminous mass! Zwicky announced its observation. At the time, the methods and the precision of measurements were not accurate and Zwicky's result were not interested for the scientific community.

The same phenomenon was again observed in 1936 by Sinclair Smith during the calculation of the Virgo Cluster's total dynamic mass. This one was 200 times more important than Edwin Hubble's estimate. According to Smith, is could be explained by the presence of matter between the galaxies of the cluster. Moreover, the galaxy clusters were still considered by a great number of astronomers as of temporary structures rather than of stable structures. This explanation was enough to justify excessive speeds.

Vera Rubin is a staff member at the Department of Terrestrial Magnetism of the Carnegie Institution of Washington, where she has been since 1965. That same year, she became the first woman permitted to observe at Palomar Observatory. The author of more than 200 papers on the structure of the Milky Way, motions within galaxies and large-scale motions in the universe, she received Carnegie Mellon University's Dickson Prize for Science in 1994 and the Royal Astronomical Society's Gold Medal in 1996. President Bill Clinton awarded her the National Medal of Science in 1993 and appointed her to the President's Committee on the National Medal of Science in 1995. Vera Rubin conducted thorough astronomical observations. It turned out that the outer stars rotating about the galactic center, moving in orbits much faster than it followed from the theory of Kepler, and with the central mass greater than "visible" by astronomers. For example, you see in Fig. 3.2.2 the orbital speed of stars (including the Sun) depending on the distance from the center of our galaxy, the Milky Way. The abscissa axis represents the distance in thousands of light-years, and axis of ordinates stands for the orbital velocity in kilometers per second.

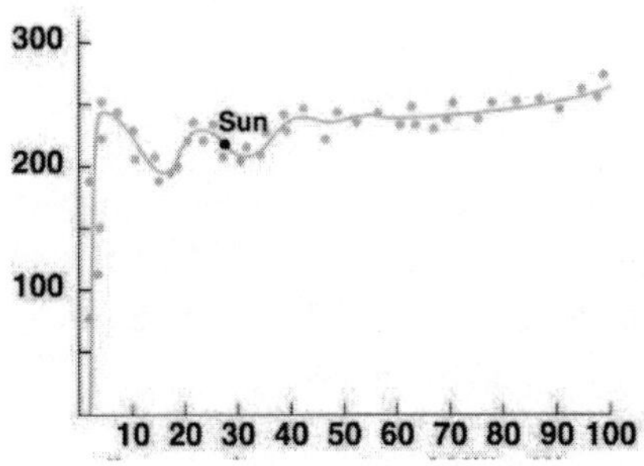

Fig. 3.2.2. Typical dependence of the orbital velocity of stars to distance (online resource).

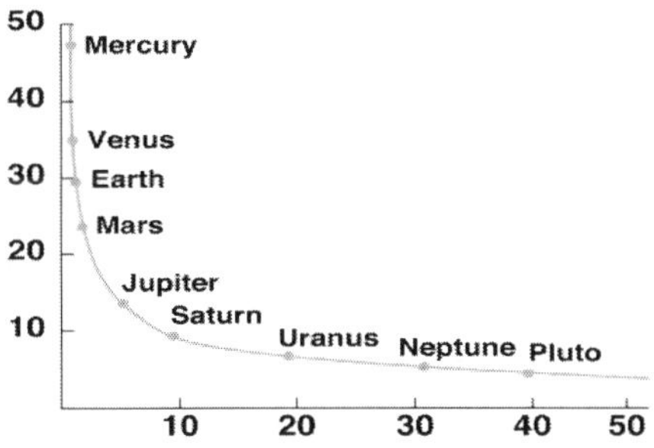

Fig. 3.2.3. The orbital speed of the planets of the solar system depending on the distance from the Sun in astronomical units (online resource).

Figure 3.2.3 shows a similar dependence for the planets of the solar system. The abscissa axis represents the distance in astronomical units, and the ordinate axis orbital speed in kilometers per second. The astronomical unit (symbol au, AU or ua) is a unit of length, roughly the distance from Earth to the Sun. This distance varies as Earth orbits the Sun, from a maximum (aphelion) to a minimum (perihelion) and back again once a year. It is taken that 1 AU $=1{,}4960\cdot 10^{11} m = 4.8481\cdot 10^{-6} pc$.

We indicate the fundamental astronomical observations; the paper (V. Rubin, W. K. Ford, Jr (1970). "Rotation of the Andromeda Nebula from a Spectroscopic Survey of Emission Regions". *Astrophysical Journal* **159**: 379) contains the first detailed study of orbital rotation in galaxies. The paper (V. Rubin, W. K. Ford, Jr, N. Thonnard (1980). "Rotational Properties of 21 Sc Galaxies with a Large Range of Luminosities and Radii from NGC 4605 (R=4kpc) to UGC 2885 (R=122kpc)". *Astrophysical Journal* **238**: 471) contains observations of a set of spiral galaxies gave convincing evidence that orbital velocities of stars in galaxies were unexpectedly high at large distances from the nucleus. This paper was influential in convincing astronomers that most of the matter in the universe is dark, and much of it is clumped about galaxies.

The “shelf” on the curve of the orbital speed is not the only paradoxical fact in the modern astrophysics; however it is enough to understand the fundamental theoretical physics is on the threshold of revolution.

3.3. Evidences of the dark matter existence from position of local physics

3.3.1. Galaxy rotation curves.

Much of the evidence comes from the motions of galaxies. A galaxy rotation curve is a plot of the orbital velocities (i.e., the speeds) of visible stars or gas in that galaxy versus their radial distance from that galaxy's center. The rotational speed of galaxies and correspondingly the orbital speed of stars do not decline with distance which leads to appearance of the "Rubin shelf" on the plot of the orbital velocities. Other orbital systems such as systems stars - planets and planets - moons that also have most of their mass at the centre but follow the Kepler's law. In the latter cases, this reflects the mass distributions within those systems. The mass observations for galaxies based on the light that they emit are far too low to explain the velocity observations. The dark matter hypothesis accounts for the missing mass, explaining the anomaly.

This situation leads to the "natural" affirmation in local astrophysical models the distribution of dark matter in galaxies explains the motion of the observed matter suggesting the presence of a roughly spherically symmetric, centrally concentrated halo of dark matter with the visible matter concentrated in a central disc.

Results of "the dark matter observations" are well known. We remind some mentioned results:

Low-surface-brightness (LSB) galaxies have a much larger visible mass deficit than others. This property simplifies the disentanglement of the dark and visible matter contributions to the rotation curves [58].

Rotation curves for some elliptical galaxies display low velocities for outlying stars. Velocity dispersion estimates of elliptical galaxies [59] with some exceptions generally indicate relatively high dark matter content.

Diffuse interstellar gas measurements of galactic edges indicate missing ordinary matter beyond the visible boundary.

Star velocity profiles seemed to indicate a concentration of dark matter in the disk of the Milky Way. The typical model for dark matter galaxies is a smooth, spherical distribution of dark matter in halos.

In 2005, astronomers claimed to have discovered a galaxy made almost entirely of dark matter, 50 million light years away in the Virgo Cluster, which was named VIRGOH121, [60]. This effect was discovered with radio frequency observations of hydrogen because VIRGOHI21 does not appear to contain visible stars.

At the same time many observations of some galaxies indicate an absence of dark matter. For example the velocity profiles of some NGC 3379 indicate an absence of dark matter.

Some results of the mentioned observations can be found in [61]. The next natural step consists in an attempt to create the map of dark matter in the Universe. Dark matter is invisible. But effect of gravitational lensing exists. Gravitational lensing (usually of more distant galaxies) can measure cluster masses without relying on observations of dynamics (e.g., velocity).

3.3.2. Gravitational lensing observations of galaxy clusters.

Gravitational lensing observations of galaxy clusters allow direct estimates of the gravitational mass based on its effect on light coming from background galaxies, since large collections of matter (dark or otherwise) gravitationally deflect light. A gravitational lensing is a distribution of matter (such as a cluster of galaxies) between a distant light source and an observer that is capable of bending the light from the source as the light travels towards the observer.

Henry Cavendish in 1784 (in an unpublished manuscript) and Johann Georg von Soldner in 1801 (published in 1804) [62] had pointed out that Newtonian gravity predicts that starlight will bend around a massive object as had already been supposed by Isaac Newton in 1704 in his famous Queries No.1 in his book Optics [63].

From the first glance we deal with the very simple idea obvious from Fig. 3.3.1.

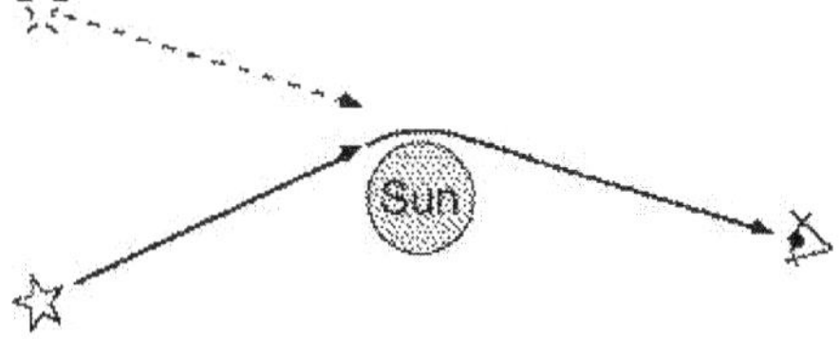

Fig. 3.3.1. The light ray from a star follows an unbound hyperbolic orbit about the Sun.

The corpuscular consideration immediately leads to two problems:

1. Photon as a particle has no the mass of the rest and the usual variant of the Newtonian gravitation law is not applicable in this situation.

2. If nevertheless we use the main ideas of gravitation between two point objects, what is the potential of interaction between these objects?

From the position of the problems formulated above, it is interesting to solve the Soldner problem using the modern formulations.

Then we proceed to calculate the deflection of a light ray by the gravitational field of a massive body.

Assumption 1. An evolution of the light ray from a distant star under the Sun's gravitational force field can be described as the scattering of a particle in a central force field.

Assumption 2. This scattering leads to the hyperbolic orbit.

Let us introduce the usual notations in the theory of scattering [64], r is radius directed from the center of attraction M_{Sun} to the moving material point m; $U(r)$ is the potential energy; φ is an angle between the direction of the radius - vector and the horizontal axes. Then we use the typical notation in the theory of hyperbola, which general picture corresponds to Fig. 3.3.2. The full solution of the problem of motion of a particle in a central force field is easiest to get, based on the laws of conservation of energy and moment. Energy of the material point m is written as

$$E=\frac{m}{2}\left[\left(\frac{dr}{dt}\right)^2+r^2\left(\frac{d\varphi}{dt}\right)^2\right]+U(r)=\frac{m}{2}\left(\frac{dr}{dt}\right)^2+\frac{L^2}{2mr^2}+U(r), \tag{3.3.1}$$

where

$$L=mr^2\frac{d\varphi}{dt}=const \tag{3.3.2}$$

is angle momentum. From (3.3.1) follows

$$dr=\sqrt{\frac{2}{m}[E-U(r)]-\frac{L^2}{m^2r^2}}dt \tag{3.3.3}$$

and from (3.3.2)

$$d\varphi=\frac{L}{mr^2}dt\,. \tag{3.3.4}$$

Comparing (3.3.3) and (3.3.4) we see

$$mr^2\frac{d\varphi}{L}=\frac{dr}{\sqrt{\frac{2}{m}[E-U(r)]-\frac{L^2}{m^2r^2}}}. \tag{3.3.5}$$

After integration we find

$$\varphi = \int \frac{\frac{L}{r^2}dr}{\sqrt{2m[E - U(r)] - \frac{L^2}{r^2}}} + const. \qquad (3.3.6)$$

The relation (3.3.6) defines the trajectory of the particle m. Let us use the Assumption 1 writing the potential energy as

$$U = -\frac{\alpha}{r}. \qquad (3.3.7)$$

In this case from (3.3.6) and (3.3.7) we have

$$\varphi = \int \frac{\frac{L}{r^2}dr}{\sqrt{2m\left[E + \frac{\alpha}{r}\right] - \frac{L^2}{r^2}}} + const$$

and after integration

$$\varphi = \arccos \frac{\frac{L}{r} - \frac{m\alpha}{L}}{\sqrt{2mE + \frac{m^2\alpha^2}{L^2}}} + const. \qquad (3.3.8)$$

Choosing the origin of the angle φ so that the constant was equal to zero and introducing the notations

$$p = \frac{L^2}{m\alpha}, \qquad (3.3.9)$$

$$e = \sqrt{1 + \frac{2EL^2}{m\alpha^2}} \qquad (3.3.10)$$

we have well known relation [64]

$$\frac{p}{r} = 1 + e\cos\varphi. \qquad (3.3.11)$$

The value $e = \sqrt{1 + \frac{b^2}{a^2}}$ (see Fig. 3.3.2) defines the eccentricity of the orbit.

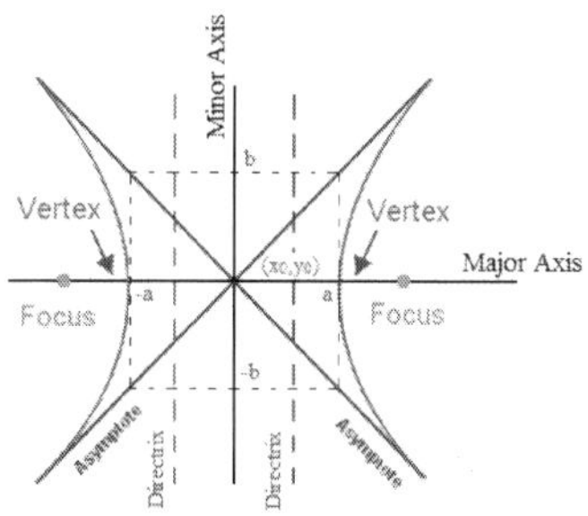

Fig. 3.3.2. The light ray from a star follows an unbound hyperbolic orbit about the Sun.

If $E \geq 0$ we have the infinite movement. If $E > 0$ the eccentricity of the orbit $e > 1$ and trajectory is a hyperbola enveloping the center of the field (focus) as shown in the Fig. 3.3.2. Perihelion distance from the center is

$$r_{\min} = \frac{b}{2} = \frac{p}{e+1}. \tag{3.3.12}$$

Using the Newton's law and (3.3.7) we find from the relation

$$U = -\frac{\alpha}{r} = \gamma_N \frac{mM_{Sun}}{r} \tag{3.3.13}$$

that

$$\alpha^2 = \gamma_N^2 m^2 M_{Sun}^2. \tag{3.3.14}$$

Let us rewrite (3.3.10) using (3.3.14) as

$$e = \sqrt{1 + \frac{2EL^2}{\gamma_N^2 m^3 M_{Sun}^2}}. \tag{3.3.15}$$

The constant values of motion can be defined in the vertex point coinciding with the Sun surface, where we have

$$E = \frac{m}{2}\left[\left(\frac{dr}{dt}\right)^2 + r^2\left(\frac{d\varphi}{dt}\right)^2\right] + U(r) = \frac{mv^2}{2} + U(r) = \frac{mv^2}{2} - \gamma_N \frac{mM_{Sun}}{R_{Sun}}, \tag{3.3.16}$$

$$L = mvR_{Sun}. \tag{3.3.17}$$

The eccentricity e from (3.3.15) is written as follows (see also (3.3.16), (3.3.17))

$$e = \sqrt{1 + \frac{2EL^2}{\gamma_N^2 m^3 M_{Sun}^2}} = \sqrt{1 + \frac{2R_{Sun}^2 c^2}{\gamma_N^2 M_{Sun}^2}\left(\frac{c^2}{2} - \gamma_N \frac{M_{Sun}}{R_{Sun}}\right)} \tag{3.3.18}$$

if the velocity v is equal to c, the light speed in vacuum.

Important conclusion: if we use the attractive potential in the form (3.3.7), mass m of the light particle cancels out in (3.3.18).

Let us produce some estimation. If $M_{Sun} = 1{,}9891 \cdot 10^{33} g$, $R_{Sun} = 6{,}9551 \cdot 10^{10} cm$, $\gamma_N = 6{,}67 \cdot 10^{-8} cm^3 g^{-1} s^{-2}$, $c = 2{,}99\,792\,458 \quad 10^{10}\, cm \cdot s^{-1}$, we obtain for the term in the round bracket of (3.3.18)

$$\gamma_N \frac{M_{Sun}}{R_{Sun}} = 1{,}9 \cdot 10^{15} \frac{cm^2}{s^2} << \frac{c^2}{2} \tag{3.3.19}$$

and

$$e = \sqrt{1 + \frac{R_{Sun}^2 c^4}{\gamma_N^2 M_{Sun}^2}}. \tag{3.3.20}$$

Analogically for (3.3.20) one obtains

$$\frac{R_{Sun}^2 c^4}{\gamma_N^2 M_{Sun}^2} = 2{,}22 \cdot 10^{11} >> 1 \tag{3.3.21}$$

and

$$e = \frac{R_{Sun}c^2}{\gamma_N M_{Sun}} = 4.71 \cdot 10^5 >> 1. \qquad (3.3.22)$$

The deflection of the light ray is illustrated in Fig. 3.3.1, with the bending greatly exaggerated for a better view of the angle of deflection. From the hyperbola theory one obtains (see Fig. 3.3.2)

$$\frac{1}{e} = \frac{a}{\sqrt{a^2 + b^2}} = \cos\varphi_N. \qquad (3.3.23)$$

The angle of deflection δ_N can be calculated (see Fig. 3.3.2 and (3.3.22), (3.3.23)) as

$$\delta_N = \pi - 2\arccos\varphi_N = \pi - 2\arccos\frac{1}{e} = \pi - 2\arccos\frac{\gamma_N M_{Sun}}{R_{Sun}c^2}. \qquad (3.3.24)$$

The relation (3.3.24) can be simplified because e^{-1} is the small value. In this case

$$\arccos e^{-1} = \frac{\pi}{2} - \arcsin e^{-1} = \frac{\pi}{2} - \left[e^{-1} + \frac{1}{2}\frac{e^{-3}}{3} + \ldots \right] \qquad (3.3.25)$$

and omitting the small second term in the squared bracket we obtain the angle of deflection δ_N

$$\delta_N = 2e^{-1} = \frac{2\gamma_N M_{Sun}}{R_{Sun}c^2} \qquad (3.3.26)$$

SOME REMARKS:

1. The first written account of the defection of light by gravity appeared in the article "On the defection of light ray from its straight motion due to the attraction of a world body which it passes closely," by Johann Soldner in 1804. In his article Soldner predicted that a light ray passing close to the solar limb would be deflected by an angle α = 0,84 arcsec.

2. More than a century later, in 1919, Albert Einstein directly addressed the influence of gravity on light. At this time Einstein's General Theory of Relativity was not fully developed. This is the reason why Einstein obtained the same value for the deflection angle as Soldner had calculated with Newtonian physics. In this paper Einstein found $\delta_N = \frac{2\gamma_N M_{Sun}}{c^2 R_{Sun}}$ = 0,83 arcsec for the deflection angle of a light ray grazing the sun (here M_{Sun} and R_{Sun} are the mass and radius of the sun, c and γ_N are the speed of light and the gravitational constant respectively). With the completion of the General Theory of Relativity in 1916, Einstein derives the formula for the deflection angle δ_E of a light

passing at a distance r from an object with mass M as $\delta_E = \frac{4\gamma_N M}{c^2 r}$. For the sun, Einstein obtained $\delta_E = \frac{4\gamma_N M_{Sun}}{c^2 R_{Sun}} = 1.74$ arcsec.

3. The first observation of light deflection was performed by noting the change in position of stars as they passed near the Sun on the celestial sphere. The observations were performed in May 1919 by Arthur Eddington, Frank Watson Dyson, and their collaborators during a total solar eclipse [65]. The solar eclipse allowed the stars near the Sun to be observed. Observations were made simultaneously in the cities of Sobral, Ceará, Brazil and in São Tomé and Principe on the west coast of Africa [66]. The observations demonstrated that the light from stars passing close to the Sun was slightly bent, so that stars appeared slightly out of position.

This value was first confirmed to within 20% by Arthur Eddington and his group during a solar total eclipse in 1919. Recently this value was confirmed to within 0,02%.

Let us consider now the lensing effect from the position of the dark matter concept.

With this aim let us investigate the Poisson equation (2.1.21), which can be written in dimensionless form as ($\tilde{G}$ is the dimensionless Newton gravitational constant $\tilde{\gamma}_N$)

$$\frac{\partial}{\partial \tilde{\mathbf{r}}} \cdot \tilde{\mathbf{g}} = -4\pi\tilde{G}\left[\tilde{\rho} - \tilde{\tau}\left(\frac{\partial\tilde{\rho}}{\partial t} + \frac{\partial}{\partial\tilde{\mathbf{r}}} \cdot \tilde{\rho}\tilde{\mathbf{v}}_0\right)\right]. \tag{3.3.27}$$

We suppose for the simplicity the stationary case with the radial symmetry. Then

$$\frac{\partial}{\partial\tilde{r}}\left(\tilde{r}^2\tilde{g}_r\right) = -\tilde{G}\left[\tilde{\rho}\tilde{r}^2 - \tilde{\tau}\frac{\partial\left(\tilde{r}^2\tilde{\rho}\tilde{v}_{0r}\right)}{\partial\tilde{r}}\right] \tag{3.3.28}$$

or after integration

$$\tilde{r}^2\tilde{g}_r = -\tilde{G}\int_0^{\tilde{r}}\left[\tilde{\rho}\tilde{r}^2\right]d\tilde{r} + \tilde{G}\int_0^{\tilde{r}}\left[\tilde{\tau}\frac{\partial\left(\tilde{r}^2\tilde{\rho}\tilde{v}_{0r}\right)}{\partial\tilde{r}}\right]d\tilde{r}. \tag{3.3.29}$$

Let us suppose that nonlocal dimensionless parameter $\tilde{\tau}$ does not depend on $\tilde{r}$. In this case we find

$$\tilde{r}^2\tilde{g}_r = -\tilde{G}\int_0^{\tilde{r}}\left[\tilde{\rho}\tilde{r}^2\right]d\tilde{r} + \tilde{G}\tilde{\tau}\tilde{r}^2\tilde{\rho}\tilde{v}_{0r} \tag{3.3.30}$$

or

$$\tilde{r}^2\tilde{g}_r = -\tilde{G}\tilde{M} + \tilde{G}\tilde{\tau}\tilde{r}^2\tilde{\rho}\tilde{v}_{0r}, \tag{3.3.31}$$

where $\widetilde{M}$ is the dimensionless mass of the central body. As a result we obtain non-local gravitation law

$$\widetilde{g}_r = -\widetilde{G}\frac{\widetilde{M}}{\widetilde{r}^2} + \widetilde{\tau}\widetilde{G}\widetilde{\rho}\widetilde{v}_{0r} \qquad (3.3.32)$$

and only in the local case we reach the classical Newton law (compare with (3.3.13))

$$\widetilde{g}_r = -\widetilde{G}\frac{\widetilde{M}}{\widetilde{r}^2}. \qquad (3.3.33)$$

In the nonlocal case gravitational acceleration

$$\widetilde{g}_r = -\widetilde{G}\left[\frac{\widetilde{M}}{\widetilde{r}^2} - \widetilde{\tau}\widetilde{\rho}\widetilde{v}_{0r}\right] \qquad (3.3.34)$$

turns into zero in a point $\widetilde{r}_{cr}$ if

$$\frac{\widetilde{M}}{\widetilde{r}_{cr}^2} = \widetilde{\tau}\widetilde{\rho}\widetilde{v}_{0r}, \qquad (3.3.35)$$

where

$$\widetilde{r}_{cr} = \sqrt{\frac{\widetilde{M}}{\widetilde{\tau}\widetilde{\rho}\widetilde{v}_{0r}}}. \qquad (3.3.36)$$

if $\widetilde{v}_{0r,cr} > 0$. Then the well known relation should be modified

$$m\widetilde{g}_r = -\widetilde{G}m\left[\frac{\widetilde{M}}{\widetilde{r}^2} - \widetilde{\tau}\widetilde{\rho}\widetilde{v}_{0r}\right] \qquad (3.3.37)$$

or the orbital velocity is equal

$$V_{orb} = \sqrt{\widetilde{G}\left[\frac{\widetilde{M}}{\widetilde{r}} - \widetilde{\tau}\widetilde{\rho}\widetilde{v}_{0r}\widetilde{r}\right]}. \qquad (3.3.38)$$

The energy flux density can be negative $\widetilde{\rho}\widetilde{v}_{0r} < 0$ that is, can be $V_{orb} > V_{orb,Newton}$. This equality may mean the introduction of additional mass which in local physics as an "additional dark matter" is considered.

Then

$$V_{orb} = \sqrt{\widetilde{G}\frac{\widetilde{M}}{\widetilde{r}}\left[1 - \frac{\widetilde{\tau}\widetilde{\rho}\widetilde{v}_{0r}\widetilde{r}^2}{\widetilde{M}}\right]}. \qquad (3.3.39)$$

For the bounded system $\widetilde{\rho}\widetilde{v}_{0r} < 0$ we have formally the additional (if you want "dark" mass)

$$M_{dark}(\widetilde{r}) = \widetilde{\tau}\widetilde{\rho}|\widetilde{v}_{0r}|\widetilde{r}^2. \qquad (3.3.40)$$

It means also that in Soldner formulae the additional mass $M_{dark}(\widetilde{r})$ should be inserted which leads to increasing effective mass M. For example (see 3.3.26)

$$\delta_N = \frac{2\gamma_N}{R_{Sun}c^2}\left(M_{Sun} + M_{dark}(\widetilde{r})\right). \qquad (3.3.41)$$

From the nonlocal Newton-Kepler relation (3.3.35) follows that anti-lensing effect can take place.

If the parameter $\tilde{\tau}$ is not dependent on $\tilde{r}$ the effective gravitational acceleration

$$\tilde{g}_r = -\tilde{G}\left[\frac{\tilde{M}}{\tilde{r}^2} - \tilde{\tau}\tilde{\rho}\tilde{v}_{0r}\right] \tag{3.3.42}$$

can be positive, negative, or zero.

The accelerated cosmological expansion was discovered in direct astronomical observations at distances of a few billion light years, almost at the edge of the observable Universe. This acceleration should be explained because mutual attraction of cosmic bodies is only capable of decelerating their scattering. As result new idea was introduced in physics about existing of a force with the opposite sign which is called universal anti-gravitation. From the position of local physics [67] - its physical source is so called dark energy that manifest itself only because of postulated property of providing anti-gravitation.

In literature we can find the numerous attempts to modify gravitational theories introducing the Einstein cosmological constant or the modified Newton force, For example the Newton law is written as

$$F(r) = -\gamma_N\left[\frac{M}{r^2} - \frac{8\pi}{3}\rho_v r\right], \tag{3.3.43}$$

where $F(r)$ is a force acting on the mass unit, ρ_v is the Einstein – Gliner vacuum density introduced also in [67, 68]. Compare now the nonlocal formula (3.3.42) (obtained from the first principles of physics) with the phenomenological (3.3.43) containing so called vacuum density.

In the limit of large distances the influence of central mass M becomes negligibly small and the field of forces is determined only by the second term in the right side of (3.3.42). It follows from relation (3.3.42) that there is a distance r_v at which the sum of the gravitation and anti-gravitation forces is equal to zero. In other words r_v is "the zero-gravitational radius". For so called Local Group of galaxies estimation of r_v is about 1Mpc, [67]. Obviously the second term in relation (3.3.42) should be defined as result of solution of the self-consistent gravitational nonlocal problem with the inclusion into consideration all transport processes. Important to underline, that General Relativistic Theory (GRT) does not contain the description of transport processes in principal.

In the following items of this chapter all calculations are realized in frame of nonlocal theory for different parameter G

$$G = \frac{\gamma_N \rho_0 x_0^2}{u_0^2} = \frac{\gamma_N M}{u_0^2 x_0}. \tag{3.3.44}$$

defining the transfer from the Kepler's to Rubin scenario. Obviously, the previously results are the particular cases realized for $G = \frac{\delta_N}{2}$ and $G = \frac{\delta_E}{4}$. The previous considerations have the obvious shortcomings, Soldner's theory should be transformed into the relativistic variant; Einstein theory has the phenomenological character and does not lead to the transport equations.

Gravity acts as a lens to bend the light from a more distant source (such as a quasar) around a massive object (such as a cluster of galaxies) lying between the source and the observer. There are two types of lensing: strong lensing produces multiple images or giant arcs near the cluster core, while weak lensing is observed as small shape distortions around the outer regions. Multiple Hubble projects have used this method to measure cluster masses. Gravitational lenses act equally on all kinds of electromagnetic radiation, not just visible light. Weak lensing effects are being studied for the cosmic microwave background as well as galaxy surveys. Strong lenses have been observed in radio and x-ray regimes as well. If a strong lens produces multiple images, there will be a relative time delay between two paths: that is, in one image the lensed object will be observed before the other image.

The first gravitational lens is discovered in 1979. It became known as the "Twin QSO" since it initially looked like two identical quasi-stellar objects. It is officially named SBS 0957+561. This gravitational lens was discovered by Dennis Walsh, Bob Carswell and Ray Weymann using the Kitt Peak National Observatory 2.1 meter telescope, [69].

In particular:

In clusters such as Abell 1689, lensing observations confirm the presence of considerably more mass than is indicated by the clusters' light. Galaxy cluster Abell 2029 comprises thousands of galaxies enveloped in a cloud of hot gas and dark matter equivalent to more than 1014 M_{Sun}. At the center of this cluster is an enormous elliptical galaxy likely formed from many smaller galaxies [70].

The most direct observational evidence comes from the Bullet Cluster. In most regions dark and visible matter are found together [71] due to their gravitational attraction. In the Bullet Cluster, lensing observations show that much of the lensing mass is separated from the X-ray-emitting baryonic mass.

Therefore we formulate the following alternative:

1. Dark matter really exists, and we are observing the effects of its gravitational attraction

or

2. Something is wrong with our understanding of gravity, causing us to mistakenly infer the existence of dark matter.

We intend to show that the item 2 is valid and the problem of the so called dark matter can be solved in the frame of nonlocal physics.

3.4. Nonlocal mathematical model in the theory of the disk galaxy rotation.

Strict consideration leads to the following system of the generalized hydrodynamic equations (GHE) written in the generalized Euler form:

(Continuity equation for species α)

$$\frac{\partial}{\partial t}\left\{\rho_\alpha-\tau_\alpha\left[\frac{\partial\rho_\alpha}{\partial t}+\frac{\partial}{\partial\mathbf{r}}\cdot(\rho_\alpha\mathbf{v}_0)\right]\right\}$$
$$+\frac{\partial}{\partial\mathbf{r}}\cdot\left\{\rho_\alpha\mathbf{v}_0-\tau_\alpha\left[\frac{\partial}{\partial t}(\rho_\alpha\mathbf{v}_0)+\frac{\partial}{\partial\mathbf{r}}\cdot(\rho_\alpha\mathbf{v}_0\mathbf{v}_0)+\ddot{\mathrm{I}}\cdot\frac{\partial p_\alpha}{\partial\mathbf{r}}-\rho_\alpha\mathbf{F}_\alpha^{(1)}-\frac{q_\alpha}{m_\alpha}\rho_\alpha\mathbf{v}_0\times\mathbf{B}\right]\right\}=R_\alpha. \quad (3.4.1)$$

(Continuity equation for mixture)

$$\frac{\partial}{\partial t}\left\{\rho-\sum_\alpha\tau_\alpha\left[\frac{\partial\rho_\alpha}{\partial t}+\frac{\partial}{\partial\mathbf{r}}\cdot(\rho_\alpha\mathbf{v}_0)\right]\right\}+\frac{\partial}{\partial\mathbf{r}}\cdot\left\{\rho\mathbf{v}_0-\sum_\alpha\tau_\alpha\left[\frac{\partial}{\partial t}(\rho_\alpha\mathbf{v}_0)+\frac{\partial}{\partial\mathbf{r}}\cdot(\rho_\alpha\mathbf{v}_0\mathbf{v}_0)\right.\right.$$
$$\left.\left.+\ddot{\mathrm{I}}\cdot\frac{\partial p_\alpha}{\partial\mathbf{r}}-\rho_\alpha\mathbf{F}_\alpha^{(1)}-\frac{q_\alpha}{m_\alpha}\rho_\alpha\mathbf{v}_0\times\mathbf{B}\right]\right\}=0. \quad (3.4.2)$$

(Momentum equation for species α)

$$\frac{\partial}{\partial t}\left\{\rho_\alpha\mathbf{v}_0-\tau_\alpha\left[\frac{\partial}{\partial t}(\rho_\alpha\mathbf{v}_0)+\frac{\partial}{\partial\mathbf{r}}\cdot\rho_\alpha\mathbf{v}_0\mathbf{v}_0+\frac{\partial p_\alpha}{\partial\mathbf{r}}-\rho_\alpha\mathbf{F}_\alpha^{(1)}\right.\right.$$
$$\left.\left.-\frac{q_\alpha}{m_\alpha}\rho_\alpha\mathbf{v}_0\times\mathbf{B}\right]\right\}-\mathbf{F}_\alpha^{(1)}\left[\rho_\alpha-\tau_\alpha\left(\frac{\partial\rho_\alpha}{\partial t}+\frac{\partial}{\partial\mathbf{r}}\cdot(\rho_\alpha\mathbf{v}_0)\right)\right]$$
$$-\frac{q_\alpha}{m_\alpha}\left\{\rho_\alpha\mathbf{v}_0-\tau_\alpha\left[\frac{\partial}{\partial t}(\rho_\alpha\mathbf{v}_0)+\frac{\partial}{\partial\mathbf{r}}\cdot\rho_\alpha\mathbf{v}_0\mathbf{v}_0+\frac{\partial p_\alpha}{\partial\mathbf{r}}-\rho_\alpha\mathbf{F}_\alpha^{(1)}\right.\right.$$
$$\left.\left.-\frac{q_\alpha}{m_\alpha}\rho_\alpha\mathbf{v}_0\times\mathbf{B}\right]\right\}\times\mathbf{B}+\frac{\partial}{\partial\mathbf{r}}\cdot\left\{\rho_\alpha\mathbf{v}_0\mathbf{v}_0+p_\alpha\ddot{\mathrm{I}}-\tau_\alpha\left[\frac{\partial}{\partial t}(\rho_\alpha\mathbf{v}_0\mathbf{v}_0\right.\right. \quad (3.4.3)$$
$$+p_\alpha\ddot{\mathrm{I}})+\frac{\partial}{\partial\mathbf{r}}\cdot\rho_\alpha(\mathbf{v}_0\mathbf{v}_0)\mathbf{v}_0+2\ddot{\mathrm{I}}\left(\frac{\partial}{\partial\mathbf{r}}\cdot(p_\alpha\mathbf{v}_0)\right)+\frac{\partial}{\partial\mathbf{r}}\cdot(\ddot{\mathrm{I}}p_\alpha\mathbf{v}_0)$$
$$\left.\left.-\mathbf{F}_\alpha^{(1)}\rho_\alpha\mathbf{v}_0-\rho_\alpha\mathbf{v}_0\mathbf{F}_\alpha^{(1)}-\frac{q_\alpha}{m_\alpha}\rho_\alpha[\mathbf{v}_0\times\mathbf{B}]\mathbf{v}_0-\frac{q_\alpha}{m_\alpha}\rho_\alpha\mathbf{v}_0[\mathbf{v}_0\times\mathbf{B}]\right]\right\}$$
$$=\int m_\alpha\mathbf{v}_\alpha J_\alpha^{st,el}d\mathbf{v}_\alpha+\int m_\alpha\mathbf{v}_\alpha J_\alpha^{st,inel}d\mathbf{v}_\alpha.$$

(Momentum equation for mixture)

$$
\begin{aligned}
&\frac{\partial}{\partial t}\left\{\rho\mathbf{v}_0-\sum_\alpha\tau_\alpha\left[\frac{\partial}{\partial t}(\rho_\alpha\mathbf{v}_0)+\frac{\partial}{\partial\mathbf{r}}\cdot\rho_\alpha\mathbf{v}_0\mathbf{v}_0+\frac{\partial p_\alpha}{\partial\mathbf{r}}-\rho_\alpha\mathbf{F}_\alpha^{(1)}\right.\right.\\
&\left.\left.-\frac{q_\alpha}{m_\alpha}\rho_\alpha\mathbf{v}_0\times\mathbf{B}\right]\right\}-\sum_\alpha\mathbf{F}_\alpha^{(1)}\left[\rho_\alpha-\tau_\alpha\left(\frac{\partial\rho_\alpha}{\partial t}+\frac{\partial}{\partial\mathbf{r}}\cdot(\rho_\alpha\mathbf{v}_0)\right)\right]\\
&-\sum_\alpha\frac{q_\alpha}{m_\alpha}\left\{\rho_\alpha\mathbf{v}_0-\tau_\alpha\left[\frac{\partial}{\partial t}(\rho_\alpha\mathbf{v}_0)+\frac{\partial}{\partial\mathbf{r}}\cdot\rho_\alpha\mathbf{v}_0\mathbf{v}_0+\frac{\partial p_\alpha}{\partial\mathbf{r}}-\rho_\alpha\mathbf{F}_\alpha^{(1)}\right.\right.\\
&\left.\left.-\frac{q_\alpha}{m_\alpha}\rho_\alpha\mathbf{v}_0\times\mathbf{B}\right]\right\}\times\mathbf{B}+\frac{\partial}{\partial\mathbf{r}}\cdot\left\{\rho\mathbf{v}_0\mathbf{v}_0+p\overset{\leftrightarrow}{\mathbf{I}}-\sum_\alpha\tau_\alpha\left[\frac{\partial}{\partial t}(\rho_\alpha\mathbf{v}_0\mathbf{v}_0\right.\right.\\
&+p_\alpha\overset{\leftrightarrow}{\mathbf{I}})+\frac{\partial}{\partial\mathbf{r}}\cdot\rho_\alpha(\mathbf{v}_0\mathbf{v}_0)\mathbf{v}_0+2\overset{\leftrightarrow}{\mathbf{I}}\left(\frac{\partial}{\partial\mathbf{r}}\cdot(p_\alpha\mathbf{v}_0)\right)+\frac{\partial}{\partial\mathbf{r}}\cdot\left(\overset{\leftrightarrow}{\mathbf{I}}p_\alpha\mathbf{v}_0\right)\\
&\left.\left.-\mathbf{F}_\alpha^{(1)}\rho_\alpha\mathbf{v}_0-\rho_\alpha\mathbf{v}_0\mathbf{F}_\alpha^{(1)}-\frac{q_\alpha}{m_\alpha}\rho_\alpha[\mathbf{v}_0\times\mathbf{B}]\mathbf{v}_0-\frac{q_\alpha}{m_\alpha}\rho_\alpha\mathbf{v}_0[\mathbf{v}_0\times\mathbf{B}]\right]\right\}=0.
\end{aligned}
\tag{3.4.4}
$$

(Energy equation for α species)

$$
\begin{aligned}
&\frac{\partial}{\partial t}\left\{\frac{\rho_\alpha v_0^2}{2}+\frac{3}{2}p_\alpha+\varepsilon_\alpha n_\alpha-\tau_\alpha\left[\frac{\partial}{\partial t}\left(\frac{\rho_\alpha v_0^2}{2}+\frac{3}{2}p_\alpha+\varepsilon_\alpha n_\alpha\right)\right.\right.\\
&\left.\left.+\frac{\partial}{\partial\mathbf{r}}\cdot\left(\frac{1}{2}\rho_\alpha v_0^2\mathbf{v}_0+\frac{5}{2}p_\alpha\mathbf{v}_0+\varepsilon_\alpha n_\alpha\mathbf{v}_0\right)-\mathbf{F}_\alpha^{(1)}\cdot\rho_\alpha\mathbf{v}_0\right]\right\}\\
&+\frac{\partial}{\partial\mathbf{r}}\cdot\left\{\frac{1}{2}\rho_\alpha v_0^2\mathbf{v}_0+\frac{5}{2}p_\alpha\mathbf{v}_0+\varepsilon_\alpha n_\alpha\mathbf{v}_0-\tau_\alpha\left[\frac{\partial}{\partial t}\left(\frac{1}{2}\rho_\alpha v_0^2\mathbf{v}_0\right.\right.\right.\\
&\left.+\frac{5}{2}p_\alpha\mathbf{v}_0+\varepsilon_\alpha n_\alpha\mathbf{v}_0\right)+\frac{\partial}{\partial\mathbf{r}}\cdot\left(\frac{1}{2}\rho_\alpha v_0^2\mathbf{v}_0\mathbf{v}_0+\frac{7}{2}p_\alpha\mathbf{v}_0\mathbf{v}_0+\frac{1}{2}p_\alpha v_0^2\overset{\leftrightarrow}{\mathbf{I}}\right.\\
&\left.+\frac{5}{2}\frac{p_\alpha^2}{\rho_\alpha}\overset{\leftrightarrow}{\mathbf{I}}+\varepsilon_\alpha n_\alpha\mathbf{v}_0\mathbf{v}_0+\varepsilon_\alpha\frac{p_\alpha}{m_\alpha}\overset{\leftrightarrow}{\mathbf{I}}\right)-\rho_\alpha\mathbf{F}_\alpha^{(1)}\cdot\mathbf{v}_0\mathbf{v}_0-p_\alpha\mathbf{F}_\alpha^{(1)}\cdot\overset{\leftrightarrow}{\mathbf{I}}\\
&-\frac{1}{2}\rho_\alpha v_0^2\mathbf{F}_\alpha^{(1)}-\frac{3}{2}\mathbf{F}_\alpha^{(1)}p_\alpha-\frac{\rho_\alpha v_0^2}{2}\frac{q_\alpha}{m_\alpha}[\mathbf{v}_0\times\mathbf{B}]-\frac{5}{2}p_\alpha\frac{q_\alpha}{m_\alpha}[\mathbf{v}_0\times\mathbf{B}]\\
&\left.\left.-\varepsilon_\alpha n_\alpha\frac{q_\alpha}{m_\alpha}[\mathbf{v}_0\times\mathbf{B}]-\varepsilon_\alpha n_\alpha\mathbf{F}_\alpha^{(1)}\right]\right\}-\left\{\rho_\alpha\mathbf{F}_\alpha^{(1)}\cdot\mathbf{v}_0\right.\\
&\left.-\tau_\alpha\left[\mathbf{F}_\alpha^{(1)}\cdot\left(\frac{\partial}{\partial t}(\rho_\alpha\mathbf{v}_0)+\frac{\partial}{\partial\mathbf{r}}\cdot\rho_\alpha\mathbf{v}_0\mathbf{v}_0+\frac{\partial}{\partial\mathbf{r}}\cdot p_\alpha\overset{\leftrightarrow}{\mathbf{I}}-\rho_\alpha\mathbf{F}_\alpha^{(1)}-q_\alpha n_\alpha[\mathbf{v}_0\times\mathbf{B}]\right)\right]\right\}\\
&=\int\left(\frac{m_\alpha v_\alpha^2}{2}+\varepsilon_\alpha\right)J_\alpha^{st,el}d\mathbf{v}_\alpha+\int\left(\frac{m_\alpha v_\alpha^2}{2}+\varepsilon_\alpha\right)J_\alpha^{st,inel}d\mathbf{v}_\alpha.
\end{aligned}
\tag{3.4.5}
$$

(Energy equation for mixture)

$$\frac{\partial}{\partial t}\left\{\frac{\rho v_0^2}{2}+\frac{3}{2}p+\sum_\alpha \varepsilon_\alpha n_\alpha-\sum_\alpha \tau_\alpha\left[\frac{\partial}{\partial t}\left(\frac{\rho_\alpha v_0^2}{2}+\frac{3}{2}p_\alpha+\varepsilon_\alpha n_\alpha\right)\right.\right.$$

$$\left.\left.+\frac{\partial}{\partial \mathbf{r}}\cdot\left(\frac{1}{2}\rho_\alpha v_0^2\mathbf{v}_0+\frac{5}{2}p_\alpha\mathbf{v}_0+\varepsilon_\alpha n_\alpha\mathbf{v}_0\right)-\mathbf{F}_\alpha^{(1)}\cdot\rho_\alpha\mathbf{v}_0\right]\right\}$$

$$+\frac{\partial}{\partial \mathbf{r}}\cdot\left\{\frac{1}{2}\rho v_0^2\mathbf{v}_0+\frac{5}{2}p\mathbf{v}_0+\mathbf{v}_0\sum_\alpha \varepsilon_\alpha n_\alpha-\sum_\alpha \tau_\alpha\left[\frac{\partial}{\partial t}\left(\frac{1}{2}\rho_\alpha v_0^2\mathbf{v}_0\right.\right.\right.$$

$$\left.+\frac{5}{2}p_\alpha\mathbf{v}_0+\varepsilon_\alpha n_\alpha\mathbf{v}_0\right)+\frac{\partial}{\partial \mathbf{r}}\cdot\left(\frac{1}{2}\rho_\alpha v_0^2\mathbf{v}_0\mathbf{v}_0+\frac{7}{2}p_\alpha\mathbf{v}_0\mathbf{v}_0+\frac{1}{2}p_\alpha v_0^2\ddot{\mathrm{I}}\right.$$

$$\left.+\frac{5}{2}\frac{p_\alpha^2}{\rho_\alpha}\ddot{\mathrm{I}}+\varepsilon_\alpha n_\alpha\mathbf{v}_0\mathbf{v}_0+\varepsilon_\alpha\frac{p_\alpha}{m_\alpha}\ddot{\mathrm{I}}\right)-\rho_\alpha\mathbf{F}_\alpha^{(1)}\cdot\mathbf{v}_0\mathbf{v}_0-p_\alpha\mathbf{F}_\alpha^{(1)}\cdot\ddot{\mathrm{I}}$$

$$-\frac{1}{2}\rho_\alpha v_0^2\mathbf{F}_\alpha^{(1)}-\frac{3}{2}\mathbf{F}_\alpha^{(1)}p_\alpha-\frac{\rho_\alpha v_0^2}{2}\frac{q_\alpha}{m_\alpha}[\mathbf{v}_0\times\mathbf{B}]-\frac{5}{2}p_\alpha\frac{q_\alpha}{m_\alpha}[\mathbf{v}_0\times\mathbf{B}]$$

$$\left.\left.-\varepsilon_\alpha n_\alpha\frac{q_\alpha}{m_\alpha}[\mathbf{v}_0\times\mathbf{B}]-\varepsilon_\alpha n_\alpha\mathbf{F}_\alpha^{(1)}\right]\right\}-\left\{\mathbf{v}_0\cdot\sum_\alpha\rho_\alpha\mathbf{F}_\alpha^{(1)}\right.$$

$$\left.-\sum_\alpha\tau_\alpha\left[\mathbf{F}_\alpha^{(1)}\cdot\left(\frac{\partial}{\partial t}(\rho_\alpha\mathbf{v}_0)+\frac{\partial}{\partial \mathbf{r}}\cdot\rho_\alpha\mathbf{v}_0\mathbf{v}_0+\frac{\partial}{\partial \mathbf{r}}\cdot p_\alpha\ddot{\mathrm{I}}-\rho_\alpha\mathbf{F}_\alpha^{(1)}-q_\alpha n_\alpha[\mathbf{v}_0\times\mathbf{B}]\right)\right]\right\}=0. \qquad (3.4.6)$$

Here $\mathbf{F}_\alpha^{(1)}$ are the forces of the non-magnetic origin, $\mathbf{B}$ - magnetic induction, $\ddot{\mathrm{I}}$ - unit tensor, q_α - charge of the α-component particle, p_α - static pressure for α-component, ε_α - internal energy for the particles of α-component, $\mathbf{v}_0$ - hydrodynamic velocity for mixture, τ_α - non-local parameter.

GHE can be applied to the physical systems from the Universe to atomic scales. All additional explanations will be done by delivering the results of modeling of corresponding physical systems with the special consideration of non-local parameters τ_α. Generally speaking to GHE should be added the system of generalized Maxwell equations (for example in the form of the generalized Poisson equation for electric potential) and gravitational equations (for example in the form of the generalized Poisson equation for gravitational potential). For example

$$\frac{\partial}{\partial \mathbf{r}}\cdot\mathbf{F}^{(1)}=-4\pi\gamma_N\left[\rho-\tau\left(\frac{\partial\rho}{\partial t}+\frac{\partial}{\partial \mathbf{r}}\cdot\rho\mathbf{v}_0\right)\right]. \qquad (3.4.7)$$

In the following I intend to show that the character features reflected on Fig 3.1.1 can be explained in the frame of Newtonian gravitation law and the non-local kinetic description created by me. Let us discuss mathematical and physical models involved into consideration taking Milky Way as an example. The Milky Way is our home galaxy. It contains over 200 billion stars including our Sun. The Milky Way has a diameter of 100,000 light years and belong to the type of a barred spiral galaxy. The Milky Way has three main parts: a disk, in which the Solar System resides, a bulge at the core, and an all encompassing halo.

This Galaxy belongs to the so called Local Group (see figure 3.4.1) of three large galaxies and over 50 smaller galaxies. The Milky Way is one of the largest galaxies in the group, second to the Andromeda Galaxy. Milky Way's closest neighbour is Canis Major Dwarf, which is about 25,000 light years away from the Earth. The Andromeda Galaxy moves towards the Milky Way Galaxy, and will meet it in about 3.75 billion years. Andromeda Galaxy moves with a speed of about 1,800 kilometers per minute.

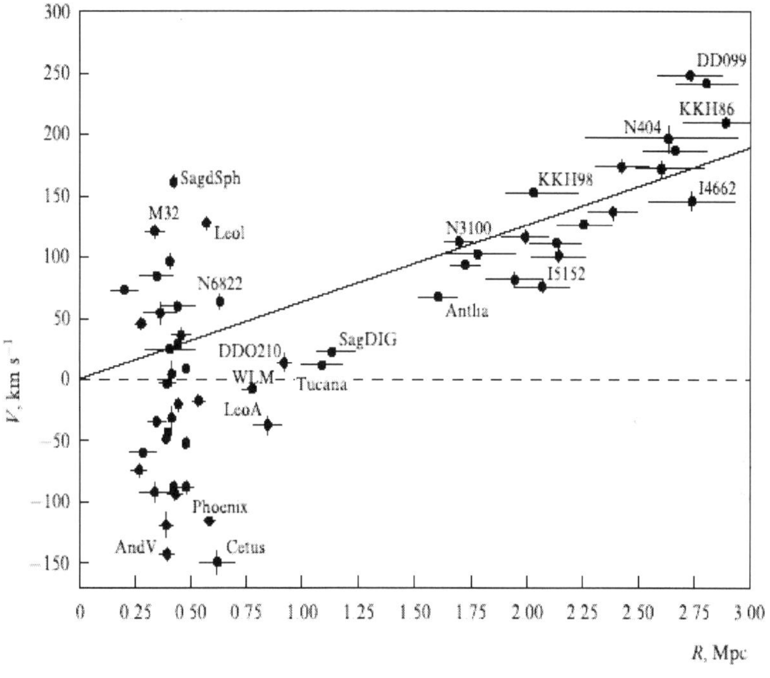

Fig. 3.4.1. Velocity-distance diagram for galaxies at distances of up to 3 Mpc for Local Group of galaxies

The data (figure 3.4.1) were obtained by Karachentsev and his collaborators as a result of the observation with the Hubble Space Telescope, (see review [67]). Each point corresponds to a galaxy with measured values of distance and line-of-site velocity in the reference frame related to the center of the Local Group. The diagram shows two distinct structures, the Local Group and the local flow of galaxies. The galaxies of the Local Group occupy a volume with the radius up to ~ 1.1 – 1.2 Mpc, but there are no galaxies in the volume whose radius is less than 0.25 Mpc. These galaxies move both away from the center (positive velocities) and toward the center (negative velocities). These galaxies form a gravitationally bound quasi-stationary system. Their average radial velocity is equal to zero. The galaxies of the local flow are located outside the group and all of them are moving from the center (positive velocities) beginning their motion near $R \approx 1$ Mpc with the velocity $v \sim 50$ km/s. By the way the measured by Karachentsev the average Hubble parameter for the Local Group is 72 ± 6 km$\cdot$s^{-1}Mpc^{-1}. Figure 3.4.1 demonstrates the effect gravitational self-catching. Effects of gravitational self-catching should be typical for Universe. The existence of "Hubble boxes" is discussed in review [67] as typical blocks of the nearby Universe. Gravitational self – catching takes place for Big Bang having given birth to the global expansion of Universe, but also for Little Bang in so called Local Group (using the Hubble's terminology) of galaxies. The following table 3.4.1 contains observation data constructed from the position local physics.

Table 3.4.1.

Observation data	
Type	Sb, Sbc, or SB(rs)bc (barred spiral galaxy)
Diameter	150–200 kly (46–61 kpc)
Thickness of thin stellar disk	≈2 kly (0.6 kpc)
Number of stars	100–400 billion [$(1–4)\times10^{11}$]
Mass	$0.8–1.5\times10^{12}\ M_{\odot}$
Angular momentum	$\approx1\times10^{67}$ J s
Sun's distance to Galactic Center	26.4 ± 1.0 kly (8.09 ± 0.31 kpc)

Sun's Galactic rotation period	240 Myr
Spiral pattern rotation period	220–360 Myr
Bar pattern rotation period	100–120 Myr
Speed relative to CMBrest frame	631 ± 20 km/s
Escape velocity at Sun's position	550 km/s
Dark matter density at Sun's position	$0.0088^{+0.0024}_{-0.0018}\ M_{\odot}\mathrm{pc}^{-3}$ or $0.35^{+0.08}_{-0.07}$ GeV cm^{-3}

Then the evolution of the Local Group (the typical Hubble box) is really fruitful field for testing of different theoretical constructions (see Fig. 3.4.2).

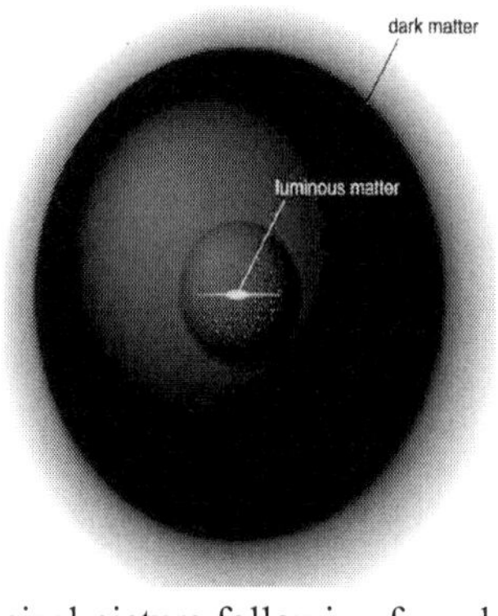

Fig. 3.4.2. The typical picture following from local astrophysics.

The main origin of Hubble effect (including the matter expansion with acceleration) is self – catching of expanding matter by the self – consistent gravitational field in conditions of the weak influence of the central massive bodies. (see also [18-20].

As we see galaxies are the extremely complicated objects. Then we need highlight the most important features for the construction the minimal adequate model for the investigation galaxies dynamics in the frame of nonlocal physics:
1. Galaxy is soliton moving in space without destruction.
2. Galaxy is a giant physical object; the radius of curvature is so large that it is possible to use a one-dimensional model corresponding to the Cartesian coordinate system.

With this aim let us consider the formation of the soliton's type of solution of the generalized hydrodynamic equations for gravitational media like galaxy in the self consistent gravitational field. Our aim consists in calculation of the self-consistent hydrodynamic moments of possible formation like gravitational soliton.

Let us investigate of the gravitational soliton formation in the frame of the non-stationary 1D Cartesian formulation. Then the system of GHE consist from the generalized Poisson equation reflecting the effects of the density and the density flux perturbations, continuity equation, motion and energy equations. This system of four equations for non-stationary 1D case is written as the deep particular case of Eqs. (3.4.1) – (3.4.6) in the form:

(Poisson equation)

$$\frac{\partial^2 \Psi}{\partial x^2} = 4\pi\gamma_N \left[\rho - \tau \left(\frac{\partial \rho}{\partial t} + \frac{\partial}{\partial x}(\rho u) \right) \right], \tag{3.4.7}$$

(continuity equation)

$$\frac{\partial}{\partial t}\left\{ \rho - \tau \left[\frac{\partial \rho}{\partial t} + \frac{\partial}{\partial x}(\rho u) \right] \right\} + \frac{\partial}{\partial x}\left\{ \rho u - \tau \left[\frac{\partial}{\partial t}(\rho u) + \frac{\partial}{\partial x}(\rho u^2) + \frac{\partial p}{\partial x} + \rho \frac{\partial \Psi}{\partial x} \right] \right\} = 0, \tag{3.4.8}$$

(motion equation)

$$\frac{\partial}{\partial t}\left\{ \rho u - \tau \left[\frac{\partial}{\partial t}(\rho u) + \frac{\partial}{\partial x}(\rho u^2) + \frac{\partial p}{\partial x} + \rho \frac{\partial \Psi}{\partial x} \right] \right\} + \frac{\partial \Psi}{\partial x}\left[\rho - \tau \left(\frac{\partial \rho}{\partial t} + \frac{\partial}{\partial x}(\rho u) \right) \right]$$
$$+ \frac{\partial}{\partial x}\left\{ \rho u^2 + p - \tau \left[\frac{\partial}{\partial t}(\rho u^2 + p) + \frac{\partial}{\partial x}(\rho u^3 + 3pu) + 2\rho u \frac{\partial \Psi}{\partial x} \right] \right\} = 0, \tag{3.4.9}$$

(energy equation)

$$\frac{\partial}{\partial t}\left\{\rho u^2+3p-\tau\left[\frac{\partial}{\partial t}\left(\rho u^2+3p\right)+\frac{\partial}{\partial x}\left(\rho u^3+5pu\right)+2\rho u\frac{\partial \Psi}{\partial x}\right]\right\}$$

$$+\frac{\partial}{\partial x}\left\{\rho u^3+5pu-\tau\left[\frac{\partial}{\partial t}\left(\rho u^3+5pu\right)+\frac{\partial}{\partial x}\left(\rho u^4\right.\right.\right.$$

$$\left.\left.\left.+8pu^2+5\frac{p^2}{\rho}\right)+\frac{\partial \Psi}{\partial x}\left(3\rho u^2+5p\right)\right]\right\} \tag{3.4.10}$$

$$+2\frac{\partial \Psi}{\partial x}\left\{\rho u-\tau\left[\frac{\partial}{\partial t}(\rho u)+\frac{\partial}{\partial x}\left(\rho u^2+p\right)+\rho\frac{\partial \Psi}{\partial x}\right]\right\}=0,$$

where u is translational velocity of the one species object, Ψ - self consistent gravitational potential ($\mathbf{g}=-\partial\Psi/\partial\mathbf{r}$ is acceleration in gravitational field), ρ is density and p is pressure, τ is non-locality parameter, γ_N is Newtonian gravitation constant.

Let us introduce the coordinate system moving along the positive direction of x- axis in ID space with velocity $C=u_0$ equal to phase velocity of considering object

$$\xi=x-Ct. \tag{3.4.11}$$

Taking into account the De Broglie relation we should wait that the group velocity u_g is equal $2u_0$. In moving coordinate system all dependent hydrodynamic values are function of (ξ,t). We investigate the possibility of the object formation of the soliton type. For this solution there is no explicit dependence on time for coordinate system moving with the phase velocity u_0. Write down the system of equations (3.4.7) - (3.4.10) in the dimensionless form, where dimensionless symbols are marked by tildes. For the scales ρ_0, $u_0, x_0=u_0t_0, \Psi_0=u_0^2$, $\gamma_{N0}=u_0^2/\left(\rho_0x_0^2\right)$ $p_0=\rho_0u_0^2$ and conditions $\tilde{C}=C/u_0=1$, the equations take the form:

(generalized Poisson equation)

$$\frac{\partial^2\tilde{\Psi}}{\partial\tilde{\xi}^2}=4\pi\tilde{\gamma}_N\left[\tilde{\rho}-\tilde{\tau}\left(-\frac{\partial\tilde{\rho}}{\partial\tilde{\xi}}+\frac{\partial}{\partial\tilde{\xi}}(\tilde{\rho}\tilde{u})\right)\right], \tag{3.4.12}$$

(continuity equation)

$$\frac{\partial\tilde{\rho}}{\partial\tilde{\xi}}-\frac{\partial\tilde{\rho}\tilde{u}}{\partial\tilde{\xi}}+\frac{\partial}{\partial\tilde{\xi}}\left\{\tilde{\tau}\left[\frac{\partial}{\partial\tilde{\xi}}\left[\tilde{p}+\tilde{\rho}\tilde{u}^2+\tilde{\rho}-2\tilde{\rho}\tilde{u}\right]+\tilde{\rho}\frac{\partial\tilde{\Psi}}{\partial\tilde{\xi}}\right]\right\}=0, \tag{3.4.13}$$

(motion equation)

$$\frac{\partial}{\partial\tilde{\xi}}\left(\tilde{\rho}\tilde{u}^2+\tilde{p}-\tilde{\rho}\tilde{u}\right)+\frac{\partial}{\partial\tilde{\xi}}\left\{\tilde{\tau}\left[\frac{\partial}{\partial\tilde{\xi}}\left(2\tilde{\rho}\tilde{u}^2-\tilde{\rho}\tilde{u}+2\tilde{p}-\tilde{\rho}\tilde{u}^3-3\tilde{p}\tilde{u}\right)+\tilde{\rho}\frac{\partial\tilde{\Psi}}{\partial\tilde{\xi}}\right]\right\}$$

$$+\frac{\partial\tilde{\Psi}}{\partial\tilde{\xi}}\left\{\tilde{\rho}-\tilde{\tau}\left[-\frac{\partial\tilde{\rho}}{\partial\tilde{\xi}}+\frac{\partial}{\partial\tilde{\xi}}\left(\tilde{\rho}\tilde{u}\right)\right]\right\}-2\frac{\partial}{\partial\tilde{\xi}}\left\{\tilde{\tau}\tilde{\rho}\tilde{u}\frac{\partial\tilde{\Psi}}{\partial\tilde{\xi}}\right\}=0, \tag{3.4.14}$$

(energy equation)

$$\frac{\partial}{\partial\tilde{\xi}}\left(\tilde{\rho}\tilde{u}^2+3\tilde{p}-\tilde{\rho}\tilde{u}^3-5\tilde{p}\tilde{u}\right)$$

$$-\frac{\partial}{\partial\tilde{\xi}}\left\{\tilde{\tau}\frac{\partial}{\partial\tilde{\xi}}\left(2\tilde{\rho}\tilde{u}^3+10\tilde{p}\tilde{u}-\tilde{\rho}\tilde{u}^2-3\tilde{p}-\tilde{\rho}\tilde{u}^4-8\tilde{p}\tilde{u}^2-5\frac{\tilde{p}^2}{\tilde{\rho}}\right)\right\}$$

$$+\frac{\partial}{\partial\tilde{\xi}}\left\{\tilde{\tau}\left(3\tilde{\rho}\tilde{u}^2+5\tilde{p}\right)\frac{\partial\tilde{\Psi}}{\partial\tilde{\xi}}\right\}-2\tilde{\rho}\tilde{u}\frac{\partial\tilde{\Psi}}{\partial\tilde{\xi}}-2\frac{\partial}{\partial\tilde{\xi}}\left\{\tilde{\tau}\tilde{\rho}\tilde{u}\frac{\partial\tilde{\Psi}}{\partial\tilde{\xi}}\right\} \tag{3.4.15}$$

$$+2\tilde{\tau}\frac{\partial\tilde{\Psi}}{\partial\tilde{\xi}}\left[-\frac{\partial}{\partial\tilde{\xi}}\left(\tilde{\rho}\tilde{u}\right)+\frac{\partial}{\partial\tilde{\xi}}\left(\tilde{\rho}\tilde{u}^2+\tilde{p}\right)+\tilde{\rho}\frac{\partial\tilde{\Psi}}{\partial\tilde{\xi}}\right]=0,$$

Some comments to the system of four ordinary non-linear equations (3.4.12) – (3.4.15):

1. Every equation from the system is of the second order and needs two conditions. The problem belongs to the class of Cauchy problems.

2. In comparison for example, with the Schrödinger theory connected with behavior of the wave function, no special conditions are applied for dependent variables including the domain of the solution existing. This domain is defined automatically in the process of the numerical solution of the concrete variant of calculations.

3. From the introduced scales ρ_0, $u_0, x_0=u_0t_0, \Psi_0=u_0^2$, $\gamma_{N0}=u_0^2/\left(\rho_0x_0^2\right)$, $p_0=\rho_0u_0^2$, only three parameters are independent, namely, ρ_0, u_0, x_0.

4. Approximation for the dimensionless non-local parameter $\tilde{\tau}$ should be introduced. In the definite sense it is not the problem of the hydrodynamic level of the physical system description (like the calculation of the kinetic coefficients in the classical hydrodynamics). Interesting to notice that quantum GHE were applied with success for calculation of atom structure [19, 20], which is considered as two species charged e,i mixture. The corresponding approximations for non-local parameters τ_i, τ_e and τ_{ei} are proposed in [19, 20]. In the theory of the atom structure after taking into account the Balmer's relation, non-local parameters τ_e transforms into

$$\tau_e=n\hbar/\left(m_eu^2\right), \tag{3.4.16}$$

where $n = 1,2,...$ is principal quantum number. As result the length scale relation was written as $x_0 = H/(m_e u_0) = n\hbar/(m_e u_0)$. But the value $\nu^{qu} = \hbar/m_e$ has the dimension $[cm^2/s]$ and can be titled as *quantum viscosity*, $\nu^{qu} = 1.1577\ cm^2/s$. Then

$$\tau_e = n\nu^{qu}/u^2. \qquad (3.4.17)$$

Introduce now the quantum Reynolds number

$$\mathrm{Re}^{qu} = u_0 x_0/\nu^{qu}. \qquad (3.4.18)$$

As result from (11.3.17), (11.3.18) follows the condition of quantization for Re^{qu}. Namely

$$\mathrm{Re}^{qu} = n, \quad n = 1,2,... \qquad (3.4.19)$$

5. Taking into account the previous considerations I introduce the following approximation for the dimensionless non-local parameter

$$\tilde{\tau} = 1/\tilde{u}^2, \qquad (3.4.20)$$

$$\tau = u_0 x_0/u^2 = \nu_0^k/u^2, \qquad (3.4.21)$$

where the scale for the kinematical viscosity is introduced $\nu_0^k = u_0 x_0$. Then we have the physically transparent result – non-local parameter is proportional to the kinematical viscosity and in inverse proportion to the square of velocity.

3.5. Mathematical modeling of the disk galaxy rotation and the problem of the dark matter.

The system of generalized hydrodynamic equations (3.4.12) – (3.4.15) (solved with the help of Maple) have the great possibilities of mathematical modeling as result of changing of eight Cauchy conditions describing the character features of initial perturbations which lead to the soliton formation. The following Maple notations on figures are used: r- density $\tilde{\rho}$, u- velocity $\tilde{u}$, p - pressure $\tilde{p}$ and v - self consistent potential $\tilde{\Psi}$.

Explanations placed under all following figures, Maple program contains Maple's notations – for example the expression $D(u)(0) = 0$ means in the usual notations $(\partial\tilde{u}/\partial\tilde{\xi})(0) = 0$, independent variable t responds to $\tilde{\xi}$.

Spiral galaxies have rather complicated geometrical forms and 3D calculations can be used. But reasonable to suppose that influence of halo on galaxy kernel is not too significant and use for calculations the spherical coordinate system. The 1D calculations in the Cartesian coordinate system correspond to calculations in the spherical coordinate system by the large radii of curvature, but have also the independent significance in another character scales.

The following figures reflect the result of soliton calculations for the case of spherical symmetry for galaxy kernel. The velocity $\tilde{u}$ corresponds to the direction of the soliton movement for spherical coordinate system on following figures. Self-consistent gravitational force F acting on the unit of mass permits to define the orbital velocity w of objects in halo, $w = \sqrt{Fr}$, or

$$\tilde{w} = \sqrt{\tilde{r} \, \partial\tilde{\Psi} / \partial\tilde{r}}, \tag{3.5.1}$$

where r is the distance from the center of galaxy. All calculations are realized for the conditions (SYSTEM I) but for different parameter

$$G = \tilde{\gamma}_N = \gamma_N / \gamma_{N0} = \gamma_N \rho_0 x_0^2 / u_0^2. \tag{3.5.2}$$

Parameter G plays the role of similarity criteria in traditional hydrodynamics. Important conclusions:

1. The following figures 3.5.1 – 3.5.8 demonstrate evolution the rotation curves from the Kepler regime (Figs. 3.5.1, 3.5.2**;** small G, like curve **A** on Fig.3.1.1) to observed (Figs. 3.5.3, 3.5.4; large G, like curve **B** on Fig. 3.1.1) for typical spiral galaxies.
2. The stars with planets (like Sun) correspond to gravitational soliton with small G and therefore originate the Kepler rotation regime.
3. Regime **B** cannot be obtained in the frame of local statistical physics in principal and authors of many papers introduce different approximations for additional "dark matter density" (as usual in Poisson equation) trying to find coincidence with data of observations.
4. From the wrong position of local theories Poisson equation (3.4.7) contains "dark matter density", continuity equation (3.4.8) contains the "flux of dark matter density", motion equation (3.4.9) includes "dark energy", the energy equation (3.4.10) has "the flux of dark energy" and so on to the "senior dark velocity moments". This entire situation is similar to the turbulent theories based on local statistical physics and empirical corrections for velocity moments.

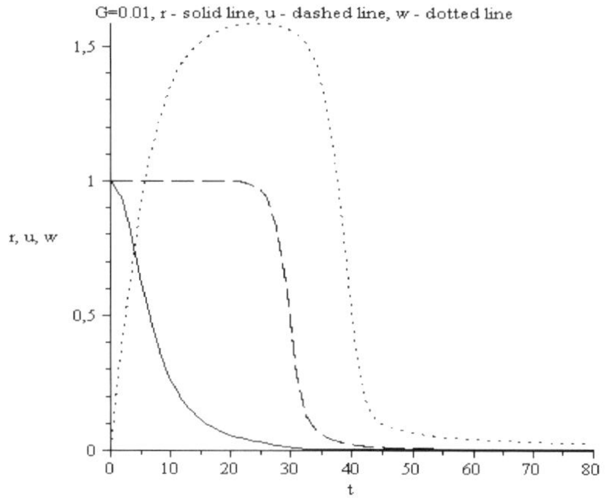

Fig. 3.5.1. r - density $\widetilde{\rho}$, u - velocity $\widetilde{u}$, w - orbital velocity $\widetilde{w}$. $G = 0.01$.

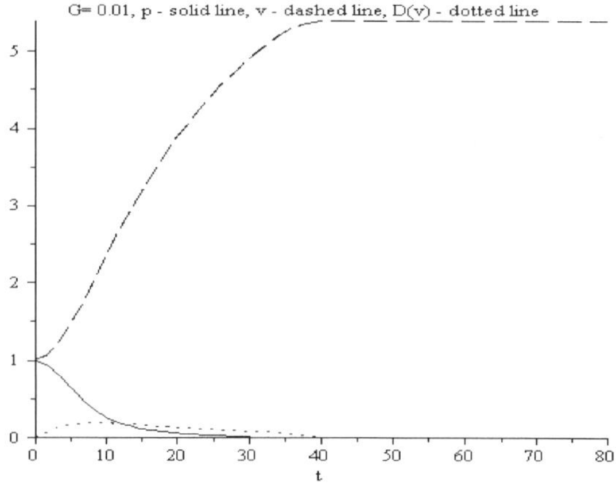

Fig. 3.5.2. p - pressure $\widetilde{p}$, v - self consistent potential in gravitational soliton, $\widetilde{\Psi}$, $D(\mathrm{v})(t) = \partial\widetilde{\Psi} / \partial\widetilde{\xi}$ in gravitational soliton.

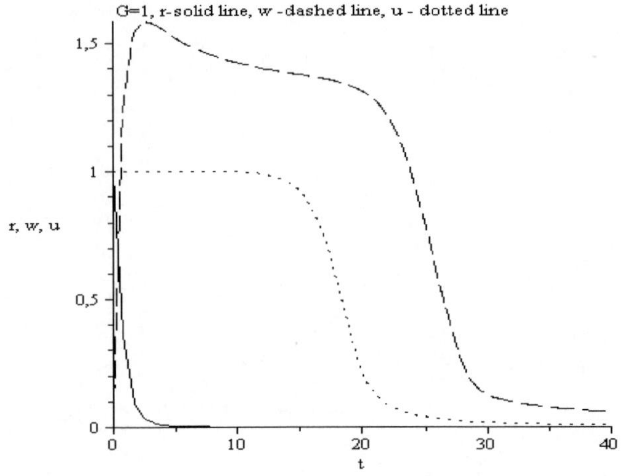

Fig. 3.5.3. r - density $\tilde{\rho}$, u - velocity $\tilde{u}$ of gravitational soliton, w - orbital velocity $\tilde{w}$. $G = 1$.

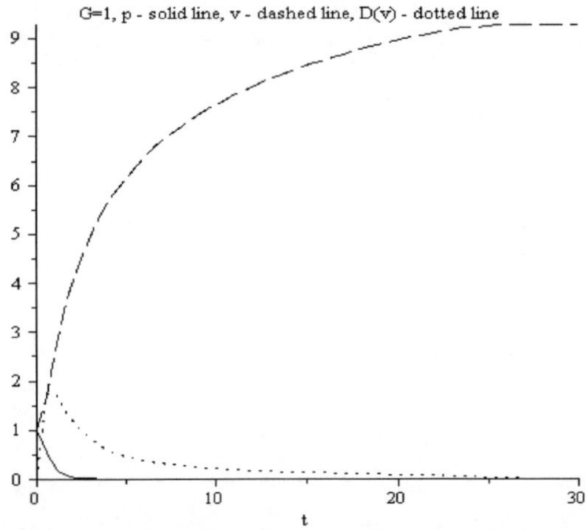

Fig. 3.5.4. p - pressure $\tilde{p}$, v - self consistent in gravitational soliton, potential $\tilde{\Psi}$, $D(\mathrm{v})(t) = \dfrac{\partial \tilde{\Psi}}{\partial \tilde{\xi}}$ in gravitational soliton, $G = 1$.

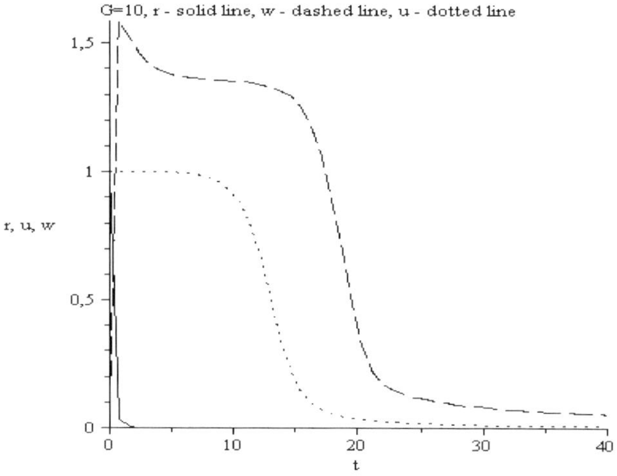

Fig. 3.5.5. r - density $\widetilde{\rho}$, u - velocity $\widetilde{u}$ of gravitational soliton, w - orbital velocity $\widetilde{w}$, $G = 10$.

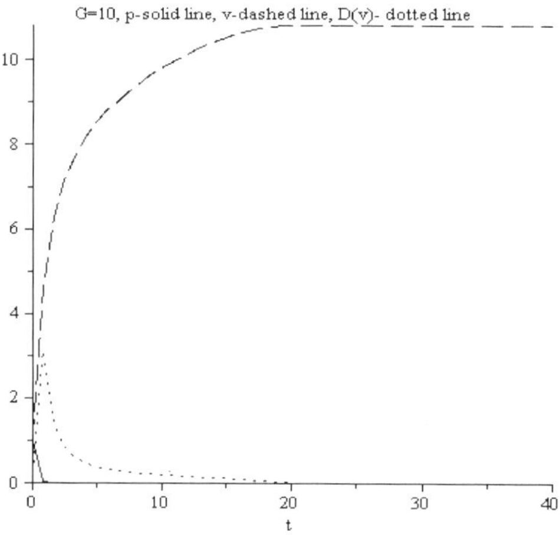

Fig. 3.5.6. p - pressure $\widetilde{p}$, v - self consistent potential $\widetilde{\Psi}$, $D(\mathrm{v})(t) = \partial\widetilde{\Psi} / \partial\widetilde{\xi}$ in gravitational soliton, $G = 10$..

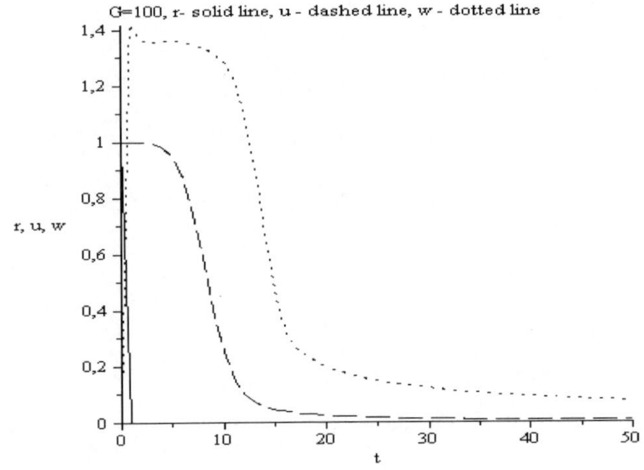

Fig. 3.5.7. r - density $\tilde{\rho}$, u - velocity $\tilde{u}$ of gravitational soliton, w - orbital velocity $\tilde{w}$. $G = 100$.

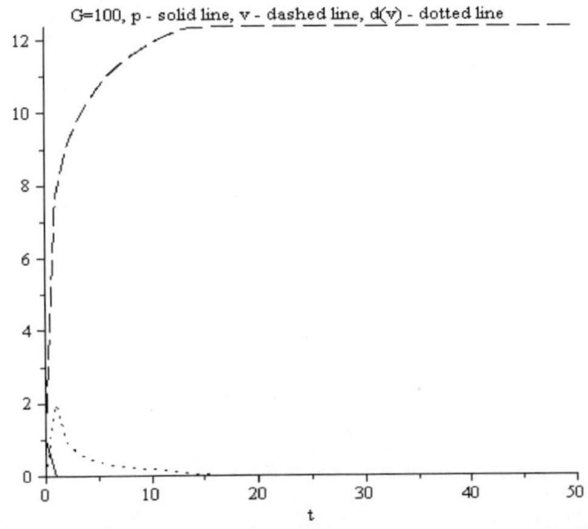

Fig. 3.5.8. p - pressure $\tilde{p}$, v - self consistent potential $\tilde{\Psi}$, $D(\mathrm{v})(t) = \partial\tilde{\Psi}/\partial\tilde{\xi}$ in gravitational soliton, $G = 100$.

As we see peculiar features of the halo movement can be explained without new concepts like "dark matter". Important to underline that the shown transformation of the Kepler's regime into the flat rotation curves for different solitons explains the "mysterious" fact of the dark matter absence in the Sun vicinity.

CHAPTER 4. NONLOCAL THEORY OF RINGS AROUND COSMIC OBJECTS

The problems of the rings formation around the cosmic bodies are discussed from the point of view of developed non-local physics theory. It is shown that the rings appearance is connected with the anti-gravitation area as a collective effect, bounded by the gravitation domains. The local physics and the transport kinetic theory in particular are not applicable to the solution of the mentioned problems. The mass loss of rings is included in consideration. The ring rotation follows Vera Rubin model.

Key words: Nonlocal Physics; Foundations of the theory of transport processes; Nonlocal hydrodynamic equations; Theory of rings around the cosmic objects. Rings with the loss of mass. Rotation of the Saturn rings

PACS: 67.55.Fa, 67.55.Hc

4.1. Preliminary remarks.

Several extremely significant problems challenge modern fundamental physics – missing antimatter after the Big Bang, and so called dark energy and dark matter. From the position of local physics the last two problems lead to affirmation that only about four percents of matter leaved for us for direct investigation because the other matter is out of our diagnostic methods. No reason to follow tremendous scientific literature devoted to investigations of these problems. But nevertheless some remarks should be done. The basic ideas of 'big bang' theory were formulated by originators—George Lemaitre, (1927) and also by George Gamow, R.A. Alpher, and R. Herman who devised the basic Big Bang model in 1948. According to the 'big bang' theory for the origin of the universe, equal amounts of matter and antimatter should have formed. Antimatter is the same as matter except that each particle has the opposite charge, magnetic moment, etc. Antimatter is supposed to be an exact counterpart to matter, down to the same mass. This has been verified in many experiments and it was shown experimentally that a proton and an antiproton have the same mass to within one part in 10 billion. At the beginning, equal amounts of matter and antimatter were created in the "big bang". The problem is that, so far, no antimatter (AM) domains have been detected in space, at least in the nearby universe. This result creates a long-standing mystery: why the big bang displays such blatant favoritism towards matter. Now there seems to be only matter or regular matter (RM) in the following theory. There have been theoretical speculations about the disappearance of antimatter, but no experimental support.

More than ten years ago, the accelerated cosmological expansion was discovered in direct astronomical observations at distances of a few billion light years, almost at the edge of the observable Universe. This acceleration should be explained because mutual attraction of cosmic bodies is only capable of decelerating their scattering. It means that we reach the revolutionary situation not only in physics but in the natural philosophy on the whole. Practically we are in front of the new challenge since Newton's Mathematical Principles of Natural Philosophy was published. As result, new idea was introduced in physics about existing of a force with the opposite sign which is called universal anti-gravitation. Its physical source is called as dark energy that manifests itself only because of postulated property of providing anti-gravitation.

It was postulated that the source of anti-gravitation is "dark matter" which inferred to exist from gravitational effects on visible matter. But from the other side dark matter is undetectable by emitted or scattered electromagnetic radiation. It means that new essences – dark matter, dark energy – were introduced in physics only with the aim to account for discrepancies between measurements of the mass of galaxies, clusters of galaxies and the entire universe made through dynamical and general relativistic means, measurements based on the mass of the visible "luminous" matter. It could be reasonable if we are speaking about small corrections to the system of knowledge achieved by mankind to the time we are living. But mentioned above discrepancies lead to affirmation, that dark matter constitutes the most part of the matter in the Universe. There is a variety in the corresponding estimations, but the situation is defined by maybe emotional, but the true exclamation which can be found between thousands Internet cues – "It is humbling, perhaps even humiliating, that we know almost nothing about 96% of what is "out there"!!

Dark matter was postulated by Swiss astrophysicist Fritz Zwicky of the California Institute of Technology in 1933. He applied the virial theorem to the Coma cluster of galaxies and obtained evidence of unseen mass. Zwicky estimated the cluster's total mass based on the motions of galaxies near its edge and compared that estimate to one based on the number of galaxies and total brightness of the cluster. He found that there was about 400 times more estimated mass than was visually observable. The gravity of the visible galaxies in the cluster would be far too small for such fast orbits, so something extra was required. This is known as the "missing mass problem". Based on these conclusions, Zwicky inferred that there must be some non-visible form of matter which would provide enough of the mass and gravity to hold the cluster together.

I do not intend to review the different speculations based on the principles of local physics. I see another problem. It is the problem of Oversimplification – but not "trivial" simplification of the important problem. The situation is much more serious – total Oversimplification based on principles of local physics, and obvious crisis, we see in astrophysics, simply reflects the general shortcomings of the local kinetic transport theory.

The formulated above problems are solved [17-20] in the frame of non-local statistical physics and the Newtonian law of gravitation.

The following conclusion of principal significance can be done from the previous consideration [see also 17-20]:

1. Madelung's quantum hydrodynamics is equivalent to the Schrödinger equation (SE) and furnishes the description of the quantum particle evolution in the form of Euler equation and continuity equation. Madelung's interpretation of SE (connected with wave function $\psi = \alpha \exp(i\beta)$) leads the probability density $\rho = \alpha^2$ and velocity $\mathbf{v} = \frac{\partial}{\partial \mathbf{r}}(\beta\hbar / m)$. Madelung quantum hydrodynamics does not lead to the energy equation on principal; the corresponding dependent variable p in the energy equation of the generalized quantum hydrodynamics developed by me can be titled as the rest quantum pressure or simply quantum pressure.
2. Generalized Boltzmann physical kinetics brings the strict approximation of non-local effects in space and time and after transmission to the local approximation leads to parameter τ, which on the quantum level corresponds to the uncertainty principle "time-energy".
3. GHE produce SE as a deep particular case of the generalized Boltzmann physical kinetics and therefore of non-local hydrodynamics.

4.2. About rings near the cosmic bodies

The Hubble Space Telescope observations of very distant supernovae showed that, a long time ago, the Universe was actually expanding more slowly than it is today. So the expansion of the Universe has not been slowing due to gravity, as everyone thought, it has been accelerating. The "local theorists" still don't know what the correct explanation is, but they have given the solution a name: dark energy, which manifests itself only because of postulated property of providing anti-gravitation.

From the position of local physics it turns out that "normal" matter is just a small fraction of the Universe. Roughly 70% of the Universe is dark energy; dark matter makes up about 25%. The rest, normal matter, is less than 5% of the Universe. The origin of the difficulties is caused by oversimplifications following from the principles of the local physics and reflects the general shortcomings of the local kinetic transport theory. In reality the dark matter is not exist. Generally speaking the anti-gravitation effects are the consequence of the physical vacuum existing. But interesting to notice that anti-gravitation effects can be demonstrated as a result of the self consistent solution of nonlocal hydrodynamic equations written in the frame of the Newtonian gravitation, in particular in the theory of rings surrounding the cosmic objects like Saturn which is under study now. Other examples of application of non-local physics framework will be presented also.

Ring systems around cosmic bodies are typical in Universe. Usually it is a disc or ring orbiting an astronomical object including galaxies. Recent evidence suggests that ring systems may also be found around other types of astronomical objects, including minor planets, moons, and brown dwarfs. For example, the spiral galaxy NGC 4594, visible from the edge, has a strip of dark matter in the diametrical transverse plane. Typical rings are composed of dust and moonlets. In the Solar System we see ring systems around Saturn, but the other three giant planets Jupiter, Uranus and Neptune also have ring systems. Rings of Saturn compose the most extensive ring system of any planet in the Solar system.

The Saturn rings are named alphabetically in the order they were discovered. The main rings are, working outward from the planet, C, B and A, with the Cassini Division, the largest gap, separating Rings B and A. Several fainter rings were discovered more recently. The D Ring is exceedingly faint and closest to the planet. The narrow F Ring is just outside the A Ring. Beyond that are two far fainter rings named G and E. The rings show a tremendous amount of structure on all scales, some related to perturbations by Saturn's moons, but much unexplained.

Rings consist of countless small particles (ranging from micrometers to meters in size and more up to kilometers across) orbiting about Saturn. The rings of Saturn are composed of billions of icy particles and rocky material. The rings have numerous gaps where particle density drops sharply.

Let's make some historical remarks. Galileo Galilei became the first person to observe Saturn's rings, though he could not see them well enough to discern their true nature.

In 1655, Christian Huygens was the first person to describe them as a disk surrounding Saturn. In 1675, Giovanni Domenico Cassini determined that Saturn's ring was composed of multiple smaller rings with gaps between them; the largest of these gaps was later named the Cassini Division. In 1787, Pierre-Simon Laplace proved that a uniform solid ring would be unstable. In 1859, James Clerk Maxwell demonstrated that a non-uniform solid ring, solid ringlets or a continuous fluid ring would also not be stable (the true affirmation), indicating that the ring must be composed of numerous small particles, all independently (the wrong affirmation) orbiting Saturn.

The rings are named alphabetically in the order they were discovered (see Table 4.1).

Table 4.1. Basic Rings

Basic elements of the structure of Saturn's rings

Name	**Distance R_r to center of Saturn, km**	**Width, km**	**Ratio R_r to radius of Saturn R_S**
Ring D	67 000—74 500	7500,	1.15 - 1.28
Ring C	74 500—92 000	17500,	1.28 - 1.58
Ring B	92 000—117 500	25 500,	1.58 - 2.02
Ring A	122 200—136 800	14600,	2.10 – 2.35
Ring F	140 210	30—500,	2.41 – 2.42
Ring G	165 800—173 800	8000,	2.85 – 2.98
Ring E	180 000—480 000	300 000,	3.09 - 8.24

There are 14 major divisions in Saturn's rings - 12 rings and 2 gaps; these are the D Ring, C Ring, B Ring, Cassini Division, A Ring, Roche Division, F Ring, Janus/Epimetheus Ring, G Ring, Methone Ring Arc, Anthe Ring Arc, Pallene Ring, E Ring and Phoebe Ring. The F ring is kept in place by two of Saturn's moons, Prometheus and Pandora, these are referred to as shepherd moons, other satellites are responsible for creating divisions in the rings as well as shepherding them. The main rings are, working outward from the planet, C, B and A, with the Cassini Division, the largest gap, separating Rings B and A. Several fainter rings were discovered more recently. The D Ring is exceedingly faint and closest to the planet. The narrow F Ring is just outside the A Ring. Beyond that are two far fainter rings named G and E. The rings show a tremendous amount of structure on all scales, some related to perturbations by Saturn's moons, but much unexplained.

Several robotic spacecrafts have observed Saturn's rings from the vicinity of the planet. The spacecraft Pioneer11's closest approach to Saturn occurred in September 1979 at a distance of 20,900 km. This spacecraft was responsible for the discovery of the F ring. Voyager 1's closest approach occurred in November 1980 at a distance of 64,200 km. Images from the spacecraft provided unprecedented detail of the ring system and revealed the existence of the G ring. Voyager2's closest approach occurred in August 1981 at a distance of 41,000 km. Voyager2 discovers many previously unseen ringlets. Cassini spacecraft entered into orbit around Saturn in July 2004, these images of the rings are the most detailed to-date, and are responsible for the discovery of yet more ringlets.

4.3. Roche limit

Let us introduce the following assumptions and restrictions discussing the Roche limit:

1. We consider a completely rigid satellite, which maintain its spherical shape until tidal forces break it apart.
2. The Roche limit for a rigid spherical satellite is the distance d, from the primary at which the gravitational force on a test mass at the surface of the object is exactly equal to the tidal force pulling the mass away from the object.
3. The Roche limit is calculated for the case of a circular orbit.
4. It is assumed that physical system is in hydrostatic equilibrium.

These assumptions, although unrealistic, greatly simplify calculations. The fourth condition is so significant that no sense to try improve theory introducing for example a model of a highly fluid satellite with the gradually deformation leading to increased tidal forces, causing the satellite to elongate.

In order to determine the Roche limit, consider a small mass m_s (as a probe particle) on the surface of the satellite closest to the primary. There are two forces acting on this mass m_s - the gravitational pull towards the satellite and the gravitational pull towards the primary. The gravitational pull F_G on the probe mass m_p towards the satellite with mass M and radius r_M can be expressed according to Newton's law of gravitation.

$$F_G = \gamma_N \frac{Mm_p}{r_M^2}. \tag{4.3.1}$$

Let us introduce three distances – satellite radius r_m, primary body radius R and the distance d between the centers of the primary body and satellite. We find the difference in the primary's gravitational pull for the probe mass on the edge of the satellite closest to the primary ball $F_G = \gamma_N \frac{Mm_p}{(d - r_M)^2}$ and pull on the center of the satellite pull on the center of the satellite $\gamma_N \frac{Mm_p}{d^2}$:

$$F_T = \gamma_N \frac{Mm_p}{(d - r_M)^2} - \gamma_N \frac{Mm_p}{d^2}, \tag{4.3.2}$$

or

$$F_T = \gamma_N Mm_p \frac{2r_M d - r_M^2}{d^4 - 2d^3 r_M^2 + r_M^2 d^2}. \tag{4.3.3}$$

In the approximation where $r_M << R$ and $R < d$, conserving the first order terms we find

$$F_T = \gamma_N Mm_p \frac{2r_M}{d^3}. \tag{4.3.4}$$

The Roche limit is reached when the gravitational force and the tidal force balance each other out.

$$F_G = F_T, \tag{4.3.5}$$

or

$$\gamma_N \frac{mm_p}{r_M^2} = \gamma_N Mm_p \frac{2r_M}{d^3}. \tag{4.3.6}$$

The probe mass m_p disappears from consideration which gives the Roche limit, d as

$$d = r_M \left(2\frac{M}{m} \right)^{1/3}. \tag{4.3.7}$$

The radius of the satellite should not appear in the expression for the limit, so it is re-written in terms of densities.

For the primary ball $M = \frac{4\pi\rho_M R^3}{3}$, and likewise $m = \frac{4\pi\rho_m r_M^3}{3}$. Then the relation (4.3.7) takes the form

$$d = r_M\left(\frac{2\rho_M R^3}{\rho_m r_m^3}\right)^{1/3} = R\left(\frac{2\rho_M}{\rho_m}\right)^{1/3} \approx 1.26R\left(\frac{\rho_M}{\rho_m}\right)^{1/3}. \qquad (4.3.8)$$

Conclusion:

1. In the approximation of a "rigid" spherical satellite, that is, under conditions of neglecting of its tidal deformation and rotation, the Roche limit depends on the radius of the central body R and the ratio of the densities of the Central body ρ_M and the satellite ρ_m.

2. Roche theory cannot be applied to statistical physical systems containing tremendous quantity of particles like the Saturn rings.

The aim of the following investigation consists in calculation of the total width of rings and their stability in the frame of nonlocal hydrodynamics. There are also problems, so to speak, of the second range:

1. Appearance the disk configuration instead of spherical symmetry;

2. Appearance of separation between rings. The solution of the first mention problem is connected with the planet axis rotation and Coriolis effects, the second problem leads to investigation of multi-component species.

4.4. Basic equations

Strict consideration leads to the following system of the generalized hydrodynamic equations (GHE) [18-20, Chapter 2] written in the generalized Euler form:

Continuity equation for species α:

$$\frac{\partial}{\partial t}\left\{\rho_\alpha - \tau_\alpha^{(0)}\left[\frac{\partial \rho_\alpha}{\partial t} + \frac{\partial}{\partial \mathbf{r}}\cdot(\rho_\alpha \mathbf{v}_0)\right]\right\} +$$

$$+\frac{\partial}{\partial \mathbf{r}}\cdot\left\{\rho_\alpha \mathbf{v}_0 - \tau_\alpha^{(0)}\left[\frac{\partial}{\partial t}(\rho_\alpha \mathbf{v}_0) + \frac{\partial}{\partial \mathbf{r}}\cdot(\rho_\alpha \mathbf{v}_0 \mathbf{v}_0) + \ddot{\mathrm{I}}\cdot\frac{\partial p_\alpha}{\partial \mathbf{r}} - \rho_\alpha \mathbf{F}_\alpha^{(1)} - \frac{q_\alpha}{m_\alpha}\rho_\alpha \mathbf{v}_0 \times \mathbf{B}\right]\right\} = R_\alpha, \qquad (4.4.1)$$

Continuity equation for mixture:

$$\frac{\partial}{\partial t}\left\{\rho-\sum_{\alpha}\tau_{\alpha}^{(0)}\left[\frac{\partial\rho_{\alpha}}{\partial t}+\frac{\partial}{\partial\mathbf{r}}\cdot(\rho_{\alpha}\mathbf{v}_{0})\right]\right\}+$$

$$+\frac{\partial}{\partial\mathbf{r}}\cdot\left\{\rho\mathbf{v}_{0}-\sum_{\alpha}\tau_{\alpha}^{(0)}\left[\frac{\partial}{\partial t}(\rho_{\alpha}\mathbf{v}_{0})+\frac{\partial}{\partial\mathbf{r}}\cdot(\rho_{\alpha}\mathbf{v}_{0}\mathbf{v}_{0})+\vec{\mathrm{I}}\cdot\frac{\partial p_{\alpha}}{\partial\mathbf{r}}-\right.\right. \tag{4.4.2}$$

$$\left.\left.-\rho_{\alpha}\mathbf{F}_{\alpha}^{(1)}-\frac{q_{\alpha}}{m_{\alpha}}\rho_{\alpha}\mathbf{v}_{0}\times\mathbf{B}\right]\right\}=0,$$

Momentum equation

$$\frac{\partial}{\partial t}\left\{\rho_{\alpha}\mathbf{v}_{0}-\tau_{\alpha}^{(0)}\left[\frac{\partial}{\partial t}(\rho_{\alpha}\mathbf{v}_{0})+\frac{\partial}{\partial\mathbf{r}}\cdot\rho_{\alpha}\mathbf{v}_{0}\mathbf{v}_{0}+\frac{\partial p_{\alpha}}{\partial\mathbf{r}}-\rho_{\alpha}\mathbf{F}_{\alpha}^{(1)}-\right.\right.$$

$$\left.\left.-\left(\frac{q_{\alpha}}{m_{\alpha}}\right)\rho_{\alpha}\mathbf{v}_{0}\times\mathbf{B}\right]\right\}-\mathbf{F}_{\alpha}^{(1)}\left[\rho_{\alpha}-\tau_{\alpha}^{(0)}\left(\frac{\partial\rho_{\alpha}}{\partial t}+\frac{\partial}{\partial\mathbf{r}}\cdot(\rho_{\alpha}\mathbf{v}_{0})\right)\right]-$$

$$-\frac{q_{\alpha}}{m_{\alpha}}\left\{\rho_{\alpha}\mathbf{v}_{0}-\tau_{\alpha}^{(0)}\left[\frac{\partial}{\partial t}(\rho_{\alpha}\mathbf{v}_{0})+\frac{\partial}{\partial\mathbf{r}}\cdot\rho_{\alpha}\mathbf{v}_{0}\mathbf{v}_{0}+\frac{\partial p_{\alpha}}{\partial\mathbf{r}}-\rho_{\alpha}\mathbf{F}_{\alpha}^{(1)}-\right.\right.$$

$$\left.\left.-\frac{q_{\alpha}}{m_{\alpha}}\rho_{\alpha}\mathbf{v}_{0}\times\mathbf{B}\right]\right\}\times\mathbf{B}+\frac{\partial}{\partial\mathbf{r}}\cdot\left\{\rho_{\alpha}\mathbf{v}_{0}\mathbf{v}_{0}+p_{\alpha}\vec{\mathrm{I}}-\tau_{\alpha}^{(0)}\left[\frac{\partial}{\partial t}(\rho_{\alpha}\mathbf{v}_{0}\mathbf{v}_{0}+\right.\right.$$

$$+p_{\alpha}\vec{\mathrm{I}})+\frac{\partial}{\partial\mathbf{r}}\cdot\left(\rho_{\alpha}(\mathbf{v}_{0}\mathbf{v}_{0})\mathbf{v}_{0}+\rho_{\alpha}\overline{(\mathbf{v}_{0}\mathbf{V}_{\alpha})\mathbf{V}_{\alpha}}+\rho_{\alpha}\overline{(\mathrm{V}_{\alpha}\mathbf{v}_{0})\mathbf{V}_{\alpha}}+\right.$$

$$\left.+\rho_{\alpha}\overline{(\mathbf{V}_{\alpha}\mathbf{V}_{\alpha})}\mathbf{v}_{0}\right)-\mathbf{F}_{\alpha}^{(1)}\rho_{\alpha}\mathbf{v}_{0}-\rho_{\alpha}\mathbf{v}_{0}\mathbf{F}_{\alpha}^{(1)}-$$

$$-\frac{q_{\alpha}}{m_{\alpha}}\rho_{\alpha}[\mathbf{v}_{0}\times\mathbf{B}]\mathbf{v}_{0}-\frac{q_{\alpha}}{m_{\alpha}}\rho_{\alpha}\overline{[\mathbf{V}_{\alpha}\times\mathbf{B}]\mathbf{V}_{\alpha}}-$$

$$\left.\left.-\frac{q_{\alpha}}{m_{\alpha}}\rho_{\alpha}\mathbf{v}_{0}[\mathbf{v}_{0}\times\mathbf{B}]-\frac{q_{\alpha}}{m_{\alpha}}\rho_{\alpha}\overline{\mathbf{V}_{\alpha}[\mathbf{V}_{\alpha}\times\mathbf{B}]}\right]\right\}=$$

$$=\int m_{\alpha}\mathrm{v}_{\alpha}J_{\alpha}^{st,el}d\mathrm{v}_{\alpha}+\int m_{\alpha}\mathrm{v}_{\alpha}J_{\alpha}^{st,inel}d\mathrm{v}_{\alpha}. \tag{4.4.3}$$

Energy equation for mixture:

$$\frac{\partial}{\partial t}\left\{\frac{\rho v_{0}^{2}}{2}+\frac{3}{2}p+\sum_{\alpha}\varepsilon_{\alpha}n_{\alpha}-\sum_{\alpha}\tau_{\alpha}^{(0)}\left[\frac{\partial}{\partial t}\left(\frac{\rho_{\alpha}v_{0}^{2}}{2}+\frac{3}{2}p_{\alpha}+\varepsilon_{\alpha}n_{\alpha}\right)+\right.\right.$$

$$\left.\left.+\frac{\partial}{\partial\mathbf{r}}\cdot\left(\frac{1}{2}\rho_{\alpha}v_{0}^{2}\mathbf{v}_{0}+\frac{5}{2}p_{\alpha}\mathbf{v}_{0}+\varepsilon_{\alpha}n_{\alpha}\mathbf{v}_{0}\right)-\mathbf{F}_{\alpha}^{(1)}\cdot\rho_{\alpha}\mathbf{v}_{0}\right]\right\}+$$

$$+\frac{\partial}{\partial\mathbf{r}}\cdot\left\{\frac{1}{2}\rho v_{0}^{2}\mathbf{v}_{0}+\frac{5}{2}p\mathbf{v}_{0}+\mathbf{v}_{0}\sum_{\alpha}\varepsilon_{\alpha}n_{\alpha}-\sum_{\alpha}\tau_{\alpha}^{(0)}\left[\frac{\partial}{\partial t}\left(\frac{1}{2}\rho_{\alpha}v_{0}^{2}\mathbf{v}_{0}+\right.\right.\right. \tag{4.4.4}$$

$$\left.+\frac{5}{2}p_{\alpha}\mathbf{v}_{0}+\varepsilon_{\alpha}n_{\alpha}\mathbf{v}_{0}\right)+\frac{\partial}{\partial\mathbf{r}}\cdot\left(\frac{1}{2}\rho_{\alpha}v_{0}^{2}\mathbf{v}_{0}\mathbf{v}_{0}+\frac{7}{2}p_{\alpha}\mathbf{v}_{0}\mathbf{v}_{0}+\frac{1}{2}p_{\alpha}v_{0}^{2}\vec{\mathrm{I}}+\right.$$

$$+\frac{5}{2}\frac{p_\alpha^2}{\rho_\alpha}\ddot{\mathrm{I}}+\varepsilon_\alpha n_\alpha \mathbf{v}_0\mathbf{v}_0+\varepsilon_\alpha\frac{p_\alpha}{m_\alpha}\ddot{\mathrm{I}}\Bigg)-\rho_\alpha\mathbf{F}_\alpha^{(1)}\cdot\mathbf{v}_0\mathbf{v}_0-p_\alpha\mathbf{F}_\alpha^{(1)}\cdot\ddot{\mathrm{I}}-$$

$$-\frac{1}{2}\rho_\alpha v_0^2\mathbf{F}_\alpha^{(1)}-\frac{3}{2}\mathbf{F}_\alpha^{(1)}p_\alpha-\frac{\rho_\alpha v_0^2}{2}\frac{q_\alpha}{m_\alpha}[\mathbf{v}_0\times\mathbf{B}]-\frac{5}{2}p_\alpha\frac{q_\alpha}{m_\alpha}[\mathbf{v}_0\times\mathbf{B}]-$$

$$-\varepsilon_\alpha n_\alpha\frac{q_\alpha}{m_\alpha}[\mathbf{v}_0\times\mathbf{B}]-\varepsilon_\alpha n_\alpha\mathbf{F}_\alpha^{(1)}\Bigg]\Bigg\}-\Bigg\{\mathbf{v}_0\cdot\sum_\alpha\rho_\alpha\mathbf{F}_\alpha^{(1)}-$$

$$-\sum_\alpha\tau_\alpha^{(0)}\Bigg[\mathbf{F}_\alpha^{(1)}\cdot\Bigg(\frac{\partial}{\partial t}(\rho_\alpha\mathbf{v}_0)+\frac{\partial}{\partial\mathbf{r}}\cdot\rho_\alpha\mathbf{v}_0\mathbf{v}_0+\frac{\partial}{\partial\mathbf{r}}\cdot p_\alpha\ddot{\mathrm{I}}-\rho_\alpha\mathbf{F}_\alpha^{(1)}-q_\alpha n_\alpha[\mathbf{v}_0\times\mathbf{B}]\Bigg)\Bigg]\Bigg\}\Bigg]=0.$$

Here $\mathbf{F}_\alpha^{(1)}$ are the forces of the non-magnetic origin, $\mathbf{B}$ - magnetic induction, $\ddot{\mathrm{I}}$ - unit tensor, q_α - charge of the α-component particle, p_α - static pressure for α-component, $\mathbf{V}_\alpha$ - thermal velocity, ε_α - internal energy for the particles of α-component, $\mathbf{v}_0$ - hydrodynamic velocity for mixture.

4.5. Basic nonlocal equations in spherical coordinates system.

Nonlocal physical kinetics leads to the strict approximation of non-local effects in space and time [18-24] and after transmission to the local approximation leads to parameter τ, which on the quantum level corresponds to the uncertainty principle “time-energy”. In the general case, the parameter τ is the non-locality parameter; in quantum hydrodynamics, its magnitude is defined by the “time-energy” uncertainty relation.

Strict consideration leads to the system of the generalized hydrodynamic equations (GHE) [19] written here for a one species physical system. We begin with the formulation of the nonlocal continuity equation in the spherical coordinate system with the independent variables r,θ,φ (radial distance r, polar angle θ and azimuth angle φ):

$$\frac{\partial}{\partial t}\left\{\rho-\tau\left[\frac{\partial\rho}{\partial t}+\frac{1}{r^2}\frac{\partial(r^2\rho v_{0r})}{\partial r}+\frac{1}{r\sin\theta}\frac{\partial(\rho v_{0\varphi})}{\partial\varphi}+\frac{1}{r\sin\theta}\frac{\partial(\rho v_{0\theta}\sin\theta)}{\partial\theta}\right]\right\}$$

$$+\frac{1}{r^2}\frac{\partial}{\partial r}\left\{r^2\left\{\rho v_{0r}-\tau\left[\frac{\partial}{\partial t}(\rho v_{0r})+\frac{1}{r^2}\frac{\partial(r^2\rho v_{0r}^2)}{\partial r}+\frac{1}{r\sin\theta}\frac{\partial(\rho v_{0\varphi}v_{0r})}{\partial\varphi}\right.\right.\right.$$

$$+\frac{1}{r\sin\theta}\frac{\partial(\rho v_{0\theta}v_{0r}\sin\theta)}{\partial\theta}-\rho g_r\Big]\Big\}\Big\}+\frac{1}{r\sin\theta}\frac{\partial}{\partial\varphi}\Big\{\rho v_{0\varphi}-\tau\Big[\frac{\partial}{\partial t}(\rho v_{0\varphi})+\frac{1}{r^2}\frac{\partial(r^2\rho v_{0r}v_{0\varphi})}{\partial r}$$

$$+\frac{1}{r\sin\theta}\frac{\partial(\rho v_{0\varphi}^2)}{\partial\varphi}+\frac{1}{r\sin\theta}\frac{\partial(\rho v_{0\theta}v_{0\varphi}\sin\theta)}{\partial\theta}-\rho g_\varphi\Big]\Big\}+\frac{1}{r\sin\theta}\frac{\partial}{\partial\theta}\Big\{\sin\theta\Big\{\rho v_{0\theta}-\tau\Big[\frac{\partial}{\partial t}(\rho v_{0\theta})$$

$$+\frac{1}{r^2}\frac{\partial(r^2\rho v_{0r}v_{0\theta})}{\partial r}+\frac{1}{r\sin\theta}\frac{\partial(\rho v_{0\varphi}v_{0\theta})}{\partial\varphi}+\frac{1}{r\sin\theta}\frac{\partial(\rho v_{0\theta}^2\sin\theta)}{\partial\theta}-\rho g_\theta\Big]\Big\}\Big\}$$

$$-\frac{1}{r^2}\frac{\partial}{\partial r}\left(\tau r^2\frac{\partial p}{\partial r}\right)-\frac{1}{r^2\sin\theta}\frac{\partial}{\partial\theta}\left(\tau\sin\theta\frac{\partial p}{\partial\theta}\right)-\frac{1}{r^2\sin^2\theta}\frac{\partial}{\partial\varphi}\left(\tau\frac{\partial p}{\partial\varphi}\right)=0, \qquad (4.5.1)$$

where p - static pressure, ρ - mass density, $\mathbf{v}_0$ - hydrodynamic velocity. In the following we consider the one-dimensional stationary physical system without the angles θ and φ dependence in derivatives, but the possible $v_{0\varphi}(r)$ dependence is taken into account in the following derivation. As a result from (4.5.1) we find

$$\frac{1}{r^2}\frac{\partial}{\partial r}\left\{r^2\left[\rho v_{0r}-\tau\left(\frac{1}{r^2}\frac{\partial(r^2\rho v_{0r}^2)}{\partial r}-\rho g_r\right)\right]\right\}-\frac{1}{r^2}\frac{\partial}{\partial r}\left(\tau r^2\frac{\partial p}{\partial r}\right)=0. \qquad (4.5.2)$$

After integrating we have

$$\rho v_{0r}-\tau\left(\frac{1}{r^2}\frac{\partial(r^2\rho v_{0r}^2)}{\partial r}-\rho g_r+\frac{\partial p}{\partial r}\right)=0. \qquad (4.5.3)$$

Now we write down motion equation onto $\mathbf{e}_\varphi$ - direction for the spherical coordinate system:

$$\frac{\partial}{\partial t}\Big\{\rho v_{0\varphi}-\tau\Big[\frac{\partial}{\partial t}(\rho v_{0\varphi})+\frac{1}{r^2}\frac{\partial(r^2\rho v_{0r}v_{0\varphi})}{\partial r}+\frac{1}{r\sin\theta}\frac{\partial(\rho v_{0\varphi}^2)}{\partial\varphi}+\frac{1}{r\sin\theta}\frac{\partial(\rho v_{0\theta}v_{0\varphi}\sin\theta)}{\partial\theta}$$

$$+\frac{1}{r\sin\theta}\frac{\partial p}{\partial\varphi}-\rho g_\varphi\Big]\Big\}-g_\varphi\Big[\rho-\tau\Big(\frac{\partial\rho}{\partial t}+\frac{1}{r^2}\frac{\partial(r^2\rho v_{0r})}{\partial r}+\frac{1}{r\sin\theta}\frac{\partial(\rho v_{0\varphi})}{\partial\varphi}+\frac{1}{r\sin\theta}\frac{\partial(\rho v_{0\theta}\sin\theta)}{\partial\theta}\Big)\Big]$$

$$+\frac{1}{r^2}\frac{\partial}{\partial r}\Big\{r^2\Big\{\rho v_{0r}v_{0\varphi}-\tau\Big[\frac{\partial}{\partial t}(\rho v_{0r}v_{0\varphi})+\frac{1}{r^2}\frac{\partial(r^2\rho v_{0r}^2v_{0\varphi})}{\partial r}+\frac{1}{r\sin\theta}\frac{\partial(\rho v_{0\varphi}^2v_{0r})}{\partial\varphi}$$

$$+\frac{1}{r\sin\theta}\frac{\partial(\rho v_{0\theta}v_{0r}v_{0\varphi}\sin\theta)}{\partial\theta}-g_r\rho v_{0\varphi}-v_{0r}\rho g_\varphi\Big]\Big\}\Big\}+\frac{1}{r\sin\theta}\frac{\partial}{\partial\varphi}\Big\{\rho v_{0\varphi}^2-\tau\Big[\frac{\partial}{\partial t}(\rho v_{0\varphi}^2)$$

$$+\frac{1}{r^2}\frac{\partial(r^2\rho v_{0r}v_{0\varphi}^2)}{\partial r}+\frac{1}{r\sin\theta}\frac{\partial(\rho v_{0\varphi}^3)}{\partial\varphi}+\frac{1}{r\sin\theta}\frac{\partial(\rho v_{0\theta}v_{0\varphi}^2\sin\theta)}{\partial\theta}-2g_\varphi\rho v_{0\varphi}\Big]\Big\}$$

$$+\frac{1}{r\sin\theta}\frac{\partial}{\partial\theta}\Big\{\sin\theta\Big\{\rho v_{0\theta}v_{0\varphi}-\tau\Big[\frac{\partial}{\partial t}(\rho v_{0\theta}v_{0\varphi})+\frac{1}{r^2}\frac{\partial(r^2\rho v_{0r}v_{0\theta}v_{0\varphi})}{\partial r}+\frac{1}{r\sin\theta}\frac{\partial(\rho v_{0\varphi}^2v_{0\theta})}{\partial\varphi}$$

$$
+\frac{1}{r\sin\theta}\frac{\partial\left(\rho v_{0\theta}^{2}v_{0\varphi}\sin\theta\right)}{\partial\theta}-g_{\theta}\rho v_{0\varphi}-v_{0\theta}\rho g_{\varphi}\Bigg]\Bigg]\Bigg\}+\frac{1}{r\sin\theta}\frac{\partial p}{\partial\varphi}-\frac{1}{r\sin\theta}\frac{\partial}{\partial\varphi}\left(\tau\frac{\partial p}{\partial t}\right)
$$

$$
-\frac{2}{r\sin\theta}\frac{\partial}{\partial\varphi}\left(\tau\left(\frac{1}{r^{2}}\frac{\partial\left(r^{2}pv_{0r}\right)}{\partial r}+\frac{1}{r\sin\theta}\frac{\partial\left(pv_{0\varphi}\right)}{\partial\varphi}+\frac{1}{r\sin\theta}\frac{\partial\left(pv_{0\theta}\sin\theta\right)}{\partial\theta}\right)\right)
$$

$$
-\frac{1}{r^{2}}\frac{\partial}{\partial r}\left(\tau r^{2}\frac{\partial\left(pv_{0\varphi}\right)}{\partial r}\right)-\frac{1}{r^{2}\sin\theta}\frac{\partial}{\partial\theta}\left(\tau\sin\theta\frac{\partial\left(pv_{0\varphi}\right)}{\partial\theta}\right)-\frac{1}{r^{2}\sin^{2}\theta}\frac{\partial}{\partial\varphi}\left(\tau\frac{\partial\left(pv_{0\varphi}\right)}{\partial\varphi}\right)=0.
$$

(4.5.4)

Let us transform this equation corresponding to the orbital motion in the stationary case. We find after excluding the angles θ and φ dependence

$$
\frac{\partial}{\partial r}\left\{r^{2}\left[\rho v_{0r}v_{0\varphi}-\tau\left(\frac{1}{r^{2}}\frac{\partial\left(r^{2}\rho v_{0r}^{2}v_{0\varphi}\right)}{\partial r}-g_{r}\rho v_{0\varphi}\right)\right]\right\}-\frac{\partial}{\partial r}\left(\tau r^{2}\frac{\partial\left(pv_{0\varphi}\right)}{\partial r}\right)=0 \tag{4.5.5}
$$

or

$$
\rho v_{0r}v_{0\varphi}-\tau\left[\frac{1}{r^{2}}\frac{\partial\left(r^{2}\rho v_{0r}^{2}v_{0\varphi}\right)}{\partial r}-g_{r}\rho v_{0\varphi}\right]-\tau\frac{\partial\left(pv_{0\varphi}\right)}{\partial r}=0 \tag{4.5.6}
$$

or

$$
\rho v_{0r}v_{0\varphi}-\tau\left[\frac{1}{r^{2}}v_{0\varphi}\frac{\partial\left(r^{2}\rho v_{0r}^{2}\right)}{\partial r}+\rho v_{0r}^{2}\frac{\partial v_{0\varphi}}{\partial r}-g_{r}\rho v_{0\varphi}+p\frac{\partial v_{0\varphi}}{\partial r}+v_{0\varphi}\frac{\partial p}{\partial r}\right]=0. \tag{4.5.7}
$$

Comparing the nonlocal continuity equation (4.5.3) written in the form

$$
\rho v_{0r}v_{0\varphi}-\tau\left(\frac{1}{r^{2}}v_{0\varphi}\frac{\partial\left(r^{2}\rho v_{0r}^{2}\right)}{\partial r}-g_{r}\rho v_{0\varphi}+v_{0\varphi}\frac{\partial p}{\partial r}\right)=0
$$

and the motion equation onto $\mathbf{e}_{\varphi}$ - direction (4.5.7) we find

$$
\left(\rho v_{0r}^{2}+p\right)\frac{\partial v_{0\varphi}}{\partial r}=0 \tag{4.5.8}
$$

or for satisfying (4.5.8) we should admit that $\frac{\partial v_{0\varphi}}{\partial r}=0$ or

$$
v_{0\varphi}=const. \tag{4.5.9}
$$

In other words, the orbital speed is constant for different radius inside of the concrete ring. Each of the rings of Saturn breaks into smaller, and those into even smaller parts.

This kind of the ring rotation corresponds to the Vera Rubin effect* [54, 55] *even in the presence of the mass transfer in the r direction. This result does not depend on the τ choice. This effect can be verified by the direct observation or with the help of robotic spacecrafts.

We have Poisson equation

$$\frac{1}{r^2}\frac{\partial}{\partial r}\left(r^2 g_r\right) = -4\pi\gamma_N\left[\rho - \tau\frac{1}{r^2}\frac{\partial\left(r^2\rho v_{0r}\right)}{\partial r}\right], \tag{4.5.10}$$

where Newton's gravitation constant $\gamma_N = 6.67\cdot 10^{-11}\frac{m^3}{\sec^2 kg}$. The condition (4.5.9) leads to the significant simplification of the following consideration.

Motion equation for the $\mathbf{e}_r$ direction is

$$\frac{\partial}{\partial t}\left\{\rho v_{0r} - \tau\left[\frac{\partial}{\partial t}(\rho v_{0r}) + \frac{1}{r^2}\frac{\partial\left(r^2\rho v_{0r}^2\right)}{\partial r} + \frac{1}{r\sin\theta}\frac{\partial\left(\rho v_{0\varphi}v_{0r}\right)}{\partial\varphi} + \frac{1}{r\sin\theta}\frac{\partial(\rho v_{0\theta}v_{0r}\sin\theta)}{\partial\theta}\right.\right.$$

$$\left.\left.+\frac{\partial p}{\partial r} - \rho g_r\right]\right\} - g_r\left[\rho - \tau\left(\frac{\partial\rho}{\partial t} + \frac{1}{r^2}\frac{\partial\left(r^2\rho v_{0r}\right)}{\partial r} + \frac{1}{r\sin\theta}\frac{\partial\left(\rho v_{0\varphi}\right)}{\partial\varphi} + \frac{1}{r\sin\theta}\frac{\partial(\rho v_{0\theta}\sin\theta)}{\partial\theta}\right)\right]$$

$$+\frac{1}{r^2}\frac{\partial}{\partial r}\left\{r^2\left\{\rho v_{0r}^2 - \tau\left[\begin{array}{l}\frac{\partial}{\partial t}\left(\rho v_{0r}^2\right) + \frac{1}{r^2}\frac{\partial\left(r^2\rho v_{0r}^3\right)}{\partial r} + \frac{1}{r\sin\theta}\frac{\partial\left(\rho v_{0\varphi}v_{0r}^2\right)}{\partial\varphi}\\ +\frac{1}{r\sin\theta}\frac{\partial\left(\rho v_{0\theta}v_{0r}^2\sin\theta\right)}{\partial\theta} - 2g_r\rho v_{0r}\end{array}\right]\right\}\right\}$$

$$+\frac{1}{r\sin\theta}\frac{\partial}{\partial\varphi}\left\{\rho v_{0\varphi}v_{0r} - \tau\left[\frac{\partial}{\partial t}\left(\rho v_{0\varphi}v_{0r}\right) + \frac{1}{r^2}\frac{\partial\left(r^2\rho v_{0\varphi}v_{0r}^2\right)}{\partial r} + \frac{1}{r\sin\theta}\frac{\partial\left(\rho v_{0\varphi}^2 v_{0r}\right)}{\partial\varphi}\right.\right.$$

$$\left.\left.+\frac{1}{r\sin\theta}\frac{\partial\left(\rho v_{0\theta}v_{0\varphi}v_{0r}\sin\theta\right)}{\partial\theta} - g_\varphi\rho v_{0r} - g_r\rho v_{0\varphi}\right]\right\} \tag{4.5.11}$$

$$+\frac{1}{r\sin\theta}\frac{\partial}{\partial\theta}\left\{\sin\theta\left\{\rho v_{0\theta}v_{0r} - \tau\left[\begin{array}{l}\frac{\partial}{\partial t}\left(\rho v_{0\theta}v_{0r}\right) + \frac{1}{r^2}\frac{\partial\left(r^2\rho v_{0\theta}v_{0r}^2\right)}{\partial r} + \frac{1}{r\sin\theta}\frac{\partial\left(\rho v_{0\varphi}v_{0\theta}v_{0r}\right)}{\partial r}\\ +\frac{1}{r\sin\theta}\frac{\partial\left(\rho v_{0\theta}^2 v_{0r}\right)}{\partial r} - g_\theta\rho v_{0r} - v_{0\theta}\rho g_r\end{array}\right]\right\}\right\}$$

$$+\frac{\partial p}{\partial r} - \frac{\partial}{\partial r}\left(\tau\frac{\partial p}{\partial t}\right) - 2\frac{\partial}{\partial r}\left(\tau\left(\frac{1}{r^2}\frac{\partial\left(r^2 p v_{0r}\right)}{\partial r} + \frac{1}{r\sin\theta}\frac{\partial\left(p v_{0\varphi}\right)}{\partial\varphi} + \frac{1}{r\sin\theta}\frac{\partial(p v_{0\theta}\sin\theta)}{\partial\theta}\right)\right)$$

$$-\frac{1}{r^2}\frac{\partial}{\partial r}\left(\tau r^2\frac{\partial(p v_{0r})}{\partial r}\right) - \frac{1}{r^2\sin\theta}\frac{\partial}{\partial\theta}\left(\tau\sin\theta\frac{\partial(p v_{0r})}{\partial\theta}\right) - \frac{1}{r^2\sin^2\theta}\frac{\partial}{\partial\varphi}\left(\tau\frac{\partial(p v_{0r})}{\partial\varphi}\right) = 0.$$

Using the previous model we have

$$-g_r\left[\rho - \tau\left(\frac{1}{r^2}\frac{\partial\left(r^2\rho v_{0r}\right)}{\partial r}\right)\right] + \frac{1}{r^2}\frac{\partial}{\partial r}\left\{r^2\left[\rho v_{0r}^2 - \tau\left(\frac{1}{r^2}\frac{\partial\left(r^2\rho v_{0r}^3\right)}{\partial r} - 2g_r\rho v_{0r}\right)\right]\right\} +$$

$$+\frac{\partial p}{\partial r} - 2\frac{\partial}{\partial r}\left(\frac{\tau}{r^2}\frac{\partial\left(r^2 p v_{0r}\right)}{\partial r}\right) - \frac{1}{r^2}\frac{\partial}{\partial r}\left(\tau r^2\frac{\partial(p v_{0r})}{\partial r}\right) = 0. \tag{4.5.12}$$

or

$$\frac{\partial p}{\partial r} - \rho g_r + \tau g_r\frac{1}{r^2}\frac{\partial\left(r^2\rho v_{0r}\right)}{\partial r} + \frac{1}{r^2}\frac{\partial}{\partial r}\left\{r^2\tau\left[g_r\rho v_{0r} - \frac{\partial v_{0r}}{\partial r}\left(p + \rho v_{0r}^2\right)\right]\right\} - 2\frac{\partial}{\partial r}\left(\tau\frac{1}{r^2}\frac{\partial\left(r^2 p v_{0r}\right)}{\partial r}\right) = 0. \tag{4.5.13}$$

Energy equation

$$\frac{\partial}{\partial t}\left\{\frac{1}{2}\rho v_0^2+\varepsilon n+\frac{3}{2}p-\tau\left[\frac{\partial}{\partial t}\left(\frac{1}{2}\rho v_0^2+\varepsilon n+\frac{3}{2}p\right)+\frac{1}{r^2}\frac{\partial}{\partial r}\left(r^2 v_{0r}\left(\frac{1}{2}\rho v_0^2+\varepsilon n+\frac{5}{2}p\right)\right)\right.\right.$$

$$+\frac{1}{r\sin\theta}\frac{\partial}{\partial\varphi}\left(v_{0\varphi}\left(\frac{1}{2}\rho v_0^2+\varepsilon n+\frac{5}{2}p\right)\right)+\frac{1}{r\sin\theta}\frac{\partial}{\partial\theta}\left(\sin\theta v_{0\theta}\left(\frac{1}{2}\rho v_0^2+\varepsilon n+\frac{5}{2}p\right)\right)$$

$$\left.\left.-\rho\left(g_r v_{0r}+g_\varphi v_{0\varphi}+g_\theta v_{0\theta}\right)\right]\right\}+\frac{1}{r^2}\frac{\partial}{\partial r}\left\{r^2\left\{\left(\frac{1}{2}\rho v_0^2+\varepsilon n+\frac{5}{2}p\right)v_{0r}-\tau\left[\frac{\partial}{\partial t}\left(\left(\frac{1}{2}\rho v_0^2+\varepsilon n+\frac{5}{2}p\right)v_{0r}\right)\right.\right.\right.$$

$$+\frac{1}{r^2}\frac{\partial}{\partial r}\left(r^2\left(\frac{1}{2}\rho v_0^2+\varepsilon n+\frac{7}{2}p\right)v_{0r}^2\right)+\frac{1}{r\sin\theta}\frac{\partial}{\partial\varphi}\left(\left(\frac{1}{2}\rho v_0^2+\varepsilon n+\frac{7}{2}p\right)v_{0\varphi}v_{0r}\right)$$

$$+\frac{1}{r\sin\theta}\frac{\partial}{\partial\theta}\left(\sin\theta\left(\frac{1}{2}\rho v_0^2+\varepsilon n+\frac{7}{2}p\right)v_{0\theta}v_{0r}\right)$$

$$\left.\left.\left.-\rho\left(g_r v_{0r}+g_\varphi v_{0\varphi}+g_\theta v_{0\theta}\right)v_{0r}-\left(\frac{1}{2}\rho v_0^2+\varepsilon n+\frac{3}{2}p\right)g_r\right]\right\}\right\}+\frac{1}{r\sin\theta}\frac{\partial}{\partial\varphi}\left\{\left(\frac{1}{2}\rho v_0^2+\varepsilon n+\frac{5}{2}p\right)v_{0\varphi}\right.$$

$$-\tau\left[\frac{\partial}{\partial t}\left(\left(\frac{1}{2}\rho v_0^2+\varepsilon n+\frac{5}{2}p\right)v_{0\varphi}\right)+\frac{1}{r^2}\frac{\partial}{\partial r}\left(r^2\left(\frac{1}{2}\rho v_0^2+\varepsilon n+\frac{7}{2}p\right)v_{0r}v_{0\varphi}\right)\right.$$

$$+\frac{1}{r\sin\theta}\frac{\partial}{\partial\varphi}\left(\left(\frac{1}{2}\rho v_0^2+\varepsilon n+\frac{7}{2}p\right)v_{0\varphi}^2\right)+\frac{1}{r\sin\theta}\frac{\partial}{\partial\theta}\left(\sin\theta\left(\frac{1}{2}\rho v_0^2+\varepsilon n+\frac{7}{2}p\right)v_{0\theta}v_{0\varphi}\right)$$

$$-\rho\left(g_r v_{0r}+g_\varphi v_{0\varphi}+g_\theta v_{0\theta}\right)v_{0\varphi}$$

$$\left.\left.-\left(\frac{1}{2}\rho v_0^2+\varepsilon n+\frac{3}{2}p\right)g_\varphi\right]\right\}+\frac{1}{r\sin\theta}\frac{\partial}{\partial\theta}\left\{\sin\theta\left\{\left(\frac{1}{2}\rho v_0^2+\varepsilon n+\frac{5}{2}p\right)v_{0\theta}-\right.\right.$$

$$\tau\left[\frac{\partial}{\partial t}\left(\left(\frac{1}{2}\rho v_0^2+\varepsilon n+\frac{5}{2}p\right)v_{0\theta}\right)+\frac{1}{r^2}\frac{\partial}{\partial r}\left(r^2\left(\frac{1}{2}\rho v_0^2+\varepsilon n+\frac{7}{2}p\right)v_{0r}v_{0\theta}\right)+\right.$$

$$\frac{1}{r\sin\theta}\frac{\partial}{\partial\varphi}\left(\left(\frac{1}{2}\rho v_0^2+\varepsilon n+\frac{7}{2}p\right)v_{0\varphi}v_{0\theta}\right)+$$

$$\left.\left.\left.+\frac{1}{r\sin\theta}\frac{\partial}{\partial\theta}\left(\sin\theta\left(\frac{1}{2}\rho v_0^2+\varepsilon n+\frac{7}{2}p\right)v_{0\theta}^2\right)-\rho\left(g_r v_{0r}+g_\varphi v_{0\varphi}+g_\theta v_{0\theta}\right)v_{0\theta}-\left(\frac{1}{2}\rho v_0^2+\varepsilon n+\frac{3}{2}p\right)g_\theta\right]\right\}\right\}$$

$$-\left\{\rho\left(g_r v_{0r}+g_\varphi v_{0\varphi}+g_\theta v_{0\theta}\right)-\tau\left[g_r\left(\frac{\partial}{\partial t}(\rho v_{0r})+\frac{1}{r^2}\frac{\partial}{\partial r}\left(r^2\rho v_{0r}^2\right)+\frac{1}{r\sin\theta}\frac{\partial}{\partial\varphi}\left(\rho v_{0\varphi}v_{0r}\right)+\right.\right.\right.$$

$$\left.+\frac{1}{r\sin\theta}\frac{\partial}{\partial\theta}\left(\rho v_{0\theta}v_{0r}\sin\theta\right)+\frac{\partial p}{\partial r}-\rho g_r\right)$$

$$+g_\varphi\left(\frac{\partial}{\partial t}(\rho v_{0\varphi})+\frac{1}{r^2}\frac{\partial}{\partial r}\left(r^2\rho v_{0r}v_{0\varphi}\right)+\frac{1}{r\sin\theta}\frac{\partial}{\partial\varphi}\left(\rho v_{0\varphi}^2\right)+\frac{1}{r\sin\theta}\frac{\partial}{\partial\theta}\left(\rho v_{0\theta}v_{0\varphi}\sin\theta\right)\right.$$

$$\left.+\frac{1}{r\sin\theta}\frac{\partial p}{\partial\varphi}-\rho g_\varphi\right)+g_\theta\left(\frac{\partial}{\partial t}(\rho v_{0\theta})+\frac{1}{r^2}\frac{\partial}{\partial r}\left(r^2\rho v_{0r}v_{0\theta}\right)+\frac{1}{r\sin\theta}\frac{\partial}{\partial\varphi}\left(\rho v_{0\varphi}v_{0\theta}\right)\right.$$

$$\left.\left.\left.+\frac{1}{r\sin\theta}\frac{\partial}{\partial\theta}\left(\rho v_{0\theta}^2\sin\theta\right)+\frac{1}{r}\frac{\partial p}{\partial\theta}-\rho g_\theta\right)\right]\right\}-\frac{1}{r^2}\frac{\partial}{\partial r}\left(\tau r^2\frac{\partial}{\partial r}\left(\frac{1}{2}pv_0^2+\varepsilon nv_0^2+\frac{5}{2}\frac{p^2}{\rho}\right)\right)$$

$$-\frac{1}{r^2\sin\theta}\frac{\partial}{\partial\theta}\left(\tau\sin\theta\frac{\partial}{\partial\theta}\left(\frac{1}{2}pv_0^2+\varepsilon nv_0^2+\frac{5}{2}\frac{p^2}{\rho}\right)\right)-\frac{1}{r^2\sin^2\theta}\frac{\partial}{\partial\varphi}\left(\tau\frac{\partial}{\partial\varphi}\left(\frac{1}{2}pv_0^2+\varepsilon nv_0^2+\frac{5}{2}\frac{p^2}{\rho}\right)\right)$$
$$+\frac{1}{r^2}\frac{\partial}{\partial r}\left(r^2\tau pg_r\right)+\frac{1}{r\sin\theta}\frac{\partial}{\partial\varphi}\left(\tau pg_\varphi\right)+\frac{1}{r\sin\theta}\frac{\partial}{\partial\theta}\left(\tau pg_\theta\sin\theta\right)=0, \tag{4.5.14}$$

where ε is the internal energy, $v_0^2=v_{0r}^2+v_{0\varphi}^2+v_{0\theta}^2$. In the frame of the previous conditions we find

$$\frac{1}{r^2}\frac{\partial}{\partial r}\left\{r^2\left\{\left(\frac{1}{2}\rho v_0^2+\frac{5}{2}p\right)v_{0r}-\tau\left[\frac{1}{r^2}\frac{\partial}{\partial r}\left(r^2\left(\frac{1}{2}\rho v_0^2+\frac{7}{2}p\right)v_{0r}^2\right)-\frac{3}{2}\left(\rho v_0^2+p\right)g_r\right]\right\}\right\}$$
$$-\left\{\rho\left(g_r v_{0r}\right)-\tau\left[g_r\left(\frac{1}{r^2}\frac{\partial}{\partial r}\left(r^2\rho v_{0r}^2\right)+\frac{\partial p}{\partial r}-\rho g_r\right)\right]\right\}-\frac{1}{r^2}\frac{\partial}{\partial r}\left(\tau r^2\frac{\partial}{\partial r}\left(\frac{1}{2}pv_0^2+\frac{5}{2}\frac{p^2}{\rho}\right)\right)$$
$$+\frac{1}{r^2}\frac{\partial}{\partial r}\left(r^2\tau pg_r\right)=0. \tag{4.5.15}$$

or

$$\frac{\partial}{\partial r}\left\{r^2\left[\left(\rho v_0^2+5p\right)v_{0r}\right]\right\}-\frac{\partial}{\partial r}\left[\tau\frac{\partial}{\partial r}\left(r^2\left(\rho v_0^2+7p\right)v_{0r}^2\right)\right]+3\frac{\partial}{\partial r}\left\{\tau r^2\rho v_0^2 g_r\right\}+5\frac{\partial}{\partial r}\left\{\tau r^2 pg_r\right\}$$
$$-2r^2\left\{\rho v_{0r}g_r-\tau\left[g_r\left(\frac{1}{r^2}\frac{\partial}{\partial r}\left(r^2\rho v_{0r}^2\right)+\frac{\partial p}{\partial r}-\rho g_r\right)\right]\right\} \tag{4.5.16}$$
$$-\frac{\partial}{\partial r}\left(\tau r^2\frac{\partial}{\partial r}\left(pv_0^2+5\frac{p^2}{\rho}\right)\right)=0$$

Let us use (4.5.3) in the form

$$\rho v_{0r}g_r=\tau\left(\frac{1}{r^2}g_r\frac{\partial\left(r^2\rho v_{0r}^2\right)}{\partial r}-\rho g_r^2+g_r\frac{\partial p}{\partial r}\right). \tag{4.5.17}$$

After substitution (4.5.17) into (4.5.16) we reach

$$\frac{\partial}{\partial r}\left\{r^2\left[\left(\rho v_0^2+5p\right)v_{0r}\right]\right\}-\frac{\partial}{\partial r}\left[\tau\frac{\partial}{\partial r}\left(r^2\left(\rho v_0^2+7p\right)v_{0r}^2\right)\right]+3\frac{\partial}{\partial r}\left\{\tau r^2\rho v_0^2 g_r\right\}+5\frac{\partial}{\partial r}\left\{\tau r^2 pg_r\right\}$$
$$-2r^2\left\{\tau\left(\frac{1}{r^2}g_r\frac{\partial\left(r^2\rho v_{0r}^2\right)}{\partial r}-\rho g_r^2+g_r\frac{\partial p}{\partial r}\right)-\tau\left[g_r\left(\frac{1}{r^2}\frac{\partial}{\partial r}\left(r^2\rho v_{0r}^2\right)+\frac{\partial p}{\partial r}-\rho g_r\right)\right]\right\}$$
$$-\frac{\partial}{\partial r}\left(\tau r^2\frac{\partial}{\partial r}\left(pv_0^2+5\frac{p^2}{\rho}\right)\right)=0. \tag{4.5.18}$$

or

$$\frac{\partial}{\partial r}\left\{r^2\left(\rho v_0^2+5p\right)v_{0r}\right\}-\frac{\partial}{\partial r}\left[\tau\frac{\partial}{\partial r}\left(r^2\left(\rho v_0^2+7p\right)v_{0r}^2\right)\right]+3\frac{\partial}{\partial r}\left\{\tau r^2\rho v_0^2 g_r\right\}+5\frac{\partial}{\partial r}\left\{\tau r^2 pg_r\right\}$$
$$-\frac{\partial}{\partial r}\left(\tau r^2\frac{\partial}{\partial r}\left(pv_0^2+5\frac{p^2}{\rho}\right)\right)=0. \tag{4.5.19}$$

After integration we find (4.5.20)

$$r^2\left(\rho v_0^2+5p\right)v_{0r}-\tau\left\{\frac{\partial}{\partial r}\left(r^2\left(\rho v_0^2+7p\right)v_{0r}^2\right)-3r^2\rho v_0^2 g_r-5r^2 p g_r+r^2\frac{\partial}{\partial r}\left(p v_0^2+5\frac{p^2}{\rho}\right)\right\}=0.$$

(4.5.20)

Obviously the constant of integration is equal to zero. Then we have the following unknown values $g_r, v_{0r}, v_{0\varphi}, \rho, p$ and five equations (4.5.3), (4.5.9), (4.5.10), (4.5.13), (4.5.20) for their definition. Write down these equations in the dimensionless form after introducing the scales: $g_0, u_0, \rho_0,\ p_0$ and for independent variable r_0;

$\tilde{\gamma}_N=\gamma_N\frac{\rho_0 r_0}{g_0}$, $\tilde{G}=\tilde{\gamma}_N=\gamma_N\frac{M}{r_0 u_0^2}$, $M=\rho_0 r_0^3$, $p_0=\rho_0 u_0^2$, $g_0=\frac{u_0^2}{r_0}$. We use the scale for τ in the form $\tau_0=\frac{r_0}{u_0}$. As a result we obtain after some transformation the following system of equations:

Poisson equation

$$\frac{\partial}{\partial\tilde{r}}\left(\tilde{r}^2\tilde{g}_r\right)+\tilde{G}\left[\tilde{\rho}\tilde{r}^2-\tilde{\tau}\frac{\partial\left(\tilde{r}^2\tilde{\rho}\tilde{v}_{0r}\right)}{\partial\tilde{r}}\right]=0, \qquad (4.5.21)$$

where $\tilde{G}=4\pi\tilde{\gamma}_N$

Continuity equation

$$\tilde{\rho}\tilde{v}_{0r}=\tilde{\tau}\left[\frac{1}{\tilde{r}^2}\frac{\partial\left(\tilde{r}^2\tilde{\rho}\tilde{v}_{0r}^2\right)}{\partial\tilde{r}}-\tilde{\rho}\tilde{g}_r+\frac{\partial\tilde{p}}{\partial\tilde{r}}\right]. \qquad (4.5.22)$$

Motion equations

$$\tilde{v}_{0\varphi}=const, \qquad (4.5.23)$$

$$\frac{\partial\tilde{p}}{\partial\tilde{r}}-\tilde{\rho}\tilde{g}_r+\tilde{\tau}\tilde{g}_r\frac{1}{\tilde{r}^2}\frac{\partial\left(\tilde{r}^2\tilde{\rho}\tilde{v}_{0r}\right)}{\partial\tilde{r}}+\frac{1}{\tilde{r}^2}\frac{\partial}{\partial\tilde{r}}\left\{\tilde{r}^2\tilde{\tau}\left[\tilde{g}_r\tilde{\rho}\tilde{v}_{0r}-\frac{\partial\tilde{v}_{0r}}{\partial\tilde{r}}\left(\tilde{p}+\tilde{\rho}\tilde{v}_{0r}^2\right)\right]\right\}$$

$$-2\frac{\partial}{\partial\tilde{r}}\left(\tilde{\tau}\frac{1}{\tilde{r}^2}\frac{\partial\left(\tilde{r}^2\tilde{p}\tilde{v}_{0r}\right)}{\partial\tilde{r}}\right)=0. \qquad (4.5.24)$$

Energy equation

$$\left(\tilde{\rho}\tilde{v}_0^2+5\tilde{p}\right)\tilde{v}_{0r}-\tilde{\tau}\left[\frac{\partial}{\partial\tilde{r}}\left(\left(\tilde{\rho}\tilde{v}_0^2+7\tilde{p}\right)\tilde{v}_{0r}^2\right)+\frac{2}{\tilde{r}}\left(\tilde{\rho}\tilde{v}_0^2+7\tilde{p}\right)\tilde{v}_{0r}^2+\frac{\partial}{\partial\tilde{r}}\left(\tilde{p}\tilde{v}_0^2+5\frac{\tilde{p}^2}{\tilde{\rho}}\right)-\left(3\tilde{\rho}\tilde{v}_0^2+5\tilde{p}\right)\tilde{g}_r\right]=0$$

(4.5.25)

Let us consider a satellite rotation about the Central body and its own axis as it shown on scheme 1. This satellite makes a direct movement (sometimes called prograde motion), the rotation motion of a planetary body in a direction similar to the orbital trip. In other words rotation around the axis corresponds to the movement direction along the orbit, in this case counterclockwise. Retrograde motion is motion in the contrary direction.

The typical explanation sounds as follows. If a satellite is formed in the gravitational field of a planet during its formation, it will orbit in the same direction in which the planet rotates. If an object is formed elsewhere and then captured by a planet, its orbit will be direct or retrograde depending on which side the first approach to the planet occurred, that is, in the direction of rotation toward or away from the satellite. The satellites of the planets, revolving in a retrograde orbit, are called irregular. Satellites of the planet, circulating in direct orbits, called regular. In the Solar system, many asteroid-sized satellites orbit in retrograde orbits, while all large satellites except Triton (the largest of Neptune's satellites) have direct orbits.

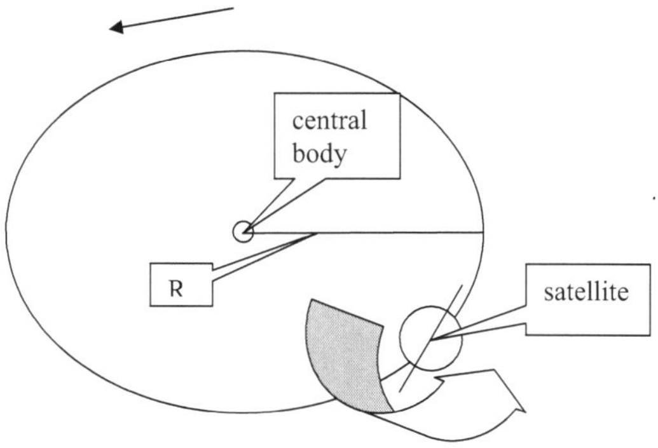

Fig. 4.5.1. Direct rotation.

Let us consider this problem in details. We suppose for the beginning that the orbital motion of a satellite occurs in accordance with Kepler's law

$$V_{orb} = \sqrt{\gamma_N M}\frac{1}{\sqrt{R}}, \qquad (4.5.26)$$

where M is mass of the central body, R is the radius of the circular orbit. Obviously all parts of satellite are moving with different orbital velocities. If the satellite radius r is significantly less than R, we find

$$\Delta V_{orb} = \sqrt{\gamma_N M}\frac{1}{\sqrt{R-r}} - \sqrt{\gamma_N M}\frac{1}{\sqrt{R+r}} \cong \sqrt{\gamma_N M}\frac{1}{\sqrt{R}}\frac{r}{R}. \qquad (4.5.27)$$

For the moon it corresponds ~ 5m/sec. Obviously, this effect should provoke the retardation motion or clockwise rotation in the considered situation. It means that the satellite formation from the initial ring follows Vera Rubin regime (see (4.5.9)).

With this aim let us investigate the Poisson equation (4.5.21), which can be written as

$$\frac{\partial}{\partial\tilde{r}}\left(\tilde{r}^2\tilde{g}_r\right)=-\tilde{G}\left[\tilde{\rho}\tilde{r}^2-\tilde{\tau}\frac{\partial\left(\tilde{r}^2\tilde{\rho}\tilde{v}_{0r}\right)}{\partial\tilde{r}}\right] \quad (4.5.28)$$

or after integration

$$\tilde{r}^2\tilde{g}_r=-\tilde{G}\int_0^{\tilde{r}}\left[\tilde{\rho}\tilde{r}^2\right]d\tilde{r}+\tilde{G}\int_0^{\tilde{r}}\left[\tilde{\tau}\frac{\partial\left(\tilde{r}^2\tilde{\rho}\tilde{v}_{0r}\right)}{\partial\tilde{r}}\right]d\tilde{r}. \quad (4.5.29)$$

Let us suppose that nonlocal dimensionless parameter $\tilde{\tau}$ does not depend on $\tilde{r}$. In this case we find

$$\tilde{r}^2\tilde{g}_r=-\tilde{G}\int_0^{\tilde{r}}\left[\tilde{\rho}\tilde{r}^2\right]d\tilde{r}+\tilde{G}\tilde{\tau}\tilde{r}^2\tilde{\rho}\tilde{v}_{0r} \quad (4.5.30)$$

or

$$\tilde{r}^2\tilde{g}_r=-\tilde{G}\tilde{M}+\tilde{G}\tilde{\tau}\tilde{r}^2\tilde{\rho}\tilde{v}_{0r}, \quad (4.5.31)$$

where $\tilde{M}$ is the dimensionless mass of the central body. As a result we obtain non-local gravitation law

$$\tilde{g}_r=-\tilde{G}\frac{\tilde{M}}{\tilde{r}^2}+\tilde{\tau}\tilde{G}\tilde{\rho}\tilde{v}_{0r} \quad (4.5.32)$$

and only in the local case we reach the classical Newton law

$$\tilde{g}_r=-\tilde{G}\frac{\tilde{M}}{\tilde{r}^2}. \quad (4.5.33)$$

In the nonlocal case gravitational acceleration

$$\tilde{g}_r=-\tilde{G}\left[\frac{\tilde{M}}{\tilde{r}^2}-\tilde{\tau}\tilde{\rho}\tilde{v}_{0r}\right] \quad (4.5.34)$$

turns into zero in a point $\tilde{r}_{cr}$ if

$$\frac{\tilde{M}}{\tilde{r}_{cr}^2}=\tilde{\tau}\tilde{\rho}\tilde{v}_{0r}, \quad (4.5.35)$$

where

$$\tilde{r}_{cr}=\sqrt{\frac{\tilde{M}}{\tilde{\tau}\tilde{\rho}\tilde{v}_{0r}}}. \quad (4.5.36)$$

if $\tilde{v}_{0r,cr}>0$. Then the well known relation should be modified

$$m\tilde{g}_r=-\tilde{G}m\left[\frac{\tilde{M}}{\tilde{r}^2}-\tilde{\tau}\tilde{\rho}\tilde{v}_{0r}\right] \quad (4.5.37)$$

or

$$V_{orb} = \sqrt{\tilde{G}\left[\frac{\tilde{M}}{\tilde{r}} - \tilde{\tau}\widetilde{\rho v}_{0r}\tilde{r}\right]}. \qquad (4.5.38)$$

The energy flux density can be negative $\widetilde{\rho v}_{0r} < 0$ that is, can be $V_{orb} > V_{orb,Newton}$. This equality may mean the introduction of additional mass as a result of the collision. In this case we obtain the direct motion.

SUMMARY:

1. If the parameter $\tilde{\tau}$ is not dependent on $\tilde{r}$ the effective gravitational acceleration

$$\tilde{g}_r = -\tilde{G}\left[\frac{\tilde{M}}{\tilde{r}^2} - \tilde{\tau}\widetilde{\rho v}_{0r}\right]$$

can be positive, negative, or zero.

2. In practical calculations, the gravitational acceleration can repeatedly turn to zero for different values of density $\tilde{\rho}$ and radial velocity $\tilde{v}_{0r}$.

3. Repeated changes in the sign $\tilde{g}_r$ leads to an oscillatory regime $\tilde{g}_r$ and the appearance of separate rings depending on the density of the mass flow $\widetilde{\rho v}_{0r}$ in the radial direction. Of course, the appearance of 3D effects, electromagnetic fields further complicate the situation and lead to the need for extensive mathematical modeling based on nonlocal transport equations.

4. If there is no radial mass transfer $\widetilde{\rho v}_{0r}$ that gravitational acceleration obeys Newton's classical law $\tilde{g}_r = -\tilde{G}\frac{\tilde{M}}{\tilde{r}^2}$.

5. The appearance of the effect of "dark matter" is associated with the considered above effects. A non-local description is inevitable. Emphasize once again that the local Boltzmann equation is the wrong equation. The gravitational equation (4.5.32) has no attitude to the so called "modified Newton equation" and reflects the collective effects in the statistical systems.

4.6. Mathematic modeling of the rings evolution

The system of equations (4.5.21) – (4.5.24) should be applied for the investigation of the transport processes in the ring systems. The transition to the study in the frame of the local case corresponds to the conversion to zero of the parameter τ in the system of equations (4.5.21) – (4.5.24). The corresponding local system of equations is written as

$$\frac{\partial}{\partial \tilde{r}}\left(\tilde{r}^2\tilde{g}_r\right) + \tilde{G}\tilde{\rho}\tilde{r}^2 = 0, \qquad (4.6.1)$$

$$\tilde{\rho}\tilde{g}_r = \frac{\partial \tilde{p}}{\partial \tilde{r}}, \qquad (4.6.2)$$

and from the local energy equation we find

$$\tilde{v}_{0r} = 0 \qquad (4.6.3)$$

with the indefinite hydrodynamic orbital velocity $\tilde{v}_{0\varphi}$. In the non-local model we can investigate two possibilities:

1. The radial velocity $v_{0r} = 0$ and
2. The radial velocity $v_{0r} \neq 0$.

In the first case rings exist without the loss of mass. In the second case the mass loss is taken into account. In the case $v_{0r} = 0$ we obtain the semi-analytical solution. Really, we find

Poisson equation

$$\frac{\partial}{\partial \tilde{r}}\left(\tilde{r}^2 \tilde{g}_r\right) + \tilde{G}\tilde{\rho}\tilde{r}^2 = 0, \qquad (4.6.4)$$

where $\tilde{G} = 4\pi\tilde{\gamma}_N$.

Continuity equation

$$\tilde{\rho}\tilde{g}_r = \frac{\partial \tilde{p}}{\partial \tilde{r}}. \qquad (4.6.5)$$

Motion equation in $\mathbf{n}_\varphi$-direction

$$\tilde{v}_{0\varphi} = const, \qquad (4.6.6)$$

Motion equation in $\mathbf{n}_r$-direction $\tilde{\rho}\tilde{g}_r = \frac{\partial \tilde{p}}{\partial \tilde{r}}$ coincides with the continuity equation (4.6.5).

Energy equation

$$\frac{\partial}{\partial \tilde{r}}\left(\tilde{p}\tilde{v}_0^2 + 5\frac{\tilde{p}^2}{\tilde{\rho}}\right) - \left(3\tilde{\rho}\tilde{v}_0^2 + 5\tilde{p}\right)\tilde{g}_r = 0 \qquad (4.6.7)$$

or

$$\frac{\partial}{\partial \tilde{r}}\left(\tilde{p}\Phi + 5\frac{\tilde{p}^2}{\tilde{\rho}}\right) - \left(3\tilde{\rho}\Phi + 5\tilde{p}\right)\tilde{g}_r = 0, \qquad (4.6.8)$$

where $\Phi = v_{0\varphi}^2$.

Let us investigate this system of equations (4.6.4) – (4.6.8), beginning with the energy equation (4.6.8). If $\Phi = 0$ equation (4.6.8) can be immediately integrated in the analytic form. Really

$$\frac{\partial}{\partial \tilde{r}}\left(\frac{\tilde{p}^2}{\tilde{\rho}}\right) - \tilde{p}\tilde{g}_r = 0. \qquad (4.6.9)$$

Using (4.6.5) we find

$$\frac{\partial}{\partial \tilde{r}}\left(\frac{\tilde{p}^2}{\tilde{\rho}}\right)-\frac{\tilde{p}}{\tilde{\rho}}\frac{\partial \tilde{p}}{\partial \tilde{r}}=0 \qquad (4.6.10)$$

or

$$\frac{\partial}{\partial \tilde{r}}\left(\frac{\tilde{p}}{\tilde{\rho}}\right)=0 \qquad (4.6.11)$$

or

$$\tilde{p}=C\tilde{\rho} \qquad (4.6.12)$$

Equation is an equation of state. In the more general case when $\Phi \neq 0$, we should apply the complete system of equations (4.6.4) – (4.6.8). But it's interesting to estimate the possible transformation of the equation of state (4.6.12). With this aim we are looking for a solution to the state equation in the same form (4.6.12). After the transformation (4.6.8) one obtains

$$5\frac{\tilde{p}}{\tilde{\rho}}\frac{\partial \tilde{p}}{\partial \tilde{r}}-5\frac{\tilde{p}^2}{\tilde{\rho}^2}\frac{\partial \tilde{\rho}}{\partial \tilde{r}}-2\Phi\frac{\partial \tilde{p}}{\partial \tilde{r}}=0 \qquad (4.6.13)$$

If $\tilde{p}=C_1\tilde{\rho}$ then

$$(5C_1-2\Phi)\frac{\partial \tilde{p}}{\partial \tilde{r}}=5C_1^2\frac{\partial \tilde{\rho}}{\partial \tilde{r}}, \qquad (4.6.14)$$

$$\tilde{p}=\tilde{\rho}\frac{5C_1^2}{5C_1-2\Phi}. \qquad (4.6.15)$$

Therefore we find a correction for (4.6.12) in the form

$$\frac{5C^2}{5C-2\Phi}=\frac{C}{1-0.4\dfrac{\Phi}{C}}=const=C_1>0. \qquad (4.6.16)$$

This correction has the sense if $\Phi \ll C$ or in other words if the hydrodynamic energy is less than the thermal energy. Let us write down the complete system describing the transport processes for the case $\tilde{v}_{0r}=0$.

$$\frac{\partial}{\partial \tilde{r}}\left(\tilde{r}^2\tilde{g}_r\right)+\tilde{G}\tilde{\rho}\tilde{r}^2=0, \qquad (4.6.17)$$

$$\frac{\partial \tilde{p}}{\partial \tilde{r}}-\tilde{\rho}\tilde{g}_r=0, \qquad (4.6.18)$$

$$\tilde{\rho}(5\tilde{p}-2\Phi\tilde{\rho})\frac{\partial \tilde{p}}{\partial \tilde{r}}-5\tilde{p}^2\frac{\partial \tilde{\rho}}{\partial \tilde{r}}=0. \qquad (4.6.19)$$

Numerical integration of the system of equations (4.6.17) – (4.6.19) is realized with the help of Maple. The corresponding results are reflected on figures 4.6.1 – 4.6.6. The initial Cauchy conditions are shown under figures, $t \leftrightarrow \tilde{r}$.

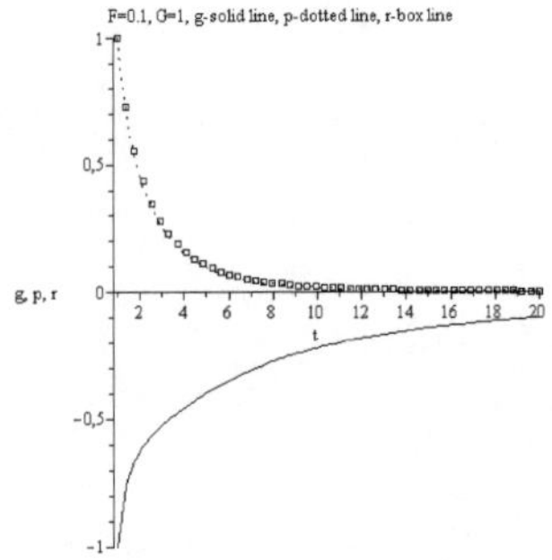

Fig. 4.6.1. g - gravitational acceleration $\widetilde{g}_r$ (solid line), p – pressure $\widetilde{p}$ (dotted line), r - density $\widetilde{\rho}$ (box line), $F = \Phi$, $\widetilde{p}(1) = 1$, $\widetilde{\rho}(1) = 1$, $\widetilde{g}_r(1) = -1$, $F = 0.1$, $G = 1$.

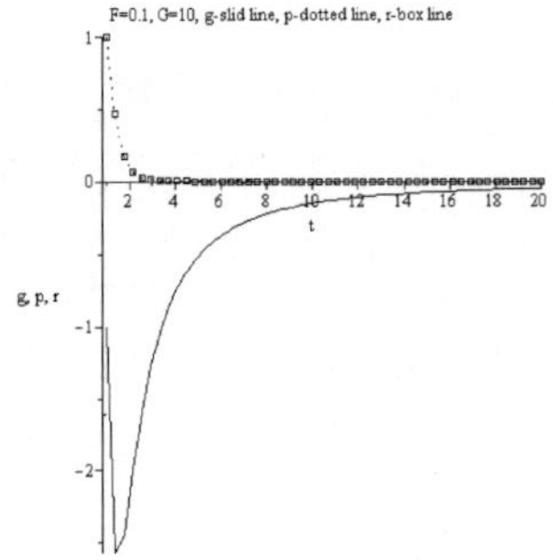

Fig. 4.6.2. g - gravitational acceleration $\widetilde{g}_r$ (solid line), p – pressure $\widetilde{p}$ (dotted line), r - density $\widetilde{\rho}$ (box line), $F = \Phi$, $\widetilde{p}(1) = 1$, $\widetilde{\rho}(1) = 1$, $\widetilde{g}_r(1) = -1$, $F = 0.1$, $G = 10$.

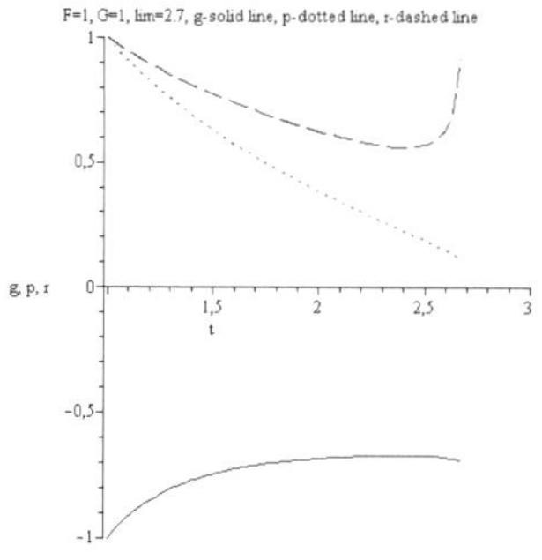

Fig. 4.6.3. g - gravitational acceleration $\tilde{g}_r$ (solid line), p – pressure $\tilde{p}$ (dotted line), r - density $\tilde{\rho}$ (dashed line), $F = \Phi$, $\tilde{p}(1) = 1$, $\tilde{\rho}(1) = 1$, $\tilde{g}_r(1) = -1$, $F = 1$, $G = 1$, $\lim = 2.7$.

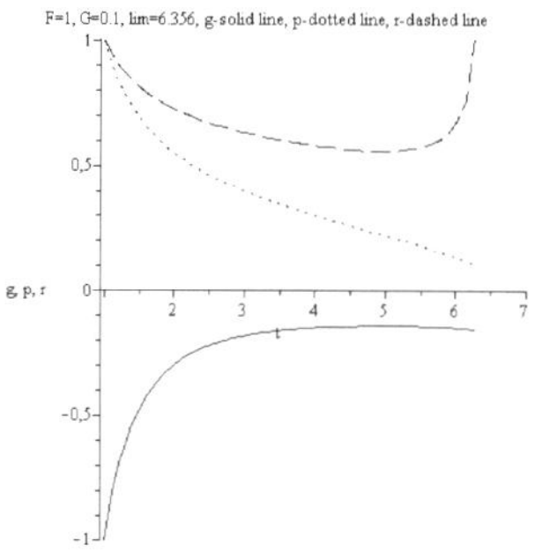

Fig. 4.6.4. g - gravitational acceleration $\tilde{g}_r$ (solid line), p – pressure $\tilde{p}$ (dotted line), r - density $\tilde{\rho}$ (dashed line), $F = \Phi$, $\tilde{p}(1) = 1$, $\tilde{\rho}(1) = 1$, $\tilde{g}_r(1) = -1$, $F = 1$, $G = 0.1$, $\lim = 6.356$.

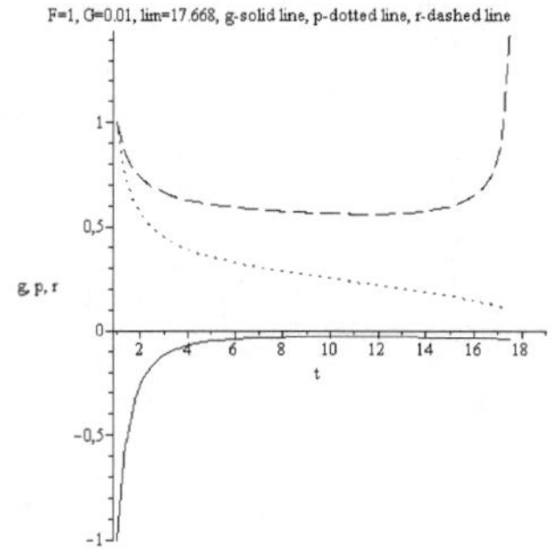

Fig. 4.6.5. g - gravitational acceleration $\widetilde{g}_r$ (solid line), p – pressure $\widetilde{p}$ (dotted line), r - density $\widetilde{\rho}$ (dashed line), $\mathrm{F}=\Phi$, $\widetilde{p}(1)=1$, $\widetilde{\rho}(1)=1$, $\widetilde{g}_r(1)=-1$, $\mathrm{F}=1$, $\mathrm{G}=0.01$, $\lim=17.668$.

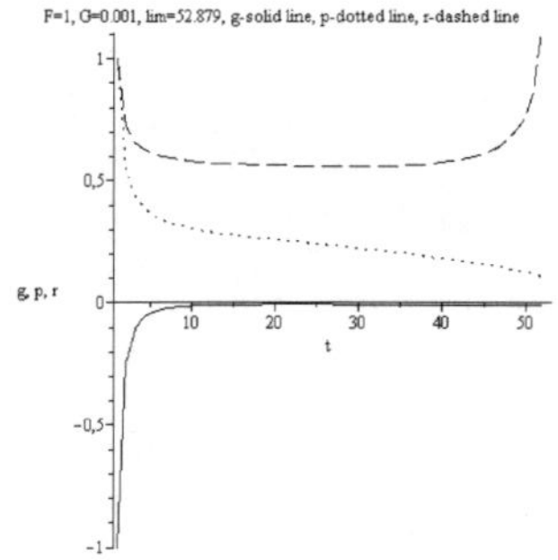

Fig. 4.6.6. g - gravitational acceleration $\widetilde{g}_r$ (solid line), p – pressure $\widetilde{p}$ (dotted line), r - density $\widetilde{\rho}$ (dashed line), $\mathrm{F}=\Phi$, $\widetilde{p}(1)=1$, $\widetilde{\rho}(1)=1$, $\widetilde{g}_r(1)=-1$, $\mathrm{F}=1$, $\mathrm{G}=0.001$, $\lim=52.879$.

Some important conclusions for the result of the mathematical modeling for the case $\widetilde{v}_{0r}=0$:

1. In the case $\widetilde{v}_{0r}=0$ the results of non-local theory do not depend on the τ choice.
2. The results reflected on figures 4.6.1 and 4.6.2 correspond to the small Φ, (see (4.6.16)).
3. The solution of the equations exists in a limited area of space for the large $\Phi=\widetilde{v}_{0\varphi}^2$ (Vera Rubin regime of the orbital motion).

4. Increasing G for the large Φ leads to diminishing area of the solution existing.

4.7. Rings with the loss of mass $(\tilde{v}_{0r} \neq 0)$.

The main theories regarding the origin of Saturn's rings are taking into account the mass transport in the radial direction. Eduard Roche in the 19th century proposed that the rings were formed after decay of a moon as a result of the tidal force activity. Other theories explore ideas about this moon disintegrated after being struck by a large comet or asteroid. The possibility exists that rings are formed from the original materials from which Saturn formed.

In this case we need to solve the general system of the nonlocal hydrodynamic equations (4.4.1) – (4.4.4) or much more simple system of equation used in the considered case. Let us write this system again:

Poisson equation

$$\frac{\partial}{\partial \tilde{r}}\left(\tilde{r}^2 \tilde{g}_r\right) + \tilde{G}\left[\tilde{\rho}\tilde{r}^2 - \tilde{\tau}\frac{\partial\left(\tilde{r}^2\tilde{\rho}\tilde{v}_{0r}\right)}{\partial \tilde{r}}\right] = 0, \qquad (4.7.1)$$

where $\tilde{G} = 4\pi\tilde{\gamma}_N$

Continuity equation

$$\tilde{\rho}\tilde{v}_{0r} = \tilde{\tau}\left[\frac{1}{\tilde{r}^2}\frac{\partial\left(\tilde{r}^2\tilde{\rho}\tilde{v}_{0r}^2\right)}{\partial \tilde{r}} - \tilde{\rho}\tilde{g}_r + \frac{\partial \tilde{p}}{\partial \tilde{r}}\right]. \qquad (4.7.2)$$

Motion equation onto $\mathbf{e}_\varphi$ - direction

$$\Phi = const, \qquad (4.7.3)$$

Motion equation onto $\mathbf{e}_r$ - direction

$$\frac{\partial \tilde{p}}{\partial \tilde{r}} - \tilde{\rho}\tilde{g}_r + \tilde{\tau}\tilde{g}_r\frac{1}{\tilde{r}^2}\frac{\partial\left(\tilde{r}^2\tilde{\rho}\tilde{v}_{0r}\right)}{\partial \tilde{r}} + \frac{1}{\tilde{r}^2}\frac{\partial}{\partial \tilde{r}}\left\{\tilde{r}^2\tilde{\tau}\left[\tilde{g}_r\tilde{\rho}\tilde{v}_{0r} - \frac{\partial \tilde{v}_{0r}}{\partial \tilde{r}}\left(\tilde{p} + \tilde{\rho}\tilde{v}_{0r}^2\right)\right]\right\}$$
$$-2\frac{\partial}{\partial \tilde{r}}\left(\tilde{\tau}\frac{1}{\tilde{r}^2}\frac{\partial\left(\tilde{r}^2\tilde{p}\tilde{v}_{0r}\right)}{\partial \tilde{r}}\right) = 0. \qquad (4.7.4)$$

Energy equation

$$\left[\tilde{\rho}(\tilde{v}_{0r}^2 + \Phi) + 5\tilde{p}\right]\tilde{v}_{0r} - \tilde{\tau}\left\{\begin{array}{l}\frac{\partial}{\partial \tilde{r}}\left[\left(\tilde{\rho}(\tilde{v}_{0r}^2 + \Phi) + 7\tilde{p}\right)\tilde{v}_{0r}^2\right] + \frac{2}{\tilde{r}}\left[\tilde{\rho}(\tilde{v}_{0r}^2 + \Phi) + 7\tilde{p}\right]\tilde{v}_{0r}^2 \\ + \frac{\partial}{\partial \tilde{r}}\left[\tilde{p}\left(\tilde{v}_{0r}^2 + \Phi\right) + 5\frac{\tilde{p}^2}{\tilde{\rho}}\right] - \left[3\tilde{\rho}(\tilde{v}_{0r}^2 + \Phi) + 5\tilde{p}\right]\tilde{g}_r\end{array}\right\} = 0 \qquad (4.7.5)$$

Numerical integration of the system of equations (4.7.1) – (4.7.5) is realized with the help of Maple. The corresponding results are reflected on figures 4.7.1 – 4.7.5. The initial Cauchy conditions are shown under figures.

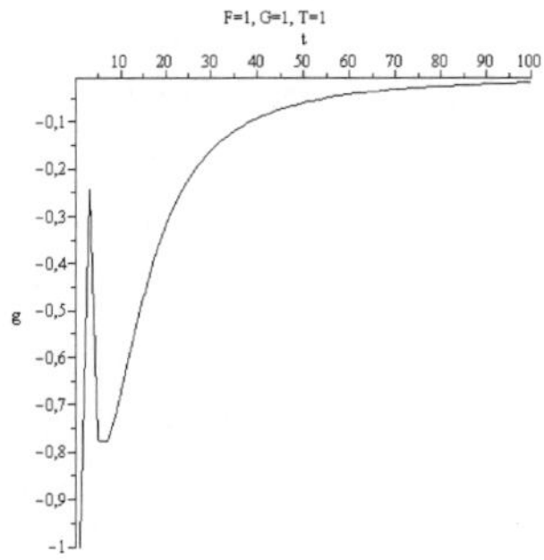

Fig. 4.7.1. $\Phi = 1, \tilde{G} = 1, \quad \tilde{\tau} = 1$ g- gravitational acceleration $\tilde{g}_r$ (solid line), $\tilde{g}_r(1) = -1$, $\tilde{p}(1) = 1$, $\tilde{\rho}(1) = 1$, $\tilde{v}_{0r}(1) = 1$, $D(\tilde{p})(1) = -1$, $D(\tilde{v}_{0r})(1) = -1$.

Let us compare figures 4.6.3 and 4.7.1. These calculation are performed without accounting for the radial transfer of mass (figure 4.6.3) and accounting for the radial transfer of mass (figure 4.7.1). These calculations lead to very different results. We see «a gap» on figure 7 reflecting the appearance of ring in the $\tilde{r}$ interval ~ 1 – 8 (see also Table 4.1). Imagine a particle inside this gravitation gap.

This position alters the orbit of anything that's in the mentioned gap, and actually has the effect of throwing it inside the gap leading to the appearance of rings.

On figure 4.7.2 there is an area where gravity changes sign and becomes positive. In other words, the gravitational acceleration vector passes the zero mark and is directed towards the rings. This looks like the manifestation of the effect of antigravity. In fact, this is a collective effect - a manifestation of the Roche effect.

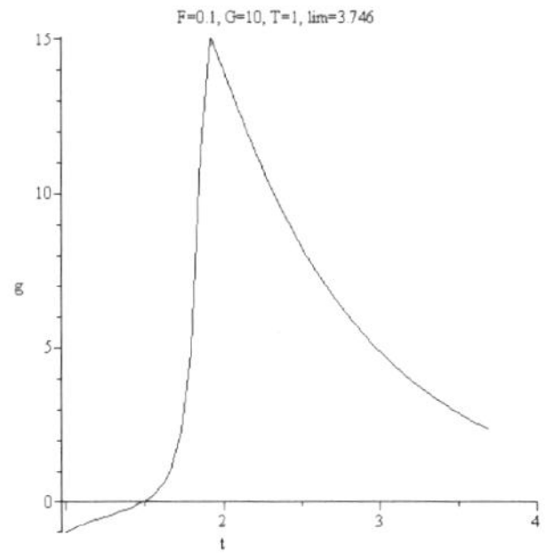

Fig. 4.7.2. $\Phi = 0.1, \widetilde{G} = 10$, $\widetilde{\tau} = 1$ g - gravitational acceleration $\widetilde{g}_r$, $\widetilde{g}_r(1) = -1$, $\widetilde{p}(1) = 1$, $\widetilde{\rho}(1) = 1$, $\widetilde{v}_{0r}(1) = 1$, $D(\widetilde{p})(1) = -0.1$, $D(\widetilde{v}_{0r})(1) = -1$, $\lim = 3.746$.

Figures 4.7.3 – 4.7.6 demonstrate the space evolution of pressure, density and radial velocity.

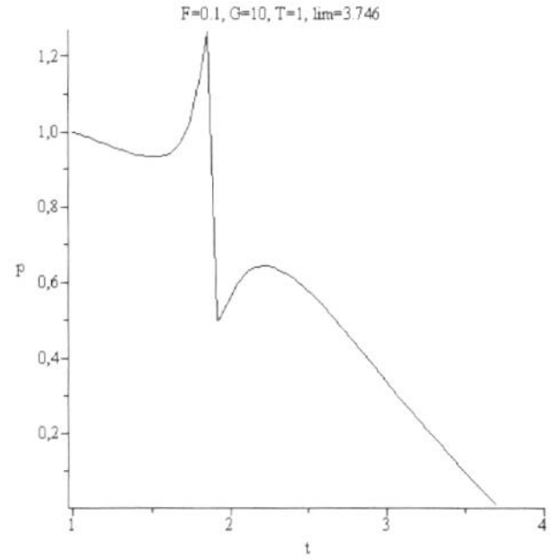

Fig. 4.7.3. $\Phi = 1, G = 10$, $\widetilde{\tau} = 1$; p - pressure $\widetilde{p}$, $\widetilde{g}_r(1) = -1$, $\widetilde{p}(1) = 1$, $\widetilde{\rho}(1) = 1$, $\widetilde{v}_{0r}(1) = 1$, $D(\widetilde{p})(1) = -0.1$, $D(\widetilde{v}_{0r})(1) = -1$, $\lim = 3.746$.

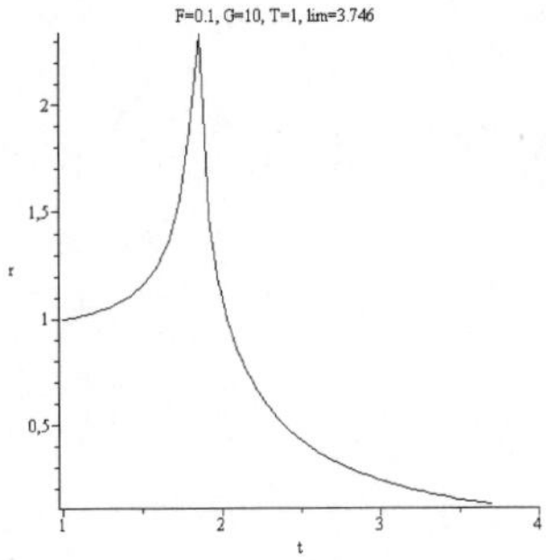

Fig. 4.7.4. $\Phi = 0.1$, $G = 10$, $\tilde{\tau} = 1$, r-density $\tilde{\rho}$ (dashed line), $\tilde{g}_r(1) = -1$, $\tilde{p}(1) = 1$, $\tilde{\rho}(1) = 1$, $\tilde{v}_{0r}(1) = 1$, $D(\tilde{p})(1) = -0.1$, $D(\tilde{v}_{0r})(1) = -1$, $\lim = 3.746$.

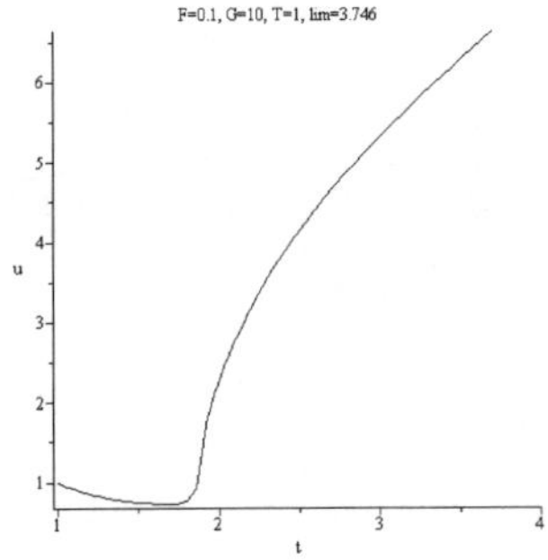

Fig. 4.7.5. $\Phi = 0.1$, $\tilde{G} = 10$, $\tilde{\tau} = 1$, velocity u - $\tilde{v}_{0r}$, $\tilde{g}_r(1) = -1$, $\tilde{p}(1) = 1$, $\tilde{\rho}(1) = 1$, $\tilde{v}_{0r}(1) = 1$, $D(\tilde{p})(1) = -0.1$, $D(\tilde{v}_{0r})(1) = -1$, $\lim = 3.746$.

The appearance of rings and disks near space objects is a typical effect in astrophysics. The disc-shaped form is explained by the presence of Coriolis forces, if the rings were formed in the upper layers of the rotating object during its formation. However, the theory of transfer processes in the interaction of the object and the rings (disk) can be constructed only within the framework of nonlocal hydrodynamics; in particular, the Roche solution is not applicable.

We consider the stationary case excluding the polar angle θ dependence. It was found from the projection of motion equation onto $\mathbf{e}_\varphi$- direction that orbital velocity $v_{0\varphi} = const$.

Two possibilities were investigated: the radial velocity $v_{0r} = 0$ and the radial velocity $v_{0r} \neq 0$. In the first case rings exist without the loss of mass. In the second case the mass loss is taken into account. The resulting system of dimensionless equations belongs to the class of Cauchy problems and requires specifying the scales of quantities and Cauchy conditions. This mathematical problem is by nature typical for aerodynamics. The selection of appropriate values opens up enormous opportunities for the study of the structures of space objects. If $v_{0r} = 0$, in the one-component case, the solution exists in the whole space $\tilde{r} \geq 1$ for rather small Φ (see figures 4.6.1, 4.6.2). The solution of the equations exists in a limited area of space for the large $\Phi = \tilde{v}_{0\varphi}^2$ (Vera Rubin regime of the orbital motion).

If there is a radial mass transfer ($v_{0r} \neq 0$), then the solution demonstrates a complex nonlinear dependence on the initial data in the finite domain of existence of the solutions. As you can see on figures 4.7.2, the Roche point appears where $\tilde{g}_r(\tilde{r})$ turns in zero. In a sense, there is an "anti-gravity zone", but in fact the area of predominant influence of ring structures. The evolution $\tilde{g}_r(\tilde{r})$ depends naturally on non-local parameter τ choosing.

Finally we should underline that the problems of anti-matter, anti-gravitation, dark energy, dark matter reflects the crisis of the local transport kinetic theory. The origin of difficulties consists in Oversimplification following from principles of local physics.

4.8. Rings in the external electromagnetic field. Basic equations.

Let us consider now the space evolution of the charged rings in the external electromagnetic field. Strict consideration leads to the system of the generalized hydrodynamic equations (GHE) [19] (see also (4.5.1) – (4.5.4)) written here for a one species physical system. We begin with the formulation of the nonlocal continuity equation in the spherical coordinate system with the independent variables r, θ, φ (radial distance r, polar angle θ and azimuth angle φ):

Continuity equation

$$\frac{\partial}{\partial t}\left\{\rho - \tau\left[\frac{\partial \rho}{\partial t} + \frac{1}{r^2}\frac{\partial\left(r^2 \rho v_{0r}\right)}{\partial r} + \frac{1}{r\sin\theta}\frac{\partial\left(\rho v_{0\varphi}\right)}{\partial \varphi} + \frac{1}{r\sin\theta}\frac{\partial\left(\rho v_{0\theta}\sin\theta\right)}{\partial \theta}\right]\right\}$$

$$+\frac{1}{r^2}\frac{\partial}{\partial r}\left\{r^2\left\{\rho v_{0r} - \tau\left[\frac{\partial}{\partial t}\left(\rho v_{0r}\right) + \frac{1}{r^2}\frac{\partial\left(r^2 \rho v_{0r}^2\right)}{\partial r} + \frac{1}{r\sin\theta}\frac{\partial\left(\rho v_{0\varphi} v_{0r}\right)}{\partial \varphi}\right.\right.\right.$$

$$+\frac{1}{r\sin\theta}\frac{\partial(\rho v_{0\theta}v_{0r}\sin\theta)}{\partial\theta}-\rho g_r-\frac{q}{m}\rho\left(v_{0\varphi}B_\theta-v_{0\theta}B_\varphi\right)\Big]\Big]\Big\}+\frac{1}{r\sin\theta}\frac{\partial}{\partial\varphi}\Big\{\rho v_{0\varphi}-\tau\Big[\frac{\partial}{\partial t}(\rho v_{0\varphi})+$$

$$\frac{1}{r^2}\frac{\partial(r^2\rho v_{0r}v_{0\varphi})}{\partial r}+\frac{1}{r\sin\theta}\frac{\partial(\rho v_{0\varphi}^2)}{\partial\varphi}+\frac{1}{r\sin\theta}\frac{\partial(\rho v_{0\theta}v_{0\varphi}\sin\theta)}{\partial\theta}-\rho g_\varphi-\frac{q}{m}\rho\left(v_{0\theta}B_r-v_{0r}B_\theta\right)\Big]\Big\}$$

$$+\frac{1}{r\sin\theta}\frac{\partial}{\partial\theta}\Big\{\sin\theta\Big\{\rho v_{0\theta}-\tau\Big[\frac{\partial}{\partial t}(\rho v_{0\theta})+\frac{1}{r^2}\frac{\partial(r^2\rho v_{0r}v_{0\theta})}{\partial r}+\frac{1}{r\sin\theta}\frac{\partial(\rho v_{0\varphi}v_{0\theta})}{\partial\varphi}+$$

$$\frac{1}{r\sin\theta}\frac{\partial(\rho v_{0\theta}^2\sin\theta)}{\partial\theta}-\rho g_\theta-\frac{q}{m}\rho\left(v_{0r}B_\varphi-v_{0\varphi}B_r\right)\Big]\Big\}\Big\}$$

$$-\frac{1}{r^2}\frac{\partial}{\partial r}\left(\tau r^2\frac{\partial p}{\partial r}\right)-\frac{1}{r^2\sin\theta}\frac{\partial}{\partial\theta}\left(\tau\sin\theta\frac{\partial p}{\partial\theta}\right)-\frac{1}{r^2\sin^2\theta}\frac{\partial}{\partial\varphi}\left(\tau\frac{\partial p}{\partial\varphi}\right)=0, \qquad (4.8.1)$$

Now we should take into account that acceleration $\mathbf{g}$ includes not only the gravitation but also the possible input of the magnetic field. The motion equation takes the form:

$$\frac{\partial}{\partial t}\Big\{\rho\mathbf{v}_0-\tau\Big[\frac{\partial}{\partial t}(\rho\mathbf{v}_0)+\frac{\partial}{\partial\mathbf{r}}\cdot\rho\mathbf{v}_0\mathbf{v}_0+\frac{\partial p}{\partial\mathbf{r}}-\rho\mathbf{g}-\frac{q}{m}\rho\mathbf{v}_0\times\mathbf{B}\Big]\Big\}-\mathbf{g}\Big[\rho-\tau\Big(\frac{\partial\rho}{\partial t}+\frac{\partial}{\partial\mathbf{r}}\cdot\rho\mathbf{v}_0\Big)\Big]-$$

$$-\frac{q}{m}\Big\{\rho\mathbf{v}_0-\tau\Big[\frac{\partial}{\partial t}(\rho\mathbf{v}_0)+\frac{\partial}{\partial\mathbf{r}}\cdot\rho\mathbf{v}_0\mathbf{v}_0+\frac{\partial p}{\partial\mathbf{r}}-\rho\mathbf{g}-\frac{q}{m}\rho\mathbf{v}_0\times\mathbf{B}\Big]\Big\}\times\mathbf{B}+$$

$$+\frac{\partial}{\partial\mathbf{r}}\cdot\Big\{\rho\mathbf{v}_0\mathbf{v}_0+p\ddot{\mathbf{I}}-\tau\Big[\frac{\partial}{\partial t}(\rho\mathbf{v}_0\mathbf{v}_0+p\ddot{\mathbf{I}})+\frac{\partial}{\partial\mathbf{r}}\cdot\rho(\mathbf{v}_0\mathbf{v}_0)\mathbf{v}_0+2\ddot{\mathbf{I}}\Big(\frac{\partial}{\partial\mathbf{r}}\cdot(p\mathbf{v}_0)\Big)+\frac{\partial}{\partial\mathbf{r}}\cdot(\ddot{\mathbf{I}}p\mathbf{v}_0)-$$

$$-\mathbf{g}\rho\mathbf{v}_0-\rho\mathbf{v}_0\mathbf{g}-\frac{q}{m}\rho[\mathbf{v}_0\times\mathbf{B}]\mathbf{v}_0-\frac{q}{m}\rho\mathbf{v}_0[\mathbf{v}_0\times\mathbf{B}]\Big]\Big\}=0.$$

(4.8.2)

Write down the equation of motion in the projection in the direction $\mathbf{e}_r$:

$$\frac{\partial}{\partial t}\left\{\rho v_{0r}-\tau\left[\frac{\partial}{\partial t}(\rho v_{0r})+\frac{1}{r^2}\frac{\partial(r^2\rho v_{0r}^2)}{\partial r}+\frac{1}{r\sin\theta}\frac{\partial(\rho v_{0\varphi}v_{0r})}{\partial\varphi}+\frac{1}{r\sin\theta}\frac{\partial(\rho v_{0\theta}v_{0r}\sin\theta)}{\partial\theta}\right.\right.$$

$$\left.\left.+\frac{1}{r}\frac{\partial p}{\partial r}-\rho g_r-\frac{q}{m}\rho(v_{0\varphi}B_\theta-v_{0\theta}B_\varphi)\right]\right\}$$

$$-g_r\left[\rho-\tau\left(\frac{\partial\rho}{\partial t}+\frac{1}{r^2}\frac{\partial(r^2\rho v_{0r})}{\partial r}+\frac{1}{r\sin\theta}\frac{\partial(\rho v_{0\varphi})}{\partial\varphi}+\frac{1}{r\sin\theta}\frac{\partial(\rho v_{0\theta}\sin\theta)}{\partial\theta}\right)\right]-$$

$$-\frac{q}{m}\left\{\rho v_{0\varphi}-\tau\left[\frac{\partial}{\partial t}(\rho v_{0\varphi})+\frac{1}{r^2}\frac{\partial(r^2\rho v_{0r}v_{0\varphi})}{\partial r}+\frac{1}{r\sin\theta}\frac{\partial(\rho v_{0\varphi}^2)}{\partial\varphi}+\frac{1}{r\sin\theta}\frac{\partial(\rho v_{0\theta}v_{0\varphi}\sin\theta)}{\partial\theta}+\right.\right.$$

$$\left.\left.+\frac{1}{r\sin\theta}\frac{\partial p}{\partial\varphi}-\rho g_\varphi-\frac{q}{m}\rho(v_{0\theta}B_r-v_{0r}B_\theta)\right]\right\}B_\theta+$$

$$+\frac{q}{m}\left\{\rho v_{0\theta}-\tau\left[\frac{\partial}{\partial t}(\rho v_{0\theta})+\frac{1}{r^2}\frac{\partial(r^2\rho v_{0r}v_{0\theta})}{\partial r}+\frac{1}{r\sin\theta}\frac{\partial(\rho v_{0\varphi}v_{0\theta})}{\partial\varphi}+\frac{1}{r\sin\theta}\frac{\partial(\rho v_{0\theta}^2\sin\theta)}{\partial\theta}+\right.\right.$$

$$\left.\left.+\frac{1}{r}\frac{\partial p}{\partial\theta}-\rho g_\theta-\frac{q}{m}\rho(v_{0r}B_\varphi-v_{0\varphi}B_r)\right]\right\}B_\varphi+$$

$$+\frac{1}{r^2}\frac{\partial}{\partial r}\left\{r^2\left\{\rho v_{0r}^2-\tau\left[\frac{\partial}{\partial t}(\rho v_{0r}^2)+\frac{1}{r^2}\frac{\partial(r^2\rho v_{0r}^3)}{\partial r}+\frac{1}{r\sin\theta}\frac{\partial(\rho v_{0r}^2v_{0\varphi})}{\partial\varphi}\right.\right.\right.$$

$$\left.\left.\left.+\frac{1}{r\sin\theta}\frac{\partial(\rho v_{0\theta}v_{0r}^2\sin\theta)}{\partial\theta}-2g_r\rho v_{0r}-2\frac{q}{m}\rho(v_{0\varphi}B_\theta-v_{0\theta}B_\varphi)v_{0r}\right]\right\}\right\}+$$

$$+\frac{1}{r\sin\theta}\frac{\partial}{\partial\varphi}\left\{\rho v_{0\varphi}v_{0r}-\tau\left[\frac{\partial}{\partial t}(\rho v_{0\varphi}v_{0r})+\frac{1}{r^2}\frac{\partial(r^2\rho v_{0\varphi}v_{0r}^2)}{\partial r}+\right.\right.$$

$$\left.\left.+\frac{1}{r\sin\theta}\frac{\partial(\rho v_{0r}v_{0\theta}v_{0\varphi}\sin\theta)}{\partial\theta}-g_\varphi\rho v_{0r}-\frac{q}{m}\rho(v_{0\theta}B_r-v_{0r}B_\theta)v_{0r}-g_r\rho v_{0\varphi}-\frac{q}{m}\rho(v_{0\varphi}B_\theta-v_{0\theta}B_\varphi)v_{0\varphi}\right]\right\}+$$

$$+\frac{1}{r\sin\theta}\frac{\partial}{\partial\theta}\left\{\sin\theta\left\{\rho v_{0\theta}v_{0r}-\tau\left[\frac{\partial}{\partial t}(\rho v_{0\theta}v_{0r})+\frac{1}{r^2}\frac{\partial(r^2\rho v_{0r}^2v_{0\theta})}{\partial r}+\frac{1}{r\sin\theta}\frac{\partial(\rho v_{0r}v_{0\theta}v_{0\varphi})}{\partial\varphi}\right.\right.\right.$$

$$\left.\left.\left.+\frac{1}{r\sin\theta}\frac{\partial(\rho v_{0\theta}^2v_{0r}\sin\theta)}{\partial\theta}-g_\theta\rho v_{0r}-\frac{q}{m}\rho(v_{0r}B_\varphi-v_{0\varphi}B_r)v_{0r}-v_{0\theta}\rho g_r-\frac{q}{m}\rho(v_{0\varphi}B_\theta-v_{0\theta}B_\varphi)v_{0\theta}\right]\right\}\right\}+$$

$$+\frac{\partial p}{\partial r}-\frac{\partial}{\partial r}\left(\tau\frac{\partial p}{\partial t}\right)-2\frac{\partial}{\partial r}\left(\tau\left(\frac{1}{r^2}\frac{\partial(r^2pv_{0r})}{\partial r}+\frac{1}{r\sin\theta}\frac{\partial(pv_{0\varphi})}{\partial\varphi}+\frac{1}{r\sin\theta}\frac{\partial(pv_{0\theta}\sin\theta)}{\partial\theta}\right)\right)-$$

$$-\frac{1}{r^2}\frac{\partial}{\partial r}\left(\tau r^2\frac{\partial(pv_{0r})}{\partial r}\right)-\frac{1}{r^2\sin\theta}\frac{\partial}{\partial\theta}\left(\tau\sin\theta\frac{\partial(pv_{0r})}{\partial\theta}\right)-\frac{1}{r^2\sin^2\theta}\frac{\partial}{\partial\varphi}\left(\tau\frac{\partial(pv_{0r})}{\partial\varphi}\right)=0. \quad (4.8.3)$$

Write down the equation of motion (4.8.2) in the projection on the direction $\mathbf{e}_\varphi$

$$
\begin{aligned}
&\frac{\partial}{\partial t}\left\{\rho v_{0\varphi}-\tau\left[\frac{\partial}{\partial t}\left(\rho v_{0\varphi}\right)+\frac{1}{r^{2}}\frac{\partial\left(r^{2}\rho v_{0r}v_{0\varphi}\right)}{\partial r}+\frac{1}{r\sin\theta}\frac{\partial\left(\rho v_{0\varphi}^{2}\right)}{\partial\varphi}+\frac{1}{r\sin\theta}\frac{\partial\left(\rho v_{0\theta}v_{0\varphi}\sin\theta\right)}{\partial\theta}\right.\right.\\
&\left.\left.+\frac{1}{r\sin\theta}\frac{\partial p}{\partial\varphi}-\rho g_{\varphi}-\frac{q}{m}\rho\left(v_{0\theta}B_{r}-v_{0r}B_{\theta}\right)\right]\right\}\\
&-g_{\varphi}\left[\rho-\tau\left(\frac{\partial\rho}{\partial t}+\frac{1}{r^{2}}\frac{\partial\left(r^{2}\rho v_{0r}\right)}{\partial r}+\frac{1}{r\sin\theta}\frac{\partial\left(\rho v_{0\varphi}\right)}{\partial\varphi}+\frac{1}{r\sin\theta}\frac{\partial\left(\rho v_{0\theta}\sin\theta\right)}{\partial\theta}\right)\right]-\\
&-\frac{q}{m}\left\{\rho v_{0\theta}-\tau\left[\frac{\partial}{\partial t}\left(\rho v_{0\theta}\right)+\frac{1}{r^{2}}\frac{\partial\left(r^{2}\rho v_{0r}v_{0\theta}\right)}{\partial r}+\frac{1}{r\sin\theta}\frac{\partial\left(\rho v_{0\varphi}v_{0\theta}\right)}{\partial\varphi}+\frac{1}{r\sin\theta}\frac{\partial\left(\rho v_{0\theta}^{2}\sin\theta\right)}{\partial\theta}+\right.\right.\\
&\left.\left.+\frac{1}{r}\frac{\partial p}{\partial\theta}-\rho g_{\theta}-\frac{q}{m}\rho\left(v_{0r}B_{\varphi}-v_{0\varphi}B_{r}\right)\right]\right\}B_{r}+\\
&+\frac{q}{m}\left\{\rho v_{0r}-\tau\left[\frac{\partial}{\partial t}\left(\rho v_{0r}\right)+\frac{1}{r^{2}}\frac{\partial\left(r^{2}\rho v_{0r}^{2}\right)}{\partial r}+\frac{1}{r\sin\theta}\frac{\partial\left(\rho v_{0\varphi}v_{0r}\right)}{\partial\varphi}+\frac{1}{r\sin\theta}\frac{\partial\left(\rho v_{0\theta}v_{0r}\sin\theta\right)}{\partial\theta}+\right.\right.\\
&\left.\left.+\frac{\partial p}{\partial r}-\rho g_{r}-\frac{q}{m}\rho\left(v_{0\varphi}B_{\theta}-v_{0\theta}B_{\varphi}\right)\right]\right\}B_{\theta}+\\
&+\frac{1}{r^{2}}\frac{\partial}{\partial r}\left\{r^{2}\left\{\rho v_{0r}v_{0\varphi}-\tau\left[\frac{\partial}{\partial t}\left(\rho v_{0r}v_{0\varphi}\right)+\frac{1}{r^{2}}\frac{\partial\left(r^{2}\rho v_{0r}^{2}v_{0\varphi}\right)}{\partial r}+\frac{1}{r\sin\theta}\frac{\partial\left(\rho v_{0\varphi}^{2}v_{0r}\right)}{\partial\varphi}\right.\right.\right.\\
&\left.\left.\left.+\frac{1}{r\sin\theta}\frac{\partial\left(\rho v_{0\theta}v_{0r}v_{0\varphi}\sin\theta\right)}{\partial\theta}-g_{r}\rho v_{0\varphi}-v_{0r}\rho g_{\varphi}-\frac{q}{m}\rho\left(v_{0\varphi}B_{\theta}-v_{0\theta}B_{\varphi}\right)v_{0\varphi}-\frac{q}{m}\rho\left(v_{0\theta}B_{r}-v_{0r}B_{\theta}\right)v_{0r}\right]\right\}\right\}+\\
&+\frac{1}{r\sin\theta}\frac{\partial}{\partial\varphi}\left\{\rho v_{0\varphi}^{2}-\tau\left[\frac{\partial}{\partial t}\left(\rho v_{0\varphi}^{2}\right)+\frac{1}{r^{2}}\frac{\partial\left(r^{2}\rho v_{0r}v_{0\varphi}^{2}\right)}{\partial r}+\right.\right.\\
&\left.\left.+\frac{1}{r\sin\theta}\frac{\partial\left(\rho v_{0\varphi}^{3}\right)}{\partial\varphi}+\frac{1}{r\sin\theta}\frac{\partial\left(\rho v_{0\theta}v_{0\varphi}^{2}\sin\theta\right)}{\partial\theta}-2g_{\varphi}\rho v_{0\varphi}-2\frac{q}{m}\rho\left(v_{0\theta}B_{r}-v_{0r}B_{\theta}\right)v_{0\varphi}\right]\right\}\\
&+\frac{1}{r\sin\theta}\frac{\partial}{\partial\theta}\left\{\sin\theta\left\{\rho v_{0\theta}v_{0\varphi}-\tau\left[\frac{\partial}{\partial t}\left(\rho v_{0\theta}v_{0\varphi}\right)+\frac{1}{r^{2}}\frac{\partial\left(r^{2}\rho v_{0r}v_{0\theta}v_{0\varphi}\right)}{\partial r}+\frac{1}{r\sin\theta}\frac{\partial\left(\rho v_{0\varphi}^{2}v_{0\theta}\right)}{\partial\varphi}\right.\right.\right.\\
&\left.\left.\left.+\frac{1}{r\sin\theta}\frac{\partial\left(\rho v_{0\theta}^{2}v_{0\varphi}\sin\theta\right)}{\partial\theta}-g_{\theta}\rho v_{0\varphi}-\frac{q}{m}\rho\left(v_{0r}B_{\varphi}-v_{0\varphi}B_{r}\right)v_{0\varphi}-v_{0\theta}\rho g_{\varphi}-\frac{q}{m}\rho\left(v_{0\theta}B_{r}-v_{0r}B_{\theta}\right)v_{0\theta}\right]\right\}\right\}\\
&+\frac{1}{r\sin\theta}\frac{\partial p}{\partial\varphi}-\frac{1}{r\sin\theta}\frac{\partial}{\partial\varphi}\left(\tau\frac{\partial p}{\partial t}\right)-\\
&-\frac{2}{r\sin\theta}\frac{\partial}{\partial\varphi}\left(\tau\left(\frac{1}{r^{2}}\frac{\partial\left(r^{2}pv_{0r}\right)}{\partial r}+\frac{1}{r\sin\theta}\frac{\partial\left(pv_{0\varphi}\right)}{\partial\varphi}+\frac{1}{r\sin\theta}\frac{\partial\left(pv_{0\theta}\sin\theta\right)}{\partial\theta}\right)\right)\\
&-\frac{1}{r^{2}}\frac{\partial}{\partial r}\left(\tau r^{2}\frac{\partial\left(pv_{0\varphi}\right)}{\partial r}\right)-\frac{1}{r^{2}\sin\theta}\frac{\partial}{\partial\theta}\left(\tau\sin\theta\frac{\partial\left(pv_{0\varphi}\right)}{\partial\theta}\right)-\frac{1}{r^{2}\sin^{2}\theta}\frac{\partial}{\partial\varphi}\left(\tau\frac{\partial\left(pv_{0\varphi}\right)}{\partial\varphi}\right)=0.
\end{aligned}
\tag{4.8.4}
$$

Write down the equation of motion (4.8.2) in the projection on the direction $\mathbf{e}_{\theta}$:

$$
\begin{aligned}
&\frac{\partial}{\partial t}\left\{\rho v_{0\theta}-\tau\left[\frac{\partial}{\partial t}(\rho v_{0\theta})+\frac{1}{r^2}\frac{\partial(r^2\rho v_{0r}v_{0\theta})}{\partial r}+\frac{1}{r\sin\theta}\frac{\partial(\rho v_{0\varphi}v_{0\theta})}{\partial\varphi}+\frac{1}{r\sin\theta}\frac{\partial(\rho v_{0\theta}^2\sin\theta)}{\partial\theta}\right.\right.\\
&\left.\left.+\frac{1}{r}\frac{\partial p}{\partial\theta}-\rho g_\theta-\frac{q}{m}\rho(v_{0r}B_\varphi-v_{0\varphi}B_r)\right]\right\}\\
&-g_\theta\left[\rho-\tau\left(\frac{\partial\rho}{\partial t}+\frac{1}{r^2}\frac{\partial(r^2\rho v_{0r})}{\partial r}+\frac{1}{r\sin\theta}\frac{\partial(\rho v_{0\varphi})}{\partial\varphi}+\frac{1}{r\sin\theta}\frac{\partial(\rho v_{0\theta}\sin\theta)}{\partial\theta}\right)\right]-\\
&-\frac{q}{m}\left\{\rho v_{0r}-\tau\left[\frac{\partial}{\partial t}(\rho v_{0r})+\frac{1}{r^2}\frac{\partial(r^2\rho v_{0r}^2)}{\partial r}+\frac{1}{r\sin\theta}\frac{\partial(\rho v_{0\varphi}v_{0r})}{\partial\varphi}+\frac{1}{r\sin\theta}\frac{\partial(\rho v_{0\theta}v_{0r}\sin\theta)}{\partial\theta}+\right.\right.\\
&\left.\left.+\frac{\partial p}{\partial r}-\rho g_r-\frac{q}{m}\rho(v_{0\varphi}B_\theta-v_{0\theta}B_\varphi)\right]\right\}B_\varphi+\\
&+\frac{q}{m}\left\{\rho v_{0\varphi}-\tau\left[\frac{\partial}{\partial t}(\rho v_{0\varphi})+\frac{1}{r^2}\frac{\partial(r^2\rho v_{0r}v_{0\varphi})}{\partial r}+\frac{1}{r\sin\theta}\frac{\partial(\rho v_{0\varphi}^2)}{\partial\varphi}+\frac{1}{r\sin\theta}\frac{\partial(\rho v_{0\theta}v_{0\varphi}\sin\theta)}{\partial\theta}+\right.\right.\\
&\left.\left.+\frac{1}{r\sin\theta}\frac{\partial p}{\partial\varphi}-\rho g_\varphi-\frac{q}{m}\rho(v_{0\theta}B_r-v_{0r}B_\theta)\right]\right\}B_r+\\
&+\frac{1}{r^2}\frac{\partial}{\partial r}\left\{r^2\left\{\rho v_{0r}v_{0\theta}-\tau\left[\frac{\partial}{\partial t}(\rho v_{0r}v_{0\theta})+\frac{1}{r^2}\frac{\partial(r^2\rho v_{0r}^2v_{0\theta})}{\partial r}+\frac{1}{r\sin\theta}\frac{\partial(\rho v_{0\varphi}v_{0r}v_{0\theta})}{\partial\varphi}\right.\right.\right.\\
&\left.\left.\left.+\frac{1}{r\sin\theta}\frac{\partial(\rho v_{0\theta}^2v_{0r}\sin\theta)}{\partial\theta}-g_r\rho v_{0\theta}-v_{0r}\rho g_\theta-\frac{q}{m}\rho(v_{0\varphi}B_\theta-v_{0\theta}B_\varphi)v_{0\theta}-\frac{q}{m}\rho(v_{0r}B_\varphi-v_{0\varphi}B_r)v_{0r}\right]\right\}\right\}+\\
&+\frac{1}{r\sin\theta}\frac{\partial}{\partial\varphi}\left\{\rho v_{0\varphi}v_{0\theta}-\tau\left[\frac{\partial}{\partial t}(\rho v_{0\varphi}v_{0\theta})+\frac{1}{r^2}\frac{\partial(r^2\rho v_{0r}v_{0\varphi}v_{0\theta})}{\partial r}+\frac{1}{r\sin\theta}\frac{\partial(\rho v_{0\varphi}^2v_{0\theta})}{\partial\varphi}+\right.\right.\\
&\left.\left.+\frac{1}{r\sin\theta}\frac{\partial(\rho v_{0\theta}^2v_{0\varphi}\sin\theta)}{\partial\theta}-g_\varphi\rho v_{0\theta}-\frac{q}{m}\rho(v_{0\theta}B_r-v_{0r}B_\theta)v_{0\theta}-g_\theta\rho v_{0\varphi}-\frac{q}{m}\rho(v_{0r}B_\varphi-v_{0\varphi}B_r)v_{0\varphi}\right]\right\}\\
&+\frac{1}{r\sin\theta}\frac{\partial}{\partial\theta}\left\{\sin\theta\left\{\rho v_{0\theta}^2-\tau\left[\frac{\partial}{\partial t}(\rho v_{0\theta}^2)+\frac{1}{r^2}\frac{\partial(r^2\rho v_{0r}v_{0\theta}^2)}{\partial r}+\frac{1}{r\sin\theta}\frac{\partial(\rho v_{0\theta}^2v_{0\varphi})}{\partial\varphi}\right.\right.\right.\\
&\left.\left.\left.+\frac{1}{r\sin\theta}\frac{\partial(\rho v_{0\theta}^3\sin\theta)}{\partial\theta}-2g_\theta\rho v_{0\theta}-\frac{q}{m}\rho(v_{0r}B_\varphi-v_{0\varphi}B_r)v_{0\theta}\right]\right\}\right\}+\frac{1}{r}\frac{\partial p}{\partial\theta}-\frac{1}{r\sin\theta}\frac{\partial}{\partial\theta}\left(\tau\frac{\partial p}{\partial t}\right)-\\
&-\frac{2}{r}\frac{\partial}{\partial\theta}\left(\tau\left(\frac{1}{r^2}\frac{\partial(r^2pv_{0r})}{\partial r}+\frac{1}{r\sin\theta}\frac{\partial(pv_{0\varphi})}{\partial\varphi}+\frac{1}{r\sin\theta}\frac{\partial(pv_{0\theta}\sin\theta)}{\partial\theta}\right)\right)\\
&-\frac{1}{r^2}\frac{\partial}{\partial r}\left(\tau r^2\frac{\partial(pv_{0\theta})}{\partial r}\right)-\frac{1}{r^2\sin\theta}\frac{\partial}{\partial\theta}\left(\tau\sin\theta\frac{\partial(pv_{0\theta})}{\partial\theta}\right)-\frac{1}{r^2\sin^2\theta}\frac{\partial}{\partial\varphi}\left(\tau\frac{\partial(pv_{0\theta})}{\partial\varphi}\right)=0. \qquad (4.8.5)
\end{aligned}
$$

Energy equation:

$$\frac{\partial}{\partial t}\Bigg\{\frac{1}{2}\rho v_0^2+\varepsilon n+\frac{3}{2}p-\tau\Bigg[\frac{\partial}{\partial t}\bigg(\frac{1}{2}\rho v_0^2+\varepsilon n+\frac{3}{2}p\bigg)+\frac{1}{r^2}\frac{\partial}{\partial r}\bigg(r^2 v_{0r}\bigg(\frac{1}{2}\rho v_0^2+\varepsilon n+\frac{5}{2}p\bigg)\bigg)+$$

$$+\frac{1}{r\sin\theta}\frac{\partial}{\partial\varphi}\bigg(v_{0\varphi}\bigg(\frac{1}{2}\rho v_0^2+\varepsilon n+\frac{5}{2}p\bigg)\bigg)+\frac{1}{r\sin\theta}\frac{\partial}{\partial\theta}\bigg(\sin\theta v_{0\theta}\bigg(\frac{1}{2}\rho v_0^2+\varepsilon n+\frac{5}{2}p\bigg)\bigg)-$$

$$-\rho\big(g_r v_{0r}+g_\varphi v_{0\varphi}+g_\theta v_{0\theta}\big)\Bigg]\Bigg\}+\frac{1}{r^2}\frac{\partial}{\partial r}\Bigg\{r^2\Bigg\{\bigg(\frac{1}{2}\rho v_0^2+\varepsilon n+\frac{5}{2}p\bigg)v_{0r}-$$

$$-\tau\Bigg[\frac{\partial}{\partial t}\bigg(\bigg(\frac{1}{2}\rho v_0^2+\varepsilon n+\frac{5}{2}p\bigg)v_{0r}\bigg)+\frac{1}{r^2}\frac{\partial}{\partial r}\bigg(r^2\bigg(\frac{1}{2}\rho v_0^2+\varepsilon n+\frac{7}{2}p\bigg)v_{0r}^2\bigg)+$$

$$+\frac{1}{r\sin\theta}\frac{\partial}{\partial\varphi}\bigg(\bigg(\frac{1}{2}\rho v_0^2+\varepsilon n+\frac{7}{2}p\bigg)v_{0\varphi}v_{0r}\bigg)+\frac{1}{r\sin\theta}\frac{\partial}{\partial\theta}\bigg(\sin\theta\bigg(\frac{1}{2}\rho v_0^2+\varepsilon n+\frac{7}{2}p\bigg)v_{0\theta}v_{0r}\bigg)-$$

$$-\rho\big(g_r v_{0r}+g_\varphi v_{0\varphi}+g_\theta v_{0\theta}\big)v_{0r}-\bigg(\frac{1}{2}\rho v_0^2+\varepsilon n+\frac{3}{2}p\bigg)g_r-$$

$$-\bigg(\frac{1}{2}\rho v_0^2+\varepsilon n+\frac{5}{2}p\bigg)\frac{q}{m}\big(v_{0\varphi}B_\theta-v_{0\theta}B_\varphi\big)\Bigg]\Bigg\}\Bigg\}+\frac{1}{r\sin\theta}\frac{\partial}{\partial\varphi}\Bigg\{\bigg(\frac{1}{2}\rho v_0^2+\varepsilon n+\frac{5}{2}p\bigg)v_{0\varphi}-$$

$$-\tau\Bigg[\frac{\partial}{\partial t}\bigg(\bigg(\frac{1}{2}\rho v_0^2+\varepsilon n+\frac{5}{2}p\bigg)v_{0\varphi}\bigg)+\frac{1}{r^2}\frac{\partial}{\partial r}\bigg(r^2\bigg(\frac{1}{2}\rho v_0^2+\varepsilon n+\frac{7}{2}p\bigg)v_{0r}v_{0\varphi}\bigg)+$$

$$+\frac{1}{r\sin\theta}\frac{\partial}{\partial\varphi}\bigg(\bigg(\frac{1}{2}\rho v_0^2+\varepsilon n+\frac{7}{2}p\bigg)v_{0\varphi}^2\bigg)+\frac{1}{r\sin\theta}\frac{\partial}{\partial\theta}\bigg(\sin\theta\bigg(\frac{1}{2}\rho v_0^2+\varepsilon n+\frac{7}{2}p\bigg)v_{0\theta}v_{0\varphi}\bigg)-$$

$$-\rho\big(g_r v_{0r}+g_\varphi v_{0\varphi}+g_\theta v_{0\theta}\big)v_{0\varphi}-\bigg(\frac{1}{2}\rho v_0^2+\varepsilon n+\frac{3}{2}p\bigg)g_\varphi-$$

$$\bigg(\frac{1}{2}\rho v_0^2+\varepsilon n+\frac{5}{2}p\bigg)\frac{q}{m}\big(v_{0\theta}B_r-v_{0r}B_\theta\big)\Bigg]\Bigg\}++\frac{1}{r\sin\theta}\frac{\partial}{\partial\theta}\Bigg\{\sin\theta\Bigg\{\bigg(\frac{1}{2}\rho v_0^2+\varepsilon n+\frac{5}{2}p\bigg)v_{0\theta}-$$

$$\tau\Bigg[\frac{\partial}{\partial t}\bigg(\bigg(\frac{1}{2}\rho v_0^2+\varepsilon n+\frac{5}{2}p\bigg)v_{0\theta}\bigg)++\frac{1}{r^2}\frac{\partial}{\partial r}\bigg(r^2\bigg(\frac{1}{2}\rho v_0^2+\varepsilon n+\frac{7}{2}p\bigg)v_{0r}v_{0\theta}\bigg)+$$

$$\frac{1}{r\sin\theta}\frac{\partial}{\partial\varphi}\bigg(\bigg(\frac{1}{2}\rho v_0^2+\varepsilon n+\frac{7}{2}p\bigg)v_{0\varphi}v_{0\theta}\bigg)+$$

$$+\frac{1}{r\sin\theta}\frac{\partial}{\partial\theta}\bigg(\sin\theta\bigg(\frac{1}{2}\rho v_0^2+\varepsilon n+\frac{7}{2}p\bigg)v_{0\theta}^2\bigg)-\rho\big(g_r v_{0r}+g_\varphi v_{0\varphi}+g_\theta v_{0\theta}\big)v_{0\theta}-\bigg(\frac{1}{2}\rho v_0^2+\varepsilon n+\frac{3}{2}p\bigg)g_\theta-$$

$$-\bigg(\frac{1}{2}\rho v_0^2+\varepsilon n+\frac{5}{2}p\bigg)\frac{q}{m}\big(v_{0r}B_\varphi-v_{0\varphi}B_r\big)\Bigg]\Bigg\}\Bigg\}-\Bigg\{\ \rho\big(g_r v_{0r}+g_\varphi v_{0\varphi}+g_\theta v_{0\theta}\big)-$$

$$-\tau\Bigg[g_r\bigg(\frac{\partial}{\partial t}(\rho v_{0r})+\frac{1}{r^2}\frac{\partial}{\partial r}\big(r^2\rho v_{0r}^2\big)+\frac{1}{r\sin\theta}\frac{\partial}{\partial\varphi}\big(\rho v_{0\varphi}v_{0r}\big)+$$

$$+\frac{1}{r\sin\theta}\frac{\partial}{\partial\theta}\big(\rho v_{0\theta}v_{0r}\sin\theta\big)+\frac{\partial p}{\partial r}-\rho g_r-qn\big(v_{0\varphi}B_\theta-v_{0\theta}B_\varphi\big)\bigg)+$$

$$+g_\varphi\bigg(\frac{\partial}{\partial t}(\rho v_{0\varphi})+\frac{1}{r^2}\frac{\partial}{\partial r}\big(r^2\rho v_{0r}v_{0\varphi}\big)+\frac{1}{r\sin\theta}\frac{\partial}{\partial\varphi}\big(\rho v_{0\varphi}^2\big)+\frac{1}{r\sin\theta}\frac{\partial}{\partial\theta}\big(\rho v_{0\theta}v_{0\varphi}\sin\theta\big)+$$

$$+\frac{1}{r\sin\theta}\frac{\partial p}{\partial\varphi}-\rho g_\varphi-qn\big(v_{0\theta}B_r-v_{0r}B_\theta\big)\bigg)+g_\theta\bigg(\frac{\partial}{\partial t}(\rho v_{0\theta})+\frac{1}{r^2}\frac{\partial}{\partial r}\big(r^2\rho v_{0r}v_{0\theta}\big)+\frac{1}{r\sin\theta}\frac{\partial}{\partial\varphi}\big(\rho v_{0\varphi}v_{0\theta}\big)+$$

$$+\frac{1}{r\sin\theta}\frac{\partial}{\partial\theta}\left(\rho v_{0\theta}^2\sin\theta\right)+\frac{1}{r}\frac{\partial p}{\partial\theta}-\rho g_\theta-qn\left(v_{0r}B_\varphi-v_{0\varphi}B_r\right)\Big)\Big]\Big\}-$$

$$-\frac{1}{r^2}\frac{\partial}{\partial r}\left(\tau r^2\frac{\partial}{\partial r}\left(\frac{1}{2}pv_0^2+\varepsilon nv_0^2+\frac{5}{2}\frac{p^2}{\rho}\right)\right)-$$

$$-\frac{1}{r^2\sin\theta}\frac{\partial}{\partial\theta}\left(\tau\sin\theta\frac{\partial}{\partial\theta}\left(\frac{1}{2}pv_0^2+\varepsilon nv_0^2+\frac{5}{2}\frac{p^2}{\rho}\right)\right)-\frac{1}{r^2\sin^2\theta}\frac{\partial}{\partial\varphi}\left(\tau\frac{\partial}{\partial\varphi}\left(\frac{1}{2}pv_0^2+\varepsilon nv_0^2+\frac{5}{2}\frac{p^2}{\rho}\right)\right)$$

$$+\frac{1}{r^2}\frac{\partial}{\partial r}\left(r^2\tau p g_r\right)+\frac{1}{r\sin\theta}\frac{\partial}{\partial\varphi}\left(\tau p g_\varphi\right)+\frac{1}{r\sin\theta}\frac{\partial}{\partial\theta}\left(\tau p g_\theta\sin\theta\right)=0\,. \tag{4.8.6}$$

The spherical coordinate system is shown in the figure 2.2.1. Figure 4.8.1 shows the magnetic field configuration for the Earth.

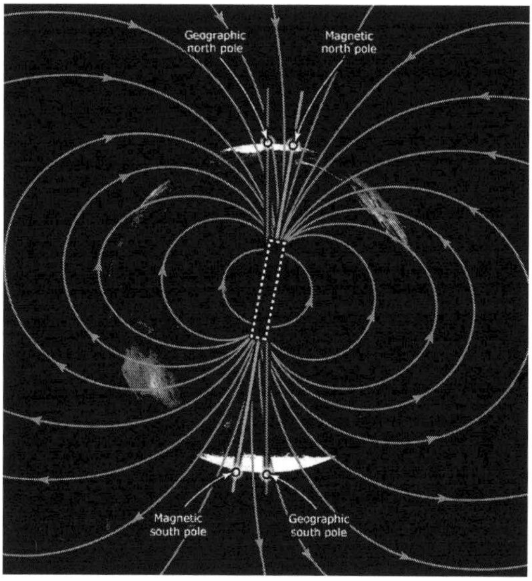

Figure 4.8.1. The Earth's magnetic field; the arrows show the direction of the magnetic induction lines.

It should be taken into account diminishing of the angle between directions defining the positions of the magnetic and geographic poles (see figure 4.8.2).

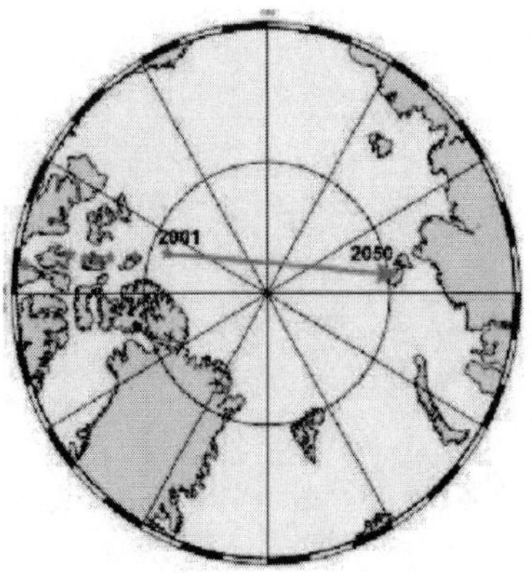

Figure 4.8.2 shows the evolution in time the north magnetic pole.

In the following we assume that (see also figure 2.2.1):

1. Stationary solutions are considered.
2. The ring is located in the Equatorial plane; geographic pole coincides with magnetic pole.
3. The thickness of the ring is neglected; the width of rings is function of r.
4. Hydrodynamic speed $\mathbf{v}_0(v_{0r}, v_{0\varphi})$, $v_{0r} = v_{0r}(r)$, and generally speaking, $v_{0\varphi} = v_{0\varphi}(r)$.
5. Magnetic intensity is $\mathbf{B}(B_\theta)$.
6. Acceleration is $\mathbf{g}(g_{r,total})$.
7. The dependences of pressure and density are $p(r)$, $\rho(r)$.
8. Acceleration $g_{r,total} \to g_r - \frac{q}{m}|E_r|$, $q = \pm e$, where e is an absolute charge value of a moving charged particle.
9. It is assumed that the main body is charged negatively (e.g., negatively charged Earth). Then, the intensity vector $\mathbf{E}(E_r)$ is directed to the center.
10. Acceleration connected with magnetic field is $\frac{q}{m} v_{0\varphi} B_\theta$, $q = \pm e$.
11. The internal particle energy $\varepsilon = 0$.

The continuity equation takes the form

$$\frac{1}{r^2}\frac{\partial}{\partial r}\left\{r^2\left\{\rho v_{0r} - \tau\left[\frac{1}{r^2}\frac{\partial\left(r^2 \rho v_{0r}^2\right)}{\partial r} - \rho g_{r,tot} - \frac{q}{m}\rho v_{0\varphi} B_\theta\right]\right\}\right\} - \frac{1}{r^2}\frac{\partial}{\partial r}\left(\tau r^2 \frac{\partial p}{\partial r}\right) = 0, \qquad (4.8.7)$$

or after integration

$$\rho v_{0r} - \tau\left[\frac{1}{r^2}\frac{\partial\left(r^2\rho v_{0r}^2\right)}{\partial r} + \frac{\partial p}{\partial r} - \rho g_{r,tot} - \frac{q}{m}\rho v_{0\varphi}B_\theta\right] = 0. \tag{4.8.8}$$

Taking into account the relation

$$g_{r,total} = g_r - \frac{q}{m}\left|E_r\right| \tag{4.8.9}$$

we find

$$\rho v_{0r} - \tau\left[\frac{1}{r^2}\frac{\partial\left(r^2\rho v_{0r}^2\right)}{\partial r} + \frac{\partial p}{\partial r} - \rho\left(g_r + \frac{q}{m}\left(v_{0\varphi}B_\theta - \left|E_r\right|\right)\right)\right] = 0. \tag{4.8.10}$$

The motion equation in the $\mathbf{e}_r$ projection is

$$\frac{\partial p}{\partial r} - g_{r,tot}\left[\rho - \tau\frac{1}{r^2}\frac{\partial\left(r^2\rho v_{0r}\right)}{\partial r}\right] - \frac{q}{m}B_\theta\left(\rho v_{0\varphi} - \tau\left[\frac{1}{r^2}\frac{\partial\left(\rho r^2 v_{0r}v_{0\varphi}\right)}{\partial r} + \frac{q}{m}B_\theta\rho v_{0r}\right]\right) +$$
$$+\frac{1}{r^2}\frac{\partial}{\partial r}\left\{r^2\left\{\rho v_{0r}^2 - \tau\left[\frac{1}{r^2}\frac{\partial\left(r^2\rho v_{0r}^3\right)}{\partial r} - 2g_{r,tot}\rho v_{0r} - 2\frac{q}{m}B_\theta\rho v_{0r}v_{0\varphi}\right]\right\}\right\}$$
$$-2\frac{\partial}{\partial r}\left(\tau\frac{1}{r^2}\frac{\partial\left(r^2 p v_{0r}\right)}{\partial r}\right) - \frac{1}{r^2}\frac{\partial}{\partial r}\left(\tau r^2\frac{\partial\left(p v_{0r}\right)}{\partial r}\right) = 0. \tag{4.8.11}$$

Let us use (4.8.8) in the form

$$\rho v_{0r}^2 = \tau\left[\frac{1}{r^2}v_{0r}\frac{\partial\left(r^2\rho v_{0r}^2\right)}{\partial r} + v_{0r}\frac{\partial p}{\partial r} - \rho v_{0r}\left(g_{r,tot} + \frac{q}{m}v_{0\varphi}B_\theta\right)\right]. \tag{4.8.12}$$

After substitution in (4.8.11) we reach

$$r^2\frac{\partial p}{\partial r} - g_{r,tot}\rho r^2 + g_{r,tot}\tau\frac{\partial\left(r^2\rho v_{0r}\right)}{\partial r} - \frac{\partial}{\partial r}\left\{r^2\tau\left(p + \rho v_{0r}^2\right)\frac{\partial v_{0r}}{\partial r}\right\} + \frac{\partial}{\partial r}\left\{r^2\tau\rho v_{0r}g_{r,tot}\right\}$$
$$-2r^2\frac{\partial}{\partial r}\left(\tau\frac{\partial\left(p v_{0r}\right)}{\partial r}\right) + 4\tau p v_{0r} - 4r\frac{\partial}{\partial r}\left(\tau p v_{0r}\right)$$
$$-\frac{q}{m}\rho B_\theta r^2\left(v_{0\varphi} - \tau v_{0r}\frac{q}{m}B_\theta\right) + \frac{q}{m}B_\theta\tau\frac{\partial\left(\rho r^2 v_{0r}v_{0\varphi}\right)}{\partial r} + \frac{\partial}{\partial r}\left\{r^2\tau\rho v_{0r}v_{0\varphi}\frac{q}{m}B_\theta\right\} = 0. \tag{4.8.13}$$

Let us now turn to the projection of the equation of motion on the direction $\mathbf{e}_\varphi$:

$$\frac{q}{m}B_\theta\left\{\rho v_{0r} - \tau\left[\frac{1}{r^2}\frac{\partial\left(r^2\rho v_{0r}^2\right)}{\partial r} + \frac{\partial p}{\partial r} - \rho g_{r,tot} - \frac{q}{m}\rho v_{0\varphi}B_\theta\right]\right\}$$
$$+\frac{1}{r^2}\frac{\partial}{\partial r}\left\{r^2\left\{\rho v_{0r}v_{0\varphi} - \tau\left[\frac{1}{r^2}\frac{\partial\left(r^2\rho v_{0r}^2 v_{0\varphi}\right)}{\partial r} - g_{r,tot}\rho v_{0\varphi} - \frac{q}{m}\rho v_{0\varphi}^2 B_\theta + \frac{q}{m}\rho v_{0r}^2 B_\theta\right]\right\}\right\}$$
$$-\frac{1}{r^2}\frac{\partial}{\partial r}\left(\tau r^2\frac{\partial\left(p v_{0\varphi}\right)}{\partial r}\right) = 0. \tag{4.8.14}$$

Let us use the continuity equation (4.8.8). We find

$$\frac{1}{r^2}\frac{\partial}{\partial r}\left\{r^2\left\{\rho v_{0r}v_{0\varphi}-\tau\left[\frac{1}{r^2}\frac{\partial\left(r^2\rho v_{0r}^2 v_{0\varphi}\right)}{\partial r}-g_{r,tot}\rho v_{0\varphi}-\frac{q}{m}\rho v_{0\varphi}^2 B_\theta+\frac{q}{m}\rho v_{0r}^2 B_\theta\right]\right\}\right\}$$

$$-\frac{1}{r^2}\frac{\partial}{\partial r}\left(\tau r^2\frac{\partial\left(p v_{0\varphi}\right)}{\partial r}\right)=0. \quad (4.8.15)$$

or after integration

$$\rho v_{0r}v_{0\varphi}-\tau\left[\frac{1}{r^2}\frac{\partial\left(r^2\rho v_{0r}^2 v_{0\varphi}\right)}{\partial r}-g_{r,tot}\rho v_{0\varphi}-\frac{q}{m}\rho v_{0\varphi}^2 B_\theta+\frac{q}{m}\rho v_{0r}^2 B_\theta\right]-\left(\tau\frac{\partial\left(p v_{0\varphi}\right)}{\partial r}\right)=0. \quad (4.8.16)$$

But (see (4.8.8))

$$\rho v_{0r}v_{0\varphi}=\tau v_{0\varphi}\left[\frac{1}{r^2}\frac{\partial\left(r^2\rho v_{0r}^2\right)}{\partial r}+\frac{\partial p}{\partial r}-\rho\left(g_{r,tot}+\frac{q}{m}\left(v_{0\varphi}B_\theta\right)\right)\right]. \quad (4.8.17)$$

Then after comparison (4.8.16) and (4.8.17) we have

$$\rho v_{0r}^2\frac{\partial v_{0\varphi}}{\partial r}+\frac{q}{m}\rho v_{0r}^2 B_\theta+p\frac{\partial v_{0\varphi}}{\partial r}=0 \quad (4.8.18)$$

or

$$\frac{\partial v_{0\varphi}}{\partial r}=-\frac{q}{m}\frac{\rho v_{0r}^2}{p+\rho v_{0r}^2}B_\theta. \quad (4.8.19)$$

It's important to notice that the orbital velocity $v_{0\varphi}=const$ if

1. $B_\theta=0$, or
2. $v_{0r}=0$, or
3. $q=0$.

Using the before formulated assumption we obtain the energy equation

$$\frac{1}{r^2}\frac{\partial}{\partial r}\left\{r^2\left\{\left(\frac{1}{2}\rho v_0^2+\frac{5}{2}p\right)v_{0r}-\right.\right.$$

$$\left.\left.\tau\left[\frac{1}{r^2}\frac{\partial}{\partial r}\left(r^2\left(\frac{1}{2}\rho v_0^2+\frac{7}{2}p\right)v_{0r}^2\right)-\rho g_{r,tot}v_{0r}^2-\left(\frac{1}{2}\rho v_0^2+\frac{3}{2}p\right)g_{r,tot}-\left(\frac{1}{2}\rho v_0^2+\frac{5}{2}p\right)\frac{q}{m}v_{0\varphi}B_\theta\right]\right\}\right\}$$

$$-g_{r,tot}\left\{\rho v_{0r}-\tau\left(\frac{1}{r^2}\frac{\partial}{\partial r}\left(r^2\rho v_{0r}^2\right)+\frac{\partial p}{\partial r}-\rho g_{r,tot}-qnv_{0\varphi}B_\theta\right)\right\} \quad (4.8.20)$$

$$-\frac{1}{r^2}\frac{\partial}{\partial r}\left(\tau r^2\frac{\partial}{\partial r}\left(\frac{1}{2}p v_0^2+\frac{5}{2}\frac{p^2}{\rho}\right)\right)+\frac{1}{r^2}\frac{\partial}{\partial r}\left(r^2\tau p g_r\right)=0.$$

Using (4.8.8) we find

$$\frac{\partial}{\partial r}\left\{r^2\left\{\left(\frac{1}{2}\rho v_0^2+\frac{5}{2}p\right)v_{0r}-\right.\right.$$

$$\left.\left.\tau\left[\frac{1}{r^2}\frac{\partial}{\partial r}\left(r^2\left(\frac{1}{2}\rho v_0^2+\frac{7}{2}p\right)v_{0r}^2\right)-\rho g_{r,tot}v_{0r}^2-\left(\frac{1}{2}\rho v_0^2+\frac{3}{2}p\right)g_{r,tot}-\left(\frac{1}{2}\rho v_0^2+\frac{5}{2}p\right)\frac{q}{m}v_{0\varphi}B_\theta\right]\right\}\right\}$$

$$-\frac{\partial}{\partial r}\left(\tau r^2\frac{\partial}{\partial r}\left(\frac{1}{2}pv_0^2+\frac{5}{2}\frac{p^2}{\rho}\right)\right)+\frac{\partial}{\partial r}\left(r^2\tau p g_{r,tot}\right)=0 \quad (4.8.21)$$

or after integration and some transformations:

$$\begin{aligned}&\left(\rho v_0^2+5p\right)v_{0r}-\tau\frac{\partial}{\partial r}\left(\left(\rho v_0^2+7p\right)v_{0r}^2+pv_0^2+5\frac{p^2}{\rho}\right)+\\&+\tau g_{r,tot}\left[3\rho v_{0r}^2+\rho v_{0\varphi}^2+5p\right]+\tau\left(\rho v_0^2+5p\right)\frac{q}{m}v_{0\varphi}B_\theta-\tau\frac{2}{r}\left(\rho v_0^2+7p\right)v_{0r}^2=0\end{aligned} \quad (4.8.22)$$

Let us use the scales used before

$$\tau_0=\frac{r_0}{u_0},\ g_0=\frac{u_0^2}{r_0},\ p_0=\rho_0u_0^2$$

and additional scales E_0, B_0 for electric and magnetic fields.

The continuity equation in the dimensionless form

$$\widetilde{\rho}\widetilde{v}_{0r}=\widetilde{\tau}\left[\frac{1}{\widetilde{r}^2}\frac{\partial\left(\widetilde{r}^2\widetilde{\rho}\widetilde{v}_{0r}^2\right)}{\partial\widetilde{r}}+\frac{\partial\widetilde{p}}{\partial\widetilde{r}}-\widetilde{\rho}\left(\widetilde{g}_r+\frac{q}{m}\left(\frac{r_0}{u_0}B_0\widetilde{v}_{0\varphi}\widetilde{B}_\theta-\frac{r_0}{u_0^2}E_0\left|\widetilde{E}_r\right|\right)\right)\right]. \quad (4.8.23)$$

The following relations take place

$$\frac{q}{m}\frac{r_0}{u_0}B_0=\frac{qu_0B_0}{mu_0^2/r_0}=\frac{F_0^{mag}}{F_0^{kin}},\ \frac{q}{m}\frac{r_0}{u_0^2}E_0=\frac{qE_0}{mu_0^2/r_0}=\frac{F_0^{el}}{F_0^{kin}}, \quad (4.8.24)$$

then

$$\widetilde{\rho}\widetilde{v}_{0r}=\widetilde{\tau}\left[\frac{1}{\widetilde{r}^2}\frac{\partial\left(\widetilde{r}^2\widetilde{\rho}\widetilde{v}_{0r}^2\right)}{\partial\widetilde{r}}+\frac{\partial\widetilde{p}}{\partial\widetilde{r}}-\widetilde{\rho}\left(\widetilde{g}_r+\frac{F_0^{mag}}{F_0^{kin}}\widetilde{v}_{0\varphi}\widetilde{B}_\theta-\frac{F_0^{el}}{F_0^{kin}}\left|\widetilde{E}_r\right|\right)\right]. \quad (4.8.25)$$

Equation (4.8.25) contains the ratios of the character magnetic and electric energies to the character kinetic energy of hydrodynamic motion.

The dimensionless motion equation on $\mathbf{e}_r$ direction:

$$\begin{aligned}&\widetilde{r}^2\frac{\partial\widetilde{p}}{\partial\widetilde{r}}-\left(\widetilde{g}_r-\frac{F_0^{el}}{F_0^{kin}}\left|\widetilde{E}_r\right|\right)\widetilde{\rho}\widetilde{r}^2+\widetilde{\tau}\left(\widetilde{g}_r-\frac{F_0^{el}}{F_0^{kin}}\left|\widetilde{E}_r\right|\right)\frac{\partial\left(\widetilde{r}^2\widetilde{\rho}\widetilde{v}_{0r}\right)}{\partial\widetilde{r}}\\&-\frac{\partial}{\partial\widetilde{r}}\left\{\widetilde{r}^2\widetilde{\tau}\left(\widetilde{p}+\widetilde{\rho}\widetilde{v}_{0r}^2\right)\frac{\partial\widetilde{v}_{0r}}{\partial\widetilde{r}}\right\}+\frac{\partial}{\partial\widetilde{r}}\left\{\widetilde{r}^2\widetilde{\tau}\widetilde{\rho}\widetilde{v}_{0r}\left(\widetilde{g}_r-\frac{F_0^{el}}{F_0^{kin}}\left|\widetilde{E}_r\right|\right)\right\}\\&-2\widetilde{r}^2\frac{\partial}{\partial\widetilde{r}}\left(\widetilde{\tau}\frac{\partial\left(\widetilde{p}\widetilde{v}_{0r}\right)}{\partial\widetilde{r}}\right)+4\widetilde{\tau}\widetilde{p}\widetilde{v}_{0r}-4\widetilde{r}\frac{\partial}{\partial\widetilde{r}}\left(\widetilde{\tau}\widetilde{p}\widetilde{v}_{0r}\right)\\&-\frac{F_0^{mag}}{F_0^{kin}}\widetilde{B}_\theta\widetilde{\rho}\widetilde{r}^2\left(\widetilde{v}_{0\varphi}-\widetilde{\tau}\widetilde{v}_{0r}\widetilde{B}_\theta\frac{F_0^{mag}}{F_0^{kin}}\right)+\frac{F_0^{mag}}{F_0^{kin}}\widetilde{\tau}\widetilde{B}_\theta\frac{\partial\left(\widetilde{\rho}\widetilde{r}^2\widetilde{v}_{0r}\widetilde{v}_{0\varphi}\right)}{\partial\widetilde{r}}+\frac{F_0^{mag}}{F_0^{kin}}\frac{\partial}{\partial\widetilde{r}}\left\{\widetilde{r}^2\widetilde{\tau}\widetilde{\rho}\widetilde{v}_{0r}\widetilde{v}_{0\varphi}\widetilde{B}_\theta\right\}=0.\end{aligned} \quad (4.8.26)$$

The dimensionless motion equation on $\mathbf{e}_\varphi$ direction:

$$\frac{\partial \widetilde{v}_{0\varphi}}{\partial \widetilde{r}} = -\frac{F_0^{mag}}{F_0^{kin}} \frac{\widetilde{\rho}\widetilde{v}_{0r}^2}{\widetilde{p} + \widetilde{\rho}\widetilde{v}_{0r}^2} \widetilde{B}_\theta , \tag{4.8.27}$$

where

$F_0^{mag} = qu_0 B_0$, $F_0^{el} = qE_0$

Component of magnetic induction vector $\widetilde{B}_\theta < 0$ for the Earth condition, then the electron orbital velocity should decrease with increasing of the ring radius

$$\left(\frac{\partial \widetilde{v}_{0\varphi}}{\partial \widetilde{r}} \right)_{el} < 0 , \tag{4.8.28}$$

and the proton orbital velocity should increase with increasing of the ring radius

$$\left(\frac{\partial \widetilde{v}_{0\varphi}}{\partial \widetilde{r}} \right)_{pr} > 0 . \tag{4.8.29}$$

Let us write down the dimensionless energy equation (4.8.21)

$$\begin{gathered} \left(\widetilde{\rho}\widetilde{v}_0^2 + 5\widetilde{p}\right)\widetilde{v}_{0r} - \widetilde{\tau} \frac{\partial}{\partial \widetilde{r}} \left(\left(\widetilde{\rho}\widetilde{v}_0^2 + 7\widetilde{p}\right)\widetilde{v}_{0r}^2 + \widetilde{p}v_0^2 + 5\frac{\widetilde{p}^2}{\widetilde{\rho}} \right) + \\ \widetilde{\tau}\widetilde{g}_{r,tot}\left(3\widetilde{\rho}\widetilde{v}_{0r}^2 + \widetilde{\rho}\widetilde{v}_{0\varphi}^2 + 5\widetilde{p}\right) + \widetilde{\tau}\left(\widetilde{\rho}\widetilde{v}_0^2 + 5\widetilde{p}\right)\widetilde{v}_{0\varphi} \frac{F_0^{mag}}{F_0^{kin}} \widetilde{B}_\theta - \widetilde{\tau}\frac{2}{r}\left(\widetilde{\rho}\widetilde{v}_0^2 + 7\widetilde{p}\right)\widetilde{v}_{0r}^2 = 0 \end{gathered} \tag{4.8.30}$$

Now we write the complete system of equations including the dimensionless Poisson equation

(Poisson equation)

$$\frac{\partial}{\partial \widetilde{r}}\left(\widetilde{r}^2 \widetilde{g}_r\right) + \widetilde{G}\left[\widetilde{\rho}\widetilde{r}^2 - \widetilde{\tau} \frac{\partial\left(\widetilde{r}^2 \widetilde{\rho}\widetilde{v}_{0r}\right)}{\partial \widetilde{r}} \right] = 0 , \tag{4.8.31}$$

(continuity equation)

$$\widetilde{\rho}\widetilde{v}_{0r} = \widetilde{\tau}\left[\frac{1}{\widetilde{r}^2} \frac{\partial\left(\widetilde{r}^2 \widetilde{\rho}\widetilde{v}_{0r}^2\right)}{\partial \widetilde{r}} + \frac{\partial \widetilde{p}}{\partial \widetilde{r}} - \widetilde{\rho}\left(\widetilde{g}_r + \frac{F_0^{mag}}{F_0^{kin}} \widetilde{v}_{0\varphi}\widetilde{B}_\theta - \frac{F_0^{el}}{F_0^{kin}} \left|\widetilde{E}_r\right| \right) \right] , \tag{4.8.32}$$

($\mathbf{e}_r$-motion equation)

$$\begin{gathered} \widetilde{r}^2 \frac{\partial \widetilde{p}}{\partial \widetilde{r}} - \left(\widetilde{g}_r - \frac{F_0^{el}}{F_0^{kin}} \left|\widetilde{E}_r\right| \right) \widetilde{\rho}\widetilde{r}^2 + \widetilde{\tau}\left(\widetilde{g}_r - \frac{F_0^{el}}{F_0^{kin}} \left|\widetilde{E}_r\right| \right) \frac{\partial\left(\widetilde{r}^2 \widetilde{\rho}\widetilde{v}_{0r}\right)}{\partial \widetilde{r}} \\ - \frac{\partial}{\partial \widetilde{r}}\left\{ \widetilde{r}^2 \widetilde{\tau}\left(\widetilde{p} + \widetilde{\rho}\widetilde{v}_{0r}^2\right) \frac{\partial \widetilde{v}_{0r}}{\partial \widetilde{r}} \right\} + \frac{\partial}{\partial \widetilde{r}}\left\{ \widetilde{r}^2 \widetilde{\tau}\widetilde{\rho}\widetilde{v}_{0r}\left(\widetilde{g}_r - \frac{F_0^{el}}{F_0^{kin}} \left|\widetilde{E}_r\right| \right) \right\} \\ - 2\widetilde{r}^2 \frac{\partial}{\partial \widetilde{r}}\left(\widetilde{\tau} \frac{\partial\left(\widetilde{p}\widetilde{v}_{0r}\right)}{\partial \widetilde{r}} \right) + 4\widetilde{\tau}\widetilde{p}\widetilde{v}_{0r} - 4\widetilde{r}\frac{\partial}{\partial \widetilde{r}}\left(\widetilde{\tau}\widetilde{p}\widetilde{v}_{0r}\right) \\ - \frac{F_0^{mag}}{F_0^{kin}} \widetilde{B}_\theta \widetilde{\rho}\widetilde{r}^2 \left(\widetilde{v}_{0\varphi} - \widetilde{\tau}\widetilde{v}_{0r}\widetilde{B}_\theta \frac{F_0^{mag}}{F_0^{kin}} \right) + \frac{F_0^{mag}}{F_0^{kin}} \widetilde{\tau}\widetilde{B}_\theta \frac{\partial\left(\widetilde{\rho}\widetilde{r}^2 \widetilde{v}_{0r}\widetilde{v}_{0\varphi}\right)}{\partial \widetilde{r}} + \frac{F_0^{mag}}{F_0^{kin}} \frac{\partial}{\partial \widetilde{r}}\left\{ \widetilde{r}^2 \widetilde{\tau}\widetilde{\rho}\widetilde{v}_{0r}\widetilde{v}_{0\varphi}\widetilde{B}_\theta \right\} = 0 , \end{gathered} \tag{4.8.33}$$

($\mathbf{e}_\varphi$-motion equation)

$$\frac{\partial \tilde{v}_{0\varphi}}{\partial \tilde{r}} = -\frac{F_0^{mag}}{F_0^{kin}} \frac{\tilde{\rho}\tilde{v}_{0r}^2}{\tilde{p} + \tilde{\rho}\tilde{v}_{0r}^2} \tilde{B}_\theta , \tag{4.8.34}$$

(energy equation)

$$\left(\tilde{\rho}\tilde{v}_0^2 + 5\tilde{p}\right)\tilde{v}_{0r} - \tilde{\tau}\frac{\partial}{\partial \tilde{r}}\left(\left(\tilde{\rho}\tilde{v}_0^2 + 7\tilde{p}\right)\tilde{v}_{0r}^2 + \tilde{p}v_0^2 + 5\frac{\tilde{p}^2}{\tilde{\rho}}\right) +$$
$$\tilde{\tau}\tilde{g}_{r,tot}\left(3\tilde{\rho}\tilde{v}_{0r}^2 + \tilde{\rho}\tilde{v}_{0\varphi}^2 + 5\tilde{p}\right) + \tilde{\tau}\left(\tilde{\rho}\tilde{v}_0^2 + 5\tilde{p}\right)\tilde{v}_{0\varphi}\frac{F_0^{mag}}{F_0^{kin}}\tilde{B}_\theta - \tilde{\tau}\frac{2}{r}\left(\tilde{\rho}\tilde{v}_0^2 + 7\tilde{p}\right)\tilde{v}_{0r}^2 = 0, \tag{4.8.35}$$

where $\tilde{G} = \tilde{\gamma}_N = \gamma_N \frac{M_0}{4\pi r_0 u_0^2}$, $p_0 = \rho_0 u_0^2$, $g_0 = \frac{u_0^2}{r_0}$.

Numerical integration of the system of equations (4.8.31) – (4.8.35) is realized with the help of Maple. The corresponding results are reflected on figures 4.8.3 – 4.8.10. The initial Cauchy conditions are:

$\tilde{p}(1) = 1$, $\tilde{v}_{0r}(1) = -1$, $\tilde{v}_{0\varphi}(1) = 0$, $\tilde{\rho}(1) = 1$, $\tilde{g}_r(1) = -1$, $\tilde{w}(1) = 0$, $D(\tilde{u})(1) = -1$.

The calculation program contains the following parameters, indicated on figures

$\mathrm{G} = \tilde{G}$, $\mathrm{T} = \tilde{\tau}$, $\mathrm{M} = \frac{q}{m}\frac{r_0}{u_0}B_0 = \frac{F_0^{mag}}{F_0^{kin}}$, $\mathrm{N} = \frac{q}{m}\frac{r_0}{u_0^2}E_0 = \frac{F_0^{el}}{F_0^{kin}}$, $\mathrm{B} = \tilde{B}_\theta$, $\mathrm{E} = \left|\tilde{E}_r\right|$

and independent scales $r_0, \tau_0, u_0, \rho_0, B_0, E_0$; $t \leftrightarrow \tilde{r}$.

Figures 4.8.3, 4.8.4 reflect the evolution of hydrodynamic parameters along the radius of electron belt in the case of $B_\theta < 0$.

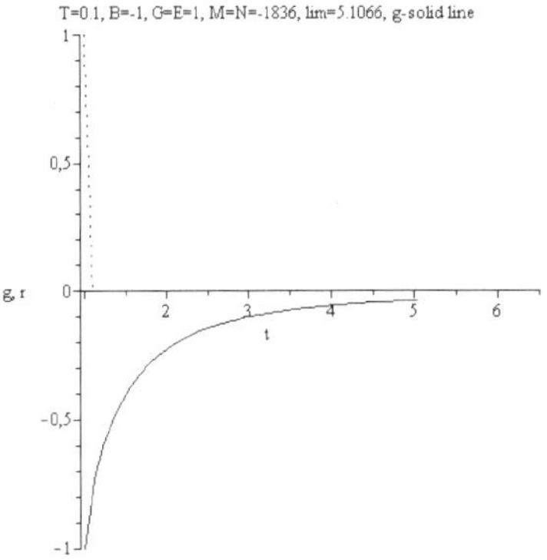

Fig. 4.8.3. g - gravitational acceleration $\tilde{g}_r$ (solid line), r - density $\tilde{\rho}$ (dotted line), $\tilde{\tau} = 0.1$, M = -1836, N = -1836, G=E=1, $\tilde{B}_\theta = -1$. lim=5.1066.

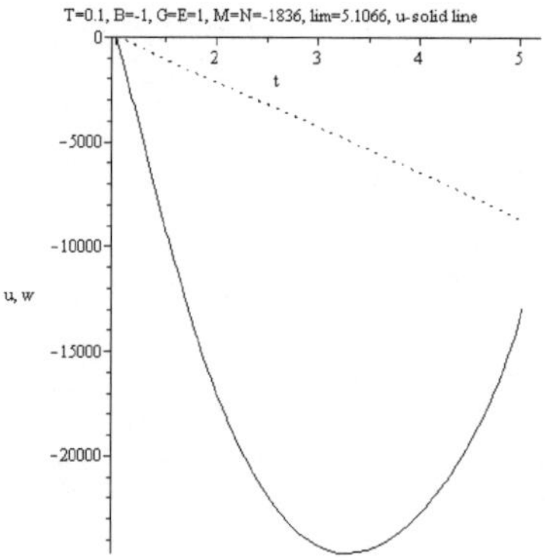

Fig. 4.8.4. u - velocity $\tilde{v}_{0r}$ (solid line), w - velocity $\tilde{v}_{0\varphi}$ (dotted line),
$\tilde{\tau} = 0.1$, M = -1836, N = -1836, G=E=1, $\tilde{B}_\theta = -1$. lim=5.1066.

Figures 4.8.5, 4.8.6 reflect the evolution of hydrodynamic parameters along the radius of proton belt in the case of $B_\theta < 0$.

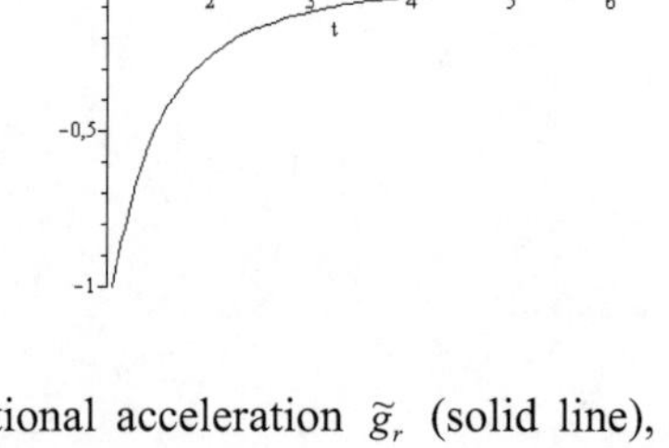

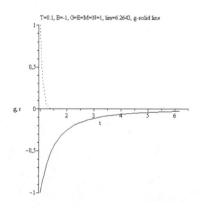

Fig. 4.8.5. g - gravitational acceleration $\tilde{g}_r$ (solid line), r - density $\tilde{\rho}$ (dotted line),
$\tilde{\tau} = 0.1$, M = 1, N = 1, G=E=1, $\tilde{B}_\theta = -1$, lim=6.2643.

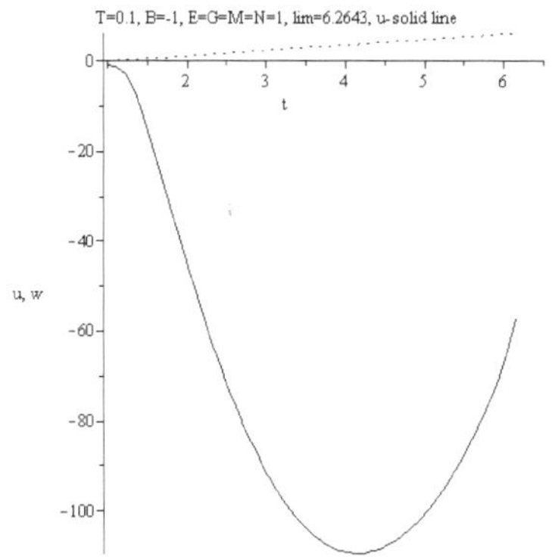

Fig. 4.8.6. u - velocity $\tilde{v}_{0r}$ (solid line), w - velocity $\tilde{v}_{0\varphi}$ (dotted line),
$\tilde{\tau} = 0.1$, $M = 1$, $N = 1$, G=E=1, $\tilde{B}_{\theta} = -1$. lim=6.2643.

Let us consider now the case of the magnetic field inversion which leads to $B_{\theta} > 0$. Figures 4.8.7, 4.8.8 reflect the evolution of hydrodynamic parameters along the radius of electron belt in the mentioned case of $B_{\theta} > 0$.

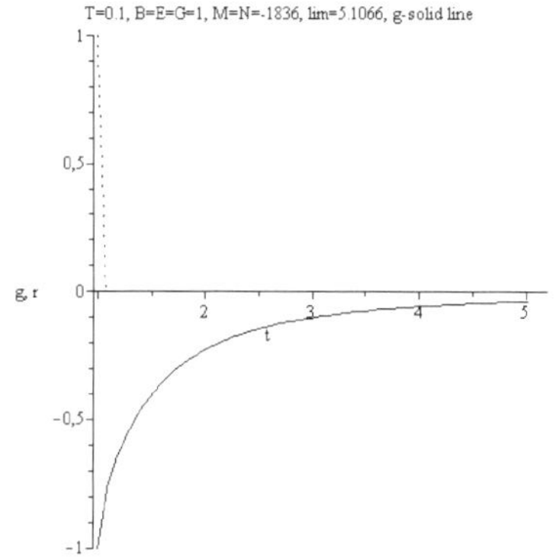

Fig. 4.8.7. g - gravitational acceleration $\tilde{g}_r$ (solid line), r - density $\tilde{\rho}$ (dotted line),
$\tilde{\tau} = 0.1$, $M = -1836$, $N = -1836$, G=E=1, $\tilde{B}_{\theta} = 1$. lim=5.1066.

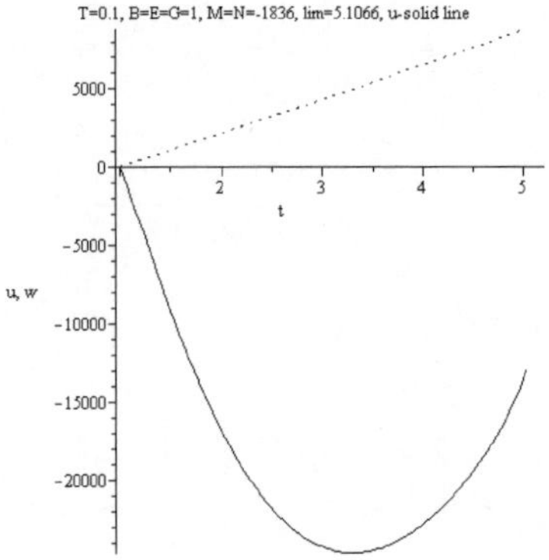

Fig. 4.8.8. u - velocity $\tilde{v}_{0r}$ (solid line), w - velocity $\tilde{v}_{0\varphi}$ (dotted line), $\tilde{\tau} = 0.1$, M = -1836, N = -1836, G=E=1, $\tilde{B}_{\theta} = 1$. lim=5.1066.

Figures 4.8.9, 4.8.10 reflect the evolution of hydrodynamic parameters along the radius of proton belt in the mentioned case of $B_{\theta} > 0$.

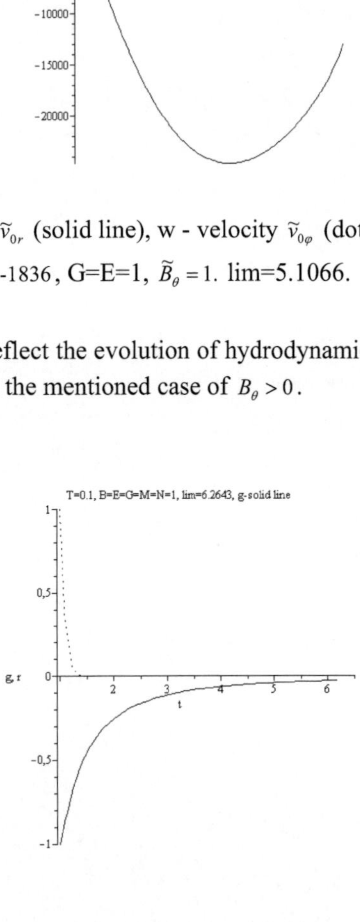

Fig. 4.8.9. g - gravitational acceleration $\tilde{g}_{r}$ (solid line), r - density $\tilde{\rho}$ (dotted line),
$\tilde{\tau} = 0.1$, M = 1, N = 1, G=E=1, $\tilde{B}_{\theta} = 1$. lim=6.2643.

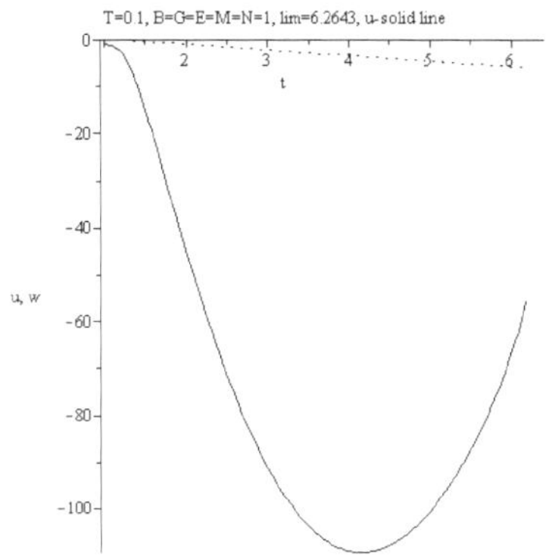

Fig. 4.8.10. u - velocity $\widetilde{v}_{0r}$ (solid line), w - velocity $\widetilde{v}_{0\varphi}$ (dotted line), $\widetilde{\tau}=0.1$, $M=1$, $N=1$, G=E=1, $\widetilde{B}_{\theta}=1$. lim=6.2643.

4.9. Discussion: Van Allen belt, magnetic field inversion and the bottleneck in biology.

A Van Allen radiation belt is a zone of energetic charged particles, most of which originate from the solar wind. These particles (RP) are captured by planet's magnetic field and held around a planet. The Earth has two such belts and sometimes others may be temporarily created. The radiation belt in the first approximation is a toroid in which following sub-belts are distinguished:

1. Internal;
2. External;
3. Sometimes for a limited period of time is formed and a third layer of RP. This phenomenon was observed, in particular, in 2013. It lasted about a month and was destroyed by an interplanetary shock wave from the Sun.

The inner belt is located at a height of from 3 to 12 thousand km above the Earth's surface, and outer - at the height of from 18 to 57 thousand km, and the Internal belt consists mainly of protons and of electrons. Although the division into internal and external belts is rather conditional (as well as the character heights), since all the near-earth space is filled with charged particles that move in the earth's magnetic field. Nevertheless, a safe zone between the internal and outer rings is usually isolated. Many years among scientists there is a debate on the topic of how it was formed, this safe area and on the origin of the process of "purification" of charged particles. Recent studies have shown that lightning is responsible for "clearing" a safe zone several thousand kilometers high; the terms used are blue jet, tiger, sprite and elves.

During high solar activity and in some geographical areas (for example, the Brazilian magnetic anomaly), the lower boundary can descend up to 200 km from the Earth. Internal radiation belt consists mainly of protons with energy of tens of MeV. It is believed that protons are formed here due to beta-decay of neutrons as a result of exposure to cosmic rays; lower energy protons are formed during geomagnetic storms. A visual image of the internal RP was obtained in 2014. The drawing resembled a "Zebra" because of the effects caused by the nature of the earth's magnetic field.

The height of the lower limit of the radiation belt changes on the same latitude as in longitude due to the inclination of the axis of Earth's magnetic field to the axis of rotation of the Earth, and on the same geographical longitude, it changes according to the latitudes because of their own form the radiation belts, due to the different height of the magnetic field lines of the Earth. For example, over the Atlantic, the increase in radiation intensity begins at an altitude of 500 km, and over Indonesia at an altitude of 1300 km

The external radiation belt is at an altitude of more than 17000 km, consisting mainly of electrons with energy of tens of Kev. With the same success you can find other estimations for the location of outer belt – it is located at an altitude of 13 000 to 60 000 kilometers and has an almost toroidal shape; consists mainly of electrons, the value of the energy which is in the range of from 0.1 to 10 MeV. In 2014, it was found that the internal boundary of the external RP is quite sharp. It is much larger in size than the internal RP. The number of particles in it varies depending on the geomagnetic storms and plasma disturbances produced by the Sun;

The outer belt is more affected by solar activity. In 2011, it was found that the flow also contains antiparticles. As a result of the interaction of the upper atmosphere with cosmic rays, antiprotons are formed. Their energy is about 60-750 MeV.

Let us now turn to the results of numerical calculations in the framework of nonlocal physics analytical and numerical calculations are realized in the frame of suggestions 1 – 11 (see Item 4.8). We have for the inner belt and the 'normal" case $B_\theta < 0$ (for the chosen Cauchy conditions):

1. Proton and electron belts exist only in bounded space area (see figures 4.8.3 - 4.8.6).
2. The width of the electron belt is less than the width of the proton belt, (figures 4.8.3, 4.8.5).
3. The orbital component of the electron velocity $\tilde{v}_{0\varphi} < 0$ and $\frac{\partial \tilde{v}_{0\varphi}}{\partial \tilde{r}} < 0$, if $\tilde{B}_\theta = -1$. (figure 4.8.4).
4. The orbital component of the proton velocity $\tilde{v}_{0\varphi} > 0$ and $\frac{\partial \tilde{v}_{0\varphi}}{\partial \tilde{r}} > 0$, if $\tilde{B}_\theta = -1$ (see figure 4.8.6).

Residual magnetism is the magnetization left behind in a ferromagnetic material (such as iron) after an external magnetic field is removed. Studies of the residual magnetization, acquired by igneous rocks when they cool down below the Curie point, indicate repeated inversions of the earth's magnetic field. In the sea crust recorded all the changes in the earth's magnetic field over the past 180 million years. The Earth's field has alternated between periods of normal polarity, in which the predominant direction of the field was the same as the present direction, and reverse polarity, in which it was the opposite. These periods are called chrons.

Reversal occurrences are statistically random. In the literature there is an opinion, that there have been 183 reversals over the last 83 million years [72, 73]. The Brunhes–Matuyama reversal was a geologic event, approximately 781,000 years ago, when the Earth magnetic field last underwent reversal. Estimations vary as to the abruptness of the reversal: it might have extended over several thousand years [72], or much more quickly, perhaps within a human lifetime, [73]. Other sources estimate that the time that it takes for a reversal to complete is on average around 7000 years for the four most recent reversals. The duration of a full reversal is typically between 2000 and 12000 years, which is one to two orders of magnitude less than the duration of magnetic chrons.

Although there have been periods in which the field reversed globally (such as the Laschamp) for several hundred years, these events are classified as excursions rather than full geomagnetic reversals. Stable polarity chrons often show large, rapid directional excursions, which occur more often than reversals, and could be seen as failed reversals. There is opinion that during such an excursion, the field reverses in the liquid outer core, but not in the solid inner core. Diffusion in the liquid outer core is on timescales of 500 years or less, while that of the solid inner core is much longer, around 3000 years.

The displacement of the magnetic poles has been recorded since 1885. Over the past 100 years, the magnetic pole in the southern hemisphere has moved almost 900 km and reached the Indian ocean. As of the beginning of 2007, the velocity of the magnetic North pole drift increased from 10 km/year in the 1970s to 60 km/year in 2004. The intensity of the earth's magnetic field falls, and unevenly. Over the past 22 years, it has decreased by an average of 1.7 %, and in some regions — for example, in the southern Atlantic ocean - by 10 %. In some places, the intensity of the magnetic field, contrary to the general trend, even increased.

The acceleration of motion of the poles (on average 3 km/year) and their movement through the corridors of the inversion of the magnetic poles suggests that the shift of the poles should not perceive the digression, but the next inversion of the magnetic field of the Earth.

Let us consider now the result of the mathematical modeling connected with chron's period $B_\theta > 0$. We have

1. Proton and electron belts exist only in bounded space area (see figures 4.8.7 - 4.8.10).
2. The width of the electron chron's belt is equal to the width on the normal period (the character widths 4.1066, see figures 4.8.7 and 4.8.3).
3. The width of the proton chron's belt is equal to the width on the normal period (5.2643). See figures 4.8.5, 4.8.9.
4. The orbital component of the electron velocity $\tilde{v}_{0\varphi} > 0$ and $\frac{\partial \tilde{v}_{0\varphi}}{\partial \tilde{r}} > 0$, (see figure 4.8.8).
5. The orbital component of the proton velocity $\tilde{v}_{0\varphi} < 0$ and $\frac{\partial \tilde{v}_{0\varphi}}{\partial \tilde{r}} < 0$, (see figure 4.8.10).
6. There is no the significant difference between the electron's velocities $\tilde{v}_{0r}$ in the normal and reversal regimes (see figures 4.8.3 and 4.8.8).
7. There is no the significant difference between the proton's velocities $\tilde{v}_{0r}$ in the normal and reversal regimes (see figures 4.8.6 and 4.8.10).

We should underline that the results of calculations are connected with the concrete parameters and Cauchy conditions chosen for an astrophysical object.

Important to notice that relation $\frac{\partial v_{0\varphi}}{\partial r} = -\frac{q}{m}\frac{\rho v_{0r}^2}{p + \rho v_{0r}^2} B_\theta$ forecasts the sign change for derivatives for chron's period. It could lead to the change of the orbital velocities and to the full reconstruction of the belts position, the breakdown of the belt capacitor and ‘the burning’ of the atmosphere.

In this case the problems arise, known as the bottleneck. A population bottleneck or genetic bottleneck is a sharp reduction in the size of a population due to environmental events, in this case due pole reversal. Verification of correlations between extinctions and reversals is difficult for a number of reasons. Larger animals are too rare in the fossil record for good statistics. Mass extinctions are global catastrophes in the history of the Earth, when a high (compared to the background level) proportion of species died out over a short geological time. During the Paleozoic (the last 540 million years) there have been five major mass extinctions and about 20 smaller ones. The last mass extinction occurred about 65 million years ago and was not the most significant, but it is best known because of the extinction of the dinosaurs. The largest of the mass extinctions (the so-called "Great extinction") 250 million years ago destroyed 90 % of the then biodiversity. This Cretaceous-Paleocene extinction event is best known for the extinction of the dinosaurs and nearly all large animal species. During this event, temperatures increased by as much as 32 degrees Celsius and sea levels rose as much as three hundred meters.

The earth's field can completely disappear during reversals. Then we can share the destiny of Mars. The Mars ' atmosphere was destroyed by the solar wind, because Mars didn't have a magnetic field to protect it. In this case no surprise that the great animals like dinosaurs disappeared. But the small animals (human beings after evolution) survived under the Earth surface.

4.10. To the nonlocal theory of the planet internal structure.

Let us consider the problem of the internal structure of planets from the position of nonlocal physics. We begin our investigation considering the old problem of hydro-magnetic dynamo (HMD). Following the accepted definition HMD is a mechanism for strengthening or maintaining a stationary (or oscillatory) state of the magnetic field by hydrodynamic movements of the conducting medium.

Most cosmic bodies (planets, stars, galaxies) and their environment have magnetic fields. The origin and observed changes of the fields are connected, as a rule, with the movements of the plasma. The idea that plasma movements can lead to an increase in the magnetic field was put forward by John Larmor in 1919. The name hydro-magnetic Dynamo arose from the similarity of the process with the operation of a dynamo machine. The peculiarity of a hydro-magnetic Dynamo is that it must be self-excited, i.e. not supported by external field sources.

In theoretical studies we believe that in the volume of plasma with a given conductivity a weak magnetic field is created as a result of an external influence or statistical fluctuations (see Item 2.7). The created field is not supported by the external field. sources. If over time the field and the total magnetic energy of the volume under consideration do not decrease, despite the action of ohmic dissipation, then a hydromagnetic Dynamo takes place.

In the local theory hydro-magnetic Dynamo is a branch of magneto-hydrodynamics. Relativistic effects, displacement currents, are usually not taken into account in the theory of a hydro-magnetic Dynamo.

It will be shown that the possibility of enhancing the initial (seed) magnetic field by the motions of the medium is associated with the Vera Rubin regime of the plasma flow. From the other side the typical estimation of the of the ohmic field attenuation leads to formula

$$\tau = 4\pi\sigma L^2 / c^2, \tag{4.10.1}$$

where L is the character linear size of the cosmic object and σ is conductivity of flow or

$$\tau = L^2 / \upsilon_m, \tag{4.10.2}$$

where υ_m is the magnetic (kinematic) viscosity (formulas are given in a Gaussian system of units). But the characteristic sizes L of the areas occupied by space are usually so large that even with moderate plasma conductivity the time τ of ohmic field attenuation are also huge. It means that the problem leads to the large dimensionless nonlocal parameter $\tilde{\tau}$ (as an example we used $\tilde{\tau} = 100$.

Let us introduce in consideration the magnetic Reynolds number

$$\mathrm{Re}_m = \frac{Lw}{\upsilon_m} \tag{4.10.3}$$

where w is an orbital velocity. Then we have

$$\mathrm{Re}_m = \frac{Lw}{\upsilon_m} = \frac{L^2 w}{L\upsilon_m} = \tau\frac{w}{L} = \tilde{\tau}. \tag{4.10.4}$$

The typical estimation for the Earth core $\mathrm{Re}_m \approx 150$.

The internal structure of the Earth is layered in spherical shells:

1) an outer silicate solid crust,
2) a highly viscous asthenosphere and mantle,
3) a liquid outer core that is much less viscous than the mantle, and
4) a solid inner core.

Scientific understanding of the internal structure of the Earth is based on observations and analysis of the seismic waves that pass through the Earth, measurements of the gravitational and magnetic fields of the Earth, and experiments with crystalline solids at pressures and temperatures characteristic of the Earth's deep interior. When an earthquake occurs, waves of three kinds occur:

1) longitudinal waves (P), can occur in any bodies-solid, liquid and gaseous; resemble sound waves; move faster than all other waves generated by an earthquake;

2) transverse waves (S) moving slower than longitudinal waves; they resemble light waves; they are shear waves, and can only occur and propagate in a solid medium;

3) a complex group of long waves (L) that are formed only in the surface parts of the earth's crust, and at depth they fade; starting from the epicenter, they cause strong displacements and destruction on the earth's surface.

All these waves diverge from the seismic center in different ways, so that at a station far from the epicenter, their arrival is recorded at different times. Later, long L waves come, since they only spread along the periphery of the Earth. The P and S waves that penetrate the Earth's body at great depths come earlier, with the faster longitudinal waves (P — primae — the first) being registered first, followed by the slower transverse waves (S — secundae — the second). If the Earth's body were uniform, the seismic rays of the P and S waves would be straight lines. A gradual increase in the density of the Earth with depth would give a concave trajectory.. If the density of the Earth changes with depth in jumps, then these concave curves must have fractures at the boundaries of media with different densities, not to mention partial reflection of waves. The study of seismic wave velocities, their nature and trajectories leads to the following conclusions:

1) when longitudinal and transverse waves pass through the Earth's body, the velocities of these waves change, which indicates changes in the properties of the medium they pass through;

2) wave speeds change abruptly, which means that changes in the properties of the environment also occur abruptly;

The thickness of the earth's crust varies from 5 to 70 km in depth from the surface. The thinnest parts of the oceanic crust that underlie the ocean basins (5-10 km) are composed of dense iron-magnesium silicate rock, such as basalt.

Below the crust is a mantle, which differs in composition and physical properties - it is more dense. The mantle of the Earth extends to a depth of 2890 km, which makes it the thickest layer of the Earth. The pressure in the lower mantle is about 140 GPa. The mantle consists of silicate rocks rich in iron and magnesium in relation to the overlying crust. High temperatures in the mantle make the silicate material ductile enough for convection of the substance in the mantle to come to the surface through faults in tectonic plates.

The average density of the Earth is $5.5\ g/cm^3$. Since the average density of surface matter is only about 3 g/cm^3, we must conclude that dense substances exist in the Earth's core. Further evidence of high core density is based on seismological data. The compaction of the substance with pressure should also be considered. The density of the upper mantle, starting from the value of 3 g/cm^3 on the surface, gradually increases with depth due to the compression of its substance. Seismic measurements show that the core is divided into two parts - a solid inner core with a radius of ~ 1220 km and a liquid outer core with a radius of ~ 3400 km.

There are in fact two sharp changes in speeds: at a depth of 60 km and at a depth of 2900 km. In other words, only the outer layer (the earth's crust) and the inner core are clearly separated. In the intermediate zone between them, as well as inside the core, there is only a change in the rate of increase in speeds. The depth for the core is 2900 km, and the average core radius is 3,500 km. The Earth core is divided into solid inner core with a radius of about 1300 km and a liquid outer core with a thickness of about 2200 km, among which stands out sometimes transition zone. The temperature on the surface of the solid core of the Earth is estimated to reach 6230±500 K and the pressure up to $3.7 \cdot 10^6 atm$, core weight - $1.9 \cdot 10^{24} kg$. In literature you can find absolutely other estimations (see also [74 – 82]).

In the center of the earth, density is about 17.2 and it changes with a particularly sharp jump (from 5.7 to 9.4) at a depth of 2900 km, and then at a depth of 5 thousand km. The first jump allows us to distinguish a dense core in the globe, and the second to subdivide this core into the outer (2900-5000 km) and the inner (from 5 thousand km to the center) parts. It is most natural to think that such a high density of the central parts is due to the enormous pressures that exist in the depths of the Earth, as a result of which matter is there in an extremely large compression state.

Figures 4.10.1 and 4.10.2 reflect the typical qualitative information obtained mainly with help seismic diagnostics.

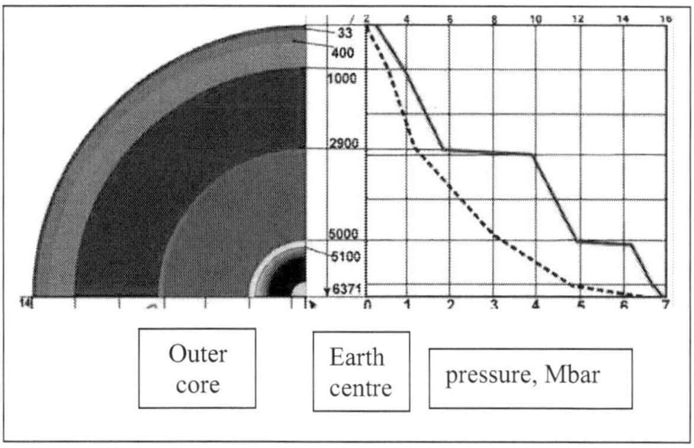

Figure 4.10.1. Earth's radial density and pressure distribution.

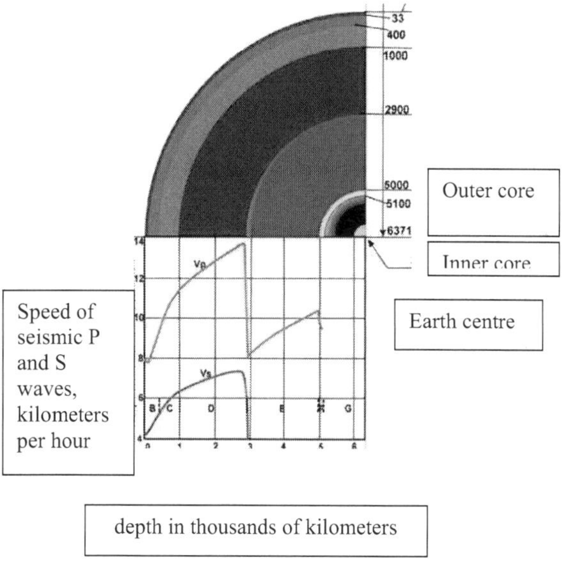

Figure 4.10.2. Speed of seismic P and S waves in the Earth's radial direction.

In the center of the earth, density is about 17.2 and it changes with a particularly sharp jump (from 5.7 to 9.4) at a depth of 2900 km, and then at a depth of 5 thousand km. The first jump allows us to distinguish a dense core in the globe, and the second to subdivide this core into the outer (2900-5000 km) and the inner (from 5 thousand km to the center) parts. It is most natural to think that such a high density of the central parts is due to the enormous pressures that exist in the depths of the Earth, as a result of which matter is there in an extremely large compression state.

It is most natural to think that such a high density of the Central parts is due to the enormous pressures that exist in the depths of the Earth, as a result of which matter is there in a state of exceptionally large compression. This explanation is now gaining more and more support. Until the pressure in the Earth reaches a certain critical limit-the density changes gradually; when this limit (apparently, 1.3 million atm) is reached, the substance jumps into a denser "metal-like" phase. Another explanation is to assume that the interior of the Earth consists of substances of greater specific gravity than the earth's crust, mainly of metals.

There is no unanimous opinion about the chemical composition of the inner parts of the planet, since we can only talk about the chemical composition of matter based mainly on data of seismic diagnostics. In connection with the above, we will consider the non-local magneto hydrodynamic aspects of the theory, leaving aside the problems of chemical composition and phase transitions.

Let write down the nonlocal system of hydrodynamic equations for partly ionized plasma.

Basic nonlocal equations in spherical coordinates system are written in Item 4.5. Therefore, the main points in the transformations of equations that correspond to the specifics of the problem will be given below. We suppose:

1. Chemical processes in the system are not taking into account.
2. System contains neutral (n), positive (i) and negative (e) particles.
3. Stationary solutions are considered.
4. Hydrodynamic speed $\mathbf{v}_0(v_{0r}, v_{0\varphi})$, $v_{0r} = v_{0r}(r)$, and generally speaking, $v_{0\varphi} = v_{0\varphi}(r)$.
5. Magnetic intensity is constant, $\mathbf{B}(B_\theta)$.
6. Acceleration is $\mathbf{g}(g_{r,total})$.
7. The dependences of pressure and densities are $p(r)$, $\rho_n(r), \rho_i(r), \rho_e(r)$..

8. Acceleration $g_{r,total} \to g_r - \frac{q}{m}|E_r|$, $q = \pm e$, where e is an absolute charge value of a moving charged particle.
9. It is assumed that the inner core is charged positively. Then, the intensity vector $\mathbf{E}(E_r)$ is calculated in the self-consistent process.
10. The internal particle energy $\varepsilon = 0$.
11. We solve the Cauchy problem. It means formally that results can be applied to an area outside the planet surface.
12. The physical processes in the inner core are not considered.

Therefore we have the system of non-dimensional equations:
Poisson equation for gravitation

$$\frac{\partial}{\partial \tilde{r}}\left(\tilde{r}^2 \tilde{g}_r\right) + \tilde{G}\left[\left(\tilde{\rho}_i + \tilde{\rho}_e + \tilde{\rho}_n\right)\tilde{r}^2 - \tilde{\tau}\frac{\partial\left(\tilde{r}^2\left(\tilde{\rho}_i + \tilde{\rho}_e + \tilde{\rho}_n\right)\tilde{v}_{0r}\right)}{\partial \tilde{r}}\right] = 0, \tag{4.10.5}$$

Poisson equation for the electric intensity

$$\frac{\partial}{\partial \tilde{r}}\left(\tilde{r}^2 \tilde{E}_r\right) = \left(\tilde{\rho}_i - \tilde{\rho}_e\right)\tilde{r}^2 - \tilde{\tau}\frac{\partial}{\partial \tilde{r}}\left[\tilde{r}^2\left(\tilde{\rho}_i - \tilde{\rho}_e\right)\tilde{v}_{0r}\right], \tag{4.10.6}$$

Continuity equation for the positive particles

$$\tilde{\rho}_i \tilde{v}_{0r} - \tilde{\tau}\left[\frac{1}{\tilde{r}^2}\frac{\partial\left(\tilde{r}^2 \tilde{\rho}_i \tilde{v}_{0r}^2\right)}{\partial \tilde{r}} - \tilde{\rho}_i \tilde{g}_r + \frac{F_0^{el}}{F_0^{kin}}\tilde{\rho}_i \tilde{E}_r - \frac{F_0^{mag}}{F_0^{kin}}\tilde{\rho}_i \tilde{v}_{0\varphi}\tilde{B}_\theta + \frac{\partial \tilde{p}}{\partial \tilde{r}}\right] = 0. \tag{4.10.7}$$

Continuity equation for the negative particles

$$\tilde{\rho}_e \tilde{v}_{0r} - \tilde{\tau}\left[\frac{1}{\tilde{r}^2}\frac{\partial\left(\tilde{r}^2 \tilde{\rho}_e \tilde{v}_{0r}^2\right)}{\partial \tilde{r}} - \tilde{\rho}_e \tilde{g}_r + \frac{F_0^{el}}{F_0^{kin}}\tilde{\rho}_e \tilde{E}_r - \frac{F_0^{mag}}{F_0^{kin}}\tilde{\rho}_e \tilde{v}_{0\varphi}\tilde{B}_\theta + \frac{\partial \tilde{p}}{\partial \tilde{r}}\right] = 0. \tag{4.10.8}$$

Continuity equation for the neutral particles

$$\tilde{\rho}_n \tilde{v}_{0r} - \tilde{\tau}\left[\frac{1}{\tilde{r}^2}\frac{\partial\left(\tilde{r}^2 \tilde{\rho}_n \tilde{v}_{0r}^2\right)}{\partial \tilde{r}} - \tilde{\rho}_n \tilde{g}_r + \frac{\partial \tilde{p}}{\partial \tilde{r}}\right] = 0. \tag{4.10.9}$$

Momentum equation for the internal orbital movement

$$\frac{\partial \tilde{v}_{0\varphi}}{\partial \tilde{r}} = \frac{F_0^{mag}}{F_0^{kin}}\left(\tilde{\rho}_e - \tilde{\rho}_i\right)\frac{\tilde{v}_{0r}^2}{\tilde{p} + \tilde{\rho}\tilde{v}_{0r}^2}\tilde{B}_\theta. \tag{4.10.10}$$

Momentum equation for the radial movement

$$
\tilde{r}^2\frac{\partial\tilde{p}}{\partial\tilde{r}}-\left(\tilde{g}_r-\frac{F_0^{el}}{F_0^{kin}}\left|\tilde{E}_r\right|\right)\tilde{\rho}\tilde{r}^2+\tilde{\tau}\left(\tilde{g}_r-\frac{F_0^{el}}{F_0^{kin}}\left|\tilde{E}_r\right|\right)\frac{\partial\left(\tilde{r}^2\tilde{\rho}\tilde{v}_{0r}\right)}{\partial\tilde{r}}
$$

$$
-\frac{\partial}{\partial\tilde{r}}\left\{\tilde{r}^2\tilde{\tau}\left(\tilde{p}+\tilde{\rho}\tilde{v}_{0r}^2\right)\frac{\partial\tilde{v}_{0r}}{\partial\tilde{r}}\right\}+\frac{\partial}{\partial\tilde{r}}\left\{\tilde{r}^2\tilde{\tau}\tilde{\rho}\tilde{v}_{0r}\left(\tilde{g}_r-\frac{F_0^{el}}{F_0^{kin}}\left|\tilde{E}_r\right|\right)\right\} \tag{4.10.11}
$$

$$
-2\tilde{r}^2\frac{\partial}{\partial\tilde{r}}\left(\tilde{\tau}\frac{\partial\left(\tilde{p}\tilde{v}_{0r}\right)}{\partial\tilde{r}}\right)+4\tilde{\tau}\tilde{p}\tilde{v}_{0r}-4\tilde{r}\frac{\partial}{\partial\tilde{r}}\left(\tilde{\tau}\tilde{p}\tilde{v}_{0r}\right)
$$

$$
-\frac{F_0^{mag}}{F_0^{kin}}\tilde{B}_\theta\tilde{\rho}\tilde{r}^2\left(\tilde{v}_{0\varphi}-\tilde{\tau}\tilde{v}_{0r}\tilde{B}_\theta\frac{F_0^{mag}}{F_0^{kin}}\right)+\frac{F_0^{mag}}{F_0^{kin}}\tilde{\tau}\tilde{B}_\theta\frac{\partial\left(\tilde{\rho}\tilde{r}^2\tilde{v}_{0r}\tilde{v}_{0\varphi}\right)}{\partial\tilde{r}}+\frac{F_0^{mag}}{F_0^{kin}}\frac{\partial}{\partial\tilde{r}}\left\{\tilde{r}^2\tilde{\tau}\tilde{\rho}\tilde{v}_{0r}\tilde{v}_{0\varphi}\tilde{B}_\theta\right\}=0\,.
$$

Energy equation

$$
\left(\tilde{\rho}\tilde{v}_0^2+5\tilde{p}\right)\tilde{v}_{0r}-\tilde{\tau}\frac{\partial}{\partial\tilde{r}}\left(\left(\tilde{\rho}\tilde{v}_0^2+7\tilde{p}\right)\tilde{v}_{0r}^2+\tilde{p}\tilde{v}_0^2+5\frac{\tilde{p}^2}{\tilde{\rho}}\right)+
$$

$$
+\tilde{\tau}\tilde{g}_{r,tot}\left[3\tilde{\rho}\tilde{v}_{0r}^2+\tilde{\rho}\tilde{v}_{0\varphi}^2+5\tilde{p}\right]+\tilde{\tau}\left(\tilde{\rho}\tilde{v}_0^2+5\tilde{p}\right)\frac{F_0^{mag}}{F_0^{kin}}\tilde{v}_{0\varphi}\tilde{B}_\theta-\tau\frac{2}{\tilde{r}}\left(\tilde{\rho}\tilde{v}_0^2+7\tilde{p}\right)\tilde{v}_{0r}^2=0, \tag{4.10.12}
$$

where $\tilde{v}_0^2=\tilde{v}_{0r}^2+\tilde{v}_{0\varphi}^2$, $\tilde{\rho}=\tilde{\rho}_n+\tilde{\rho}_i+\tilde{\rho}_e$.

Remarks:

1. These equations are written down in the dimensionless form after introducing the scales: $g_0, u_0, \rho_0,\ p_0$ and for independent variable r_0; (see also Item 4.5), $\mathrm{E}\leftrightarrow\tilde{E}$, $\mathrm{B}\leftrightarrow\tilde{B}_\theta$, $\tilde{\gamma}_N=\gamma_N\frac{\rho_0 r_0}{g_0}$, $\tilde{G}=\tilde{\gamma}_N=\gamma_N\frac{\mu}{r_0u_0^2}$, $\mu=\rho_0r_0^3$, $p_0=\rho_0u_0^2$, $g_0=\frac{u_0^2}{r_0}$. We use the scale for τ in the form $\tau_0=\frac{r_0}{u_0}$. Equations contain dimensionless parameters (see also (4.8.24)) $\frac{e}{m}\frac{r_0}{u_0}B_0=\frac{eu_0B_0}{mu_0^2/r_0}=\frac{F_0^{mag}}{F_0^{kin}}$, $\frac{e}{m}\frac{r_0}{u_0^2}E_0=\frac{eE_0}{mu_0^2/r_0}=\frac{F_0^{el}}{F_0^{kin}}$, $\mathrm{M}=\frac{F_0^{mag}}{F_0^{kin}}$, $\mathrm{N}=\frac{F_0^{el}}{F_0^{kin}}$, $\mathrm{t}\leftrightarrow\tilde{r}$.

Numerical integration of the system of equations (4.9.5) – (4.9.12) is realized with the help of Maple. The corresponding results are reflected on figures 4.10.3 – 4.10.6, u - velocity $\tilde{v}_{0r}$, w - velocity $\tilde{v}_{0\varphi}$, g - gravitational acceleration $\tilde{g}_r$, p-pressure $\tilde{p}$, T-$\tilde{\tau}$, n - density $\tilde{\rho}_n$, $\mathrm{G}\leftrightarrow\tilde{G}$

The following Cauchy conditions are used in the following calculations:

```
p(0.1)=1,u(0.1)=1,g(0.1)=-1,r(0.1)=0.4,s(0.1)=0.3,
n(0.1)=0.3, w(0.1)=0.01, D(u)(0.1)=1, E(0.1)=10
```

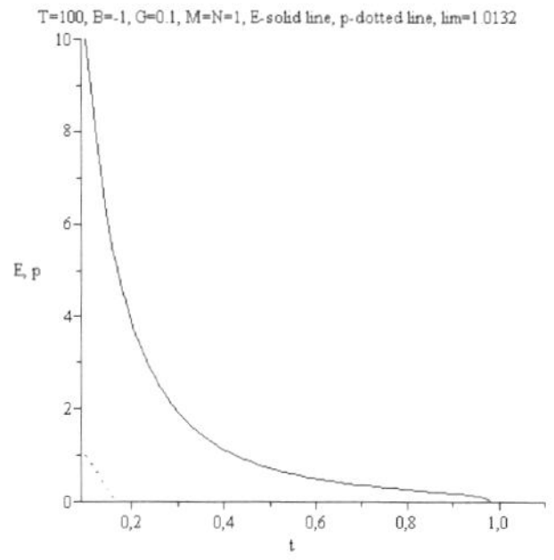

Fig. 4.10.3. E- electric intensity $\widetilde{E}$ (solid line), p - pressure $\widetilde{p}$ (dotted line), $T = \widetilde{\tau} = 100$, M=N=1, G=0.1, $\mathrm{B} = \widetilde{B}_\theta = -1$. lim=1.0132.

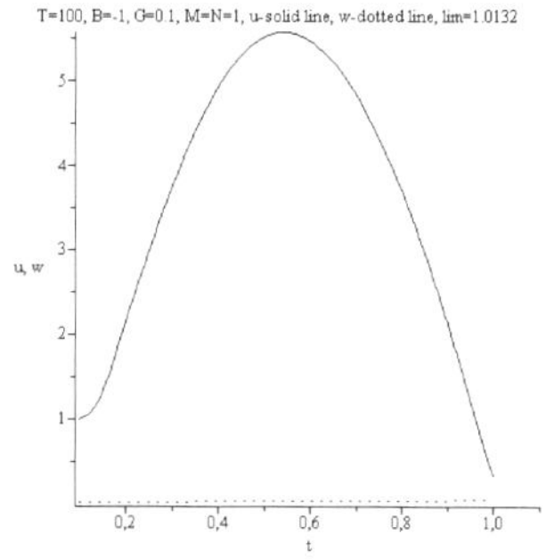

Fig. 4.10.4. u - velocity $\widetilde{v}_{0r}$ (solid line), w - velocity $\widetilde{v}_{0\varphi}$ (dotted line), $T = \widetilde{\tau} = 100$, M=N=1, G=0.1, $\mathrm{B} = \widetilde{B}_\theta = -1$. lim=1.0132.

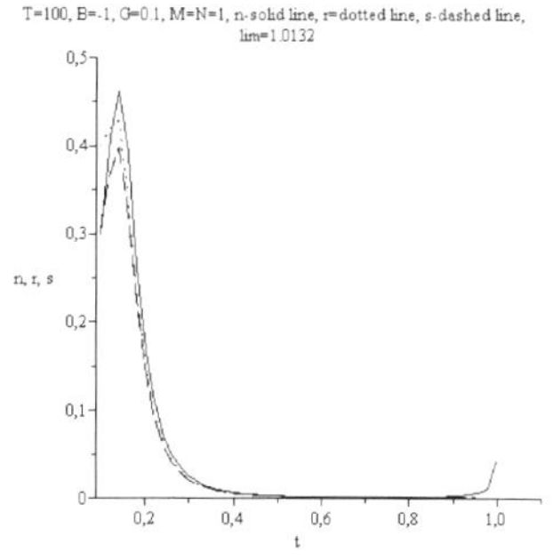

Fig. 4.10.5. n- density $\widetilde{\rho}_n$ (solid line), r- density $\widetilde{\rho}_i$ (dotted line), s- density $\widetilde{\rho}_e$ (dashed line), $T = \widetilde{\tau} = 100$, M=N=1, G=0.1, $\mathrm{B} = \widetilde{B}_\theta = -1$. lim=1.0132.

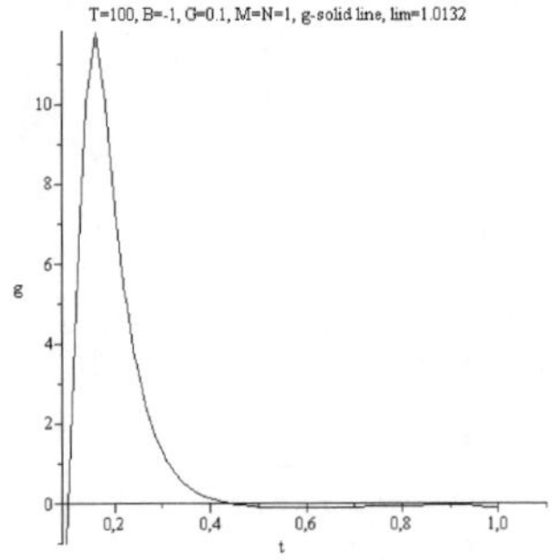

Fig. 4.10.6. $g \leftrightarrow \tilde{g}$ - gravitational acceleration (solid line), $T = \tilde{\tau} = 100$, M=N=1, G=0.1, $B = \tilde{B}_\theta = -1$. lim=1.0132.

The nonlocal model has the tremendous potential for the future investigations. For example we can include the self consistent calculation of magnetic field in the scheme of calculations using generalized Maxwell equation. In this case the magnetic induction vector is dependent value and for the $\tilde{B}_\theta$ calculation we should add the nonlocal Maxwell equation

$$\frac{1}{\tilde{r}}\frac{\partial}{\partial \tilde{r}}\left(\tilde{r}\tilde{B}_\theta\right) = \frac{4\pi}{c^2}u_0^2\frac{F_0^{el}}{F_0^{mag}}\left[\left(\tilde{\rho}_i - \tilde{\rho}_e\right)\tilde{v}_{0\varphi} - \tilde{\tau}\left(\frac{1}{\tilde{r}^2}\frac{\partial\left(\tilde{r}^2\left(\tilde{\rho}_i - \tilde{\rho}_e\right)\tilde{v}_{0r}\tilde{v}_{0\varphi}\right)}{\partial \tilde{r}} + \left(\tilde{\rho}_i - \tilde{\rho}_e\right)\tilde{v}_{0r}\tilde{B}_\theta\right)\right]. \quad (4.10.13)$$

Cauchy conditions:

```
p(0.1)=1,u(0.1)=1,g(0.1)=-1,r(0.1)=0.4,s(0.1)=0.3,
n(0.1)=0.3, w(0.1)=0.1, D(u)(0.1)=1, E(0.1)=10,
B(0.1)=-1.
```
(4.10.14)

In figures 4.10.7 – 4.7.11

$$K = 4\pi\frac{u_0^2}{c^2}\frac{F_0^{el}}{F_0^{mag}}. \quad (4.10.15)$$

The following figures 4.10.7 – 4.10.12 reflect the result of calculations for conditions (4.10.14).

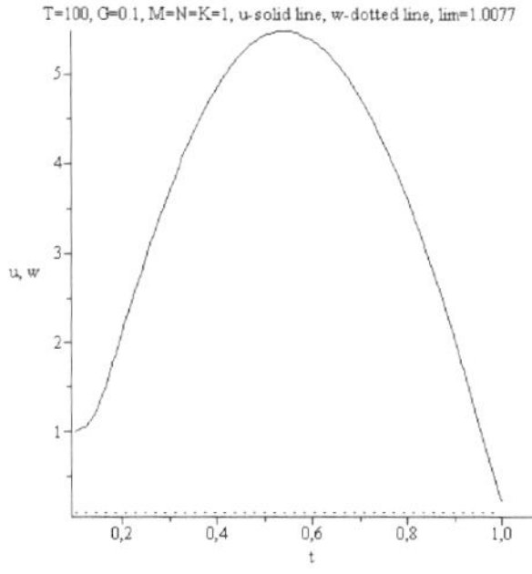

Fig. 4.10.7. u - velocity $\widetilde{v}_{0r}$ (solid line), w - velocity $\widetilde{v}_{0\varphi}$ (dotted line), $T = \widetilde{\tau} = 100$, K=M=N=1, G=0.1, lim=1.0077.

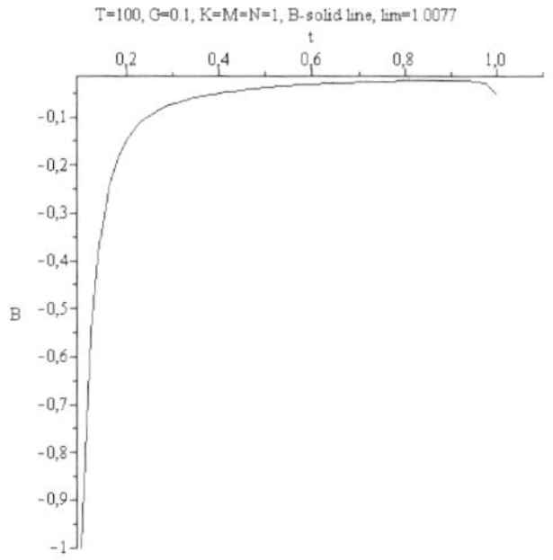

Fig. 4.10.8. B- magnetic induction $\widetilde{B}_\theta$.
$T = \widetilde{\tau} = 100$, K=M=N=1, G=0.1, lim=1.0077.

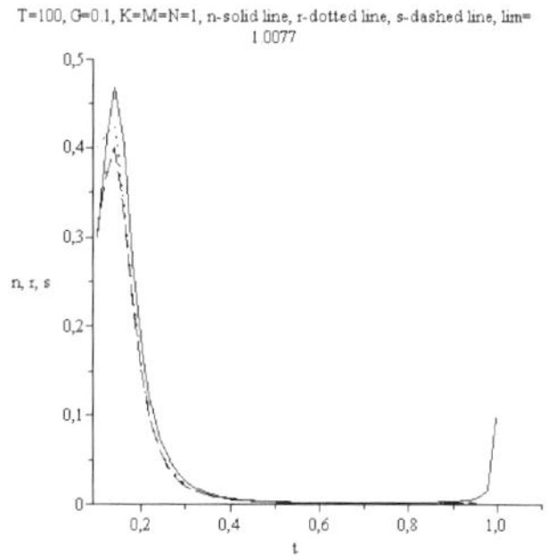

Fig. 4.10.9. n- density $\widetilde{\rho}_n$ (solid line), r- density $\widetilde{\rho}_i$ (dotted line), s- density $\widetilde{\rho}_e$ (dashed line), $T = \widetilde{\tau} = 100$, K=M=N=1, G=0.1, lim=1.0077.

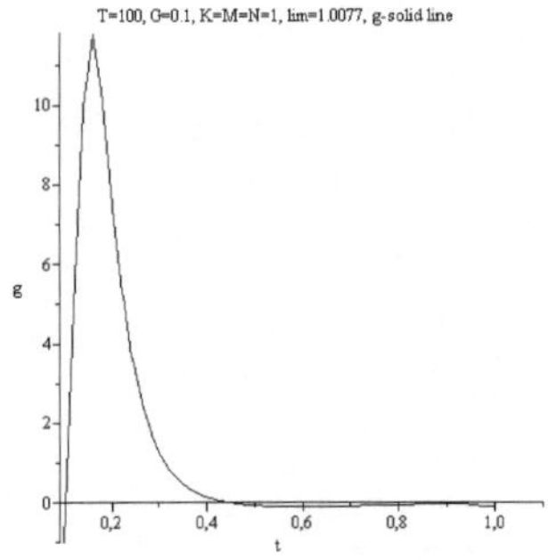

Fig. 4.10.10. g $\leftrightarrow \tilde{g}$ - gravitational acceleration (solid line), $T = \tilde{\tau} = 100$, K=M=N=1, G=0.1, lim=1.0077.

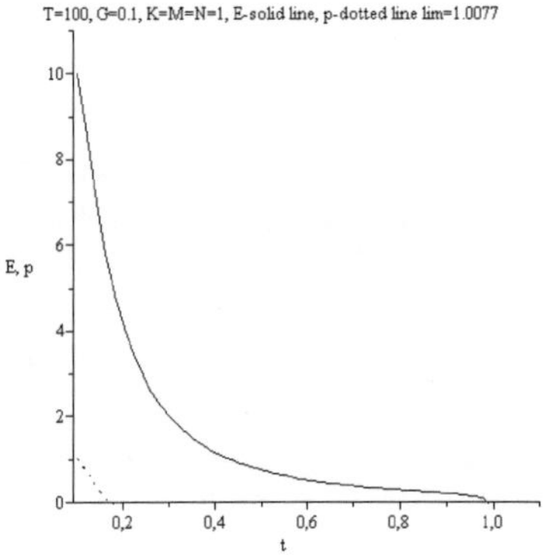

Fig. 4.10.11. E- electric intensity $\tilde{E}$ (solid line), p - pressure $\tilde{p}$ (dotted line),

Conclusion.

1. In the literature (see for example [83]) you can find studies of the extreme values of gravitational acceleration g_r. Let us consider this problem in details. Poisson equation (4.5.10) can be written in the form

$$\frac{\partial}{\partial \tilde{r}}\left(\tilde{r}^2 \tilde{g}_r\right) + \tilde{G}\left[\tilde{\rho}\tilde{r}^2 - \tilde{\tau}\frac{\partial\left(\tilde{r}^2 \tilde{\rho}\tilde{v}_{0r}\right)}{\partial \tilde{r}}\right] = 0, \tag{4.10.16}$$

or

$$\tilde{r}^2 \frac{\partial \tilde{g}_r}{\partial \tilde{r}} + 2\tilde{r}\tilde{g}_r + \tilde{G}\left[\tilde{\rho}\tilde{r}^2 - \tilde{\tau}\frac{\partial\left(\tilde{r}^2 \tilde{\rho}\tilde{v}_{0r}\right)}{\partial \tilde{r}}\right] = 0. \tag{4.10.17}$$

The extreme values of gravitational acceleration g_r correspond to the equation

$$\tilde{g}_{r,ext} = \frac{\tilde{G}}{2}\left[\tilde{\tau}\frac{1}{\tilde{r}}\frac{\partial\left(\tilde{r}^2\tilde{\rho}\tilde{v}_{0r}\right)}{\partial\tilde{r}} - \tilde{\rho}\tilde{r}\right]_{ext} . \quad (4.10.18)$$

As we see the value of $\tilde{g}_{r,ext}$ and the position $\tilde{r}_{ext}$ depends on the hydrodynamic values even in the case $\tilde{\tau} = 0$ (or $\tilde{v}_{0r} = 0$). The artificial constructions with the different pre - defined $\tilde{\rho}(\tilde{r})$ dependency has no real practical sense; moreover the gravitational acceleration $\tilde{g}_r$ does not contain the dependence on azimuthal velocity $\tilde{v}_{0\varphi}$ in the explicit form.

2. As we see from figures 4.10.4 and 4.10.7 the orbital velocity $\tilde{v}_{0\varphi} = const$. I should underline that it is the typical result for many variants of calculations defined by the Cauchy conditions. In other words, the orbital motions in the Vera Rubin mode are typical for the Universe - from the rotation of stars around the center of Galaxies to the undamped Dynamo in the cores of planets. The detection of a rotation regime with a constant orbital velocity (instead of the Kepler regime) led to attempts to detect "dark matter". We can express a paradoxical thought - there is no need to look for the dark matter. We have dark matter under our feet in the form of an undamped dynamo.

4.11. Hydrodynamic theory of the Searle's effect.

In 1946, Prof. John Searle of Great Britain made a fundamental discovery in areas of the nature of magnetism. While working at Mortimer, Berkshire, he discovered that if the magnets in the form of rollers made according to the new technology are placed around the outside of the ring magnet, then with a certain number of rollers, they come into independent motion around the ring magnet. Once in motion, the rollers increase their speed until they reach dynamic equilibrium. Since 1952 the Searle has produced and tested more than 10 generators with a group of employees, the largest of which was disc-shaped and reached 10 meters in diameter.

Searle's work has never been published in scientific or technical literature, but many the researchers were aware of these results. A patent was applied for with the title, but later revoked.

In Internet, the situation has remained virtually unchanged for many years. 10 years ago, there was a surge of attention to this invention. Then interest in the Searle generator began to wane. It was also found that when rotating magnetic rollers, the device creates an electrostatic potential difference whose vector is directed along the radius from the rollers to the ring magnet. In this case, the fixed ring is positively charged, and the rollers - negatively.

Four years in a row (from 1968 to 1972) every first Sunday of the month John's neighbors observed inexplicable phenomena. In the hands professors came to life, spinning and generating energy from unusual generators; disks with a diameter of half a meter to 10 meters, they rose into the air and made controlled flights from London to Cornwall and back. BBC TV journalists have started making a documentary about the extraordinary devices. It was shown on television. The result was unexpected: the local electricity Committee accused John Searle of stealing electricity. The electricians didn't believe that his lab was powered by its own source. The scientist was jailed for 10 months. During this time, a strange fire occurred in the laboratory, but before it all the equipment, drawings and mysterious inventions disappeared.

The previous information was taken from Internet. Let us consider now the Searle's effect from the position of nonlocal physics. We intend to use the spherical coordinate system shown as figure 4.11.1.

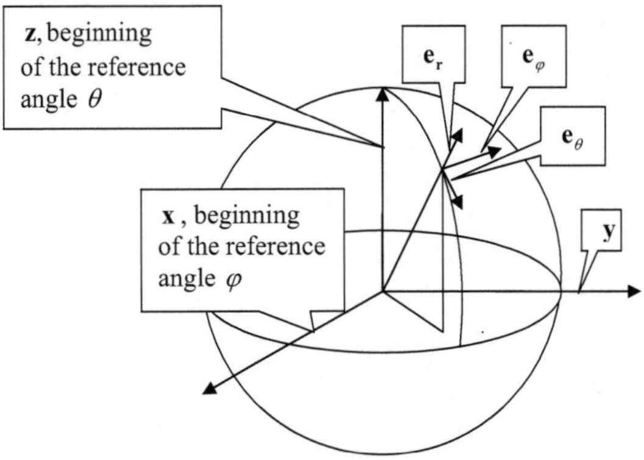

Figure 4.11.1. Spherical coordinate system.

Figure 4.11.2 contains the principal element of the Searle's generator (SG). Figure 4.11.2 shows the basic SG in its simplest form, consisting of one stationary annular ring-shaped magnet, called the plate, and a number of moving cylinder-shaped rods called runners.

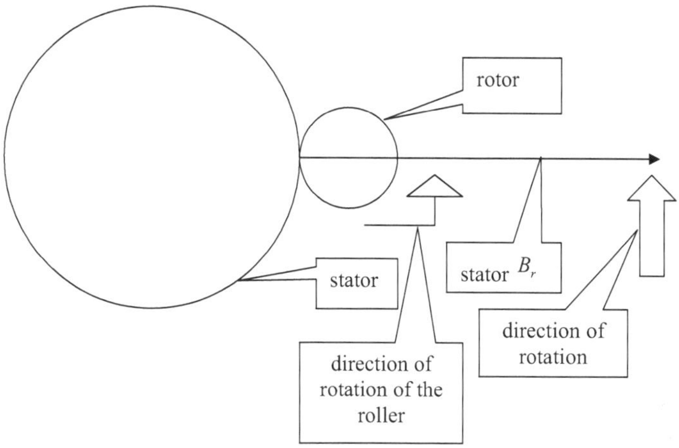

Fig. 4.11.2. The principal element of the Searle's generator (SG)

A more complex (multi-row) design consisted of several rotary rings (sections), shown in Fig. 4.11.3.

Figure 4.11.3. Multi-row design.

Searle found that the rollers, if given a small boost, could move faster around the ring. This creates an electric potential difference in the radial direction between the ring and the rollers. As follows from the published materials, at the first test, an unexpected event occurred: the generator, without ceasing to rotate, began to

climb up, disconnected from the accelerating engine and rose to a height of about 50 feet. Here it paused a little, accelerating more and more, and began to emit a pink glow around it, ionizing the air. Then he continued up and out of sight.
It is clear that such a fantastic result requires serious verification, and if it is confirmed - an adequate theoretical explanation. Moreover, the successful development of this field can significantly change the fundamental foundations of physics and open up an almost inexhaustible source of energy.

I repeat that the previous information was taken from Internet. It is obvious, that the following increasing the roller numbers leads to the hydrodynamic theory of rings around the large flat circular magnet. The "particles" of rings have the small radius $r_{rol} << r_{disk}$. The rollers considered as particles have the internal energy like "spin effect" in quantum mechanics. With this aim let us consider a coil show in Fig. 4.11.4.

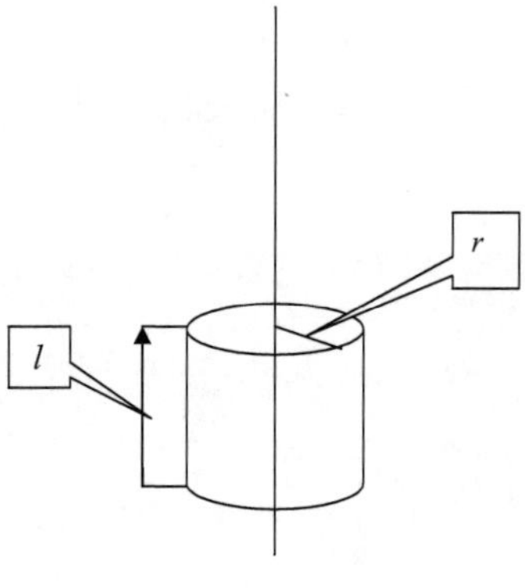

Figure 4.11.4. A coil configuration.

We use notations: L - the inductance in Henry; N - number of turns in the coil; μ - magnetic permeability; μ_0 - vacuum permeability, μ_0 = $1.25663706212(19)\times10^{-6}$ H/m.; S - the cross-sectional area of the core; l - length of the midline of the core; W_{mag} - magnetic field energy; W_{mech} - energy of rotational motion of the roller; I - amperage.

The magnetic energy is

$$W_{mag} = \frac{LI^2}{2}, \tag{4.11.1}$$

where $L = \frac{\mu\mu_0 N^2 S}{l}$. (4.11.2)

Then roller-particle has the internal magnetic energy.

$$W_{mag} = \frac{\mu\mu_0 N^2 S I^2}{2l}, \quad (4.11.3)$$

But the roller has also mechanical energy of the rotation origin. Namely

$$W_{mech,rot} = \frac{\mathrm{I}_{\mathrm{rot}}\omega^2}{2}, \quad (4.11.4)$$

where

$$\mathrm{I}_{\mathrm{rot}} = \mathrm{I}_{\mathrm{cyl}} = \frac{mr^2}{2}, \quad (4.11.5)$$

then

$$W_{mech,rot} = \frac{mr^2\omega^2}{4}. \quad (4.11.6)$$

The total internal energy is

$$W_{\mathrm{int}} = W_{mag} + W_{mech,rot} = \frac{\mu\mu_0 N^2 S I^2}{2l} + \frac{mr^2\omega^2}{4}. \quad (4.11.7)$$

But for a coil the B_θ component is written as

$$B_\theta = \frac{\mu\mu_0}{l} NI. \quad (4.11.8)$$

Then

$$W = W_{mag} + W_{mech,rot} = \frac{lS}{2\mu\mu_0}\frac{(\mu\mu_0)^2 N^2 I^2}{l^2} + \frac{mr^2\omega^2}{4} = \frac{lS}{2\mu\mu_0}B_\theta^2 + \frac{mr^2\omega^2}{4}. \quad (4.11.9)$$

Therefore the internal energy of the pseudo-particle is

$$\varepsilon = \frac{lS}{2\mu\mu_0}B_\theta^2 + \frac{mr^2\omega^2}{4}, \quad (4.11.10)$$

and the hydrodynamic description leads to the internal energy for the volume unit

$$\varepsilon n = \frac{1}{2\mu\mu_0}B_\theta^2 + \frac{\rho r_{coil}^2 \omega_{coil}^2}{4}. \quad (4.11.11)$$

or

$$2\varepsilon n = \frac{1}{\mu\mu_0}B_\theta^2 + \frac{\rho r_{coil}^2 \omega_{coil}^2}{2}. \quad (4.11.12)$$

Let us consider now the Searle's effect from the position of nonlocal hydrodynamics. Strict consideration leads to the system of the generalized hydrodynamic equations (GHE) [19] (see also (4.8.1) – (4.8.6)) written here for a one species physical system.

We consider 1D stationary model ($\theta = \pi/2$, independent variable is r) with unknown variables $\rho, g_r, p, v_{0\varphi}, v_{0\theta}$. We begin the derivation of the corresponding system of equations with the formulation of the nonlocal continuity equation in the spherical coordinate system with the independent variables r,θ,φ (radial distance r, polar angle θ and azimuth angle φ; figure 4.11.1):

Continuity equation

$$\frac{\partial}{\partial t}\left\{\rho-\tau\left[\frac{\partial \rho}{\partial t}+\frac{1}{r^2}\frac{\partial\left(r^2\rho v_{0r}\right)}{\partial r}+\frac{1}{r\sin\theta}\frac{\partial\left(\rho v_{0\varphi}\right)}{\partial\varphi}+\frac{1}{r\sin\theta}\frac{\partial\left(\rho v_{0\theta}\sin\theta\right)}{\partial\theta}\right]\right\}$$

$$+\frac{1}{r^2}\frac{\partial}{\partial r}\left\{r^2\left\{\rho v_{0r}-\tau\left[\frac{\partial}{\partial t}\left(\rho v_{0r}\right)+\frac{1}{r^2}\frac{\partial\left(r^2\rho v_{0r}^2\right)}{\partial r}+\frac{1}{r\sin\theta}\frac{\partial\left(\rho v_{0\varphi}v_{0r}\right)}{\partial\varphi}\right.\right.\right.$$

$$\left.\left.\left.+\frac{1}{r\sin\theta}\frac{\partial\left(\rho v_{0\theta}v_{0r}\sin\theta\right)}{\partial\theta}-\rho g_r-\frac{q}{m}\rho\left(v_{0\varphi}B_\theta-v_{0\theta}B_\varphi\right)\right]\right\}\right\}+\frac{1}{r\sin\theta}\frac{\partial}{\partial\varphi}\left\{\rho v_{0\varphi}-\tau\left[\frac{\partial}{\partial t}\left(\rho v_{0\varphi}\right)+\right.\right.$$

$$\left.\left.\frac{1}{r^2}\frac{\partial\left(r^2\rho v_{0r}v_{0\varphi}\right)}{\partial r}+\frac{1}{r\sin\theta}\frac{\partial\left(\rho v_{0\varphi}^2\right)}{\partial\varphi}+\frac{1}{r\sin\theta}\frac{\partial\left(\rho v_{0\theta}v_{0\varphi}\sin\theta\right)}{\partial\theta}-\rho g_\varphi-\frac{q}{m}\rho\left(v_{0\theta}B_r-v_{0r}B_\theta\right)\right]\right\}$$

$$+\frac{1}{r\sin\theta}\frac{\partial}{\partial\theta}\left\{\sin\theta\left\{\rho v_{0\theta}-\tau\left[\frac{\partial}{\partial t}\left(\rho v_{0\theta}\right)+\frac{1}{r^2}\frac{\partial\left(r^2\rho v_{0r}v_{0\theta}\right)}{\partial r}+\frac{1}{r\sin\theta}\frac{\partial\left(\rho v_{0\varphi}v_{0\theta}\right)}{\partial\varphi}+\right.\right.\right.$$

$$\left.\left.\left.\frac{1}{r\sin\theta}\frac{\partial\left(\rho v_{0\theta}^2\sin\theta\right)}{\partial\theta}-\rho g_\theta-\frac{q}{m}\rho\left(v_{0r}B_\varphi-v_{0\varphi}B_r\right)\right]\right\}\right\}$$

$$-\frac{1}{r^2}\frac{\partial}{\partial r}\left(\tau r^2\frac{\partial p}{\partial r}\right)-\frac{1}{r^2\sin\theta}\frac{\partial}{\partial\theta}\left(\tau\sin\theta\frac{\partial p}{\partial\theta}\right)-\frac{1}{r^2\sin^2\theta}\frac{\partial}{\partial\varphi}\left(\tau\frac{\partial p}{\partial\varphi}\right)=0, \qquad (4.11.13)$$

For the chosen model we have from (4.11.13)

$$\rho g_r+\frac{q}{m}\rho v_{0\varphi}B_\theta-\frac{\partial p}{\partial r}=0. \qquad (4.11.14)$$

Write down the equation of motion in the projection in the direction $\mathbf{e}_r$:

$$\frac{\partial}{\partial t}\left\{\rho v_{0r}-\tau\left[\frac{\partial}{\partial t}(\rho v_{0r})+\frac{1}{r^2}\frac{\partial\left(r^2\rho v_{0r}^2\right)}{\partial r}+\frac{1}{r\sin\theta}\frac{\partial\left(\rho v_{0\varphi}v_{0r}\right)}{\partial\varphi}+\frac{1}{r\sin\theta}\frac{\partial\left(\rho v_{0\theta}v_{0r}\sin\theta\right)}{\partial\theta}\right.\right.$$

$$\left.\left.+\frac{1}{r}\frac{\partial p}{\partial r}-\rho g_r-\frac{q}{m}\rho\left(v_{0\varphi}B_\theta-v_{0\theta}B_\varphi\right)\right]\right\}$$

$$-g_r\left[\rho-\tau\left(\frac{\partial\rho}{\partial t}+\frac{1}{r^2}\frac{\partial\left(r^2\rho v_{0r}\right)}{\partial r}+\frac{1}{r\sin\theta}\frac{\partial\left(\rho v_{0\varphi}\right)}{\partial\varphi}+\frac{1}{r\sin\theta}\frac{\partial\left(\rho v_{0\theta}\sin\theta\right)}{\partial\theta}\right)\right]-$$

$$-\frac{q}{m}\left\{\rho v_{0\varphi}-\tau\left[\frac{\partial}{\partial t}\left(\rho v_{0\varphi}\right)+\frac{1}{r^2}\frac{\partial\left(r^2\rho v_{0r}v_{0\varphi}\right)}{\partial r}+\frac{1}{r\sin\theta}\frac{\partial\left(\rho v_{0\varphi}^2\right)}{\partial\varphi}+\frac{1}{r\sin\theta}\frac{\partial\left(\rho v_{0\theta}v_{0\varphi}\sin\theta\right)}{\partial\theta}+\right.\right.$$

$$\left.\left.+\frac{1}{r\sin\theta}\frac{\partial p}{\partial\varphi}-\rho g_\varphi-\frac{q}{m}\rho\left(v_{0\theta}B_r-v_{0r}B_\theta\right)\right]\right\}B_\theta+$$

$$+\frac{q}{m}\left\{\rho v_{0\theta}-\tau\left[\frac{\partial}{\partial t}\left(\rho v_{0\theta}\right)+\frac{1}{r^2}\frac{\partial\left(r^2\rho v_{0r}v_{0\theta}\right)}{\partial r}+\frac{1}{r\sin\theta}\frac{\partial\left(\rho v_{0\varphi}v_{0\theta}\right)}{\partial\varphi}+\frac{1}{r\sin\theta}\frac{\partial\left(\rho v_{0\theta}^2\sin\theta\right)}{\partial\theta}+\right.\right.$$

$$\left.\left.+\frac{1}{r}\frac{\partial p}{\partial\theta}-\rho g_\theta-\frac{q}{m}\rho\left(v_{0r}B_\varphi-v_{0\varphi}B_r\right)\right]\right\}B_\varphi+$$

$$+\frac{1}{r^2}\frac{\partial}{\partial r}\left\{r^2\left\{\rho v_{0r}^2-\tau\left[\frac{\partial}{\partial t}\left(\rho v_{0r}^2\right)+\frac{1}{r^2}\frac{\partial\left(r^2\rho v_{0r}^3\right)}{\partial r}+\frac{1}{r\sin\theta}\frac{\partial\left(\rho v_{0r}^2v_{0\varphi}\right)}{\partial\varphi}\right.\right.\right.$$

$$\left.\left.\left.+\frac{1}{r\sin\theta}\frac{\partial\left(\rho v_{0\theta}v_{0r}^2\sin\theta\right)}{\partial\theta}-2g_r\rho v_{0r}-2\frac{q}{m}\rho\left(v_{0\varphi}B_\theta-v_{0\theta}B_\varphi\right)v_{0r}\right]\right\}\right\}+$$

$$+\frac{1}{r\sin\theta}\frac{\partial}{\partial\varphi}\left\{\rho v_{0\varphi}v_{0r}-\tau\left[\frac{\partial}{\partial t}\left(\rho v_{0\varphi}v_{0r}\right)+\frac{1}{r^2}\frac{\partial\left(r^2\rho v_{0\varphi}v_{0r}^2\right)}{\partial r}+\right.\right.$$

$$\left.\left.+\frac{1}{r\sin\theta}\frac{\partial\left(\rho v_{0r}v_{0\theta}v_{0\varphi}\sin\theta\right)}{\partial\theta}-g_\varphi\rho v_{0r}-\frac{q}{m}\rho\left(v_{0\theta}B_r-v_{0r}B_\theta\right)v_{0r}-g_r\rho v_{0\varphi}-\frac{q}{m}\rho\left(v_{0\varphi}B_\theta-v_{0\theta}B_\varphi\right)v_{0\varphi}\right]\right\}$$

$$+\frac{1}{r\sin\theta}\frac{\partial}{\partial\theta}\left\{\sin\theta\left\{\rho v_{0\theta}v_{0r}-\tau\left[\frac{\partial}{\partial t}\left(\rho v_{0\theta}v_{0r}\right)+\frac{1}{r^2}\frac{\partial\left(r^2\rho v_{0r}^2v_{0\theta}\right)}{\partial r}+\frac{1}{r\sin\theta}\frac{\partial\left(\rho v_{0r}v_{0\theta}v_{0\varphi}\right)}{\partial\varphi}\right.\right.\right.$$

$$\left.\left.\left.+\frac{1}{r\sin\theta}\frac{\partial\left(\rho v_{0\theta}^2v_{0r}\sin\theta\right)}{\partial\theta}-g_\theta\rho v_{0r}-\frac{q}{m}\rho\left(v_{0r}B_\varphi-v_{0\varphi}B_r\right)v_{0r}-v_{0\theta}\rho g_r-\frac{q}{m}\rho\left(v_{0\varphi}B_\theta-v_{0\theta}B_\varphi\right)v_{0\theta}\right]\right\}\right\}$$

$$+\frac{\partial p}{\partial r}-\frac{\partial}{\partial r}\left(\tau\frac{\partial p}{\partial t}\right)-2\frac{\partial}{\partial r}\left(\tau\left(\frac{1}{r^2}\frac{\partial\left(r^2pv_{0r}\right)}{\partial r}+\frac{1}{r\sin\theta}\frac{\partial\left(pv_{0\varphi}\right)}{\partial\varphi}+\frac{1}{r\sin\theta}\frac{\partial\left(pv_{0\theta}\sin\theta\right)}{\partial\theta}\right)\right)-$$

$$-\frac{1}{r^2}\frac{\partial}{\partial r}\left(\tau r^2\frac{\partial\left(pv_{0r}\right)}{\partial r}\right)-\frac{1}{r^2\sin\theta}\frac{\partial}{\partial\theta}\left(\tau\sin\theta\frac{\partial\left(pv_{0r}\right)}{\partial\theta}\right)-\frac{1}{r^2\sin^2\theta}\frac{\partial}{\partial\varphi}\left(\tau\frac{\partial\left(pv_{0r}\right)}{\partial\varphi}\right)=0.$$

(4.11.15)

For the chosen model we have

$$\frac{\partial p}{\partial r}-g_r\rho-\frac{q}{m}\left[\rho v_{0\varphi}+\tau\frac{q}{m}\rho v_{0\theta}B_r\right]B_\theta=0. \qquad (4.11.16)$$

The both equations (4.11.14) and (4.11.16) are self-consistent if

$$v_{0\varphi} >> \tau \frac{q}{m} v_{0\theta} B_r \,. \tag{4.11.17}$$

It is reasonable to remark that $\tau \frac{q}{m} B_r$ is dimensionless value. In this case the θ-component of the magnet induction B_θ is known value $B_\theta = \frac{\mu\mu_0}{l} NI$ (see also (4.11.8)). We leave only one equation (4.11.14) written here as

$$\rho g_r + \frac{e}{m} \rho v_{0\varphi} B_\theta - \frac{\partial p}{\partial r} = 0 , \tag{4.11.18}$$

where in SI – system $e/m = -1.7588 \cdot 10^{11} C/kg$.

Write down the equation of motion (4.8.2) in the projection on the direction $\mathbf{e}_\varphi$

$$\frac{\partial}{\partial t}\left\{ \rho v_{0\varphi} - \tau\left[\frac{\partial}{\partial t}(\rho v_{0\varphi}) + \frac{1}{r^2}\frac{\partial(r^2 \rho v_{0r} v_{0\varphi})}{\partial r} + \frac{1}{r\sin\theta}\frac{\partial(\rho v_{0\varphi}^2)}{\partial \varphi} + \frac{1}{r\sin\theta}\frac{\partial(\rho v_{0\theta} v_{0\varphi}\sin\theta)}{\partial \theta} \right.\right.$$

$$\left.\left. + \frac{1}{r\sin\theta}\frac{\partial p}{\partial \varphi} - \rho g_\varphi - \frac{q}{m}\rho(v_{0\theta}B_r - v_{0r}B_\theta) \right]\right\}$$

$$- g_\varphi\left[\rho - \tau\left(\frac{\partial \rho}{\partial t} + \frac{1}{r^2}\frac{\partial(r^2 \rho v_{0r})}{\partial r} + \frac{1}{r\sin\theta}\frac{\partial(\rho v_{0\varphi})}{\partial \varphi} + \frac{1}{r\sin\theta}\frac{\partial(\rho v_{0\theta}\sin\theta)}{\partial \theta} \right)\right] -$$

$$- \frac{q}{m}\left\{ \rho v_{0\theta} - \tau\left[\frac{\partial}{\partial t}(\rho v_{0\theta}) + \frac{1}{r^2}\frac{\partial(r^2 \rho v_{0r} v_{0\theta})}{\partial r} + \frac{1}{r\sin\theta}\frac{\partial(\rho v_{0\varphi} v_{0\theta})}{\partial \varphi} + \frac{1}{r\sin\theta}\frac{\partial(\rho v_{0\theta}^2\sin\theta)}{\partial \theta} + \right.\right.$$

$$\left.\left. + \frac{1}{r}\frac{\partial p}{\partial \theta} - \rho g_\theta - \frac{q}{m}\rho(v_{0r}B_\varphi - v_{0\varphi}B_r) \right]\right\} B_r +$$

$$+ \frac{q}{m}\left\{ \rho v_{0r} - \tau\left[\frac{\partial}{\partial t}(\rho v_{0r}) + \frac{1}{r^2}\frac{\partial(r^2 \rho v_{0r}^2)}{\partial r} + \frac{1}{r\sin\theta}\frac{\partial(\rho v_{0\varphi} v_{0r})}{\partial \varphi} + \frac{1}{r\sin\theta}\frac{\partial(\rho v_{0\theta} v_{0r}\sin\theta)}{\partial \theta} + \right.\right.$$

$$\left.\left. + \frac{\partial p}{\partial r} - \rho g_r - \frac{q}{m}\rho(v_{0\varphi}B_\theta - v_{0\theta}B_\varphi) \right]\right\} B_\theta +$$

$$+ \frac{1}{r^2}\frac{\partial}{\partial r}\left\{ r^2\left\{ \rho v_{0r} v_{0\varphi} - \tau\left[\frac{\partial}{\partial t}(\rho v_{0r} v_{0\varphi}) + \frac{1}{r^2}\frac{\partial(r^2 \rho v_{0r}^2 v_{0\varphi})}{\partial r} + \frac{1}{r\sin\theta}\frac{\partial(\rho v_{0\varphi}^2 v_{0r})}{\partial \varphi} \right.\right.\right.$$

$$\left.\left.\left. + \frac{1}{r\sin\theta}\frac{\partial(\rho v_{0\theta} v_{0r} v_{0\varphi}\sin\theta)}{\partial \theta} - g_r \rho v_{0\varphi} - v_{0r}\rho g_\varphi - \frac{q}{m}\rho(v_{0\varphi}B_\theta - v_{0\theta}B_\varphi)v_{0\varphi} - \frac{q}{m}\rho(v_{0\theta}B_r - v_{0r}B_\theta)v_{0r} \right]\right\}\right\} +$$

$$+ \frac{1}{r\sin\theta}\frac{\partial}{\partial \varphi}\left\{ \rho v_{0\varphi}^2 - \tau\left[\frac{\partial}{\partial t}(\rho v_{0\varphi}^2) + \frac{1}{r^2}\frac{\partial(r^2 \rho v_{0r} v_{0\varphi}^2)}{\partial r} + \right.\right.$$

$$\left.\left. + \frac{1}{r\sin\theta}\frac{\partial(\rho v_{0\varphi}^3)}{\partial \varphi} + \frac{1}{r\sin\theta}\frac{\partial(\rho v_{0\theta} v_{0\varphi}^2\sin\theta)}{\partial \theta} - 2 g_\varphi \rho v_{0\varphi} - 2\frac{q}{m}\rho(v_{0\theta}B_r - v_{0r}B_\theta)v_{0\varphi} \right]\right\}$$

$$+ \frac{1}{r\sin\theta}\frac{\partial}{\partial \theta}\left\{ \sin\theta\left\{ \rho v_{0\theta} v_{0\varphi} - \tau\left[\frac{\partial}{\partial t}(\rho v_{0\theta} v_{0\varphi}) + \frac{1}{r^2}\frac{\partial(r^2 \rho v_{0r} v_{0\theta} v_{0\varphi})}{\partial r} + \frac{1}{r\sin\theta}\frac{\partial(\rho v_{0\varphi}^2 v_{0\theta})}{\partial \varphi} \right.\right.\right.$$

$$+\frac{1}{r\sin\theta}\frac{\partial\left(\rho v_{0\theta}^{2}v_{0\varphi}\sin\theta\right)}{\partial\theta}-g_{\theta}\rho v_{0\varphi}-\frac{q}{m}\rho\left(v_{0r}B_{\varphi}-v_{0\varphi}B_{r}\right)v_{0\varphi}-v_{0\theta}\rho g_{\varphi}-\frac{q}{m}\rho\left(v_{0\theta}B_{r}-v_{0r}B_{\theta}\right)v_{0\theta}\Bigg]\Bigg]\Bigg\}$$

$$+\frac{1}{r\sin\theta}\frac{\partial p}{\partial\varphi}-\frac{1}{r\sin\theta}\frac{\partial}{\partial\varphi}\left(\tau\frac{\partial p}{\partial t}\right)-$$

$$-\frac{2}{r\sin\theta}\frac{\partial}{\partial\varphi}\left(\tau\left(\frac{1}{r^{2}}\frac{\partial\left(r^{2}pv_{0r}\right)}{\partial r}+\frac{1}{r\sin\theta}\frac{\partial\left(pv_{0\varphi}\right)}{\partial\varphi}+\frac{1}{r\sin\theta}\frac{\partial\left(pv_{0\theta}\sin\theta\right)}{\partial\theta}\right)\right)$$

$$-\frac{1}{r^{2}}\frac{\partial}{\partial r}\left(\tau r^{2}\frac{\partial\left(pv_{0\varphi}\right)}{\partial r}\right)-\frac{1}{r^{2}\sin\theta}\frac{\partial}{\partial\theta}\left(\tau\sin\theta\frac{\partial\left(pv_{0\varphi}\right)}{\partial\theta}\right)-\frac{1}{r^{2}\sin^{2}\theta}\frac{\partial}{\partial\varphi}\left(\tau\frac{\partial\left(pv_{0\varphi}\right)}{\partial\varphi}\right)=0.$$

(4.11.19)

For $\mathbf{e}_{\varphi}$ – projection we obtain

$$-\frac{q}{m}\left[\rho v_{0\theta}-\tau\frac{q}{m}\rho v_{0\varphi}B_{r}\right]B_{r}+\frac{q}{m}\left\{\rho v_{0r}-\tau\left[\frac{\partial p}{\partial r}-\rho g_{r}-\frac{q}{m}\rho v_{0\varphi}B_{\theta}\right]\right\}B_{\theta}+$$

$$+\frac{1}{r^{2}}\frac{\partial}{\partial r}\left\{r^{2}\tau\rho v_{0\varphi}\left[g_{r}+\frac{q}{m}v_{0\varphi}B_{\theta}\right]\right\}-\frac{1}{r^{2}}\frac{\partial}{\partial r}\left(\tau r^{2}\frac{\partial\left(pv_{0\varphi}\right)}{\partial r}\right)=0. \qquad (4.11.20)$$

Using (4.11.14) we find

$$\frac{q}{m}\rho\left(v_{0r}B_{\theta}-v_{0\theta}B_{r}\right)+\tau\left(\frac{q}{m}\right)^{2}\rho v_{0\varphi}B_{r}^{2}+\frac{1}{r^{2}}\frac{\partial}{\partial r}\left\{r^{2}\tau v_{0\varphi}\left[\rho g_{r}+\frac{q}{m}v_{0\varphi}\rho B_{\theta}\right]\right\}$$

$$-\frac{1}{r^{2}}\frac{\partial}{\partial r}\left(\tau r^{2}\frac{\partial\left(pv_{0\varphi}\right)}{\partial r}\right)=0. \qquad (4.11.21)$$

For the Searle scheme $v_{0r}=0$ and (4.11.21) can be simplified using also the relation

$$\rho g_{r}+\frac{q}{m}\rho v_{0\varphi}B_{\theta}=\frac{\partial p}{\partial r}. \qquad (4.11.22)$$

$$\tau\left(\frac{q}{m}\right)^{2}\rho v_{0\varphi}B_{r}^{2}+\frac{1}{r^{2}}\frac{\partial}{\partial r}\left\{r^{2}\tau v_{0\varphi}\left[\rho g_{r}+\frac{q}{m}v_{0\varphi}\rho B_{\theta}\right]\right\}-\frac{1}{r^{2}}\frac{\partial}{\partial r}\left(\tau r^{2}\frac{\partial\left(pv_{0\varphi}\right)}{\partial r}\right)-\frac{q}{m}\rho v_{0\theta}B_{r}=0.$$

(4.11.23)

or

$$\tau\left(\frac{q}{m}\right)^{2}\rho v_{0\varphi}B_{r}^{2}-\frac{1}{r^{2}}\frac{\partial}{\partial r}\left(\tau r^{2}p\frac{\partial v_{0\varphi}}{\partial r}\right)-\frac{q}{m}\rho v_{0\theta}B_{r}=0. \qquad (4.11.24)$$

From (4.11.24) immediately follows that in local case ($\tau=0$) $v_{0\theta}\equiv 0$ and the disk levitation can not be realized.

Write down the equation of motion (4.8.2) in the projection on the direction $\mathbf{e}_{\theta}$:

$$
\begin{aligned}
&\frac{\partial}{\partial t}\left\{\rho v_{0\theta}-\tau\left[\frac{\partial}{\partial t}(\rho v_{0\theta})+\frac{1}{r^2}\frac{\partial\left(r^2\rho v_{0r}v_{0\theta}\right)}{\partial r}+\frac{1}{r\sin\theta}\frac{\partial\left(\rho v_{0\varphi}v_{0\theta}\right)}{\partial\varphi}+\frac{1}{r\sin\theta}\frac{\partial\left(\rho v_{0\theta}^2\sin\theta\right)}{\partial\theta}\right.\right.\\
&\left.\left.+\frac{1}{r}\frac{\partial p}{\partial\theta}-\rho g_\theta-\frac{q}{m}\rho\left(v_{0r}B_\varphi-v_{0\varphi}B_r\right)\right]\right\}\\
&-g_\theta\left[\rho-\tau\left(\frac{\partial\rho}{\partial t}+\frac{1}{r^2}\frac{\partial\left(r^2\rho v_{0r}\right)}{\partial r}+\frac{1}{r\sin\theta}\frac{\partial\left(\rho v_{0\varphi}\right)}{\partial\varphi}+\frac{1}{r\sin\theta}\frac{\partial\left(\rho v_{0\theta}\sin\theta\right)}{\partial\theta}\right)\right]-\\
&-\frac{q}{m}\left\{\rho v_{0r}-\tau\left[\frac{\partial}{\partial t}(\rho v_{0r})+\frac{1}{r^2}\frac{\partial\left(r^2\rho v_{0r}^2\right)}{\partial r}+\frac{1}{r\sin\theta}\frac{\partial\left(\rho v_{0\varphi}v_{0r}\right)}{\partial\varphi}+\frac{1}{r\sin\theta}\frac{\partial\left(\rho v_{0\theta}v_{0r}\sin\theta\right)}{\partial\theta}+\right.\right.\\
&\left.\left.+\frac{\partial p}{\partial r}-\rho g_r-\frac{q}{m}\rho\left(v_{0\varphi}B_\theta-v_{0\theta}B_\varphi\right)\right]\right\}B_\varphi+\\
&+\frac{q}{m}\left\{\rho v_{0\varphi}-\tau\left[\frac{\partial}{\partial t}(\rho v_{0\varphi})+\frac{1}{r^2}\frac{\partial\left(r^2\rho v_{0r}v_{0\varphi}\right)}{\partial r}+\frac{1}{r\sin\theta}\frac{\partial\left(\rho v_{0\varphi}^2\right)}{\partial\varphi}+\frac{1}{r\sin\theta}\frac{\partial\left(\rho v_{0\theta}v_{0\varphi}\sin\theta\right)}{\partial\theta}+\right.\right.\\
&\left.\left.+\frac{1}{r\sin\theta}\frac{\partial p}{\partial\varphi}-\rho g_\varphi-\frac{q}{m}\rho\left(v_{0\theta}B_r-v_{0r}B_\theta\right)\right]\right\}B_r+\\
&+\frac{1}{r^2}\frac{\partial}{\partial r}\left\{r^2\left\{\rho v_{0r}v_{0\theta}-\tau\left[\frac{\partial}{\partial t}(\rho v_{0r}v_{0\theta})+\frac{1}{r^2}\frac{\partial\left(r^2\rho v_{0r}^2v_{0\theta}\right)}{\partial r}+\frac{1}{r\sin\theta}\frac{\partial\left(\rho v_{0\varphi}v_{0r}v_{0\theta}\right)}{\partial\varphi}\right.\right.\right.\\
&\left.\left.\left.+\frac{1}{r\sin\theta}\frac{\partial\left(\rho v_{0\theta}^2v_{0r}\sin\theta\right)}{\partial\theta}-g_r\rho v_{0\theta}-v_{0r}\rho g_\theta-\frac{q}{m}\rho\left(v_{0\varphi}B_\theta-v_{0\theta}B_\varphi\right)v_{0\theta}-\frac{q}{m}\rho\left(v_{0r}B_\varphi-v_{0\varphi}B_r\right)v_{0r}\right]\right\}\right\}\\
&+\frac{1}{r\sin\theta}\frac{\partial}{\partial\varphi}\left\{\rho v_{0\varphi}v_{0\theta}-\tau\left[\frac{\partial}{\partial t}(\rho v_{0\varphi}v_{0\theta})+\frac{1}{r^2}\frac{\partial\left(r^2\rho v_{0r}v_{0\varphi}v_{0\theta}\right)}{\partial r}+\frac{1}{r\sin\theta}\frac{\partial\left(\rho v_{0\varphi}^2v_{0\theta}\right)}{\partial\varphi}+\right.\right.\\
&\left.\left.+\frac{1}{r\sin\theta}\frac{\partial\left(\rho v_{0\theta}^2v_{0\varphi}\sin\theta\right)}{\partial\theta}-g_\varphi\rho v_{0\theta}-\frac{q}{m}\rho\left(v_{0\theta}B_r-v_{0r}B_\theta\right)v_{0\theta}-g_\theta\rho v_{0\varphi}-\frac{q}{m}\rho\left(v_{0r}B_\varphi-v_{0\varphi}B_r\right)v_{0\varphi}\right]\right\}\\
&+\frac{1}{r\sin\theta}\frac{\partial}{\partial\theta}\left\{\sin\theta\left\{\rho v_{0\theta}^2-\tau\left[\frac{\partial}{\partial t}(\rho v_{0\theta}^2)+\frac{1}{r^2}\frac{\partial\left(r^2\rho v_{0r}v_{0\theta}^2\right)}{\partial r}+\frac{1}{r\sin\theta}\frac{\partial\left(\rho v_{0\theta}^2v_{0\varphi}\right)}{\partial\varphi}\right.\right.\right.\\
&\left.\left.\left.+\frac{1}{r\sin\theta}\frac{\partial\left(\rho v_{0\theta}^3\sin\theta\right)}{\partial\theta}-2g_\theta\rho v_{0\theta}-\frac{q}{m}\rho\left(v_{0r}B_\varphi-v_{0\varphi}B_r\right)v_{0\theta}\right]\right\}\right\}+\frac{1}{r}\frac{\partial p}{\partial\theta}-\frac{1}{r\sin\theta}\frac{\partial}{\partial\theta}\left(\tau\frac{\partial p}{\partial t}\right)-\\
&-\frac{2}{r}\frac{\partial}{\partial\theta}\left(\tau\left(\frac{1}{r^2}\frac{\partial\left(r^2pv_{0r}\right)}{\partial r}+\frac{1}{r\sin\theta}\frac{\partial\left(pv_{0\varphi}\right)}{\partial\varphi}+\frac{1}{r\sin\theta}\frac{\partial\left(pv_{0\theta}\sin\theta\right)}{\partial\theta}\right)\right)\\
&-\frac{1}{r^2}\frac{\partial}{\partial r}\left(\tau r^2\frac{\partial\left(pv_{0\theta}\right)}{\partial r}\right)-\frac{1}{r^2\sin\theta}\frac{\partial}{\partial\theta}\left(\tau\sin\theta\frac{\partial\left(pv_{0\theta}\right)}{\partial\theta}\right)-\frac{1}{r^2\sin^2\theta}\frac{\partial}{\partial\varphi}\left(\tau\frac{\partial\left(pv_{0\theta}\right)}{\partial\varphi}\right)=0.
\end{aligned}
\tag{4.11.25}
$$

We find in the case

$$
\frac{q}{m}\left[\rho v_{0\varphi}+\tau\frac{q}{m}\rho v_{0\theta}B_r\right]B_r+\frac{1}{r^2}\frac{\partial}{\partial r}\left[r^2v_{0\theta}\rho\tau\left(g_r+\frac{q}{m}v_{0\varphi}B_\theta\right)\right]-\frac{1}{r^2}\frac{\partial}{\partial r}\left(\tau r^2\frac{\partial\left(pv_{0\theta}\right)}{\partial r}\right)=0.
\tag{4.11.26}
$$

and using (4.11.22) we reach

$$\frac{q}{m}\left[\rho v_{0\varphi}+\tau\frac{q}{m}\rho v_{0\theta}B_r\right]B_r+\frac{1}{r^2}\frac{\partial}{\partial r}\left[\tau r^2 v_{0\theta}\frac{\partial p}{\partial r}\right]-\frac{1}{r^2}\frac{\partial}{\partial r}\left(\tau r^2\frac{\partial(pv_{0\theta})}{\partial r}\right)=0. \quad (4.11.27)$$

Write down now the energy equation:

$$\frac{\partial}{\partial t}\left\{\frac{1}{2}\rho v_0^2+\varepsilon n+\frac{3}{2}p-\tau\left[\frac{\partial}{\partial t}\left(\frac{1}{2}\rho v_0^2+\varepsilon n+\frac{3}{2}p\right)+\frac{1}{r^2}\frac{\partial}{\partial r}\left(r^2 v_{0r}\left(\frac{1}{2}\rho v_0^2+\varepsilon n+\frac{5}{2}p\right)\right)+\right.\right.$$
$$+\frac{1}{r\sin\theta}\frac{\partial}{\partial\varphi}\left(v_{0\varphi}\left(\frac{1}{2}\rho v_0^2+\varepsilon n+\frac{5}{2}p\right)\right)+\frac{1}{r\sin\theta}\frac{\partial}{\partial\theta}\left(\sin\theta v_{0\theta}\left(\frac{1}{2}\rho v_0^2+\varepsilon n+\frac{5}{2}p\right)\right)-$$
$$\left.\left.-\rho(g_r v_{0r}+g_\varphi v_{0\varphi}+g_\theta v_{0\theta})\quad\right]\right\}+\frac{1}{r^2}\frac{\partial}{\partial r}\left\{r^2\left\{\left(\frac{1}{2}\rho v_0^2+\varepsilon n+\frac{5}{2}p\right)v_{0r}-\right.\right.$$
$$-\tau\left[\frac{\partial}{\partial t}\left(\left(\frac{1}{2}\rho v_0^2+\varepsilon n+\frac{5}{2}p\right)v_{0r}\right)+\frac{1}{r^2}\frac{\partial}{\partial r}\left(r^2\left(\frac{1}{2}\rho v_0^2+\varepsilon n+\frac{7}{2}p\right)v_{0r}^2\right)+\right.$$
$$+\frac{1}{r\sin\theta}\frac{\partial}{\partial\varphi}\left(\left(\frac{1}{2}\rho v_0^2+\varepsilon n+\frac{7}{2}p\right)v_{0\varphi}v_{0r}\right)+\frac{1}{r\sin\theta}\frac{\partial}{\partial\theta}\left(\sin\theta\left(\frac{1}{2}\rho v_0^2+\varepsilon n+\frac{7}{2}p\right)v_{0\theta}v_{0r}\right)-$$
$$-\rho(g_r v_{0r}+g_\varphi v_{0\varphi}+g_\theta v_{0\theta})v_{0r}-\left(\frac{1}{2}\rho v_0^2+\varepsilon n+\frac{3}{2}p\right)g_r-$$
$$\left.\left.\left.-\left(\frac{1}{2}\rho v_0^2+\varepsilon n+\frac{5}{2}p\right)\frac{q}{m}(v_{0\varphi}B_\theta-v_{0\theta}B_\varphi)\right]\right\}\right\}+\frac{1}{r\sin\theta}\frac{\partial}{\partial\varphi}\left\{\left(\frac{1}{2}\rho v_0^2+\varepsilon n+\frac{5}{2}p\right)v_{0\varphi}-\right.$$
$$-\tau\left[\frac{\partial}{\partial t}\left(\left(\frac{1}{2}\rho v_0^2+\varepsilon n+\frac{5}{2}p\right)v_{0\varphi}\right)+\frac{1}{r^2}\frac{\partial}{\partial r}\left(r^2\left(\frac{1}{2}\rho v_0^2+\varepsilon n+\frac{7}{2}p\right)v_{0r}v_{0\varphi}\right)+\right.$$
$$+\frac{1}{r\sin\theta}\frac{\partial}{\partial\varphi}\left(\left(\frac{1}{2}\rho v_0^2+\varepsilon n+\frac{7}{2}p\right)v_{0\varphi}^2\right)+\frac{1}{r\sin\theta}\frac{\partial}{\partial\theta}\left(\sin\theta\left(\frac{1}{2}\rho v_0^2+\varepsilon n+\frac{7}{2}p\right)v_{0\theta}v_{0\varphi}\right)-$$
$$-\rho(g_r v_{0r}+g_\varphi v_{0\varphi}+g_\theta v_{0\theta})v_{0\varphi}-\left(\frac{1}{2}\rho v_0^2+\varepsilon n+\frac{3}{2}p\right)g_\varphi-$$
$$\left.\left.\left(\frac{1}{2}\rho v_0^2+\varepsilon n+\frac{5}{2}p\right)\frac{q}{m}(v_{0\theta}B_r-v_{0r}B_\theta)\right]\right\}++\frac{1}{r\sin\theta}\frac{\partial}{\partial\theta}\left\{\sin\theta\left\{\left(\frac{1}{2}\rho v_0^2+\varepsilon n+\frac{5}{2}p\right)v_{0\theta}-\right.\right.$$
$$\tau\left[\frac{\partial}{\partial t}\left(\left(\frac{1}{2}\rho v_0^2+\varepsilon n+\frac{5}{2}p\right)v_{0\theta}\right)++\frac{1}{r^2}\frac{\partial}{\partial r}\left(r^2\left(\frac{1}{2}\rho v_0^2+\varepsilon n+\frac{7}{2}p\right)v_{0r}v_{0\theta}\right)+\right.$$
$$\frac{1}{r\sin\theta}\frac{\partial}{\partial\varphi}\left(\left(\frac{1}{2}\rho v_0^2+\varepsilon n+\frac{7}{2}p\right)v_{0\varphi}v_{0\theta}\right)+$$
$$+\frac{1}{r\sin\theta}\frac{\partial}{\partial\theta}\left(\sin\theta\left(\frac{1}{2}\rho v_0^2+\varepsilon n+\frac{7}{2}p\right)v_{0\theta}^2\right)-\rho(g_r v_{0r}+g_\varphi v_{0\varphi}+g_\theta v_{0\theta})v_{0\theta}-\left(\frac{1}{2}\rho v_0^2+\varepsilon n+\frac{3}{2}p\right)g_\theta-$$
$$\left.\left.\left.-\left(\frac{1}{2}\rho v_0^2+\varepsilon n+\frac{5}{2}p\right)\frac{q}{m}(v_{0r}B_\varphi-v_{0\varphi}B_r)\right]\right\}\right\}-\left\{\quad\rho(g_r v_{0r}+g_\varphi v_{0\varphi}+g_\theta v_{0\theta})-\right.$$
$$-\tau\left[g_r\left(\frac{\partial}{\partial t}(\rho v_{0r})+\frac{1}{r^2}\frac{\partial}{\partial r}(r^2\rho v_{0r}^2)+\frac{1}{r\sin\theta}\frac{\partial}{\partial\varphi}(\rho v_{0\varphi}v_{0r})+\right.\right.$$
$$\left.+\frac{1}{r\sin\theta}\frac{\partial}{\partial\theta}(\rho v_{0\theta}v_{0r}\sin\theta)+\frac{\partial p}{\partial r}-\rho g_r-qn(v_{0\varphi}B_\theta-v_{0\theta}B_\varphi)\right)+$$

$$+g_\varphi\left(\frac{\partial}{\partial t}(\rho v_{0\varphi})+\frac{1}{r^2}\frac{\partial}{\partial r}(r^2\rho v_{0r}v_{0\varphi})+\frac{1}{r\sin\theta}\frac{\partial}{\partial\varphi}(\rho v_{0\varphi}^2)+\frac{1}{r\sin\theta}\frac{\partial}{\partial\theta}(\rho v_{0\theta}v_{0\varphi}\sin\theta)+\right.$$

$$\left.+\frac{1}{r\sin\theta}\frac{\partial p}{\partial\varphi}-\rho g_\varphi-qn(v_{0\theta}B_r-v_{0r}B_\theta)\right)+g_\theta\left(\frac{\partial}{\partial t}(\rho v_{0\theta})+\frac{1}{r^2}\frac{\partial}{\partial r}(r^2\rho v_{0r}v_{0\theta})+\frac{1}{r\sin\theta}\frac{\partial}{\partial\varphi}(\rho v_{0\varphi}v_{0\theta})\right.$$

$$\left.\left.\left.+\frac{1}{r\sin\theta}\frac{\partial}{\partial\theta}(\rho v_{0\theta}^2\sin\theta)+\frac{1}{r}\frac{\partial p}{\partial\theta}-\rho g_\theta-qn(v_{0r}B_\varphi-v_{0\varphi}B_r)\right)\right]\right\}-$$

$$-\frac{1}{r^2}\frac{\partial}{\partial r}\left(\tau r^2\frac{\partial}{\partial r}\left(\frac{1}{2}pv_0^2+\varepsilon nv_0^2+\frac{5}{2}\frac{p^2}{\rho}\right)\right)-$$

$$-\frac{1}{r^2\sin\theta}\frac{\partial}{\partial\theta}\left(\tau\sin\theta\frac{\partial}{\partial\theta}\left(\frac{1}{2}pv_0^2+\varepsilon nv_0^2+\frac{5}{2}\frac{p^2}{\rho}\right)\right)-\frac{1}{r^2\sin^2\theta}\frac{\partial}{\partial\varphi}\left(\tau\frac{\partial}{\partial\varphi}\left(\frac{1}{2}pv_0^2+\varepsilon nv_0^2+\frac{5}{2}\frac{p^2}{\rho}\right)\right)$$

$$+\frac{1}{r^2}\frac{\partial}{\partial r}(r^2\tau pg_r)+\frac{1}{r\sin\theta}\frac{\partial}{\partial\varphi}(\tau pg_\varphi)+\frac{1}{r\sin\theta}\frac{\partial}{\partial\theta}(\tau pg_\theta\sin\theta)=0. \qquad (4.11.28)$$

Energy equation for the considering case:

$$\frac{1}{r^2}\frac{\partial}{\partial r}\left\{r^2\tau\left[\left(\frac{1}{2}\rho v_0^2+\varepsilon n+\frac{3}{2}p\right)g_r+\left(\frac{1}{2}\rho v_0^2+\varepsilon n+\frac{5}{2}p\right)\frac{q}{m}v_{0\varphi}B_\theta\right]\right\}+$$

$$+\tau g_r\left(\frac{\partial p}{\partial r}-\rho g_r-qnv_{0\varphi}B_\theta\right)-\frac{1}{r^2}\frac{\partial}{\partial r}\left(\tau r^2\frac{\partial}{\partial r}\left(\frac{1}{2}pv_0^2+\varepsilon nv_0^2+\frac{5}{2}\frac{p^2}{\rho}\right)\right)+\frac{1}{r^2}\frac{\partial}{\partial r}(r^2\tau pg_r)=0.$$

$$(4.11.29)$$

Using (4.11.22) we have

$$\frac{1}{r^2}\frac{\partial}{\partial r}\left\{r^2\tau\left[\left(\frac{1}{2}\rho v_0^2+\varepsilon n+\frac{3}{2}p\right)g_r+\left(\frac{1}{2}\rho v_0^2+\varepsilon n+\frac{5}{2}p\right)\frac{q}{m}v_{0\varphi}B_\theta\right]\right\}-$$

$$-\frac{1}{r^2}\frac{\partial}{\partial r}\left(\tau r^2\frac{\partial}{\partial r}\left(\frac{1}{2}pv_0^2+\varepsilon nv_0^2+\frac{5}{2}\frac{p^2}{\rho}\right)\right)+\frac{1}{r^2}\frac{\partial}{\partial r}(r^2\tau pg_r)=0. \qquad (4.11.30)$$

or

$$\left(\frac{1}{2}\rho v_0^2+\varepsilon n+\frac{3}{2}p\right)g_r+\left(\frac{1}{2}\rho v_0^2+\varepsilon n+\frac{5}{2}p\right)\frac{q}{m}v_{0\varphi}B_\theta-$$

$$-\frac{\partial}{\partial r}\left(\frac{1}{2}pv_0^2+\varepsilon nv_0^2+\frac{5}{2}\frac{p^2}{\rho}\right)+pg_r=0. \qquad (4.11.31)$$

or

$$\frac{\partial}{\partial r}\left(pv_0^2+2\varepsilon nv_0^2+5\frac{p^2}{\rho}\right)-(\rho v_0^2+2\varepsilon n+5p)\left(g_r+\frac{q}{m}v_{0\varphi}B_\theta\right)=0. \qquad (4.11.32)$$

But (see (4.11.22)) $\rho g_r+\frac{q}{m}\rho v_{0\varphi}B_\theta=\frac{\partial p}{\partial r}$. Then

$$\frac{\partial}{\partial r}\left(pv_0^2+2\varepsilon nv_0^2+5\frac{p^2}{\rho}\right)-\frac{1}{\rho}(\rho v_0^2+2\varepsilon n+5p)\frac{\partial p}{\partial r}=0 \qquad (4.11.33)$$

or

$$5\frac{\partial}{\partial r}\left(\frac{p^2}{\rho}\right)+\frac{\partial}{\partial r}\left[v_0^2(p+2\varepsilon n)\right]-\left(v_0^2+2\frac{\varepsilon n}{\rho}\right)\frac{\partial p}{\partial r}-5\frac{p}{\rho}\frac{\partial p}{\partial r}=0 \tag{4.11.34}$$

or

$$5\frac{\partial}{\partial r}\left(\frac{p^2}{\rho}\right)+p\frac{\partial v_0^2}{\partial r}+2\frac{\partial}{\partial r}\left[v_0^2\varepsilon n\right]-2\frac{\varepsilon n}{\rho}\frac{\partial p}{\partial r}-5\frac{p}{\rho}\frac{\partial p}{\partial r}=0 \tag{4.11.35}$$

or

$$5p\frac{\partial}{\partial r}\left(\frac{p}{\rho}\right)+p\frac{\partial v_0^2}{\partial r}+2\frac{\partial}{\partial r}\left[v_0^2\varepsilon n\right]-2\frac{\varepsilon n}{\rho}\frac{\partial p}{\partial r}=0. \tag{4.11.36}$$

where

$$2\varepsilon n=\frac{V_{coil}}{\mu\mu_0}B_\theta^2+\frac{S_{coil}\omega_{coil}^2}{2\pi}\rho. \tag{4.11.37}$$

where V_{coil} is the coil volume.

We have the following system of equations (written partly again) for the five unknown values $\rho, g_r, p, v_{0\varphi}, v_{0\theta}$:

Continuum equation

$$\rho g_r+\frac{q}{m}\rho v_{0\varphi}B_\theta-\frac{\partial p}{\partial r}=0, \tag{4.11.38}$$

Motion equation $\mathbf{e}_r$ coincides with the previous equation if $\rho v_{0\varphi} >> \tau\frac{q}{m}\rho v_{0\theta}B_r$.

Motion equation $\mathbf{e}_\varphi$, $\mathbf{e}_\varphi$ – projection.

$$\tau\left(\frac{q}{m}\right)^2\rho v_{0\varphi}B_r^2-\frac{1}{r^2}\frac{\partial}{\partial r}\left(\tau r^2 p\frac{\partial v_{0\varphi}}{\partial r}\right)-\frac{q}{m}\rho v_{0\theta}B_r=0. \tag{4.11.39}$$

Motion equation $\mathbf{e}_\theta$, $\mathbf{e}_\theta$ – projection

$$\frac{q}{m}\rho v_{0\varphi}B_r-\frac{1}{r^2}\frac{\partial}{\partial r}\left(\tau r^2 p\frac{\partial v_{0\theta}}{\partial r}\right)=0. \tag{4.11.40}$$

From the equation immediately follows that in local physics $v_{0\varphi}=0$ even if $B_r\neq 0$.

Energy equation

$$5p\frac{\partial}{\partial r}\left(\frac{p}{\rho}\right)+p\frac{\partial v_0^2}{\partial r}+2\frac{\partial}{\partial r}\left(v_0^2\varepsilon n\right)-2\frac{\varepsilon n}{\rho}\frac{\partial p}{\partial r}=0. \tag{4.11.41}$$

where

$$2\varepsilon n=\frac{V_{coil}}{\mu\mu_0}B_\theta^2+\frac{S_{coil}\omega_{coil}^2}{2\pi}\rho.$$

The fifth equation we need is Poisson equation which is written here as before in the dimensionless form.

$$\frac{\partial}{\partial\widetilde{r}}\left(\widetilde{r}^{2}\widetilde{g}_{r}\right)+\widetilde{G}\widetilde{\rho}\widetilde{r}^{2}=0\,. \tag{4.11.42}$$

Let us write down the full system of equations in the dimensionless form using the scales:

Let us use the scales used before $\tau_0, r_0, u_0, g_0, p_0, B_0$.

$$\tau_0=\frac{r_0}{u_0}\,,\ g_0=\frac{u_0^2}{r_0}\,,\ p_0=\rho_0 u_0^2\,,\ \widetilde{G}=4\pi\widetilde{\gamma}_N\,,\ \widetilde{\gamma}_N=\gamma_N\frac{\rho_0 r_0}{g_0}\,.$$

The continuity equation in the dimensionless form

$$\widetilde{\rho}\widetilde{g}_r+\frac{q}{m}\tau_0 B_0\widetilde{v}_{0\varphi}\widetilde{\rho}\widetilde{B}_\theta-\frac{\partial\widetilde{p}}{\partial\widetilde{r}}=0\,. \tag{4.11.43}$$

Let us introduce the dimensionless parameter $A=\frac{q}{m}\tau_0 B_0$. We have

$$\widetilde{\rho}\widetilde{g}_r+A\widetilde{v}_{0\varphi}\widetilde{\rho}\widetilde{B}_\theta-\frac{\partial\widetilde{p}}{\partial\widetilde{r}}=0\,. \tag{4.11.44}$$

Motion equation $\mathbf{e}_\varphi$, $\mathbf{e}_\varphi$ – projection in the dimensionless form.

$$A^2\widetilde{\tau}\widetilde{\rho}\widetilde{v}_{0\varphi}\widetilde{B}_r^2-\frac{1}{\widetilde{r}^2}\frac{\partial}{\partial\widetilde{r}}\left(\widetilde{\tau}\widetilde{r}^2\widetilde{p}\frac{\partial\widetilde{v}_{0\varphi}}{\partial\widetilde{r}}\right)-A\widetilde{\rho}\widetilde{v}_{0\theta}\widetilde{B}_r=0\,. \tag{4.11.45}$$

Motion equation $\mathbf{e}_\theta$, $\mathbf{e}_\theta$ – projection in the dimensionless form.

$$A\widetilde{\rho}\widetilde{v}_{0\varphi}\widetilde{B}_r-\frac{1}{\widetilde{r}^2}\frac{\partial}{\partial\widetilde{r}}\left(\widetilde{\tau}\widetilde{r}^2\widetilde{p}\frac{\partial\widetilde{v}_{0\theta}}{\partial\widetilde{r}}\right)=0\,. \tag{4.11.46}$$

Energy equation in the dimensionless form.

$$5p\frac{\partial}{\partial r}\left(\frac{p}{\rho}\right)+p\frac{\partial}{\partial r}\left(v_{0\varphi}^2+v_{0\theta}^2\right)+\frac{\partial}{\partial r}\left[\left(v_{0\varphi}^2+v_{0\theta}^2\right)\left(\frac{1}{\mu\mu_0}B_\theta^2+\frac{S_{coil}\omega_{coil}^2}{2\pi}\rho\right)\right]-$$
$$-\frac{1}{\rho}\left(\frac{1}{\mu\mu_0}B_\theta^2+\frac{S_{coil}\omega_{coil}^2}{2\pi}\rho\right)\frac{\partial p}{\partial r}=0, \tag{4.11.47}$$

or

$$5\widetilde{p}\frac{\partial}{\partial\widetilde{r}}\left(\frac{\widetilde{p}}{\widetilde{\rho}}\right)+\widetilde{p}\frac{\partial}{\partial\widetilde{r}}\left(\widetilde{v}_{0\varphi}^2+\widetilde{v}_{0\theta}^2\right)+\frac{\partial}{\partial\widetilde{r}}\left[\left(\widetilde{v}_{0\varphi}^2+\widetilde{v}_{0\theta}^2\right)\left(\frac{1}{\mu\mu_0}B_\theta^2\frac{1}{\rho_0 u_0^2}+\frac{S_{coil}\omega_{coil}^2}{2\pi}\widetilde{\rho}\frac{1}{u_0^2}\right)\right]-$$
$$-\frac{1}{\widetilde{\rho}}\left(\frac{1}{\mu\mu_0}B_\theta^2\frac{1}{\rho_0 u_0^2}+\frac{S_{coil}\omega_{coil}^2}{2\pi}\widetilde{\rho}\frac{1}{u_0^2}\right)\frac{\partial\widetilde{p}}{\partial\widetilde{r}}=0.$$

Let us introduce the notation

$$\widetilde{S}=\frac{S}{\pi r_0^2}\,,\ \widetilde{\omega}_{coil}^2=\omega_{coil}^2\tau_0^2\,,\ C=2\frac{p_{mag}}{p_{kin}},\ D=\frac{\widetilde{S}_{coil}\widetilde{\omega}_{coil}^2}{2}\,,\ p_{kin}=\rho_0 u_0^2\,,\ p_{mag}\frac{1}{\mu\mu_0}\frac{B_\theta^2}{2} \tag{4.11.48}$$

Then

$$5\tilde{p}\frac{\partial}{\partial\tilde{r}}\left(\frac{\tilde{p}}{\tilde{\rho}}\right)+\tilde{p}\frac{\partial}{\partial\tilde{r}}\left(\tilde{v}_{0\varphi}^2+\tilde{v}_{0\theta}^2\right)+\frac{\partial}{\partial\tilde{r}}\left[\left(\tilde{v}_{0\varphi}^2+\tilde{v}_{0\theta}^2\right)\left(\frac{1}{\mu\mu_0}B_\theta^2\frac{1}{\rho_0 u_0^2}+\frac{\tilde{S}_{coil}\tilde{\omega}_{coil}^2}{2}\tilde{\rho}\right)\right]-$$
$$-\frac{1}{\tilde{\rho}}\left(\frac{1}{\mu\mu_0}B_\theta^2\frac{1}{\rho_0 u_0^2}+\frac{\tilde{S}_{coil}\tilde{\omega}_{coil}^2}{2}\tilde{\rho}\right)\frac{\partial\tilde{p}}{\partial\tilde{r}}=0,$$

(4.11.49)

where μ_0 is a permeability constant. Then

$$5\tilde{p}\frac{\partial}{\partial\tilde{r}}\left(\frac{\tilde{p}}{\tilde{\rho}}\right)+\tilde{p}\frac{\partial}{\partial\tilde{r}}\left(\tilde{v}_{0\varphi}^2+\tilde{v}_{0\theta}^2\right)+\frac{\partial}{\partial\tilde{r}}\left[\left(\tilde{v}_{0\varphi}^2+\tilde{v}_{0\theta}^2\right)\left(2\frac{p_{mag}}{p_{kin}}+\frac{\tilde{S}_{coil}\tilde{\omega}_{coil}^2}{2}\tilde{\rho}\right)\right]-$$
$$-\frac{1}{\tilde{\rho}}\left(2\frac{p_{mag}}{p_{kin}}+\frac{\tilde{S}_{coil}\tilde{\omega}_{coil}^2}{2}\tilde{\rho}\right)\frac{\partial\tilde{p}}{\partial\tilde{r}}=0 \qquad (4.11.50)$$

$$5\tilde{p}\frac{\partial}{\partial\tilde{r}}\left(\frac{\tilde{p}}{\tilde{\rho}}\right)+\tilde{p}\frac{\partial}{\partial\tilde{r}}\left(\tilde{v}_{0\varphi}^2+\tilde{v}_{0\theta}^2\right)+\frac{\partial}{\partial\tilde{r}}\left[\left(\tilde{v}_{0\varphi}^2+\tilde{v}_{0\theta}^2\right)\left(C+D\tilde{\rho}\right)\right]-\frac{1}{\tilde{\rho}}\left(C+D\tilde{\rho}\right)\frac{\partial\tilde{p}}{\partial\tilde{r}}=0.$$

(4.11.51)

Finally we have the following system of dimensionless equation (if $v_{0\varphi}>>\tau\frac{q}{m}v_{0\theta}B_r$) with unknown values $p,g_r,v_{0\theta},v_{0\varphi},\rho$, and parameters $A=\frac{q}{m}\tau_0 B_0$, $C=2\frac{p_{mag}}{p_{kin}}$, $D=\frac{\tilde{S}_{coil}\tilde{\omega}_{coil}^2}{2}$.

Poisson equation

$$\frac{\partial}{\partial\tilde{r}}\left(\tilde{r}^2\tilde{g}_r\right)+\tilde{G}\tilde{\rho}\tilde{r}^2=0, \qquad (4.11.52)$$

Continuity equation and motion equation, $\mathbf{e}_r$ - projection

$$\tilde{\rho}\tilde{g}_r+A\tilde{v}_{0\varphi}\tilde{\rho}\tilde{B}_\theta-\frac{\partial\tilde{p}}{\partial\tilde{r}}=0, \qquad (4.11.53)$$

Motion equation, $\mathbf{e}_\varphi$ - projection

$$A\tilde{\rho}\tilde{B}_r(A\tilde{\tau}\tilde{v}_{0\varphi}\tilde{B}_r-\tilde{v}_{0\theta})-\frac{1}{\tilde{r}^2}\frac{\partial}{\partial\tilde{r}}\left(\tilde{\tau}\tilde{r}^2\tilde{p}\frac{\partial\tilde{v}_{0\varphi}}{\partial\tilde{r}}\right)=0, \qquad (4.11.54)$$

Motion equation $\mathbf{e}_\theta$ - projection

$$A\tilde{\rho}\tilde{v}_{0\varphi}\tilde{B}_r-\frac{1}{\tilde{r}^2}\frac{\partial}{\partial\tilde{r}}\left(\tilde{\tau}\tilde{r}^2\tilde{p}\frac{\partial\tilde{v}_{0\theta}}{\partial\tilde{r}}\right)=0, \qquad (4.11.55)$$

Energy equation

$$5\tilde{p}\frac{\partial}{\partial\tilde{r}}\left(\frac{\tilde{p}}{\tilde{\rho}}\right)+\tilde{p}\frac{\partial}{\partial\tilde{r}}\left(\tilde{v}_{0\varphi}^2+\tilde{v}_{0\theta}^2\right)+\frac{\partial}{\partial\tilde{r}}\left[\left(\tilde{v}_{0\varphi}^2+\tilde{v}_{0\theta}^2\right)\left(C+D\tilde{\rho}\right)\right]-\frac{1}{\tilde{\rho}}\left(C+D\tilde{\rho}\right)\frac{\partial\tilde{p}}{\partial\tilde{r}}=0, \qquad (4.11.56)$$

Maxwell equation

$$\frac{\partial E_r}{\partial r}=0. \qquad (4.11.57)$$

Conclusion:

1. In the frame of local physics Searle effect cannot be explained. For this case if $\tau = 0$, the velocities $v_{0\varphi} = 0,\ v_{0\theta} = 0$.

2. The closed system of equations (4.11.52) – (4.11.57) is 1D Cauchy problem. The corresponding energy equation does not contain nonlocal parameter τ in the first approximation.

3. Equation (4.1.58) leads to appearance of the potential difference in radial direction.

4. The system of equations (4.11.52) – (4.11.57) can be solved using numerical methods for the different parameters A, C and D.

Interesting to estimate the solution of equation (4.11.54) if $A\tilde{\tau}\tilde{v}_{0\varphi}\tilde{B}_r >> \tilde{v}_{0\theta}$ and $\tilde{p} \sim const$ and $\tilde{\rho} \sim const$. In this approximation we find

$$\frac{1}{\tilde{r}^2}\frac{\partial}{\partial\tilde{r}}\left(\tilde{r}^2\frac{\partial\tilde{v}_{0\varphi}}{\partial\tilde{r}}\right) - E\tilde{v}_{0\varphi} = 0, \tag{4.11.58}$$

where

$$E = A^2B_r^2\tilde{\tau}\frac{\tilde{\rho}}{\tilde{p}}. \tag{4.11.59}$$

Figure 4.11.5 contains the solution of equation (4.11.58) for the case $E = 1$.

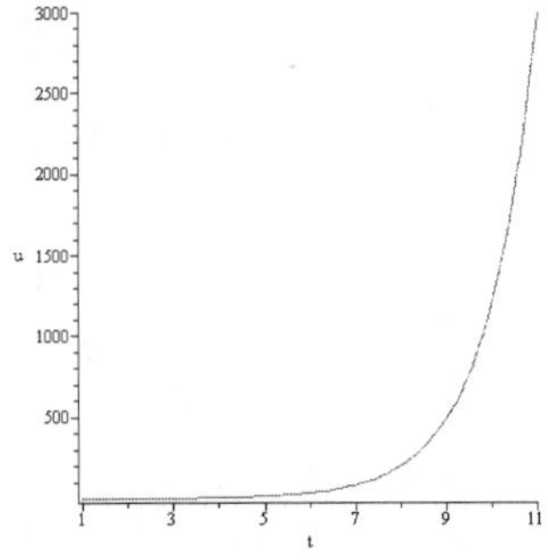

Figure 4.11.5. The orbital velocity $\tilde{v}_{0\varphi}(\tilde{r})$ as solution of equation (4.11.58), $E = 1$, $\tilde{v}_{0\varphi}(1) = 1,\ D[\tilde{v}_{0\varphi}(1)] = 1$.

As we see in this approximation the solution exists in a limited area, for the real situation the orbital roller velocity is practically the same along radius. It looks like Vera Rubin style of rotation.

CHAPTER 5. SOLITONS IN NONLOCAL PHYSICS

5.1. Nonlocal physics and special and general theory of relativity.

Let us investigate the possible connection between nonlocal physics and special theory of relativity (STR). The underlying STR experiment (which has in the following years tremendous variants) belongs to Albert A. Michelson and Edward W. Morley. The Michelson–Morley experiment was performed and published in November, 1887 [84]. They compared the speed of light in perpendicular directions, in an attempt to detect the relative motion of matter through some stationary medium called aether.

The result was negative, in that the expected difference between the speed of light in the direction of movement through the presumed aether, and the speed at right angles, was found not to exist. Michelson–Morley type experiments have been repeated many times with steadily increasing sensitivity. The result is considered as the evidence against the aether theory, and initiated a line of research that eventually led to special relativity, which rules out a stationary aether. The figure 5.1.1 shows the Michelson - Morley device. Calculate the time for which the light will pass the distance to the mirror in the horizontal direction. In one second light travels c meters, and the aether wind blows it in v meters back. Therefore, the actual speed will be equal $(c-v)$. It means that light will reach the mirror over $t = \frac{L_{\Rightarrow}}{c-v}$.

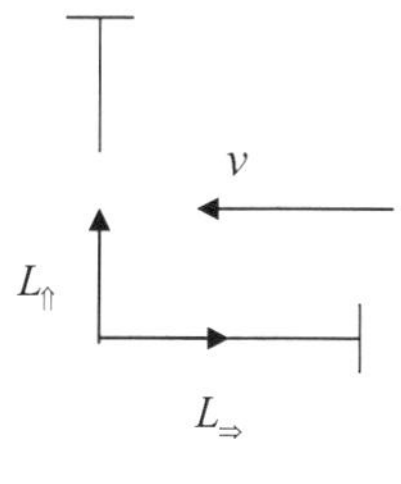

Fig. 5.1.1 The principal scheme of Michelson - Morley experiment.

Obviously the way back will take time $t = \frac{L_{\Rightarrow}}{c+v}$. Total time spent:

$$t_1 = \frac{L_{\Rightarrow}}{c+v} + \frac{L_{\Rightarrow}}{c-v} = \frac{2L_{\Rightarrow}c}{c^2 - v^2}. \qquad (5.1.1)$$

Calculate the elapsed time for moving in the vertical direction. In one second the aether wind will shift the light on the v meters to the left.

In other words the stationary observer should see the real velocity of the vertical movement as $u = c\cos\phi = \sqrt{c^2 - v^2}$. Then the real rate of convergence of the light with mirror (reflected on Fig. 5.1.1 as the upper mirror) is $u = \sqrt{c^2 - v^2}$.

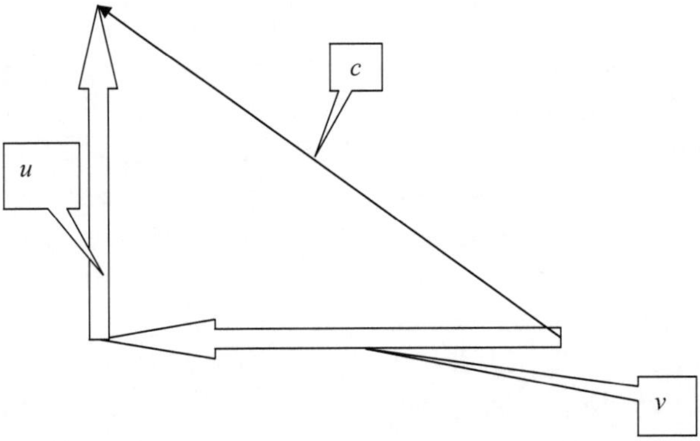

Fig. 5.1.2. Real velocity of the vertical movement

Moving in the opposite direction leads to the symmetrical situation. Thus,

$$t_2 = \frac{2L_{\Uparrow}}{\sqrt{c^2 - v^2}}. \qquad (5.1.2)$$

The time difference is

$$t_1 - t_2 = \frac{2L_{\Rightarrow}c}{c^2 - v^2} - \frac{2L_{\Uparrow}}{\sqrt{c^2 - v^2}} = \frac{2c}{c^2 - v^2}\left[L_{\Rightarrow} - L_{\Uparrow}\frac{\sqrt{c^2 - v^2}}{c}\right] = \frac{2c}{c^2 - v^2}\left[L_{\Rightarrow} - L_{\Uparrow}\sqrt{1 - \frac{v^2}{c^2}}\right]. \qquad (5.1.3)$$

Some conclusions:

1. The mentioned above configuration known as Michelson-Morley experiment (1887) would have detected the earth's motion through the supposed luminiferous aether that most physicists at the time believed was the medium in which light waves propagated. From the first glance the null result of that experiment leads to the condition (see (5.1.3))

$$t_1 - t_2 = 0. \qquad (5.1.4)$$

2. But relation (5.1.4) obtained for the *closed* thermodynamic system without taking into account the direct influence of physical vacuum PV (or in old terminology) luminiferous aether.
3. In principal we consider the *open* thermodynamic system interacting with physical vacuum (PV). But the relation (5.1.1) - (5.1.3) obtained for classic dynamic system without taking into account the direct influence of PV on the mentioned system.
4. Nevertheless we intend to construct simplified theory *excluding* the direct PV influence. This fact leads to kinematic relation

$$L_{\Rightarrow} = L_{\Uparrow}\sqrt{1-\frac{v^2}{c^2}}. \qquad (5.1.5)$$

Let us consider this situation in detail from the position of the nonlocal physics. The Michelson installation can be considered as a device delivering particles moving with the velocities v in the open probe contour filled by PV. The corresponding nonlocal parameter is (see Item 2.6)

$$\tau_D = \frac{H_D}{v^2}. \qquad (5.1.6)$$

For photons we have (υ_f is frequency)

$$\tau_{ph} h\upsilon_f = h, \qquad (5.1.7)$$

or

$$\tau_{ph} = \frac{1}{\upsilon_f}. \qquad (5.1.8)$$

Now we can rewrite the relation (5.1.3) in the form

$$t_1 - t_2 = \frac{2c}{c^2 - v^2}\left[L_{\Rightarrow} - L_{\Uparrow}\sqrt{1-\frac{v^2}{c^2}}\right] = \frac{2c\tau_D}{\tau_D c^2 - H_D}\left[L_{\Rightarrow} - L_{\Uparrow}\sqrt{1-\frac{H_D}{\tau_D c^2}}\right]. \qquad (5.1.9)$$

Michelson's experiment assumes that the length of the instrument's shoulders does not change when rotated to a right angle.

In this case from the position of nonlocal physics

$$t_1 - t_2 = 0 \qquad (5.1.10)$$

only if

$$H_D \to 0. \qquad (5.1.11)$$

or if the PV viscosity tends to zero. As we see this affirmation contradicts the Heisenberg's uncertainty principle.

Moreover, it could be said that the uncertainty principle reflects the existence of Physical Vacuum. From the physical point of view it means that for the realizations (5.1.10) we should exclude the influence of PV in the explicit form. Then (if $H_D \to 0$)

$$t_1 - t_2 \to \frac{2}{c}\left[L_{\Rightarrow} - L_{\Uparrow}\right] = 0. \qquad (5.1.12)$$

H.A. Lorentz was aware in the aether existence. In his lectures on theoretical physics delivered at the University of Leiden he wrote [85], Chapter 1, Paragraph 8: «Reduction in the direction of movement»):

"The negative result of Michelson's experiment can be explained by assuming that the length of the instrument's shoulders changes when rotated to a right angle....This size dependence on the orientation relative to the Earth's motion is not as surprising as it might seem at first. Indeed, the size is determined by molecular forces, and since the latter are transmitted over the aether, on the contrary it would be strange if the state of motion of the latter does not affect the size of bodies. The nature of molecular forces unknown to us; however, if we assume that they are transmitted through the aether in the same way as the electrical forces, then we can build a theory of this reduction, which gives the value of the latter, exactly corresponding to the value necessary to explain the zero effect of the Michelson's experiment. The size of this reduction will be 6,5 cm for the diameter of the Earth and 1/200 microns for the rod length of 1 m."

No difficulties to reproduce the Lorentz' estimation; for example for the rod reduction $L_{rr} = \sqrt{1 - \frac{9 \cdot 10^2}{9 \cdot 10^{10}}} = L\left(1 - \frac{1}{2}10^{-8}\right)m$ we have ($v_{earth} = 30 km/s,\ c = 3 \cdot 10^5 km/s$).

Let us remind now the corresponding consideration in the special relativistic theory. Deduce the equations of transformation from one inertial reference system to another. We use the standard inertial frames K and K' which are set up such that the x and x' axes coincide; the y and y' axes and z and z' axes are parallel. Let the system K' moves relative to the system along the x-axis with velocity υ. Then $y' = y,\ z' = z$. Seen from K, that K' moves in the positive x-direction with speed υ and, seen from K', that K moves in the negative x' -direction with speed υ (see Fig. 5.1.3). Furthermore, it is imagined that in each inertial frame there is an infinite set of recording clocks at rest in the frame and synchronized with each other. Clocks in both frames are set to zero when the origins O and O' coincide.

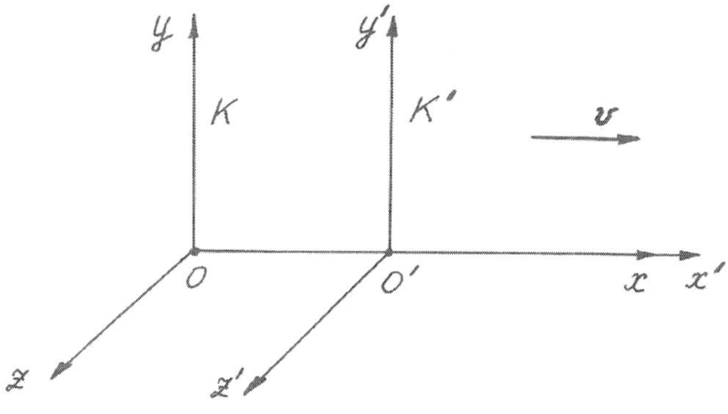

Fig. 5.1.3. Inertial frames K and K'.

Since space and time are homogeneous, the transformations sought are linear functions of the form

$$x = \gamma x' + \beta t', \qquad (5.1.13)$$

$$x' = \hat{\gamma} x + \hat{\beta} t, \qquad (5.1.14)$$

where $\gamma, \hat{\gamma}, \beta, \hat{\beta}$ are constants. For the point O we have $x = 0$, $x' = -\upsilon t'$. Substituting these values into (5.1.13), we obtain $\beta = \gamma\upsilon$. Let us now consider a point O'. For this point $x' = 0$, $x = \upsilon t$. Substituting these values into (5.1.14), we obtain $\hat{\beta} = -\hat{\gamma}\upsilon$. Substituting β and $\hat{\beta}$ in (5.1.13), (5.1.14) and taking into account that $\gamma = \hat{\gamma}$ (because of the equality of the systems K and K′) we find

$$x = \gamma(x' + \upsilon t'), \qquad (5.1.15)$$

$$x' = \gamma(x - \upsilon t). \qquad (5.1.16)$$

The step of principal significance: to determine the coefficient γ we use the principle of the constancy of the speed of light in both frames.

Let at the time moment $t = t' = 0$ from the point $O = O'$ in the direction of the axes x and x' sends a light signal that produces a flash of light on the screen. This screen is located at the point with x-coordinate in system K and x' coordinate in system K′. Then

$$x = ct, \; x' = ct'. \qquad (5.1.17)$$

Substituting (5.1.17) in (5.1.15), (5.1.16), we obtain

$$ct = \gamma(c + \upsilon)t', \qquad (5.1.18)$$

$$ct' = \gamma(c - \upsilon)t. \qquad (5.1.19)$$

Multiplying respectively left and right parts (5.1.18) and (5.1.19), we have

$$c^2 = \gamma^2(c^2 - \upsilon^2), \qquad (5.1.20)$$

$$\gamma = \frac{1}{\sqrt{1-\frac{\upsilon^2}{c^2}}}. \tag{5.1.21}$$

Substituting γ in (5.1.18), (5.1.19) and using (5.1.17) we reach

$$x = \frac{x' + \upsilon t'}{\sqrt{1-\frac{\upsilon^2}{c^2}}}, \tag{5.1.22}$$

$$x' = \frac{x - \upsilon t}{\sqrt{1-\frac{\upsilon^2}{c^2}}}. \tag{5.1.23}$$

Now we derive the transformation for time, expressing t from (5.1.23) and using (5.1.22):

$$t = \frac{1}{\upsilon}\left(x - x'\sqrt{1-\frac{\upsilon^2}{c^2}}\right) = \frac{1}{\upsilon}\left(\frac{x' + \upsilon t'}{\sqrt{1-\frac{\upsilon^2}{c^2}}} - \frac{x'\left(1-\frac{\upsilon^2}{c^2}\right)}{\sqrt{1-\frac{\upsilon^2}{c^2}}}\right) = \frac{t' + \frac{\upsilon}{c^2}x'}{\sqrt{1-\frac{\upsilon^2}{c^2}}}. \tag{5.1.24}$$

Thus, the formulae of transformations, called Lorentz transformations are of the form:

$$x = \frac{x' + \upsilon t'}{\sqrt{1-\frac{\upsilon^2}{c^2}}},\ y = y',\ z = z',\ t = \frac{t' + \frac{\upsilon}{c^2}x'}{\sqrt{1-\frac{\upsilon^2}{c^2}}}. \tag{5.1.25}$$

Reverse conversions can be obtained by replacing υ ($-\upsilon$)

$$x' = \frac{x - \upsilon t}{\sqrt{1-\frac{\upsilon^2}{c^2}}},\ y' = y,\ z' = z,\ t' = \frac{t - \frac{\upsilon}{c^2}x}{\sqrt{1-\frac{\upsilon^2}{c^2}}}. \tag{5.1.26}$$

We turn to the Minkowski coordinates

$$x^\alpha = (ct, x, y, z) = \left(x^0, x^1, x^{,2}, x^{,3}\right), \tag{5.1.27}$$

designation of the upper index in the form like ",2" is done for the purpose to avoid misunderstandings with the exponent in the formula. Lorentz transformations (5.1.26) can be written as

$$x'^0 = \left(x^0 - \frac{\upsilon}{c}x^1\right)\gamma,\ x'^1 = \left(x^1 - \frac{\upsilon}{c}x^0\right)\gamma,\ x'^{,2} = x^{,2},\ x'^{,3} = x^{,3}, \tag{5.1.28}$$

or, in matrix form,

$$X' = \begin{pmatrix} x'^0 \\ x'^1 \\ x'^{,2} \\ x'^{,3} \end{pmatrix} = \begin{pmatrix} \gamma & -\frac{\upsilon}{c}\gamma & 0 & 0 \\ -\frac{\upsilon}{c}\gamma & \gamma & 0 & 0 \\ 0 & 0 & 1 & 0 \\ 0 & 0 & 0 & 1 \end{pmatrix} \begin{pmatrix} x^0 \\ x^1 \\ x^{,2} \\ x^{,3} \end{pmatrix} = \ddot{\Gamma} X . \tag{5.1.29}$$

The symbol «$\ddot{\Gamma}$» emphasizes that «$\ddot{\Gamma}$» is a matrix

$$\ddot{\Gamma} = \begin{pmatrix} \gamma & -\frac{\upsilon}{c}\gamma & 0 & 0 \\ -\frac{\upsilon}{c}\gamma & \gamma & 0 & 0 \\ 0 & 0 & 1 & 0 \\ 0 & 0 & 0 & 1 \end{pmatrix} \tag{5.1.30}$$

Get some consequences of the Lorentz transformations.

Let in the system K lie the rod parallel to the axis x. Its length in this system is $l_0 = x_2 - x_1$ - a self - length of the rod. In accordance with (5.1.22) we have

$$x_1 = \frac{x_1' + \upsilon t'}{\sqrt{1 - \frac{\upsilon^2}{c^2}}}, \quad x_2 = \frac{x_2' + \upsilon t'}{\sqrt{1 - \frac{\upsilon^2}{c^2}}}, \tag{5.1.31}$$

where x_1' and x_2' - are the coordinates of the ends of the rod at the same time moment t'.

$$l_0 = x_2 - x_1 = \frac{x_2' - x_1'}{\sqrt{1 - \frac{\upsilon^2}{c^2}}} = \frac{l}{\sqrt{1 - \frac{\upsilon^2}{c^2}}}, \tag{5.1.32}$$

or

$$l = l_0 \sqrt{1 - \frac{\upsilon^2}{c^2}} . \tag{5.1.33}$$

Compare now the relations (5.1.5) and (5.1.33), we have the identical relations. This result is called as Lorentzian reduced size.

Since the transverse dimensions of the body in its motion does not change, then the body volume is reduced similarly

$$V = V_0 \sqrt{1 - \frac{\upsilon^2}{c^2}} . \tag{5.1.34}$$

Interesting to notice, that Lorentz was aware in the aether existing and claimed in defense of his hypothesis that the size of the Michelson installation should be reduced in the direction of motion for the share $\sqrt{1 - \frac{v^2}{c^2}}$; indeed, in this case $t_1 = t_2$, (see (5.1.3)).

The origin of contradiction consists in situation when the *open* thermodynamic system is considered as a *closed* one. In other words the mirrors should not be considered as fixed objects. Then special theory of relativity is *kinematic* theory which allows avoiding PV effects in the *explicit* form from consideration. This affirmation is valid for the situation when the ratio of the object velocity to the light velocity in an inertial coordinate system is not small, [20].

Criticism of general relativity (GR) is well known topic in theoretical physics (see for example [86]). No reason to discuss here the shortcomings of GR. Nevertheless we should notice:

1. GR does not contain the conservation laws, in other words GR can't serve as a basement for investigation of transport processes in physical systems.
2. GR is a phenomenological generalization of the Poisson equation with the aim to organize the transfer to the Newtonian gravitation.
3. Poisson equation has no interpretation even in Madelung-Schrödinger quantum mechanics (QM). Then we have no chance to obtain the unified GR-QM theory.
4. GR postulates that the rate of transmission of gravitational interactions is equal to the speed of light. Laplace and Poincaré [87, 88] believed that the rate of transmission of gravitational interactions is several orders of magnitude higher than the speed of light; extremely important problem since the time of Laplace and Poincaré.
5. The existence of a singularity of solutions.
6. In many cases, the result of the calculations is simply adjusted to the desired one using a small number of experimental data (including the situation with the Λ-term and Soldner problem discussed in Item 3.3).

5.2. Wave packets in Schrödinger quantum mechanics

The adequate soliton description is the problem of the principal significance in theoretical physics including Madelung-Schrödinger quantum mechanics (MSQM). Schrödinger assumed, that the spatial evolution of a quantum object (such as an electron) can be described as the motion of a wave packet, in other words, a soliton. But Pauli showed that the wave packet, built on Schrödinger, is spreading in space [89]. Really, the non-stationary 1D Schrödinger equation (SE) can be writes as

$$i\hbar\frac{\partial\psi}{\partial t}=-\frac{\hbar^2}{2m}\Delta\psi\,, \tag{5.2.1}$$

where ψ is the wave function. In the ID case we have

$$i\frac{\partial\psi}{\partial t}=-\frac{\hbar}{2m}\frac{\partial^2\psi}{\partial x^2}\,. \tag{5.2.2}$$

Let us introduce the scales $t_0, x_0=\sqrt{\frac{\hbar}{m}t_0}$. Introducing the dimensionless time $\widetilde{t}$ and Cartesian distance $\widetilde{x}$ for (5.2.2) we find ($\hbar=1.054572\ erg\cdot s$)

$$i\frac{\partial\psi}{\partial\widetilde{t}}=-\frac{1}{2}\frac{\partial^2\psi}{\partial\widetilde{x}^2}\,. \tag{5.2.3}$$

The solution (5.2.3) has the form

$$\psi(\widetilde{x},\widetilde{t})=\frac{\sqrt[4]{\frac{2}{\pi}}}{\sqrt{1+2i\widetilde{t}}}e^{-\frac{1}{4}\widetilde{k}_0^2}e^{-\frac{1}{1+2i\widetilde{t}}\left(\widetilde{x}-\frac{i\widetilde{k}_0}{2}\right)^2}, \tag{5.2.4}$$

if

$$\psi(\widetilde{x},0)=\sqrt[4]{\frac{2}{\pi}}e^{-\frac{1}{4}\widetilde{k}_0^2}e^{-\left(\widetilde{x}-\frac{i\widetilde{k}_0}{2}\right)^2}, \tag{5.2.5}$$

where $\widetilde{k}_0$ is the dimensionless wave number. Interesting to notice that

$$\psi(\widetilde{x},0)=\sqrt[4]{\frac{2}{\pi}}e^{-\frac{1}{4}\widetilde{k}_0^2}e^{-\left(\widetilde{x}^2-\widetilde{x}\widetilde{k}_0 i-\frac{\widetilde{k}_0^2}{4}\right)} \tag{5.2.6}$$

and

$$|\psi(\widetilde{x},0)|^2=\psi\psi^*=\sqrt{\frac{2}{\pi}}e^{-\frac{1}{2}\widetilde{k}_0^2}e^{-2\left\{\widetilde{x}^2-\frac{\widetilde{k}_0^2}{4}\right\}}. \tag{5.2.7}$$

The identity (5.2.3) can be proved after substitution (5.2.4) into (5.2.3). For example

$$\begin{aligned} i\frac{\partial\psi}{\partial\widetilde{t}}=&\frac{\sqrt[4]{\frac{2}{\pi}}}{\left(1+2i\widetilde{t}\right)^{3/2}}e^{-\frac{1}{4}\widetilde{k}_0^2}e^{-\frac{1}{1+2i\widetilde{t}}\left(\widetilde{x}-\frac{i\widetilde{k}_0}{2}\right)^2}+\\ &-\frac{\sqrt[4]{\frac{2}{\pi}}}{\left(1+2i\widetilde{t}\right)^{1/2}}e^{-\frac{1}{4}\widetilde{k}_0^2}e^{-\frac{1}{1+2i\widetilde{t}}\left(\widetilde{x}-\frac{i\widetilde{k}_0}{2}\right)^2}\left[\left(\widetilde{x}-\frac{i\widetilde{k}_0}{2}\right)^2\frac{2}{\left(1+2i\widetilde{t}\right)^2}\right] \end{aligned} \tag{5.2.8}$$

or

$$i\frac{\partial\psi}{\partial\tilde{t}}=\frac{\sqrt[4]{\frac{2}{\pi}}}{\left(1+2i\tilde{t}\right)^{3/2}}e^{-\frac{1}{4}\tilde{k}_0^2}e^{-\frac{1}{1+2i\tilde{t}}\left(\tilde{x}-\frac{i\tilde{k}_0}{2}\right)^2}\left[1-\frac{2}{1+2i\tilde{t}}\left(\tilde{x}-\frac{i\tilde{k}_0}{2}\right)^2\right]. \tag{5.2.9}$$

After calculation

$$\frac{\partial^2}{\partial\tilde{x}^2}\psi\left(\tilde{x},\tilde{t}\right)=-\frac{2\sqrt[4]{\frac{2}{\pi}}}{\left(1+2i\tilde{t}\right)^{\frac{3}{2}}}e^{-\frac{1}{4}\tilde{k}_0^2}e^{-\frac{1}{1+2i\tilde{t}}\left(\tilde{x}-\frac{i\tilde{k}_0}{2}\right)^2}\left\{1-\frac{2}{1+2i\tilde{t}}\left(\tilde{x}-\frac{i\tilde{k}_0}{2}\right)^2\right\} \tag{5.2.10}$$

and comparing (5.2.9) and (5.2.10) we find identity (5.2.3).

Let us find now $\left|\psi\left(\tilde{x},\tilde{t}\right)\right|^2=\psi\psi^*$. With this aim we should obtain the complex conjugate value ψ^*. We have the transformed wave function ψ

$$\psi\left(\tilde{x},\tilde{t}\right)=\frac{\sqrt[4]{\frac{2}{\pi}}}{\sqrt{1+2i\tilde{t}}}e^{-\frac{1}{4}\tilde{k}_0^2}e^{-\frac{1}{1+4\tilde{t}^2}\left[\tilde{x}^2-\frac{\tilde{k}_0^2}{4}-2i\tilde{x}\tilde{k}_0-2i\tilde{t}\left(\tilde{x}^2-\frac{\tilde{k}_0^2}{4}-2i\tilde{x}\tilde{k}_0\right)\right]}=$$
$$=\frac{\sqrt[4]{\frac{2}{\pi}}}{\sqrt{1+4\tilde{t}^2}}e^{-\frac{1}{4}\tilde{k}_0^2}e^{-\frac{1}{1+4\tilde{t}^2}\left[\tilde{x}^2-\frac{\tilde{k}_0^2}{4}-4\tilde{t}\tilde{x}\tilde{k}_0\right]}e^{\frac{i}{1+4\tilde{t}^2}\left[2\tilde{x}\tilde{k}_0+2\tilde{t}\tilde{x}^2-\tilde{t}\frac{\tilde{k}_0^2}{2}\right]}\sqrt{1-2i\tilde{t}}. \tag{5.2.11}$$

Using the De Moivre formula (1707) we obtain

$$\psi\left(\tilde{x},\tilde{t}\right)=\sqrt[4]{\frac{2}{\pi\left(1+4\tilde{t}^2\right)}}e^{-\frac{1}{4}\tilde{k}_0^2}e^{-\frac{1}{1+4\tilde{t}^2}\left[\tilde{x}^2-\frac{\tilde{k}_0^2}{4}-4\tilde{t}\tilde{x}\tilde{k}_0\right]}e^{i\left\{\frac{1}{1+4\tilde{t}^2}\left[2\tilde{x}\tilde{k}_0+2\tilde{t}\tilde{x}^2-\tilde{t}\frac{\tilde{k}_0^2}{2}\right]+\arctan\left(-4\tilde{t}\right)\right\}}. \tag{5.2.12}$$

Then

$$\psi^*\left(\tilde{x},\tilde{t}\right)=\sqrt[4]{\frac{2}{\pi\left(1+4\tilde{t}^2\right)}}e^{-\frac{1}{4}\tilde{k}_0^2}e^{-\frac{1}{1+4\tilde{t}^2}\left[\tilde{x}^2-\frac{\tilde{k}_0^2}{4}-4\tilde{t}\tilde{x}\tilde{k}_0\right]}e^{-i\left\{\frac{1}{1+4\tilde{t}^2}\left[2\tilde{x}\tilde{k}_0+2\tilde{t}\tilde{x}^2-\tilde{t}\frac{\tilde{k}_0^2}{2}\right]+\arctan\left(-4\tilde{t}\right)\right\}} \tag{5.2.13}$$

Now we can calculate

$$\left|\psi\left(\tilde{x},\tilde{t}\right)\right|^2=\psi\psi^*=\sqrt{\frac{2}{\pi\left(1+4\tilde{t}^2\right)}}e^{-\frac{1}{2}\tilde{k}_0^2}e^{-\frac{2}{1+4\tilde{t}^2}\left\{\tilde{x}^2-\frac{\tilde{k}_0^2}{4}-4\tilde{t}\tilde{k}_0\tilde{x}\right\}}. \tag{5.2.14}$$

For zero time moment we reach from (5.2.14)

$$\left|\psi\left(\tilde{x},0\right)\right|^2=\psi\psi^*=\sqrt{\frac{2}{\pi}}e^{-\frac{1}{2}\tilde{k}_0^2}e^{-2\left\{\tilde{x}^2-\frac{\tilde{k}_0^2}{4}\right\}} \tag{5.2.15}$$

and we reveal coinsiding (5.2.7) and (5.2.15).

It is well known that basic Schrödinger equation (SE) of quantum mechanics firstly was introduced as a quantum mechanical postulate. The obvious next step should be done and was realized by E. Madelung in 1927 – the derivation of special hydrodynamic form of SE after introduction wave function ψ_w as

$$\psi_w(x, y, z, t) = \alpha(x, y, z, t)\ e^{i\beta(x,y,z,t)}. \tag{5.2.16}$$

Using (5.2.16) and separating the real and imagine parts of SE one obtains (all details in Item 7.2)

$$\frac{\partial \alpha^2}{\partial t} + \frac{\partial}{\partial \mathbf{r}} \cdot \left(\frac{\alpha^2 \hbar}{m} \frac{\partial \beta}{\partial \mathbf{r}} \right) = 0, \tag{5.2.17}$$

and Eq. (5.2.14) immediately transforms in continuity equation if the identifications for density and velocity take place

$$\rho = \alpha^2, \tag{5.2.18}$$

$$\mathbf{v} = \frac{\partial}{\partial \mathbf{r}}(\beta\hbar / m) \tag{5.2.19}$$

Then in the Schrödinger-Madelung model for this case

$$\rho = \left|\psi(\tilde{x}, \tilde{t})\right|^2 = \psi\psi^* = \sqrt{\frac{2}{\pi(1+4\tilde{t}^2)}} e^{-\frac{1}{2}\tilde{k}_0^2} e^{-\frac{2}{1+4\tilde{t}^2}\left\{\tilde{x}^2 - \frac{\tilde{k}_0^2}{4} - 4\tilde{t}\tilde{k}_0\tilde{x}\right\}}. \tag{5.2.20}$$

Then, an impression of the dispersive behavior of this wave packet is obvious by looking at the probability density (5.2.17). For the large $\tilde{t}$

$$\rho = \left|\psi(\tilde{x}, \tilde{t})\right|^2 = \frac{1}{\tilde{t}} \frac{1}{\sqrt{2\pi}} e^{-\frac{1}{2}\tilde{k}_0^2} e^{-\frac{1}{2\tilde{t}^2}\left\{\tilde{x}^2 - \frac{\tilde{k}_0^2}{4} - 4\tilde{t}\tilde{k}_0\tilde{x}\right\}} \sim \frac{1}{\tilde{t}} e^{\frac{2}{\tilde{t}}\tilde{k}_0\tilde{x}} \sim \frac{1}{t^2}. \tag{5.2.21}$$

It is evident that this dispersive wave packet, while moving with constant group velocity ($\tilde{k}_0$=const), is delocalizing rapidly (if $\tilde{t} \to \infty$). This fact leads to dramatic consequences not only for the theoretical physics but for biology also (see Item 7.7).

The nonlocal physics radically improve the situation; as a result we obtain stable solitons (see the following text).

5.3. Non-stationary 1D solitons in the nonlocal physics ($\tau = const$).

The 1D non-stationsary GHE in the potential field of forces can be written as

(continuity equation)

$$\frac{\partial}{\partial t}\left\{\rho-\tau\left[\frac{\partial\rho}{\partial t}+\frac{\partial}{\partial x}(\rho v_0)\right]\right\}+\frac{\partial}{\partial x}\left\{\rho v_0-\tau\left[\frac{\partial}{\partial t}(\rho v_0)+\right.\right.$$
$$\left.\left.+\frac{\partial}{\partial x}\left(\rho v_0^2\right)+\frac{\partial p}{\partial x}+\rho\frac{\partial U}{\partial x}\right]\right\}=0. \tag{5.3.1}$$

(motion equation)

$$\frac{\partial}{\partial t}\left\{\rho v_0-\tau\left[\frac{\partial}{\partial t}(\rho v_0)+\frac{\partial}{\partial x}\left(\rho v_0^2\right)+\frac{\partial p}{\partial x}+\rho\frac{\partial U}{\partial x}\right]\right\}+$$
$$+\frac{\partial U}{\partial x}\left[\rho-\tau\left(\frac{\partial\rho}{\partial t}+\frac{\partial}{\partial x}(\rho v_0)\right)\right]+ \tag{5.3.2}$$
$$+\frac{\partial}{\partial x}\left\{\rho v_0^2+p-\tau\left[\frac{\partial}{\partial t}\left(\rho v_0^2+p\right)+\frac{\partial}{\partial x}\left(\rho v_0^3+3pv_0\right)+2\rho v_0\frac{\partial U}{\partial x}\right]\right\}=0,$$

(energy equation)

$$\frac{\partial}{\partial t}\left\{\rho v_0^2+3p-\tau\left[\frac{\partial}{\partial t}\left(\rho v_0^2+3p\right)+\frac{\partial}{\partial x}\left(\rho v_0^3+5pv_0\right)+2\rho v_0\frac{\partial U}{\partial x}\right]\right\}+$$
$$+\frac{\partial}{\partial x}\left\{\rho v_0^3+5pv_0-\tau\left[\frac{\partial}{\partial t}\left(\rho v_0^3+5pv_0\right)+\frac{\partial}{\partial x}\left(\rho v_0^4+\right.\right.\right.$$
$$\left.\left.\left.+8pv_0^2+5\frac{p^2}{\rho}\right)+\frac{\partial U}{\partial x}\left(3\rho v_0^2+5p\right)\right]\right\}+ \tag{5.3.3}$$
$$+2\frac{\partial U}{\partial x}\left\{\rho v_0-\tau\left[\frac{\partial}{\partial t}(\rho v_0)+\frac{\partial}{\partial x}\left(\rho v_0^2+p\right)+\rho\frac{\partial U}{\partial x}\right]\right\}=0.$$

We believe that $\tau = const,\ v_0 = u$, we use the following system of scales:

$$\rho_0,\ u_0,\ t_0=\tau^{(0)}, x_0=u_0t_0,\ U_0=u_0^2,\ p_0=\rho_0u_0^2.$$

We are looking for wave solutions. To this end, we use a moving coordinate system. The system moves to the right in the direction of increasing positive values $\tilde{x}$

$$\tilde{\xi}=\tilde{x}-\tilde{C}\tilde{t}. \tag{5.3.4}$$

We calculate the derivatives, noting that in the moving coordinate system all the introduced dependent hydrodynamic variables are functions $\tilde{\xi}$. In particular,

$$\frac{\partial\tilde{\rho}}{\partial\tilde{t}}=\frac{\partial\tilde{\rho}}{\partial\tilde{\xi}}\frac{\partial\tilde{\xi}}{\partial\tilde{t}}=-\tilde{C}\frac{\partial\tilde{\rho}}{\partial\tilde{\xi}}. \tag{5.3.5}$$

Likewise,

$$\frac{\partial}{\partial \tilde{t}}(\tilde{\rho}\tilde{u}) = -\tilde{C}\frac{\partial}{\partial \tilde{\xi}}(\tilde{\rho}\tilde{u}). \tag{5.3.6}$$

From continuity equation

$$\begin{gathered}\frac{\partial}{\partial t}\left\{\rho - \tau\left[\frac{\partial \rho}{\partial t} + \frac{\partial}{\partial x}(\rho u)\right]\right\} + \frac{\partial}{\partial x}\left\{\rho - \tau\left[\frac{\partial}{\partial t}(\rho) + \right.\right. \\ \left.\left. + \frac{\partial}{\partial x}(\rho u^2) + \frac{\partial p}{\partial x} + \rho\frac{\partial U}{\partial x}\right]\right\} = 0,\end{gathered} \tag{5.3.7}$$

follows

$$\begin{gathered}-\tilde{C}\frac{\partial \tilde{\rho}}{\partial \tilde{\xi}} - \tilde{C}^2\frac{\partial^2 \tilde{\rho}}{\partial \tilde{\xi}^2} + \tilde{C}\frac{\partial^2}{\partial \tilde{\xi}^2}(\tilde{\rho}\tilde{u}) + \\ + \frac{\partial}{\partial \tilde{\xi}}\left\{\tilde{\rho}\tilde{u} + \tilde{C}\frac{\partial}{\partial \tilde{\xi}}(\tilde{\rho}\tilde{u}) - \frac{\partial}{\partial \tilde{\xi}}(\tilde{\rho}\tilde{u}^2) - \frac{\partial \tilde{p}}{\partial \tilde{\xi}} - \tilde{\rho}\frac{\partial \tilde{U}}{\partial \tilde{\xi}}\right\} = 0\end{gathered}, \tag{5.3.8}$$

Let be $\tilde{C} = 1$.

$$\begin{gathered}-\frac{\partial \tilde{\rho}}{\partial \tilde{\xi}} - \frac{\partial^2 \tilde{\rho}}{\partial \tilde{\xi}^2} + \frac{\partial^2}{\partial \tilde{\xi}^2}(\tilde{\rho}\tilde{u}) + \\ + \frac{\partial}{\partial \tilde{\xi}}\left\{\tilde{\rho}\tilde{u} + \frac{\partial}{\partial \tilde{\xi}}(\tilde{\rho}\tilde{u}) - \frac{\partial}{\partial \tilde{\xi}}(\tilde{\rho}\tilde{u}^2) - \frac{\partial \tilde{p}}{\partial \tilde{\xi}} - \tilde{\rho}\frac{\partial \tilde{U}}{\partial \tilde{\xi}}\right\} = 0\end{gathered} \tag{5.3.9}$$

or

$$-\frac{\partial \tilde{\rho}}{\partial \tilde{\xi}} - \frac{\partial^2 \tilde{\rho}}{\partial \tilde{\xi}^2} + 2\frac{\partial^2}{\partial \tilde{\xi}^2}(\tilde{\rho}\tilde{u}) + \frac{\partial}{\partial \tilde{\xi}}\left\{\tilde{\rho}\tilde{u} - \frac{\partial}{\partial \tilde{\xi}}(\tilde{\rho}\tilde{u}^2) - \frac{\partial \tilde{p}}{\partial \tilde{\xi}} - \tilde{\rho}\frac{\partial \tilde{U}}{\partial \tilde{\xi}}\right\} = 0. \tag{5.3.10}$$

Single integration is possible. However, we will carry out further transformations

$$\frac{\partial^2 \tilde{\rho}}{\partial \tilde{\xi}^2} + \frac{\partial \tilde{\rho}}{\partial \tilde{\xi}} - 2\frac{\partial^2}{\partial \tilde{\xi}^2}(\tilde{\rho}\tilde{u}) - \frac{\partial}{\partial \tilde{\xi}}(\tilde{\rho}\tilde{u}) + \frac{\partial^2}{\partial \tilde{\xi}^2}(\tilde{\rho}\tilde{u}^2) + \frac{\partial^2 \tilde{p}}{\partial \tilde{\xi}^2} + \frac{\partial}{\partial \tilde{\xi}}\left(\tilde{\rho}\frac{\partial \tilde{U}}{\partial \tilde{\xi}}\right) = 0 \tag{5.3.11}$$

From the motion equation

$$\begin{gathered}\frac{\partial}{\partial t}\left\{\rho u - \tau^{(0)}\left[\frac{\partial}{\partial t}(\rho u) + \frac{\partial}{\partial x}(\rho u^2) + \frac{\partial p}{\partial x} + \rho\frac{\partial U}{\partial x}\right]\right\} + \\ + \frac{\partial U}{\partial x}\left[\rho - \tau\left(\frac{\partial \rho}{\partial t} + \frac{\partial}{\partial x}(\rho u)\right)\right] + \\ + \frac{\partial}{\partial x}\left\{\rho u^2 + p - \tau\left[\frac{\partial}{\partial t}(\rho u^2 + p) + \frac{\partial}{\partial x}(\rho u^3 + 3pu) + 2\rho u\frac{\partial U}{\partial x}\right]\right\} = 0\end{gathered} \tag{5.3.12}$$

follows

$$-\widetilde{C}\frac{\partial}{\partial\widetilde{\xi}}(\widetilde{\rho}\widetilde{u})+\widetilde{C}\frac{\partial}{\partial\widetilde{\xi}}\left\{-\widetilde{C}\frac{\partial}{\partial\widetilde{\xi}}(\widetilde{\rho}\widetilde{u})+\widetilde{\rho}\frac{\partial\widetilde{U}}{\partial\widetilde{\xi}}+\frac{\partial}{\partial\widetilde{\xi}}\left(\widetilde{\rho}\widetilde{u}^{2}\right)+\frac{\partial\widetilde{p}}{\partial\widetilde{\xi}}\right\}+$$

$$+\frac{\partial\widetilde{U}}{\partial\widetilde{\xi}}\left(\widetilde{\rho}+\widetilde{C}\frac{\partial\widetilde{\rho}}{\partial\widetilde{\xi}}-\frac{\partial}{\partial\widetilde{\xi}}(\widetilde{\rho}\widetilde{u})\right)+\frac{\partial}{\partial\widetilde{\xi}}\left\{\begin{array}{l}\widetilde{\rho}\widetilde{u}^{2}+\widetilde{p}+\widetilde{C}\frac{\partial}{\partial\widetilde{\xi}}\left(\widetilde{\rho}\widetilde{u}^{2}\right)+\widetilde{C}\frac{\partial\widetilde{p}}{\partial\widetilde{\xi}}-\\ -\frac{\partial}{\partial\widetilde{\xi}}\left(\widetilde{\rho}\widetilde{u}^{3}\right)-3\frac{\partial}{\partial\widetilde{\xi}}(\widetilde{p}\widetilde{u})-2\widetilde{\rho}\widetilde{u}\frac{\partial\widetilde{U}}{\partial\widetilde{\xi}}\end{array}\right\}=0,$$

(5.3.13)

or if $\widetilde{C}=1$

$$-\frac{\partial}{\partial\widetilde{\xi}}(\widetilde{\rho}\widetilde{u})+\frac{\partial}{\partial\widetilde{\xi}}\left\{\begin{array}{l}-\frac{\partial}{\partial\widetilde{\xi}}(\widetilde{\rho}\widetilde{u})+\widetilde{\rho}\frac{\partial\widetilde{U}}{\partial\widetilde{\xi}}+2\frac{\partial}{\partial\widetilde{\xi}}\left(\widetilde{\rho}\widetilde{u}^{2}\right)+2\frac{\partial\widetilde{p}}{\partial\widetilde{\xi}}+\widetilde{\rho}\widetilde{u}^{2}+\widetilde{p}-\\ -\frac{\partial}{\partial\widetilde{\xi}}\left(\widetilde{\rho}\widetilde{u}^{3}\right)-3\frac{\partial}{\partial\widetilde{\xi}}(\widetilde{p}\widetilde{u})-2\widetilde{\rho}\widetilde{u}\frac{\partial\widetilde{U}}{\partial\widetilde{\xi}}\end{array}\right\}$$

$$+\frac{\partial\widetilde{U}}{\partial\widetilde{\xi}}\left(\widetilde{\rho}+\frac{\partial\widetilde{\rho}}{\partial\widetilde{\xi}}-\frac{\partial}{\partial\widetilde{\xi}}(\widetilde{\rho}\widetilde{u})\right)=0,$$

(5.3.14)

or

$$\frac{\partial^{2}}{\partial\widetilde{\xi}^{2}}(\widetilde{\rho}\widetilde{u})+\frac{\partial}{\partial\widetilde{\xi}}(\widetilde{\rho}\widetilde{u})-\frac{\partial}{\partial\widetilde{\xi}}\left(\widetilde{\rho}\frac{\partial\widetilde{U}}{\partial\widetilde{\xi}}\right)-2\frac{\partial^{2}}{\partial\widetilde{\xi}^{2}}\left(\widetilde{\rho}\widetilde{u}^{2}\right)-2\frac{\partial^{2}\widetilde{p}}{\partial\widetilde{\xi}^{2}}-\frac{\partial}{\partial\widetilde{\xi}}\left(\widetilde{\rho}\widetilde{u}^{2}\right)-\frac{\partial\widetilde{p}}{\partial\widetilde{\xi}}+$$

$$+\frac{\partial^{2}}{\partial\widetilde{\xi}^{2}}\left(\widetilde{\rho}\widetilde{u}^{3}\right)+3\frac{\partial^{2}}{\partial\widetilde{\xi}^{2}}(\widetilde{p}\widetilde{u})+2\frac{\partial}{\partial\widetilde{\xi}}\left(\widetilde{\rho}\widetilde{u}\frac{\partial\widetilde{U}}{\partial\widetilde{\xi}}\right)-\frac{\partial\widetilde{U}}{\partial\widetilde{\xi}}\left(\widetilde{\rho}+\frac{\partial\widetilde{\rho}}{\partial\widetilde{\xi}}-\frac{\partial}{\partial\widetilde{\xi}}(\widetilde{\rho}\widetilde{u})\right)=0,$$

(5.3.15)

or

$$\frac{\partial^{2}}{\partial\widetilde{\xi}^{2}}(\widetilde{\rho}\widetilde{u})+\frac{\partial}{\partial\widetilde{\xi}}(\widetilde{\rho}\widetilde{u})-2\frac{\partial^{2}}{\partial\widetilde{\xi}^{2}}\left(\widetilde{\rho}\widetilde{u}^{2}\right)-2\frac{\partial^{2}\widetilde{p}}{\partial\widetilde{\xi}^{2}}-\frac{\partial}{\partial\widetilde{\xi}}\left(\widetilde{\rho}\widetilde{u}^{2}\right)-\frac{\partial\widetilde{p}}{\partial\widetilde{\xi}}+\frac{\partial^{2}}{\partial\widetilde{\xi}^{2}}\left(\widetilde{\rho}\widetilde{u}^{3}\right)+$$

$$+3\frac{\partial^{2}}{\partial\widetilde{\xi}^{2}}(\widetilde{p}\widetilde{u})+2\frac{\partial}{\partial\widetilde{\xi}}\left(\widetilde{\rho}\widetilde{u}\frac{\partial\widetilde{U}}{\partial\widetilde{\xi}}\right)-\frac{\partial}{\partial\widetilde{\xi}}\left(\widetilde{\rho}\frac{\partial\widetilde{U}}{\partial\widetilde{\xi}}\right)-\frac{\partial\widetilde{U}}{\partial\widetilde{\xi}}\left(\widetilde{\rho}+\frac{\partial\widetilde{\rho}}{\partial\widetilde{\xi}}-\frac{\partial}{\partial\widetilde{\xi}}(\widetilde{\rho}\widetilde{u})\right)=0,$$

(5.3.16)

From the energy equation

$$\frac{\partial}{\partial t}\left\{\rho u^{2}+3p-\tau\left[\frac{\partial}{\partial t}\left(\rho u^{2}+3p\right)+\frac{\partial}{\partial x}\left(\rho u^{3}+5pu\right)+2\rho u\frac{\partial U}{\partial x}\right]\right\}+$$

$$+\frac{\partial}{\partial x}\left\{\rho u^{3}+5pu-\tau\left[\frac{\partial}{\partial t}\left(\rho u^{3}+5pu\right)+\frac{\partial}{\partial x}\left(\rho u^{4}+\right.\right.\right.$$

$$\left.\left.\left.+8pu^{2}+5\frac{p^{2}}{\rho}\right)+\frac{\partial U}{\partial x}\left(3\rho u^{2}+5p\right)\right]\right\}+$$

$$+2\frac{\partial U}{\partial x}\left\{\rho u-\tau\left[\frac{\partial}{\partial t}(\rho u)+\frac{\partial}{\partial x}\left(\rho u^{2}+p\right)+\rho\frac{\partial U}{\partial x}\right]\right\}=0$$

(5.3.17)

we have

$$-\widetilde{C}\frac{\partial}{\partial\widetilde{\xi}}\left(\widetilde{\rho}\widetilde{u}^{2}\right)-3\widetilde{C}\frac{\partial\widetilde{p}}{\partial\widetilde{\xi}}+\widetilde{C}\frac{\partial}{\partial\widetilde{\xi}}\left\{\begin{array}{l}-\widetilde{C}\frac{\partial}{\partial\widetilde{\xi}}\left(\widetilde{\rho}\widetilde{u}^{2}\right)-3\widetilde{C}\frac{\partial\widetilde{p}}{\partial\widetilde{\xi}}+\frac{\partial}{\partial\widetilde{\xi}}\left(\widetilde{\rho}\widetilde{u}^{3}\right)+\\+5\frac{\partial}{\partial\widetilde{\xi}}\left(\widetilde{p}\widetilde{u}\right)+2\widetilde{\rho}\widetilde{u}\frac{\partial\widetilde{U}}{\partial\widetilde{\xi}}\end{array}\right\}+$$

$$+\frac{\partial}{\partial\widetilde{\xi}}\left\{\begin{array}{l}\widetilde{\rho}\widetilde{u}^{3}+5\widetilde{p}\widetilde{u}+\widetilde{C}\frac{\partial}{\partial\widetilde{\xi}}\left(\widetilde{\rho}\widetilde{u}^{3}\right)+5\widetilde{C}\frac{\partial}{\partial\widetilde{\xi}}\left(\widetilde{p}\widetilde{u}\right)-\frac{\partial}{\partial\widetilde{\xi}}\left(\widetilde{\rho}\widetilde{u}^{4}\right)-8\frac{\partial}{\partial\widetilde{\xi}}\left(\widetilde{p}\widetilde{u}^{2}\right)-\\-5\frac{\partial}{\partial\widetilde{\xi}}\frac{\widetilde{p}^{2}}{\widetilde{\rho}}-\frac{\partial\widetilde{U}}{\partial\widetilde{\xi}}\left(5\widetilde{p}+3\widetilde{\rho}\widetilde{u}^{2}\right)\end{array}\right\}+$$

$$+2\frac{\partial\widetilde{U}}{\partial\widetilde{\xi}}\left(\widetilde{\rho}\widetilde{u}+\widetilde{C}\frac{\partial}{\partial\widetilde{\xi}}\left(\widetilde{\rho}\widetilde{u}\right)-\frac{\partial}{\partial\widetilde{\xi}}\left(\widetilde{\rho}\widetilde{u}^{2}\right)-\frac{\partial\widetilde{p}}{\partial\widetilde{\xi}}-\widetilde{\rho}\frac{\partial\widetilde{U}}{\partial\widetilde{\xi}}\right)=0, \tag{5.3.18}$$

and if $\widetilde{C}=1$ we reach

$$-\frac{\partial}{\partial\widetilde{\xi}}\left(\widetilde{\rho}\widetilde{u}^{2}\right)-3\frac{\partial\widetilde{p}}{\partial\widetilde{\xi}}-\frac{\partial^{2}}{\partial\widetilde{\xi}^{2}}\left(\widetilde{\rho}\widetilde{u}^{2}\right)-3\frac{\partial^{2}\widetilde{p}}{\partial\widetilde{\xi}^{2}}+\frac{\partial^{2}}{\partial\widetilde{\xi}^{2}}\left(\widetilde{\rho}\widetilde{u}^{3}\right)+5\frac{\partial^{2}}{\partial\widetilde{\xi}^{2}}\left(\widetilde{p}\widetilde{u}\right)+$$

$$+2\frac{\partial}{\partial\widetilde{\xi}}\left(\widetilde{\rho}\widetilde{u}\frac{\partial\widetilde{U}}{\partial\widetilde{\xi}}\right)+\frac{\partial}{\partial\widetilde{\xi}}\left(\widetilde{\rho}\widetilde{u}^{3}\right)+5\frac{\partial}{\partial\widetilde{\xi}}\left(\widetilde{p}\widetilde{u}\right)+\frac{\partial^{2}}{\partial\widetilde{\xi}^{2}}\left(\widetilde{\rho}\widetilde{u}^{3}\right)+5\frac{\partial^{2}}{\partial\widetilde{\xi}^{2}}\left(\widetilde{p}\widetilde{u}\right)-\frac{\partial^{2}}{\partial\widetilde{\xi}^{2}}\left(\widetilde{\rho}\widetilde{u}^{4}\right)$$

$$-8\frac{\partial^{2}}{\partial\widetilde{\xi}^{2}}\left(\widetilde{p}\widetilde{u}^{2}\right)-5\frac{\partial^{2}}{\partial\widetilde{\xi}^{2}}\frac{\widetilde{p}^{2}}{\widetilde{\rho}}-\frac{\partial}{\partial\widetilde{\xi}}\left[\frac{\partial\widetilde{U}}{\partial\widetilde{\xi}}\left(5\widetilde{p}+3\widetilde{\rho}\widetilde{u}^{2}\right)\right]+$$

$$+2\frac{\partial\widetilde{U}}{\partial\widetilde{\xi}}\left(\widetilde{\rho}\widetilde{u}+\frac{\partial}{\partial\widetilde{\xi}}\left(\widetilde{\rho}\widetilde{u}\right)-\frac{\partial}{\partial\widetilde{\xi}}\left(\widetilde{\rho}\widetilde{u}^{2}\right)-\frac{\partial\widetilde{p}}{\partial\widetilde{\xi}}-\widetilde{\rho}\frac{\partial\widetilde{U}}{\partial\widetilde{\xi}}\right)=0, \tag{5.3.19}$$

or

$$3\frac{\partial^{2}\widetilde{p}}{\partial\widetilde{\xi}^{2}}+\frac{\partial}{\partial\widetilde{\xi}}\left(\widetilde{\rho}\widetilde{u}^{2}\right)+3\frac{\partial\widetilde{p}}{\partial\widetilde{\xi}}+\frac{\partial^{2}}{\partial\widetilde{\xi}^{2}}\left(\widetilde{\rho}\widetilde{u}^{2}\right)-2\frac{\partial^{2}}{\partial\widetilde{\xi}^{2}}\left(\widetilde{\rho}\widetilde{u}^{3}\right)-10\frac{\partial^{2}}{\partial\widetilde{\xi}^{2}}\left(\widetilde{p}\widetilde{u}\right)-$$

$$-2\frac{\partial}{\partial\widetilde{\xi}}\left(\widetilde{\rho}\widetilde{u}\frac{\partial\widetilde{U}}{\partial\widetilde{\xi}}\right)-\frac{\partial}{\partial\widetilde{\xi}}\left(\widetilde{\rho}\widetilde{u}^{3}\right)-5\frac{\partial}{\partial\widetilde{\xi}}\left(\widetilde{p}\widetilde{u}\right)+\frac{\partial^{2}}{\partial\widetilde{\xi}^{2}}\left(\widetilde{\rho}\widetilde{u}^{4}\right)+8\frac{\partial^{2}}{\partial\widetilde{\xi}^{2}}\left(\widetilde{p}\widetilde{u}^{2}\right)+5\frac{\partial^{2}}{\partial\widetilde{\xi}^{2}}\frac{\widetilde{p}^{2}}{\widetilde{\rho}}$$

$$+\frac{\partial}{\partial\widetilde{\xi}}\left[\frac{\partial\widetilde{U}}{\partial\widetilde{\xi}}\left(5\widetilde{p}+3\widetilde{\rho}\widetilde{u}^{2}\right)\right]-2\frac{\partial\widetilde{U}}{\partial\widetilde{\xi}}\left(\widetilde{\rho}\widetilde{u}+\frac{\partial}{\partial\widetilde{\xi}}\left(\widetilde{\rho}\widetilde{u}\right)-\frac{\partial}{\partial\widetilde{\xi}}\left(\widetilde{\rho}\widetilde{u}^{2}\right)-\frac{\partial\widetilde{p}}{\partial\widetilde{\xi}}-\widetilde{\rho}\frac{\partial\widetilde{U}}{\partial\widetilde{\xi}}\right)=0, \tag{5.3.20}$$

As a result we have the following system of equations (continuity, motion and energy equations correspondingly)

$$\frac{\partial^{2}\widetilde{\rho}}{\partial\widetilde{\xi}^{2}}+\frac{\partial\widetilde{\rho}}{\partial\widetilde{\xi}}-2\frac{\partial^{2}}{\partial\widetilde{\xi}^{2}}\left(\widetilde{\rho}\widetilde{u}\right)-\frac{\partial}{\partial\widetilde{\xi}}\left(\widetilde{\rho}\widetilde{u}\right)+\frac{\partial^{2}}{\partial\widetilde{\xi}^{2}}\left(\widetilde{\rho}\widetilde{u}^{2}\right)+\frac{\partial^{2}\widetilde{p}}{\partial\widetilde{\xi}^{2}}+\frac{\partial}{\partial\widetilde{\xi}}\left(\widetilde{\rho}\frac{\partial\widetilde{U}}{\partial\widetilde{\xi}}\right)=0 \tag{5.3.21}$$

$$\frac{\partial^2}{\partial\tilde{\xi}^2}(\tilde{\rho}\tilde{u})+\frac{\partial}{\partial\tilde{\xi}}(\tilde{\rho}\tilde{u})-2\frac{\partial^2}{\partial\tilde{\xi}^2}(\tilde{\rho}\tilde{u}^2)-2\frac{\partial^2\tilde{p}}{\partial\tilde{\xi}^2}-\frac{\partial}{\partial\tilde{\xi}}(\tilde{\rho}\tilde{u}^2)-\frac{\partial\tilde{p}}{\partial\tilde{\xi}}+\frac{\partial^2}{\partial\tilde{\xi}^2}(\tilde{\rho}\tilde{u}^3)+$$

$$+3\frac{\partial^2}{\partial\tilde{\xi}^2}(\tilde{p}\tilde{u})+2\frac{\partial}{\partial\tilde{\xi}}\left(\tilde{\rho}\tilde{u}\frac{\partial\tilde{U}}{\partial\tilde{\xi}}\right)-\frac{\partial}{\partial\tilde{\xi}}\left(\tilde{\rho}\frac{\partial\tilde{U}}{\partial\tilde{\xi}}\right)-\frac{\partial\tilde{U}}{\partial\tilde{\xi}}\left(\tilde{\rho}+\frac{\partial\tilde{\rho}}{\partial\tilde{\xi}}-\frac{\partial}{\partial\tilde{\xi}}(\tilde{\rho}\tilde{u})\right)=0, \tag{5.3.22}$$

$$3\frac{\partial^2\tilde{p}}{\partial\tilde{\xi}^2}+\frac{\partial}{\partial\tilde{\xi}}(\tilde{\rho}\tilde{u}^2)+3\frac{\partial\tilde{p}}{\partial\tilde{\xi}}+\frac{\partial^2}{\partial\tilde{\xi}^2}(\tilde{\rho}\tilde{u}^2)-2\frac{\partial^2}{\partial\tilde{\xi}^2}(\tilde{\rho}\tilde{u}^3)-10\frac{\partial^2}{\partial\tilde{\xi}^2}(\tilde{p}\tilde{u})-$$

$$-2\frac{\partial}{\partial\tilde{\xi}}\left(\tilde{\rho}\tilde{u}\frac{\partial\tilde{U}}{\partial\tilde{\xi}}\right)-\frac{\partial}{\partial\tilde{\xi}}(\tilde{\rho}\tilde{u}^3)-5\frac{\partial}{\partial\tilde{\xi}}(\tilde{p}\tilde{u})+\frac{\partial^2}{\partial\tilde{\xi}^2}(\tilde{\rho}\tilde{u}^4)+8\frac{\partial^2}{\partial\tilde{\xi}^2}(\tilde{p}\tilde{u}^2)+5\frac{\partial^2}{\partial\tilde{\xi}^2}\frac{\tilde{p}^2}{\tilde{\rho}}$$

$$+\frac{\partial}{\partial\tilde{\xi}}\left[\frac{\partial\tilde{U}}{\partial\tilde{\xi}}(5\tilde{p}+3\tilde{\rho}\tilde{u}^2)\right]-2\frac{\partial\tilde{U}}{\partial\tilde{\xi}}\left(\tilde{\rho}\tilde{u}+\frac{\partial}{\partial\tilde{\xi}}(\tilde{\rho}\tilde{u})-\frac{\partial}{\partial\tilde{\xi}}(\tilde{\rho}\tilde{u}^2)-\frac{\partial\tilde{p}}{\partial\tilde{\xi}}-\tilde{\rho}\frac{\partial\tilde{U}}{\partial\tilde{\xi}}\right)=0, \tag{5.3.23}$$

Consider the case for which $\tilde{U}=\tilde{\xi}^2$, (oscillator). Then. $\frac{\partial\tilde{U}}{\partial\tilde{\xi}}=2\tilde{\xi}$. We can use the following Maple programme:

```
> dsolve[interactive]({
diff(r(t),t$2)+diff(r(t),t)-2*diff(r(t)*u(t),t$2)-
diff(r(t)*u(t),t)+diff(r(t)*u(t)^2,t$2)+diff(p(t),t$2
)+2*diff(r(t)*t,t)=0,
diff(r(t)*u(t),t$2)+diff(r(t)*u(t),t)-
2*diff(r(t)*u(t)^2,t$2)-2*diff(p(t),t$2)-
diff(r(t)*u(t)^2,t)-
diff(p(t),t)+diff(r(t)*u(t)^3,t$2)+3*diff(p(t)*u(t),t
$2)+4*diff(r(t)*u(t)*t,t)-2*diff(r(t)*t,t)-
2*t*(r(t)+diff(r(t),t)-diff(r(t)*u(t),t))=0,
3*diff(p(t),t$2)+diff(r(t)*u(t)^2,t)+3*diff(p(t),t)+d
iff(r(t)*u(t)^2,t$2)-2*diff(r(t)*u(t)^3,t$2)-
10*diff(p(t)*u(t),t$2)-4*diff(t*r(t)*u(t),t)-
diff(r(t)*u(t)^3,t)-
5*diff(p(t)*u(t),t)+diff(r(t)*u(t)^4,t$2)+8*diff(p(t)
*u(t)^2,t$2)+5*diff(p(t)^2/r(t),t$2)+diff(2*t*(5*p(t)
+3*r(t)*u(t)^2),t)-4*t*(r(t)*u(t)+diff(r(t)*u(t),t)-
diff(r(t)*u(t)^2,t)-diff(p(t),t)-2*t*r(t))=0,
diff(q(t),t)=r(t)*diff(u(t),t)+u(t)*diff(r(t),t),
r(0)=1,D(r)(0)=0,u(0)=1,D(u)(0)=0,p(0)=10,D(p)(0)=0,q
(0)=1});
```

```
Initializing Java runtime environment.
```

We use the Maple notations, for example D(u)(0) means $\left[\frac{\partial u}{\partial t}\right]_{t=0}$.

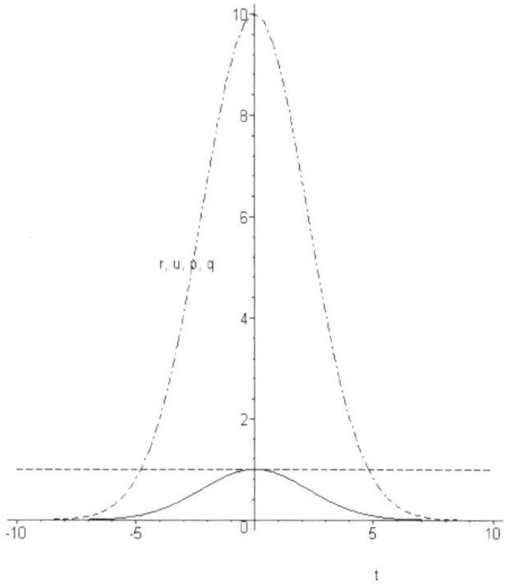

Figure. 5.3.1.
r - density, solid line, u - velocity, dashed line,
p - pressure, dash-dot line, q - impulse, dotted line.

The results presented in Fig. 5.3.1 and obtained by the Runge-Kutta method, should be interpreted as the formation of an "ideal" soliton. Namely, the velocity of all elements of a solitary wave is strictly constant, and the numerical method does not capture the presence of possible singular regions of the solution. Thus, if at the initial time a perturbation of the hydrodynamic parameters specified in the initial conditions is formed, the soliton propagates at a constant speed along the axis direction x.

On figures 5.3.2 – 5.3.4 the results are presented for other Cauchy conditions.

```
> dsolve[interactive]({
diff(r(t),t$2)+diff(r(t),t)-2*diff(r(t)*u(t),t$2)-
diff(r(t)*u(t),t)+diff(r(t)*u(t)^2,t$2)+diff(p(t),t$2
)+2*diff(r(t)*t,t)=0,
diff(r(t)*u(t),t$2)+diff(r(t)*u(t),t)-
2*diff(r(t)*u(t)^2,t$2)-2*diff(p(t),t$2)-
```

```
diff(r(t)*u(t)^2,t)-
diff(p(t),t)+diff(r(t)*u(t)^3,t$2)+3*diff(p(t)*u(t),t
$2)+4*diff(r(t)*u(t)*t,t)-2*diff(r(t)*t,t)-
2*t*(r(t)+diff(r(t),t)-diff(r(t)*u(t),t))=0,
3*diff(p(t),t$2)+diff(r(t)*u(t)^2,t)+3*diff(p(t),t)+d
iff(r(t)*u(t)^2,t$2)-2*diff(r(t)*u(t)^3,t$2)-
10*diff(p(t)*u(t),t$2)-4*diff(t*r(t)*u(t),t)-
diff(r(t)*u(t)^3,t)-
5*diff(p(t)*u(t),t)+diff(r(t)*u(t)^4,t$2)+8*diff(p(t)
*u(t)^2,t$2)+5*diff(p(t)^2/r(t),t$2)+diff(2*t*(5*p(t)
+3*r(t)*u(t)^2),t)-4*t*(r(t)*u(t)+diff(r(t)*u(t),t)-
diff(r(t)*u(t)^2,t)-diff(p(t),t)-2*t*r(t))=0,
diff(q(t),t)=r(t)*diff(u(t),t)+u(t)*diff(r(t),t),
r(0)=1,D(r)(0)=0,u(0)=1,D(u)(0)=0,p(0)=1,D(p)(0)=0,q(
0)=1});
```

Solution with the help of the Livermore solver for the stiff equations.

```
Initializing Java runtime environment.
Warning, could not obtain numerical solution at all
points, plot may be incomplete
```

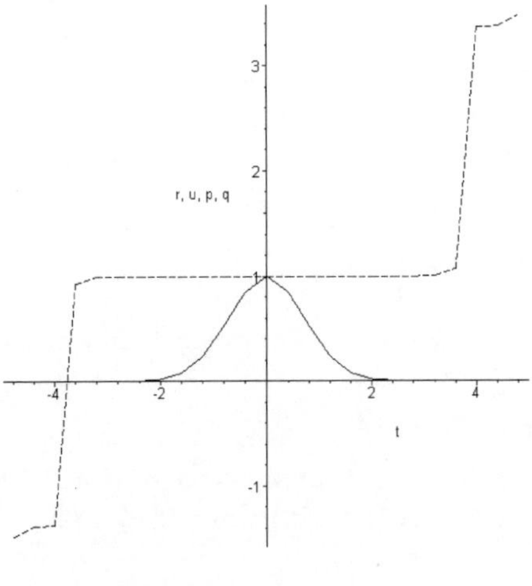

Figure 5.3.2. r - density, solid line, u - velocity, dashed line, p - pressure, dash-dot line, q - impulse, dotted line.

```
> dsolve[interactive]({
diff(r(t),t$2)+diff(r(t),t)-2*diff(r(t)*u(t),t$2)-
diff(r(t)*u(t),t)+diff(r(t)*u(t)^2,t$2)+diff(p(t),t$2
)+2*diff(r(t)*t,t)=0,
diff(r(t)*u(t),t$2)+diff(r(t)*u(t),t)-
2*diff(r(t)*u(t)^2,t$2)-2*diff(p(t),t$2)-
diff(r(t)*u(t)^2,t)-
diff(p(t),t)+diff(r(t)*u(t)^3,t$2)+3*diff(p(t)*u(t),t
$2)+4*diff(r(t)*u(t)*t,t)-2*diff(r(t)*t,t)-
2*t*(r(t)+diff(r(t),t)-diff(r(t)*u(t),t))=0,
3*diff(p(t),t$2)+diff(r(t)*u(t)^2,t)+3*diff(p(t),t)+d
iff(r(t)*u(t)^2,t$2)-2*diff(r(t)*u(t)^3,t$2)-
10*diff(p(t)*u(t),t$2)-4*diff(t*r(t)*u(t),t)-
diff(r(t)*u(t)^3,t)-
5*diff(p(t)*u(t),t)+diff(r(t)*u(t)^4,t$2)+8*diff(p(t)
*u(t)^2,t$2)+5*diff(p(t)^2/r(t),t$2)+diff(2*t*(5*p(t)
+3*r(t)*u(t)^2),t)-4*t*(r(t)*u(t)+diff(r(t)*u(t),t)-
diff(r(t)*u(t)^2,t)-diff(p(t),t)-2*t*r(t))=0,
diff(q(t),t)=r(t)*diff(u(t),t)+u(t)*diff(r(t),t),
r(0)=1,D(r)(0)=0,u(0)=1,D(u)(0)=0,p(0)=.1,D(p)(0)=0,q
(0)=1});
Warning, cannot evaluate the solution further right
of 4.4000000. Warning, cannot evaluate the solution
further left of -4.4000000, probably a singularity
```

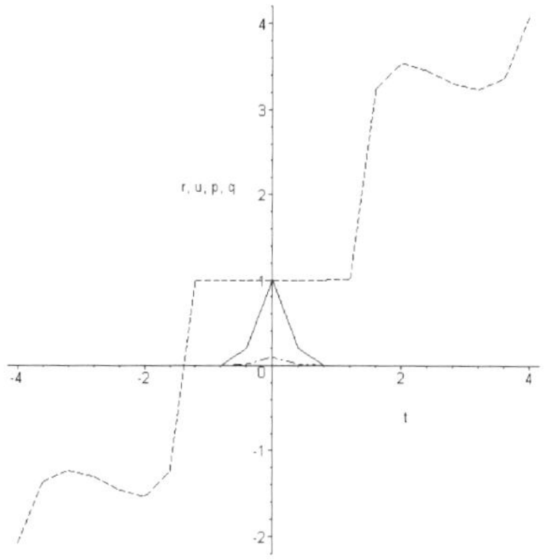

Figure 5.3.3. r - density, solid line, u - velocity, dashed line, p - pressure, dash-dot line, q - impulse, dotted line.

```
> dsolve[interactive]({
diff(r(t),t$2)+diff(r(t),t)-2*diff(r(t)*u(t),t$2)-
diff(r(t)*u(t),t)+diff(r(t)*u(t)^2,t$2)+diff(p(t),t$2
)+2*diff(r(t)*t,t)=0,
diff(r(t)*u(t),t$2)+diff(r(t)*u(t),t)-
2*diff(r(t)*u(t)^2,t$2)-2*diff(p(t),t$2)-
diff(r(t)*u(t)^2,t)-
diff(p(t),t)+diff(r(t)*u(t)^3,t$2)+3*diff(p(t)*u(t),t
$2)+4*diff(r(t)*u(t)*t,t)-2*diff(r(t)*t,t)-
2*t*(r(t)+diff(r(t),t)-diff(r(t)*u(t),t))=0,
3*diff(p(t),t$2)+diff(r(t)*u(t)^2,t)+3*diff(p(t),t)+d
iff(r(t)*u(t)^2,t$2)-2*diff(r(t)*u(t)^3,t$2)-
10*diff(p(t)*u(t),t$2)-4*diff(t*r(t)*u(t),t)-
diff(r(t)*u(t)^3,t)-
5*diff(p(t)*u(t),t)+diff(r(t)*u(t)^4,t$2)+8*diff(p(t)
*u(t)^2,t$2)+5*diff(p(t)^2/r(t),t$2)+diff(2*t*(5*p(t)
+3*r(t)*u(t)^2),t)-4*t*(r(t)*u(t)+diff(r(t)*u(t),t)-
diff(r(t)*u(t)^2,t)-diff(p(t),t)-2*t*r(t))=0,
diff(q(t),t)=r(t)*diff(u(t),t)+u(t)*diff(r(t),t),
r(0)=10,D(r)(0)=0,u(0)=1,D(u)(0)=0,p(0)=1,D(p)(0)=0,q
(0)=10});
Warning, cannot evaluate the solution further right
of 4.4000000. Warning, cannot evaluate the solution
further left of -4.4000000, probably a singularity
```

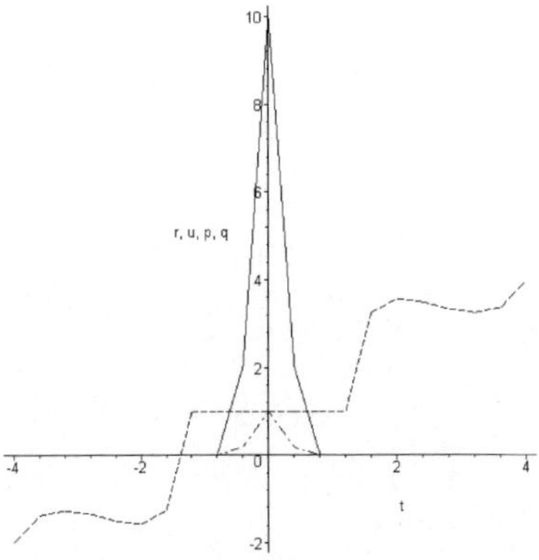

Figure 5.3.4. r - density, solid line, u - velocity, dashed line, p - pressure, dash-dot line, q - impulse, dotted line.

Let us investigate now the soliton defined by two oscillators, for which $\widetilde{U}=\widetilde{\xi}^2+(\widetilde{\xi}-1)^2$. Then $\frac{\partial\widetilde{U}}{\partial\widetilde{\xi}}=2\widetilde{\xi}+2(\widetilde{\xi}-1)=2(2\widetilde{\xi}-1)$, and we obtain the following system of equations;

continuity equation

$$\frac{\partial^2\widetilde{\rho}}{\partial\widetilde{\xi}^2}+(4\widetilde{\xi}-1)\frac{\partial\widetilde{\rho}}{\partial\widetilde{\xi}}-2\frac{\partial^2}{\partial\widetilde{\xi}^2}(\widetilde{\rho}\widetilde{u})-\frac{\partial}{\partial\widetilde{\xi}}(\widetilde{\rho}\widetilde{u})+\frac{\partial^2}{\partial\widetilde{\xi}^2}(\widetilde{\rho}\widetilde{u}^2)+\frac{\partial^2\widetilde{p}}{\partial\widetilde{\xi}^2}+4\widetilde{\rho}=0, \tag{5.3.24}$$

motion equation

$$\frac{\partial^2}{\partial\widetilde{\xi}^2}(\widetilde{\rho}\widetilde{u})+\frac{\partial}{\partial\widetilde{\xi}}(\widetilde{\rho}\widetilde{u})-2\frac{\partial^2}{\partial\widetilde{\xi}^2}(\widetilde{\rho}\widetilde{u}^2)-2\frac{\partial^2\widetilde{p}}{\partial\widetilde{\xi}^2}-\frac{\partial}{\partial\widetilde{\xi}}(\widetilde{\rho}\widetilde{u}^2)-\frac{\partial\widetilde{p}}{\partial\widetilde{\xi}}+\frac{\partial^2}{\partial\widetilde{\xi}^2}(\widetilde{\rho}\widetilde{u}^3)+$$
$$+3\frac{\partial^2}{\partial\widetilde{\xi}^2}(\widetilde{p}\widetilde{u})+3(4\widetilde{\xi}-2)\frac{\partial}{\partial\widetilde{\xi}}(\widetilde{\rho}\widetilde{u})+8\widetilde{\rho}\widetilde{u}-2(4\widetilde{\xi}-2)\frac{\partial\widetilde{\rho}}{\partial\widetilde{\xi}}-(4\widetilde{\xi}+2)\widetilde{\rho}=0, \tag{5.3.25}$$

energy equation

$$3\frac{\partial^2\widetilde{p}}{\partial\widetilde{\xi}^2}+\frac{\partial}{\partial\widetilde{\xi}}(\widetilde{\rho}\widetilde{u}^2)+3\frac{\partial\widetilde{p}}{\partial\widetilde{\xi}}+\frac{\partial^2}{\partial\widetilde{\xi}^2}(\widetilde{\rho}\widetilde{u}^2)-2\frac{\partial^2}{\partial\widetilde{\xi}^2}(\widetilde{\rho}\widetilde{u}^3)-10\frac{\partial^2}{\partial\widetilde{\xi}^2}(\widetilde{p}\widetilde{u})-$$
$$-2\frac{\partial}{\partial\widetilde{\xi}}\left[\widetilde{\rho}\widetilde{u}(4\widetilde{\xi}-2)\right]-\frac{\partial}{\partial\widetilde{\xi}}(\widetilde{\rho}\widetilde{u}^3)-5\frac{\partial}{\partial\widetilde{\xi}}(\widetilde{p}\widetilde{u})+\frac{\partial^2}{\partial\widetilde{\xi}^2}(\widetilde{\rho}\widetilde{u}^4)+8\frac{\partial^2}{\partial\widetilde{\xi}^2}(\widetilde{p}\widetilde{u}^2)+$$
$$+5\frac{\partial^2}{\partial\widetilde{\xi}^2}\frac{\widetilde{p}^2}{\widetilde{\rho}}+\frac{\partial}{\partial\widetilde{\xi}}\left[(4\widetilde{\xi}-2)(5\widetilde{p}+3\widetilde{\rho}\widetilde{u}^2)\right]-$$
$$-2(4\widetilde{\xi}-2)\left(\widetilde{\rho}\widetilde{u}+\frac{\partial}{\partial\widetilde{\xi}}(\widetilde{\rho}\widetilde{u})-\frac{\partial}{\partial\widetilde{\xi}}(\widetilde{\rho}\widetilde{u}^2)-\frac{\partial\widetilde{p}}{\partial\widetilde{\xi}}-\widetilde{\rho}(4\widetilde{\xi}-2)\right)=0, \tag{5.3.26}$$

Maple programme

```
> dsolve[interactive]({
diff(r(t),t$2)+(4*t-1)*diff(r(t),t)-
2*diff(r(t)*u(t),t$2)-
diff(r(t)*u(t),t)+diff(r(t)*u(t)^2,t$2)+diff(p(t),t$2
)+4*r(t)=0,

diff(r(t)*u(t),t$2)+diff(r(t)*u(t),t)-
2*diff(r(t)*u(t)^2,t$2)-2*diff(p(t),t$2)-
diff(r(t)*u(t)^2,t)-
diff(p(t),t)+diff(r(t)*u(t)^3,t$2)+3*diff(p(t)*u(t),t
$2)+3*(4*t-2)*diff(r(t)*u(t),t)+8*r(t)*u(t)-2*(4*t-
2)*diff(r(t),t)-(4*t+2)*r(t)=0,
```

```
3*diff(p(t),t$2)+diff(r(t)*u(t)^2,t)+3*diff(p(t),t)+d
iff(r(t)*u(t)^2,t$2)-2*diff(r(t)*u(t)^3,t$2)-
10*diff(p(t)*u(t),t$2)-2*diff((4*t-2)*r(t)*u(t),t)-
diff(r(t)*u(t)^3,t)-
5*diff(p(t)*u(t),t)+diff(r(t)*u(t)^4,t$2)+8*diff(p(t)
*u(t)^2,t$2)+5*diff(p(t)^2/r(t),t$2)+diff((4*t-
2)*(5*p(t)+3*r(t)*u(t)^2),t)-2*(4*t-
2)*(r(t)*u(t)+diff(r(t)*u(t),t)-diff(r(t)*u(t)^2,t)-
diff(p(t),t)-r(t)*(4*t-2))=0,
diff(q(t),t)=r(t)*diff(u(t),t)+u(t)*diff(r(t),t),
r(0.5)=1,D(r)(0.5)=0,u(0.5)=1,D(u)(0.5)=0,p(0.5)=1,D(
p)(0.5)=0,q(0.5)=1});
```

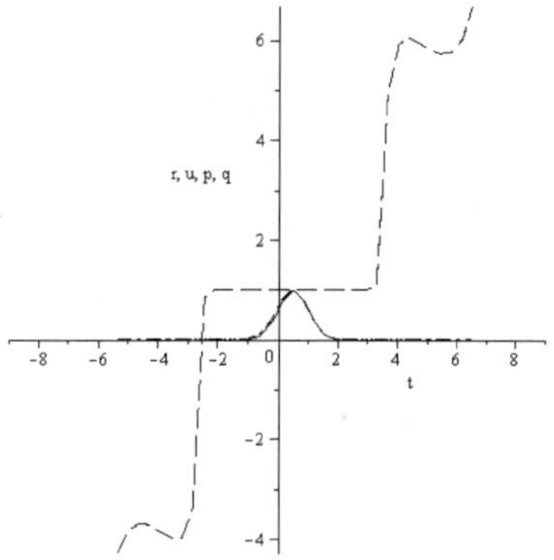

Figure 5.3.5.
r - density, solid line, u - velocity, dashed line,
p - pressure, dash-dot line, q - impulse, dotted line.

```
Warning, cannot evaluate the solution further right
of 6.5972, probably a singularity

Warning, cannot evaluate the solution further left of
-5.5797, probably a singularity
```

Take into account that Cauchy conditions correspond to $t = \tilde{\xi} = 0.5$.

Figure 5.3.6 reflects the soliton formation for Cauchy conditions

```
r(0.5)=1,D(r)(0.5)=0,u(0.5)=1,D(u)(0.5)=0,p(0.5)=10,D
(p)(0.5)=0,q(0.5)=1});
```

```
Initializing Java runtime environment.
```

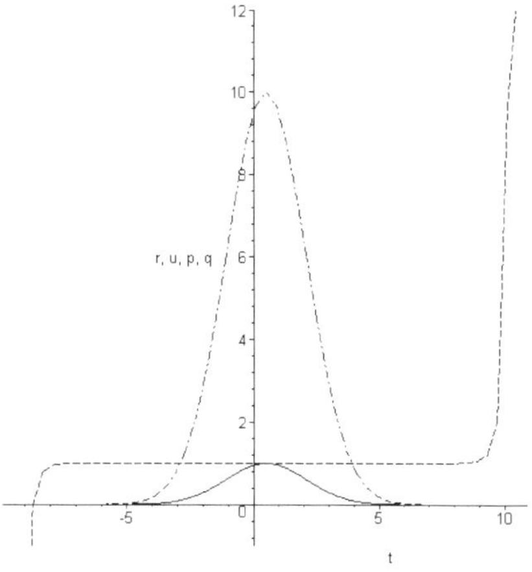

Figure 5.3.6.
r - density, solid line, u - velocity, dashed line,
p - pressure, dash-dot line, q - impulse, dotted line.

5.4. Non-stationary 1D solitons in the nonlocal physics ($\tau \neq const$).

We have a system of equations:

$$\frac{\partial}{\partial t}\left\{\rho-\tau\left[\frac{\partial \rho}{\partial t}+\frac{\partial}{\partial x}(\rho u)\right]\right\}+\frac{\partial}{\partial x}\left\{\rho v_0-\tau\left[\frac{\partial}{\partial t}(\rho u)+\right.\right.$$
$$\left.\left.+\frac{\partial}{\partial x}\left(\rho u^2\right)+\frac{\partial p}{\partial x}+\rho\frac{\partial U}{\partial x}\right]\right\}=0, \tag{5.4.1}$$

$$\frac{\partial}{\partial t}\left\{\rho u-\tau\left[\frac{\partial}{\partial t}(\rho u)+\frac{\partial}{\partial x}\left(\rho u^2\right)+\frac{\partial p}{\partial x}+\rho\frac{\partial U}{\partial x}\right]\right\}+$$
$$+\frac{\partial U}{\partial x}\left[\rho-\tau\left(\frac{\partial \rho}{\partial t}+\frac{\partial}{\partial x}(\rho u)\right)\right]+ \tag{5.4.2}$$
$$+\frac{\partial}{\partial x}\left\{\rho u^2+p-\tau\left[\frac{\partial}{\partial t}\left(\rho u^2+p\right)+\frac{\partial}{\partial x}\left(\rho u^3+3pu\right)+2\rho u\frac{\partial U}{\partial x}\right]\right\}=0,$$

$$\frac{\partial}{\partial t}\left\{\rho u^2+3p-\tau\left[\frac{\partial}{\partial t}\left(\rho u^2+3p\right)+\frac{\partial}{\partial x}\left(\rho u^3+5pu\right)+2\rho u\frac{\partial U}{\partial x}\right]\right\}+$$

$$+\frac{\partial}{\partial x}\left\{\rho u^3+5pu-\tau\left[\frac{\partial}{\partial t}\left(\rho u^3+5pu\right)+\frac{\partial}{\partial x}\left(\rho u^4+\right.\right.\right.$$

$$\left.\left.\left.+8pu^2+5\frac{p^2}{\rho}\right)+\frac{\partial U}{\partial x}\left(3\rho u^2+5p\right)\right]\right\}+$$

$$+2\frac{\partial U}{\partial x}\left\{\rho u-\tau\left[\frac{\partial}{\partial t}(\rho u)+\frac{\partial}{\partial x}\left(\rho u^2+p\right)+\rho\frac{\partial U}{\partial x}\right]\right\}=0.$$

(5.4.3)

We intend to use τ – approximation in the form

$$\tau=\tau^{(qu)}=\frac{\hbar}{4m}\frac{1}{u^2}. \qquad (5.4.4)$$

The relation (5.4.4) is due to the existence of Heisenberg's uncertainty principle in terms of time – energy. It is intuitively clear that the nonlocality effect should decrease with increasing particle velocity. The effect should not depend on the direction of the particle velocity. Therefore, the effect of nonlocality becomes inversely proportional to the square of the velocity or, otherwise, the energy of the particles (see also Item 2.6).

Now we use the following scale system:

$$\rho_0,\ u_0, x_0=u_0 t_0, U_0=u_0^2,\ t_0=\frac{\hbar}{4m}\frac{1}{u_0^2}. \qquad (5.4.5)$$

Then

$$\tau=\tau^{(qu)}=\frac{\hbar}{4m}\frac{1}{u^2}=t_0\frac{u_0^2}{u^2}=t_0\frac{1}{\tilde{u}^2}. \qquad (5.4.6)$$

The dimensionless continuity equation is written as

$$-\frac{\partial}{\partial\tilde{\xi}}\left\{\tilde{\rho}-\frac{1}{\tilde{u}^2}\left[-\frac{\partial\tilde{\rho}}{\partial\tilde{\xi}}+\frac{\partial}{\partial\tilde{\xi}}(\tilde{\rho}\tilde{u})\right]\right\}+$$

$$+\frac{\partial}{\partial\tilde{\xi}}\left\{\tilde{\rho}\tilde{u}-\frac{1}{\tilde{u}^2}\left[-\frac{\partial}{\partial\tilde{\xi}}(\tilde{\rho}\tilde{u})+\frac{\partial}{\partial\tilde{\xi}}\left(\tilde{\rho}\tilde{u}^2\right)+\frac{\partial\tilde{p}}{\partial\tilde{\xi}}+\tilde{\rho}\frac{\partial\tilde{U}}{\partial\tilde{\xi}}\right]\right\}=0, \qquad (5.4.7)$$

and after integration

$$\tilde{\rho}(\tilde{u}-1)\tilde{u}^2=\frac{\partial}{\partial\tilde{\xi}}\left(\tilde{\rho}\tilde{u}^2+\tilde{p}-2\tilde{\rho}\tilde{u}+\tilde{\rho}\right) \qquad (5.4.8)$$

because the integration constant is equal to zero, if $u(0)=\rho(0)=1$, $\frac{\partial\tilde{p}}{\partial\tilde{\xi}}(0)=\frac{\partial\tilde{u}}{\partial\tilde{\xi}}(0)=0$.

Note that the Maple software package allows the numerical integration of the generalized equations of continuity, motion and energy with minimal transformations of the mentioned equations. We present these transformations.

Reduction of the continuity equation to an integrable form in Maple:

$$\frac{\partial\tilde{\rho}}{\partial\tilde{\xi}}-\frac{\partial\tilde{\rho}\tilde{u}}{\partial\tilde{\xi}}+\frac{\partial}{\partial\tilde{\xi}}\left\{\frac{1}{\tilde{u}^{2}}\left[\frac{\partial}{\partial\tilde{\xi}}\left(\tilde{p}+\tilde{\rho}+\tilde{\rho}\tilde{u}^{2}-2\tilde{\rho}\tilde{u}\right)+\tilde{\rho}\frac{\partial\tilde{U}}{\partial\tilde{\xi}}\right]\right\}=0, \quad (5.4.9)$$

Reduction of the motion equation to the form integrable in Maple:

$$\begin{aligned}&\frac{\partial}{\partial\tilde{\xi}}\left(\tilde{\rho}\tilde{u}^{2}+\tilde{p}-\tilde{\rho}\tilde{u}\right)+\\&+\frac{\partial}{\partial\tilde{\xi}}\left\{\frac{1}{\tilde{u}^{2}}\left[\frac{\partial}{\partial\tilde{\xi}}\left(2\tilde{\rho}\tilde{u}^{2}-\tilde{\rho}\tilde{u}+2\tilde{p}-\tilde{\rho}\tilde{u}^{3}-3\tilde{p}\tilde{u}\right)+\tilde{\rho}\frac{\partial\tilde{U}}{\partial\tilde{\xi}}\right]\right\}\\&+\frac{\partial\tilde{U}}{\partial\tilde{\xi}}\left\{\tilde{\rho}-\frac{1}{\tilde{u}^{2}}\left[-\frac{\partial\tilde{\rho}}{\partial\tilde{\xi}}+\frac{\partial}{\partial\tilde{\xi}}\left(\tilde{\rho}\tilde{u}\right)\right]\right\}-2\frac{\partial}{\partial\tilde{\xi}}\left\{\frac{\tilde{\rho}}{\tilde{u}}\frac{\partial\tilde{U}}{\partial\tilde{\xi}}\right\}=0,\end{aligned} \quad (5.4.10)$$

Reduction of the energy equation to the form integrable in Maple.

$$\begin{aligned}&-\frac{\partial}{\partial\tilde{\xi}}\left(\tilde{\rho}\tilde{u}^{2}+3\tilde{p}\right)+\\&+\frac{\partial}{\partial\tilde{\xi}}\left\{\frac{1}{\tilde{u}^{2}}\left[-\frac{\partial}{\partial\tilde{\xi}}\left(\tilde{\rho}\tilde{u}^{2}+3\tilde{p}\right)+\frac{\partial}{\partial\tilde{\xi}}\left(\tilde{\rho}\tilde{u}^{3}+5\tilde{p}\tilde{u}\right)+2\tilde{p}\tilde{u}\frac{\partial\tilde{U}}{\partial\tilde{\xi}}\right]\right\}+\\&+\frac{\partial}{\partial\tilde{\xi}}\left(\tilde{\rho}\tilde{u}^{3}+5\tilde{p}\tilde{u}\right)-\\&-\frac{\partial}{\partial\tilde{\xi}}\left\{\frac{1}{\tilde{u}^{2}}\left[\frac{\partial}{\partial\tilde{\xi}}\left(\tilde{\rho}\tilde{u}^{4}+8\tilde{p}\tilde{u}^{2}+5\frac{\tilde{p}^{2}}{\tilde{\rho}}\right)+\left(3\tilde{\rho}\tilde{u}^{2}+5\tilde{p}\right)\frac{\partial\tilde{U}}{\partial\tilde{\xi}}-\frac{\partial}{\partial\tilde{\xi}}\left(\tilde{\rho}\tilde{u}^{3}+5\tilde{p}\tilde{u}\right)\right]\right\}\\&+2\tilde{p}\tilde{u}\frac{\partial\tilde{U}}{\partial\tilde{\xi}}-\frac{2}{\tilde{u}^{2}}\frac{\partial\tilde{U}}{\partial\tilde{\xi}}\left[-\frac{\partial}{\partial\tilde{\xi}}\left(\tilde{\rho}\tilde{u}\right)+\frac{\partial}{\partial\tilde{\xi}}\left(\tilde{\rho}\tilde{u}^{2}+\tilde{p}\right)+\tilde{\rho}\frac{\partial\tilde{U}}{\partial\tilde{\xi}}\right]=0,\end{aligned}$$

(5.4.11)

or

$$\begin{aligned}&\frac{\partial}{\partial\tilde{\xi}}\left(\tilde{\rho}\tilde{u}^{2}+3\tilde{p}-\tilde{\rho}\tilde{u}^{3}-5\tilde{p}\tilde{u}\right)-\\&-\frac{\partial}{\partial\tilde{\xi}}\left\{\frac{1}{\tilde{u}^{2}}\frac{\partial}{\partial\tilde{\xi}}\left(2\tilde{\rho}\tilde{u}^{3}+10\tilde{p}\tilde{u}-\tilde{\rho}\tilde{u}^{2}-3\tilde{p}-\tilde{\rho}\tilde{u}^{4}-8\tilde{p}\tilde{u}^{2}-5\frac{\tilde{p}^{2}}{\tilde{\rho}}\right)\right\}\\&+\frac{\partial}{\partial\tilde{\xi}}\left\{\frac{1}{\tilde{u}^{2}}\left(3\tilde{\rho}\tilde{u}^{2}+5\tilde{p}\right)\frac{\partial\tilde{U}}{\partial\tilde{\xi}}\right\}-2\tilde{p}\tilde{u}\frac{\partial\tilde{U}}{\partial\tilde{\xi}}-2\frac{\partial}{\partial\tilde{\xi}}\left\{\frac{\tilde{p}}{\tilde{u}}\frac{\partial\tilde{U}}{\partial\tilde{\xi}}\right\}+\\&+\frac{2}{\tilde{u}^{2}}\frac{\partial\tilde{U}}{\partial\tilde{\xi}}\left[-\frac{\partial}{\partial\tilde{\xi}}\left(\tilde{\rho}\tilde{u}\right)+\frac{\partial}{\partial\tilde{\xi}}\left(\tilde{\rho}\tilde{u}^{2}+\tilde{p}\right)+\tilde{\rho}\frac{\partial\tilde{U}}{\partial\tilde{\xi}}\right]=0,\end{aligned} \quad (5.4.12)$$

In the absence of a potential the system of equations (5.4.13) – (5.4.15)

$$\frac{\partial\tilde{\rho}}{\partial\tilde{\xi}}-\frac{\partial\tilde{\rho}\tilde{u}}{\partial\tilde{\xi}}+\frac{\partial}{\partial\tilde{\xi}}\left\{\frac{1}{\tilde{u}^{2}}\left[\frac{\partial}{\partial\tilde{\xi}}\left(\tilde{p}+\tilde{\rho}+\tilde{\rho}\tilde{u}^{2}-2\tilde{\rho}\tilde{u}\right)\right]\right\}=0, \qquad (5.4.13)$$

$$\frac{\partial}{\partial\tilde{\xi}}\left(\tilde{\rho}\tilde{u}^{2}+\tilde{p}-\tilde{\rho}\tilde{u}\right)+\frac{\partial}{\partial\tilde{\xi}}\left\{\frac{1}{\tilde{u}^{2}}\left[\frac{\partial}{\partial\tilde{\xi}}\left(2\tilde{\rho}\tilde{u}^{2}-\tilde{\rho}\tilde{u}+2\tilde{p}-\tilde{\rho}\tilde{u}^{3}-3\tilde{p}\tilde{u}\right)\right]\right\}=0,$$

(5.4.14)

$$\frac{\partial}{\partial\tilde{\xi}}\left(\tilde{\rho}\tilde{u}^{2}+3\tilde{p}-\tilde{\rho}\tilde{u}^{3}-5\tilde{p}\tilde{u}\right)-$$

$$-\frac{\partial}{\partial\tilde{\xi}}\left\{\frac{1}{\tilde{u}^{2}}\frac{\partial}{\partial\tilde{\xi}}\left(2\tilde{\rho}\tilde{u}^{3}+10\tilde{p}\tilde{u}-\tilde{\rho}\tilde{u}^{2}-3\tilde{p}-\tilde{\rho}\tilde{u}^{4}-8\tilde{p}\tilde{u}^{2}-5\frac{\tilde{p}^{2}}{\tilde{\rho}}\right)\right\}=0,$$

(5.4.15)

has only the trivial solution.

5.5. Numerical solution of the equations of continuity, motion, and energy under the Heisenberg uncertainty principle. Quantum oscillator $\tilde{U}=\tilde{\xi}^{2}$.

The system of generalized hydrodynamic equations is integrated $\tilde{U}=\tilde{\xi}^{2}$.

$$\frac{\partial\tilde{\rho}}{\partial\tilde{\xi}}-\frac{\partial\tilde{\rho}\tilde{u}}{\partial\tilde{\xi}}+\frac{\partial}{\partial\tilde{\xi}}\left\{\frac{1}{\tilde{u}^{2}}\left[\frac{\partial}{\partial\tilde{\xi}}\left(\tilde{p}+\tilde{\rho}+\tilde{\rho}\tilde{u}^{2}-2\tilde{\rho}\tilde{u}\right)+2\tilde{\rho}\tilde{\xi}\right]\right\}=0, \qquad (5.5.1)$$

$$\frac{\partial}{\partial\tilde{\xi}}\left(\tilde{\rho}\tilde{u}^{2}+\tilde{p}-\tilde{\rho}\tilde{u}\right)+$$

$$+\frac{\partial}{\partial\tilde{\xi}}\left\{\frac{1}{\tilde{u}^{2}}\left[\frac{\partial}{\partial\tilde{\xi}}\left(2\tilde{\rho}\tilde{u}^{2}-\tilde{\rho}\tilde{u}+2\tilde{p}-\tilde{\rho}\tilde{u}^{3}-3\tilde{p}\tilde{u}\right)+2\tilde{\rho}\tilde{\xi}\right]\right\}+ \qquad (5.5.2)$$

$$+2\tilde{\xi}\left\{\tilde{\rho}-\frac{1}{\tilde{u}^{2}}\left[-\frac{\partial\tilde{\rho}}{\partial\tilde{\xi}}+\frac{\partial}{\partial\tilde{\xi}}\left(\tilde{\rho}\tilde{u}\right)\right]\right\}-4\frac{\partial}{\partial\tilde{\xi}}\left\{\frac{\tilde{\rho}}{\tilde{u}}\tilde{\xi}\right\}=0,$$

$$\frac{\partial}{\partial\tilde{\xi}}\left(\tilde{\rho}\tilde{u}^{2}+3\tilde{p}-\tilde{\rho}\tilde{u}^{3}-5\tilde{p}\tilde{u}\right)-$$

$$-\frac{\partial}{\partial\tilde{\xi}}\left\{\frac{1}{\tilde{u}^{2}}\frac{\partial}{\partial\tilde{\xi}}\left(2\tilde{\rho}\tilde{u}^{3}+10\tilde{p}\tilde{u}-\tilde{\rho}\tilde{u}^{2}-3\tilde{p}-\tilde{\rho}\tilde{u}^{4}-8\tilde{p}\tilde{u}^{2}-5\frac{\tilde{p}^{2}}{\tilde{\rho}}\right)\right\}+$$

$$+\frac{\partial}{\partial\tilde{\xi}}\left\{\frac{1}{\tilde{u}^{2}}\left(3\tilde{\rho}\tilde{u}^{2}+5\tilde{p}\right)\frac{\partial\tilde{U}}{\partial\tilde{\xi}}\right\}-4\tilde{\rho}\tilde{u}\tilde{\xi}-4\frac{\partial}{\partial\tilde{\xi}}\left\{\frac{\tilde{\rho}}{\tilde{u}}\tilde{\xi}\right\}+$$

$$+\frac{4}{\tilde{u}^{2}}\tilde{\xi}\left[-\frac{\partial}{\partial\tilde{\xi}}\left(\tilde{\rho}\tilde{u}\right)+\frac{\partial}{\partial\tilde{\xi}}\left(\tilde{\rho}\tilde{u}^{2}+\tilde{p}\right)+2\tilde{\rho}\tilde{\xi}\right]=0,$$

(5.5.3)

Let us demonsrate the change of functions with increasing density perturbations from $\widetilde{\rho} = r(t) = 0.1$ to $\widetilde{\rho} = r(t) = 15$. Calculations at values are presented: $r(t)$=0.1, $r(t)$=0.5, $r(t)$=0.7, $r(t)$=1, $r(t)$=5, $r(t)$=15.

```
> dsolve[interactive]({
diff(r(t)*(1-
u(t)),t)+diff((diff(p(t)+r(t)+r(t)*u(t)^2-
2*r(t)*u(t),t))/u(t)^2,t)+2*diff(t*r(t)/u(t)^2,t)=0,
diff(r(t)*u(t)^2+p(t)-
r(t)*u(t),t)+diff((diff(2*r(t)*u(t)^2+2*p(t)-
r(t)*u(t)-r(t)*u(t)^3-
3*p(t)*u(t),t))/u(t)^2,t)+2*diff(t*r(t)/u(t)^2,t)+2*t
*(r(t)-(diff(r(t)*(u(t)-1),t))/u(t)^2)-
4*diff(r(t)*t/u(t),t)=0,
diff(r(t)*u(t)^2+3*p(t)-r(t)*u(t)^3-5*p(t)*u(t),t)-
diff((diff(2*r(t)*u(t)^3+10*p(t)*u(t)-r(t)*u(t)^2-
3*p(t)-r(t)*u(t)^4-8*p(t)*u(t)^2-
5*p(t)^2/r(t),t))/u(t)^2,t)+2*diff(t*(3*r(t)*u(t)^2+5
*p(t))/u(t)^2,t)-4*t*r(t)*u(t)-
4*diff(t*r(t)/u(t),t)+4*t*(2*r(t)*t+diff(p(t)+r(t)*u(
t)^2-r(t)*u(t),t))/u(t)^2=0,
u(0)=1,p(0)=1,r(0)=.1,D(u)(0)=0,D(p)(0)=0,D(r)(0)=0})
;
```

The calculation was performed by the Runge-Kutta method of the fifth order of accuracy.

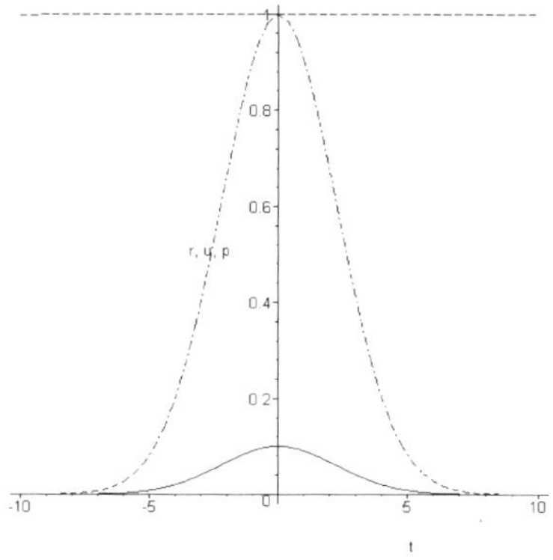

Figure 5.5.1 r - density, solid line, u - velocity, dashed line, p - pressure, dash-dot line.

```
> dsolve[interactive]({
diff(r(t)*(1-
u(t)),t)+diff((diff(p(t)+r(t)+r(t)*u(t)^2-
2*r(t)*u(t),t))/u(t)^2,t)+2*diff(t*r(t)/u(t)^2,t)=0,
diff(r(t)*u(t)^2+p(t)-
r(t)*u(t),t)+diff((diff(2*r(t)*u(t)^2+2*p(t)-
r(t)*u(t)-r(t)*u(t)^3-
3*p(t)*u(t),t))/u(t)^2,t)+2*diff(t*r(t)/u(t)^2,t)+2*t
*(r(t)-(diff(r(t)*(u(t)-1),t))/u(t)^2)-
4*diff(r(t)*t/u(t),t)=0,
diff(r(t)*u(t)^2+3*p(t)-r(t)*u(t)^3-5*p(t)*u(t),t)-
diff((diff(2*r(t)*u(t)^3+10*p(t)*u(t)-r(t)*u(t)^2-
3*p(t)-r(t)*u(t)^4-8*p(t)*u(t)^2-
5*p(t)^2/r(t),t))/u(t)^2,t)+2*diff(t*(3*r(t)*u(t)^2+5
*p(t))/u(t)^2,t)-4*t*r(t)*u(t)-
4*diff(t*r(t)/u(t),t)+4*t*(2*r(t)*t+diff(p(t)+r(t)*u(
t)^2-r(t)*u(t),t))/u(t)^2=0,
u(0)=1,p(0)=1,r(0)=.5,D(u)(0)=0,D(p)(0)=0,D(r)(0)=0})
;
Initializing Java runtime environment.
Warning, could not obtain numerical solution at all
points, plot may be incomplete
```

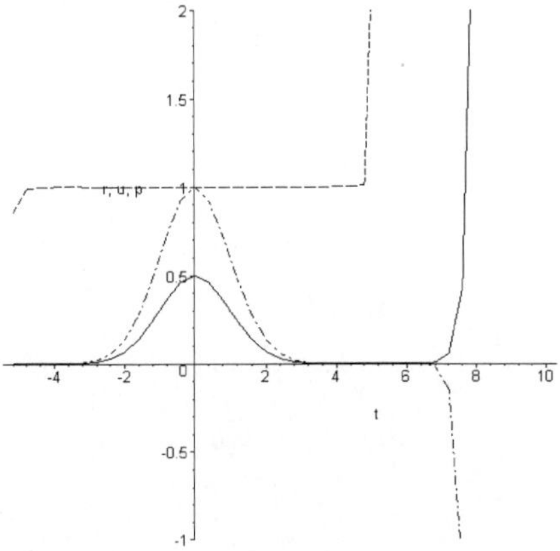

Figure 5.5.2.
r - density, solid line, u - velocity, dashed line,
p - pressure, dash-dot line.

```
> dsolve[interactive]({
diff(r(t)*(1-
u(t)),t)+diff((diff(p(t)+r(t)+r(t)*u(t)^2-
2*r(t)*u(t),t))/u(t)^2,t)+2*diff(t*r(t)/u(t)^2,t)=0,d
iff(r(t)*u(t)^2+p(t)-
r(t)*u(t),t)+diff((diff(2*r(t)*u(t)^2+2*p(t)-
r(t)*u(t)-r(t)*u(t)^3-
3*p(t)*u(t),t))/u(t)^2,t)+2*diff(t*r(t)/u(t)^2,t)+2*t
*(r(t)-(diff(r(t)*(u(t)-1),t))/u(t)^2)-
4*diff(r(t)*t/u(t),t)=0,diff(r(t)*u(t)^2+3*p(t)-
r(t)*u(t)^3-5*p(t)*u(t),t)-
diff((diff(2*r(t)*u(t)^3+10*p(t)*u(t)-r(t)*u(t)^2-
3*p(t)-r(t)*u(t)^4-8*p(t)*u(t)^2-
5*p(t)^2/r(t),t))/u(t)^2,t)+2*diff(t*(3*r(t)*u(t)^2+5
*p(t))/u(t)^2,t)-4*t*r(t)*u(t)-
4*diff(t*r(t)/u(t),t)+4*t*(2*r(t)*t+diff(p(t)+r(t)*u(
t)^2-
r(t)*u(t),t))/u(t)^2=0,u(0)=1,p(0)=1,r(0)=.7,D(u)(0)=
0,D(p)(0)=0,D(r)(0)=0});
Initializing Java runtime environment.
Warning, could not obtain numerical solution at all
points, plot may be incomplete
```

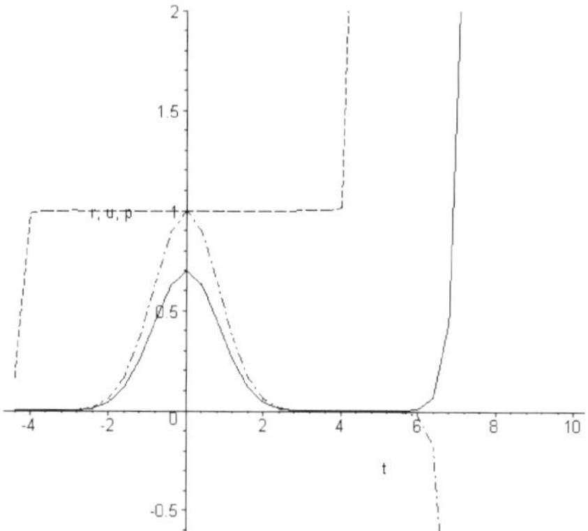

Figure 5.5.3. r - density, solid line, u - velocity, dashed line, p - pressure, dash-dot line.

```
> dsolve[interactive]({
diff(r(t)*(1-
u(t)),t)+diff((diff(p(t)+r(t)+r(t)*u(t)^2-
2*r(t)*u(t),t))/u(t)^2,t)+2*diff(t*r(t)/u(t)^2,t)=0,
diff(r(t)*u(t)^2+p(t)-
r(t)*u(t),t)+diff((diff(2*r(t)*u(t)^2+2*p(t)-
r(t)*u(t)-r(t)*u(t)^3-
3*p(t)*u(t),t))/u(t)^2,t)+2*diff(t*r(t)/u(t)^2,t)+2*t
*(r(t)-(diff(r(t)*(u(t)-1),t))/u(t)^2)-
4*diff(r(t)*t/u(t),t)=0,
diff(r(t)*u(t)^2+3*p(t)-r(t)*u(t)^3-5*p(t)*u(t),t)-
diff((diff(2*r(t)*u(t)^3+10*p(t)*u(t)-r(t)*u(t)^2-
3*p(t)-r(t)*u(t)^4-8*p(t)*u(t)^2-
5*p(t)^2/r(t),t))/u(t)^2,t)+2*diff(t*(3*r(t)*u(t)^2+5
*p(t))/u(t)^2,t)-4*t*r(t)*u(t)-
4*diff(t*r(t)/u(t),t)+4*t*(2*r(t)*t+diff(p(t)+r(t)*u(
t)^2-r(t)*u(t),t))/u(t)^2=0,
u(0)=1,p(0)=1,r(0)=1,D(u)(0)=0,D(p)(0)=0,D(r)(0)=0});
```

```
Initializing Java runtime environment.
```

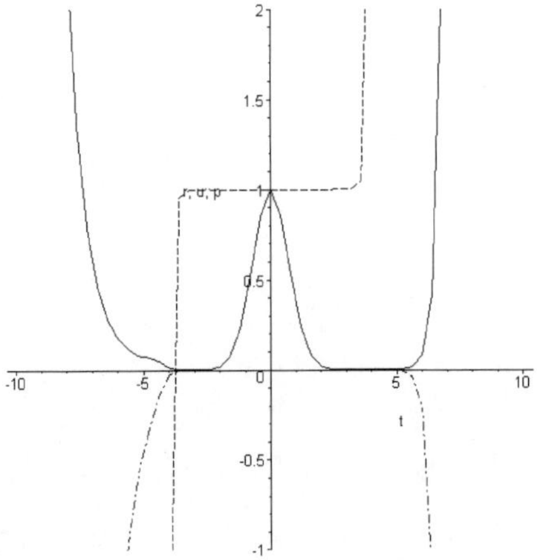

Figure 5.5.4.
r - density, solid line, u - velocity, dashed line,
p - pressure, dash-dot line.

```
> dsolve[interactive]({
diff(r(t)*(1-
u(t)),t)+diff((diff(p(t)+r(t)+r(t)*u(t)^2-
2*r(t)*u(t),t))/u(t)^2,t)+2*diff(t*r(t)/u(t)^2,t)=0,
diff(r(t)*u(t)^2+p(t)-
r(t)*u(t),t)+diff((diff(2*r(t)*u(t)^2+2*p(t)-
r(t)*u(t)-r(t)*u(t)^3-
3*p(t)*u(t),t))/u(t)^2,t)+2*diff(t*r(t)/u(t)^2,t)+2*t
*(r(t)-(diff(r(t)*(u(t)-1),t))/u(t)^2)-
4*diff(r(t)*t/u(t),t)=0,
diff(r(t)*u(t)^2+3*p(t)-r(t)*u(t)^3-5*p(t)*u(t),t)-
diff((diff(2*r(t)*u(t)^3+10*p(t)*u(t)-r(t)*u(t)^2-
3*p(t)-r(t)*u(t)^4-8*p(t)*u(t)^2-
5*p(t)^2/r(t),t))/u(t)^2,t)+2*diff(t*(3*r(t)*u(t)^2+5
*p(t))/u(t)^2,t)-4*t*r(t)*u(t)-
4*diff(t*r(t)/u(t),t)+4*t*(2*r(t)*t+diff(p(t)+r(t)*u(
t)^2-r(t)*u(t),t))/u(t)^2=0,
u(0)=1,p(0)=1,r(0)=5,D(u)(0)=0,D(p)(0)=0,D(r)(0)=0});

Warning, could not obtain numerical solution at all
points, plot may be incomplete
```

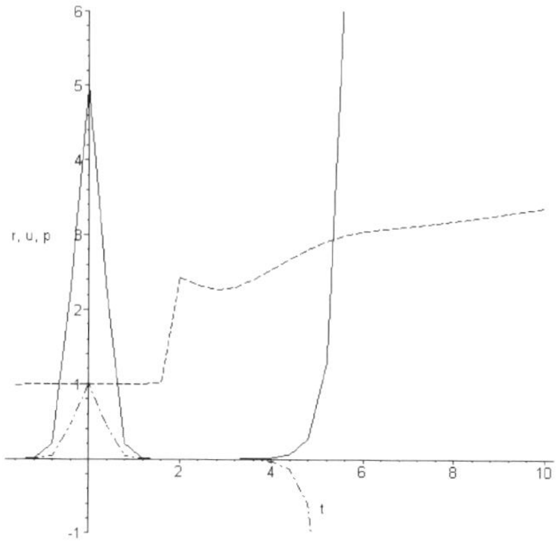

Figure 5.5.5.

r - density, solid line, u - velocity, dashed line,

p - pressure, dash-dot line.

```
> dsolve[interactive]({
diff(r(t)*(1-
u(t)),t)+diff((diff(p(t)+r(t)+r(t)*u(t)^2-
2*r(t)*u(t),t))/u(t)^2,t)+2*diff(t*r(t)/u(t)^2,t)=0,
diff(r(t)*u(t)^2+p(t)-
r(t)*u(t),t)+diff((diff(2*r(t)*u(t)^2+2*p(t)-
r(t)*u(t)-r(t)*u(t)^3-
3*p(t)*u(t),t))/u(t)^2,t)+2*diff(t*r(t)/u(t)^2,t)+2*t
*(r(t)-(diff(r(t)*(u(t)-1),t))/u(t)^2)-
4*diff(r(t)*t/u(t),t)=0,
diff(r(t)*u(t)^2+3*p(t)-r(t)*u(t)^3-5*p(t)*u(t),t)-
diff((diff(2*r(t)*u(t)^3+10*p(t)*u(t)-r(t)*u(t)^2-
3*p(t)-r(t)*u(t)^4-8*p(t)*u(t)^2-
5*p(t)^2/r(t),t))/u(t)^2,t)+2*diff(t*(3*r(t)*u(t)^2+5
*p(t))/u(t)^2,t)-4*t*r(t)*u(t)-
4*diff(t*r(t)/u(t),t)+4*t*(2*r(t)*t+diff(p(t)+r(t)*u(
t)^2-r(t)*u(t),t))/u(t)^2=0,
u(0)=1,p(0)=1,r(0)=15,D(u)(0)=0,D(p)(0)=0,D(r)(0)=0})
;
```

```
Warning, could not obtain numerical solution at all
points, plot may be incomplete
```

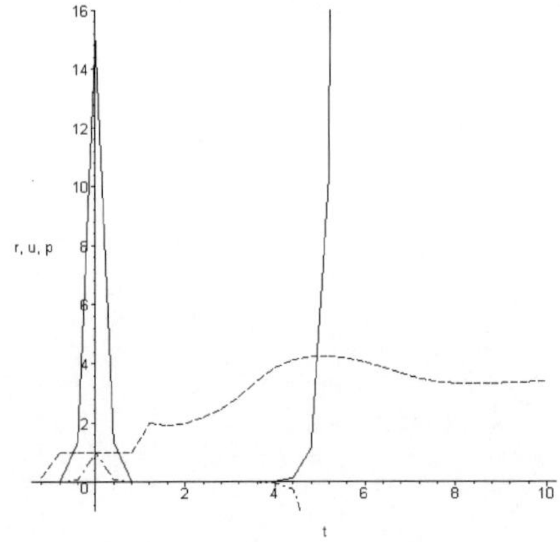

Figure 5.5.6.
r - density, solid line, u - velocity, dashed line,
p - pressure, dash-dot line.

Figures 5.5.1 – 5.5.6 show how the region of existence of the soliton narrows as the initial density perturbation increases. We demonstrate further the role of the pressure increasing from $\widetilde{p}(0)=0.1$ to $\widetilde{p}(0)=50$ for the soliton evolution, (figures 5.5.7 – 5.5.9).

```
> dsolve[interactive]({
diff(r(t)*(1-
u(t)),t)+diff((diff(p(t)+r(t)+r(t)*u(t)^2-
2*r(t)*u(t),t))/u(t)^2,t)+2*diff(t*r(t)/u(t)^2,t)=0,
diff(r(t)*u(t)^2+p(t)-
r(t)*u(t),t)+diff((diff(2*r(t)*u(t)^2+2*p(t)-
r(t)*u(t)-r(t)*u(t)^3-
3*p(t)*u(t),t))/u(t)^2,t)+2*diff(t*r(t)/u(t)^2,t)+2*t
*(r(t)-(diff(r(t)*(u(t)-1),t))/u(t)^2)-
4*diff(r(t)*t/u(t),t)=0,
diff(r(t)*u(t)^2+3*p(t)-r(t)*u(t)^3-5*p(t)*u(t),t)-
diff((diff(2*r(t)*u(t)^3+10*p(t)*u(t)-r(t)*u(t)^2-
3*p(t)-r(t)*u(t)^4-8*p(t)*u(t)^2-
5*p(t)^2/r(t),t))/u(t)^2,t)+2*diff(t*(3*r(t)*u(t)^2+5
*p(t))/u(t)^2,t)-4*t*r(t)*u(t)-
4*diff(t*r(t)/u(t),t)+4*t*(2*r(t)*t+diff(p(t)+r(t)*u(
t)^2-r(t)*u(t),t))/u(t)^2=0,
u(0)=1,p(0)=.1,r(0)=1,D(u)(0)=0,D(p)(0)=0,D(r)(0)=0})
;
```

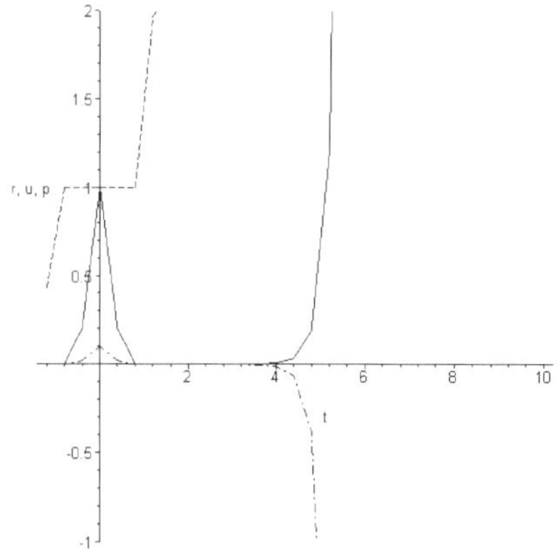

Figure 5.5.7. r - density, solid line, u - velocity, dashed line, p - pressure, dash-dot line.

```
> dsolve[interactive]({
diff(r(t)*(1-
u(t)),t)+diff((diff(p(t)+r(t)+r(t)*u(t)^2-
2*r(t)*u(t),t))/u(t)^2,t)+2*diff(t*r(t)/u(t)^2,t)=0,
diff(r(t)*u(t)^2+p(t)-
r(t)*u(t),t)+diff((diff(2*r(t)*u(t)^2+2*p(t)-
r(t)*u(t)-r(t)*u(t)^3-
3*p(t)*u(t),t))/u(t)^2,t)+2*diff(t*r(t)/u(t)^2,t)+2*t
*(r(t)-(diff(r(t)*(u(t)-1),t))/u(t)^2)-
4*diff(r(t)*t/u(t),t)=0,
diff(r(t)*u(t)^2+3*p(t)-r(t)*u(t)^3-5*p(t)*u(t),t)-
diff((diff(2*r(t)*u(t)^3+10*p(t)*u(t)-r(t)*u(t)^2-
3*p(t)-r(t)*u(t)^4-8*p(t)*u(t)^2-
5*p(t)^2/r(t),t))/u(t)^2,t)+2*diff(t*(3*r(t)*u(t)^2+5
*p(t))/u(t)^2,t)-4*t*r(t)*u(t)-
4*diff(t*r(t)/u(t),t)+4*t*(2*r(t)*t+diff(p(t)+r(t)*u(
t)^2-r(t)*u(t),t))/u(t)^2=0,
u(0)=1,p(0)=10,r(0)=1,D(u)(0)=0,D(p)(0)=0,D(r)(0)=0})
;
```

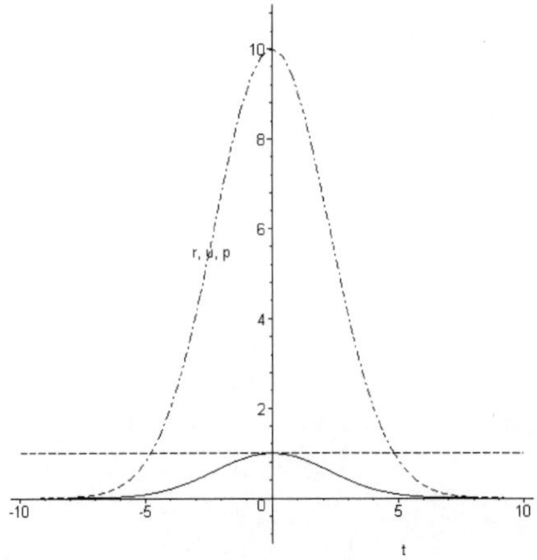

Figure 5.5.8.

r - density, solid line, u - velocity, dashed line,

p - pressure, dash-dot line.

```
> dsolve[interactive]({
diff(r(t)*(1-
u(t)),t)+diff((diff(p(t)+r(t)+r(t)*u(t)^2-
2*r(t)*u(t),t))/u(t)^2,t)+2*diff(t*r(t)/u(t)^2,t)=0,
diff(r(t)*u(t)^2+p(t)-
r(t)*u(t),t)+diff((diff(2*r(t)*u(t)^2+2*p(t)-
r(t)*u(t)-r(t)*u(t)^3-
3*p(t)*u(t),t))/u(t)^2,t)+2*diff(t*r(t)/u(t)^2,t)+2*t
*(r(t)-(diff(r(t)*(u(t)-1),t))/u(t)^2)-
4*diff(r(t)*t/u(t),t)=0,
diff(r(t)*u(t)^2+3*p(t)-r(t)*u(t)^3-5*p(t)*u(t),t)-
diff((diff(2*r(t)*u(t)^3+10*p(t)*u(t)-r(t)*u(t)^2-
3*p(t)-r(t)*u(t)^4-8*p(t)*u(t)^2-
5*p(t)^2/r(t),t))/u(t)^2,t)+2*diff(t*(3*r(t)*u(t)^2+5
*p(t))/u(t)^2,t)-4*t*r(t)*u(t)-
4*diff(t*r(t)/u(t),t)+4*t*(2*r(t)*t+diff(p(t)+r(t)*u(
t)^2-r(t)*u(t),t))/u(t)^2=0,
u(0)=1,p(0)=50,r(0)=1,D(u)(0)=0,D(p)(0)=0,D(r)(0)=0})
;
```

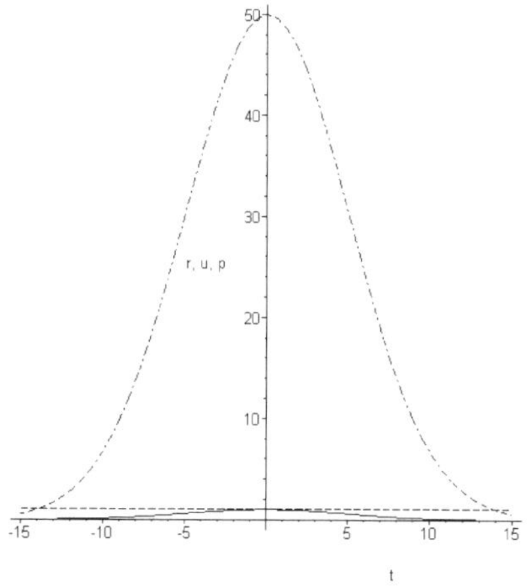

Figure 5.5.9.
r - density, solid line, u - velocity, dashed line,
p - pressure, dash-dot line.

The following are calculations for the quantum oscillator when the displacement is proportional $\tilde{\xi}^{10}$.

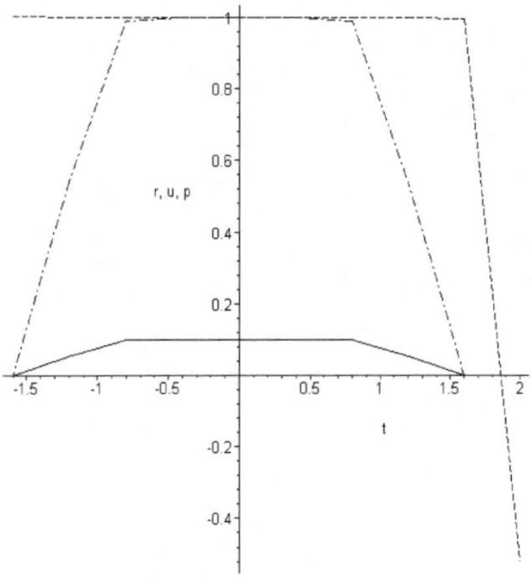

Figure 5.5.10.
r - density, solid line, u - velocity, dashed line,
p - pressure, dash-dot line.

The following are calculations for the quantum anharmonic oscillator when the displacement is proportional $\left(\tilde{\xi}^2 + \tilde{\xi}^{10}\right)$.

```
> dsolve[interactive]({
diff(r(t)*(1-
u(t)),t)+diff((diff(p(t)+r(t)+r(t)*u(t)^2-
2*r(t)*u(t),t))/u(t)^2,t)+diff((2*t+10*t^9)*r(t)/u(t)
^2,t)=0,
diff(r(t)*u(t)^2+p(t)-
r(t)*u(t),t)+diff((diff(2*r(t)*u(t)^2+2*p(t)-
r(t)*u(t)-r(t)*u(t)^3-
3*p(t)*u(t),t))/u(t)^2,t)+diff((2*t+10*t^9)*r(t)/u(t)
^2,t)+(2*t+10*t^9)*(r(t)-(diff(r(t)*(u(t)-
1),t))/u(t)^2)-2*diff(r(t)*(2*t+10*t^9)/u(t),t)=0,
diff(r(t)*u(t)^2+3*p(t)-r(t)*u(t)^3-5*p(t)*u(t),t)-
diff((diff(2*r(t)*u(t)^3+10*p(t)*u(t)-r(t)*u(t)^2-
```

```
3*p(t)-r(t)*u(t)^4-8*p(t)*u(t)^2-
5*p(t)^2/r(t),t))/u(t)^2,t)+diff((2*t+10*t^9)*(3*r(t)
*u(t)^2+5*p(t))/u(t)^2,t)-2*(2*t+10*t^9)*r(t)*u(t)-
2*diff((2*t+10*t^9)*r(t)/u(t),t)+2*(2*t+10*t^9)*(r(t)
*(2*t+10*t^9)+diff(p(t)+r(t)*u(t)^2-
r(t)*u(t),t))/u(t)^2=0,
u(0)=1,p(0)=1,r(0)=.1,D(u)(0)=0,D(p)(0)=0,D(r)(0)=0})
;
```

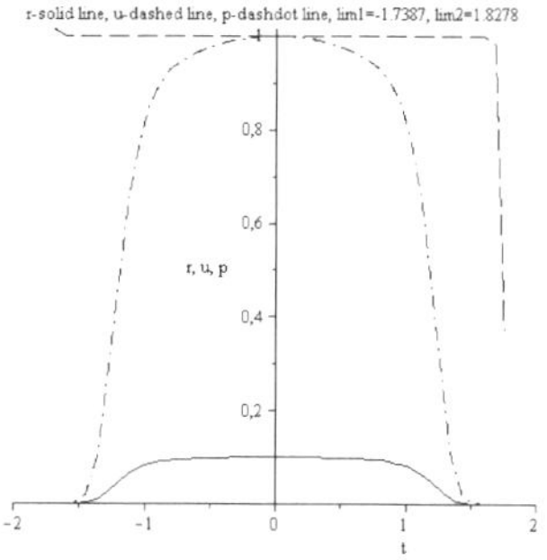

Figure 5.5.11.
r - density, solid line, u - velocity, dashed line,
p - pressure, dash-dot line, lim1=-1.7387, lim2=1.8278.

5.6. Numerical solution of the equations of continuity, motion, and energy under the Heisenberg uncertainty principle. Two displaced quantum oscillators.

In the following we realize numerical solution of the equations of continuity, motion, and energy under the Heisenberg uncertainty principle, two displaced quantum oscillators for which $\tilde{U} = \tilde{\xi}^2 + (\tilde{\xi} - 1)^2$. In this case $\frac{\partial \tilde{U}}{\partial \tilde{\xi}} = 2\tilde{\xi} + 2(\tilde{\xi} - 1) = 2(2\tilde{\xi} - 1)$.

We have the system of equations:

$$\frac{\partial \tilde{\rho}}{\partial \tilde{\xi}} - \frac{\partial \tilde{\rho}\tilde{u}}{\partial \tilde{\xi}} + \frac{\partial}{\partial \tilde{\xi}}\left\{\frac{1}{\tilde{u}^2}\left[\frac{\partial}{\partial \tilde{\xi}}\left(\tilde{p} + \tilde{\rho} + \tilde{\rho}\tilde{u}^2 - 2\tilde{\rho}\tilde{u}\right) + 2\left(2\tilde{\xi} - 1\right)\tilde{\rho}\right]\right\} = 0, \qquad (5.6.1)$$

$$\frac{\partial}{\partial\tilde{\xi}}\left(\tilde{\rho}\tilde{u}^2+\tilde{p}-\tilde{\rho}\tilde{u}\right)+$$

$$+\frac{\partial}{\partial\tilde{\xi}}\left\{\frac{1}{\tilde{u}^2}\left[\frac{\partial}{\partial\tilde{\xi}}\left(2\tilde{\rho}\tilde{u}^2-\tilde{\rho}\tilde{u}+2\tilde{p}-\tilde{\rho}\tilde{u}^3-3\tilde{p}\tilde{u}\right)+2\left(2\tilde{\xi}-1\right)\tilde{\rho}\right]\right\}+ \qquad (5.6.2)$$

$$+2\left(2\tilde{\xi}-1\right)\left\{\tilde{\rho}-\frac{1}{\tilde{u}^2}\left[-\frac{\partial\tilde{\rho}}{\partial\tilde{\xi}}+\frac{\partial}{\partial\tilde{\xi}}\left(\tilde{\rho}\tilde{u}\right)\right]\right\}-4\frac{\partial}{\partial\tilde{\xi}}\left\{\frac{\tilde{\rho}}{\tilde{u}}\left(2\tilde{\xi}-1\right)\right\}=0,$$

$$\frac{\partial}{\partial\tilde{\xi}}\left(\tilde{\rho}\tilde{u}^2+3\tilde{p}-\tilde{\rho}\tilde{u}^3-5\tilde{p}\tilde{u}\right)-$$

$$-\frac{\partial}{\partial\tilde{\xi}}\left\{\frac{1}{\tilde{u}^2}\frac{\partial}{\partial\tilde{\xi}}\left(2\tilde{\rho}\tilde{u}^3+10\tilde{p}\tilde{u}-\tilde{\rho}\tilde{u}^2-3\tilde{p}-\tilde{\rho}\tilde{u}^4-8\tilde{p}\tilde{u}^2-5\frac{\tilde{p}^2}{\tilde{\rho}}\right)\right\}+$$

$$+2\frac{\partial}{\partial\tilde{\xi}}\left\{\frac{1}{\tilde{u}^2}\left(3\tilde{\rho}\tilde{u}^2+5\tilde{p}\right)\left(2\tilde{\xi}-1\right)\right\}-4\tilde{\rho}\tilde{u}\left(2\tilde{\xi}-1\right)-4\frac{\partial}{\partial\tilde{\xi}}\left\{\frac{\tilde{\rho}}{\tilde{u}}\left(2\tilde{\xi}-1\right)\right\}+$$

$$+\frac{4}{\tilde{u}^2}\left(2\tilde{\xi}-1\right)\left[-\frac{\partial}{\partial\tilde{\xi}}\left(\tilde{\rho}\tilde{u}\right)+\frac{\partial}{\partial\tilde{\xi}}\left(\tilde{\rho}\tilde{u}^2+\tilde{p}\right)+2\left(2\tilde{\xi}-1\right)\tilde{\rho}\right]=0,$$

(5.6.3)

```
> dsolve[interactive]({
diff(r(t)*(1-
u(t)),t)+diff((diff(p(t)+r(t)+r(t)*u(t)^2-
2*r(t)*u(t),t))/u(t)^2,t)+2*diff((2*t-
1)*r(t)/u(t)^2,t)=0,
diff(r(t)*u(t)^2+p(t)-
r(t)*u(t),t)+diff(diff(2*r(t)*u(t)^2+2*p(t)-
r(t)*u(t)-r(t)*u(t)^3-
3*p(t)*u(t),t)/u(t)^2,t)+2*diff((2*t-
1)*r(t)/u(t)^2,t)+2*(2*t-1)*r(t)-2*(2*t-
1)*diff(r(t)*(u(t)-1),t)/u(t)^2-4*diff(r(t)*(2*t-
1)/u(t),t)=0,
diff(r(t)*u(t)^2+3*p(t)-r(t)*u(t)^3-5*p(t)*u(t),t)-
diff(diff(2*r(t)*u(t)^3+10*p(t)*u(t)-r(t)*u(t)^2-
3*p(t)-r(t)*u(t)^4-8*p(t)*u(t)^2-
5*p(t)^2/r(t),t)/u(t)^2,t)+2*diff((2*t-
1)*(3*r(t)*u(t)^2+5*p(t))/u(t)^2,t)-4*(2*t-
1)*r(t)*u(t)-4*diff((2*t-1)*r(t)/u(t),t)+4*(2*t-
1)*(2*r(t)*(2*t-1)+diff(p(t)+r(t)*u(t)^2-
r(t)*u(t),t))/u(t)^2=0,
u(0.5)=1,p(0.5)=10,r(0.5)=1,D(u)(0.5)=0,D(p)(0.5)=0,D
(r)(0.5)=0});
```

Notice that Cauchy conditions refer to $\tilde{\xi} = 0.5$, $\tilde{\xi}$ is t on figures.

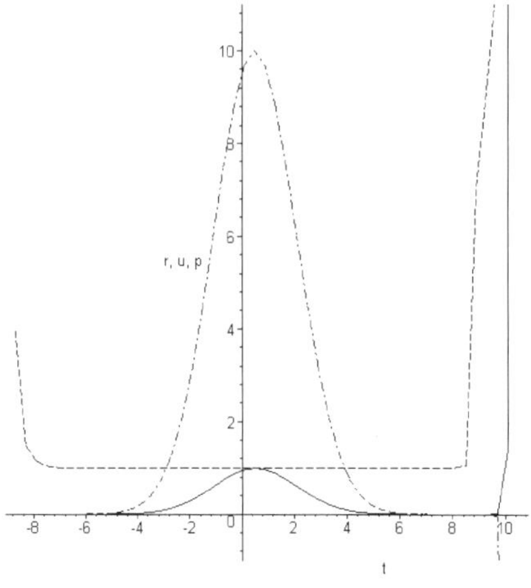

Figure 5.6.1.
r - density, solid line, u - velocity, dashed line,
p - pressure, dash-dot line.

The following figure 5.6.2 reflects calculations fot the Cauchy conditions `u(0.5)=1,p(0.5)=1,r(0.5)=1,D(u)(0.5)=0,D(p)(0.5)=0,D(r)(0.5)=0.`

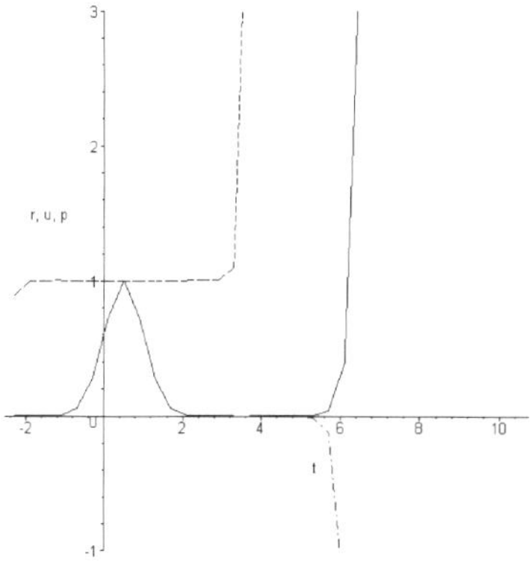

Figure 5.6.2. r - density, solid line, u - velocity, dashed line,
p - pressure, dash-dot line.

Figures 5.6.1 and 5.6.2 ilustrate solitons located between two singular regions.

5.7. Conclusion to Chapter 5.

1. Within the framework of a unified approach, non-local hydrodynamics is an effective tool for studying a variety of physical problems from atmospheric phenomena to quantum mechanics.
2. The discovery of differential equations that can lead to solutions of the soliton type has always been an event in mathematics and mechanics. As you can see, the appearance of solitons in nonlocal theory is an "ordinary", often occurring fact. In many cases, the theory leads to the appearance of discrete levels for derivatives of hydrodynamic quantities.
3. In nonlocal hydrodynamics, solitons exist for quite complex systems, such as a progressively moving oscillator and a combination of oscillators. These formations mimic the movement of molecules. The natural next step is to study the interaction and, in particular, the collision of solitons. It can be hypothesized that the collision of solitons can lead to the birth of a set of solitons ("fragments"), which causes the transition to the hydrodynamic description in the theoretical study of the collision of heavy particles in colliders.
4. The artificial exclusion of the energy equation from consideration (as it was implicitly postulated by Schrödinger) only complicates the theory aimed at searching for solitary waves and often leads to non-physical results.
5. Quantum mechanics of Schrödinger leads to the "spread" of wave packets simulating an elementary particle. However, the appearance of quantum solitons in nonlocal theory allows us to agree with the Schrödinger hypothesis, which proposed to treat quantum effects as the evolution of matter waves in time and space.

CHAPTER 6. THE THEORY OF HIGH-TEMPERATURE SUPERCONDUCTIVITY.

6.1. Preliminary remarks.

It is well known that superconductivity (SC) was discovered more than 100 years ago in the laboratory of Heike Kamerlingh Onnes, at Leiden University in the Netherlands. It was done on 8 April 1911, after testing for electrical resistance in a sample of mercury at 3 K. H. Kamerlingh Onnes found that at 4.2 K the resistance in a solid mercury wire immersed in liquid helium suddenly vanished. He immediately realized the significance of the discovery [90]. He reported that "Mercury has passed into a new state, which on account of its extraordinary electrical properties may be called the superconductive state". Superconductivity is the phenomenon of complete absence of resistance during the flow of electric current, as well as ideal diamagnetism (that is, "pushing out" the magnetic field from the sample: the magnetic field does not penetrate deep into the material).

Quantum mechanics created in the 1920s provided an underlying model for the structure of ordinary metals. Metal atoms form a regular crystalline lattice with tightly bound inner core of electrons. But their loosely attached outer electrons become unbound, collecting into a mobile "electron cloud". Under the influence of an electric field, these free electrons will drift throughout the lattice, forming the basis of conductivity. But random thermal fluctuations scatter the electrons, interrupting their forward motion and dissipating energy — thereby producing electrical resistance. If some metals are cooled to temperatures close to absolute zero, the electrons suddenly shift into a highly ordered state and travel collectively without deviating from their path. Below a critical temperature T_c (or better to say a narrow temperature diapason ΔT) the electrical resistance falls to zero, and they become superconductors. In the case of low temperature SC ΔT is about $0{,}001 \div 0{,}1$ K, for high temperature SC ΔT can be more than 1 K. From position of non-local physics it means that the solution of the generalized non-local quantum equations transforms into soliton's type without destruction in space and time.

In the May issue of Physical Review two experimental papers [91, 92] (both received by the journal on March 24th, 1950) were describing measurements of the critical temperature of mercury for different isotopes, reporting that "there is a systematic decrease of transition temperature with increasing mass" [91], and that [92] "From these results one may infer that the transition temperature of a superconductor is a function of the nuclear mass, the lighter the mass the higher the transition temperature. From experiments follow that for crystal lattices of the different isotopes the relation takes place

$$T_c\sqrt{M} = const, \tag{6.1.1}$$

where M is isotopic mass and $const$ is the same for all isotopes. The frequency of the lattice vibration ω is connected with the square root of M

$$\omega \sim 1/\sqrt{M}. \tag{6.1.2}$$

It means that the interaction between electrons and lattice vibrations (phonons) was responsible for superconductivity.

It should be noticed that on May 16th, 1950, Herbert Fröhlich's paper entitled "Theory of the Superconducting State. I. The Ground State at the Absolute Zero of Temperature" was received by the Physical Review [93]. This theoretical paper also proposed that the interaction between electrons and lattice vibrations (phonons) was responsible for superconductivity. The paper made no mention of the experimental papers [91, 92], moreover later Herbert Fröhlich stated that the isotope effect experiments "have just come to my notice" and pointed out that the formalism in his May 16th paper ([93]) in fact predicted the effect. The question of priority is discussed until now [94].

Significant step in explanation of the behavior of superconducting materials consists in creation of BCS theory (John Bardeen, Leon N. Cooper, and John R. Schrieffer, 1957, [95]). From the qualitative point of view the physical model looks as follows. Two forces of the electric origin influence on the electrons behavior in a metal – the repulsion between electrons and attraction between electrons and positive ions that make up the rigid lattice of the metal.

Let us estimate the character scale Δr of the phonon interaction. Phonon energy is $\hbar\omega_D \sim \hbar v_s / a$, where ω_D is Debye frequency, v_s – sound speed, a - the lattice constant. For example the lattice constant for a common carbon diamond is a = 3.57Å at 300 K. The character impulse is $\Delta p \sim \hbar\omega_D / v_F$, where v_F $(\sim 10^6 m/\sec)$ – electron velocity near Fermi surface. Then the scale Δr can be found using the Heisenberg uncertainty relation

$$\Delta r \sim \hbar / \Delta p \sim v_F / \omega_D \sim \frac{v_F}{v_s} a \sim \sqrt{\frac{M}{m}} a, \tag{6.1.3}$$

where M, m – ion and electron masses respectively. Usually, $\Delta r \sim 10^{-5} \div 10^{-6}$ см.

The mentioned attraction distorts the ion lattice, increasing the local positive charge density of the lattice. This perturbation of the positive charge can attract other electrons. At long distances this attraction between electrons due to the displaced ions can overcome the electrons' repulsion due to their negative charge, and cause them to pair up. A Cooper pair (described in 1956 by Leon Cooper) has special construction:

1. Electrons are fermions, but a Cooper pair is a composite boson as its total spin is integer. As result the wave functions are symmetric under particle interchange, and they are allowed to be in the same state. The Cooper pairs "condense" in a body into the same ground quantum state.
2. If the electric current is absent, the combined impulse of a Cooper pair is equal to zero. After application of the external electric field a Cooper pair receives the additional impulse

$$(\mathbf{p}+\mathbf{p}')+(-\mathbf{p}+\mathbf{p}')=2\mathbf{p}', \qquad (6.1.4)$$

if the initial impulse of the first electron was $\mathbf{p}$ and the second one $(-\mathbf{p})$. The impulse of the Cooper pair is

$$p_C = 2mv \qquad (6.1.5)$$

The electrons in a pair are not necessarily close together; because the interaction is long range. The typical estimation is $\sim 10^{-4}$ cm. This distance is usually greater than the average inter-electron distance. As result a Cooper pair begins to move as a single object under influence of the self-consistent electric field. As a superconductor is warmed, its Cooper pairs separate into individual electrons, and the material becomes no superconducting. In other words thermal energy can break the pairs. In Internet the animations can be found (see for example bcs.anim.GIF and Fig. 6.1.1) for illustration of the mentioned motion.

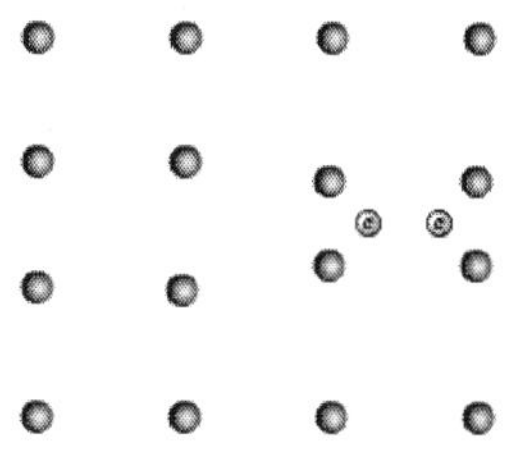

Fig. 6.1.1. A shot from animation illustrating a cooper pair movement (bcs.anim.GIF).

The following remarks should be taken into account by using such kind of animations:

1. The distance between electrons in a Cooper pair practically much more than the distance between neighboring ions in the crystal lattice.
2. By the concurrent motion of many Cooper pairs the lattice ions perform the oscillations along the directed motion of electrons.

From the previous consideration follows that we have quantum hydrodynamic non-local effects.

Later in June 1986, physicists Georg Bednorz and Alex Müller at the IBM Laboratory in Zurich, Switzerland, reported that they had created a material that became superconducting at 35 K. Extremely important that they were looking not at metals, but at insulating materials called copper oxides. Ceramics $YBa_2Cu_3O_7$ and TlBaCaCuO became superconducting at 93 K. For high temperature SC classic BCS theory can't be applied. Finishing the introduction is reasonable to cite the beginning of the BCS-paper [95]: "Since the discovery of the isotope effect, it has been known that superconductivity arises from the interaction between electrons and lattice vibrations, but it has proved difficult to construct an adequate theory based on this concept."

The ideal diamagnetism of the superconductor can be explained by the fact that an undamped current begins to flow along the surface of the sample, the magnetic field of which completely compensates the external magnetic field. The density of the undamped current shielding the external magnetic field decreases rapidly as it moves away from the surface into the superconductor. Accordingly, in this area, the external magnetic field decreases from a certain value on the surface to zero in depth. This phenomenon was discovered in 1933 by German physicists Walter Meisner and Robert Oxenfeld and is called the Meisner–Oxenfeld effect. The state is considered to be superconducting if it meets two requirements: the absence of resistance and the ejection of the magnetic field from the sample (the Meisner–Oxenfeld effect).

The Meissner effect (or Meissner–Ochsenfeld effect) [96] is the expulsion of a magnetic field from a superconductor during its transition to the superconducting state. This phenomenon was discovered by measuring the magnetic field distribution outside superconducting tin and lead samples. A superconductor with little or no magnetic field within it is said to be in the Meissner state.

The Meissner state breaks down when the applied magnetic field is too strong. Superconductors can be divided into two classes according to how this breakdown occurs. In type-1 superconductors, superconductivity is abruptly destroyed when the strength of the applied field rises above a critical value H_c. In type-II superconductors, raising the applied field past a critical value H_{c1} leads to a mixed state (also known as the vortex state) in which an increasing amount of magnetic flux penetrates the material, but there remains no resistance to the electric current as long as the current is not too large.

The Meissner effect was given a phenomenological explanation by the brothers Fritz and Heinz London, who introduced the phenomenological relation

$$\Delta\mathbf{H} = \frac{1}{\lambda^2}\mathbf{H}, \qquad (6.1.6)$$

where **H** is the magnetic field and λ is the London penetration depth. This London equation predicts that the magnetic field in a superconductor decays exponentially decays from whatever value it possesses at the surface.

The first theory satisfactorily describing the phenomenon of superconductivity is the theory of Bardeen–Cooper–Schrieffer (BCS theory). In April of 1957 Bardeen, Cooper and Schrieffer published a short paper in *Physical Review* entitled "Microscopic Theory of Superconductivity." They submitted their full detailed report, appropriately titled "Theory of Superconductivity," to *the Physical Review* in July 1957, and it was published in December. Bardeen, Cooper, and Schrieffer were awarded the Nobel Prize in 1972 for their theory of superconductivity. This was Bardeen's second Nobel Prize in physics–his first was shared with William Shockley and Walter Brattain for the transistor in 1956.

This is the theory of low-temperature superconductivity. Its essence is as follows: the electrons in the substance, through interaction with the vibrations of the crystal lattice of the material (phonons), are combined into pairs, called Cooper, and behave as if a single "organism" with huge atomic dimensions. As a result, the electronic system of Cooper pairs "does not notice" obstacles when it flows through the material (that is, it experiences zero resistance).

Without any doubt, the main task of technologists — specialists in "applied" superconductivity is to create a superconductor with room critical temperature T_c. Of course, it is difficult to search for such materials at random, so physicists come to the aid of material scientists, who try to indicate the direction of their search with their models. Although, as history shows, in the case of superconductivity, rather, there is a reverse process — technologists find HTSC materials, theorists build a model. However, if the theory of high-temperature superconductivity were to be constructed, the search for substances with room T_c would certainly become easier.

When in 1986 Johannes Bednorz and Karl Muller, employees of the Zurich branch of IBM Corporation, discovered the ability of ceramics based on copper oxide, lanthanum and barium at 30 K to move into a superconducting state, it was the first stage on the way to high-temperature superconductivity. Since it was opened a lot of substances related to high temperature superconductors, but no real success of building a theoretical model that well describes the observed properties of high-temperature superconductivity.

Attempts to apply the theory of BCS to the explanation of high-temperature superconductivity have not been successful; currently, there are more than a dozen different models in their approaches, each of which separately gives some correct predictions. By now recognized record the TC value of 135 K possesses $HgBa_2Ca_2Cu_3O_{8+d}$, opened in Moscow State University in 1993.

Thus, it can be stated that the search for substances with the properties of high-temperature superconductors is made at random without a single strategy based on underlying fundamental theory. It will be further shown that the solution of the problem should be based on the creation of artificial materials based on the application of nonlocal physics in the theory of quantum dots.

The main aim of the following consideration consists in construction "an adequate theory based on this concept", the theory distinguished from BCS.

6.2. Numerical solution of the equations of continuity, motion and energy of the model problem of quantum dot theory taking into account the Heisenberg uncertainty principle.

First of all, we must explain the use of the term "quantum dots" in the nonlocal theory of high-temperature superconductivity. Until now, the field of application of quantum dot technology had nothing to do with non-local physics in general, and the theory of high-temperature superconductivity in particular.

Until now quantum dots (QDs) are tiny semiconductor particles a few nanometers in size, having optical and electronics properties that differ from larger particles due to the quantum mechanical effects. They are a central topic in nanotechnology. When the quantum dots are illuminated by UV light, an electron in the quantum dot can be excited to a state of higher energy. In the case of a semiconducting quantum dot, this process corresponds to the transition of an electron from the valence band to the conducting band. The excited electron can drop back into the valence band releasing its energy by the emission of light. The color of that light depends on the energy difference between the conducting band and the valence band. Quantum dots are sometimes referred to as artificial atoms. Quantum dots have properties intermediate between bulk semiconductors and discrete atoms or molecules. Potential applications of quantum dots include single-electron transistors, solar cells, LEDs. lasers, quantum computing and so on.

Definition.

Under the quantum dots in high-temperature superconductivity (QDHTS), we understand the nano-material, providing the creation of such a potential, in which there is no destruction of electronic solitons, current carriers in the conductor.

We show that such potentials, which do not destroy (but, on the contrary, support) the wave of solitons, do exist. Let us transform nonlocal Maxwell equation

$$\frac{\partial}{\partial x}E = 4\pi\left[\rho_e - \tau\left(\frac{\partial \rho_e}{\partial t} - \frac{\partial}{\partial x}(\rho_e u)\right)\right], \tag{6.2.1}$$

where ρ_e is the electron charge density, or

$$-\frac{\partial^2}{\partial x^2}U_e = 4\pi\left[n_e - \tau\left(\frac{\partial n_e}{\partial t} - \frac{\partial}{\partial x}(n_e u)\right)\right]e, \tag{6.2.2}$$

where U_e is electrical potential and n_e is the electron number density. Equation (6.2.2) can be written in terms of wave parameters ($\xi = x - Ct$). Namely

$$-\frac{\partial^2}{\partial \xi^2}U_e = 4\pi\frac{e}{m_e}\left[\rho - \tau\left(-C\frac{\partial \rho}{\partial \xi} - \frac{\partial}{\partial \xi}(\rho u)\right)\right], \tag{6.2.3}$$

where ρ is the mass density, or introducing the absolute electron charge and potential $U = U_e / m_e$ we find

$$\frac{\partial^2}{\partial \xi^2}U = 4\pi\frac{|e|}{m_e^2}\left[\rho + \tau\left(C\frac{\partial \rho}{\partial \xi} + \frac{\partial}{\partial \xi}(\rho u)\right)\right]. \tag{6.2.4}$$

We use the following system of scales:

$$C_0 = x_0\frac{1}{\tau_0},\ \widetilde{C} = 1,\ \rho_0 = \frac{m_e}{4\pi x_0^3},\ U_0 = \frac{|e|}{m_e x_0},\ u_0 = \sqrt{\frac{\hbar}{4m_e}} = \frac{1}{2}\sqrt{\frac{\hbar}{m_e}}, \tag{6.2.5}$$

$$\tau = \tau^{(qu)} = t_0\frac{1}{\widetilde{u}^2} = t_0\frac{u_0^2}{u^2} = \frac{\hbar}{4m_e}\frac{1}{u^2}\tau_0,\ \tau_0 = \frac{x_0}{u_0} = 2x_0\sqrt{\frac{m_e}{\hbar}},\ C_0 = 2\sqrt{\frac{\hbar}{m_e}} = 2.1519\frac{cm}{s}. \tag{6.2.6}$$

The single independent scale is x_0.

Taking into account $\hbar = 1.054572\cdot 10^{-27} erg\cdot s$, $m_e = 0.9109383\cdot 10^{-27} g$, we have

$$\sqrt{\frac{\hbar}{m_e}} = 1.0759538\frac{cm}{s},\ \sqrt{\frac{m_e}{\hbar}} = 0.964058\frac{s}{cm},\ \tilde{\tau} = \frac{1}{\tilde{u}^2}. \tag{6.2.7}$$

The considered physical system works in Meissner regime, and then we needn't to use the influence of magnetic field. We reach the system of dimensionless equations

$$\frac{\partial^2}{\partial\tilde{\xi}^2}\tilde{U} = \tilde{\rho} + \frac{1}{\tilde{u}^2}\frac{\partial}{\partial\tilde{\xi}}[\tilde{\rho}(1+\tilde{u})] \tag{6.2.8}$$

$$\frac{\partial\tilde{\rho}}{\partial\tilde{\xi}} - \frac{\partial\tilde{\rho}\tilde{u}}{\partial\tilde{\xi}} + \frac{\partial}{\partial\tilde{\xi}}\left\{\frac{1}{\tilde{u}^2}\left[\frac{\partial}{\partial\tilde{\xi}}\left(\tilde{p} + \tilde{\rho} + \tilde{\rho}\tilde{u}^2 - 2\tilde{\rho}\tilde{u}\right) + \tilde{\rho}\frac{\partial\tilde{U}}{\partial\tilde{\xi}}\right]\right\} = 0, \tag{6.2.9}$$

$$\begin{aligned} &\frac{\partial}{\partial\tilde{\xi}}\left(\tilde{\rho}\tilde{u}^2 + \tilde{p} - \tilde{\rho}\tilde{u}\right) + \\ &+ \frac{\partial}{\partial\tilde{\xi}}\left\{\frac{1}{\tilde{u}^2}\left[\frac{\partial}{\partial\tilde{\xi}}\left(2\tilde{\rho}\tilde{u}^2 - \tilde{\rho}\tilde{u} + 2\tilde{p} - \tilde{\rho}\tilde{u}^3 - 3\tilde{p}\tilde{u}\right) + \tilde{\rho}\frac{\partial\tilde{U}}{\partial\tilde{\xi}}\right]\right\} + \\ &+ \frac{\partial\tilde{U}}{\partial\tilde{\xi}}\left\{\tilde{\rho} - \frac{1}{\tilde{u}^2}\left[-\frac{\partial\tilde{\rho}}{\partial\tilde{\xi}} + \frac{\partial}{\partial\tilde{\xi}}(\tilde{\rho}\tilde{u})\right]\right\} - 2\frac{\partial}{\partial\tilde{\xi}}\left\{\frac{\tilde{\rho}}{\tilde{u}}\frac{\partial\tilde{U}}{\partial\tilde{\xi}}\right\} = 0, \end{aligned} \tag{6.2.10}$$

$$\begin{aligned} &\frac{\partial}{\partial\tilde{\xi}}\left(\tilde{\rho}\tilde{u}^2 + 3\tilde{p} - \tilde{\rho}\tilde{u}^3 - 5\tilde{p}\tilde{u}\right) - \\ &- \frac{\partial}{\partial\tilde{\xi}}\left\{\frac{1}{\tilde{u}^2}\frac{\partial}{\partial\tilde{\xi}}\left(2\tilde{\rho}\tilde{u}^3 + 10\tilde{p}\tilde{u} - \tilde{\rho}\tilde{u}^2 - 3\tilde{p} - \tilde{\rho}\tilde{u}^4 - 8\tilde{p}\tilde{u}^2 - 5\frac{\tilde{p}^2}{\tilde{\rho}}\right)\right\} + \\ &+ \frac{\partial}{\partial\tilde{\xi}}\left\{\frac{1}{\tilde{u}^2}\left(3\tilde{\rho}\tilde{u}^2 + 5\tilde{p}\right)\frac{\partial\tilde{U}}{\partial\tilde{\xi}}\right\} - 2\tilde{\rho}\tilde{u}\frac{\partial\tilde{U}}{\partial\tilde{\xi}} - 2\frac{\partial}{\partial\tilde{\xi}}\left\{\frac{\tilde{p}}{\tilde{u}}\frac{\partial\tilde{U}}{\partial\tilde{\xi}}\right\} + \\ &+ \frac{2}{\tilde{u}^2}\frac{\partial\tilde{U}}{\partial\tilde{\xi}}\left[-\frac{\partial}{\partial\tilde{\xi}}(\tilde{\rho}\tilde{u}) + \frac{\partial}{\partial\tilde{\xi}}\left(\tilde{\rho}\tilde{u}^2 + \tilde{p}\right) + \tilde{\rho}\frac{\partial\tilde{U}}{\partial\tilde{\xi}}\right] = 0, \end{aligned} \tag{6.2.11}$$

```
>dsolve[interactive]({
diff(r(t)*(1-
u(t)),t)+diff((diff(p(t)+r(t)+r(t)*u(t)^2-
2*r(t)*u(t),t))/u(t)^2,t)+diff(r(t)*diff(v(t),t)/u(t)
^2,t)=0,
diff(r(t)*u(t)^2+p(t)-
r(t)*u(t),t)+diff(diff(2*r(t)*u(t)^2+2*p(t)-
r(t)*u(t)-r(t)*u(t)^3-
3*p(t)*u(t),t)/u(t)^2,t)+diff(diff(v(t),t)*r(t)/u(t)^
2,t)+r(t)*diff(v(t),t)-diff(v(t),t)*diff(r(t)*(u(t)-
1),t)/u(t)^2-
2*diff(diff(v(t),t)*r(t)/u(t),t)=0,
```

```
diff(r(t)*u(t)^2+3*p(t)-r(t)*u(t)^3-5*p(t)*u(t),t)-
diff(diff(2*r(t)*u(t)^3+10*p(t)*u(t)-r(t)*u(t)^2-
3*p(t)-r(t)*u(t)^4-8*p(t)*u(t)^2-
5*p(t)^2/r(t),t)/u(t)^2,t)+diff(diff(v(t),t)*(3*r(t)*
u(t)^2+5*p(t))/u(t)^2,t)-2*r(t)*diff(v(t),t)*u(t)-
2*diff(r(t)*diff(v(t),t)/u(t),t)+2*diff(v(t),t)*(r(t)
*diff(v(t),t)+diff(p(t)+r(t)*u(t)^2-
r(t)*u(t),t))/u(t)^2=0,
diff(v(t),t$2)=r(t)+(1/u(t)^2)*diff(r(t)*(1+u(t)),t),
u(0)=1,p(0)=1,r(0)=1,D(u)(0)=0,D(p)(0)=0,D(r)(0)=0,D(
v)(0)=0,v(0)=10});
```

As you see Cauchy conditions are:

`u(0)=1,p(0)=1,r(0)=1,D(u)(0)=0,D(p)(0)=0,D(r)(0)=0, D(v)(0)=0,v(0)=10.`

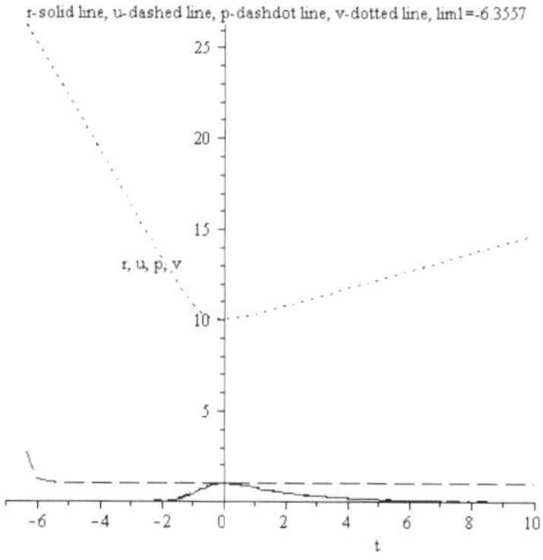

Figure 6.2.1. Density r - solid line, velocity u - dashed line, pressure p – dash-dot line, self-consistent potential v - dotted line, lim1=-6.3557.

The following figures reflect the result of calculations for the Cauchy conditions:

`u(0)=1,p(0)=1,r(0)=1,D(u)(0)=0,D(p)(0)=0,D(r)(0)=0, D(v)(0)=0,v(0)=1.`

(decrease in the previous initial potential in ten times).

```
> dsolve[interactive]({
diff(r(t)*(1-
u(t)),t)+diff((diff(p(t)+r(t)+r(t)*u(t)^2-
2*r(t)*u(t),t))/u(t)^2,t)+diff(r(t)*diff(v(t),t)/u(t)
^2,t)=0,
diff(r(t)*u(t)^2+p(t)-
r(t)*u(t),t)+diff(diff(2*r(t)*u(t)^2+2*p(t)-
r(t)*u(t)-r(t)*u(t)^3-
3*p(t)*u(t),t)/u(t)^2,t)+diff(diff(v(t),t)*r(t)/u(t)^
2,t)+r(t)*diff(v(t),t)-diff(v(t),t)*diff(r(t)*(u(t)-
1),t)/u(t)^2-
2*diff(diff(v(t),t)*r(t)/u(t),t)=0,
diff(r(t)*u(t)^2+3*p(t)-r(t)*u(t)^3-5*p(t)*u(t),t)-
diff(diff(2*r(t)*u(t)^3+10*p(t)*u(t)-r(t)*u(t)^2-
3*p(t)-r(t)*u(t)^4-8*p(t)*u(t)^2-
5*p(t)^2/r(t),t)/u(t)^2,t)+diff(diff(v(t),t)*(3*r(t)*
u(t)^2+5*p(t))/u(t)^2,t)-2*r(t)*diff(v(t),t)*u(t)-
2*diff(r(t)*diff(v(t),t)/u(t),t)+2*diff(v(t),t)*(r(t)
*diff(v(t),t)+diff(p(t)+r(t)*u(t)^2-
r(t)*u(t),t))/u(t)^2=0,
diff(v(t),t$2)=r(t)+(1/u(t)^2)*diff(r(t)*(1+u(t)),t),
u(0)=1,p(0)=1,r(0)=1,D(u)(0)=0,D(p)(0)=0,D(r)(0)=0,D(
v)(0)=0,v(0)=1});
```

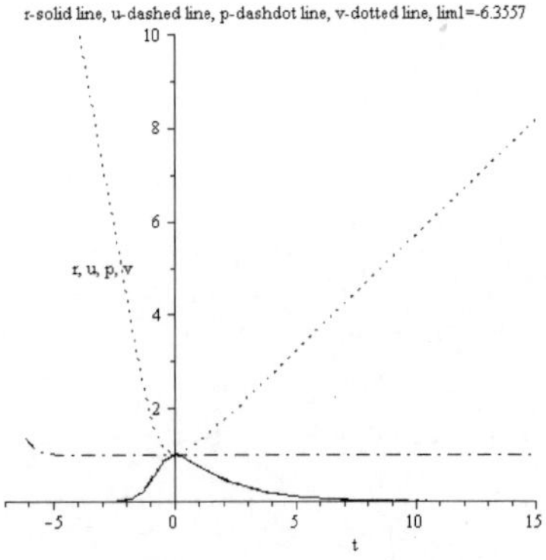

Figure 6.2.2. Density r - solid line, velocity u - dashed line, pressure p – dash-dot line, self-consistent potential v - dotted line, lim1=-6.3557.

It's a variant for the Cauchy conditions

```
u(0)=1,p(0)=1,r(0)=1,D(u)(0)=0,D(p)(0)=0,D(r)(0)=0,
D(v)(0)=0,v(0)=0.1,
```

(decrease in the previous initial potential in ten times).

```
>dsolve[interactive]({
diff(r(t)*(1-
u(t)),t)+diff((diff(p(t)+r(t)+r(t)*u(t)^2-
2*r(t)*u(t),t))/u(t)^2,t)+diff(r(t)*diff(v(t),t)/u(t)
^2,t)=0,
diff(r(t)*u(t)^2+p(t)-
r(t)*u(t),t)+diff(diff(2*r(t)*u(t)^2+2*p(t)-
r(t)*u(t)-r(t)*u(t)^3-
3*p(t)*u(t),t)/u(t)^2,t)+diff(diff(v(t),t)*r(t)/u(t)^
2,t)+r(t)*diff(v(t),t)-diff(v(t),t)*diff(r(t)*(u(t)-
1),t)/u(t)^2-
2*diff(diff(v(t),t)*r(t)/u(t),t)=0,
diff(r(t)*u(t)^2+3*p(t)-r(t)*u(t)^3-5*p(t)*u(t),t)-
diff(diff(2*r(t)*u(t)^3+10*p(t)*u(t)-r(t)*u(t)^2-
3*p(t)-r(t)*u(t)^4-8*p(t)*u(t)^2-
5*p(t)^2/r(t),t)/u(t)^2,t)+diff(diff(v(t),t)*(3*r(t)*
u(t)^2+5*p(t))/u(t)^2,t)-2*r(t)*diff(v(t),t)*u(t)-
2*diff(r(t)*diff(v(t),t)/u(t),t)+2*diff(v(t),t)*(r(t)
*diff(v(t),t)+diff(p(t)+r(t)*u(t)^2-
r(t)*u(t),t))/u(t)^2=0,
diff(v(t),t$2)=r(t)+(1/u(t)^2)*diff(r(t)*(1+u(t)),t),
u(0)=1,p(0)=1,r(0)=1,D(u)(0)=0,D(p)(0)=0,D(r)(0)=0,D(
v)(0)=0,v(0)=.1});
```

```
Initializing Java runtime environment.
Warning, could not obtain numerical solution at all
points, plot may be incomplete
```

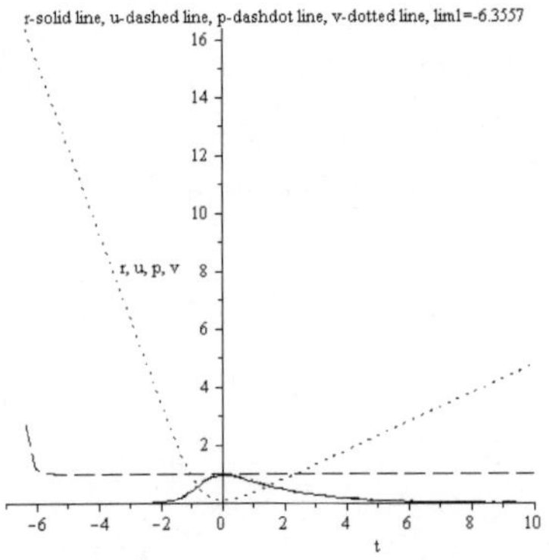

Figure 6.2.3. Density r - solid line, velocity u - dashed line, pressure p – dash-dot line, self-consistent potential v - dotted line, lim1=-6.3557.

Now we change the pressure in the Cauchy conditions,
u(0)=1,p(0)=2,r(0)=1,D(u)(0)=0,D(p)(0)=0,D(r)(0)=0,
D(v)(0)=0,v(0)=1.

```
>dsolve[interactive]({
diff(r(t)*(1-
u(t)),t)+diff((diff(p(t)+r(t)+r(t)*u(t)^2-
2*r(t)*u(t),t))/u(t)^2,t)+diff(r(t)*diff(v(t),t)/u(t)
^2,t)=0,
diff(r(t)*u(t)^2+p(t)-
r(t)*u(t),t)+diff(diff(2*r(t)*u(t)^2+2*p(t)-
r(t)*u(t)-r(t)*u(t)^3-
3*p(t)*u(t),t)/u(t)^2,t)+diff(diff(v(t),t)*r(t)/u(t)^
2,t)+r(t)*diff(v(t),t)-diff(v(t),t)*diff(r(t)*(u(t)-
1),t)/u(t)^2-
2*diff(diff(v(t),t)*r(t)/u(t),t)=0,
diff(r(t)*u(t)^2+3*p(t)-r(t)*u(t)^3-5*p(t)*u(t),t)-
diff(diff(2*r(t)*u(t)^3+10*p(t)*u(t)-r(t)*u(t)^2-
3*p(t)-r(t)*u(t)^4-8*p(t)*u(t)^2-
5*p(t)^2/r(t),t)/u(t)^2,t)+diff(diff(v(t),t)*(3*r(t)*
u(t)^2+5*p(t))/u(t)^2,t)-2*r(t)*diff(v(t),t)*u(t)-
2*diff(r(t)*diff(v(t),t)/u(t),t)+2*diff(v(t),t)*(r(t)
*diff(v(t),t)+diff(p(t)+r(t)*u(t)^2-
r(t)*u(t),t))/u(t)^2=0,
```

```
diff(v(t),t$2)=r(t)+(1/u(t)^2)*diff(r(t)*(1+u(t)),t),
u(0)=1,p(0)=2,r(0)=1,D(u)(0)=0,D(p)(0)=0,D(r)(0)=0,D(
v)(0)=0,v(0)=1});
Warning, could not obtain numerical solution at all
points, plot may be incomplete
```

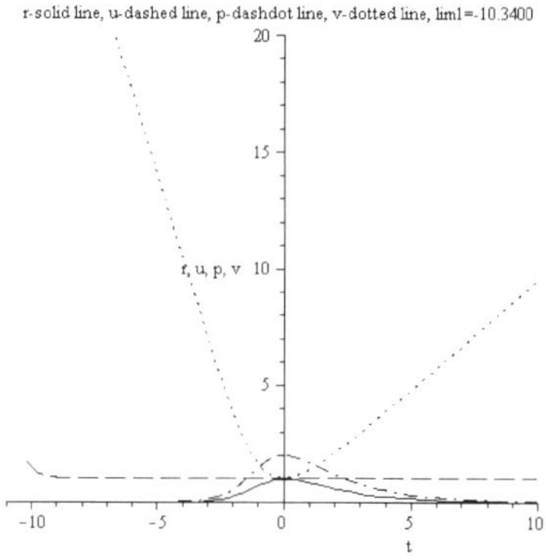

Figure 6.2.4. Density r - solid line, velocity u - dashed line, pressure p – dash-dot line, self-consistent potential v - dotted line, lim1=-10.3400.

Let us change now density in Cauchy conditions, namely
`u(0)=1,p(0)=1,r(0)=5,D(u)(0)=0,D(p)(0)=0,D(r)(0)=0,D(v)(0)=0, v(0)=1.`

The corresponding program in language Maple is

```
>dsolve[interactive]({
diff(r(t)*(1-
u(t)),t)+diff((diff(p(t)+r(t)+r(t)*u(t)^2-
2*r(t)*u(t),t))/u(t)^2,t)+diff(r(t)*diff(v(t),t)/u(t)
^2,t)=0,
diff(r(t)*u(t)^2+p(t)-
r(t)*u(t),t)+diff(diff(2*r(t)*u(t)^2+2*p(t)-
r(t)*u(t)-r(t)*u(t)^3-
3*p(t)*u(t),t)/u(t)^2,t)+diff(diff(v(t),t)*r(t)/u(t)^
2,t)+r(t)*diff(v(t),t)-diff(v(t),t)*diff(r(t)*(u(t)-
1),t)/u(t)^2-
2*diff(diff(v(t),t)*r(t)/u(t),t)=0,
```

```
diff(r(t)*u(t)^2+3*p(t)-r(t)*u(t)^3-5*p(t)*u(t),t)-
diff(diff(2*r(t)*u(t)^3+10*p(t)*u(t)-r(t)*u(t)^2-
3*p(t)-r(t)*u(t)^4-8*p(t)*u(t)^2-
5*p(t)^2/r(t),t)/u(t)^2,t)+diff(diff(v(t),t)*(3*r(t)*
u(t)^2+5*p(t))/u(t)^2,t)-2*r(t)*diff(v(t),t)*u(t)-
2*diff(r(t)*diff(v(t),t)/u(t),t)+2*diff(v(t),t)*(r(t)
*diff(v(t),t)+diff(p(t)+r(t)*u(t)^2-
r(t)*u(t),t))/u(t)^2=0,
diff(v(t),t$2)=r(t)+(1/u(t)^2)*diff(r(t)*(1+u(t)),t),
u(0)=1,p(0)=1,r(0)=5,D(u)(0)=0,D(p)(0)=0,D(r)(0)=0,D(
v)(0)=0,v(0)=1});
```

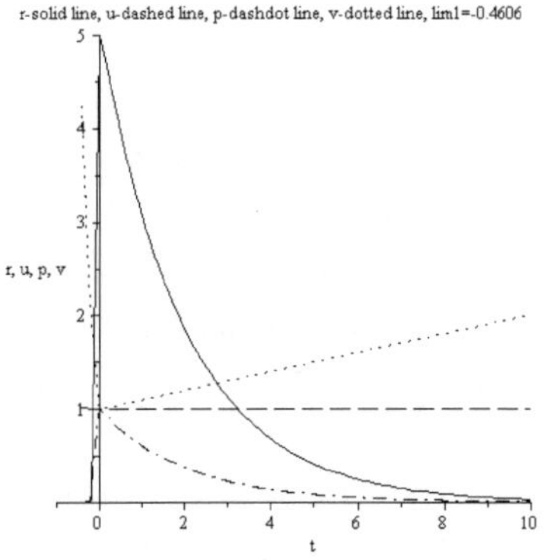

Figure 6.2.5. Density r - solid line, velocity u - dashed line, pressure p – dash-dot line, self-consistent potential v - dotted line, lim1=-0.4606.

Until now we investigated the space evolution of solitons moving with the phase velocity. Let us “spoil” this condition taking, for example, in Cauchy conditions u(0)=2. Namely we use

```
u(0)=2,p(0)=1,r(0)=1,D(u)(0)=0,D(p)(0)=0,D(r)(0)=0,D(
v)(0)=0, v(0)=1
> dsolve[interactive]({
diff(r(t)*(1-
u(t)),t)+diff((diff(p(t)+r(t)+r(t)*u(t)^2-
2*r(t)*u(t),t))/u(t)^2,t)+diff(r(t)*diff(v(t),t)/u(t)
^2,t)=0,
```

```
diff(r(t)*u(t)^2+p(t)-
r(t)*u(t),t)+diff(diff(2*r(t)*u(t)^2+2*p(t)-
r(t)*u(t)-r(t)*u(t)^3-
3*p(t)*u(t),t)/u(t)^2,t)+diff(diff(v(t),t)*r(t)/u(t)^
2,t)+r(t)*diff(v(t),t)-diff(v(t),t)*diff(r(t)*(u(t)-
1),t)/u(t)^2-
2*diff(diff(v(t),t)*r(t)/u(t),t)=0,
diff(r(t)*u(t)^2+3*p(t)-r(t)*u(t)^3-5*p(t)*u(t),t)-
diff(diff(2*r(t)*u(t)^3+10*p(t)*u(t)-r(t)*u(t)^2-
3*p(t)-r(t)*u(t)^4-8*p(t)*u(t)^2-
5*p(t)^2/r(t),t)/u(t)^2,t)+diff(diff(v(t),t)*(3*r(t)*
u(t)^2+5*p(t))/u(t)^2,t)-2*r(t)*diff(v(t),t)*u(t)-
2*diff(r(t)*diff(v(t),t)/u(t),t)+2*diff(v(t),t)*(r(t)
*diff(v(t),t)+diff(p(t)+r(t)*u(t)^2-
r(t)*u(t),t))/u(t)^2=0,
diff(v(t),t$2)=r(t)+(1/u(t)^2)*diff(r(t)*(1+u(t)),t),
u(0)=2,p(0)=1,r(0)=1,D(u)(0)=0,D(p)(0)=0,D(r)(0)=0,D(
v)(0)=0,v(0)=1});
```

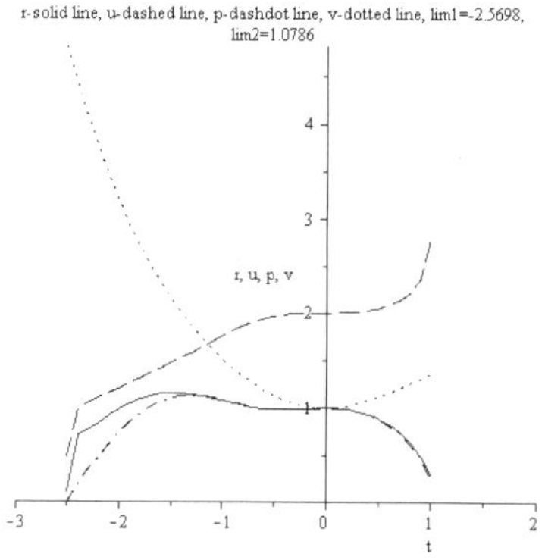

Figure 6.2.6. Density r - solid line, velocity u - dashed line, pressure p – dash-dot line, self-consistent potential v - dotted line, lim1=-2.5698, lim2=1.0786.

As you can see, an attempt to organize the movement of the electron wave at a speed different from the phase speed leads to the immediate destruction of the soliton.

The previous calculations allow defining the correlation lengths as the lengths of moving soliton for all reasonable temperature diapason.

Now we deliver some conclusions:

1. BCS theory of superconductivity needs to exchange phonons between two electrons for creating Cooper pairs quasi-particles close to the Fermi level.
2. BCS theory explains superconductivity using the concept of cooper pairs formed from the continual exchange of phonons between two electrons due to lattice distortions.
3. As they are bosons thus they are not limited by the Pauli's exclusion principle and thus they try to share the same state.
3. Immediately the main shortcoming of BCS arises – the temperature restrictions connected with Debye temperature. Namely $k_B T_D$ is roughly equal to the phonon energy of the minimum wavelength mode, and so we can interpret the Debye temperature [97] as the temperature at which the highest-frequency mode (and hence every mode) is excited. Such a limit T_c was calculated in the past to be around 30K.
4. Such cooper pairs can only form below a temperature of ~30K as too great of lattice vibrations causes too much scattering of the electrons to be able to form cooper pairs. That is to say, upper 30K couldn't exist superconductivity without having a crystalline lattice broken. This is in short the incompatibility between BCS and the high T_c superconductors which present a much higher critical temperature. Hence, BCS theory is limited as it only explains superconductivity in type 1 superconductors (pure metals) not type 2 superconductors (alloys, ceramics with higher T_c than 30K)
5. For solving such difficulty there are many models, but one is quite well developed uses magnons instead of phonons as exchange particles between the electrons (having an anti-ferromagnetic background in their insulation phase) allowing bound pairs in states with d-symmetry. This is called d-superconductivity; there is also p-superconductivity and s-superconductivity (which coincides with the usual BCS).
6. BCS fails to predict the effects of the actual superconductivity or which materials are superconducting. In other words BCS does not describe transport processes. Instead, it simply provides an explanation for the 'events'.

7. The developed nonlocal theory does not contain temperature restrictions and leads to the generalized transport equations as a basement for the following creation of HT superconductors.

6.3. To the theory of ion superconductivity.

The well-established term ion superconductivity is used for ion conductors with ultra-high (but still finite) conductivity. Real ionic superconductivity has not been realized. In most ionic crystals, the ions of each variety occupy quite certain positions, and the number of these positions corresponds exactly to the number of available ions. For example, in a NaCl crystal, each Na^+ ion is located in the center of the octahedron, the vertices of which are occupied by Cl^- ions, and vice versa, each Cl^- ion is located in a symmetrical environment of six Na^+ ions. This rigid order begins to be disturbed to some extent only at high temperatures, when the amplitude of the ion oscillations increases so much that some particles are able to leave their places in the nodes of the crystal lattice and move to the internodes or to the surface of the crystal.

The appearance of free nodes (ion vacancies) makes possible the ionic conductivity, which although increases with temperature, but remains quite small even near the melting temperature. The presence of a large number of vacancies randomly located in the crystal lattice, in fact, means a violation of the strict long-range order. Such a lack of long-range order is typical for liquids. A solid electrolyte can be imagined as a rigid ordered frame formed by some ions, inside which there is a fluid "liquid" formed by ions of another kind — just as in metals, conductive "liquid" form electrons.

However, if the conductivity of metals increases with decreasing temperature, in solid electrolytes it increases when heated. There is a problem of creation of superconducting solid electrolytes; in other words, such crystalline substances that would have extremely high ionic conductivity already at room temperature.

The more rigid and ordered the crystal lattice formed by ions of one class, and the more erratic and mobile the ions of another class, the lower the temperature at which the solid electrolyte can work. One of the already created ion superconductors, capable of operating at room temperature, has a composition of Ag4RbI5 and is obtained by fusion of silver and rubidium iodides. As soon as this compound was discovered, it was immediately used as a solid electrolyte in miniature solid-phase batteries intended for space: Such a battery, using the energy of the interaction of silver with iodine, is able to give a steady current for years in the temperature range from -55 to +75°C.

But it is even more tempting to create solid electrolytes that conduct electric current as a result of the movement of hydrogen ions — protons. Let us realize now the mathematical modeling of the soliton movement created by protons. In this case we have following system of the dimensionless equations.

$$\frac{\partial^2}{\partial\tilde{\xi}^2}\tilde{U} = -\tilde{\rho} - \frac{1}{\tilde{u}^2}\frac{\partial}{\partial\tilde{\xi}}[\tilde{\rho}(1+\tilde{u})] \tag{6.3.1}$$

$$\frac{\partial\tilde{\rho}}{\partial\tilde{\xi}} - \frac{\partial\tilde{\rho}\tilde{u}}{\partial\tilde{\xi}} + \frac{\partial}{\partial\tilde{\xi}}\left\{\frac{1}{\tilde{u}^2}\left[\frac{\partial}{\partial\tilde{\xi}}\left(\tilde{p} + \tilde{\rho} + \tilde{\rho}\tilde{u}^2 - 2\tilde{\rho}\tilde{u}\right) + \tilde{\rho}\frac{\partial\tilde{U}}{\partial\tilde{\xi}}\right]\right\} = 0, \tag{6.3.2}$$

$$\begin{aligned}
&\frac{\partial}{\partial\tilde{\xi}}\left(\tilde{\rho}\tilde{u}^2 + \tilde{p} - \tilde{\rho}\tilde{u}\right) + \\
&+\frac{\partial}{\partial\tilde{\xi}}\left\{\frac{1}{\tilde{u}^2}\left[\frac{\partial}{\partial\tilde{\xi}}\left(2\tilde{\rho}\tilde{u}^2 - \tilde{\rho}\tilde{u} + 2\tilde{p} - \tilde{\rho}\tilde{u}^3 - 3\tilde{p}\tilde{u}\right) + \tilde{\rho}\frac{\partial\tilde{U}}{\partial\tilde{\xi}}\right]\right\} + \\
&+\frac{\partial\tilde{U}}{\partial\tilde{\xi}}\left\{\tilde{\rho} - \frac{1}{\tilde{u}^2}\left[-\frac{\partial\tilde{\rho}}{\partial\tilde{\xi}} + \frac{\partial}{\partial\tilde{\xi}}(\tilde{\rho}\tilde{u})\right]\right\} - 2\frac{\partial}{\partial\tilde{\xi}}\left\{\frac{\tilde{\rho}}{\tilde{u}}\frac{\partial\tilde{U}}{\partial\tilde{\xi}}\right\} = 0,
\end{aligned} \tag{6.3.3}$$

$$\begin{aligned}
&\frac{\partial}{\partial\tilde{\xi}}\left(\tilde{\rho}\tilde{u}^2 + 3\tilde{p} - \tilde{\rho}\tilde{u}^3 - 5\tilde{p}\tilde{u}\right) - \\
&-\frac{\partial}{\partial\tilde{\xi}}\left\{\frac{1}{\tilde{u}^2}\frac{\partial}{\partial\tilde{\xi}}\left(2\tilde{\rho}\tilde{u}^3 + 10\tilde{p}\tilde{u} - \tilde{\rho}\tilde{u}^2 - 3\tilde{p} - \tilde{\rho}\tilde{u}^4 - 8\tilde{p}\tilde{u}^2 - 5\frac{\tilde{p}^2}{\tilde{\rho}}\right)\right\} + \\
&+\frac{\partial}{\partial\tilde{\xi}}\left\{\frac{1}{\tilde{u}^2}\left(3\tilde{\rho}\tilde{u}^2 + 5\tilde{p}\right)\frac{\partial\tilde{U}}{\partial\tilde{\xi}}\right\} - 2\tilde{\rho}\tilde{u}\frac{\partial\tilde{U}}{\partial\tilde{\xi}} - 2\frac{\partial}{\partial\tilde{\xi}}\left\{\frac{\tilde{\rho}}{\tilde{u}}\frac{\partial\tilde{U}}{\partial\tilde{\xi}}\right\} + \\
&+\frac{2}{\tilde{u}^2}\frac{\partial\tilde{U}}{\partial\tilde{\xi}}\left[-\frac{\partial}{\partial\tilde{\xi}}(\tilde{\rho}\tilde{u}) + \frac{\partial}{\partial\tilde{\xi}}\left(\tilde{\rho}\tilde{u}^2 + \tilde{p}\right) + \tilde{\rho}\frac{\partial\tilde{U}}{\partial\tilde{\xi}}\right] = 0,
\end{aligned} \tag{6.3.4}$$

created for the system of scales:

$$C_0 = x_0\frac{1}{\tau_0},\ \tilde{C} = 1,\ \rho_0 = \frac{m_p}{4\pi x_0^3},\ U_0 = \frac{|e|}{m_p x_0},\ u_0 = \frac{1}{2}\sqrt{\frac{\hbar}{m_p}}, \tag{6.3.5}$$

$$\tau = \tau^{(\kappa\epsilon)} = t_0\frac{1}{\tilde{u}^2} = t_0\frac{u_0^2}{u^2} = \frac{\hbar}{4m_p}\frac{1}{u^2}\tau_0,\ \tau_0 = \frac{x_0}{u_0} = 2x_0\sqrt{\frac{m_p}{\hbar}}. \tag{6.3.6}$$

$$m_p = 1.672622\cdot10^{-24}g,\ \hbar = 1.054572\cdot10^{-27}erg\cdot s,\ \sqrt{\frac{\hbar}{m_p}} = \sqrt{\frac{10.54572}{1.672622}10^{-4}} = 2.511\cdot10^{-2}\frac{cm}{s},$$

$$u_0 = \frac{1}{2}\sqrt{\frac{\hbar}{m_p}} = 0.12555\frac{mm}{s}. \tag{6.3.7}$$

```
>dsolve[interactive]({
diff(r(t)*(1-
u(t)),t)+diff((diff(p(t)+r(t)+r(t)*u(t)^2-
2*r(t)*u(t),t))/u(t)^2,t)+diff(r(t)*diff(v(t),t)/u(t)
^2,t)=0,
diff(r(t)*u(t)^2+p(t)-
r(t)*u(t),t)+diff(diff(2*r(t)*u(t)^2+2*p(t)-
r(t)*u(t)-r(t)*u(t)^3-
3*p(t)*u(t),t)/u(t)^2,t)+diff(diff(v(t),t)*r(t)/u(t)^
2,t)+r(t)*diff(v(t),t)-diff(v(t),t)*diff(r(t)*(u(t)-
1),t)/u(t)^2-
2*diff(diff(v(t),t)*r(t)/u(t),t)=0,
diff(r(t)*u(t)^2+3*p(t)-r(t)*u(t)^3-5*p(t)*u(t),t)-
diff(diff(2*r(t)*u(t)^3+10*p(t)*u(t)-r(t)*u(t)^2-
3*p(t)-r(t)*u(t)^4-8*p(t)*u(t)^2-
5*p(t)^2/r(t),t)/u(t)^2,t)+diff(diff(v(t),t)*(3*r(t)*
u(t)^2+5*p(t))/u(t)^2,t)-2*r(t)*diff(v(t),t)*u(t)-
2*diff(r(t)*diff(v(t),t)/u(t),t)+2*diff(v(t),t)*(r(t)
*diff(v(t),t)+diff(p(t)+r(t)*u(t)^2-
r(t)*u(t),t))/u(t)^2=0,
-diff(v(t),t$2)=
r(t)+(1/u(t)^2)*diff(r(t)*(1+u(t)),t),
u(0)=1,p(0)=1,r(0)=1,D(u)(0)=0,D(p)(0)=0,D(r)(0)=0,D(
v)(0)=0,v(0)=10});
```

As you see Cauchy conditions are:

```
u(0)=1,p(0)=1,r(0)=1,D(u)(0)=0,D(p)(0)=0,D(r)(0)=0,
D(v)(0)=0,v(0)=10.
```

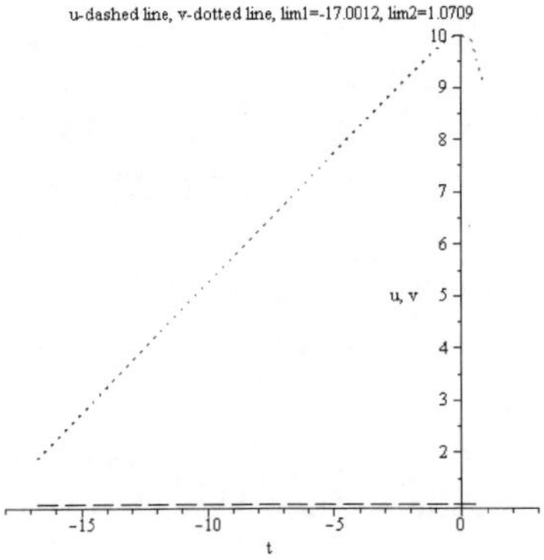

Figure 6.3.1. Velocity u-dashed line, self-consistent potential v -dotted line, lim1=-17.0012, lim2=1.0709.

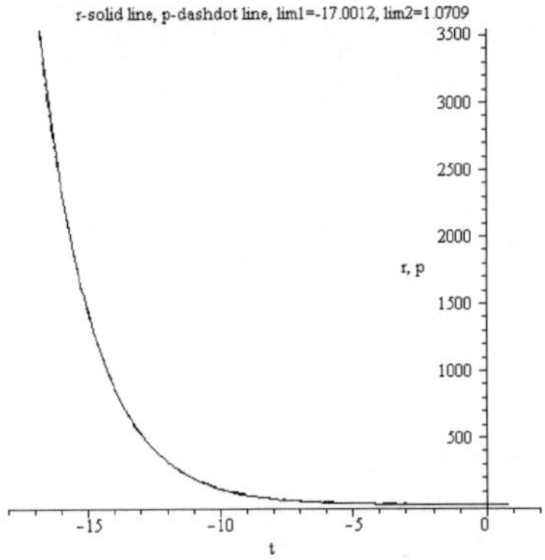

Figure 6.3.2. Density r-solid line, pressure p-dash-dot line, lim1=-17.0012, lim2=1.0709.

The following figures reflect the result of calculations for the Cauchy conditions:

`u(0)=1,p(0)=1,r(0)=1,D(u)(0)=0,D(p)(0)=0,D(r)(0)=0, D(v)(0)=0,v(0)=1.`

(decrease in the previous initial potential in ten times).

```
> dsolve[interactive]({
diff(r(t)*(1-
u(t)),t)+diff((diff(p(t)+r(t)+r(t)*u(t)^2-
2*r(t)*u(t),t))/u(t)^2,t)+diff(r(t)*diff(v(t),t)/u(t)
^2,t)=0,
diff(r(t)*u(t)^2+p(t)-
r(t)*u(t),t)+diff(diff(2*r(t)*u(t)^2+2*p(t)-
r(t)*u(t)-r(t)*u(t)^3-
3*p(t)*u(t),t)/u(t)^2,t)+diff(diff(v(t),t)*r(t)/u(t)^
2,t)+r(t)*diff(v(t),t)-diff(v(t),t)*diff(r(t)*(u(t)-
1),t)/u(t)^2-
2*diff(diff(v(t),t)*r(t)/u(t),t)=0,
diff(r(t)*u(t)^2+3*p(t)-r(t)*u(t)^3-5*p(t)*u(t),t)-
diff(diff(2*r(t)*u(t)^3+10*p(t)*u(t)-r(t)*u(t)^2-
3*p(t)-r(t)*u(t)^4-8*p(t)*u(t)^2-
5*p(t)^2/r(t),t)/u(t)^2,t)+diff(diff(v(t),t)*(3*r(t)*
u(t)^2+5*p(t))/u(t)^2,t)-2*r(t)*diff(v(t),t)*u(t)-
2*diff(r(t)*diff(v(t),t)/u(t),t)+2*diff(v(t),t)*(r(t)
*diff(v(t),t)+diff(p(t)+r(t)*u(t)^2-
r(t)*u(t),t))/u(t)^2=0,
-diff(v(t),t$2)=
r(t)+(1/u(t)^2)*diff(r(t)*(1+u(t)),t),
u(0)=1,p(0)=1,r(0)=1,D(u)(0)=0,D(p)(0)=0,D(r)(0)=0,D(
v)(0)=0,v(0)=1});
```

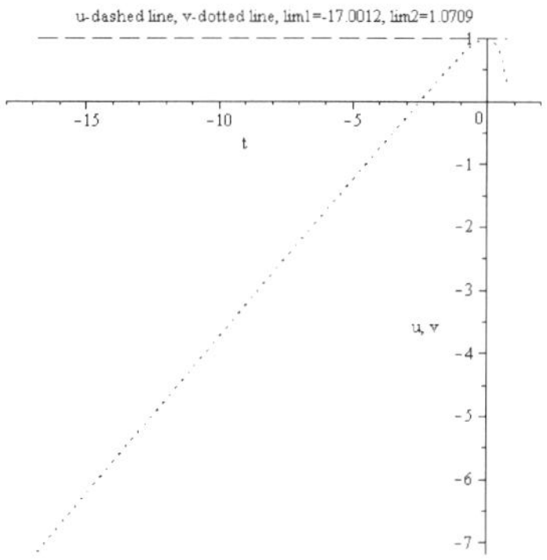

Figure 6.3.3. Velocity u-dashed line, self-consistent potential v -dotted line, lim1=-17.0012, lim2=1.0709.

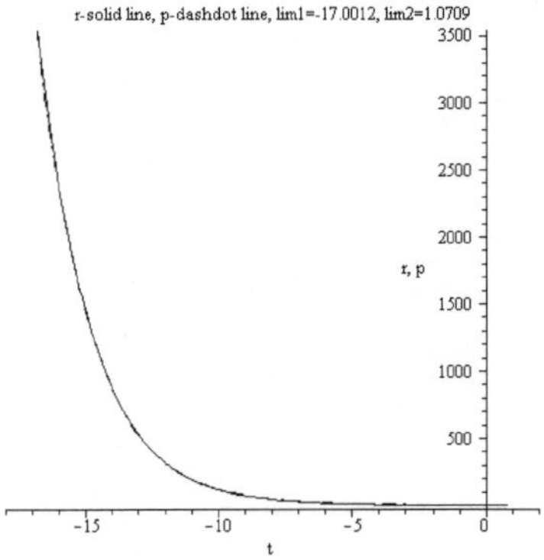

Figure 6.3.4. Density r-solid line, pressure p-dash-dot line, lim1=-17.0012, lim2=1.0709.

It's a variant for the Cauchy conditions
```
u(0)=1,p(0)=1,r(0)=1,D(u)(0)=0,D(p)(0)=0,D(r)(0)=0,
D(v)(0)=0,v(0)=0.1,
```
(decrease in the previous initial potential in ten times).

```
>dsolve[interactive]({
diff(r(t)*(1-
u(t)),t)+diff((diff(p(t)+r(t)+r(t)*u(t)^2-
2*r(t)*u(t),t))/u(t)^2,t)+diff(r(t)*diff(v(t),t)/u(t)
^2,t)=0,
diff(r(t)*u(t)^2+p(t)-
r(t)*u(t),t)+diff(diff(2*r(t)*u(t)^2+2*p(t)-
r(t)*u(t)-r(t)*u(t)^3-
3*p(t)*u(t),t)/u(t)^2,t)+diff(diff(v(t),t)*r(t)/u(t)^
2,t)+r(t)*diff(v(t),t)-diff(v(t),t)*diff(r(t)*(u(t)-
1),t)/u(t)^2-
2*diff(diff(v(t),t)*r(t)/u(t),t)=0,
diff(r(t)*u(t)^2+3*p(t)-r(t)*u(t)^3-5*p(t)*u(t),t)-
diff(diff(2*r(t)*u(t)^3+10*p(t)*u(t)-r(t)*u(t)^2-
3*p(t)-r(t)*u(t)^4-8*p(t)*u(t)^2-
5*p(t)^2/r(t),t)/u(t)^2,t)+diff(diff(v(t),t)*(3*r(t)*
u(t)^2+5*p(t))/u(t)^2,t)-2*r(t)*diff(v(t),t)*u(t)-
2*diff(r(t)*diff(v(t),t)/u(t),t)+2*diff(v(t),t)*(r(t)
```

```
*diff(v(t),t)+diff(p(t)+r(t)*u(t)^2-
r(t)*u(t),t))/u(t)^2=0,
-diff(v(t),t$2)=
r(t)+(1/u(t)^2)*diff(r(t)*(1+u(t)),t),
u(0)=1,p(0)=1,r(0)=1,D(u)(0)=0,D(p)(0)=0,D(r)(0)=0,D(
v)(0)=0,v(0)=.1});
```

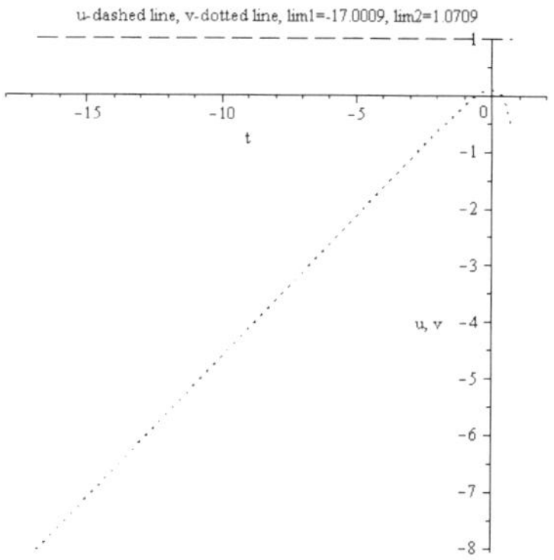

Figure 6.3.5. Velocity u-dashed line, self-consistent potential v -dotted line, lim1=-17.0009, lim2=1.0709.

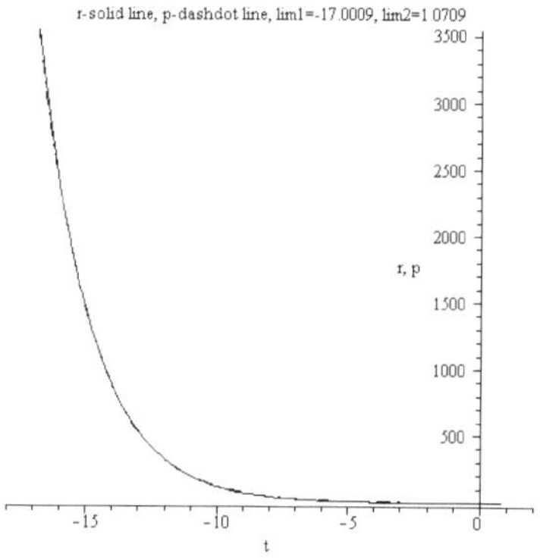

Figure 6.3.6. Density r-solid line, pressure p-dash-dot line, lim1=-17.0009, lim2=1.0709.

Now we change the pressure in the Cauchy conditions.

```
u(0)=1,p(0)=2,r(0)=1,D(u)(0)=0,D(p)(0)=0,D(r)(0)=0,
D(v)(0)=0,v(0)=1.
```

```
>dsolve[interactive]({
diff(r(t)*(1-
u(t)),t)+diff((diff(p(t)+r(t)+r(t)*u(t)^2-
2*r(t)*u(t),t))/u(t)^2,t)+diff(r(t)*diff(v(t),t)/u(t)
^2,t)=0,
diff(r(t)*u(t)^2+p(t)-
r(t)*u(t),t)+diff(diff(2*r(t)*u(t)^2+2*p(t)-
r(t)*u(t)-r(t)*u(t)^3-
3*p(t)*u(t),t)/u(t)^2,t)+diff(diff(v(t),t)*r(t)/u(t)^
2,t)+r(t)*diff(v(t),t)-diff(v(t),t)*diff(r(t)*(u(t)-
1),t)/u(t)^2-
2*diff(diff(v(t),t)*r(t)/u(t),t)=0,
diff(r(t)*u(t)^2+3*p(t)-r(t)*u(t)^3-5*p(t)*u(t),t)-
diff(diff(2*r(t)*u(t)^3+10*p(t)*u(t)-r(t)*u(t)^2-
3*p(t)-r(t)*u(t)^4-8*p(t)*u(t)^2-
5*p(t)^2/r(t),t)/u(t)^2,t)+diff(diff(v(t),t)*(3*r(t)*
u(t)^2+5*p(t))/u(t)^2,t)-2*r(t)*diff(v(t),t)*u(t)-
2*diff(r(t)*diff(v(t),t)/u(t),t)+2*diff(v(t),t)*(r(t)
*diff(v(t),t)+diff(p(t)+r(t)*u(t)^2-
r(t)*u(t),t))/u(t)^2=0,
-diff(v(t),t$2)=
r(t)+(1/u(t)^2)*diff(r(t)*(1+u(t)),t),
u(0)=1,p(0)=2,r(0)=1,D(u)(0)=0,D(p)(0)=0,D(r)(0)=0,D(
v)(0)=0,v(0)=1});
```

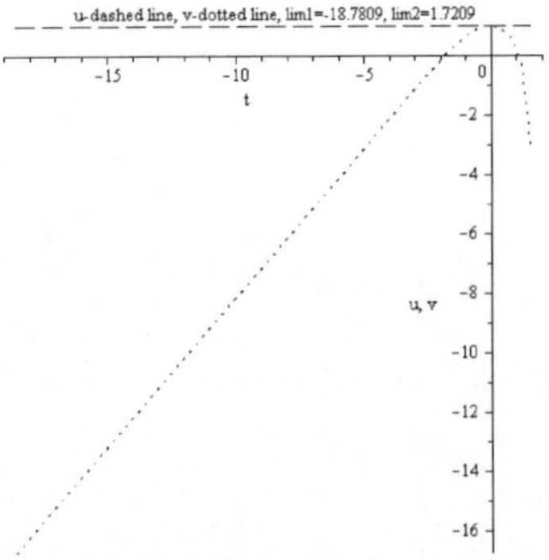

Figure 6.3.7. Velocity u-dashed line, self-consistent potential v -dotted line, lim1=-18.7809, lim2=1.7209.

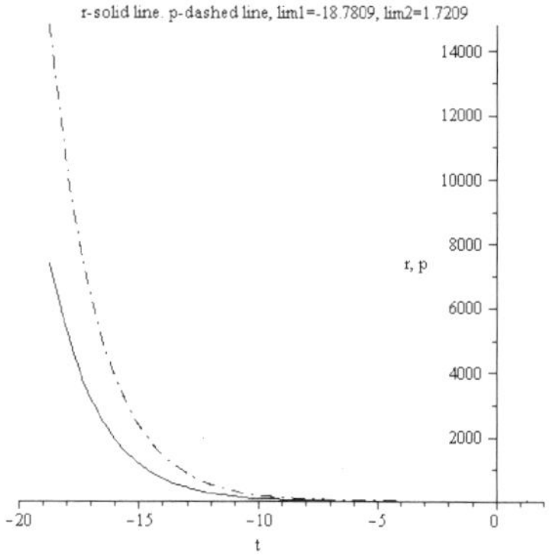

Figure 6.3.8. Density r-solid line, pressure p-dash-dot line, lim1=-18.7809, lim2=1.7209.

Let us change now density in Cauchy conditions, namely

```
u(0)=1,p(0)=1,r(0)=5,D(u)(0)=0,D(p)(0)=0,D(r)(0)=0,D(
v)(0)=0, v(0)=1.
```

The corresponding program in language Maple is

```
>dsolve[interactive]({
diff(r(t)*(1-
u(t)),t)+diff((diff(p(t)+r(t)+r(t)*u(t)^2-
2*r(t)*u(t),t))/u(t)^2,t)+diff(r(t)*diff(v(t),t)/u(t)
^2,t)=0,
diff(r(t)*u(t)^2+p(t)-
r(t)*u(t),t)+diff(diff(2*r(t)*u(t)^2+2*p(t)-
r(t)*u(t)-r(t)*u(t)^3-
3*p(t)*u(t),t)/u(t)^2,t)+diff(diff(v(t),t)*r(t)/u(t)^
2,t)+r(t)*diff(v(t),t)-diff(v(t),t)*diff(r(t)*(u(t)-
1),t)/u(t)^2-
2*diff(diff(v(t),t)*r(t)/u(t),t)=0,
diff(r(t)*u(t)^2+3*p(t)-r(t)*u(t)^3-5*p(t)*u(t),t)-
diff(diff(2*r(t)*u(t)^3+10*p(t)*u(t)-r(t)*u(t)^2-
3*p(t)-r(t)*u(t)^4-8*p(t)*u(t)^2-
5*p(t)^2/r(t),t)/u(t)^2,t)+diff(diff(v(t),t)*(3*r(t)*
```

```
u(t)^2+5*p(t))/u(t)^2,t)-2*r(t)*diff(v(t),t)*u(t)-
2*diff(r(t)*diff(v(t),t)/u(t),t)+2*diff(v(t),t)*(r(t)
*diff(v(t),t)+diff(p(t)+r(t)*u(t)^2-
r(t)*u(t),t))/u(t)^2=0,
-diff(v(t),t$2)=
r(t)+(1/u(t)^2)*diff(r(t)*(1+u(t)),t),
u(0)=1,p(0)=1,r(0)=5,D(u)(0)=0,D(p)(0)=0,D(r)(0)=0,D(
v)(0)=0,v(0)=1});
```

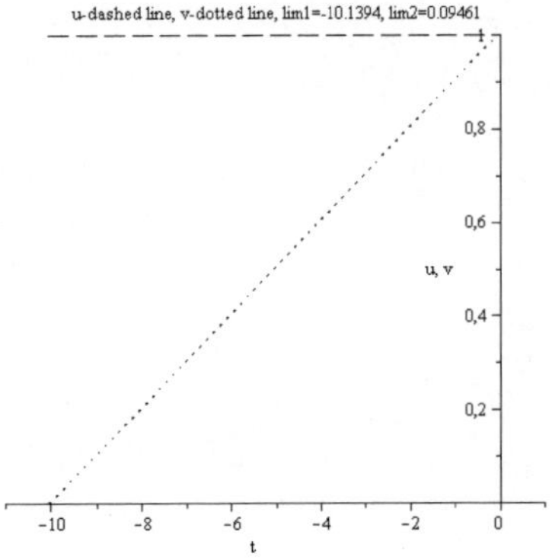

Figure 6.3.9. Velocity u-dashed line, self-consistent potential v -dotted line, lim1=-10.1394, lim2=0.09461.

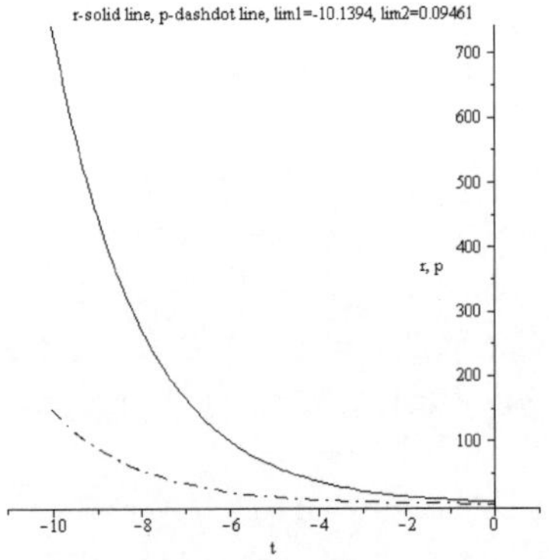

Figure 6.3.10. Density r-solid line, pressure p-dash-dot line, lim1=-10.1394, lim2=0.09461.

Until now we investigated the space evolution of solitons moving with the phase velocity. Let us "spoil" this condition taking, for example, in Cauchy conditions u(0)=2. Namely we use

```
u(0)=2,p(0)=1,r(0)=1,D(u)(0)=0,D(p)(0)=0,D(r)(0)=0,D(
v)(0)=0, v(0)=1
```

```
>dsolve[interactive]({
diff(r(t)*(1-
u(t)),t)+diff((diff(p(t)+r(t)+r(t)*u(t)^2-
2*r(t)*u(t),t))/u(t)^2,t)+diff(r(t)*diff(v(t),t)/u(t)
^2,t)=0,
diff(r(t)*u(t)^2+p(t)-
r(t)*u(t),t)+diff(diff(2*r(t)*u(t)^2+2*p(t)-
r(t)*u(t)-r(t)*u(t)^3-
3*p(t)*u(t),t)/u(t)^2,t)+diff(diff(v(t),t)*r(t)/u(t)^
2,t)+r(t)*diff(v(t),t)-diff(v(t),t)*diff(r(t)*(u(t)-
1),t)/u(t)^2-
2*diff(diff(v(t),t)*r(t)/u(t),t)=0,
diff(r(t)*u(t)^2+3*p(t)-r(t)*u(t)^3-5*p(t)*u(t),t)-
diff(diff(2*r(t)*u(t)^3+10*p(t)*u(t)-r(t)*u(t)^2-
3*p(t)-r(t)*u(t)^4-8*p(t)*u(t)^2-
5*p(t)^2/r(t),t)/u(t)^2,t)+diff(diff(v(t),t)*(3*r(t)*
u(t)^2+5*p(t))/u(t)^2,t)-2*r(t)*diff(v(t),t)*u(t)-
2*diff(r(t)*diff(v(t),t)/u(t),t)+2*diff(v(t),t)*(r(t)
*diff(v(t),t)+diff(p(t)+r(t)*u(t)^2-
r(t)*u(t),t))/u(t)^2=0,
-diff(v(t),t$2)=
r(t)+(1/u(t)^2)*diff(r(t)*(1+u(t)),t),
u(0)=2,p(0)=1,r(0)=1,D(u)(0)=0,D(p)(0)=0,D(r)(0)=0,D(
v)(0)=0,v(0)=1});
```

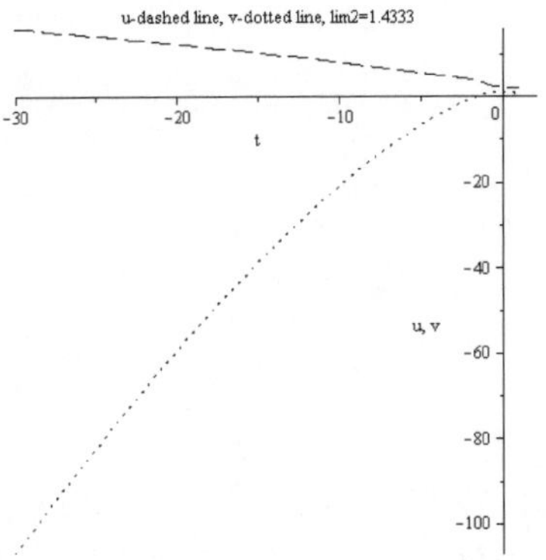

Figure 6.3.11. Velocity u-dashed line, self-consistent potential v -dotted line, lim2=1.4333.

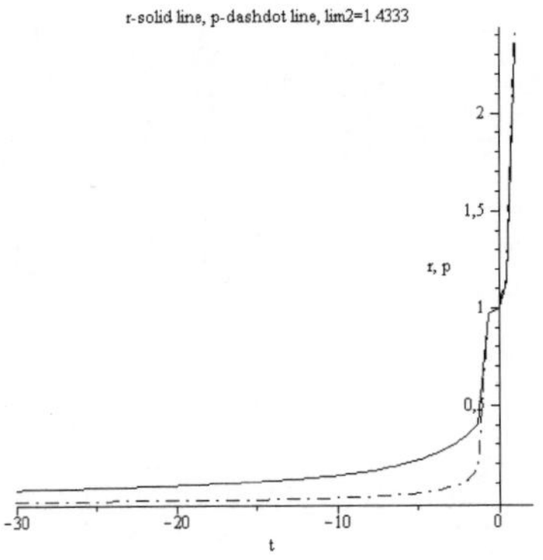

Figure 6.3.12. Density r-solid line, pressure p-dash-dot line, lim2=1.4333.

As you can see,

1. An attempt to organize the movement of the ion wave at a speed different from the phase speed leads to the immediate destruction of the soliton.
2. The previous calculations allow defining the correlation lengths as the lengths of moving soliton for all reasonable temperature diapason.
3. From the point of view of nonlocal physics ion superconductivity can be realized.

6.4. Superconducting soliton motion in the two component physical system.

In general case the strict consideration leads to the following system of the non-local quantum hydrodynamic equations written in the GHE form for multi-component species:

Continuity equation for species α:

$$\frac{\partial}{\partial t}\left\{\rho_\alpha-\tau_\alpha\left[\frac{\partial\rho_\alpha}{\partial t}+\frac{\partial}{\partial\mathbf{r}}\cdot(\rho_\alpha\mathbf{v}_0)\right]\right\}+$$
$$+\frac{\partial}{\partial\mathbf{r}}\cdot\left\{\rho_\alpha\mathbf{v}_0-\tau_\alpha\left[\frac{\partial}{\partial t}(\rho_\alpha\mathbf{v}_0)+\frac{\partial}{\partial\mathbf{r}}\cdot(\rho_\alpha\mathbf{v}_0\mathbf{v}_0)+\ddot{\mathrm{I}}\cdot\frac{\partial p_\alpha}{\partial\mathbf{r}}-\rho_\alpha\mathbf{F}_\alpha^{(1)}-\frac{q_\alpha}{m_\alpha}\rho_\alpha\mathbf{v}_0\times\mathbf{B}\right]\right\}=R_\alpha. \quad (6.4.1)$$

Continuity equation for mixture:

$$\frac{\partial}{\partial t}\left\{\rho-\sum_\alpha\tau_\alpha\left[\frac{\partial\rho_\alpha}{\partial t}+\frac{\partial}{\partial\mathbf{r}}\cdot(\rho_\alpha\mathbf{v}_0)\right]\right\}+\frac{\partial}{\partial\mathbf{r}}\cdot\left\{\rho\mathbf{v}_0-\sum_\alpha\tau_\alpha\left[\frac{\partial}{\partial t}(\rho_\alpha\mathbf{v}_0)+\frac{\partial}{\partial\mathbf{r}}\cdot(\rho_\alpha\mathbf{v}_0\mathbf{v}_0)+\right.\right.$$
$$\left.\left.+\ddot{\mathrm{I}}\cdot\frac{\partial p_\alpha}{\partial\mathbf{r}}-\rho_\alpha\mathrm{F}_\alpha^{(1)}-\frac{q_\alpha}{m_\alpha}\rho_\alpha\mathbf{v}_0\times\mathbf{B}\right]\right\}=0.$$

(6.4.2)

Momentum equation for species α:

$$\frac{\partial}{\partial t}\left\{\rho_\alpha\mathbf{v}_0-\tau_\alpha\left[\frac{\partial}{\partial t}(\rho_\alpha\mathbf{v}_0)+\frac{\partial}{\partial\mathbf{r}}\cdot\rho_\alpha\mathbf{v}_0\mathbf{v}_0+\frac{\partial p_\alpha}{\partial\mathbf{r}}-\rho_\alpha\mathbf{F}_\alpha^{(1)}-\right.\right.$$
$$\left.\left.-\frac{q_\alpha}{m_\alpha}\rho_\alpha\mathbf{v}_0\times\mathbf{B}\right]\right\}-\mathbf{F}_\alpha^{(1)}\left[\rho_\alpha-\tau_\alpha\left(\frac{\partial\rho_\alpha}{\partial t}+\frac{\partial}{\partial\mathbf{r}}(\rho_\alpha\mathbf{v}_0)\right)\right]-$$
$$-\frac{q_\alpha}{m_\alpha}\left\{\rho_\alpha\mathbf{v}_0-\tau_\alpha\left[\frac{\partial}{\partial t}(\rho_\alpha\mathbf{v}_0)+\frac{\partial}{\partial\mathbf{r}}\cdot\rho_\alpha\mathbf{v}_0\mathbf{v}_0+\frac{\partial p_\alpha}{\partial\mathbf{r}}-\rho_\alpha\mathbf{F}_\alpha^{(1)}-\right.\right.$$
$$\left.\left.-\frac{q_\alpha}{m_\alpha}\rho_\alpha\mathbf{v}_0\times\mathbf{B}\right]\right\}\times\mathbf{B}+\frac{\partial}{\partial\mathbf{r}}\cdot\left\{\rho_\alpha\mathbf{v}_0\mathbf{v}_0+p_\alpha\ddot{\mathrm{I}}-\tau_\alpha\left[\frac{\partial}{\partial t}(\rho_\alpha\mathbf{v}_0\mathbf{v}_0+\right.\right. \quad (6.4.3)$$
$$+p_\alpha\ddot{\mathrm{I}})+\frac{\partial}{\partial\mathbf{r}}\cdot\rho_\alpha(\mathbf{v}_0\mathbf{v}_0)\mathbf{v}_0+2\ddot{\mathrm{I}}\left(\frac{\partial}{\partial\mathbf{r}}\cdot(p_\alpha\mathbf{v}_0)\right)+\frac{\partial}{\partial\mathbf{r}}\cdot(\ddot{\mathrm{I}}p_\alpha\mathbf{v}_0)-$$
$$\left.\left.-\mathbf{F}_\alpha^{(1)}\rho_\alpha\mathbf{v}_0-\rho_\alpha\mathbf{v}_0\mathbf{F}_\alpha^{(1)}-\frac{q_\alpha}{m_\alpha}\rho_\alpha[\mathbf{v}_0\times\mathbf{B}]\mathbf{v}_0-\frac{q_\alpha}{m_\alpha}\rho_\alpha\mathbf{v}_0[\mathbf{v}_0\times\mathbf{B}]\right]\right\}=$$
$$=\int m_\alpha\mathbf{v}_\alpha J_\alpha^{st,el}d\mathbf{v}_\alpha+\int m_\alpha\mathbf{v}_\alpha J_\alpha^{st,inel}d\mathbf{v}_\alpha.$$

Momentum equation for mixture

$$
\begin{aligned}
&\frac{\partial}{\partial t}\left\{\rho\mathbf{v}_0-\sum_\alpha\tau_\alpha\left[\frac{\partial}{\partial t}(\rho_\alpha\mathbf{v}_0)+\frac{\partial}{\partial\mathbf{r}}\cdot\rho_\alpha\mathbf{v}_0\mathbf{v}_0+\frac{\partial p_\alpha}{\partial\mathbf{r}}-\rho_\alpha\mathbf{F}_\alpha^{(1)}-\right.\right.\\
&\left.\left.-\frac{q_\alpha}{m_\alpha}\rho_\alpha\mathbf{v}_0\times\mathbf{B}\right]\right\}-\sum_\alpha\mathbf{F}_\alpha^{(1)}\left[\rho_\alpha-\tau_\alpha\left(\frac{\partial\rho_\alpha}{\partial t}+\frac{\partial}{\partial\mathbf{r}}(\rho_\alpha\mathbf{v}_0)\right)\right]-\\
&-\sum_\alpha\frac{q_\alpha}{m_\alpha}\left\{\rho_\alpha\mathbf{v}_0-\tau_\alpha\left[\frac{\partial}{\partial t}(\rho_\alpha\mathbf{v}_0)+\frac{\partial}{\partial\mathbf{r}}\cdot\rho_\alpha\mathbf{v}_0\mathbf{v}_0+\frac{\partial p_\alpha}{\partial\mathbf{r}}-\rho_\alpha\mathbf{F}_\alpha^{(1)}-\right.\right.\\
&\left.\left.-\frac{q_\alpha}{m_\alpha}\rho_\alpha\mathbf{v}_0\times\mathbf{B}\right]\right\}\times\mathbf{B}+\frac{\partial}{\partial\mathbf{r}}\cdot\left\{\rho\mathbf{v}_0\mathbf{v}_0+p\overleftrightarrow{\mathbf{I}}-\sum_\alpha\tau_\alpha\left[\frac{\partial}{\partial t}(\rho_\alpha\mathbf{v}_0\mathbf{v}_0+\right.\right.\\
&+p_\alpha\overleftrightarrow{\mathbf{I}})+\frac{\partial}{\partial\mathbf{r}}\cdot\rho_\alpha(\mathbf{v}_0\mathbf{v}_0)\mathbf{v}_0+2\overleftrightarrow{\mathbf{I}}\left(\frac{\partial}{\partial\mathbf{r}}\cdot(p_\alpha\mathbf{v}_0)\right)+\frac{\partial}{\partial\mathbf{r}}\cdot\left(\overleftrightarrow{\mathbf{I}}p_\alpha\mathbf{v}_0\right)-\\
&\left.\left.-\mathbf{F}_\alpha^{(1)}\rho_\alpha\mathbf{v}_0-\rho_\alpha\mathbf{v}_0\mathbf{F}_\alpha^{(1)}-\frac{q_\alpha}{m_\alpha}\rho_\alpha[\mathbf{v}_0\times\mathbf{B}]\mathbf{v}_0-\frac{q_\alpha}{m_\alpha}\rho_\alpha\mathbf{v}_0[\mathbf{v}_0\times\mathbf{B}]\right]\right\}=0
\end{aligned}
\tag{6.4.4}
$$

Energy equation for α species

$$
\begin{aligned}
&\frac{\partial}{\partial t}\left\{\frac{\rho_\alpha v_0^2}{2}+\frac{3}{2}p_\alpha+\varepsilon_\alpha n_\alpha-\tau_\alpha\left[\frac{\partial}{\partial t}\left(\frac{\rho_\alpha v_0^2}{2}+\frac{3}{2}p_\alpha+\varepsilon_\alpha n_\alpha\right)+\right.\right.\\
&\left.\left.+\frac{\partial}{\partial\mathbf{r}}\cdot\left(\frac{1}{2}\rho_\alpha v_0^2\mathbf{v}_0+\frac{5}{2}p_\alpha\mathbf{v}_0+\varepsilon_\alpha n_\alpha\mathbf{v}_0\right)-\mathbf{F}_\alpha^{(1)}\cdot\rho_\alpha\mathbf{v}_0\right]\right\}+\\
&+\frac{\partial}{\partial\mathbf{r}}\cdot\left\{\frac{1}{2}\rho_\alpha v_0^2\mathbf{v}_0+\frac{5}{2}p_\alpha\mathbf{v}_0+\varepsilon_\alpha n_\alpha\mathbf{v}_0-\tau_\alpha\left[\frac{\partial}{\partial t}\left(\frac{1}{2}\rho_\alpha v_0^2\mathbf{v}_0+\right.\right.\right.\\
&\left.+\frac{5}{2}p_\alpha\mathbf{v}_0+\varepsilon_\alpha n_\alpha\mathbf{v}_0\right)+\frac{\partial}{\partial\mathbf{r}}\cdot\left(\frac{1}{2}\rho_\alpha v_0^2\mathbf{v}_0\mathbf{v}_0+\frac{7}{2}p_\alpha\mathbf{v}_0\mathbf{v}_0+\frac{1}{2}p_\alpha v_0^2\overleftrightarrow{\mathbf{I}}+\right.\\
&\left.+\frac{5}{2}\frac{p_\alpha^2}{\rho_\alpha}\overleftrightarrow{\mathbf{I}}+\varepsilon_\alpha n_\alpha\mathbf{v}_0\mathbf{v}_0+\varepsilon_\alpha\frac{p_\alpha}{m_\alpha}\overleftrightarrow{\mathbf{I}}\right)-\rho_\alpha\mathbf{F}_\alpha^{(1)}\cdot\mathbf{v}_0\mathbf{v}_0-p_\alpha\mathbf{F}_\alpha^{(1)}\cdot\overleftrightarrow{\mathbf{I}}-\\
&-\frac{1}{2}\rho_\alpha v_0^2\mathbf{F}_\alpha^{(1)}-\frac{3}{2}\mathbf{F}_\alpha^{(1)}p_\alpha-\frac{\rho_\alpha v_0^2}{2}\frac{q_\alpha}{m_\alpha}[\mathbf{v}_0\times\mathbf{B}]-\frac{5}{2}p_\alpha\frac{q_\alpha}{m_\alpha}[\mathbf{v}_0\times\mathbf{B}]-\\
&\left.\left.-\varepsilon_\alpha n_\alpha\frac{q_\alpha}{m_\alpha}[\mathbf{v}_0\times\mathbf{B}]-\varepsilon_\alpha n_\alpha\mathbf{F}_\alpha^{(1)}\right]\right\}-\\
&\left\{\rho_\alpha\mathbf{F}_\alpha^{(1)}\cdot\mathbf{v}_0-\tau_\alpha\left[\mathbf{F}_\alpha^{(1)}\cdot\left(\frac{\partial}{\partial t}(\rho_\alpha\mathbf{v}_0)+\frac{\partial}{\partial\mathbf{r}}\cdot\rho_\alpha\mathbf{v}_0\mathbf{v}_0+\frac{\partial}{\partial\mathbf{r}}\cdot p_\alpha\overleftrightarrow{\mathbf{I}}-\rho_\alpha\mathbf{F}_\alpha^{(1)}-q_\alpha n_\alpha[\mathbf{v}_0\times\mathbf{B}]\right)\right]\right\}=\\
&=\int\left(\frac{m_\alpha v_\alpha^2}{2}+\varepsilon_\alpha\right)J_\alpha^{st,el}d\mathbf{v}_\alpha+\int\left(\frac{m_\alpha v_\alpha^2}{2}+\varepsilon_\alpha\right)J_\alpha^{st,inel}d\mathbf{v}_\alpha.
\end{aligned}
\tag{6.4.5}
$$

Energy equation for mixture:

$$\frac{\partial}{\partial t}\left\{\frac{\rho v_0^2}{2}+\frac{3}{2}p+\sum_\alpha \varepsilon_\alpha n_\alpha-\sum_\alpha \tau_\alpha\left[\frac{\partial}{\partial t}\left(\frac{\rho_\alpha v_0^2}{2}+\frac{3}{2}p_\alpha+\varepsilon_\alpha n_\alpha\right)+\right.\right.$$

$$\left.\left.+\frac{\partial}{\partial \mathbf{r}}\cdot\left(\frac{1}{2}\rho_\alpha v_0^2\mathbf{v}_0+\frac{5}{2}p_\alpha\mathbf{v}_0+\varepsilon_\alpha n_\alpha\mathbf{v}_0\right)-\mathbf{F}_\alpha^{(1)}\cdot\rho_\alpha\mathbf{v}_0\right]\right\}+$$

$$+\frac{\partial}{\partial \mathbf{r}}\cdot\left\{\frac{1}{2}\rho v_0^2\mathbf{v}_0+\frac{5}{2}p\mathbf{v}_0+\mathbf{v}_0\sum_\alpha\varepsilon_\alpha n_\alpha-\sum_\alpha\tau_\alpha\left[\frac{\partial}{\partial t}\left(\frac{1}{2}\rho_\alpha v_0^2\mathbf{v}_0+\right.\right.\right.$$

$$\left.+\frac{5}{2}p_\alpha\mathbf{v}_0+\varepsilon_\alpha n_\alpha\mathbf{v}_0\right)+\frac{\partial}{\partial \mathbf{r}}\cdot\left(\frac{1}{2}\rho_\alpha v_0^2\mathbf{v}_0\mathbf{v}_0+\frac{7}{2}p_\alpha\mathbf{v}_0\mathbf{v}_0+\frac{1}{2}p_\alpha v_0^2\ddot{\mathrm{I}}+\right.$$

$$\left.+\frac{5}{2}\frac{p_\alpha^2}{\rho_\alpha}\ddot{\mathrm{I}}+\varepsilon_\alpha n_\alpha\mathbf{v}_0\mathbf{v}_0+\varepsilon_\alpha\frac{p_\alpha}{m_\alpha}\ddot{\mathrm{I}}\right)-\rho_\alpha\mathbf{F}_\alpha^{(1)}\cdot\mathbf{v}_0\mathbf{v}_0-p_\alpha\mathbf{F}_\alpha^{(1)}\cdot\ddot{\mathrm{I}}-$$

$$-\frac{1}{2}\rho_\alpha v_0^2\mathbf{F}_\alpha^{(1)}-\frac{3}{2}\mathbf{F}_\alpha^{(1)}p_\alpha-\frac{\rho_\alpha v_0^2}{2}\frac{q_\alpha}{m_\alpha}[\mathbf{v}_0\times\mathbf{B}]-\frac{5}{2}p_\alpha\frac{q_\alpha}{m_\alpha}[\mathbf{v}_0\times\mathbf{B}]-$$

$$\left.\left.-\varepsilon_\alpha n_\alpha\frac{q_\alpha}{m_\alpha}[\mathbf{v}_0\times\mathbf{B}]-\varepsilon_\alpha n_\alpha\mathbf{F}_\alpha^{(1)}\right]\right\}-\left\{\mathbf{v}_0\cdot\sum_\alpha\rho_\alpha\mathbf{F}_\alpha^{(1)}-\right.$$

$$\left.-\sum_\alpha\tau_\alpha\left[\mathbf{F}_\alpha^{(1)}\cdot\left(\frac{\partial}{\partial t}(\rho_\alpha\mathbf{v}_0)+\frac{\partial}{\partial \mathbf{r}}\cdot\rho_\alpha\mathbf{v}_0\mathbf{v}_0+\frac{\partial}{\partial \mathbf{r}}\cdot p_\alpha\ddot{\mathrm{I}}-\rho_\alpha\mathbf{F}_\alpha^{(1)}-q_\alpha n_\alpha[\mathbf{v}_0\times\mathbf{B}]\right)\right]\right\}=0.$$

(6.4.6)

Here $\mathbf{F}_\alpha^{(1)}$ are the forces (acting on the mass unit) of the non-magnetic origin, $\mathbf{B}$ - magnetic induction, $\ddot{\mathrm{I}}$ - unit tensor, q_α - charge of the α-component particle, p_α - static pressure for α-component, ε_α - internal energy for the particles of α-component, $\mathbf{v}_0$ - hydrodynamic velocity for mixture, τ_α - non-local parameter.

In the following we intend to obtain the soliton's type of solution of the generalized hydrodynamic equations (GHE). The non-stationary 1D model will be used with taking into account the energy equation, external forces and non-locality parameter τ defined by the "time-energy" uncertainty relation of Heisenberg. Then GHE contain Poisson equation (reflected fluctuations of charges and flux of the charges density), two continuity equations for positive (lattice ions) and negative (electrons) species, momentum equation and two energy equations for positive and negative species. This system of six non-stationary 1D equations is written as:

(Generalized Poisson equation):

$$\frac{\partial^2\psi}{\partial x^2}=-4\pi e\left\{\left[n_i-\tau_i\left(\frac{\partial n_i}{\partial t}+\frac{\partial}{\partial x}(n_i u)\right)\right]-\left[n_e-\tau_e\left(\frac{\partial n_e}{\partial t}+\frac{\partial}{\partial x}(n_e u)\right)\right]\right\}. \quad (6.4.7)$$

(Continuity equation for ions):

$$\frac{\partial}{\partial t}\left\{\rho_i-\tau_i\left[\frac{\partial\rho_i}{\partial t}+\frac{\partial}{\partial x}(\rho_i u)\right]\right\}+\frac{\partial}{\partial x}\left\{\rho_i u-\tau_i\left[\frac{\partial}{\partial t}(\rho_i u)+\frac{\partial}{\partial x}(\rho_i u^2)+\frac{\partial p_i}{\partial x}-\rho_i F_i\right]\right\}=0. \quad (6.4.8)$$

(Continuity equation for electrons):

$$\frac{\partial}{\partial t}\left\{\rho_e-\tau_e\left[\frac{\partial\rho_e}{\partial t}+\frac{\partial}{\partial x}(\rho_e u)\right]\right\}+\frac{\partial}{\partial x}\left\{\rho_e u-\tau_e\left[\frac{\partial}{\partial t}(\rho_e u)+\frac{\partial}{\partial x}(\rho_e u^2)+\frac{\partial p_e}{\partial x}-\rho_e F_e\right]\right\}=0. \quad (6.4.9)$$

(Momentum equation):

$$\frac{\partial}{\partial t}\left\{\rho u-\tau_i\left[\frac{\partial}{\partial t}(\rho_i u)+\frac{\partial}{\partial x}(p_i+\rho_i u^2)-\rho_i F_i\right]-\tau_e\left[\frac{\partial}{\partial t}(\rho_e u)+\frac{\partial}{\partial x}(p_e+\rho_e u^2)-\rho_e F_e\right]\right\}-$$
$$-\rho_i F_i-\rho_e F_e+F_i\tau_i\left(\frac{\partial\rho_i}{\partial t}+\frac{\partial}{\partial x}(\rho_i u)\right)+F_e\tau_e\left(\frac{\partial\rho_e}{\partial t}+\frac{\partial}{\partial x}(\rho_e u)\right)+$$
$$+\frac{\partial}{\partial x}\left\{\begin{matrix}\rho u^2+p-\tau_i\left[\frac{\partial}{\partial t}(\rho_i u^2+p_i)+\frac{\partial}{\partial x}(\rho_i u^3+3p_i u)-2\rho_i u F_i\right]- \\ -\tau_e\left[\frac{\partial}{\partial t}(\rho_e u^2+p_e)+\frac{\partial}{\partial x}(\rho_e u^3+3p_e u)\right]-2\rho_e u F_e\end{matrix}\right\}=0.$$

(6.4.10)

(Energy equation for ions):

$$\frac{\partial}{\partial t}\left\{\rho_i u^2+3p_i-\tau_i\left[\frac{\partial}{\partial t}(\rho_i u^2+3p_i)+\frac{\partial}{\partial x}(\rho_i u^3+5p_i u)-2\rho_i F_i u\right]\right\}+$$
$$+\frac{\partial}{\partial x}\left\{\rho_i u^3+5p_i u-\tau_i\left[\frac{\partial}{\partial t}(\rho_i u^3+5p_i u)+\frac{\partial}{\partial x}\left(\rho_i u^4+8p_i u^2+5\frac{p_i^2}{\rho_i}\right)-F_i(3\rho_i u^2+5p_i)\right]\right\}-$$
$$-2u\rho_i F_i+2\tau_i F_i\left[\frac{\partial}{\partial t}(\rho_i u)+\frac{\partial}{\partial x}(\rho_i u^2+p_i)-\rho_i F_i\right]=-\frac{p_i-p_e}{\tau_{ei}}.$$

(6.4.11)

(Energy equation for electrons):

$$\frac{\partial}{\partial t}\left\{\rho_e u^2+3p_e-\tau_e\left[\frac{\partial}{\partial t}(\rho_e u^2+3p_e)+\frac{\partial}{\partial x}(\rho_e u^3+5p_e u)-2\rho_e F_e u\right]\right\}+$$
$$+\frac{\partial}{\partial x}\left\{\rho_e u^3+5p_e u-\tau_e\left[\frac{\partial}{\partial t}(\rho_e u^3+5p_e u)+\frac{\partial}{\partial x}\left(\rho_e u^4+8p_e u^2+5\frac{p_e^2}{\rho_e}\right)-F_e(3\rho_e u^2+5p_e)\right]\right\}-$$
$$-2u\rho_e F_e+2\tau_e F_e\left[\frac{\partial}{\partial t}(\rho_e u)+\frac{\partial}{\partial x}(\rho_e u^2+p_e)-\rho_e F_e\right]=-\frac{p_e-p_i}{\tau_{ei}},$$

(6.4.12)

where u is velocity of the directed motion of combined quantum object (phonon-electron), n_i and n_e – numerical density of the charged species, F_i and

F_e – forces (of potential and non-potential origin), acting on the mass unit of the charged particles. The right hand sides of the energy equations are written in the relaxation forms following from BGK kinetic approximation.

For acting potential forces of the electrical origin the relations are valid

$$F_i^{(pot)} = -\frac{e}{m_i}\frac{\partial \psi}{\partial x}, \tag{6.4.13}$$

$$F_e^{(pot)} = \frac{e}{m_e}\frac{\partial \psi}{\partial x}, \tag{6.4.14}$$

where ψ – scalar potential. On principal GHE (and therefore GQH) needn't in using of the "time-energy" uncertainty relation for estimation of the value of the non-locality parameter τ. Moreover the "time-energy" uncertainty relation does not produce the exact relations and from position of non-local physics is only the simplest estimation of the non-local effects. Really, let us consider two neighboring physically infinitely small volumes $\mathbf{PhSV_1}$ and $\mathbf{PhSV_2}$ in a non-equilibrium system. Obviously the time τ should tends to diminish with increasing of the velocities u of particles invading in the nearest neighboring physically infinitely small volume ($\mathbf{PhSV_1}$ or $\mathbf{PhSV_2}$):

$$\tau = K/u^n . \tag{6.4.15}$$

But the value τ cannot depend on the velocity direction and naturally to tie τ with the particle kinetic energy, then

$$\tau = K/mu^2 , \tag{6.4.16}$$

where K is a coefficient of proportionality, which reflects the state of physical system. In the simplest case K is equal to Plank constant $\hbar$ and relation (6.4.16) became compatible with the Heisenberg relation.

Introduce approximations for τ_i and τ_i using (6.4.16)

$$\tau_i = \hbar/m_i u^2 , \quad \tau_e = \hbar/m_e u^2 . \tag{6.4.17}$$

For electron-phonon non-local parameter τ_{ei} the following relation is applicable

$$\frac{1}{\tau_{ei}} = \frac{1}{\tau_e} + \frac{1}{\tau_i}. \tag{6.4.18}$$

For this case parameter τ_{ei} corresponds to the relaxation time for the positive and negative species and to Heisenberg relation for combined particle. Really

$$\frac{1}{\tau_{ei}} = \frac{\tau_e + \tau_i}{\tau_e \tau_i} = \frac{\dfrac{\hbar}{m_e u^2} + \dfrac{\hbar}{m_i u^2}}{\dfrac{\hbar^2}{u^4} \dfrac{1}{m_e m_i}} = \frac{u^2}{\hbar}(m_e + m_i). \tag{6.4.19}$$

Then

$$u^2 (m_e + m_i) \tau_{ei} = \hbar. \tag{6.4.20}$$

Formula (6.4.19) is obvious consequence of uncertainty relation for combined particle which mass is $m_i + m_e$. Energy equation of the generalized quantum hydrodynamics contain pressures p_i, p_e, which can be named as the quantum pressure of the non-local origin. In the definite sense these pressures can be considered as analog of the Bose condensate pressure.

6.5. Combined quantum solitons in the self-consistent electric field.

Let us formulate the problem in detail. The non-stationary 1D motion of the combined phonon-electron soliton is considered under influence of the self-consistent electric forces of the potential and non-potential origin. It should be shown that mentioned soliton can exists without a chemical bond formation. For better understanding of situation let us investigate the situation for the case when the external forces are absent. Introduce the coordinate system moving along the positive direction of the x axis in 1D space with the velocity $C = u_0$, which is equal to the phase velocity of this quantum object.

$$\xi = x - Ct. \tag{6.5.1}$$

Taking into account de Broglie relation we should wait that the group velocity u_g is equal to $2u_0$.

Really the energy of a relativistic particle is

$$E = mc^2, \tag{6.5.2}$$

where

$$m = m_0 \left(1 - \frac{v_g^2}{c^2}\right)^{-1/2} \tag{6.5.3}$$

and c is the light velocity, v_g is the group velocity, m_0 – the particle rest mass. Relation (6.5.2) can be written as

$$E = \mathrm{p}\frac{c^2}{v_g} \tag{6.5.4}$$

where

$$\mathrm{p} = m v_g \tag{6.5.5}$$

is the particle impulse. In the non-relativistic approach the relation (6.5.4) takes the form $$E = \frac{1}{2} m_0 v_g^2 . \qquad (6.5.6)$$

Using the dualism principle in the de Broglie interpretation we have for the particle energy

$$E = \hbar\omega = \hbar k v_{ph} , \qquad (6.5.7)$$

where ω is the circular frequency, $v_{ph} = \frac{\omega}{\kappa}$ – the phase velocity, $\kappa = 2\pi / \lambda$ is the wave number and λ is the wave length. Correspondingly the particle impulse p is

$$\mathrm{p} = \hbar k \qquad (6.5.8)$$

and using (6.5.8),

$$E = \mathrm{p} v_{ph} . \qquad (6.5.9)$$

Then in the non-relativistic case

$$E = \frac{1}{2} m_0 v_g^2 = \frac{1}{2} \mathrm{p} v_g . \qquad (6.5.10)$$

From (6.5.9) and (6.5.10) for the non-relativistic case one obtains

$$v_g = 2 v_{ph} . \qquad (6.5.11)$$

Then we should wait that the indestructible soliton has the velocity v_{ph} in the coordinate system moving with the phase velocity v_{ph}.

If we pass on the moving coordinate system, all dependent hydrodynamic values will be functions of (ξ, t). But we investigate the possibility of the creation of the combined quantum object of the soliton type. For this case the explicit time dependence of solutions does not exist in mentioned coordinate system moving with the phase velocity u_0.

Write down the system of equations (6.4.7) - (6.4.12) for the two component mixture of charged particles without taking into account the component's internal energy in the dimensionless form, where dimensionless symbols are marked by tildes. We begin with introduction the scales for velocity

$$[u] = u_0 \qquad (6.5.12)$$

and for coordinate x

$$\frac{\hbar}{m_e u_0} = x_0 . \qquad (6.5.13)$$

Generalized Poisson equation (6.4.7)

$$\frac{\partial^2 \psi}{\partial x^2} = -4\pi e \left\{ \left[n_i - \frac{\hbar}{m_i u^2} u_0 \left(-\frac{\partial n_i}{\partial x} + \frac{\partial}{\partial x}(n_i \tilde{u}) \right) \right] - \left[n_e - \frac{\hbar}{m_e u^2} u_0 \left(-\frac{\partial n_e}{\partial x} + \frac{\partial}{\partial x}(n_e \tilde{u}) \right) \right] \right\} \qquad (6.5.14)$$

takes the form

$$\frac{\partial^2\tilde{\psi}}{\partial\tilde{\xi}^2}=-\left\{\frac{m_e}{m_i}\left[\tilde{\rho}_i-\frac{1}{u^2}\frac{m_e}{m_i}\left(-\frac{\partial\tilde{\rho}_i}{\partial\xi}+\frac{\partial}{\partial\xi}(\tilde{\rho}_i\tilde{u})\right)\right]-\left[\tilde{\rho}_e-\frac{1}{\tilde{u}^2}\left(-\frac{\partial\tilde{\rho}_e}{\partial\xi}+\frac{\partial}{\partial\xi}(\tilde{\rho}_e\tilde{u})\right)\right]\right\} \qquad (6.5.15)$$

if the potential scale ψ_0 and the density scale ρ_0 are chosen as (e is absolute electron charge)

$$\psi_0=\frac{m_e}{e}u_0^2, \qquad (6.5.16)$$

$$\rho_0=\frac{m_e^4}{4\pi\hbar^2e^2}u_0^4. \qquad (6.5.17)$$

Scaling forces are

$$\rho_iF_i=-\frac{u_0^2}{x_0}\rho_0\frac{m_e}{m_i}\frac{\partial\tilde{\psi}}{\partial\tilde{\xi}}\tilde{\rho}_i, \qquad (6.5.18)$$

$$\rho_eF_e=-\frac{u_0^2}{x_0}\rho_0\frac{\partial\tilde{\psi}}{\partial\tilde{\xi}}\tilde{\rho}_e. \qquad (6.5.19)$$

Strictly speaking we should take into account the self-consistent magnetic field. By the Lorentz normalization the classic Poisson equation is

$$\Delta\psi-\frac{\varepsilon\mu}{c^2}\frac{\partial^2\psi}{\partial t^2}=-\frac{4\pi}{\varepsilon}\rho, \qquad (6.5.20)$$

where ε, μ are dielectric and magnetic permeability and c – the light velocity. As we see, in Eq. (6.5.20) the second time derivative is omitted as small value of the u_0^2/c^2 order. In relations (6.5.18), (6.5.19) the derivatives of the vector potential $\mathbf{A}$ on time are also omitted as the small values of the u_0/c order. Then here the self consistent and external magnetic fields are not considered.

Analogical transformations should be applied to other equations of the system (6.4.7) – (6.4.11). As result one obtains the six non-linear dimensionless ordinary differential equations

$$\frac{\partial^2\tilde{\psi}}{\partial\tilde{\xi}^2}=-\left\{\frac{m_e}{m_i}\left[\tilde{\rho}_i-\frac{1}{\tilde{u}^2}\frac{m_e}{m_i}\left(-\frac{\partial\tilde{\rho}_i}{\partial\tilde{\xi}}+\frac{\partial}{\partial\tilde{\xi}}(\tilde{\rho}_i\tilde{u})\right)\right]-\left[\tilde{\rho}_e-\frac{1}{\tilde{u}^2}\left(-\frac{\partial\tilde{\rho}_e}{\partial\tilde{\xi}}+\frac{\partial}{\partial\tilde{\xi}}(\tilde{\rho}_e\tilde{u})\right)\right]\right\}, \qquad (6.5.21)$$

$$\frac{\partial\tilde{\rho}_i}{\partial\tilde{\xi}}-\frac{\partial\tilde{\rho}_i\tilde{u}}{\partial\tilde{\xi}}+\frac{m_e}{m_i}\frac{\partial}{\partial\tilde{\xi}}\left\{\frac{1}{\tilde{u}^2}\left[\frac{\partial}{\partial\tilde{\xi}}\left(\tilde{p}_i+\tilde{\rho}_i+\tilde{\rho}_i\tilde{u}^2-2\tilde{\rho}_i\tilde{u}_i\right)+\frac{m_e}{m_i}\tilde{\rho}_i\frac{\partial\tilde{\psi}}{\partial\tilde{\xi}}\right]\right\}=0, \qquad (6.5.22)$$

$$\frac{\partial\tilde{\rho}_e}{\partial\tilde{\xi}}-\frac{\partial\tilde{\rho}_e\tilde{u}}{\partial\tilde{\xi}}+\frac{\partial}{\partial\tilde{\xi}}\left\{\frac{1}{\tilde{u}^2}\left[\frac{\partial}{\partial\tilde{\xi}}\left(\tilde{p}_e+\tilde{\rho}_e+\tilde{\rho}_e\tilde{u}^2-2\tilde{\rho}_e\tilde{u}_e\right)-\tilde{\rho}_e\frac{\partial\tilde{\psi}}{\partial\tilde{\xi}}\right]\right\}=0, \qquad (6.5.23)$$

$$
\begin{aligned}
&\frac{\partial}{\partial \tilde{\xi}}\left\{(\tilde{\rho}_i+\tilde{\rho}_e)\tilde{u}^2+\tilde{p}_i+\tilde{p}_e-(\tilde{\rho}_i+\tilde{\rho}_e)\tilde{u}\right\}+\\
&+\frac{\partial}{\partial \tilde{\xi}}\left\{\begin{array}{l}\dfrac{1}{\tilde{u}^2}\dfrac{m_e}{m_i}\left[\dfrac{\partial}{\partial \tilde{\xi}}\left(2\tilde{p}_i+2\tilde{p}_i\tilde{u}^2-\tilde{\rho}_i\tilde{u}-\tilde{\rho}_i\tilde{u}^3-3\tilde{p}_i\tilde{u}\right)+\tilde{\rho}_i\dfrac{m_e}{m_i}\dfrac{\partial \tilde{\psi}}{\partial \tilde{\xi}}\right]+\\
+\dfrac{1}{\tilde{u}^2}\left[\dfrac{\partial}{\partial \tilde{\xi}}\left(2\tilde{p}_e+2\tilde{p}_e\tilde{u}^2-\tilde{\rho}_e\tilde{u}-\tilde{\rho}_e\tilde{u}^3-3\tilde{p}_e\tilde{u}\right)-\tilde{\rho}_e\dfrac{\partial \tilde{\psi}}{\partial \tilde{\xi}}\right]\end{array}\right\}+\\
&+\tilde{\rho}_i\frac{m_e}{m_i}\frac{\partial \tilde{\psi}}{\partial \tilde{\xi}}-\tilde{\rho}_e\frac{\partial \tilde{\psi}}{\partial \tilde{\xi}}-\frac{\partial \tilde{\psi}}{\partial \tilde{\xi}}\frac{1}{\tilde{u}^2}\left(\frac{m_e}{m_i}\right)^2\left(-\frac{\partial \tilde{\rho}_i}{\partial \tilde{\xi}}+\frac{\partial}{\partial \tilde{\xi}}(\tilde{\rho}_i\tilde{u})\right)+\\
&+\frac{\partial \tilde{\psi}}{\partial \tilde{\xi}}\frac{1}{\tilde{u}^2}\left(-\frac{\partial \tilde{\rho}_e}{\partial \tilde{\xi}}+\frac{\partial}{\partial \tilde{\xi}}(\tilde{\rho}_e\tilde{u})\right)-2\frac{\partial}{\partial \tilde{\xi}}\left\{\frac{1}{\tilde{u}}\frac{\partial \tilde{\psi}}{\partial \tilde{\xi}}\left[\left(\frac{m_e}{m_i}\right)^2\tilde{\rho}_i-\tilde{\rho}_e\right]\right\}=0
\end{aligned}
\tag{6.5.24}
$$

$$
\begin{aligned}
&\frac{\partial}{\partial \tilde{\xi}}\left\{\tilde{\rho}_i\tilde{u}^3+5\tilde{p}_i\tilde{u}-\tilde{\rho}_i\tilde{u}^2-3\tilde{p}_i\right\}+\frac{\partial}{\partial \xi}\left\{\frac{1}{\tilde{u}^2}\frac{m_{\text{в}}}{m_i}\left[\frac{\partial}{\partial \tilde{\xi}}\left(2\tilde{\rho}_i\tilde{u}^3+10\tilde{p}_i\tilde{u}-\tilde{\rho}_i\tilde{u}^4-8\tilde{p}_i\tilde{u}^2-\right.\right.\right.\\
&\left.\left.\left.-5\frac{\tilde{p}_i^{\,2}}{\tilde{\rho}_i}-\tilde{\rho}_i\tilde{u}^2-3\tilde{p}_i\right)+\frac{m_{\text{в}}}{m_i}\frac{\partial \tilde{\psi}}{\partial \tilde{\xi}}(2\tilde{\rho}_i\tilde{u}-3\tilde{\rho}_i\tilde{u}^2-5\tilde{p}_i)\right]\right\}+2\frac{m_{\text{в}}}{m_i}\tilde{\rho}_i\tilde{u}\frac{\partial \tilde{\psi}}{\partial \tilde{\xi}}-\\
&-2\frac{\partial \tilde{\varphi}}{\partial \xi}\frac{1}{\tilde{u}^2}\left(\frac{m_{\text{в}}}{m_i}\right)^2\left[\frac{\partial}{\partial \tilde{\xi}}(\tilde{\rho}_i\tilde{u}^2+\tilde{p}_i-\tilde{\rho}_i\tilde{u})+\tilde{\rho}_i\frac{m_{\text{в}}}{m_i}\frac{\partial \tilde{\psi}}{\partial \tilde{\xi}}\right]=\\
&=-(\tilde{p}_i-\tilde{p}_{\text{в}})\tilde{u}^2\left(1+\frac{m_i}{m_{\text{в}}}\right)
\end{aligned}
\tag{6.5.25}
$$

$$
\begin{aligned}
&\frac{\partial}{\partial \tilde{\xi}}\left\{\tilde{\rho}_{\text{в}}\tilde{u}^3+5\tilde{p}_{\text{в}}\tilde{u}-\tilde{\rho}_{\text{в}}\tilde{u}^2-3\tilde{p}_{\text{в}}\right\}+\frac{\partial}{\partial \tilde{\xi}}\left\{\frac{1}{\tilde{u}^2}\left[\frac{\partial}{\partial \tilde{\xi}}\left(2\tilde{\rho}_{\text{в}}\tilde{u}^3+10\tilde{p}_{\text{в}}\tilde{u}-\tilde{\rho}_{\text{в}}\tilde{u}^4-8\tilde{p}_{\text{в}}\tilde{u}^2-\right.\right.\right.\\
&\left.\left.\left.-5\frac{\tilde{p}_{\text{в}}^{\,2}}{\tilde{\rho}_{\text{в}}}-\tilde{\rho}_{\text{в}}\tilde{u}^2-3\tilde{p}_{\text{в}}\right)+\frac{\partial \tilde{\psi}}{\partial \tilde{\xi}}(3\tilde{\rho}_{\text{в}}\tilde{u}^2+5\tilde{p}_{\text{в}}-2\tilde{\rho}_{\text{в}}\tilde{u})\right]\right\}-2\tilde{\rho}_{\text{в}}\tilde{u}\frac{\partial \tilde{\psi}}{\partial \tilde{\xi}}+\\
&+2\frac{\partial \tilde{\psi}}{\partial \tilde{\xi}}\frac{1}{\tilde{u}^2}\left[\frac{\partial}{\partial \tilde{\xi}}(\tilde{\rho}_{\text{в}}\tilde{u}^2+\tilde{p}_{\text{в}}-\tilde{\rho}_{\text{в}}\tilde{u})-\tilde{\rho}_{\text{в}}\frac{\partial \tilde{\psi}}{\partial \tilde{\xi}}\right]=-(\tilde{p}_{\text{в}}-\tilde{p}_i)\left(1+\frac{m_i}{m_{\text{в}}}\right)\tilde{u}^2
\end{aligned}
\tag{6.5.26}
$$

Some comments to Eqs. (6.5.21 – 6.5.26):

1. Every equation from the system (6.5.21 – 6.5.26) is of the second order and needs two conditions. The problem belongs to the class of Cauchy problems.
2. In comparison with the Schrödinger theory connected with behavior of the wave function, no special conditions are applied for dependent variables including the domain of the solution existing. This domain is defined automatically in the process of the numerical solution of the concrete variant of calculations.
3. From the introduced scales

$$u_0,\ x_0 = \frac{\hbar}{m_e}\frac{1}{u_0},\ \psi_0 = \frac{m_e}{e}u_0^2,\ \rho_0 = \frac{m_e^4}{4\pi\hbar^2 e^2}u_0^4,\ p_0 = \rho_0 u_0^2 = \frac{m_e^4}{4\pi\hbar^2 e^2}u_0^6 \qquad (6.5.27)$$

only one parameter is independent – the phase velocity u_0 of the combined quantum object. From this point of view the obtained solutions which will be discussed below have the universal character defined only by Cauchy conditions.

4. Introduced scales have the connection with the character values in the Schrödinger theory of the hydrogen atom. Really in the Schrödinger theory the probability maximum corresponds to the Bohr's orbits and for the state $1s$ the orbit radius $a = \frac{\hbar^2}{me^2} \cong 0.53\cdot 10^{-8}$ cm, and the orbit velocity $V_{\text{orb}} = \frac{e}{\sqrt{m_e a}} = \frac{e^2}{\hbar} = \frac{\hbar}{m_e a}$.

For example taking as the velocity scale $u_0 = V_{\text{orb}}$ we have for the numerical density scale $n_0 = \frac{\rho_0}{m_e} = \frac{m_e^3}{4\pi\hbar^2 e^2}u_0^4 = \frac{\hbar^2}{4\pi e^2 m_e a^4} = \frac{1}{4\pi a^3}$. But the probability density for the Schrödinger atom at the origin of the coordinates for 1s state corresponds to value $(\Psi_{100})^2_{r=0} = \frac{1}{\pi a^3}$. Then for this scale choice (with an accuracy of numerical coefficient) $n_0 \approx (\Psi_{100})^2_{r=0}$. The difference is connected with the choice of the object geometry and coordinate system.

6.6. The results of the mathematical modeling.

The system of generalized quantum hydrodynamic equations (6.5.21) – (6.5.26) have the great possibilities of mathematical modeling as result of changing of twelve Cauchy conditions describing the character features of initial perturbations which lead to the soliton formation.

On this step of investigation we intend to demonstrate the influence of difference conditions on the soliton formation. The following figures reflect some results of calculations realized according to the system of equations (6.5.21) - (6.5.26) with the help of Maple. The following notations on figures are used: r- density $\tilde{\rho}_i$, s- density $\tilde{\rho}_e$ (solid lines), u- velocity $\tilde{u}$ (dashed line), p - pressure $\tilde{p}_i$, q - pressure $\tilde{p}_e$ and v - self consistent potential $\tilde{\psi}$. Explanations placed under all following figures, Maple program contains Maple's notations – for example the expression $D(u)(0) = 0$ means in usual notations $\frac{\partial \tilde{u}}{\partial \tilde{\xi}}(0) = 0$, independent variable t responds to $\tilde{\xi}$.

There is the problem of principle significance – is it possible after a perturbation (defined by Cauchy conditions) to obtain the quantum object of the soliton's kind as result of the self-organization of ionized matter? In the case of the positive answer, what is the origin of existence of this stable object?

We use the following Maple program:

```
> dsolve[interactive]({
diff(v(t),t$2)=-r(t)*(L/H)+(L/H)^2*diff(r(t)*u(t)-
r(t),t)/u(t)^2+
s(t)-diff(s(t)*u(t)-s(t),t)/u(t)^2,
diff(r(t)*(1-
u(t)),t)+(L/H)*diff(diff(p(t)+r(t)+r(t)*u(t)^2-
2*r(t)*u(t),t)/u(t)^2,t)+(L/H)^2*diff(r(t)*diff(v(t),
t)/u(t)^2,t)=0,
diff(s(t)*(1-
u(t)),t)+diff((diff(q(t)+s(t)+s(t)*u(t)^2-
2*s(t)*u(t),t))/u(t)^2,t)-
diff(s(t)*diff(v(t),t)/u(t)^2,t)=0,
diff((r(t)+s(t))*u(t)^2+p(t)+q(t)-
(r(t)+s(t))*u(t),t)+
diff(diff(2*r(t)*u(t)^2+2*p(t)-r(t)*u(t)-r(t)*u(t)^3-
3*p(t)*u(t),t)/(u(t)^2*(H/L)),t)+
diff(diff(2*s(t)*u(t)^2+2*q(t)-s(t)*u(t)-s(t)*u(t)^3-
3*q(t)*u(t),t)/u(t)^2,t)+
diff(r(t)*diff(v(t),t)*(L/H)^2/u(t)^2,t)-
diff(s(t)*diff(v(t),t)/u(t)^2,t)+
r(t)*diff(v(t),t)*(L/H)-s(t)*diff(v(t),t)-
(L/H)^2*diff(v(t),t)*diff(r(t)*(u(t)-1),t)/u(t)^2+
diff(v(t),t)*diff(s(t)*(u(t)-1),t)/u(t)^2-
2*diff(((L/H)^2*r(t)-s(t))*diff(v(t),t)/u(t),t)=0,
diff(r(t)*u(t)^3+5*p(t)*u(t)-r(t)*u(t)^2-3*p(t),t)+
(L/H)*diff(diff(2*r(t)*u(t)^3+10*p(t)*u(t)-
r(t)*u(t)^4-8*p(t)*u(t)^2-5*p(t)^2/r(t)-r(t)*u(t)^2-
3*p(t),t)/u(t)^2,t)+
(L/H)^2*diff((2*r(t)*u(t)-3*r(t)*u(t)^2-
5*p(t))*diff(v(t),t)/u(t)^2,t)+
2*(L/H)*r(t)*diff(v(t),t)*u(t)-
```

```
2*(L/H)^2*diff(v(t),t)*diff(r(t)*u(t)^2+p(t)-
r(t)*u(t),t)/u(t)^2-
2*(L/H)^3*r(t)*diff(v(t),t)^2/u(t)^2=-(p(t)-
q(t))*u(t)^2*((L+H)/L),
diff(s(t)*u(t)^3+5*q(t)*u(t)-s(t)*u(t)^2-3*q(t),t)+
diff(diff(2*s(t)*u(t)^3+10*q(t)*u(t)-s(t)*u(t)^4-
8*q(t)*u(t)^2-5*q(t)^2/s(t)-s(t)*u(t)^2-
3*q(t),t)/u(t)^2,t)+
diff(diff(v(t),t)*(3*s(t)*u(t)^2+5*q(t)-
2*s(t)*u(t))/u(t)^2,t)-
2*s(t)*diff(v(t),t)*u(t)+
2*diff(v(t),t)*diff(s(t)*u(t)^2+q(t)-
s(t)*u(t),t)/u(t)^2-2*s(t)*diff(v(t),t)^2/u(t)^2=-
(q(t)-p(t))*u(t)^2*((L+H)/L),
v(0)=1,r(0)=1,s(0)=1/1838,u(0)=1,p(0)=1,q(0)=.95,
D(v)(0)=0,D(r)(0)=0,D(s)(0)=0,D(u)(0)=0,D(p)(0)=0,D(q
)(0)=0
});
```

Figures 6.6.1, 6.6.2 reflect the calculations for the Cauchy conditions

```
v(0)=1,r(0)=1,s(0)=1/1838,u(0)=1,p(0)=1,q(0)=.95,
D(v)(0)=0,D(r)(0)=0,D(s)(0)=0,D(u)(0)=0,D(p)(0)=0,D(q
)(0)=0
```

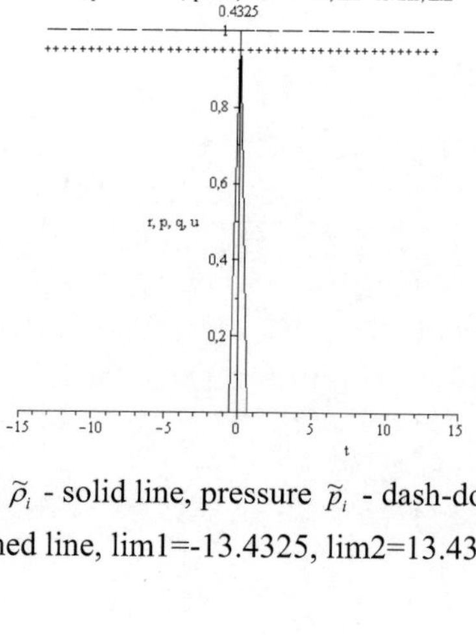

Figure 6.6.1. density $\widetilde{\rho}_i$ - solid line, pressure $\widetilde{p}_i$ - dash-dot line, $\widetilde{p}_e$ - cross, u-dashed line, lim1=-13.4325, lim2=13.4325.

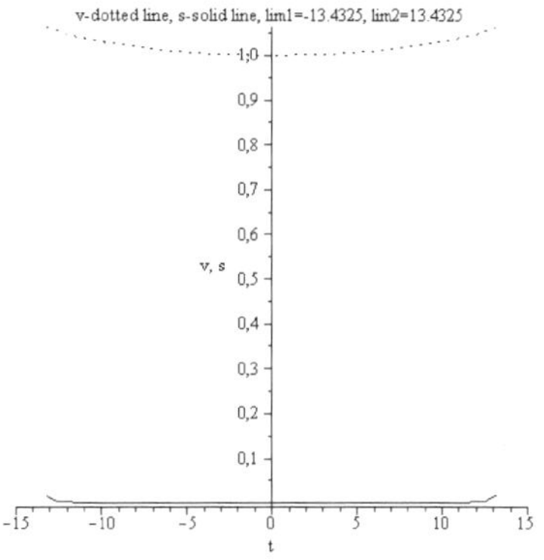

Figure 6.6.2. density $\widetilde{\rho}_e$ - solid line, potential $\widetilde{\psi}$ - dotted line, lim1=-13.4325, lim2=13.4325.

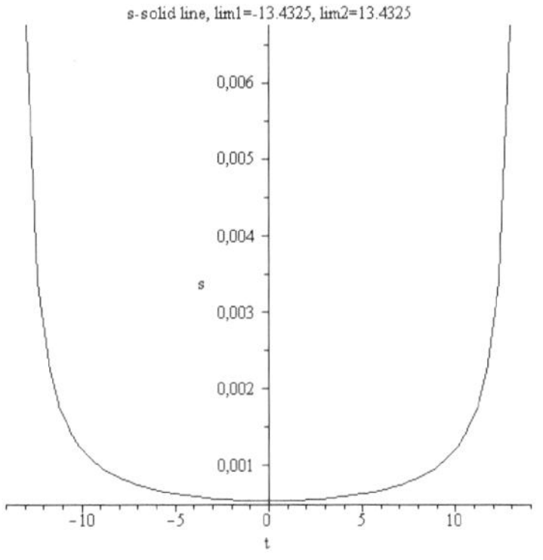

Figure 6.6.3. density $\widetilde{\rho}_e$ - solid line, lim1=-13.4325, lim2=13.4325.

Increase the pressure $\widetilde{p}_i$ of protons in 10 times, leaving the other conditions the Cauchy problem without changing

```
v(0)=1,r(0)=1,s(0)=1/1838,u(0)=1,p(0)=10,q(0)=.95,
D(v)(0)=0,D(r)(0)=0,D(s)(0)=0,D(u)(0)=0,D(p)(0)=0,D(q
)(0)=0,
```

see figures 6.6.4, - 6.6.6.

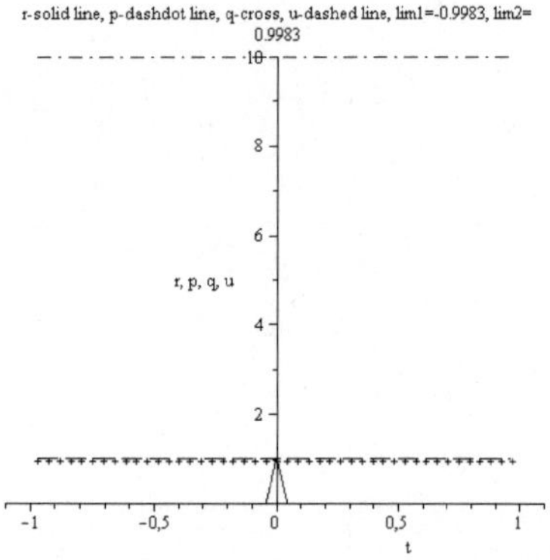

Figure 6.6.4. density $\tilde{\rho}_i$ - solid line, pressure $\tilde{p}_i$ - dashdot line, $\tilde{p}_e$ - cross, u-dashed line,
lim1=-0.9983, lim2=0.9983.

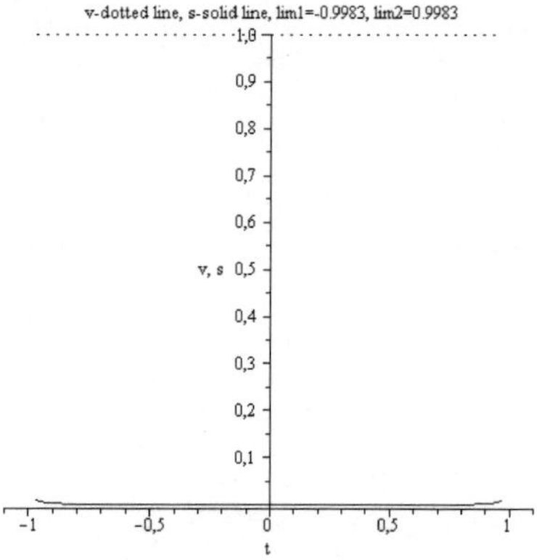

Figure 6.6.5. density $\tilde{\rho}_e$ - solid line, potential $\tilde{\psi}$ - dotted line,
lim1=-0.9983, lim2=0.9983.

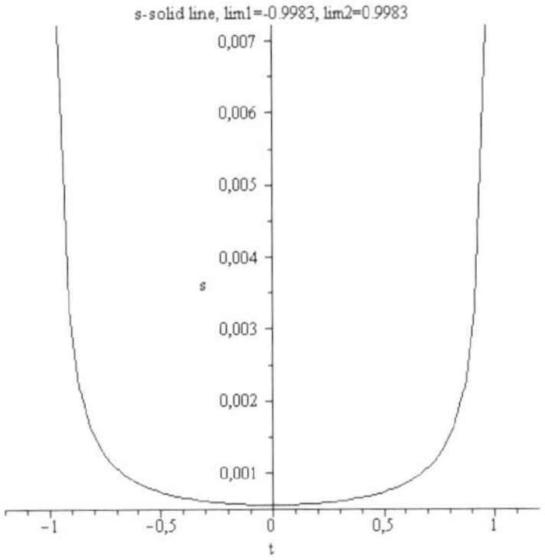

Figure 6.6.6. density $\widetilde{\rho}_e$ - solid line,
lim1=-0.9983, lim2=0.9983.

The appearance of the difference between initial electron and proton quantum pressure leads to the creation of a proton wave front between two electronic fronts (figures 6.6.1 – 6.6.4). Increasing $\widetilde{p}_i(0)$ leads to diminishing of the soliton size.

Let us now the Cauchy conditions with equal initial pressures $\widetilde{p}_i(0)$ and $\widetilde{p}_e(0)$, namely

```
v(0)=1,r(0)=1,s(0)=1/1838,u(0)=1,p(0)=1,q(0)=1,
D(v)(0)=0,D(r)(0)=0,D(s)(0)=0,D(u)(0)=0,D(p)(0)=0,D(q
)(0)=0,
```

We find, figure 6.6.7:

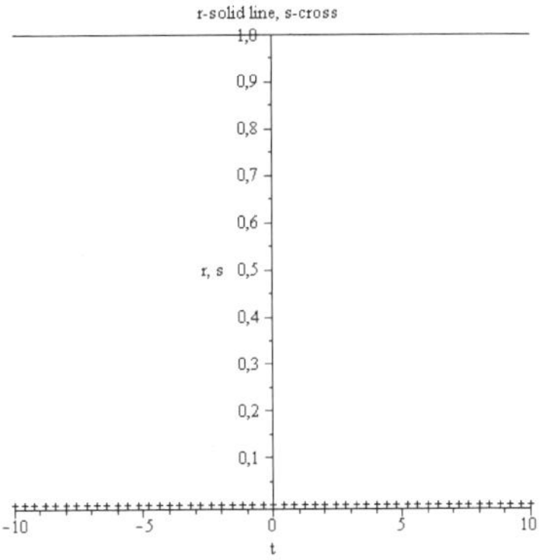

Figure 6.6.7. density $\widetilde{\rho}_e$ - solid line, density s - cross,

As we see in this case the proton wave front disappeared.
In the theory of a solid body, the elastic vibrations of the crystal lattice are described as the motion of phonons — quanta of sound waves. In these terms, electron pairing occurs through the exchange of phonons, or electron-phonon interaction. We can say that electrons are attracted by emitting and absorbing phonons. This mechanism is the basis of the BCS theory. However, the initial Cooper model is more general, since it indicates the possibility of pairing electrons under the influence of any effective attraction, not necessarily due to the exchange of phonons.

The conclusion was formulated:

1. The stability of the quantum object is result of the self-consistent influence of electric forces and quantum pressures.
2. In the absence of the external electric field the combined soliton corresponding to BCS structure can exists if $\tilde{p}_i(0) \neq \tilde{p}_e(0)$. This inequality does not correspond to energy of chemical bond.
3. Stability can be achieved if soliton has *negative* shell and *positive* nuclei and $\tilde{p}_i(0) > \tilde{p}_e(0)$. Increasing the difference $p_i(0) - p_e(0)$ lead to diminishing of the character domain occupied by soliton. Stability can be also achieved if soliton has *positive* shell and *negative* kernel but $\tilde{p}_i(0) < \tilde{p}_e(0)$.

For illustration of item 3 let us consider the calculations when the energy of the chemical bond is equal to zero, $\tilde{p}_i(0) < \tilde{p}_e(0)$, in the absence of the external electric field. With this aim let the initial perturbations are used (see Figs. 6.6.8, 6.6.9):

```
v(0)=1,r(0)=1,s(0)=1/1838,u(0)=1,p(0)=0.95,
q(0)=1,
D(v)(0)=0,D(r)(0)=0,D(s)(0)=0,D(u)(0)=0,
D(p)(0)=0,D(q)(0)=0
```

As expected figure 6.6.7 looks like typical curves for free particles in the Schrödinger theory. But phonon - electron interaction does not lead to a chemical bonded system. It means that $\tilde{p}_i(0) - \tilde{p}_e(0) = 0$ and creation of the combined electron-phonon soliton can be realized in the superconducting system only in the external electric field posed by the lattice. In other words as result of polarization the "estafette" bond mechanism is appearing leading to wave solitons placed in bounded area of space.

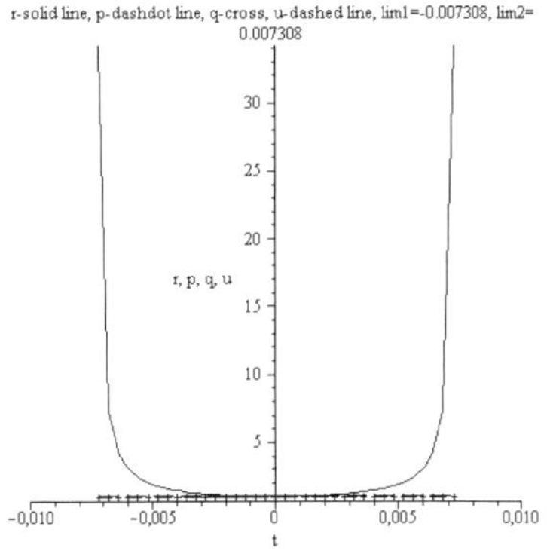

Figure 6.6.8. density $\tilde{\rho}_i$ - solid line, pressure $\tilde{p}_i$ - dashdot line, $\tilde{p}_e$ - cross, u-dashed line,
lim1=-0.007308, lim2=0.007308.

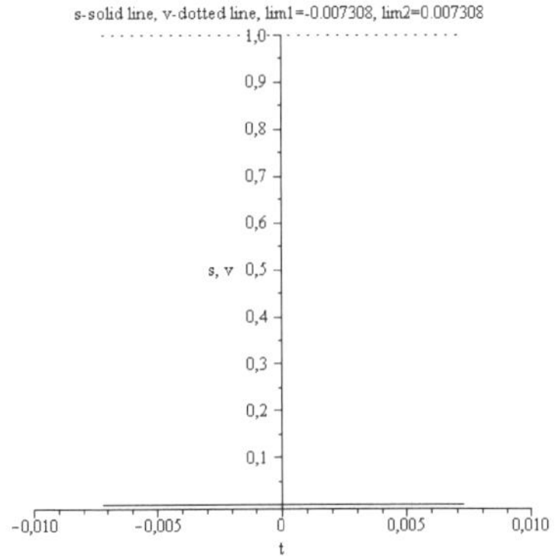

Figure 6.6.9. density $\tilde{\rho}_e$ - solid line, potential $\tilde{\psi}$ – dotted line,
lim1=-0.007308, lim2=0.007308.

As an example let us consider the situation when the soliton is catching by the external periodical non-potential longitudinal electric field

$$F_i^{(npot)} = \frac{eE}{m_i}\cos\left(kx - \omega t\right), \tag{6.6.1}$$

for which the phase velocity is $\omega / k = u_0$. In this case $\xi = x - Ct$, $\xi = x - u_0 t$ and (6.6.1) takes the form

$$F_i^{(npot)} = \frac{eE}{m_i}\cos\left[\frac{2\pi}{\lambda}x_0\tilde{\xi}\right],\ \frac{\hbar}{m_e u_0} = x_0 \tag{6.6.2}$$

But the value $\nu^{qu} = \hbar / m_e$ has the dimension $[cm^2/s]$ and can be titled as quantum viscosity, $\nu^{qu} = 1.1577\ cm^2/s$. Introduce the quantum velocity $\nu_h^{qu} = h / m_e = 2\pi\nu^{qu}$ in relation (6.6.2)

$$\rho_i F_i^{(npot)} = \rho_0\tilde{\rho}_i \frac{eE}{m_i}\cos\left[\frac{1}{\lambda}\frac{h}{m_e u_0}\tilde{\xi}\right] = \rho_0\tilde{\rho}_i \frac{eE}{m_i}\cos\left[\frac{1}{\lambda}\frac{\nu_h^{qu}}{u_0}\tilde{\xi}\right]. \tag{6.6.3}$$

Expression under cosines sign forms the similarity criteria which can be named as quantum Reynolds number,

$$\mathrm{Re}^{\mathrm{qu}} = \frac{\lambda u_0}{\nu_h^{qu}}. \tag{6.6.4}$$

From (6.6.3) follows

$$\rho_i F_i^{npot} = \rho_0\tilde{\rho}_i \frac{eE}{m_i}\cos\left[\frac{1}{\mathrm{Re}^{\mathrm{qu}}}\tilde{\xi}\right]. \tag{6.6.5}$$

The effective force acting on the positive charges is written as

$$\rho_i F_i^{(pot)} + \rho_i F_i^{(npot)} = -\frac{u_0^2}{x_0}\frac{m_e}{m_i}\rho_0\tilde{\rho}_i\left[\frac{\partial\tilde{\psi}}{\partial\tilde{\xi}} - eE\frac{x_0}{m_e u_0^2}\cos\left(\frac{1}{\mathrm{Re}^{\mathrm{qu}}}\tilde{\xi}\right)\right]. \tag{6.6.6}$$

Symbolize

$$\mathrm{E}^{\mathrm{qu}} = eE\frac{x_0}{m_e u_0^2}. \tag{6.6.7}$$

and introduce $\mathrm{F}_0 = \frac{eE}{m_e}$ as the scale of the external force, acting on the mass unit of the positive charge, which the absolute value is e. Then

$$\mathrm{E}^{\mathrm{qu}} = \frac{\mathrm{F}_0 x_0}{u_0^2} \tag{6.6.8}$$

is the similarity criteria reflecting the ratio the character work of the external force to the kinetic energy of the mass unit. We have

$$\rho_i F_i^{(pot)} + \rho_i F_i^{(npot)} = -\frac{u_0^2}{x_0}\frac{m_e}{m_i}\rho_0\tilde{\rho}_i\left[\frac{\partial\tilde{\psi}}{\partial\tilde{\xi}} - \mathrm{E}^{\mathrm{qu}}\cos\left(\frac{1}{\mathrm{Re}^{\mathrm{qu}}}\tilde{\xi}\right)\right]. \tag{6.6.8}$$

Analogically for electrons

$$\rho_e F_e^{(pot)} + \rho_e F_e^{(npot)} = \frac{u_0^2}{x_0}\rho_0\tilde{\rho}_e\left[\frac{\partial\tilde{\psi}}{\partial\tilde{\xi}} - \mathrm{E}^{\mathrm{qu}}\cos\left(\frac{1}{\mathrm{Re}^{\mathrm{qu}}}\tilde{\xi}\right)\right]. \tag{6.6.9}$$

In the dimensionless form we have

$$\tilde{\rho}_i\tilde{F}_i^{(pot)} + \tilde{\rho}_i\tilde{F}_i^{(npot)} = -\frac{m_e}{m_i}\tilde{\rho}_i\left[\frac{\partial\tilde{\psi}}{\partial\tilde{\xi}} - \mathrm{E}^{\mathrm{qu}}\cos\left(\frac{1}{\mathrm{Re}^{\mathrm{qu}}}\tilde{\xi}\right)\right], \tag{6.6.10}$$

$$\tilde{\rho}_e \tilde{F}_e^{(pot)} + \tilde{\rho}_e \tilde{F}_e^{(npot)} = \tilde{\rho}_e \left[\frac{\partial \tilde{\psi}}{\partial \tilde{\xi}} - \mathrm{E}^{\mathrm{qu}} \cos\left(\frac{1}{\mathrm{Re}^{\mathrm{qu}}} \tilde{\xi} \right) \right]. \tag{6.6.11}$$

Expressions (6.6.10), (6.6.11) should be introduced in the system of quantum hydrodynamic equations (6.5.21) - (6.5.26). The similarity criteria E^{qu} and $\mathrm{Re}^{\mathrm{qu}}$ are parameters of calculations.

$$\frac{\partial^2 \tilde{\varphi}}{\partial \tilde{\xi}^2} = -\left\{ \frac{m_e}{m_i} \left[\tilde{\rho}_i - \frac{1}{\tilde{u}^2} \frac{m_e}{m_i} \left(-\frac{\partial \tilde{p}_i}{\partial \tilde{\xi}} + \frac{\partial}{\partial \tilde{\xi}} (\tilde{\rho}_i \tilde{u}) \right) \right] - \left[\tilde{\rho}_e - \frac{1}{\tilde{u}^2} \left(-\frac{\partial \tilde{p}_e}{\partial \tilde{\xi}} + \frac{\partial}{\partial \tilde{\xi}} (\tilde{\rho}_e \tilde{u}) \right) \right] \right\}, \tag{6.6.12}$$

$$\begin{gathered} \frac{\partial \tilde{\rho}_i}{\partial \tilde{\xi}} - \frac{\partial \tilde{\rho}_i \tilde{u}}{\partial \tilde{\xi}} + \\ + \frac{m_e}{m_i} \frac{\partial}{\partial \tilde{\xi}} \left\{ \frac{1}{\tilde{u}^2} \left[\frac{\partial}{\partial \tilde{\xi}} \left(\tilde{p}_i + \tilde{\rho}_i + \tilde{\rho}_i \tilde{u}^2 - 2 \tilde{\rho}_i \tilde{u}_i \right) + \frac{m_e}{m_i} \tilde{\rho}_i \left[\frac{\partial \tilde{\psi}}{\partial \tilde{\xi}} - \mathrm{E}^{\mathrm{qu}} \cos\left(\frac{1}{\mathrm{Re}^{qu}} \tilde{\xi} \right) \right] \right] \right\} = 0, \end{gathered} \tag{6.6.13}$$

$$\frac{\partial \tilde{\rho}_e}{\partial \tilde{\xi}} - \frac{\partial \tilde{\rho}_e \tilde{u}}{\partial \tilde{\xi}} + \frac{\partial}{\partial \tilde{\xi}} \left\{ \frac{1}{\tilde{u}^2} \left[\frac{\partial}{\partial \tilde{\xi}} \left(\tilde{p}_e + \tilde{\rho}_e + \tilde{\rho}_e \tilde{u}^2 - 2 \tilde{\rho}_e \tilde{u}_e \right) - \tilde{\rho}_e \left[\frac{\partial \tilde{\psi}}{\partial \tilde{\xi}} - \mathrm{E}^{\mathrm{qu}} \cos\left(\frac{1}{\mathrm{Re}^{qu}} \tilde{\xi} \right) \right] \right] \right\} = 0, \tag{6.6.14}$$

$$\begin{gathered} \frac{\partial}{\partial \tilde{\xi}} \left\{ (\tilde{\rho}_i + \tilde{\rho}_e) \tilde{u}^2 + \tilde{p}_i + \tilde{p}_e - (\tilde{\rho}_i + \tilde{\rho}_e) \tilde{u} \right\} + \\ + \frac{\partial}{\partial \tilde{\xi}} \left\{ \begin{aligned} & \frac{1}{\tilde{u}^2} \frac{m_e}{m_i} \left[\frac{\partial}{\partial \tilde{\xi}} \left(2\tilde{p}_i + 2\tilde{p}_i \tilde{u}^2 - \tilde{\rho}_i \tilde{u} - \tilde{\rho}_i \tilde{u}^3 - 3 \tilde{p}_i \tilde{u} \right) + \tilde{\rho}_i \frac{m_e}{m_i} \left[\frac{\partial \tilde{\psi}}{\partial \tilde{\xi}} - \mathrm{E}^{\mathrm{qu}} \cos\left(\frac{1}{\mathrm{Re}^{qu}} \tilde{\xi} \right) \right] \right] + \\ & + \frac{1}{\tilde{u}^2} \left[\frac{\partial}{\partial \tilde{\xi}} \left(2\tilde{p}_e + 2\tilde{p}_e \tilde{u}^2 - \tilde{\rho}_e \tilde{u} - \tilde{\rho}_e \tilde{u}^3 - 3 \tilde{p}_e \tilde{u} \right) - \tilde{\rho}_e \left[\frac{\partial \tilde{\psi}}{\partial \tilde{\xi}} - \mathrm{E}^{\mathrm{qu}} \cos\left(\frac{1}{\mathrm{Re}^{qu}} \tilde{\xi} \right) \right] \right] \end{aligned} \right\} + \\ + \tilde{\rho}_i \frac{m_e}{m_i} \left[\frac{\partial \tilde{\psi}}{\partial \tilde{\xi}} - \mathrm{E}^{\mathrm{qu}} \cos\left(\frac{1}{\mathrm{Re}^{qu}} \tilde{\xi} \right) \right] - \tilde{\rho}_e \left[\frac{\partial \tilde{\psi}}{\partial \tilde{\xi}} - \mathrm{E}^{\mathrm{qu}} \cos\left(\frac{1}{\mathrm{Re}^{qu}} \tilde{\xi} \right) \right] - \\ - \left[\frac{\partial \tilde{\psi}}{\partial \tilde{\xi}} - \mathrm{E}^{\mathrm{qu}} \cos\left(\frac{1}{\mathrm{Re}^{qu}} \tilde{\xi} \right) \right] \frac{1}{\tilde{u}^2} \left(\frac{m_e}{m_i} \right)^2 \left(-\frac{\partial \tilde{p}_i}{\partial \tilde{\xi}} + \frac{\partial}{\partial \tilde{\xi}} (\tilde{\rho}_i \tilde{u}) \right) + \\ + \left[\frac{\partial \tilde{\psi}}{\partial \tilde{\xi}} - \mathrm{E}^{\mathrm{qu}} \cos\left(\frac{1}{\mathrm{Re}^{qu}} \tilde{\xi} \right) \right] \frac{1}{\tilde{u}^2} \left(-\frac{\partial \tilde{p}_e}{\partial \tilde{\xi}} + \frac{\partial}{\partial \tilde{\xi}} (\tilde{\rho}_e \tilde{u}) \right) - \\ - 2 \frac{\partial}{\partial \tilde{\xi}} \left\{ \frac{1}{\tilde{u}} \left[\frac{\partial \tilde{\psi}}{\partial \tilde{\xi}} - \mathrm{E}^{\mathrm{qu}} \cos\left(\frac{1}{\mathrm{Re}^{qu}} \tilde{\xi} \right) \right] \left[\left(\frac{m_e}{m_i} \right)^2 \tilde{\rho}_i - \tilde{\rho}_e \right] \right\} = 0, \end{gathered} \tag{6.6.15}$$

$$\frac{\partial}{\partial\tilde{\xi}}\{\tilde{\rho}_i\tilde{u}^3+5\tilde{p}_i\tilde{u}-\tilde{\rho}_i\tilde{u}^2-3\tilde{p}_i\}+\frac{\partial}{\partial\xi}\left\{\frac{1}{\tilde{u}^2}\frac{m_e}{m_i}\left[\frac{\partial}{\partial\tilde{\xi}}\left(2\tilde{\rho}_i\tilde{u}^3+10\tilde{p}_i\tilde{u}-\tilde{\rho}_i\tilde{u}^4-8\tilde{p}_i\tilde{u}^2-\right.\right.\right.$$

$$\left.\left.\left.-5\frac{\tilde{p}_i^{\,2}}{\tilde{\rho}_i}-\tilde{\rho}_i\tilde{u}^2-3\tilde{p}_i\right)+\frac{m_e}{m_i}\left[\frac{\partial\tilde{\psi}}{\partial\tilde{\xi}}-\mathrm{E}^{\mathrm{qu}}\cos\left(\frac{1}{\mathrm{Re}^{qu}}\tilde{\xi}\right)\right](2\tilde{\rho}_i\tilde{u}-3\tilde{\rho}_i\tilde{u}^2-5\tilde{p}_i)\right]\right\}+$$

$$+2\frac{m_e}{m_i}\tilde{\rho}_i\tilde{u}\left[\frac{\partial\tilde{\psi}}{\partial\tilde{\xi}}-\mathrm{E}^{\mathrm{qu}}\cos\left(\frac{1}{\mathrm{Re}^{qu}}\tilde{\xi}\right)\right]-$$

$$-2\left[\frac{\partial\tilde{\psi}}{\partial\tilde{\xi}}-\mathrm{E}^{\mathrm{qu}}\cos\left(\frac{1}{\mathrm{Re}^{qu}}\tilde{\xi}\right)\right]\frac{1}{\tilde{u}^2}\left(\frac{m_e}{m_i}\right)^2\left[\frac{\partial}{\partial\tilde{\xi}}(\tilde{\rho}_i\tilde{u}^2+\tilde{p}_i-\tilde{\rho}_i\tilde{u})+\tilde{\rho}_i\frac{m_e}{m_i}\left[\frac{\partial\tilde{\psi}}{\partial\tilde{\xi}}-\mathrm{E}^{\mathrm{qu}}\cos\left(\frac{1}{\mathrm{Re}^{qu}}\tilde{\xi}\right)\right]\right]$$

$$=-(\tilde{p}_i-\tilde{p}_e)\tilde{u}^2\left(1+\frac{m_i}{m_e}\right)$$

$$(6.6.16)$$

$$\frac{\partial}{\partial\tilde{\xi}}\{\tilde{\rho}_e\tilde{u}^3+5\tilde{p}_e\tilde{u}-\tilde{\rho}_e\tilde{u}^2-3\tilde{p}_e\}+\frac{\partial}{\partial\tilde{\xi}}\left\{\frac{1}{\tilde{u}^2}\left[\frac{\partial}{\partial\tilde{\xi}}\left(2\tilde{\rho}_e\tilde{u}^3+10\tilde{p}_e\tilde{u}-\tilde{\rho}_e\tilde{u}^4-8\tilde{p}_e\tilde{u}^2-\right.\right.\right.$$

$$\left.\left.\left.-5\frac{\tilde{p}_e^{\,2}}{\tilde{\rho}_e}-\tilde{\rho}_e\tilde{u}^2-3\tilde{p}_e\right)+\left[\frac{\partial\tilde{\psi}}{\partial\tilde{\xi}}-\mathrm{E}^{\mathrm{qu}}\cos\left(\frac{1}{\mathrm{Re}^{qu}}\tilde{\xi}\right)\right](3\tilde{\rho}_e\tilde{u}^2+5\tilde{p}_e-2\tilde{\rho}_e\tilde{u})\right]\right\}-$$

$$-2\tilde{\rho}_e\tilde{u}\left[\frac{\partial\tilde{\psi}}{\partial\tilde{\xi}}-\mathrm{E}^{\mathrm{qu}}\cos\left(\frac{1}{\mathrm{Re}^{qu}}\tilde{\xi}\right)\right]+$$

$$+2\left[\frac{\partial\tilde{\psi}}{\partial\tilde{\xi}}-\mathrm{E}^{\mathrm{qu}}\cos\left(\frac{1}{\mathrm{Re}^{qu}}\tilde{\xi}\right)\right]\frac{1}{\tilde{u}^2}\left[\frac{\partial}{\partial\tilde{\xi}}(\tilde{\rho}_e\tilde{u}^2+\tilde{p}_e-\tilde{\rho}_e\tilde{u})-\tilde{\rho}_e\left[\frac{\partial\tilde{\psi}}{\partial\tilde{\xi}}-\mathrm{E}^{\mathrm{qu}}\cos\left(\frac{1}{\mathrm{Re}^{qu}}\tilde{\xi}\right)\right]\right]=$$

$$=-(\tilde{p}_e-\tilde{p}_i)\left(1+\frac{m_i}{m_e}\right)\tilde{u}^2.$$

$$(6.6.17)$$

Let us show some results of calculations in external (and self-consistent) electric field for the following Cauchy conditions (written in Maple notations): $\mathrm{E}^{\mathrm{qu}}=1$, $\mathrm{Re}^{\mathrm{qu}}=1$, $\tilde{p}_e(0)=\tilde{p}_i(0)$,

```
v(0)=1,r(0)=1,s(0)=1/1838,u(0)=1,p(0)=1,q(0)=1,
D(v)(0)=0,D(r)(0)=0,D(s)(0)=0,D(u)(0)=0,D(p)(0)=0,D(q
)(0)=0.
> dsolve[interactive]({
diff(v(t),t$2)=-r(t)*(L/H)+(L/H)^2*diff(r(t)*u(t)-
r(t),t)/u(t)^2+
s(t)-diff(s(t)*u(t)-s(t),t)/u(t)^2,
diff(r(t)*(1-
u(t)),t)+(L/H)*diff(diff(p(t)+r(t)+r(t)*u(t)^2-
2*r(t)*u(t),t)/u(t)^2,t)+(L/H)^2*diff(r(t)*(diff(v(t)
,t)-E*cos(t/R))/u(t)^2,t)=0,
```

```
diff(s(t)*(1-
u(t)),t)+diff((diff(q(t)+s(t)+s(t)*u(t)^2-
2*s(t)*u(t),t))/u(t)^2,t)-diff(s(t)*(diff(v(t),t)-
E*cos(t/R))/u(t)^2,t)=0,
diff((r(t)+s(t))*u(t)^2+p(t)+q(t)-
(r(t)+s(t))*u(t),t)+
diff(diff(2*r(t)*u(t)^2+2*p(t)-r(t)*u(t)-r(t)*u(t)^3-
3*p(t)*u(t),t)/(u(t)^2*(H/L)),t)+
diff(diff(2*s(t)*u(t)^2+2*q(t)-s(t)*u(t)-s(t)*u(t)^3-
3*q(t)*u(t),t)/u(t)^2,t)+
diff(r(t)*(diff(v(t),t)-
E*cos(t/R))*(L/H)^2/u(t)^2,t)-
diff(s(t)*(diff(v(t),t)-E*cos(t/R))/u(t)^2,t)+
r(t)*(diff(v(t),t)-E*cos(t/R))*(L/H)-
s(t)*(diff(v(t),t)-E*cos(t/R))-
(L/H)^2*(diff(v(t),t)-E*cos(t/R))*diff(r(t)*(u(t)-
1),t)/u(t)^2+
(diff(v(t),t)-E*cos(t/R))*diff(s(t)*(u(t)-
1),t)/u(t)^2-
2*diff(((L/H)^2*r(t)-s(t))*(diff(v(t),t)-
E*cos(t/R))/u(t),t)=0,
diff(r(t)*u(t)^3+5*p(t)*u(t)-r(t)*u(t)^2-3*p(t),t)+
(L/H)*diff(diff(2*r(t)*u(t)^3+10*p(t)*u(t)-
r(t)*u(t)^4-8*p(t)*u(t)^2-5*p(t)^2/r(t)-r(t)*u(t)^2-
3*p(t),t)/u(t)^2,t)+
(L/H)^2*diff((2*r(t)*u(t)-3*r(t)*u(t)^2-
5*p(t))*(diff(v(t),t)-E*cos(t/R))/u(t)^2,t)+
2*(L/H)*r(t)*(diff(v(t),t)-E*cos(t/R))*u(t)-
2*(L/H)^2*(diff(v(t),t)-
E*cos(t/R))*diff(r(t)*u(t)^2+p(t)-
r(t)*u(t),t)/u(t)^2-
2*(L/H)^3*r(t)*(diff(v(t),t)-E*cos(t/R))^2/u(t)^2=-
(p(t)-q(t))*u(t)^2*((L+H)/L),
diff(s(t)*u(t)^3+5*q(t)*u(t)-s(t)*u(t)^2-3*q(t),t)+
diff(diff(2*s(t)*u(t)^3+10*q(t)*u(t)-s(t)*u(t)^4-
8*q(t)*u(t)^2-5*q(t)^2/s(t)-s(t)*u(t)^2-
3*q(t),t)/u(t)^2,t)+
```

```
diff((diff(v(t),t)-E*cos(t/R))*(3*s(t)*u(t)^2+5*q(t)-
2*s(t)*u(t))/u(t)^2,t)-
2*s(t)*(diff(v(t),t)-E*cos(t/R))*u(t)+
2*(diff(v(t),t)-E*cos(t/R))*diff(s(t)*u(t)^2+q(t)-
s(t)*u(t),t)/u(t)^2-2*s(t)*(diff(v(t),t)-
E*cos(t/R))^2/u(t)^2=-(q(t)-p(t))*u(t)^2*((L+H)/L),
v(0)=1,r(0)=1,s(0)=1/1838,u(0)=1,p(0)=1,q(0)=1,
D(v)(0)=0,D(r)(0)=0,D(s)(0)=0,D(u)(0)=0,D(p)(0)=0,D(q
)(0)=0
});
```

The following figures 6.6.10 – 6.6.15 fulfilled for the different combinations of E^{qu}, Re^{qu}.

Cauchy conditions

```
v(0)=1,r(0)=1,s(0)=1/1838,u(0)=1,p(0)=1,q(0)=1,
D(v)(0)=0,D(r)(0)=0,D(s)(0)=0,D(u)(0)=0,D(p)(0)=0,D(q
)(0)=0
```

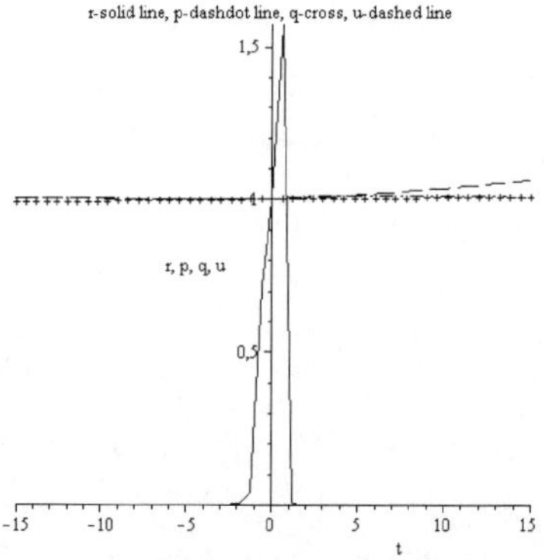

Figure 6.6.10. density $\widetilde{\rho}_i$ - solid line, pressure $\widetilde{p}_i$ - dashdot line, $\widetilde{p}_e$ - cross, u-dashed line.

$E^{qu} = 1$, $Re^{qu} = 1$.

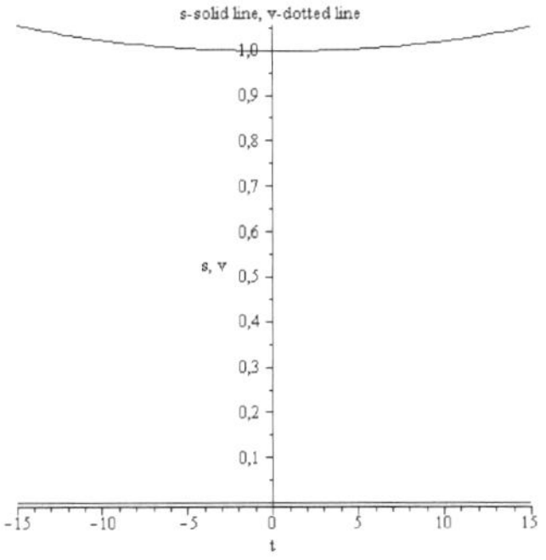

Figure 6.6.11. density $\widetilde{\rho}_e$ - solid line, potential $\widetilde{\psi}$ – dotted line, $\mathrm{E}^{qu} = 1$, $\mathrm{Re}^{qu} = 1$.

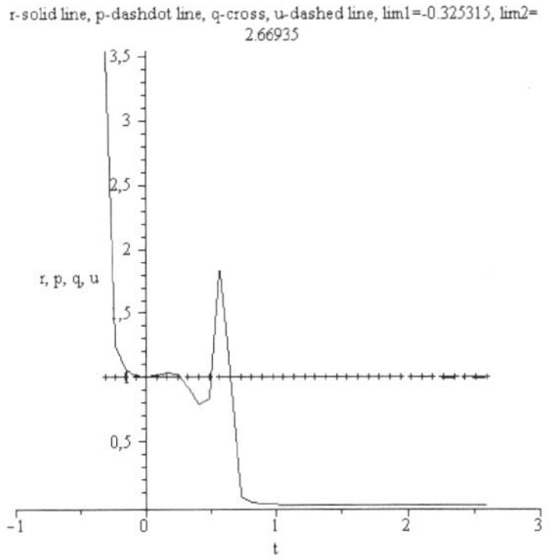

Figure 6.6.12. density $\widetilde{\rho}_i$ - solid line, pressure $\widetilde{p}_i$ - dashdot line, $\widetilde{p}_e$ - cross, u-dashed line. $\mathrm{E}^{qu} = 10$, $\mathrm{Re}^{qu} = 10$.

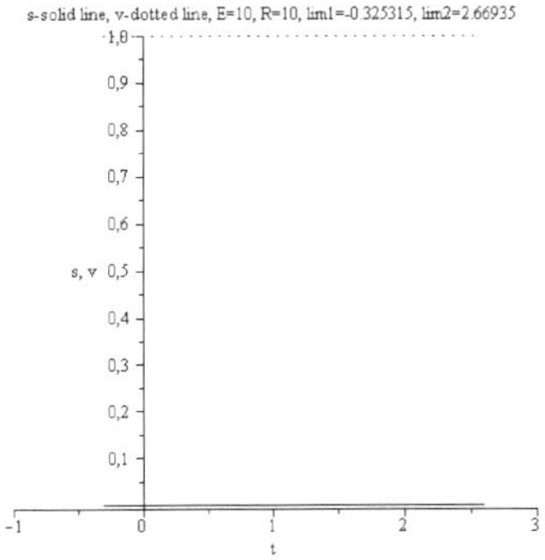

Figure 6.6.13. density $\widetilde{\rho}_e$ - solid line, potential $\widetilde{\psi}$ – dotted line, $\mathrm{E}^{qu} = 10$, $\mathrm{Re}^{qu} = 10$.

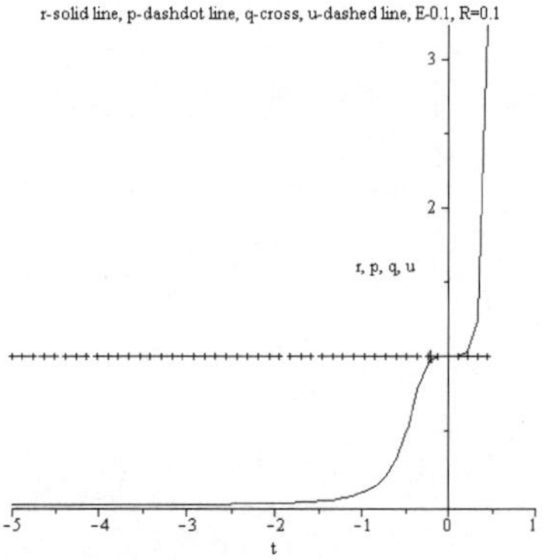

Figure 6.6.14. density $\tilde{\rho}_i$ - solid line, pressure $\tilde{p}_i$ - dashdot line, $\tilde{p}_e$ - cross, u-dashed line.

$E^{qu} = 0.1$, $Re^{qu} = 0.1$, lim2=0.486201.

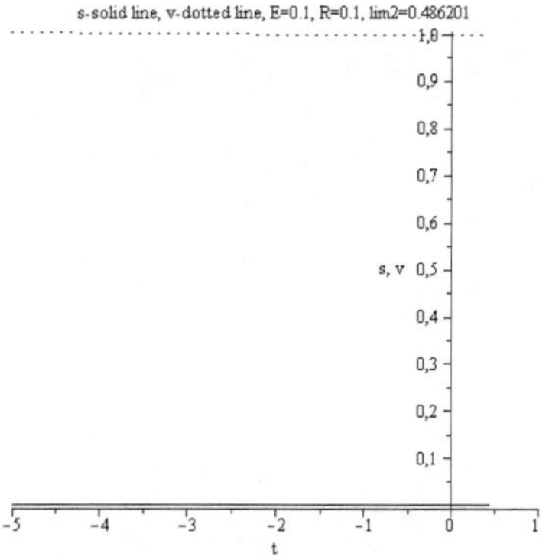

Figure 6.6.15. density $\tilde{\rho}_e$ - solid line, potential $\tilde{\psi}$ – dotted line,

$E = 0.1$, $Re^{qu} = 0.1$.

The electric field of real lattices can have the complicated configuration. For analytical expression for forces created by ions of the crystal lattice, Fourier approximation can be used. Let us consider for example the influence of the quadratic harmonics by the same other conditions of calculations. For the lattice ions

$$\rho_i F_i^{(pot)} + \rho_i F_i^{(npot)} = -\frac{u_0^2}{x_0}\frac{m_e}{m_i}\rho_0\tilde{\rho}_i\left[\frac{\partial\tilde{\psi}}{\partial\tilde{\xi}} - E^{qu}\cos^2\left(\frac{2\pi}{Re^{qu}}\tilde{\xi}\right)\right]. \tag{6.6.18}$$

Analogically for electrons

$$\rho_e F_e^{(pot)} + \rho_e F_e^{(npot)} = \frac{u_0^2}{x_0} \rho_0 \tilde{\rho}_e \left[\frac{\partial \tilde{\psi}}{\partial \tilde{\xi}} - \mathrm{E}^{\mathrm{qu}} \cos^2 \left(\frac{2\pi}{\mathrm{Re}^{qu}} \tilde{\xi} \right) \right]. \qquad (6.6.19)$$

The results of calculations on Figs. 6.6.16 – 6.6.18 are shown ($\mathrm{E}^{\mathrm{qu}} = 1$, $\mathrm{Re}^{\mathrm{qu}} = 1$).

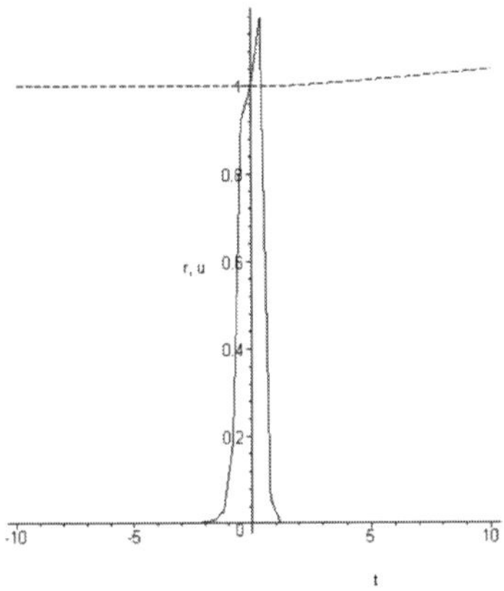

Fig. 6.6.16. r- density $\tilde{\rho}_i$, u- velocity $\tilde{u}$.

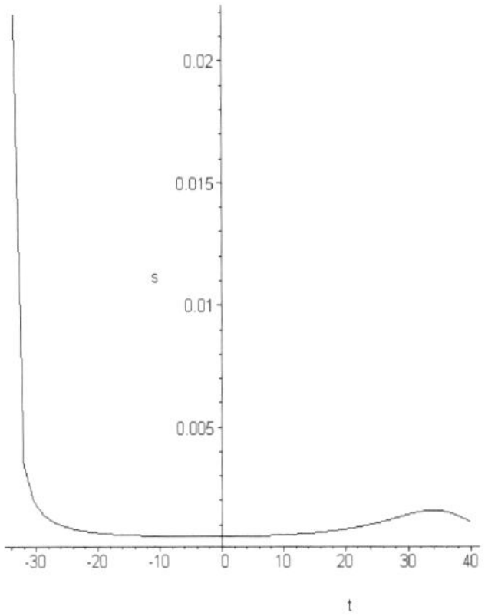

Fig. 6.6.17. s- density $\tilde{\rho}_s$.

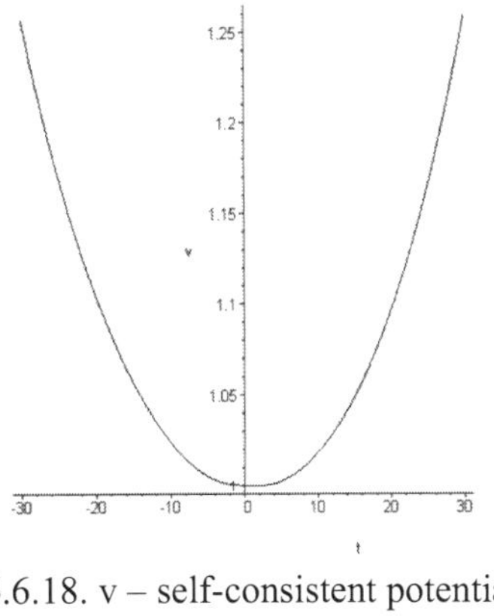

Fig. 6.6.18. v – self-consistent potential $\tilde{\psi}$.

The previous figures display the typical quantum objects placed in *the bounded region* of 1D space, all parts of these objects are moving with the same velocity. Namely from calculations follow that in coordinate system moving with the phase velocity, indestructible soliton has the velocity equal to the phase velocity. Moreover the attempt to impose to soliton to move with another group velocity leads to the soliton destruction. As we see from calculations, in the superconductivity regime the “estafette” movement of the soliton system “lattice ion – electron” is realized without creation of a chemical bond. The dependences $\widetilde{p}_e(\widetilde{\xi}),\widetilde{p}_i(\widetilde{\xi})$ define the conditions of the stability of the electron – ion pair. The destruction of the SC regime is the solitons destruction, depending on many conditions.

Research of superconductors is curried out very actively. But in spite of obvious success the following conclusion could be established:

1. Contemporary theories of superconductivity based on the Schrödinger equation, practically exhaust their arguments and have no possibility to explain effects of the high temperature superconductivity.
2. Contemporary theories of superconductivity (including BCS) based on the Schrödinger equation, can’t propose the principles of search and creation of superconducting materials.
3. The necessity exists of creation of principal new non-local quantum theories of superconductivity.

From position of the quantum hydrodynamics the problem of search and creation of superconductive materials come to the search of materials which lattices ensure the soliton movement without destruction. In my opinion the mentioned materials can be created artificially using the technology of the special introduction of quantum dots in matrices on the basement of proposed quantum hydrodynamics. It is known that technology of material creation with special quantum dots exists now in other applications.

CHAPTER 7. STRUCTURE OF "ELEMENTARY" PARTICLES, ATOMS AND PLASMOIDS

7.1. Plasmoids in the atmosphere and laboratories

Reports of the observation of ball lightning regularly appear in the press, but until recently the essence of this phenomenon remained a mystery. The purpose of the following consideration is to apply the methods of nonlocal physics to the study of long-lived (quasi-stationary) solitary plasma objects, which we will call plasmoids. Introduction to the definition of the requirement of privacy of the object is fundamental, because it allows you to separate the phenomenon from the lights of St. Elmo — glow near individual objects, which is observed in stormy weather at high electric field strength. St. Elmo's lights are attached to objects, and are treated as a corona discharge glow in the vicinity of these objects.

The term "plasmoid" is not unambiguous; in the literature, a plasmoid is often understood as a limited configuration of magnetic fields and plasma. Further, we will see that the long-lived plasma formation, generally speaking, does not require the introduction of either an external or self-consistent magnetic field. The use of the term "ball lightning" is even less preferable since the shape of an object can vary from spherical (or irregular spherical) to pear-shaped. Laboratory plasmoids can be even more complex.

Internet resources contain numerous photos of plasmoids.

Here are two known old photos of plasmoids taken from a distance of about 200 m and confirmed by visual observations. In 1933, an oval mass suddenly appeared in front of the photographer who was shooting thunderstorms (Fig. 7.1.1).

A dazzling ball that was seen by several more people slowly descended to the ground. The photographer estimated its diameter at 35 cm; the ball remained for about 10 seconds. Figure 7.1.2 corresponds ball lightning like fireworks. A ball with a diameter of about 50 cm appeared in front of the photographer in circumstances similar to the previous case. The ball rushed down and a few meters above the ground flew in different directions, like fireworks. The photographer reported that he clearly saw a glowing body at a distance of 200 m and that there was no other light sources in his field of vision.

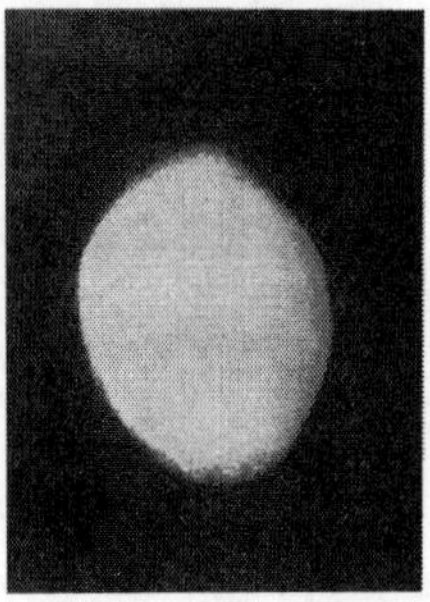

Fig. 7.1.1. Oval fireball.

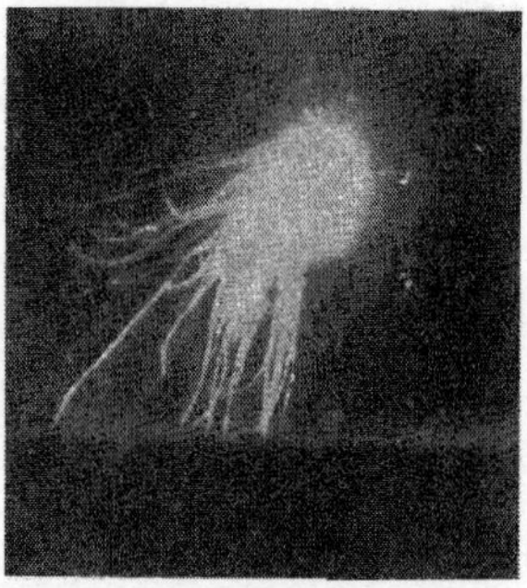

Fig. 7.1.2. "Fireworks" fireball.

Analysis of the descriptions of eyewitnesses has shown that BL:

1. The BL radiation of heat and radiant energy before its destruction is so small that it leaves no trace even when flying almost closely;

2. BL has a clear boundary separating it from the environment. BL motion does not cause this boundary to blur in the air (as in combustion, for example). Shell of BL sustainable and resilient in the face of strong deformation (with penetration through cracks and openings).

3. BL has a large spread of energy values, judging by the destruction;

4. BL is able to carry a large amount of electric charge, which can not carry a normal body of the same volume and mass.

5. BL has abnormally (relative to the known isolated plasma formations) a great time of life.

You can formulate a few questions, the answers to which should give a complete theory of ball lightning:

Why is ball lightning so stable? After all, if it is a gaseous formation, then at such temperatures this gas or plasma will immediately mix with the surrounding air. What prevents such mixing?

Why ball lightning does not float?

How does a ball lightning manage to exist for such a long time?

Where in the ball lightning such energy reserves (estimated, a typical ball lightning contains tens and hundreds of kilojoules)?

If BL is just a charge, it should be attracted to the surrounding bodies. Why are there no simple laws of electrostatics?

From the perspective of nonlocal quantum hydrodynamics, the problem of the Tunguska "meteorite» is of particular interest. The term "meteorite" is not suitable for the description of the phenomenon and is used in the literature only to refer to the event — the Tunguska phenomenon. The shape of the body is described as round, spherical or cylindrical; the color is red, yellow or white; there was no smoke trail, but some eyewitnesses tell of bright rainbow stripes extending behind the body.

The Tunguska phenomenon (TP) exploded in the air near the river Podkamennaya Tunguska river (about 60 km North and 20 km West from the village of Vanavara) 17 (30) June 1908 at 7 o'clock 14,5 ± 0,8 minutes local time (0 h 14,5 min UTC). The power of the explosion is estimated at 40-50 megatons ($10^{23}-10^{24}$ erg, $10^{13}-10^{14}$kJ), which corresponds to the energy of the most powerful hydrogen bomb. The power of the explosion is so great that almost no version of the explosion as a result of the physical system of exothermic chemical reactions. The explosion on Tunguska was heard 800 km from the epicenter, the blast wave knocked down the forest on the area of 2000 km^2; in a radius of 200 km windows were broken of some houses; seismic wave recorded seismic stations in Irkutsk, Tashkent, Tbilisi and yen. Shortly after the explosion, a magnetic storm began, lasting 5 hours.

In the Yenisei basin, the fireball moved from the Southeast to the Northwest. A survey of witnesses conducted in 1920-30-ies, led the first researchers of the problem (L. A. Kulik, I. S. Astapovich and E. L. Krinov) to the conclusion that the "cosmic object" flew in the direction from South to North. However, the analysis of the vector structure of forest felling and burn injuries gives a spread in azimuth from 114° to 95°, which indicates the movement of TP almost from East to West. Disagreements in the eyewitness accounts are so great that there were assumptions about the maneuvers in the atmosphere of the alien spacecraft and its catastrophe.

Not to believe a few hundred witnesses is impossible — this means that the TP before the explosion had a flight path, absolutely atypical for space objects invading the earth's atmosphere. This inconsistency does not end there [98]:

1. Thundering sounds were observed not only during and after the TP flight, but also before it. Obviously, the reason for the advanced sound effects could not be a shock wave in front of the head of a hypothetical cosmic body.

2. The flight ended with an explosion at an altitude of 7-10 km above the uninhabited area of the taiga. The blast wave was recorded by many observatories around the world. Within a few days on the territory from the Atlantic to Central Siberia there was an intense glow of the sky and glowing clouds. However, strange events began even before the TP explosion. Three days before the event, starting from June 27, 1908, in Europe, the European part

of Russia and Western Siberia, unusual atmospheric phenomena were observed: silver clouds, bright twilight, solar halo. British astronomer William Denning wrote that on the night of June 30, the sky over Bristol was so bright that the stars were almost invisible; the entire Northern part of the sky was red, and the East — green. The unusual atmospheric lighting effects that preceded the explosion peaked on July 1.

3. Reliable information about the substance TP does not exist, despite all the efforts of researchers.

4. At the site of the alleged fall of the meteorite knocked down the forest on a large area, but in the place that was supposed to be the epicenter of the explosion, the forest remained standing, and any traces of the meteorite crater were absent. The total radioactivity in the epicenter of the explosion, somehow different from the natural background, was not noted.

5. There are axisymmetric deviations from the strict radiality, existing in the projection area of the trajectory and representing a trace of the shock wave. This would not be surprising if these deviations from radiality existed before the epicenter of the explosion. But they existed after the explosion. This means that the hypothesis of an explosion of frozen gases or ice comet disappears.

To date there is no generally accepted physical model of the phenomena, explains all the essential features of the evolution of the TP. The situation is paradoxical in a way reminiscent of the situation in the theory of ball lightning (BL). In the theory of ball lightning, within the framework of local statistical physics of transport processes, all models aimed at explaining the existence of solitary plasma formations are sorted out. The question is — what can be BL?

All models are sorted out — it turns out that all (local) models are unsatisfactory. At the same time, the proposed explanations of the TP phenomenon are not only numerous and diverse, but often correspond to the level of science fiction, and not real physics. P.I. Privalov published in the Russian journal “Young technician” (1969-08, page 22-25) article "Guide to help compilers of hypotheses related to the fall of the Tunguska meteorite", which described seventy-seven theories about its fall, known on January 1, 1969 (no saying about their numerous combination). The current state of TP research is reflected in the proceedings of Siberian scientific conferences (see also [98]). In particular, from 1 to 3 may 2008 in Tomsk was held Siberian anniversary scientific conference "100 years of the Tunguska meteorite", "50 years of KSE" (complex Amateur expedition).

In our opinion, the only real explanation for the effect of Tunguska phenomenon (TP) is the appearance of TP as a giant plasmoid of earth origin as a result of powerful electromagnetic

The ball lightning (BL) problem might be considered as the unique one. Over the past two centuries several hundreds of hypotheses of ball lightning structure have been proposed [99], and now from time to time new hypotheses are still emerging.

We have now the sea of observational data. These data were statistically treated and were checked for reliability. The main results of this procedure are:

1) data observed in different parts of the Earth which are in good agreement with each other [99- 105],

2) all these data describe one and the same natural phenomenon [102-107].

The following characteristics of ball lightning might be considered as the main ones:

1. Its ability to liberate up to 10^9 J of energy in a matter of several tens of seconds. Nevertheless it is not an upper limit, because the Tunguska phenomenon can be treated as a giant BL explosion.

2. The peculiar character of its movement (absence of convection, movement against the wind, floating along conductors).

3. The lifetime up to several minutes, quiet dying or destruction with explosion.

4. The mechanism of its luminosity in the visible range of spectrum (light power 10-1000 W, colour - red, orange, silver, rainbow, possibility of fast colour changing, stability of emission power during its lifetime).

5. Absence of heat emission, and burns at close contact.

6. The presence or absence of noise and odour, accompanying its appearance.

7. Its ability to penetrate through obstacles (glasses, nets) with or without damaging them.

8. Its capability to change form, split into fragments and penetrate through chinks.

9. Its ability to lift heavy objects and to perform mechanical work.

The characteristic sizes of ball lightning are reported to vary from the size of the pea diameter to ~ 13 m. There are reports of extremely large balls — 27 and even 260 meters in diameter. Obviously, the size estimate depended on the distance to the object, which in turn was determined only approximately. Balloons observed at close range, were generally attributed to smaller diameters; when observed from afar, it was reported, usually on the larger size. The author of the monograph personally observed a ball lightning (diameter about 7-10 cm), which flew during a thunderstorm in the country from the electrical outlet and slowly moving through the room went into the chimney of the fireplace.

Ball lightning is a serious danger to the observer. In 1753, Georg Richman, a full member of the St. Petersburg Academy of Sciences, was killed by a ball lightning strike. He created a device to study atmospheric electricity. When at the next meeting, Richman heard that the storm was coming; he urgently went home with the engraver to capture the phenomenon. During the experiment, the blue-orange ball flew out of the device and hit the scientist directly on the forehead. There was a deafening roar. Richman fell dead, and the engraver was stunned and knocked down. He later described what happened. On the forehead of the scientist was a little dark crimson stain, his clothes were parched, and shoes torn. Door shattered into splinters, and the door blew off its hinges. Later inspection of a scene was made personally by M. V. Lomonosov.

There is a reason to believe that the death of Gagarin was due to a collision his aircraft with atmospheric plasmoid, [19].

The author of the article personally watched the ball lightning (diameter about 7-10 cm) which flew during a thunderstorm at the cottage from the electrical outlet and slowly moved through the room went into the chimney of the fireplace.

There are many reports collected and analyzed today on observations of long-lived large-scale plasmoids in atmosphere and under water [107-111]. These events were reported by military sailors, pilots and radar specialists. Typical characteristics and parameters of these plasmoids are the follows: • Diameter 3-10 m, • Altitude 10-20 km, • Depth 0- 10 km, • Cruise velocity in air 2 - 4 kmps, • Cruise velocity in water 300 kmph, • Life time 0.1 - 10 hours.

Many of these plasmoids are invisible in radio-frequency range for external probing EM radiation. For example, radar couldn't record some of these plasmoids. There is a strong electromagnetic impact of these plasmoids on board electronic equipment arranged on flight or sea vehicles. This long-lived plasmoid has a high electric surface potential which is up to 10 kV. So, this plasmoid is charged (non-neutral) plasma formation. It is revealed that aerodynamic drag of charged plasmoid is very small in air and water flows. So, it can move against a wind and a water flow. The artificial primary plasmoid can be divided in two or three secondary plasmoids. There is also an opposite process of primary small plasmoids conglomeration to a single large secondary plasmoid.

In recent years, there have been reports of giant electrical discharges in the upper atmosphere at altitudes from 30 to 150 kilometers, which are often identified with unidentified flying objects (UFO). Moreover, there are reports [112, 113] about underwater UFO in the oceans. The appearance of underwater plasmoids with a diameter of three to ten meters is associated with electric discharges that occur when the tectonic plates are shifted.

At the same time the efforts are initiated to obtain the artificial ball lightning. Often they are undertaken in the hope of fortune, of occasional success. These attempts are inspired by the apparent simplicity of ball lightning creating in nature, where it is most likely generated by a discharge of a linear lightning. However the success has not been yet achieved on that way. The cause of this situation is obvious - no underlying theory.

The number of appearances of ball lightning, not directly related to the storm, is small. According to Barry, 90% of occurrences were observed during thunderstorms. It is not surprising that experimenters trying to reproduce the ball lightning in the laboratory use water as one of the electrodes. In particular, A. I. Egorov and S. I. Stepanov [114] describe a device that allows obtaining luminous plasmoids – artificial ball lightning – with high reproducibility. Plasmoids are obtained as a result of a high – voltage discharge in the air, one electrode is solid, the other electrode is the surface of the water. To study the life time and electrical properties of plasmoids created measuring equipment and received several thousands of plasmoids. A significant part of the charge is concentrated on the glowing shell of the plasmoid.

A. G. Oreshko [115] reports on the experimental production of spherical plasmoids. The core of plasmoids has an excessive negative charge, and the outer spherical layer has, on the contrary, an excess positive charge. For us the mentioned experimental works are interesting by the fact that the excess peripheral charge of plasmoids can be positive or negative depending on the organization of the experiment.

Since there is no solution to the problem of the nature of the Tunguska phenomenon within the framework of local physics and, in our opinion, can not be found, it seems appropriate to consider the effect by methods of nonlocal physics. We have already created in previous chapters the nonlocal theory of transport processes and the theory of motion of quantum solitons.

Periodically, new aspects concerning the ball lightning are discussed at international symposiums. The intriguing appearance and characteristics of the ball lightning have given rise to a wide variety of models proposed for explaining the phenomenon. Practically the mentioned models cover the tremendous area possible mechanisms from complex chemical phenomenon to processes related to the behavior of antimatter. No reason to go into details of mentioned models. All these models are insufficient and have one common feature – they are constructed in the frame of local physics. Here I intend to show that application of the non-local hydrodynamic description leads to the ball lightning (BL) phenomenon as the result of the self-organization of the ionized matter. About terminology – maybe more reasonable to use the term plasmoid. But it will be shown that the influence of the external or internal magnetic field can be taken into account but existence of magnetic field is not the principal restriction for stable BL. As usual plasmoid is considered usually as a coherent structure of plasma and magnetic fields. In this connection I conserve in the following the term BL for the non-equilibrium structure of ionized matter existing in the bounded space domain in the self-consistent electric field.

What is the origin of all difficulties with the creation of the adequate BL theory?

1. The BL theory should be a particular case of the corresponding quantum nonlocal soliton theory.
2. The application of the BL transport equations should lead to Cauchy problems but not to boundary problems.
3. The BL theory should reflect the separation effects of charges in BL.
4. It means that the creation of the BL theory is equal to creation of the atom structure calculation with simultaneous self-consistent consideration nucleus + electron shell.
5. Nonlocal physics responds to these demands.

As you can see, the appearance of plasmoids is so diverse that the use of non-stationary 3D difference schemes becomes very desirable. Yet this is only a secondary problem. The most important thing is the possibility of theoretical explanation of the existence of solitary plasmoids. In Chapter 5 it is established that nonlocal quantum hydrodynamics allows to simulate the evolution of quantum solitons. The purpose of the following investigation is to apply the methods of non-local physics to the study of long-lived (quasi-stationary) solitary plasma objects, which we will further call also as plasmoids.

We underline a fundamentally important requirement for an adequate theory of solitary atomic structures. The theory should lead to the description of a bounded atomic structure *as a result of solving the Cauchy problem*, not the boundary value problem. It immediately follows that Schrödinger's theory is unsuitable for a strict description of such objects.

No reason to discuss "local" theories. Moreover we intend to proof the theorem - all the lightning's balls models based on local physics are wrong in principal.

Let us now turn to the mathematical modeling of solitary plasmoids based on the methods of nonlocal quantum hydrodynamics.

7.2. Basic nonlocal equations of quantum hydrodynamics

It is well known that basic Schrödinger equation (SE) [116-120] of quantum mechanics firstly was introduced as a quantum mechanical postulate. The obvious next step should be done and was realized by E. Madelung in 1927 – the derivation of special hydrodynamic form of SE after introduction wave function ψ_w as

$$\psi_w(x,y,z,t) = \alpha(x,y,z,t)\ e^{i\beta(x,y,z,t)}. \tag{7.2.1}$$

Using (7.2.1) and separating the real and imagine parts of SE one obtains

$$\frac{\partial \alpha^2}{\partial t} + \frac{\partial}{\partial \mathbf{r}} \cdot \left(\frac{\alpha^2 \hbar}{m} \frac{\partial \beta}{\partial \mathbf{r}} \right) = 0, \tag{7.2.2}$$

and Eq. (7.2.2) immediately transforms in continuity equation if the identifications for density and velocity

$$\rho = \alpha^2, \tag{7.2.3}$$

$$\mathbf{v} = \frac{\partial}{\partial \mathbf{r}}(\beta\hbar / m) \tag{7.2.4}$$

introduce in Eq. (7.2.2). Identification for velocity (7.2.2) is obvious because for 1D flow

$$v = \frac{\partial}{\partial x}(\beta\hbar / m) = \frac{\hbar}{m}\frac{\partial}{\partial x}\left[-\frac{1}{\hbar}(E_k t - px) \right] = \frac{1}{m}\frac{\partial}{\partial x}(px) = v_\phi, \tag{7.2.5}$$

where v_ϕ is phase velocity. The existence of the condition (7.2.5) means that the corresponding flow has potential

$$\Psi = \beta\hbar / m. \tag{7.2.6}$$

As result two effective hydrodynamic equations take place:

$$\frac{\partial \rho}{\partial t} + \frac{\partial}{\partial \mathbf{r}} \cdot (\rho \mathbf{v}) = 0, \tag{7.2.7}$$

$$\frac{\partial \mathbf{v}}{\partial t} + \frac{1}{2}\frac{\partial}{\partial \mathbf{r}} v^2 = -\frac{1}{m}\frac{\partial}{\partial \mathbf{r}}\left(U - \frac{\hbar^2}{2m}\frac{\Delta\alpha}{\alpha} \right). \tag{7.2.8}$$

But

$$\frac{\Delta\alpha}{\alpha}=\frac{\Delta\alpha^2}{2\alpha^2}-\frac{1}{\alpha^2}\left(\frac{\partial\alpha}{\partial\mathbf{r}}\right)^2, \tag{7.2.9}$$

and the relation (7.2.9) transforms (7.2.8) in particular case of the Euler motion equation

$$\frac{\partial\mathbf{v}}{\partial t}+(\mathbf{v}\cdot\frac{\partial}{\partial\mathbf{r}})\mathbf{v}=-\frac{1}{m}\frac{\partial}{\partial\mathbf{r}}U^*, \tag{7.2.10}$$

where introduced the efficient potential

$$U^*=U-\frac{\hbar^2}{4m\rho}\left[\Delta\rho-\frac{1}{2\rho}\left(\frac{\partial\rho}{\partial\mathbf{r}}\right)^2\right]. \tag{7.2.11}$$

Additive quantum part of potential can be written in the so called Bohm form

$$\frac{\hbar^2}{2m\sqrt{\rho}}\Delta\sqrt{\rho}=\frac{\hbar^2}{4m\rho}\left[\Delta\rho-\frac{1}{2\rho}\left(\frac{\partial\rho}{\partial\mathbf{r}}\right)^2\right]. \tag{7.2.12}$$

Then

$$U^*=U+U_{qu}=U-\frac{\hbar^2}{2m\sqrt{\rho}}\Delta\sqrt{\rho}=U-\frac{\hbar^2}{4m\rho}\left[\Delta\rho-\frac{1}{2\rho}\left(\frac{\partial\rho}{\partial\mathbf{r}}\right)^2\right]. \tag{7.2.13}$$

Some remarks:

a) SE transforms in hydrodynamic form without additional assumptions. But numerical methods of hydrodynamics are very good developed. As result at the end of seventieth of the last century we realized the systematic calculation of quantum problems using quantum hydrodynamics (see for example [17].

b) SE reduces to the system of continuity equation and particular case of the Euler equation with the additional potential proportional to $\hbar^2$. The physical sense and the origin of the Bohm potential are established in [19, 28, 29].

c) SE (obtained in the frame of the theory of classical complex variables) cannot contain the energy equation in principle. As result in many cases the palliative approach is used when for solution of dissipative quantum problems the classical hydrodynamics is used with insertion of additional Bohm potential in the system of hydrodynamic equations.

d) The system of the generalized quantum hydrodynamic equations contains energy equation written for unknown dependent value which can be specified as quantum pressure p_α of non-local origin.

Strict consideration leads to the following system of the generalized hydrodynamic equations (GHE) [18-22] written in the generalized Euler form:

Continuity equation for species α :

$$\frac{\partial}{\partial t}\left\{\rho_\alpha - \tau_\alpha\left[\frac{\partial \rho_\alpha}{\partial t}+\frac{\partial}{\partial \mathbf{r}}\cdot(\rho_\alpha \mathbf{v}_0)\right]\right\}+$$
$$+\frac{\partial}{\partial \mathbf{r}}\cdot\left\{\rho_\alpha \mathbf{v}_0 - \tau_\alpha\left[\frac{\partial}{\partial t}(\rho_\alpha \mathbf{v}_0)+\frac{\partial}{\partial \mathbf{r}}\cdot(\rho_\alpha \mathbf{v}_0\mathbf{v}_0)+\vec{\mathrm{I}}\cdot\frac{\partial p_\alpha}{\partial \mathbf{r}}-\right.\right. \tag{7.2.14}$$
$$\left.\left.-\rho_\alpha \mathbf{F}_\alpha^{(1)}-\frac{q_\alpha}{m_\alpha}\rho_\alpha \mathbf{v}_0\times\mathbf{B}\right]\right\}=R_\alpha,$$

and continuity equation for mixture

$$\frac{\partial}{\partial t}\left\{\rho - \sum_\alpha \tau_\alpha\left[\frac{\partial \rho_\alpha}{\partial t}+\frac{\partial}{\partial \mathbf{r}}\cdot(\rho_\alpha \mathbf{v}_0)\right]\right\}+$$
$$+\frac{\partial}{\partial \mathbf{r}}\cdot\left\{\rho \mathbf{v}_0 - \sum_\alpha \tau_\alpha\left[\frac{\partial}{\partial t}(\rho_\alpha \mathbf{v}_0)+\frac{\partial}{\partial \mathbf{r}}\cdot(\rho_\alpha \mathbf{v}_0\mathbf{v}_0)+\vec{\mathrm{I}}\cdot\frac{\partial p_\alpha}{\partial \mathbf{r}}-\right.\right. \tag{7.2.15}$$
$$\left.\left.-\rho_\alpha \mathbf{F}_\alpha^{(1)}-\frac{q_\alpha}{m_\alpha}\rho_\alpha \mathbf{v}_0\times\mathbf{B}\right]\right\}=0,$$

Momentum equation for species

$$\frac{\partial}{\partial t}\left\{\rho_\alpha \mathbf{v}_0 - \tau_\alpha\left[\frac{\partial}{\partial t}(\rho_\alpha \mathbf{v}_0)+\frac{\partial}{\partial \mathbf{r}}\cdot\rho_\alpha \mathbf{v}_0\mathbf{v}_0+\frac{\partial p_\alpha}{\partial \mathbf{r}}-\rho_\alpha \mathbf{F}_\alpha^{(1)}-\right.\right.$$
$$\left.\left.-\frac{q_\alpha}{m_\alpha}\rho_\alpha \mathbf{v}_0\times\mathbf{B}\right]\right\}-\mathbf{F}_\alpha^{(1)}\left[\rho_\alpha-\tau_\alpha\left(\frac{\partial \rho_\alpha}{\partial t}+\frac{\partial}{\partial \mathbf{r}}(\rho_\alpha \mathbf{v}_0)\right)\right]-$$
$$-\frac{q_\alpha}{m_\alpha}\left\{\rho_\alpha \mathbf{v}_0 - \tau_\alpha\left[\frac{\partial}{\partial t}(\rho_\alpha \mathbf{v}_0)+\frac{\partial}{\partial \mathbf{r}}\cdot\rho_\alpha \mathbf{v}_0\mathbf{v}_0+\frac{\partial p_\alpha}{\partial \mathbf{r}}-\rho_\alpha \mathbf{F}_\alpha^{(1)}-\right.\right.$$
$$\left.\left.-\frac{q_\alpha}{m_\alpha}\rho_\alpha \mathbf{v}_0\times\mathbf{B}\right]\right\}\times\mathbf{B}+\frac{\partial}{\partial \mathbf{r}}\cdot\left\{\rho_\alpha \mathbf{v}_0\mathbf{v}_0+p_\alpha\vec{\mathrm{I}}-\tau_\alpha\left[\frac{\partial}{\partial t}(\rho_\alpha \mathbf{v}_0\mathbf{v}_0+\right.\right. \tag{7.2.16}$$
$$+p_\alpha\vec{\mathrm{I}})+\frac{\partial}{\partial \mathbf{r}}\cdot\rho_\alpha(\mathbf{v}_0\mathbf{v}_0)\mathbf{v}_0+2\vec{\mathrm{I}}\left(\frac{\partial}{\partial \mathbf{r}}\cdot(p_\alpha \mathbf{v}_0)\right)+\frac{\partial}{\partial \mathbf{r}}\cdot\left(\vec{\mathrm{I}}p_\alpha \mathbf{v}_0\right)-$$
$$\left.\left.-\mathbf{F}_\alpha^{(1)}\rho_\alpha \mathbf{v}_0-\rho_\alpha \mathbf{v}_0\mathbf{F}_\alpha^{(1)}-\frac{q_\alpha}{m_\alpha}\rho_\alpha[\mathbf{v}_0\times\mathbf{B}]\mathbf{v}_0-\frac{q_\alpha}{m_\alpha}\rho_\alpha \mathbf{v}_0[\mathbf{v}_0\times\mathbf{B}]\right]\right\}=$$
$$=\int m_\alpha \mathbf{v}_\alpha J_\alpha^{st,el}d\mathbf{v}_\alpha+\int m_\alpha \mathbf{v}_\alpha J_\alpha^{st,inel}d\mathbf{v}_\alpha .$$

Generalized moment equation for mixture

$$
\begin{aligned}
&\frac{\partial}{\partial t}\left\{\rho\mathbf{v}_0-\sum_\alpha\tau_\alpha\left[\frac{\partial}{\partial t}(\rho_\alpha\mathbf{v}_0)+\frac{\partial}{\partial\mathbf{r}}\cdot\rho_\alpha\mathbf{v}_0\mathbf{v}_0+\frac{\partial p_\alpha}{\partial\mathbf{r}}-\rho_\alpha\mathbf{F}_\alpha^{(1)}-\right.\right.\\
&\left.\left.-\frac{q_\alpha}{m_\alpha}\rho_\alpha\mathbf{v}_0\times\mathbf{B}\right]\right\}-\sum_\alpha\mathbf{F}_\alpha^{(1)}\left[\rho_\alpha-\tau_\alpha\left(\frac{\partial\rho_\alpha}{\partial t}+\frac{\partial}{\partial\mathbf{r}}(\rho_\alpha\mathbf{v}_0)\right)\right]-\\
&-\sum_\alpha\frac{q_\alpha}{m_\alpha}\left\{\rho_\alpha\mathbf{v}_0-\tau_\alpha^{(0)}\left[\frac{\partial}{\partial t}(\rho_\alpha\mathbf{v}_0)+\frac{\partial}{\partial\mathbf{r}}\cdot\rho_\alpha\mathbf{v}_0\mathbf{v}_0+\frac{\partial p_\alpha}{\partial\mathbf{r}}-\rho_\alpha\mathbf{F}_\alpha^{(1)}-\right.\right.\\
&\left.\left.-\frac{q_\alpha}{m_\alpha}\rho_\alpha\mathbf{v}_0\times\mathbf{B}\right]\right\}\times\mathbf{B}+\frac{\partial}{\partial\mathbf{r}}\cdot\left\{\rho\mathbf{v}_0\mathbf{v}_0+p\ddot{\mathrm{I}}-\sum_\alpha\tau_\alpha\left[\frac{\partial}{\partial t}(\rho_\alpha\mathbf{v}_0\mathbf{v}_0+\right.\right.\\
&+p_\alpha\ddot{\mathrm{I}})+\frac{\partial}{\partial\mathbf{r}}\cdot\rho_\alpha(\mathbf{v}_0\mathbf{v}_0)\mathbf{v}_0+2\ddot{\mathrm{I}}\left(\frac{\partial}{\partial\mathbf{r}}\cdot(p_\alpha\mathbf{v}_0)\right)+\frac{\partial}{\partial\mathbf{r}}\cdot(\ddot{\mathrm{I}}p_\alpha\mathbf{v}_0)-\\
&\left.\left.-\mathbf{F}_\alpha^{(1)}\rho_\alpha\mathbf{v}_0-\rho_\alpha\mathbf{v}_0\mathbf{F}_\alpha^{(1)}-\frac{q_\alpha}{m_\alpha}\rho_\alpha[\mathbf{v}_0\times\mathbf{B}]\mathbf{v}_0-\frac{q_\alpha}{m_\alpha}\rho_\alpha\mathbf{v}_0[\mathbf{v}_0\times\mathbf{B}]\right]\right\}=0
\end{aligned}
\tag{7.2.17}
$$

Energy equation for component

$$
\begin{aligned}
&\frac{\partial}{\partial t}\left\{\frac{\rho_\alpha v_0^2}{2}+\frac{3}{2}p_\alpha+\varepsilon_\alpha n_\alpha-\tau_\alpha\left[\frac{\partial}{\partial t}\left(\frac{\rho_\alpha v_0^2}{2}+\frac{3}{2}p_\alpha+\varepsilon_\alpha n_\alpha\right)+\right.\right.\\
&\left.\left.+\frac{\partial}{\partial\mathbf{r}}\cdot\left(\frac{1}{2}\rho_\alpha v_0^2\mathbf{v}_0+\frac{5}{2}p_\alpha\mathbf{v}_0+\varepsilon_\alpha n_\alpha\mathbf{v}_0\right)-\mathbf{F}_\alpha^{(1)}\cdot\rho_\alpha\mathbf{v}_0\right]\right\}+\\
&+\frac{\partial}{\partial\mathbf{r}}\cdot\left\{\frac{1}{2}\rho_\alpha v_0^2\mathbf{v}_0+\frac{5}{2}p_\alpha\mathbf{v}_0+\varepsilon_\alpha n_\alpha\mathbf{v}_0-\tau_\alpha\left[\frac{\partial}{\partial t}\left(\frac{1}{2}\rho_\alpha v_0^2\mathbf{v}_0+\right.\right.\right.\\
&\left.+\frac{5}{2}p_\alpha\mathbf{v}_0+\varepsilon_\alpha n_\alpha\mathbf{v}_0\right)+\frac{\partial}{\partial\mathbf{r}}\cdot\left(\frac{1}{2}\rho_\alpha v_0^2\mathbf{v}_0\mathbf{v}_0+\frac{7}{2}p_\alpha\mathbf{v}_0\mathbf{v}_0+\frac{1}{2}p_\alpha v_0^2\ddot{\mathrm{I}}+\right.\\
&\left.+\frac{5}{2}\frac{p_\alpha^2}{\rho_\alpha}\ddot{\mathrm{I}}+\varepsilon_\alpha n_\alpha\mathbf{v}_0\mathbf{v}_0+\varepsilon_\alpha\frac{p_\alpha}{m_\alpha}\ddot{\mathrm{I}}\right)-\rho_\alpha\mathbf{F}_\alpha^{(1)}\cdot\mathbf{v}_0\mathbf{v}_0-p_\alpha\mathbf{F}_\alpha^{(1)}\cdot\ddot{\mathrm{I}}-\\
&-\frac{1}{2}\rho_\alpha v_0^2\mathbf{F}_\alpha^{(1)}-\frac{3}{2}\mathbf{F}_\alpha^{(1)}p_\alpha-\frac{\rho_\alpha v_0^2}{2}\frac{q_\alpha}{m_\alpha}[\mathbf{v}_0\times\mathbf{B}]-\frac{5}{2}p_\alpha\frac{q_\alpha}{m_\alpha}[\mathbf{v}_0\times\mathbf{B}]-\\
&\left.\left.-\varepsilon_\alpha n_\alpha\frac{q_\alpha}{m_\alpha}[\mathbf{v}_0\times\mathbf{B}]-\varepsilon_\alpha n_\alpha\mathbf{F}_\alpha^{(1)}\right]\right\}-\left\{\rho_\alpha\mathbf{F}_\alpha^{(1)}\cdot\mathbf{v}_0-\tau_\alpha\left[\mathbf{F}_\alpha^{(1)}\cdot\right.\right.\\
&\left.\left.\cdot\left(\frac{\partial}{\partial t}(\rho_\alpha\mathbf{v}_0)+\frac{\partial}{\partial\mathbf{r}}\cdot\rho_\alpha\mathbf{v}_0\mathbf{v}_0+\frac{\partial}{\partial\mathbf{r}}\cdot p_\alpha\ddot{\mathrm{I}}-\rho_\alpha\mathbf{F}_\alpha^{(1)}-q_\alpha n_\alpha[\mathbf{v}_0\times\mathbf{B}]\right)\right]\right\}=\\
&=\int\left(\frac{m_\alpha v_\alpha^2}{2}+\varepsilon_\alpha\right)J_\alpha^{st,el}d\mathbf{v}_\alpha+\int\left(\frac{m_\alpha v_\alpha^2}{2}+\varepsilon_\alpha\right)J_\alpha^{st,inel}d\mathbf{v}_\alpha.
\end{aligned}
\tag{7.2.18}
$$

and after summation the generalized energy equation for mixture

$$\frac{\partial}{\partial t}\left\{\frac{\rho v_0^2}{2}+\frac{3}{2}p+\sum_\alpha \varepsilon_\alpha n_\alpha-\sum_\alpha \tau_\alpha\left[\frac{\partial}{\partial t}\left(\frac{\rho_\alpha v_0^2}{2}+\frac{3}{2}p_\alpha+\varepsilon_\alpha n_\alpha\right)+\right.\right.$$

$$\left.\left.+\frac{\partial}{\partial \mathbf{r}}\cdot\left(\frac{1}{2}\rho_\alpha v_0^2\mathbf{v}_0+\frac{5}{2}p_\alpha\mathbf{v}_0+\varepsilon_\alpha n_\alpha\mathbf{v}_0\right)-\mathbf{F}_\alpha^{(1)}\cdot\rho_\alpha\mathbf{v}_0\right]\right\}+$$

$$+\frac{\partial}{\partial \mathbf{r}}\cdot\left\{\frac{1}{2}\rho v_0^2\mathbf{v}_0+\frac{5}{2}p\mathbf{v}_0+\mathbf{v}_0\sum_\alpha\varepsilon_\alpha n_\alpha-\sum_\alpha\tau_\alpha\left[\frac{\partial}{\partial t}\left(\frac{1}{2}\rho_\alpha v_0^2\mathbf{v}_0+\right.\right.\right.$$

$$\left.+\frac{5}{2}p_\alpha\mathbf{v}_0+\varepsilon_\alpha n_\alpha\mathbf{v}_0\right)+\frac{\partial}{\partial \mathbf{r}}\cdot\left(\frac{1}{2}\rho_\alpha v_0^2\mathbf{v}_0\mathbf{v}_0+\frac{7}{2}p_\alpha\mathbf{v}_0\mathbf{v}_0+\frac{1}{2}p_\alpha v_0^2\ddot{\mathrm{I}}+\right.$$

$$\left.+\frac{5}{2}\frac{p_\alpha^2}{\rho_\alpha}\ddot{\mathrm{I}}+\varepsilon_\alpha n_\alpha\mathbf{v}_0\mathbf{v}_0+\varepsilon_\alpha\frac{p_\alpha}{m_\alpha}\ddot{\mathrm{I}}\right)-\rho_\alpha\mathbf{F}_\alpha^{(1)}\cdot\mathbf{v}_0\mathbf{v}_0-p_\alpha\mathbf{F}_\alpha^{(1)}\cdot\ddot{\mathrm{I}}-$$

$$-\frac{1}{2}\rho_\alpha v_0^2\mathbf{F}_\alpha^{(1)}-\frac{3}{2}\mathbf{F}_\alpha^{(1)}p_\alpha-\frac{\rho_\alpha v_0^2}{2}\frac{q_\alpha}{m_\alpha}[\mathbf{v}_0\times\mathbf{B}]-\frac{5}{2}p_\alpha\frac{q_\alpha}{m_\alpha}[\mathbf{v}_0\times\mathbf{B}]-$$

$$\left.\left.-\varepsilon_\alpha n_\alpha\frac{q_\alpha}{m_\alpha}[\mathbf{v}_0\times\mathbf{F}]-\varepsilon_\alpha n_\alpha\mathbf{F}_\alpha^{(1)}\right]\right\}-\mathbf{v}_0\cdot\sum_\alpha\rho_\alpha\mathbf{F}_\alpha^{(1)}+$$

$$+\sum_\alpha\tau_\alpha\mathbf{F}_\alpha^{(1)}\cdot\left[\frac{\partial}{\partial t}(\rho_\alpha\mathbf{v}_0)+\frac{\partial}{\partial \mathbf{r}}\cdot\rho_\alpha\mathbf{v}_0\mathbf{v}_0+\frac{\partial}{\partial \mathbf{r}}\cdot p_\alpha\ddot{\mathrm{I}}-\rho_\alpha\mathbf{F}_\alpha^{(1)}-q_\alpha n_\alpha[\mathbf{v}_0\times\mathbf{B}]\right]=0.$$

(7.2.19)

Here $\mathbf{F}_\alpha^{(1)}$ are the forces of the non-magnetic origin, $\mathbf{B}$ - magnetic induction, $\ddot{\mathrm{I}}$ - unit tensor, q_α - charge of the α-component particle, p_α - static pressure for α-component, ε_α - internal energy for the particles of α-component, $\mathbf{v}_0$ - hydrodynamic velocity for mixture. For calculations in the self-consistent electro-magnetic field the system of non-local Maxwell equations should be added.

In the following I demonstrate applying of generalized non-local quantum hydrodynamic equations (7.2.14) – (7.2.19) to investigation of the one species system - the proton and electron internal structures.

7.3. Proton internal structure.

Let us consider a positive charged physical system placed in a bounded region of a space. Internal energy ε_α of this one species object and a possible influence of the magnetic field are not taken into account. The character linear scale of this region will be defined as result of the self-consistent solution of the generalized non-local quantum hydrodynamic equations. Suppose also that the mentioned physical object for simplicity has the spherical form and the system (7.2.14) – (7.2.19) takes the form:

(continuity equation)

$$\frac{\partial}{\partial t}\left\{\rho-\tau\left[\frac{\partial\rho}{\partial t}+\frac{1}{r^2}\frac{\partial(r^2\rho v_{0r})}{\partial r}\right]\right\}+\frac{1}{r^2}\frac{\partial}{\partial r}\left\{r^2\left\{\rho v_{0r}-\tau\left[\frac{\partial}{\partial t}(\rho v_{0r})+\frac{1}{r^2}\frac{\partial(r^2\rho v_{0r}^2)}{\partial r}+q\frac{\partial\Psi}{\partial r}\right]\right\}\right\}-$$

$$-\frac{1}{r^2}\frac{\partial}{\partial r}\left(\tau r^2\frac{\partial p}{\partial r}\right)=0, \tag{7.3.1}$$

(momentum equation)

$$\frac{\partial}{\partial t}\left\{\rho v_{0r}-\tau\left[\frac{\partial}{\partial t}(\rho v_{0r})+\frac{1}{r^2}\frac{\partial(r^2\rho v_{0r}^2)}{\partial r}+\frac{\partial p}{\partial r}+q\frac{\partial\Psi}{\partial r}\right]\right\}+\frac{q}{\rho}\frac{\partial\Psi}{\partial r}\left[\rho-\tau\left(\frac{\partial\rho}{\partial t}+\frac{1}{r^2}\frac{\partial(r^2\rho v_{0r})}{\partial r}\right)\right]+$$

$$+\frac{1}{r^2}\frac{\partial}{\partial r}\left\{r^2\left\{\rho v_{0r}^2-\tau\left[\frac{\partial}{\partial t}(\rho v_{0r}^2)+\frac{1}{r^2}\frac{\partial(r^2\rho v_{0r}^3)}{\partial r}+2q\frac{\partial\Psi}{\partial r}v_{0r}\right]\right\}\right\}+$$

$$+\frac{\partial p}{\partial r}-\frac{\partial}{\partial r}\left(\tau\frac{\partial p}{\partial t}\right)-2\frac{\partial}{\partial r}\left(\frac{\tau}{r^2}\frac{\partial(r^2 p v_{0r})}{\partial r}\right)-\frac{1}{r^2}\frac{\partial}{\partial r}\left(\tau r^2\frac{\partial(p v_{0r})}{\partial r}\right)=0. \tag{7.3.2}$$

(energy equation)

$$\frac{\partial}{\partial t}\left\{\frac{1}{2}\rho v_{0r}^2+\frac{3}{2}p-\tau\left[\frac{\partial}{\partial t}\left(\frac{1}{2}\rho v_{0r}^2+\frac{3}{2}p\right)+\frac{1}{r^2}\frac{\partial}{\partial r}\left(r^2 v_{0r}\left(\frac{1}{2}\rho v_{0r}^2+\frac{5}{2}p\right)\right)+q\frac{\partial\Psi}{\partial r}v_{0r}\right]\right\}+$$

$$+\frac{1}{r^2}\frac{\partial}{\partial r}\left\{r^2\left\{\left(\frac{1}{2}\rho v_{0r}^2+\frac{5}{2}p\right)v_{0r}-\tau\left[\frac{\partial}{\partial t}\left(\left(\frac{1}{2}\rho v_{0r}^2+\frac{5}{2}p\right)v_{0r}\right)+\frac{1}{r^2}\frac{\partial}{\partial r}\left(r^2\left(\frac{1}{2}\rho v_{0r}^2+\frac{7}{2}p\right)v_{0r}^2\right)+\right.\right.\right.$$

$$\left.\left.\left.+q\frac{\partial\Psi}{\partial r}v_{0r}^2+\frac{q}{\rho}\frac{\partial\Psi}{\partial r}\left(\frac{1}{2}\rho v_{0r}^2+\frac{3}{2}p\right)\right]\right\}\right\}+\left\{q\frac{\partial\Psi}{\partial r}v_{0r}-\right.$$

$$\left.-\tau\left[\frac{q}{\rho}\frac{\partial\Psi}{\partial r}\left(\frac{\partial}{\partial t}(\rho v_{0r})+\frac{1}{r^2}\frac{\partial}{\partial r}(r^2\rho v_{0r}^2)+\frac{\partial p}{\partial r}+q\frac{\partial\Psi}{\partial r}\right)\right]\right\}-\frac{1}{r^2}\frac{\partial}{\partial r}\left(\tau r^2\frac{\partial}{\partial r}\left(\frac{1}{2}p v_{0r}^2+\frac{5}{2}\frac{p^2}{\rho}\right)\right)-$$

$$-\frac{1}{r^2}\frac{\partial}{\partial r}\left(r^2\tau p\frac{q}{\rho}\frac{\partial\Psi}{\partial r}\right)=0, \tag{7.3.3}$$

where Ψ is potential *acting on the unit of charge*. Moreover let us admit that stationary physical system is at the rest, namely $v_{0r}=0$ and $\frac{\partial}{\partial t}\equiv 0$.

Is it possible to obtain the soliton type solution for this object under these stiff conditions? Let us show that the system (7.3.1) – (7.3.3) admit such kind of solutions. For mentioned case the system can be written as:

Poisson equation is

$$\frac{1}{r^2}\frac{\partial}{\partial r}\left(r^2\frac{\partial\Psi}{\partial r}\right)=-4\pi n, \tag{7.3.4}$$

where n is the number density of charge.

Continuity equation:

$$\frac{\partial}{\partial r}\left\{\tau r^2\left(\frac{\partial p}{\partial r}+q\frac{\partial\Psi}{\partial r}\right)\right\}=0, \tag{7.3.5}$$

where q is the positive charge (*per the unit of volume*) of the one species quantum object.

Momentum equation:

$$\frac{\partial p}{\partial r}+q\frac{\partial \Psi}{\partial r}=0. \qquad (7.3.6)$$

Equation (7.3.5) is satisfied for all parameter of non-locality if Eq. (7.3.6) is fulfilled. Energy equation takes the form (omitting the internal energy ε):

$$-\frac{1}{r^2}\frac{5}{2}\frac{\partial}{\partial r}\left\{r^2\tau p\frac{q}{\rho}\frac{\partial \Psi}{\partial r}\right\}+\tau\frac{q}{\rho}\frac{\partial \Psi}{\partial r}\left[\frac{\partial p}{\partial r}+q\frac{\partial \Psi}{\partial r}\right]-\frac{1}{r^2}\frac{5}{2}\frac{\partial}{\partial r}\left(\tau r^2\frac{\partial}{\partial r}\left(\frac{p^2}{\rho}\right)\right)=0 \qquad (7.3.7)$$

or using (7.3.6)

$$\frac{\partial}{\partial r}\left\{r^2\tau p\frac{q}{\rho}\frac{\partial \Psi}{\partial r}\right\}+\frac{\partial}{\partial r}\left(\tau r^2\frac{\partial}{\partial r}\left(\frac{p^2}{\rho}\right)\right)=0. \qquad (7.3.8)$$

From (7.3.8) follows

$$\tau p\frac{q}{\rho}r^2\frac{\partial \Psi}{\partial r}+\tau r^2\frac{\partial}{\partial r}\left(\frac{p^2}{\rho}\right)=C, \qquad (7.3.9)$$

where C is constant of integration. If the non-locality parameter τ does not depend explicitly on r and the left side of Eq. (7.3.9) turns into zero if $r=0$, then $C=0$. Eq. (7.3.9) is written as

$$p\frac{q}{\rho}\frac{\partial \Psi}{\partial r}+\frac{\partial}{\partial r}\left(\frac{p^2}{\rho}\right)=0 \qquad (7.3.10)$$

or using (7.3.6)

$$\frac{\partial}{\partial r}\left(\frac{p}{q}\right)=0, \qquad (7.3.11)$$

which leads to the solution with new constant of integration C

$$p=Cq. \qquad (7.3.12)$$

From (7.3.6), (7.3.12) one obtains

$$\ln\frac{q}{C_1}=-\frac{\Psi}{C}. \qquad (7.3.13)$$

with new constant of integration C_1. Let us use these constants as scales, namely $C=\Psi_0$, $C_1=q_0$ denoting of dimensionless values by wave $\tilde{q}=q/q_0$, $\tilde{\Psi}=\Psi/\Psi_0$,

$\Psi_0=\frac{1}{r_0}$, $q_0=\frac{e}{4\pi r_0^3}$,

$p_0=\frac{q_0}{r_0}=\frac{e}{4\pi r_0^2}\frac{1}{r_0^2}$, where e is the absolute value of the electron charge. From (7.3.13) follows

$$q=C_1\exp\left(-\frac{\Psi}{C}\right), \qquad (7.3.14)$$

or

$$q = q_0 \exp\left(-\widetilde{\Psi}\right). \tag{7.3.15}$$

or

$$\widetilde{q} = \exp\left(-\widetilde{\Psi}\right). \tag{7.3.16}$$

Equation (7.3.4) transforms into dimensionless equation

$$\frac{\partial}{\partial \widetilde{r}}\left(\widetilde{r}^2 \frac{\partial \widetilde{\Psi}}{\partial \widetilde{r}}\right) = -\widetilde{r}^2 \exp\left(-\widetilde{\Psi}\right), \tag{7.3.17}$$

After substitution $\partial\Psi/\partial r$ from the equation (see also (7.3.6))

$$\frac{\partial \widetilde{\Psi}}{\partial \widetilde{r}} = -\frac{1}{\widetilde{q}}\frac{\partial \widetilde{p}}{\partial \widetilde{r}} \tag{7.3.18}$$

in the equation (7.3.17) and using (7.3.16) we find

$$\frac{\partial}{\partial \widetilde{r}}\left(\widetilde{r}^2 \frac{1}{\widetilde{q}}\frac{\partial \widetilde{q}}{\partial \widetilde{r}}\right) = \widetilde{r}^2 \widetilde{q}. \tag{7.3.19}$$

Analogically using (7.3.12) in the form

$$\widetilde{p} p_0 = \widetilde{q} q_0 \frac{1}{r_0}.$$

$$\widetilde{p} = \widetilde{q} \tag{7.3.20}$$

one obtains

$$\frac{\partial}{\partial \widetilde{r}}\left(\widetilde{r}^2 \frac{1}{\widetilde{p}}\frac{\partial \widetilde{p}}{\partial \widetilde{r}}\right) = \widetilde{r}^2 \widetilde{p}. \tag{7.3.21}$$

Equations (7.3.19), (7.3.21) have the same dimensionless solutions.

Figures 7.3.1 and 7.3.2 reflect the solutions of (7.3.17), (7.3.19) correspondingly. Maple notations are used ($v = \widetilde{\Psi}$, $D(v)(t) = \frac{\partial \widetilde{\Psi}}{\partial \widetilde{r}}$, $q = \widetilde{q}$). Cauchy conditions for this calculations: $v(0) = \widetilde{\Psi}(0) = 1$, $D(v)(0) = \frac{\partial \widetilde{\Psi}}{\partial \widetilde{r}}(0) = 0$; $\widetilde{q}(0) = e^{-1}$, $D(q)(0) = \frac{\partial \widetilde{q}}{\partial \widetilde{r}}(0) = 0$.

```
dsolve[interactive]({
diff(t^2*diff(v(t),t),t)=-t^2*exp(-v(t)),
v(0)=1,D(v)(0)=0
});
dsolve[interactive]({
diff(t^2*diff(q(t),t)/q(t),t)=t^2*q(t),
q(0)=exp(-1),D(q)(0)=0
});
```

Condition `q(0)=exp(-1)` follows from relation (7.3.16) and `v(0)=1`.

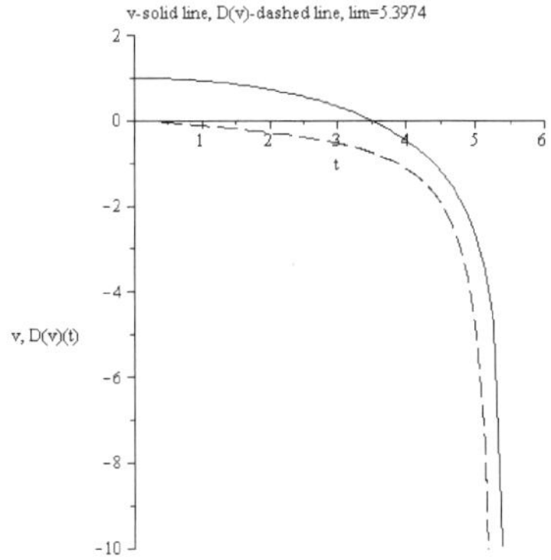

Figure 7.3.1. $v = \Psi(\tilde{r})$, $D(v)(t) = \frac{\partial \tilde{\Psi}}{\partial \tilde{r}}(\tilde{r})$ for proton, $v = \tilde{\Psi}(\tilde{r})$ - solid line, lim=5.3974.

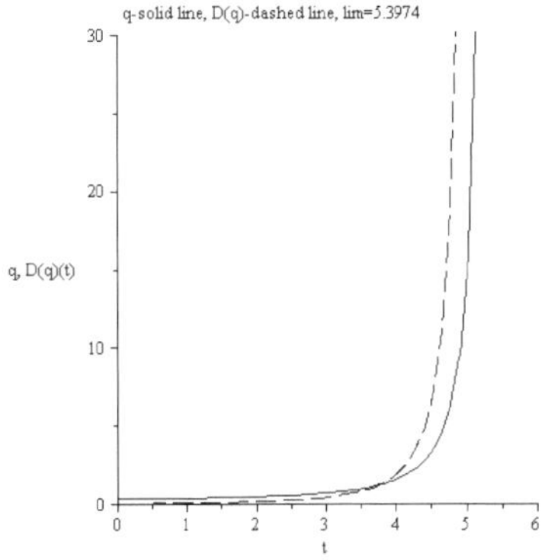

Figure 7.3.2. $q = \tilde{q}(\tilde{r})$, $D(q)(t) = D(\tilde{q})(\tilde{r})$ for proton.

Proton charge q_p is equal to

$$q_p = \int_0^{r_p} 4\pi r^2 q(r) dr = 4\pi r_0^3 q_0 \int_0^{\tilde{r}_p} \tilde{r}^2 \tilde{q} d\tilde{r} = 4\pi r_0^3 q_0 \int_0^{\tilde{r}_p} \frac{\partial}{\partial \tilde{r}} \left(\tilde{r}^2 \frac{1}{\tilde{q}} \frac{\partial \tilde{q}}{\partial \tilde{r}} \right) d\tilde{r} =$$
$$= 4\pi r_0^3 \frac{e}{4\pi r_0^3} \int_0^{\tilde{r}_p} \frac{\partial}{\partial \tilde{r}} \left(\tilde{r}^2 \frac{1}{\tilde{q}} \frac{\partial \tilde{q}}{\partial \tilde{r}} \right) d\tilde{r} = e \int_0^{\tilde{r}_p} \frac{\partial}{\partial \tilde{r}} \left(\tilde{r}^2 \frac{1}{\tilde{q}} \frac{\partial \tilde{q}}{\partial \tilde{r}} \right) d\tilde{r} = e \tilde{r}_p^2 \left[\frac{\partial \ln \tilde{q}}{\partial \tilde{r}} \right]_{\tilde{r} = \tilde{r}_p} \quad (7.3.22)$$

or

$$\tilde{r}_p^2 \left[\frac{\partial \ln \tilde{q}}{\partial \tilde{r}} \right]_{\tilde{r}=\tilde{r}_p} = 1. \qquad (7.3.23)$$

Relation (7.3.23) delivers the natural boundary condition for the external area of proton.

$$\tilde{r}_p^2 \left[\frac{1}{\tilde{q}} \frac{\partial \tilde{q}}{\partial \tilde{r}} \right]_{\tilde{r}=\tilde{r}_p} = 1. \qquad (7.3.24)$$

Let us consider figure (7.3.3). In the point $\tilde{r} \cong 1.92$ we have $\frac{1}{\tilde{q}}\frac{\partial \tilde{q}}{\partial \tilde{r}} \cong 1$ ($\tilde{q} = 0.4690, \partial\tilde{q}/\partial\tilde{r} = 0.1276$))

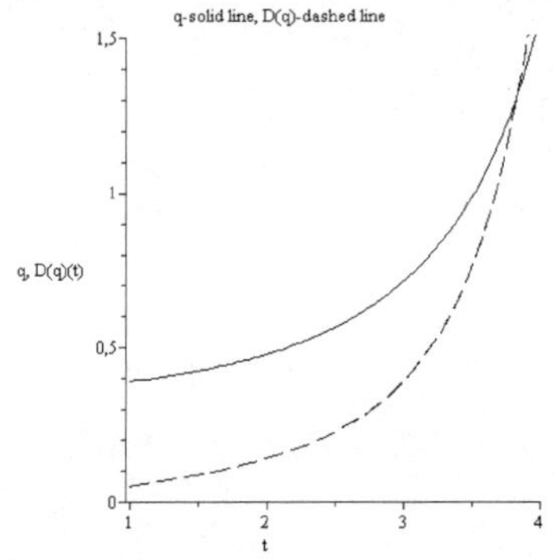

Figure 7.3.3. $\mathrm{q} = \tilde{q}(\tilde{r})$, $\mathrm{D(q)(t)} = D(\tilde{q})(\tilde{r})$ for proton.

Then for chosen Cauchy conditions $\tilde{r}_p = 1.92$ or $r_p = 1.92 r_0$. The typical experimental value of the proton radius is $0.831 \cdot 10^{-15} m$. Then $r_0 = 0.433 \cdot 10^{-15} m$ and $\tilde{\Psi}_p = 0.7572$, $\Psi_p = 0.7572 / r_0 = 1.748 \cdot 10^{15} m^{-1}$, $D(\tilde{\Psi})(\tilde{r}_p) = -0.2721$ (see also figure 7.3.4).

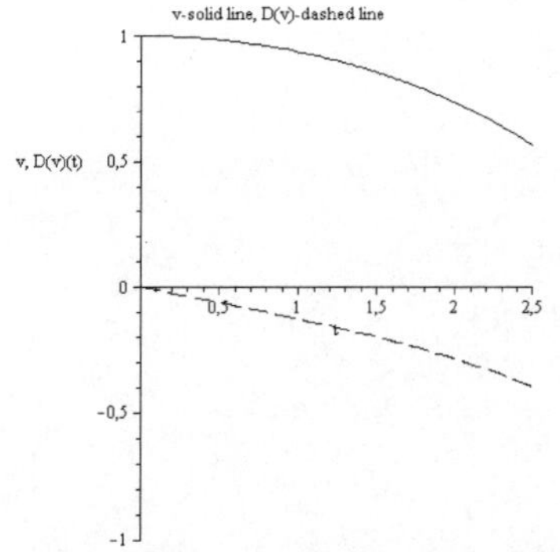

Figure 7.3.4. $\mathrm{v} = \tilde{\mathrm{v}}(\tilde{r})$, $\mathrm{D(v)(t)} = D(\tilde{\Psi})(\tilde{r})$ for proton.

The same dimensionless solutions exist for positron.

7.4. Electron internal structure.

Now we can apply the previous theory to the calculation of the internal electron structure. It leads to the very old question, if the electron does not have an internal structure, how does it maintain itself as an entity? Why does it not disintegrate? As before we intend to consider the electron at the rest placed in the self-consistent intrinsic electric field without an intrinsic magnetic field.

In our electron model, we no longer regard the electron as a point-like particle. Similar to the proton's electric charge, which has continuum distribution inside of the proton, we make the same basic assumptions based on the application of the non-local theory. On this step of investigation no reason to introduce the simplest model of electron spin like a spinning electrically charged ball or much more complicated theory which leads to the magnetic charge continuum distribution inside of the electron using the Dirac monopole speculations.

In the analogical theory we should take into account the change of the charge sign. We should wait for changing sign in equations (7.3.17) and (7.319) defining potential $\tilde{\Psi}$ and charge $\tilde{q}$ correspondingly. Equation (7.3.21) (defining the pressure $\tilde{p}$ evolution) should conserve the previous form. Let consider this affirmations in details.

The Poisson equation can be written in the form

$$\frac{1}{r^2}\frac{\partial}{\partial r}\left(r^2\frac{\partial \Psi}{\partial r}\right)=4\pi n, \qquad (7.4.1)$$

where Ψ - is potential *acting on the unit of charge* scalar electric potential and n is the number density for particles having the negative charge.

Momentum equation:

$$\frac{\partial p}{\partial r}+q\frac{\partial \Psi}{\partial r}=0, \qquad (7.4.2)$$

where q is the negative charge (*per the unit of volume*) of the one species quantum object.

Energy equation takes the form (omitting the internal energy ε):

$$-\frac{1}{r^2}\frac{5}{2}\frac{\partial}{\partial r}\left\{r^2\tau p\frac{q}{\rho}\frac{\partial \Psi}{\partial r}\right\}+\tau\frac{q}{\rho}\frac{\partial \Psi}{\partial r}\left[\frac{\partial p}{\partial r}+q\frac{\partial \Psi}{\partial r}\right]-\frac{1}{r^2}\frac{5}{2}\frac{\partial}{\partial r}\left(\tau r^2\frac{\partial}{\partial r}\left(\frac{p^2}{\rho}\right)\right)=0 \qquad (7.4.3)$$

or using (7.4.2)

$$\frac{\partial}{\partial r}\left\{r^2\tau p\frac{q}{\rho}\frac{\partial\Psi}{\partial r}\right\}+\frac{\partial}{\partial r}\left(\tau r^2\frac{\partial}{\partial r}\left(\frac{p^2}{\rho}\right)\right)=0\,. \quad (7.4.4)$$

From (7.4.4) follows

$$\tau p\frac{q}{\rho}r^2\frac{\partial\Psi}{\partial r}+\tau r^2\frac{\partial}{\partial r}\left(\frac{p^2}{\rho}\right)=C\,, \quad (7.4.5)$$

where C is constant of integration. If the non-locality parameter τ does not depend explicitly on r and the left side of Eq. (7.4.5) turns into zero if $r=0$, then $C=0$. Eq. (7.4.5) is written as

$$p\frac{q}{\rho}\frac{\partial\Psi}{\partial r}+\frac{\partial}{\partial r}\left(\frac{p^2}{\rho}\right)=0 \quad (7.4.6)$$

or using (7.4.2)

$$\frac{\partial}{\partial r}\left(\frac{p}{q}\right)=0\,, \quad (7.4.7)$$

which leads to the solution with new constant of integration C

$$p=Cq\,. \quad (7.4.8)$$

From (7.4.2), (7.4.8) one obtains

$$\frac{\partial q}{\partial r}+\frac{q}{C}\frac{\partial\Psi}{\partial r}=0 \quad (7.4.9)$$

$$\ln\frac{q}{C_1}=-\frac{\Psi}{C}. \quad (7.4.10)$$

with new constant of integration C_1. Let us use these constants as scales, namely $C=-|\Psi_0|$, $C_1=-q_0$ denoting of dimensionless values by wave $\tilde{q}=q/q_0$, $\tilde{\Psi}=\Psi/|\Psi_0|$, $|\Psi_0|=\frac{1}{r_0}$, $q_0=\frac{e}{4\pi r_0^3}$, $p_0=\frac{q_0}{r_0}=\frac{e}{4\pi r_0^2}\frac{1}{r_0^2}$, where e is the absolute value of the electron charge. From (7.4.10) follows

$$q=C_1\exp\left(\frac{\Psi}{|\Psi_0|}\right), \quad (7.4.11)$$

or

$$\tilde{q}=-\exp(\tilde{\Psi}). \quad (7.4.12)$$

Equation (7.4.1) transforms into dimensionless equation

$$\frac{1}{r^2}\frac{\partial}{\partial r}\left(r^2\frac{\partial\Psi}{\partial r}\right)=-\frac{1}{e}4\pi q \quad (7.4.13)$$

or

$$\frac{1}{\tilde{r}^2}\frac{\partial}{\partial\tilde{r}}\left(\tilde{r}^2\frac{\partial\tilde{\Psi}}{\partial\tilde{r}}\right)=4\pi\frac{1}{e/r_0^3}q_0\exp(\tilde{\Psi}) \quad (7.4.14)$$

or

$$\frac{1}{\widetilde{r}^2}\frac{\partial}{\partial\widetilde{r}}\left(\widetilde{r}^2\frac{\partial\widetilde{\Psi}}{\partial\widetilde{r}}\right)=\exp\left(\widetilde{\Psi}\right). \tag{7.4.15}$$

After substitution $\partial\Psi/\partial r$ from the equation (see also (7.4.2))

$$\frac{\partial\widetilde{\Psi}}{\partial\widetilde{r}}=-\frac{1}{\widetilde{q}}\frac{\partial\widetilde{p}}{\partial\widetilde{r}} \tag{7.4.16}$$

in the equation (7.4.15) we find

$$\frac{1}{\widetilde{r}^2}\frac{\partial}{\partial\widetilde{r}}\left(\widetilde{r}^2\frac{1}{\widetilde{q}}\frac{\partial\widetilde{p}}{\partial\widetilde{r}}\right)=-\exp\left(\widetilde{\Psi}\right) \tag{7.4.17}$$

or using (7.4.12) one obtains

$$\frac{\partial}{\partial\widetilde{r}}\left(\widetilde{r}^2\frac{1}{\widetilde{q}}\frac{\partial\widetilde{p}}{\partial\widetilde{r}}\right)=\widetilde{r}^2\widetilde{q}\,. \tag{7.4.18}$$

Equation (7.4.8) is written as

$$\widetilde{p}p_0=-\widetilde{q}q_0\frac{1}{r_0}. \tag{7.4.19}$$

or

$$\widetilde{p}=-\widetilde{q} \tag{7.4.20}$$

one obtains

$$\frac{\partial}{\partial\widetilde{r}}\left(\widetilde{r}^2\frac{1}{q}\frac{\partial\widetilde{q}}{\partial\widetilde{r}}\right)=-\widetilde{r}^2\widetilde{q}\,, \tag{7.4.21}$$

$$\frac{\partial}{\partial\widetilde{r}}\left(\widetilde{r}^2\frac{1}{\widetilde{p}}\frac{\partial\widetilde{p}}{\partial\widetilde{r}}\right)=\widetilde{r}^2\widetilde{p}\,. \tag{7.4.22}$$

Equations (7.4.17), (7.4.21) and (7.4.22) confirm affirmations related to the sign changing in equations. have the same dimensionless solutions.

Figures 7.4.1 - 7.4.6 reflect the solutions of equations (7.4.15), (7.4.17) and (7.4.20). Maple notations are used ($\mathrm{v}=\widetilde{\Psi}$, $\mathrm{D(v)(t)}=\frac{\partial\widetilde{\Psi}}{\partial\widetilde{r}}$, $\mathrm{q}=\widetilde{q}$). Cauchy conditions for these calculations are indicated in figures:

$\mathrm{v}(0)=\widetilde{\psi}(0)=1$, $\mathrm{D(v)(0)}=\frac{\partial\widetilde{\Psi}}{\partial\widetilde{r}}(0)=0$; $\widetilde{q}(0)=e^{-1}$, $\mathrm{D(q)(0)}=\frac{\partial\widetilde{q}}{\partial\widetilde{r}}(0)=0$.

Programs written in Marple:

```
dsolve[interactive]({
diff(t^2*diff(v(t),t),t)=t^2*exp(v(t)),
v(0)=1,D(v)(0)=0
});
dsolve[interactive]({
diff(t^2*diff(q(t),t)/q(t),t)=-t^2*q(t),
```

```
q(0)=-exp(-1),D(q)(0)=0
});
dsolve[interactive]({
diff(t^2*diff(p(t),t)/p(t),t)=t^2*p(t),
p(0)=exp(-1),D(p)(0)=0
});
```

```
> dsolve[interactive]({
  diff(t^2*diff(q(t),t)/q(t),t) =-t^2
      *q(t),
  q(0) =-exp(-1), D(q)(0) = 0
  });
```

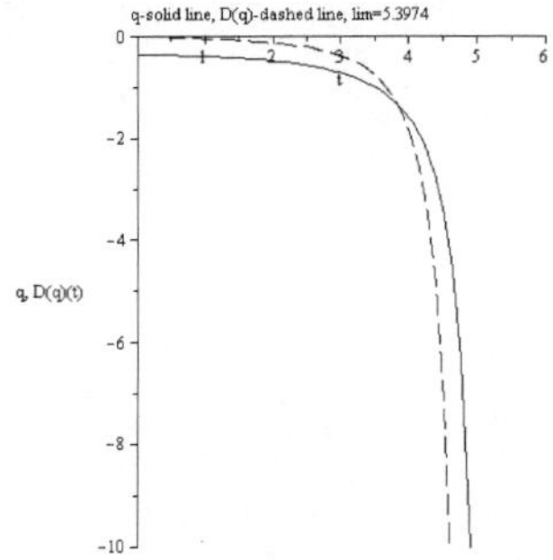

Figure 7.4.1. $q = \widetilde{q}(\widetilde{r})$, solid line; $D(q)(t) = \frac{\partial \widetilde{q}}{\partial \widetilde{r}}(\widetilde{r})$, dashed line for electron.

```
> dsolve[interactive]({
  diff(t^2*diff(q(t),t)/q(t),t) =-t^2
      *q(t),
  q(0) =-1/10^8, D(q)(0) = 0
  });
```

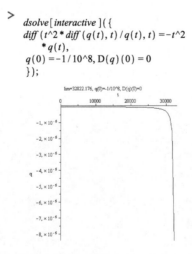

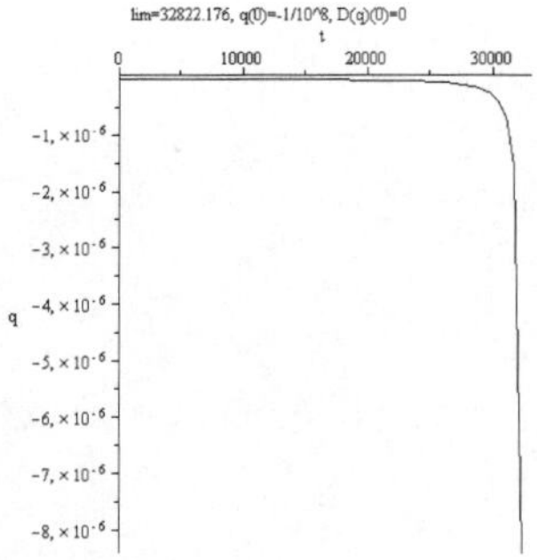

Figure 7.4.2. $q = \widetilde{q}(\widetilde{r})$, solid line for electron.

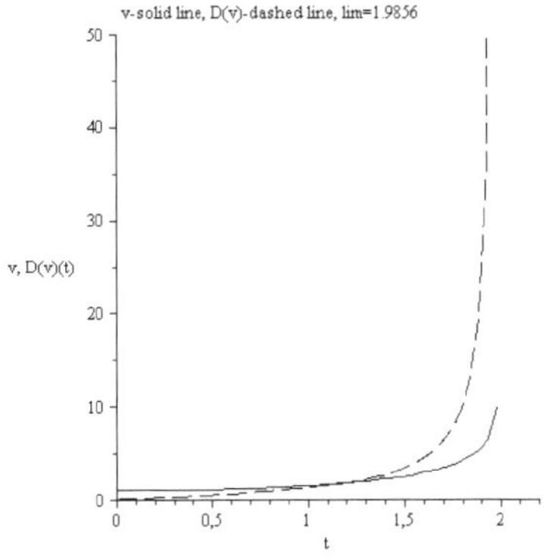

$$v(0)=\widetilde{\Psi}(0)=1,\ D(v)(0)=\frac{\partial\widetilde{\Psi}}{\partial\widetilde{r}}(0)=0..$$

Figure 7.4.3. $v=\widetilde{\Psi}(\widetilde{r}),\ D(v)(t)=\frac{\partial\widetilde{\Psi}}{\partial\widetilde{r}}(\widetilde{r})$ for electron, solid line $v=\widetilde{\Psi}(\widetilde{r})$.

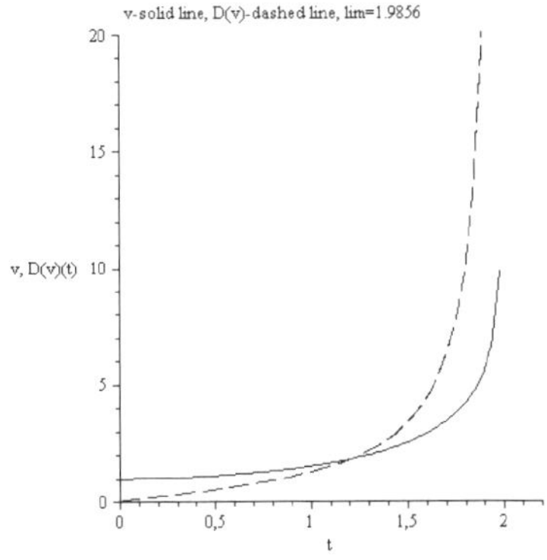

$$v(0)=\widetilde{\Psi}(0)=1,\ D(v)(0)=\frac{\partial\widetilde{\Psi}}{\partial\widetilde{r}}(0)=0..$$

Figure 7.4.4. $v=\widetilde{\Psi}(\widetilde{r}),\ D(v)(t)=\frac{\partial\widetilde{\Psi}}{\partial\widetilde{r}}(\widetilde{r})$ for electron, solid line $v=\widetilde{\Psi}(\widetilde{r})$.

```
dsolve[interactive]({
diff(t^2*diff(v(t), t), t) = t^2
    *exp(v(t)),
v(0) = 1/10^8, D(v)(0) = 0
});
```

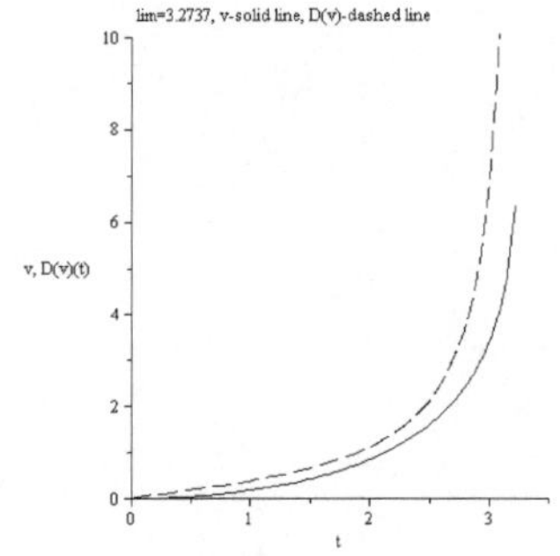

Figure 7.4.5. $\mathrm{v} = \widetilde{\Psi}(\widetilde{r})$, $\mathrm{D(v)(t)} = \frac{\partial \widetilde{\Psi}}{\partial \widetilde{r}}(\widetilde{r})$ for electron, solid line $\mathrm{v} = \widetilde{\Psi}(\widetilde{r})$.

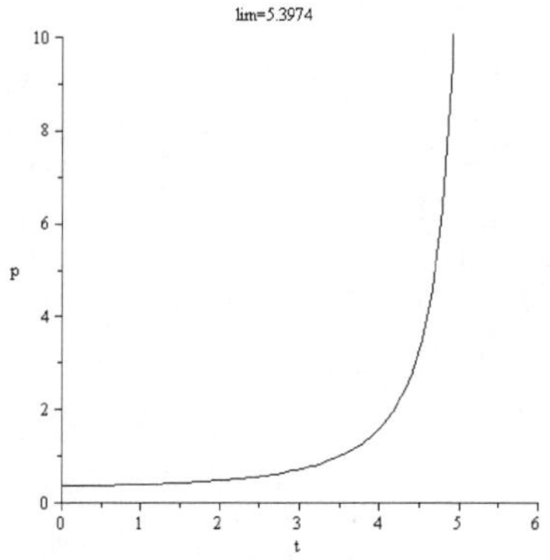

Figure 7.4.6. $\mathrm{p} = \widetilde{p}(\widetilde{r})$ for electron.

Electron charge q_e is equal to

$$\begin{aligned} q_e &= \int_0^{r_e} 4\pi r^2 q(r) dr = 4\pi r_0^3 q_0 \int_0^{\widetilde{r}_e} \widetilde{r}^2 \widetilde{q} d\widetilde{r} = -4\pi r_0^3 q_0 \int_0^{\widetilde{r}_e} \frac{\partial}{\partial \widetilde{r}} \left(\widetilde{r}^2 \frac{1}{\widetilde{q}} \frac{\partial \widetilde{q}}{\partial \widetilde{r}} \right) d\widetilde{r} = \\ &= -4\pi r_0^3 \frac{e}{4\pi r_0^3} \int_0^{\widetilde{r}_e} \frac{\partial}{\partial \widetilde{r}} \left(\widetilde{r}^2 \frac{1}{\widetilde{q}} \frac{\partial \widetilde{q}}{\partial \widetilde{r}} \right) d\widetilde{r} = -e \int_0^{\widetilde{r}_e} \frac{\partial}{\partial \widetilde{r}} \left(\widetilde{r}^2 \frac{1}{\widetilde{q}} \frac{\partial \widetilde{q}}{\partial \widetilde{r}} \right) d\widetilde{r} = -e \widetilde{r}_e^2 \left[\frac{\partial \ln \widetilde{q}}{\partial \widetilde{r}} \right]_{\widetilde{r} = \widetilde{r}_p} \end{aligned} \quad (7.4.23)$$

or $(q_e = -e)$

$$\widetilde{r}_e^2 \left[\frac{\partial \ln \widetilde{q}}{\partial \widetilde{r}} \right]_{\widetilde{r} = \widetilde{r}_e} = 1. \quad (7.4.24)$$

For the best transparency of the problem, we intend to compare our results with the Schrödinger model (Schrödinger model of the year 1926, first communication). It means that we consider the stationary state of the electron shell having the radial symmetry without spin. Consider the interaction of two charged particles according to Coulomb's law. The stationary Schrödinger equation for the wave function of the system ψ_{sys} has the form

$$\frac{\hbar^2}{2m_e}\frac{\partial^2\psi_{sys}}{\partial r_e^2}+\frac{\hbar^2}{2m_c}\frac{\partial^2\psi_{sys}}{\partial r_c^2}+\left(E_{tot}+\frac{Ze^2}{r}\right)\psi_{sys}=0, \qquad (7.4.25)$$

here $r_e=|\mathbf{r}_e|$ and $r_c=|\mathbf{r}_c|$; $\mathbf{r}_e$ and $\mathbf{r}_c$ are the radius vectors of the electron and the nucleus (core) respectively, E_{tot} is the total energy of the system. Note that the dimension of the wave function is $\left[cm^{-d/2}\right]$, where d is the dimension of the problem. We introduce the position of the center of inertia of particles

$$\mathbf{R}=\frac{m_e\mathbf{r}_e+m_c\mathbf{r}_c}{m_e+m_c} \qquad (7.4.26)$$

and the electron relative to the nucleus

$$\mathbf{r}_{ec}=\mathbf{r}_e-\mathbf{r}_c \qquad (7.4.27)$$

Let's replace the variables in the differentiation operators in the left part (7.4.7)

$$\frac{\partial^2}{\partial r_e^2}=\frac{\partial^2}{\partial r_{ec}^2}+\left(\frac{m_e}{m_e+m_c}\right)\frac{\partial^2}{\partial R^2}, \qquad (7.4.28)$$

$$\frac{\partial^2}{\partial r_c^2}=\frac{\partial^2}{\partial r_{ec}^2}+\left(\frac{m_c}{m_e+m_c}\right)\frac{\partial^2}{\partial R^2}. \qquad (7.4.29)$$

Substituting (7.4.28) and (7.4.29) in (7.4.25), we come to the equation

$$\frac{\hbar^2}{2m_e}\left[\frac{\partial^2\psi_{sys}}{\partial r_{ec}^2}+\left(\frac{m_e}{m_e+m_c}\right)\frac{\partial^2\psi_{sys}}{\partial R^2}\right]+\frac{\hbar^2}{2m_c}\left[\frac{\partial^2\psi_{sys}}{\partial r_{ec}^2}+\left(\frac{m_c}{m_e+m_c}\right)\frac{\partial^2\psi_{sys}}{\partial R^2}\right]+\left(E_{tot}+\frac{Ze^2}{r_{ec}}\right)\psi_{sys}=0$$

(7.4.30)

or

$$\frac{\hbar^2}{2}\left(\frac{1}{m_e}+\frac{1}{m_c}\right)\left[\frac{\partial^2\psi_{sys}}{\partial r_{ec}^2}+\frac{\hbar^2}{2}\left(\frac{1}{m_e+m_c}\right)\frac{\partial^2\psi_{sys}}{\partial R^2}\right]+\left(E_{tot}+\frac{Ze^2}{r_{ec}}\right)\psi_{sys}=0. \qquad (7.4.31)$$

It allows for separation of variables. Imagine a wave function as a product

$$\psi_{sys}=\psi(r_{ec})\psi(R). \qquad (7.4.32)$$

After dividing (7.4.31) on $\psi_{sys}=\psi(r_{ec})\psi(R)$ we find:

$$\frac{\hbar^2}{2}\left(\frac{1}{m_e}+\frac{1}{m_c}\right)\frac{1}{\psi(r_{ec})}\frac{\partial^2\psi_{sys}}{\partial r_{ec}^2}+\left(E_{tot}+\frac{Ze^2}{r_{ec}}\right)=-\frac{\hbar^2}{2}\left(\frac{1}{m_e+m_c}\right)\frac{1}{\psi(R)}\frac{\partial^2\psi_{sys}}{\partial R^2}, \qquad (7.4.33)$$

The total energy E_{tot} of system is composed of its total electron energy E_{el} and the energy E_{cm} of the motion of the center of mass of the electron and the nucleus:

$$E_{tot}=E_{el}+E_{cm}. \qquad (7.4.34)$$

Then

$$\frac{\hbar^2}{2}\left(\frac{1}{m_e}+\frac{1}{m_c}\right)\frac{1}{\psi(r_{ec})}\frac{\partial^2\psi(r_{ec})}{\partial r_{ec}^2}+\left(E_{el}+\frac{Ze^2}{r_{ec}}\right)=-\frac{\hbar^2}{2}\frac{1}{m_e+m_c}\frac{1}{\psi(R)}\frac{\partial^2\psi(R)}{\partial R^2}-E_{cm}. \quad (7.4.35)$$

The left and right sides of the last equation depend on different variables, so each of them must be equal to a constant. Equation

$$\frac{\hbar^2}{2}\frac{1}{m_e+m_c}\frac{1}{\psi(R)}\frac{\partial^2\psi(R)}{\partial R^2}+E_{cm}=-const \quad (7.4.36)$$

and

$$\frac{\hbar^2}{2}\left(\frac{1}{m_e}+\frac{1}{m_c}\right)\frac{1}{\psi(r_{ec})}\frac{\partial^2\psi(r_{ec})}{\partial r_{ec}^2}+\left(E_e+\frac{Ze^2}{r_{ec}}\right)=const. \quad (7.4.37)$$

We can choose const equal to unit, it is connected only with choosing of the reference level for energy. If $m_e << m_c$, then the usual form of the Schrödinger equation can be used:

$$\frac{\hbar^2}{2m_e}\frac{\partial^2\psi(r_{ec})}{\partial r_{ec}^2}+\left(E_e+\frac{Ze^2}{r_{ec}}\right)\psi(r_{ec})=0. \quad (7.4.38)$$

Equation (7.4.36) describes the motion of the center of mass, and the equation (7.4.38) is the Schrödinger equation for relative electron motion in the Coulomb force field. In (7.4.20) practically the last traces of the nucleus are lost.

Operator $\frac{\partial^2}{\partial r_{ec}^2}$ is Laplace operator and in the spherical coordinate system leads to the equation

$$\frac{1}{r^2}\frac{\partial}{\partial r}\left(r^2\frac{\partial\psi}{\partial r}\right)+\frac{1}{r^2\sin\theta}\frac{\partial}{\partial\theta}\left(\sin\theta\frac{\partial\psi}{\partial r}\right)+\frac{1}{r^2\sin\theta}\frac{\partial^2\psi(r)}{\partial\varphi^2}+\frac{2m_e}{\hbar^2}\left(E_e+\frac{Ze^2}{r}\right)\psi=0. \quad (7.4.39)$$

In the case of the radial symmetry we have

$$\frac{1}{r^2}\frac{\partial}{\partial r}\left(r^2\frac{\partial\psi}{\partial r}\right)+\frac{2m_e}{\hbar^2}\left(E_e+\frac{Ze^2}{r}\right)\psi=0. \quad (7.4.40)$$

In the bound state, the energy of the particle E_e is taken to be negative. Instead, we will use the de Broglie wave number k_{dB}:

$$k_{dB}^2=-\frac{2m_eE_e}{\hbar^2}. \quad (7.4.41)$$

Let's enter the scale of the length

$$b=\frac{2Zm_ee^2}{\hbar^2}, \quad (7.4.42)$$

for hydrogen atom

$$b_H=\frac{2m_ee^2}{\hbar^2} \quad (7.4.43)$$

or

$$b_H = \frac{2}{a_0} \tag{7.4.44}$$

where a_0 is Bohr radius. In these notations equation (7.4.40) (written for the one dimension spherical system) takes the following standard form [116 – 120]:

$$\frac{\partial}{\partial r}\left(r^2\frac{\partial\psi}{\partial r}\right) = r^2\left(k_{dB}^2 - \frac{b}{r}\right)\psi \,. \tag{7.4.45}$$

Schrödinger-Madelung model leads (see (7.2.7), (7.2.10)) in stationary case for the rest electron transforms in the system of equations to equation

$$\frac{\hbar^2}{4m\rho}\left[\Delta\rho - \frac{1}{2\rho}\left(\frac{\partial\rho}{\partial\mathbf{r}}\right)^2\right] = U \,, \tag{7.4.46}$$

or

$$\frac{\hbar^2}{4m_e}\left[\Delta n - \frac{1}{2n}\left(\frac{\partial n}{\partial\mathbf{r}}\right)^2\right] = Un \tag{7.4.47}$$

or

$$\frac{\hbar^2}{4m_e}\left[\Delta q - \frac{1}{2q}\left(\frac{\partial q}{\partial\mathbf{r}}\right)^2\right] = \Psi q \tag{7.4.48}$$

As a result we have the following system of equations written in the dimensionless form

$$\frac{\partial^2\tilde{q}}{\partial\tilde{r}^2} + \frac{2}{\tilde{r}}\frac{\partial\tilde{q}}{\partial\tilde{r}} - \frac{1}{2\tilde{q}}\left(\frac{\partial\tilde{q}}{\partial\tilde{r}}\right)^2 - \tilde{\Psi}\tilde{q} = 0 \,, \tag{7.4.49}$$

$$\frac{\partial^2\tilde{\Psi}}{\partial\tilde{r}^2} + \frac{2}{\tilde{r}}\frac{\partial\tilde{\Psi}}{\partial\tilde{r}} = 4\pi\tilde{q} \,, \tag{7.4.50}$$

for the following scales $q_0 = \frac{e}{r_0^3}, \Psi_0 = \frac{e}{r_0}, \; r_0 = \frac{\hbar^2}{4m_e e}$.

Figures 7.4.7 and 7.4.8 reflect the solutions of equations (7.4.49), (7.4.50) for the Madelung model.

```
dsolve[interactive]({
t*diff(diff(q(t),t),t)+2*diff(q(t),t)-
t*(diff(q(t),t))^2/(2*q(t))=t*q(t)*v(t),
t*diff(diff(v(t),t),t)+2*diff(q(t),t)=4*P*t*q(t),
q(0)=exp(-1),D(q)(0)=0, v(0)=1, D(v)(0)=0
});
```

$P = \pi$.

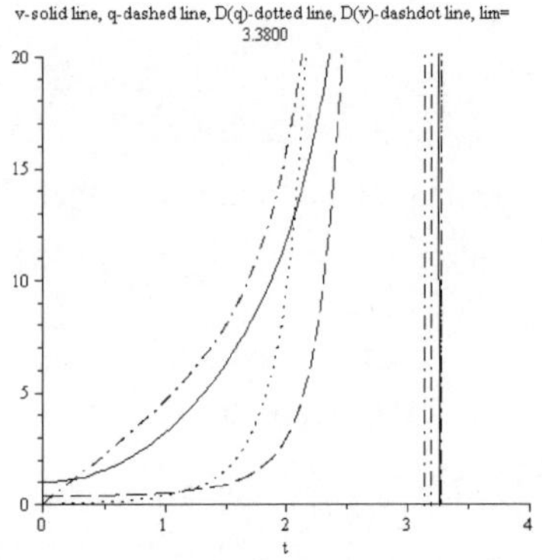

Fig. 7.4.7. Evolution potential $\mathrm{v} \to \widetilde{\Psi}(\widetilde{r})$, charge density $\mathrm{q} \to \widetilde{q}(\widetilde{r})$, charge density derivative $\mathrm{D(q)} \to \dfrac{\partial \widetilde{q}}{\partial \widetilde{r}}$ and potential derivative $\mathrm{D(v)} \to \dfrac{\partial \widetilde{\Psi}}{\partial \widetilde{r}}$.

```
dsolve[interactive]({
t*diff(diff(q(t), t), t) + 2*diff(q(t),
    t) -t*(diff(q(t), t))^2/(2*q(t))
    = t*q(t)*v(t),
t*diff(diff(v(t), t), t) + 2*diff(q(t), t)
    = 4*P*t*q(t),
v(0) = 1/10^8, D(v)(0) = 0, q(0) = 1
    /10^8, D(q)(0) = 0
});
```

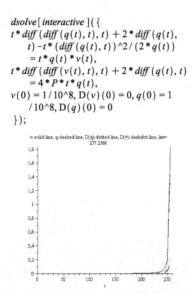

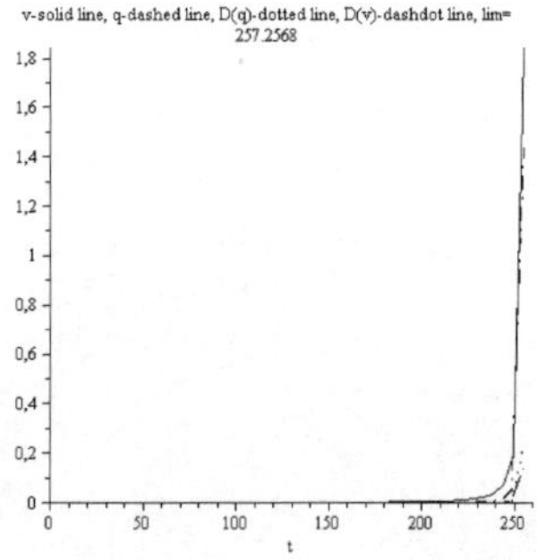

Fig. 7.4.8. Evolution potential $\mathrm{v} \to \widetilde{\Psi}(\widetilde{r})$, charge density $\mathrm{q} \to \widetilde{q}(\widetilde{r})$, charge density derivative $\mathrm{D(q)} \to \dfrac{\partial \widetilde{q}}{\partial \widetilde{r}}$ and potential derivative $\mathrm{D(v)} \to \dfrac{\partial \widetilde{\Psi}}{\partial \widetilde{r}}$.

On the whole, the nature of the change in the curves of the potential, derivative of the potential, and charge density in the nonlocal model and the Madelung hydrodynamics is similar. However, the areas where the solution exists are very different. For the calculation of the potential evolution in the frame of nonlocal model we needn't the value of the charge magnitude in the center of the electron (compare (7.4.15) and (7.4.49), (7.4.50)).

7.5. Two component atom structure

Let us write down now the system of the generalized hydrodynamic equations in the spherical coordinate system for the one dimensional non-stationary case.

Poisson equation should be added

$$\frac{1}{r^2}\frac{\partial}{\partial r}\left(r^2\frac{\partial\Psi}{\partial r}\right)=-4\pi e\left\{\left[n_i-\tau_i\frac{1}{r^2}\frac{\partial\left(r^2 n_i v_{0r}\right)}{\partial r}\right]-\left[n_e-\tau_e\frac{1}{r^2}\frac{\partial\left(r^2 n_e v_{0r}\right)}{\partial r}\right]\right\}, \quad (7.5.1)$$

where n_i, n_e - number densities, $\mathbf{v}_0$ - hydrodynamic velocity, Ψ - scalar electric potential, e is absolute value of the electron charge.

Continuity equation for ions

$$\frac{\partial}{\partial t}\left\{\rho_i-\tau_i\left[\frac{\partial\rho_i}{\partial t}+\frac{1}{r^2}\frac{\partial\left(r^2\rho_i v_{0r}\right)}{\partial r}\right]\right\}$$

$$+\frac{1}{r^2}\frac{\partial}{\partial r}\left\{r^2\left\{\rho_i v_{0r}-\tau\left[\frac{\partial}{\partial t}\left(\rho_i v_{0r}\right)+\frac{1}{r^2}\frac{\partial\left(r^2\rho_i v_{0r}^2\right)}{\partial r}+q_\alpha\frac{\partial\Psi}{\partial r}\right]\right\}\right\}-\frac{1}{r^2}\frac{\partial}{\partial r}\left(\tau r^2\frac{\partial p}{\partial r}\right)=0, \quad (7.5.2)$$

Continuity equation for electrons

$$\frac{\partial}{\partial t}\left\{\rho_e-\tau\left[\frac{\partial\rho_e}{\partial t}+\frac{1}{r^2}\frac{\partial\left(r^2\rho_e v_{0r}\right)}{\partial r}\right]\right\}$$

$$+\frac{1}{r^2}\frac{\partial}{\partial r}\left\{r^2\left\{\rho_e v_{0r}-\tau\left[\frac{\partial}{\partial t}\left(\rho_e v_{0r}\right)+\frac{1}{r^2}\frac{\partial\left(r^2\rho_e v_{0r}^2\right)}{\partial r}+q_\alpha\frac{\partial\Psi}{\partial r}\right]\right\}\right\}-\frac{1}{r^2}\frac{\partial}{\partial r}\left(\tau r^2\frac{\partial p}{\partial r}\right)=0, \quad (7.5.3)$$

where

$$q_\alpha=e_\alpha n_\alpha \quad (7.5.4)$$

and e_α is charge of the α-particles, n_α is the number density of the α-species, Ψ is potential related to the unit of charge. The system of the one dimensional non-stationary equations for a many species charged objects in rest $((\mathbf{v}_0=0)$ is written as

Poisson equation:

$$\frac{1}{r^2}\frac{\partial}{\partial r}\left(r^2\frac{\partial \Psi}{\partial r}\right) = -4\pi(n_i - n_e), \qquad (7.5.5)$$

- continuity equation

$$\frac{\partial}{\partial t}\left[\rho_\alpha - \tau_\alpha \frac{\partial \rho_\alpha}{\partial t}\right] - \frac{1}{r^2}\frac{\partial}{\partial r}\left[r^2\tau_\alpha\left(q_\alpha\frac{\partial \Psi}{\partial r} + \frac{\partial p_\alpha}{\partial r}\right)\right] = 0, \qquad (7.5.6)$$

- momentum equation, $\mathbf{e}_r$ projection

$$-\frac{\partial}{\partial t}\left\{\tau_\alpha\left[\frac{\partial p_\alpha}{\partial r} + q_\alpha\frac{\partial \Psi}{\partial r}\right]\right\} + \frac{q_\alpha}{\rho_\alpha}\frac{\partial \Psi}{\partial r}\left[\rho_\alpha - \tau_\alpha\left(\frac{\partial \rho_\alpha}{\partial t}\right)\right]$$

$$+\frac{\partial p_\alpha}{\partial r} - \frac{\partial}{\partial r}\left(\tau_\alpha\frac{\partial p_\alpha}{\partial t}\right) = \int m_\alpha v_{\alpha r} J_\alpha^{st,el} d\mathbf{v}_\alpha + \int m_\alpha v_{\alpha r} J_\alpha^{st,inel} d\mathbf{v}_\alpha, \qquad (7.5.7)$$

- energy equation

$$\frac{\partial}{\partial t}\left\{\varepsilon_\alpha n_\alpha + \frac{3}{2}p_\alpha - \tau_\alpha\frac{\partial}{\partial t}\left(\varepsilon_\alpha n_\alpha + \frac{3}{2}p_\alpha\right)\right\} + \tau_\alpha\frac{q_\alpha}{\rho_\alpha}\frac{\partial \Psi}{\partial r}\left(\frac{\partial p_\alpha}{\partial r} + q_\alpha\frac{\partial \Psi}{\partial r}\right)$$

$$-\frac{1}{r^2}\frac{\partial}{\partial r}\left\{\tau_\alpha r^2\left[\frac{\partial}{\partial r}\left[\frac{p_\alpha}{\rho_\alpha}\left(\frac{5}{2}p_\alpha + \varepsilon_\alpha n_\alpha\right)\right] + \left(\frac{5}{2}p_\alpha + \varepsilon_\alpha n_\alpha\right)\frac{q_\alpha}{\rho_\alpha}\frac{\partial \Psi}{\partial r}\right]\right\} = \qquad (7.5.8)$$

$$\int\left(\frac{m_\alpha v_\alpha^2}{2} + \varepsilon_\alpha\right)J_\alpha^{st,el} d\mathbf{v}_\alpha.$$

In nonlocal quantum hydrodynamics internal energy ε_α is proportional to spin of particles α,

for electron $\varepsilon_{el} = \frac{\hbar}{2}\left(\omega \pm \frac{e}{m_e c}B\right)$, if $\mathbf{B}$ is directed along the spin direction.

After multiplication continuity equation (7.5.6) by ε_α we find

$$\frac{\partial}{\partial t}\left[\varepsilon_\alpha n_\alpha - \tau_\alpha\frac{\partial \varepsilon_\alpha n_\alpha}{\partial t}\right] - \frac{1}{r^2}\frac{\partial}{\partial r}\left[r^2\tau_\alpha\left(\frac{q_\alpha}{m_\alpha}\varepsilon_\alpha\frac{\partial \Psi}{\partial r} + \frac{\varepsilon_\alpha}{m_\alpha}\frac{\partial p_\alpha}{\partial r}\right)\right] = 0. \qquad (7.5.9)$$

Subtract the equation (7.5.9) by term from the equation (7.5.8)

$$\frac{3}{2}\frac{\partial}{\partial t}\left\{p_\alpha - \tau_\alpha\frac{\partial p_\alpha}{\partial t}\right\} + \tau_\alpha\frac{q_\alpha}{\rho_\alpha}\frac{\partial \Psi}{\partial r}\left(\frac{\partial p_\alpha}{\partial r} + q_\alpha\frac{\partial \Psi}{\partial r}\right)$$

$$-\frac{1}{r^2}\frac{\partial}{\partial r}\left\{\tau_\alpha r^2\left[\frac{\partial}{\partial r}\left[\frac{p_\alpha}{\rho_\alpha}\left(\frac{5}{2}p_\alpha + \varepsilon_\alpha n_\alpha\right)\right] + \left(\frac{5}{2}p_\alpha + \varepsilon_\alpha n_\alpha\right)\frac{q_\alpha}{\rho_\alpha}\frac{\partial \Psi}{\partial r}\right]\right\} + \qquad (7.5.10)$$

$$+\frac{1}{r^2}\frac{\partial}{\partial r}\left[r^2\tau_\alpha\left(\frac{q_\alpha}{m_\alpha}\varepsilon_\alpha\frac{\partial \Psi}{\partial r} + \frac{\varepsilon_\alpha}{m_\alpha}\frac{\partial p_\alpha}{\partial r}\right)\right] = \int\left(\frac{m_\alpha v_\alpha^2}{2} + \varepsilon_\alpha\right)J_\alpha^{st,el} d\mathbf{v}_\alpha.$$

or

$$\frac{3}{2}\frac{\partial}{\partial t}\left\{p_\alpha-\tau_\alpha\frac{\partial p_\alpha}{\partial t}\right\}+\tau_\alpha\frac{q_\alpha}{\rho_\alpha}\frac{\partial\Psi}{\partial r}\left(\frac{\partial p_\alpha}{\partial r}+q_\alpha\frac{\partial\Psi}{\partial r}\right)$$
$$-\frac{1}{r^2}\frac{\partial}{\partial r}\left\{\tau_\alpha r^2\frac{\partial}{\partial r}\left[\frac{p_\alpha}{\rho_\alpha}\left(\frac{5}{2}p_\alpha+\varepsilon_\alpha n_\alpha\right)\right]\right\}- \tag{7.5.11}$$
$$-\frac{1}{r^2}\frac{\partial}{\partial r}\left\{\tau_\alpha r^2\left[\frac{5}{2}p_\alpha\frac{q_\alpha}{\rho_\alpha}\frac{\partial\Psi}{\partial r}-\frac{\varepsilon_\alpha}{m_\alpha}\frac{\partial p_\alpha}{\partial r}\right]\right\}=\int\left(\frac{m_\alpha v_\alpha^2}{2}+\varepsilon_\alpha\right)J_\alpha^{st,el}d\mathbf{v}_\alpha.$$

For the particular case of the one species system it follows from (7.5.11)

$$\frac{3}{2}\frac{\partial}{\partial t}\left\{p-\tau\frac{\partial p}{\partial t}\right\}+\tau\frac{q}{\rho}\frac{\partial\Psi}{\partial r}\left(\frac{\partial p}{\partial r}+q\frac{\partial\Psi}{\partial r}\right)$$
$$-\frac{1}{r^2}\frac{\partial}{\partial r}\left\{\tau r^2\frac{\partial}{\partial r}\left[\frac{p}{\rho}\left(\frac{5}{2}p+\varepsilon n\right)\right]\right\}-\frac{1}{r^2}\frac{\partial}{\partial r}\left\{\tau r^2\left[\frac{5}{2}p\frac{q}{\rho}\frac{\partial\Psi}{\partial r}-\frac{\varepsilon}{m}\frac{\partial p}{\partial r}\right]\right\}=0. \tag{7.5.12}$$

For the Schrödinger model $\varepsilon_\alpha=0$. We have energy equation

$$\frac{3}{2}\frac{\partial}{\partial t}\left\{p_\alpha-\tau_\alpha\frac{\partial}{\partial t}p_\alpha\right\}+\tau_\alpha\frac{q_\alpha}{\rho_\alpha}\frac{\partial\Psi}{\partial r}\left(\frac{\partial p_\alpha}{\partial r}+q_\alpha\frac{\partial\Psi}{\partial r}\right)$$
$$-\frac{5}{2}\frac{1}{r^2}\frac{\partial}{\partial r}\left\{\tau_\alpha r^2\left[\frac{\partial}{\partial r}\left(\frac{p_\alpha^2}{\rho_\alpha}\right)+p_\alpha\frac{q_\alpha}{\rho_\alpha}\frac{\partial\Psi}{\partial r}\right]\right\}=\int\frac{m_\alpha v_\alpha^2}{2}J_\alpha^{st,el}d\mathbf{v}_\alpha. \tag{7.5.13}$$

Let us notice:

1. The solution of non-local equations for the spherically symmetric plasma object is considered; this object is in the rest, the external magnetic field is absent, but the self- consistent electric field is taken into account.
2. In many cases the final formulation of the problem contains only the external parameters of the system and *doesn't contain the non-local parameters*. The mentioned solutions lead to appearance of objects like solitons with the separated negative and positive parts placed in the finite space domain.
3. The solution has the self-consistent character and no needs to formulate the boundary conditions on infinity.

The consideration of the stationary case leads to the following simplification of the system of equations:

$$\frac{1}{r^2}\frac{\partial}{\partial r}\left(r^2\frac{\partial\Psi}{\partial r}\right)=-4\pi(n_i-n_e), \tag{7.5.14}$$

$$q_\alpha\frac{\partial\Psi}{\partial r}+\frac{\partial p_\alpha}{\partial r}=0, \tag{7.5.15}$$

$$q_\alpha\frac{\partial\Psi}{\partial r}+\frac{\partial p_\alpha}{\partial r}=\int m_\alpha v_{\alpha r}J_\alpha^{st,el}d\mathbf{v}_\alpha+\int m_\alpha v_{\alpha r}J_\alpha^{st,inel}d\mathbf{v}_\alpha, \tag{7.5.16}$$

$$\tau_\alpha \frac{q_\alpha}{\rho_\alpha}\frac{\partial \Psi}{\partial r}\left(\frac{\partial p_\alpha}{\partial r}+q_\alpha \frac{\partial \Psi}{\partial r}\right)$$
$$-\frac{5}{2}\frac{1}{r^2}\frac{\partial}{\partial r}\left\{\tau_\alpha r^2\left[\frac{\partial}{\partial r}\left(\frac{p_\alpha^2}{\rho_\alpha}\right)+p_\alpha \frac{q_\alpha}{\rho_\alpha}\frac{\partial \Psi}{\partial r}\right]\right\}=\int \frac{m_\alpha v_\alpha^2}{2} J_\alpha^{st,el} d\mathbf{v}_\alpha, \tag{7.5.17}$$

where Ψ - scalar electric potential (acting on the unit of charge) and q_α is a value of charge (with the corresponding sign) per the unit of volume; $q_\alpha = \pm e n_\alpha$, e is the absolute electron charge.

Using (7.5.15) we find from (7.5.17)

$$-\frac{5}{2}\frac{1}{r^2}\frac{\partial}{\partial r}\left\{\tau_\alpha r^2\left[\frac{\partial}{\partial r}\left(\frac{p_\alpha^2}{\rho_\alpha}\right)+p_\alpha \frac{q_\alpha}{\rho_\alpha}\frac{\partial \Psi}{\partial r}\right]\right\}=\int \frac{m_\alpha v_\alpha^2}{2} J_\alpha^{st,el} d\mathbf{v}_\alpha \tag{7.5.18}$$

or

$$-\frac{5}{2}\frac{1}{r^2}\frac{\partial}{\partial r}\left\{\tau_\alpha r^2\left[\frac{p_\alpha}{\rho_\alpha}\frac{\partial p_\alpha}{\partial r}+p_\alpha \frac{\partial}{\partial r}\left(\frac{p_\alpha}{\rho_\alpha}\right)+p_\alpha \frac{q_\alpha}{\rho_\alpha}\frac{\partial \Psi}{\partial r}\right]\right\}=\int \frac{m_\alpha v_\alpha^2}{2} J_\alpha^{st,el} d\mathbf{v}_\alpha. \tag{7.5.19}$$

or using (7.5.15)

$$-\frac{5}{2}\frac{1}{r^2}\frac{\partial}{\partial r}\left\{\tau_\alpha r^2 p_\alpha \frac{\partial}{\partial r}\left(\frac{p_\alpha}{\rho_\alpha}\right)\right\}=\int \frac{m_\alpha v_\alpha^2}{2} J_\alpha^{st,el} d\mathbf{v}_\alpha. \tag{7.5.20}$$

Collision integral in the right side of (7.5.20) corresponds to the energy rate of the α species per unit volume per unit time. Then we have the following system of equations:

$$q_\alpha \frac{\partial \Psi}{\partial r}+\frac{\partial p_\alpha}{\partial r}=0, \tag{7.5.21}$$

$$\frac{1}{r^2}\frac{\partial}{\partial r}\left(r^2 \frac{\partial \Psi}{\partial r}\right)=-4\pi(n_i-n_e), \tag{7.5.22}$$

$$\frac{1}{r^2}\frac{\partial}{\partial r}\left\{\tau_\alpha r^2 p_\alpha \frac{\partial}{\partial r}\left(\frac{p_\alpha}{\rho_\alpha}\right)\right\}=-\frac{2}{5}\int \frac{m_\alpha v_\alpha^2}{2} J_\alpha^{st,el} d\mathbf{v}_\alpha. \tag{7.5.23}$$

Nonlocal kinetic equation is more complicated from the mathematical point of view than Boltzmann equation. But local part of collision integrals in nonlocal and Boltzmann models are the same. In this regard, it is important to search for and develop various alternatives approaches based on certain simplifications of the local collision integral. One of such simplifications is the approximation of the collision integral by the relaxation models. Currently, many different models have been developed, the most popular are the model Bhatnagar – Gross – Krook (BGK) [121], ellipsoidal statistical model (ES) [122], Shakhov model (S-model) [123] and models with a frequency depending on the molecular velocity [124, 125]. BGK model is in particular the approximating model of the first approximation for pseudo-Maxwell molecules. One of the significant drawbacks of this approximation is the wrong value of the Prandtl number Pr in the transition to the hydrodynamic regime. Nevertheless, this is a very important model that gives the correct qualitative behavior of the kinetic solution and on its basis an effective method for calculation was created. To obtain the correct Prandtl number, an ellipsoidal statistical model was proposed in [122], and several other models. Practically all models lead in Boltzmann theory to a modification of Π-parameter in (1.2.10) like

$$\Pi = 1 - \lambda, \tag{7.5.24}$$

where $-0.5 \le \lambda < 1$. For the integral collision terms we can use an analog of the BGK approximation.

For adiabatic case Ehrenfest supposes that (see also (1.2.30))

$$2\overline{T}\tau = \Omega_1, \Omega_2, ... \tag{7.5.25}$$

where $\Omega_1, \Omega_2, ...$ are adiabatic invariants. Obviously for Plank's oscillator

$$2\overline{T}\tau = nh. \tag{7.5.26}$$

Obviously, each exactly conserved (invariant) quantity is an adiabatic invariant. For example L. Brillouin (Chapter 7 "Boltzmann's formula and adiabatic invariants" in [126, see also 127]) writes "We have shown that for all systems that are capable of oscillating in accord with a purely-sinusoidal law, the quantity τE will be an adiabatic invariant, where E represents the total energy. It was to such systems that Planck first applied the idea of quanta by writing that

$$\tau E = \frac{E}{\upsilon} = nh, \ n \text{ integer}. \tag{7.5.27}$$

For these pure oscillators, the total energy will then be equal to an integer number times $h\upsilon$."

Then the adiabatic theorem and consequences of this theory deliver the general quantization conditions for non-local quantum hydrodynamics, in particular

$$\tau_e = \frac{n}{\upsilon_e} \text{ for electronic shell,} \tag{7.5.28}$$

$$\tau_e = \frac{k}{\upsilon_i} \text{ for nucleus,} \tag{7.5.29}$$

where n is shell quantum number and k is nucleus quantum number.

Then the adiabatic theorem and consequences of this theory deliver the general quantization conditions for non-local quantum hydrodynamics.

In the modified BGK approximation we reach the system of equations (indexes "i" and "e" can be treated also as corresponding to internal (nucleus) and external (shell) areas:

$$\frac{5}{2}\frac{\partial}{\partial r}\left\{r^2 p_i \tau_i \frac{\partial}{\partial r}\left(\frac{p_i}{n_i}\right)\right\} = m_i \frac{p_i - p_e}{\tau_{ei}} r^2, \tag{7.5.30}$$

$$\frac{5}{2}\frac{\partial}{\partial r}\left\{r^2 p_e \tau_e \frac{\partial}{\partial r}\left(\frac{p_e}{n_e}\right)\right\} = m_e \frac{p_e - p_i}{\tau_{ei}} r^2, \tag{7.5.31}$$

$$e n_i \frac{\partial \Psi}{\partial r} + \frac{\partial p_i}{\partial r} = 0, \tag{7.5.32}$$

$$- e n_e \frac{\partial \Psi}{\partial r} + \frac{\partial p_e}{\partial r} = 0, \tag{7.5.33}$$

$$\frac{\partial}{\partial r}\left(r^2 \frac{\partial \Psi}{\partial r}\right) = -4\pi [n_i - n_e] r^2. \tag{7.5.34}$$

In the frame of local physics $(\tau_e = 0, \tau_i = 0, \tau_{ei} = 0)$ *we have from* (7.5.30) - (7.5.34) *only trivial solutions, namely*

$$p_e = p_i,\ n_i = n_e,\ \Psi = const. \tag{7.5.35}$$

Equations (7.5.30) - (7.5.34) can be rewritten in the hydrodynamic dimensionless form using the scales: n_0, p_0, Ψ_0, r_0. Equations (7.5.30) - (7.5.34) take the form

$$- e\frac{n_0 \Psi_0}{p_0} \widetilde{n}_e \frac{\partial \widetilde{\Psi}}{\partial \widetilde{r}} + \frac{\partial \widetilde{p}_e}{\partial \widetilde{r}} = 0, \tag{7.5.36}$$

$$e\frac{n_0 \Psi_0}{p_0} \widetilde{n}_i \frac{\partial \widetilde{\Psi}}{\partial \widetilde{r}} + \frac{\partial \widetilde{p}_i}{\partial \widetilde{r}} = 0, \tag{7.5.37}$$

$$\frac{\Psi_0}{4\pi n_0 r_0^2} \frac{1}{\widetilde{r}^2} \frac{\partial}{\partial \widetilde{r}}\left(\widetilde{r}^2 \frac{\partial \widetilde{\Psi}}{\partial \widetilde{r}}\right) = -[\widetilde{n}_i - \widetilde{n}_e]. \tag{7.5.38}$$

Let us introduce the dimensionless coefficients

$$e\frac{n_0 \Psi_0}{p_0} = \mathrm{B} \tag{7.5.39}$$

and

$$\mathrm{A}^{-1} = \frac{\Psi_0}{4\pi r_0^2 n_0}. \tag{7.5.40}$$

We find the following system of equations

$$- \mathrm{B} \widetilde{n}_e \frac{\partial \widetilde{\Psi}}{\partial \widetilde{r}} + \frac{\partial \widetilde{p}_e}{\partial \widetilde{r}} = 0, \tag{7.5.41}$$

$$\mathrm{B} \widetilde{n}_i \frac{\partial \widetilde{\Psi}}{\partial \widetilde{r}} + \frac{\partial \widetilde{p}_i}{\partial \widetilde{r}} = 0, \tag{7.5.42}$$

$$\frac{1}{\widetilde{r}^2} \frac{\partial}{\partial \widetilde{r}}\left(\widetilde{r}^2 \frac{\partial \widetilde{\Psi}}{\partial \widetilde{r}}\right) = -\mathrm{A}[\widetilde{n}_i - \widetilde{n}_e]. \tag{7.5.43}$$

$$\frac{5}{2}\tau_i \tau_{ei} \frac{p_0}{m_i n_0 r_0^2} \frac{\partial}{\partial \widetilde{r}}\left\{\widetilde{r}^2 \widetilde{p}_i \frac{\partial}{\partial \widetilde{r}}\left(\frac{\widetilde{p}_i}{\widetilde{n}_i}\right)\right\} = (\widetilde{p}_i - \widetilde{p}_e)\widetilde{r}^2, \tag{7.5.44}$$

$$\frac{5}{2}\tau_e\tau_{ei}\frac{p_0}{m_e n_0 r_0^2}\frac{\partial}{\partial\tilde{r}}\left\{\tilde{r}^2\tilde{p}_e\frac{\partial}{\partial\tilde{r}}\left(\frac{\tilde{p}_e}{\tilde{n}_e}\right)\right\}=(\tilde{p}_e-\tilde{p}_i)\tilde{r}^2, \qquad (7.5.45)$$

Let us introduce the nonlocal kinematic viscosities

$$\nu_i=\frac{5}{2}\tau_{ei}\frac{p_0}{m_i n_0}, \qquad (7.5.46)$$

$$\nu_e=\frac{5}{2}\tau_{ei}\frac{p_0}{m_e n_0} \qquad (7.5.47)$$

and nonlocal Reynolds numbers using the definitions

$$\mathrm{Re}_i=LV_i/\nu_i, \qquad (7.5.48)$$

$$\mathrm{Re}_e=LV_e/\nu_e, \qquad (7.5.49)$$

where the linear scale is $L=r_0$, character velocities $V_i=r_0/\tau_i$, $V_e=r_0/\tau_e$. Then equations (7.5.44), (7.5.45) and (7.5.43) take the hydrodynamic form and we three equations of the BGK type. Then we have the transformed system of equations

$$\frac{1}{\mathrm{Re}_i}\frac{\partial}{\partial\tilde{r}}\left[\tilde{r}^2\tilde{p}_i\frac{\partial}{\partial\tilde{r}}\left(\frac{\tilde{p}_i}{\tilde{n}_i}\right)\right]=\tilde{r}^2(\tilde{p}_i-\tilde{p}_e), \qquad (7.5.50)$$

$$\frac{1}{\mathrm{Re}_e}\frac{\partial}{\partial\tilde{r}}\left[\tilde{r}^2\tilde{p}_e\frac{\partial}{\partial\tilde{r}}\left(\frac{\tilde{p}_e}{\tilde{n}_e}\right)\right]=\tilde{r}^2(\tilde{p}_e-\tilde{p}_i). \qquad (7.5.51)$$

$$\frac{1}{\mathrm{A}}\frac{\partial}{\partial\tilde{r}}\left(\tilde{r}^2\frac{\partial\tilde{\Psi}}{\partial\tilde{r}}\right)=\tilde{r}^2[\tilde{n}_e-\tilde{n}_i]. \qquad (7.5.52)$$

and equations (7.5.41), (7.5.42). In the frame of the developed theory the Poisson equation now is not more than one of the BGK equations in the chosen approximation. It is interesting to notice an analogy between Poisson equation (7.5.52) and Schrödinger equation (7.4.45).

Then $\frac{1}{\mathrm{Re}_i}$, $\frac{1}{\mathrm{Re}_e}$, $\frac{1}{A}$ are dimensionless relaxation times for the collision integrals in (7.5.20) and the $\tilde{\Psi}$ rate. We find the system of equations of the hydrodynamic type (7.5.50) – (7.5.52) and (7.5.41), (7.5.42) with hydrodynamic parameters $\mathrm{A},\mathrm{B},\mathrm{Re}_i,\mathrm{Re}_e$.

We have the equations written as complete system

$$\frac{1}{\mathrm{Re}_i}\frac{\partial}{\partial\tilde{r}}\left[\tilde{r}^2\tilde{p}_i\frac{\partial}{\partial\tilde{r}}\left(\frac{\tilde{p}_i}{\tilde{n}_i}\right)\right]=\tilde{r}^2(\tilde{p}_i-\tilde{p}_e), \qquad (7.5.53)$$

$$\frac{1}{\mathrm{Re}_e}\frac{\partial}{\partial\tilde{r}}\left[\tilde{r}^2\tilde{p}_e\frac{\partial}{\partial\tilde{r}}\left(\frac{\tilde{p}_e}{\tilde{n}_e}\right)\right]=\tilde{r}^2(\tilde{p}_e-\tilde{p}_i). \qquad (7.5.54)$$

$$\frac{1}{\mathrm{A}}\frac{\partial}{\partial\tilde{r}}\left(\tilde{r}^2\frac{\partial\tilde{\Psi}}{\partial\tilde{r}}\right)=\tilde{r}^2[\tilde{n}_e-\tilde{n}_i]. \qquad (7.5.55)$$

$$- B\widetilde{n}_e \frac{\partial \widetilde{\Psi}}{\partial \widetilde{r}} + \frac{\partial \widetilde{p}_e}{\partial \widetilde{r}} = 0, \qquad (7.5.56)$$

$$B\widetilde{n}_i \frac{\partial \widetilde{\Psi}}{\partial \widetilde{r}} + \frac{\partial \widetilde{p}_i}{\partial \widetilde{r}} = 0, \qquad (7.5.57)$$

In the following Maple program $C \leftrightarrow \mathrm{Re}_i$, $E \leftrightarrow \mathrm{Re}_e$.

```
dsolve[interactive]({
-B*diff(s(t),t)*diff(v(t),t)-
B*s(t)*diff(v(t),t$2)+diff(q(t),t$2)=0,
B*diff(r(t),t)*diff(v(t),t)+B*r(t)*diff(v(t),t$2)+
diff(p(t),t$2)=0,
diff(t^2*diff(v(t),t),t)=-A*t^2*(r(t)-s(t)),
(1/C)*diff(t^2*p(t)*diff(p(t)/r(t),t),t)=t^2*(p(t)-
q(t)),
(1/E)*diff(t^2*q(t)*diff(q(t)/s(t),t),t)=t^2*(q(t)-
p(t)),

v(0)=1,D(v)(0)=0, r(0)=1, D(r)(0)=0, s(0)=0.01,
D(s)(0)=0,
p(0)=1, q(0)=0.9, D(p)(0)=0, D(q)(0)=0
    });
```

Let us introduce now quantization in the developed theory. The following transformations lead to quantization of the mentioned Reynolds numbers. Let us use now the discussed before the quantum adiabatic approximations for nonlocal parameters (7.5.28), (7.5.29). We obtain

$$\frac{5}{2}\frac{\partial}{\partial \widetilde{r}}\left\{\widetilde{r}^2 \widetilde{p}_i \frac{\partial}{\partial \widetilde{r}}\left(\frac{\widetilde{p}_i}{\widetilde{n}_i}\right)\right\} = \frac{m_i}{M}(\widetilde{p}_i - \widetilde{p}_e)\frac{\widetilde{\upsilon}_i}{k}\left[\frac{\widetilde{\upsilon}_e}{n} + \frac{\widetilde{\upsilon}_i}{k}\right]\widetilde{r}^2, \qquad (7.5.58)$$

$$\frac{5}{2}\frac{\partial}{\partial \widetilde{r}}\left\{\widetilde{r}^2 \widetilde{p}_e \frac{\partial}{\partial \widetilde{r}}\left(\frac{\widetilde{p}_e}{\widetilde{n}_e}\right)\right\} = \frac{m_e}{M}(\widetilde{p}_e - \widetilde{p}_i)\frac{\widetilde{\upsilon}_e}{n}\left[\frac{\widetilde{\upsilon}_e}{n} + \frac{\widetilde{\upsilon}_i}{k}\right]\widetilde{r}^2, \qquad (7.5.59)$$

where the following notation is introduced for the mass scale:

$$M = \frac{p_0}{r_0^2 n_0 \upsilon_0^2}. \qquad (7.5.60)$$

Comparing (7.5.44) and (7.5.55) we find

$$\mathrm{Re}_i = \frac{2}{5}\frac{m_i}{M}\frac{\widetilde{\upsilon}_i}{k}\left[\frac{\widetilde{\upsilon}_e}{n} + \frac{\widetilde{\upsilon}_i}{k}\right], \qquad (7.5.61)$$

and comparing (7.5.45) and (7.5.56)

$$\mathrm{Re}_e = \frac{2}{5}\frac{m_e}{M}\frac{\tilde{\upsilon}_e}{n}\left[\frac{\tilde{\upsilon}_e}{n} + \frac{\tilde{\upsilon}_i}{k}\right]. \qquad (7.5.62)$$

We will start with the study of the problem of fundamental importance – is it possible after the primary perturbation determined by Cauchy conditions to obtain an object of the soliton type located in a limited area of space and being a product of self-organization of ionized matter?

Some typical calculations are displayed on figures 7.5.1 – 7.5.7. The following Maple notations on figures are used: v – potential $\tilde{\Psi}$, s - $\tilde{n}_e$, r - $\tilde{n}_i$, q - $\tilde{p}_e$, p - $\tilde{p}_i$ and t – independent variable $\tilde{r}$. The system of external parameters A, B, Re_e, Re_i leads to the vast possibilities of mathematical modeling. Explanations placed under all following figures. In all numerical examples we use Cauchy conditions

```
v(0)=1,D(v)(0)=D(q)(0)=D(p)(0)=D(r)(0)=D(s)(0)=0,
s(0)=0.01, r(0)=1
```

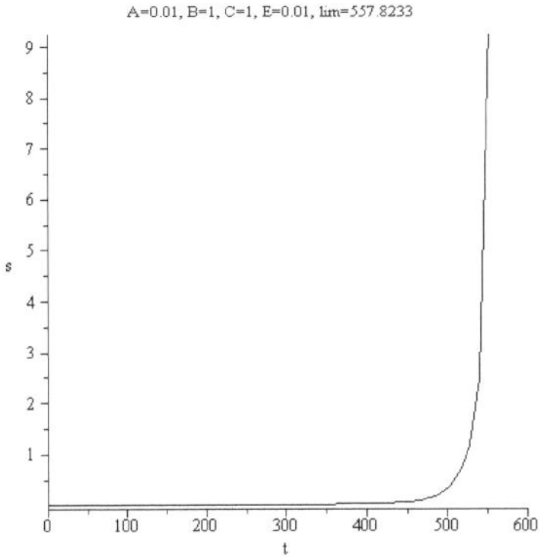

Fig. 7.5.1. Dependence $s(t) \leftrightarrow \tilde{n}_e(\tilde{r})$, $\tilde{p}_i(0)=1$, $\tilde{p}_e(0)=0.9$, $\tilde{r}_{\lim}=557.8233$.

$A=0.01$, $\mathrm{Re}_e=0.01$, $\mathrm{Re}_i=1$

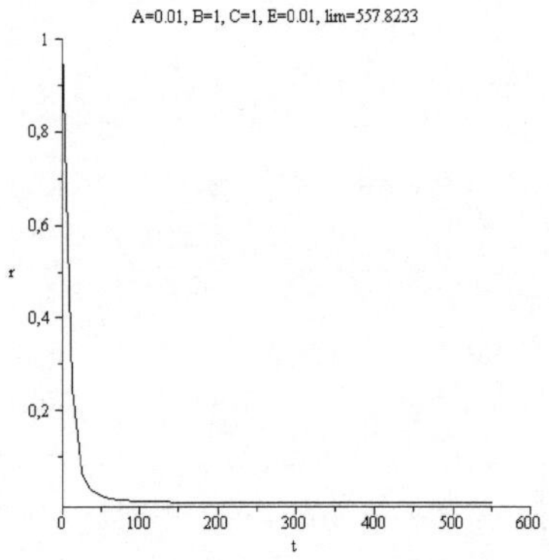

Fig. 7.5.2. Dependence $\mathrm{r(t)} \leftrightarrow \tilde{n}_i(\tilde{r})$, $\tilde{p}_i(0)=1$, $\tilde{p}_e(0)=0.9$, $\tilde{r}_{\lim}=557.8233$.
$\mathrm{A}=0.01$, $\mathrm{Re_e}=0.01$, $\mathrm{Re_i}=1$.

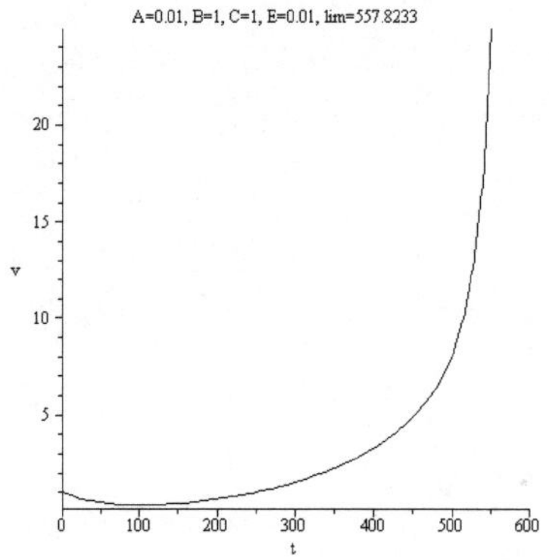

Fig. 7.5.3. Dependence $\mathrm{v(t)} \leftrightarrow \Psi(\tilde{r})$, $\tilde{p}_i(0)=1$, $\tilde{p}_e(0)=0.9$, $\tilde{r}_{\lim}=557.8233$, $\mathrm{A}=0.01$,
$\mathrm{Re_e}=0.01$, $\mathrm{Re_i}=1$.

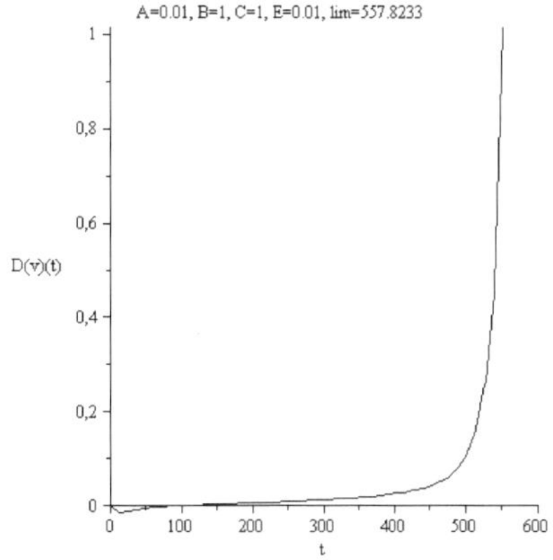

Fig. 7.5.4. Dependence $\mathrm{D(v)}(t) \leftrightarrow \dfrac{\partial \widetilde{\Psi}}{\partial \widetilde{r}}$, $\widetilde{r}_{\lim} = 557.8233$, $\mathrm{A} = 0.01$, $\mathrm{Re_e} = 0.01$, $\mathrm{Re_i} = 1$, $\widetilde{p}_i(0) = 1$, $\widetilde{p}_e(0) = 0.9$.

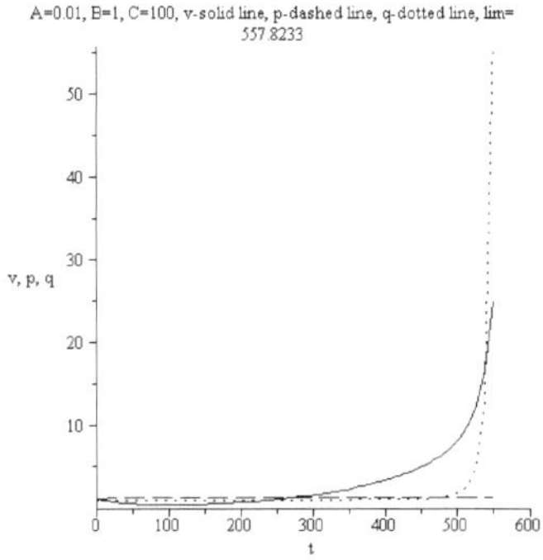

Fig. 7.5.5. Dependence $\mathrm{v}(t) \leftrightarrow \Psi(\widetilde{r})$, $\mathrm{p} \leftrightarrow \widetilde{p}_i(\widetilde{r})$, $\mathrm{q} \leftrightarrow \widetilde{p}_e(\widetilde{r})$, $\widetilde{p}_i(0) = 1$, $\widetilde{p}_e(0) = 0.9$, $\widetilde{r}_{\lim} = 557.8233$, $\mathrm{A} = 0.01$, $\mathrm{Re_e} = 0.01$, $\mathrm{Re_i} = 1$.

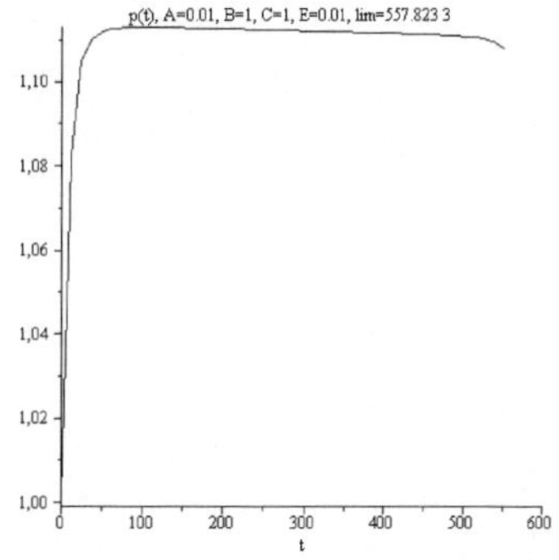

Fig. 7.5.6. Dependence $p(t) \leftrightarrow \tilde{p}_i(\tilde{r})$, $\tilde{r}_{\lim} = 557.8233$, $A = 0.01$, $Re_e = 0.01$, $Re_i = 1$, $\tilde{p}_i(0) = 1$, $\tilde{p}_e(0) = 0.9$.

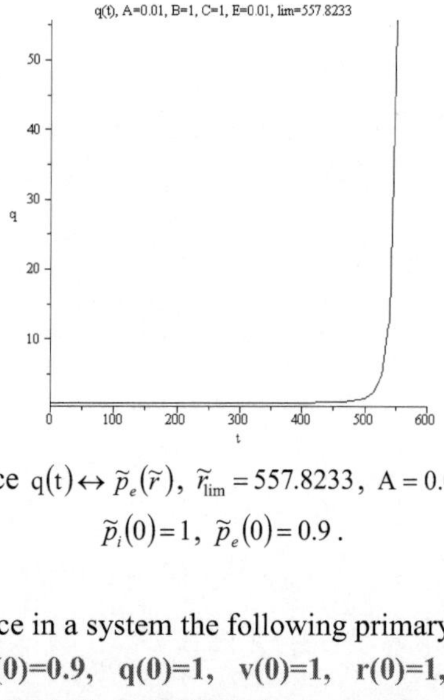

Fig. 7.5.7. Dependence $q(t) \leftrightarrow \tilde{p}_e(\tilde{r})$, $\tilde{r}_{\lim} = 557.8233$, $A = 0.01$, $Re_e = 0.01$, $Re_i = 1$, $\tilde{p}_i(0) = 1$, $\tilde{p}_e(0) = 0.9$.

Now we introduce in a system the following primary disturbances:

(Option 1): **p(0)=0.9, q(0)=1, v(0)=1, r(0)=1, s(0)=1, D(p)(0)=0, D(q)(0)=0, D(v)(0)=0, D(r)(0)=0, D(s)(0)=0;** $A = B = Re_e = Re_i = 1$.

(Option 2): **p(0)=1, q(0)=0.9, v(0)=1, r(0)=1, s(0)=1, D(p)(0)=0, D(q)(0)=0, D(v)(0)=0, D(r)(0)=0, D(s)(0)=0;** $A = B = Re_e = Re_i = 1$.

(Option 3): **p(0)=0.9, q(0)=1, v(0)=1, r(0)=1, s(0)=1, D(p)(0)=0, D(q)(0)=0, D(v)(0)=0, D(r)(0)=0, D(s)(0)=0;** $A = B = 1$, $Re_e = Re_i = 0.1$.

(Option 4): **p(0)=1, q(0)=0.9, v(0)=1, r(0)=1, s(0)=1, D(p)(0)=0, D(q)(0)=0, D(v)(0)=0, D(r)(0)=0, D(s)(0)=0;** $A = B = 1$, $Re_e = Re_i = 0.1$.

(Option 5): **p(0)=1, q(0)=1, v(0)=1, r(0)=1, s(0)=1, D(p)(0)=0, D(q)(0)=0, D(v)(0)=0, D(r)(0)=0, D(s)(0)=0;** $A = B = Re_e = Re_i = 1$.

Results of calculations are reflected in figures 7.5.7 – 7.5.16.

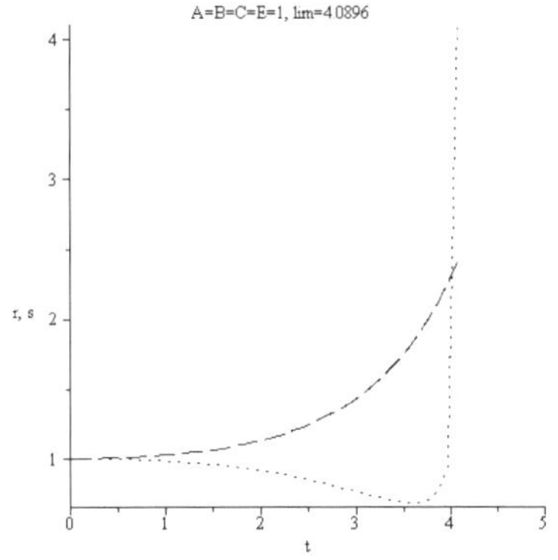

Fig. 7.5.7. r- density $\tilde{n}_i$ (dashed line), s- density $\tilde{n}_e$ (dotted line) in quantum soliton.
lim=4.0896, Option 1.

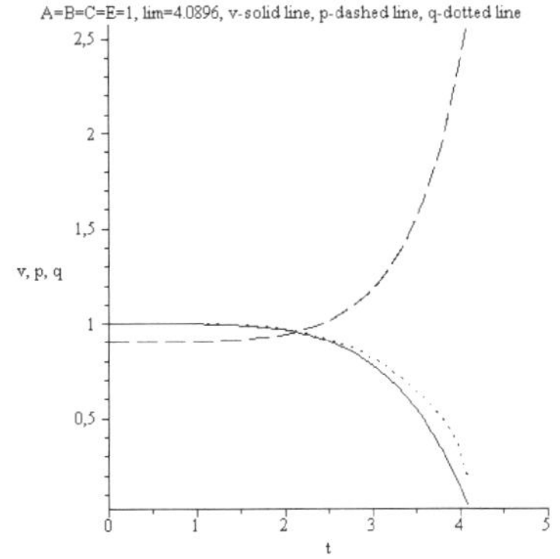

Fig. 7.5.8. v-potential $\tilde{\Psi}$ (solid line), p- pressure $\tilde{p}_i$ (dashed line), q- pressure $\tilde{p}_e$, (dotted line), in quantum soliton, lim=4.0896, Option 1.

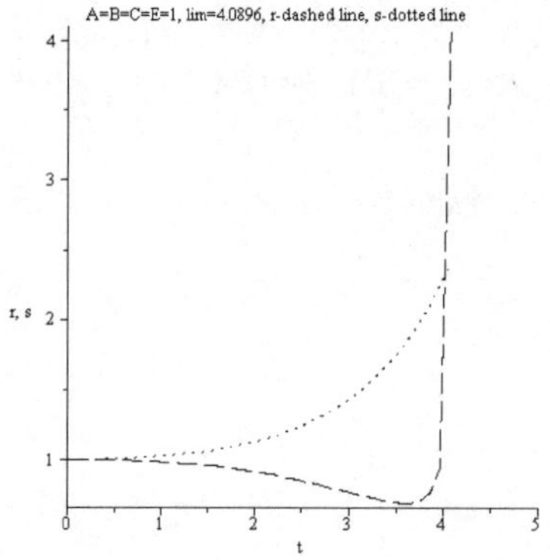

Fig. 7.5.9. r- density $\widetilde{n}_i$ (dashed line), s- density $\widetilde{n}_e$ (dotted line) in quantum soliton.
lim=4.0896, Option 2.

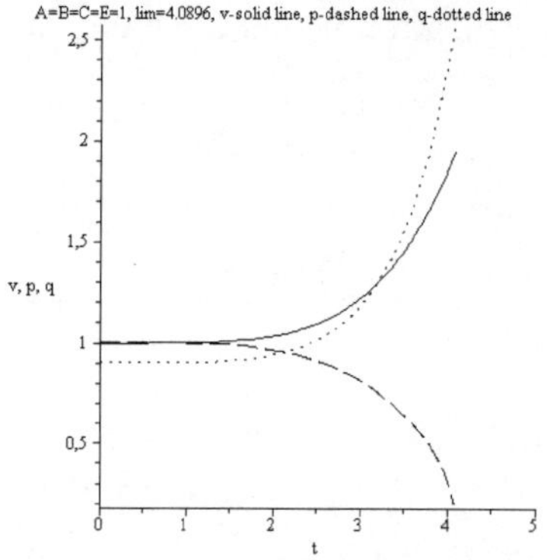

Fig. 7.5.10. v-potential $\widetilde{\Psi}$ (solid line), p- pressure $\widetilde{p}_i$ (dashed line), q- pressure $\widetilde{p}_e$, (dotted line), in quantum soliton, lim=4.0896, Option 2.

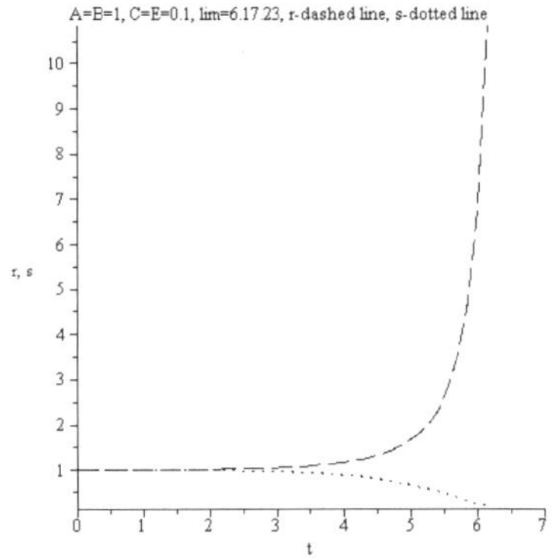

Fig. 7.5.11. r- density $\tilde{n}_i$ (dashed line), s- density $\tilde{n}_e$ (dotted line) in quantum soliton,
lim=6.1723, Option 3.

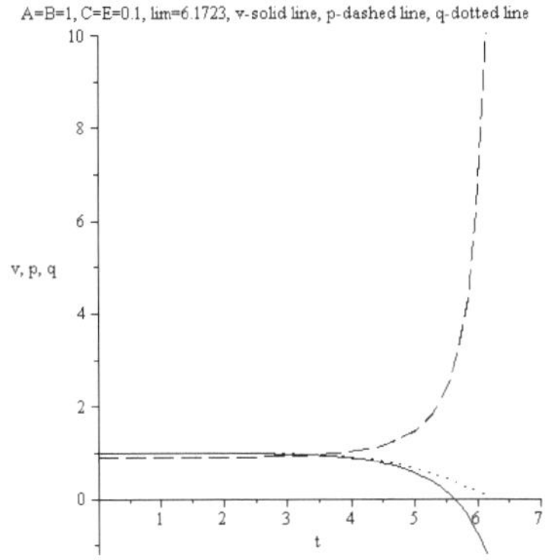

Fig. 7.5.12. v-potential $\tilde{\Psi}$ (solid line), p- pressure $\tilde{p}_i$ (dashed line), q- pressure $\tilde{p}_e$, (dotted line), in quantum soliton, lim=6.1723, Option 3.

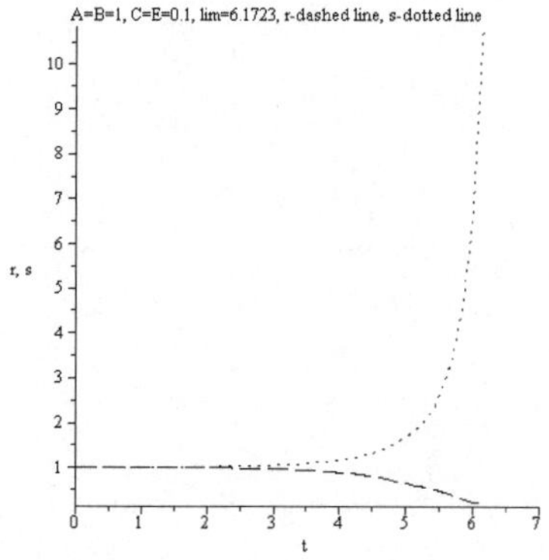

Fig. 7.5.13. r- density $\tilde{n}_i$ (dashed line), s- density $\tilde{n}_e$ (dotted line) in quantum soliton.
lim=6.1723, Option 4.

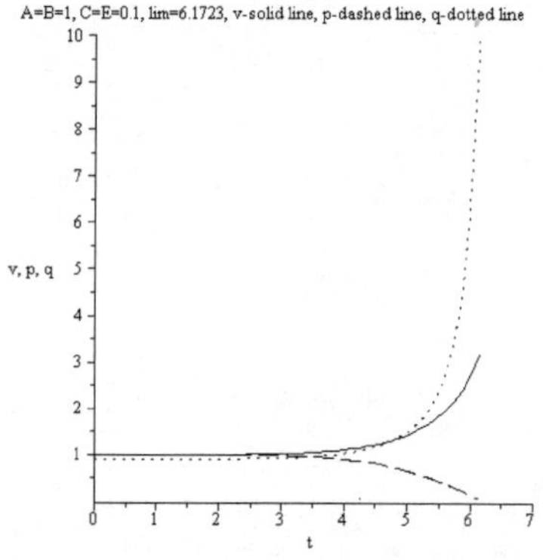

Fig. 7.5.14. v-potential $\tilde{\Psi}$ (solid line), p- pressure $\tilde{p}_i$ (dashed line), q- pressure $\tilde{p}_e$, (dotted line), in quantum soliton, lim=6.1723, Option 4.

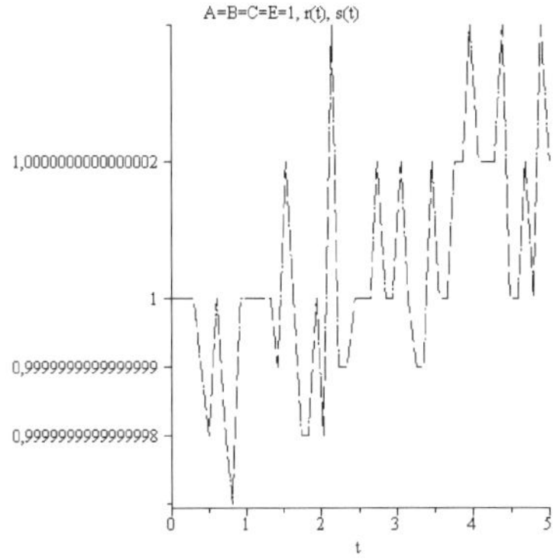

Fig. 7.5.15. r- density $\widetilde{n}_i$ (dashed line), s- density $\widetilde{n}_e$ (dotted line) in quantum soliton. Option 5.

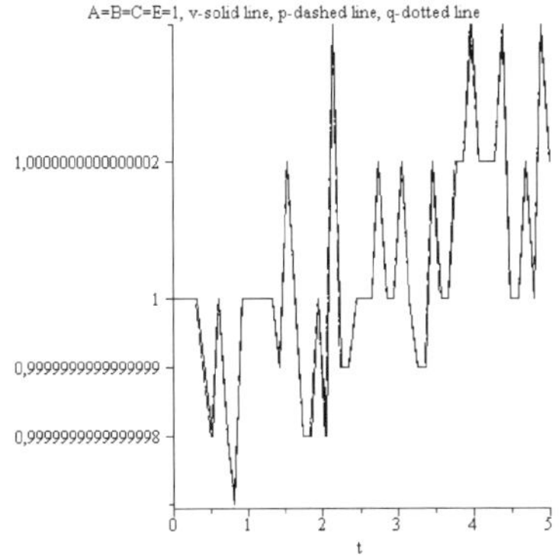

Fig. 7.5.16. v-potential $\widetilde{\Psi}$ (solid line), p- pressure $\widetilde{p}_i$ (dashed line), q- pressure $\widetilde{p}_e$, (dotted line), in quantum soliton, Option 5.

We draw conclusions using the results of the calculations:

1. A plasmoid is a non-equilibrium product of self-organization of ionized matter located in a limited region of space. A non-equilibrium object has an excess (in relation to the equilibrium configuration) charge of one sign and a lack of charges of another sign along the radial direction. Figures 7.5.5 – 7.5.14 show the existence of two spherical layers whose size is determined by Cauchy conditions and parameters $A, B, \mathrm{Re}_i, \mathrm{Re}_e$. The stability of the plasma object is achieved as a result of the equilibrium of self-consistent forces of electrostatic

origin and gas-kinetic pressure of non-local origin. In this case, the outer spherical electric layer can bear a negative charge if $\tilde{p}_i(0) < \tilde{p}_e(0)$ or positive charge if $\tilde{p}_i(0) > \tilde{p}_e(0)$. As follows from the given experimental data [114, 115], both of these cases are implemented in practice and are determined by the specific features of the organization of the experiment.
2. If the initial gradient of pressures is absent or $\tilde{p}_i(0) = \tilde{p}_e(0)$ then calculations lead to physical natural results - plasma fluctuations (figures 7.5.15 and 7.5.16).
3. Mathematical modeling implemented in the framework of non-local physics leads to the existence of a stable plasma object even in the absence of a magnetic field.
4. In the considered theory, there is no need to use external boundary conditions. The radial size of the plasmoid is produced "automatically" in the process of solving the Cauchy problem as a domain of existence of the solution.

As it follows from the calculations, the separated charges in plasmoid can correspond to the model of the spherical capacitor. The maximum energy that can be stored in a capacitor is limited by the breakdown voltage. But the breakdown process can have rather lengthy character realized in the several stages. This fact can explain the anomalies in the Tunguska Object (TO) behavior. TO can be considered as a giant atmospheric plasmoid - BL.

The spherical capacitor energy W is written as

$$W = 2\pi\varepsilon_0\varepsilon \frac{R_1 R_2}{R_2 - R_1}(\Delta\psi)^2, \tag{7.5.63}$$

where $\Delta\psi = \psi_1 - \psi_2$, is the potential difference between the conductors for a given charge q on each. The voltage between the spheres can be found by integrating the electric field along a radial line:

$$\Delta\psi = \psi_1 - \psi_2 = \frac{q}{4\pi\varepsilon_0\varepsilon}\int_{R_1}^{R_2}\frac{dr}{r^2} = \frac{q}{4\pi\varepsilon_0\varepsilon}\left(\frac{1}{R_1} - \frac{1}{R_2}\right), \tag{7.5.64}$$

If $R_2 >> R_1$, then

$$W = 2\pi\varepsilon_0\varepsilon R_1(\Delta\psi)^2. \tag{7.5.65}$$

The force $\mathbf{F} = -\frac{dW_p}{dr}\frac{\mathbf{r}}{r}$, acting on the internal conductor

$$F_{\text{in}} = -\frac{\partial W_p}{\partial R_1} \cong 2\pi\varepsilon_0\varepsilon(\Delta\psi)^2, \tag{7.5.66}$$

does not depend in the first approximation on the radius of the internal sphere. For the external sphere, the force acts in the opposite direction.

$$F_{ex} = -\frac{\partial W_p}{\partial R_2} = -2\pi\varepsilon_0\varepsilon_1(\Delta\psi)^2 \frac{R_1^2}{(R_2 - R_1)^2}. \quad (7.5.67)$$

If $R_2 >> R_1$, then

$$F_{ex} = -\frac{\partial W_p}{\partial R_2} = -2\pi\varepsilon_0\varepsilon_1(\Delta\psi)^2 \left(\frac{R_1}{R_2}\right)^2, \quad (7.5.68)$$

If for the TO $W = 10^{16}\,\mathrm{J}$, radius of the internal sphere is 100 m, $\varepsilon = 1$, then $\Delta\psi = 1.34 \cdot 10^{12}\,\mathrm{V}$.

Electrostatic generator (which uses a moving belt to accumulate very high amounts of electrical potential on a hollow metal globe on the top of the stand) was invented by American physicist Robert J. Van de Graaf in 1929. The potential difference achieved in Van de Graaff generators reaches $7 \cdot 10^6$ volts in the 30th of the last century.

A Marx generator (Arkadyev – Marks generator in the Russian scientific literature) generates a high-voltage pulse. The circuit generates a high-voltage pulse by charging a number of capacitors in parallel, then suddenly connecting them in series. Marx generators are used in high energy physics experiments, as well as to simulate the effects of lightning on power line gear and aviation equipment. The high-voltage pulse can reach up to 10^7 V. The mega-joule estimates are known for the ball lightings.

7.6. Schrödinger "resonance" idea instead of quantum jumps. Neutron structure.

Several extremely significant problems challenge modern fundamental physics – missing antimatter after the Big Bang, and so called dark energy and dark matter. From the position of local physics the last two problems lead to affirmation that only about four percents of matter leaved for us for direct investigation because the other matter is out of our diagnostic methods.

More than ten years ago, the accelerated cosmological expansion was discovered in direct astronomical observations at distances of a few billion light years, almost at the edge of the observable Universe. This acceleration should be explained because mutual attraction of cosmic bodies is only capable of decelerating their scattering. It means that we reach the revolutionary situation not only in physics but in the natural philosophy on the whole. Practically we are in front of the new challenge since Newton's Mathematical Principles of Natural Philosophy was published. As result, new idea was introduced in physics about existing of a force with the opposite sign which is called universal anti-gravitation.

Between these global (and rather new problems) we have very old problem about the physical sense of wave function and quantum jumps. When surveying the literature, one often gets the impression that Schrödinger held several distinct interpretations of quantum mechanics, and practically in all case he denied the interpretation of the Copenhagen group [128]. It is known the most impressive Schrödinger reaction: "If we have to go on with these damned quantum jumps, then I'm sorry that I ever got involved". Scientists generally recognize the great importance of his contributions to the interpretation of quantum mechanics. But as a rule, only the lines of argument and ingenious thought-experiments by which Schrödinger challenged the current orthodoxy.

On the face of it, none of Schrödinger's own positive suggestions appear to have had any lasting influence. He objects in particular to the notion of 'stationary states', and above all to 'quantum jumping' between those states. He regards these concepts as hangovers from the old Bohr quantum theory, of 1913 [123], and entirely unmotivated by anything in the mathematics of the new theory of 1926 [116-120]. He would like to regard the wave function itself as the complete picture, and completely determined by the Schrödinger equation, and so evolving smoothly without 'quantum jumps'.

At an early stage, he had tried to replace 'particles' by wave packets (Schrödinger, 1926); but wave packets diffuse. And the paper of 1952 [129] ends with the admission that Schrödinger does not see how, for the present, to account the definiteness of physical reality including particle tracks in track chambers with the indefiniteness, the waviness, of the wave function. It is the problem like the Schrödinger's cat. Schrödinger tried to solve these complex problems (without success) from the position of the resonance effects [129]. In other words, is it possible to speak about continuous effects in reality and quantum jumps only as shortcomings of Bohr and Schrödinger phenomenological theories? From this point of view it is interesting to remind the abstract (containing only one sentence) of the Madelung paper [37]: "Es wird gezeigt, daß man die Schrödingersche Gleichung des Einelektronenproblems in die Form der hydrodynamischen Gleichungen transformieren kann" (It is shown that the Schrödinger equation for one-electron problems can be transformed into the form of hydrodynamic equations).

In the last years significant experimental and theoretical efforts were realized with the aim to clarify the physical situation. Authors of [130] wrote

"The times at which the discontinuous jump transitions occur are reputed to be fundamentally unpredictable. Can there be, despite the indeterminism of quantum physics, a possibility to know if a quantum jump is about to occur or not? Here, we answer this question affirmatively by experimentally demonstrating that the jump from the ground to an excited state of a superconducting artificial three-level atom can be tracked as it follows a predictable "flight," by monitoring the population of an auxiliary energy level coupled to the ground state. The experimental results demonstrate that the jump evolution when completed is continuous, coherent, and deterministic".

We intend to show that nonlocal physics (in this case of the local limit of nonlocal equations) can lead to waving solutions in the area where the Schrödinger equation leads to the jump solutions. We should underline that the nonlocal theory is constructed on the underlying first principles of physics.

With this aim let us investigate the asymptotic of the system of equations of the hydrodynamic type (see Item 7.5), when the electron quantum numbers $k,n \to \infty$ or $\mathrm{Re}_i \to 0, \mathrm{Re}_e \to 0$.

We find

$$\frac{\partial}{\partial \widetilde{r}}\left(\frac{\widetilde{p}_i}{\widetilde{n}_i}\right)=0, \tag{7.6.1}$$

$$\frac{\partial}{\partial \widetilde{r}}\left(\frac{\widetilde{p}_e}{\widetilde{n}_e}\right)=0 \tag{7.6.2}$$

We prolong the transformations by integrating (7.6.1) and (7.6.2).

$$\widetilde{p}_i = \mathrm{P}\widetilde{n}_i, \tag{7.6.3}$$

$$\widetilde{p}_e = \mathrm{E}\widetilde{n}_e. \tag{7.6.4}$$

Relation (7.6.3), (7.6.4) have the transparent physical sense. Really we have

$$\frac{p_\alpha}{\rho_\alpha} = const \tag{7.6.5}$$

or

$$\frac{5}{2}\frac{p_\alpha}{\rho_\alpha} + \frac{\varepsilon_\alpha}{m_\alpha} = const, \tag{7.6.6}$$

if we use the energy equation (7.5.8). Internal energy ε_α reflects the spin existence. In the general case in the absence of magnetic field

$$\frac{5}{2}\frac{p_e}{\rho_e} + \frac{\hbar}{m_e}\omega(\Psi) = const, \tag{7.6.7}$$

where $h/m_e = 1.158 \ cm^2/s$ is kinematic quantum viscosity. As follows from (7.6.7) internal energy is implicit function of potential. Omitting the spin dependence for bound system in Schrödinger restrictions we find the system (see also (7.5.41) and (7.5.42)):

$$-\mathrm{B}\tilde{n}_e\frac{\partial\tilde{\Psi}}{\partial\tilde{r}}+\frac{\partial\tilde{p}_e}{\partial\tilde{r}}=0, \qquad (7.6.8)$$

$$\mathrm{B}\tilde{n}_i\frac{\partial\tilde{\Psi}}{\partial\tilde{r}}+\frac{\partial\tilde{p}_i}{\partial\tilde{r}}=0 \qquad (7.6.9)$$

and the last transformed equation of the BGK type.

$$\frac{1}{\tilde{r}^2}\frac{\partial}{\partial\tilde{r}}\left(\tilde{r}^2\frac{\partial\tilde{\Psi}}{\partial\tilde{r}}\right)=-\mathrm{A}[\tilde{n}_i-\tilde{n}_e]. \qquad (7.6.10)$$

Relations (7.6.3) and (7.6.4) correspond to the well known laws of the energy conservation and can be considered also as equations of state for the positive and negative particles. The dimensionless parameters E and P are proportional to the total internal energy of the electron shell and the nucleus of the atom correspondingly.

After substitution (7.6.3) in (7.6.9) and (7.6.4) in (7.6.8) we obtain

$$-\mathrm{B}\tilde{n}_e\frac{\partial\tilde{\Psi}}{\partial\tilde{r}}+\mathrm{E}\frac{\partial\tilde{n}_e}{\partial\tilde{r}}=0, \qquad (7.6.11)$$

$$\mathrm{B}\tilde{n}_i\frac{\partial\tilde{\Psi}}{\partial\tilde{r}}+\mathrm{P}\frac{\partial\tilde{n}_i}{\partial\tilde{r}}=0 \qquad (7.6.12)$$

or

$$-\mathrm{B}\frac{\partial\tilde{\Psi}}{\partial\tilde{r}}+\mathrm{E}\frac{\partial\ln\tilde{n}_e}{\partial\tilde{r}}=0, \qquad (7.6.13)$$

$$\mathrm{B}\frac{\partial\tilde{\Psi}}{\partial\tilde{r}}+\mathrm{P}\frac{\partial\ln\tilde{n}_i}{\partial\tilde{r}}=0. \qquad (7.6.14)$$

Then (introducing new integration constants)

$$\mathrm{E}\ln\tilde{n}_e-\mathrm{B}\tilde{\Psi}=\mathrm{C}, \qquad (7.6.15)$$

$$\mathrm{P}\ln\tilde{n}_i+\mathrm{B}\tilde{\Psi}=\mathrm{D}, \qquad (7.6.16)$$

$$\tilde{n}_e=\exp\left[\frac{1}{\mathrm{E}}\left(\mathrm{C}+\mathrm{B}\tilde{\Psi}\right)\right], \qquad (7.6.17)$$

$$\tilde{n}_i=\exp\left[\frac{1}{\mathrm{P}}\left(\mathrm{D}-\mathrm{B}\tilde{\Psi}\right)\right]. \qquad (7.6.18)$$

Other interpretation of (7.6.17) and (7.6.18):

$$\tilde{n}_e=\tilde{n}_{e0}e^{B\tilde{\Psi}/\mathrm{E}}, \qquad (7.6.19)$$

$$\tilde{n}_i=\tilde{n}_{i0}e^{-B\tilde{\Psi}/\mathrm{P}}, \qquad (7.6.20)$$

where

$$\tilde{n}_{e,0}=\tilde{n}_{e,\tilde{\Psi}=0}=\exp\frac{\mathrm{C}}{\mathrm{E}},\ \tilde{n}_{i,0}=\tilde{n}_{i,\tilde{\Psi}=0}=\exp\frac{\mathrm{D}}{\mathrm{P}}. \qquad (7.6.21)$$

In particular from (7.6.19) (7.6.20) follow

$$\tilde{n}_e^{\mathrm{E}}\tilde{n}_i^{\mathrm{P}} = const\,. \tag{7.6.22}$$

Using (7.6.10) and (7.6.19), (7.6.20) we reach an equation

$$\frac{1}{\tilde{r}^2}\frac{\partial}{\partial\tilde{r}}\left(\tilde{r}^2\frac{\partial\tilde{\Psi}}{\partial\tilde{r}}\right) = \mathrm{A}\left\{\tilde{n}_{e,0}\exp\left[\frac{\mathrm{B}}{\mathrm{E}}\tilde{\Psi}\right] - \tilde{n}_{i,0}\exp\left[-\frac{\mathrm{B}}{\mathrm{P}}\tilde{\Psi}\right]\right\} \tag{7.6.23}$$

or

$$\frac{1}{\tilde{r}^2}\frac{\partial}{\partial\tilde{r}}\left(\tilde{r}^2\frac{\partial\tilde{\Psi}}{\partial\tilde{r}}\right) = \mathrm{A}\left\{\exp\left[\frac{C}{\mathrm{E}} + \frac{\mathrm{B}}{\mathrm{E}}\tilde{\Psi}\right] - \exp\left[\frac{\mathrm{D}}{\mathrm{P}} - \frac{\mathrm{B}}{\mathrm{P}}\tilde{\Psi}\right]\right\}. \tag{7.6.24}$$

Let us use (7.6.24) with the aim to find extremes of the potential $\tilde{\Psi}$. From (7.6.24) follows that the condition for the extremes existence is written as

$$\exp\left[\frac{\mathrm{D}}{\mathrm{P}} - \frac{\mathrm{B}}{\mathrm{P}}\tilde{\Psi}\right] - \exp\left[\frac{\mathrm{C}}{\mathrm{E}} + \frac{\mathrm{B}}{\mathrm{E}}\tilde{\Psi}\right] = 0, \tag{7.6.25}$$

or

$$\frac{\mathrm{D}}{\mathrm{P}} - \frac{\mathrm{B}}{\mathrm{P}}\tilde{\Psi} = \frac{\mathrm{C}}{\mathrm{E}} + \frac{\mathrm{B}}{\mathrm{E}}\tilde{\Psi}, \tag{7.6.26}$$

or

$$\tilde{\Psi} = -\frac{1}{\mathrm{B}}\frac{\mathrm{CP} - \mathrm{ED}}{\mathrm{E} + \mathrm{P}}. \tag{7.6.27}$$

Let us define constants in (7.6.27) in the frame of Schrödinger theory, taking

$$\mathrm{B} = n^2, \; \Psi = E_n, \tag{7.6.28}$$

$$Ry = \frac{\Psi_0}{\mathrm{E} + \mathrm{P}}(\mathrm{CP} - \mathrm{ED}), \tag{7.6.29}$$

where n is principal quantum number, the value $T_{total} = \mathrm{E} + \mathrm{P}$ is the dimensionless total thermal energy of the system nucleus +shell and Ry is the generalized Rydberg number.

It is known that the Rydberg constant is a fundamental physical constant used in formulas to calculate the energy levels and radiation frequencies of atoms. It was introduced by the Swedish scientist Johannes Robert Rydberg in 1890 in the study of the radiation spectra of atoms. This constant originally appeared as an empirical fitting parameter in the Rydberg formula describing the spectral series of hydrogen.

Let us introduce the dimensionless Rydberg constant $\overline{Ry} = \frac{Ry}{\Psi_0}$. Then

$$\overline{Ry} = \frac{\mathrm{EP}}{\mathrm{E} + \mathrm{P}}\left(\frac{\mathrm{C}}{\mathrm{E}} - \frac{\mathrm{D}}{\mathrm{P}}\right) = \frac{T_{el}T_{nu}}{T_{el} + T_{nu}}\left(\frac{\mathrm{C}}{\mathrm{E}} - \frac{\mathrm{D}}{\mathrm{P}}\right) = \frac{T_{el}T_{nu}}{T_{total}}\left(\frac{\mathrm{C}}{\mathrm{E}} - \frac{\mathrm{D}}{\mathrm{P}}\right) = \frac{T_{el}T_{nu}}{T_{total}}F_{fit}, \tag{7.6.30}$$

where

$$F_{fit} = \frac{\mathrm{C}}{\mathrm{E}} - \frac{\mathrm{D}}{\mathrm{P}} \tag{7.6.31}$$

is fitting coefficient.

From (7.6.28), (7.6.29) follow the classical formula

$$E_n = -\frac{Ry}{n^2}, \qquad (7.6.32)$$

where for hydrogen atom $Ry = 13.6$ eV, (1eV = $1{,}6\cdot 10^{-19}$ J). The choice $\mathrm{B} = n^2$ leads to the specified choice of scales, namely

$$e\frac{n_0 \Psi_0}{p_0} = n^2. \qquad (7.6.33)$$

Then

$$e\Psi = -\frac{p_0}{n_0}\frac{\mathrm{CP} - \mathrm{ED}}{\mathrm{E} + \mathrm{P}}. \qquad (7.6.34)$$

Obviously p_0 / n_0 is the scale of the thermal energy. Of course the formulae (7.6.28) and (7.6.29) can be transformed in other classical forms:

$$\upsilon_{lk} = \frac{E_l - E_k}{h} = Ry\left[\frac{1}{k^2} - \frac{1}{l^2}\right], \qquad (7.6.35)$$

$$\upsilon_{lk} = \frac{E_l - E_k}{h} = \frac{m_e e^4}{64\pi^3\hbar^3\varepsilon_0^2}\left[\frac{1}{k^2} - \frac{1}{l^2}\right]. \qquad (7.6.36)$$

In figure 7.6.1 the typical hydrogen spectrum is shown.

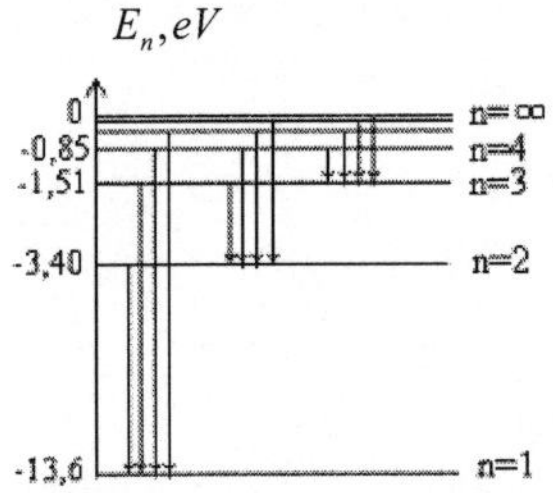

Fig. 7.6.1. Hydrogen spectrum.

Equation (7.6.23) can be easily numerically integrated if the system of external parameters A, B, C, D, E, P is known. Let us demonstrate results of some calculations (see figures 7.6.2 – 7.6.6). The following Maple notations on figures are used: v – potential $\tilde{\Psi}$, x(t) - $\tilde{n}_e(\tilde{r})$, y(t) - $\tilde{n}_i(\tilde{r})$, H - $\tilde{n}_{e0}$, Q - $\tilde{n}_{i0}$, and t – independent variable $\tilde{r}$. The system of external parameters $A, B, C, D,$ E, P leads to the vast possibilities of mathematical modeling. Explanations placed under all following figures. In all numerical examples we use Cauchy conditions

v(0)=1,D(v)(0)=0, x(0)=0.01, y(0)=0.99

```
dsolve[interactive]({

diff(t^2*diff(v(t), t), t) = A·t^2*(H
    *exp(B·v(t)/E) - Q*exp(-B·v(t)
    /P)),
-B·x(t)*diff(v(t), t) + E*diff(x(t),
    t) = 0,
B·y(t)*diff(v(t), t) + P*diff(y(t), t)
    = 0,
v(0) = 1, D(v)(0) = 0, y(0) = 0.99, x(0)
    = .01
});
```

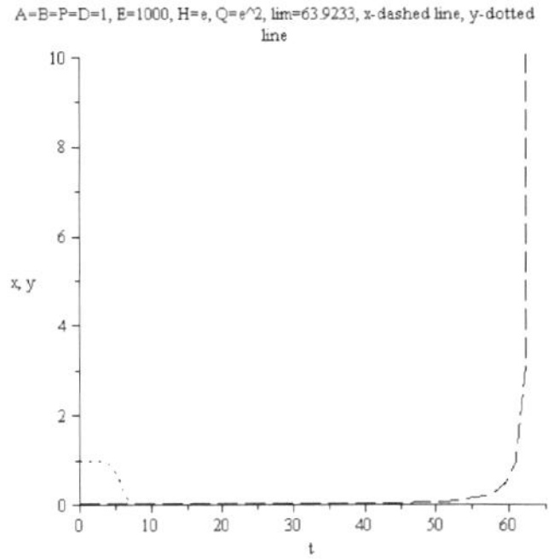

Fig. 7.6.2. Dependence x(t)$\leftrightarrow \tilde{n}_e(\tilde{r})$, y(t)$\leftrightarrow \tilde{n}_i(\tilde{r})$, x(t) – dashed line, y(t) – dotted line,

$\tilde{r}_{\lim} = 63.9233$, A=B=P=D=1, E=1000, H=e, $\mathrm{Q} = \mathrm{e}^2$.

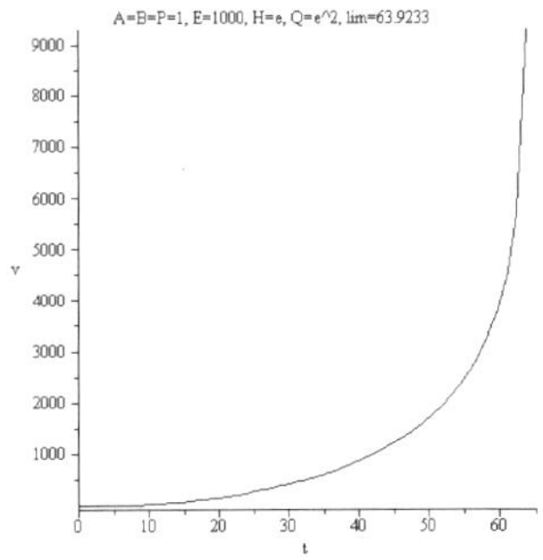

Fig. 7.6.3. Dependence v(t)$\leftrightarrow \tilde{\Psi}(\tilde{r})$, $\tilde{r}_{\lim} = 63.9233$, A=B=P=D=1, E=1000, H=e, $\mathrm{Q} = \mathrm{e}^2$.

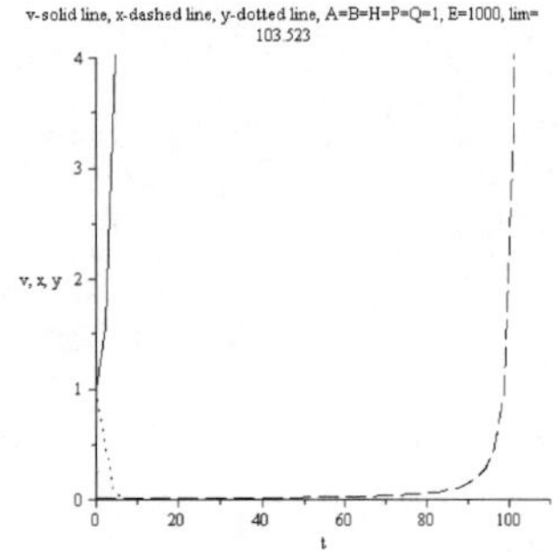

Fig. 7.6.4. Dependence $v(t) \leftrightarrow \tilde{\Psi}(\tilde{r})$, $x(t) \leftrightarrow \tilde{n}_e(\tilde{r})$, $y(t) \leftrightarrow \tilde{n}_i(\tilde{r})$, v(t) – solid line, x(t) – dashed line, y(t) – dotted line, $\tilde{r}_{\lim} = 103.523$, A=B=H=P=Q=1, E=1000.

Figures 7.6.5 and 7.6.6 reflect the typical picture of atom structure with the separated positive (internal) atomic nucleus and negative (external) shell, if $H = \tilde{n}_{e0} = \tilde{n}_{e,\tilde{\Psi}=0} = 1$, $Q = \tilde{n}_{i0} = \tilde{n}_{i,\tilde{\Psi}=0} = 1$.

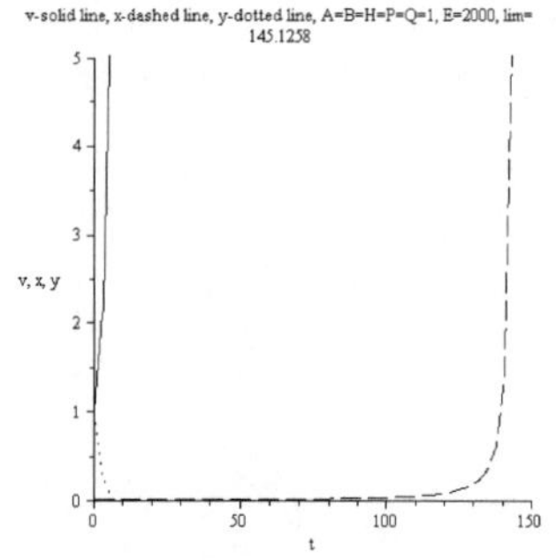

Fig. 7.6.5. Dependence $v(t) \leftrightarrow \tilde{\Psi}(\tilde{r})$, $x(t) \leftrightarrow \tilde{n}_e(\tilde{r})$, $y(t) \leftrightarrow \tilde{n}_i(\tilde{r})$, v(t) – solid line, x(t) – dashed line, y(t) – dotted line, $\tilde{r}_{\lim} = 145.1258$, A=B=H=P=Q=1, E=2000.

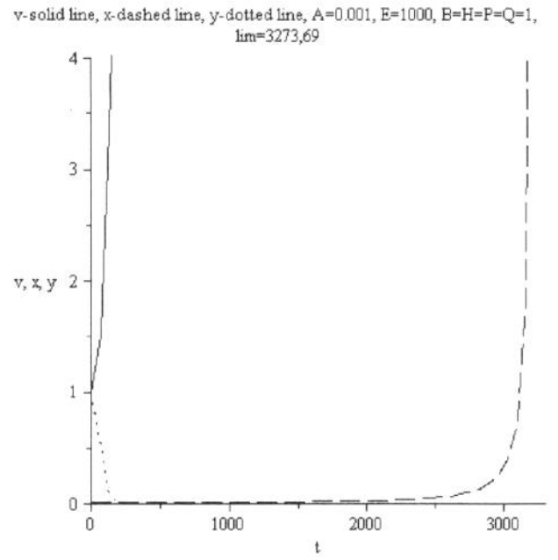

Fig. 7.6.6. Dependence v(t) $\leftrightarrow \tilde{\Psi}(\tilde{r})$, x(t) $\leftrightarrow \tilde{n}_e(\tilde{r})$, y(t) $\leftrightarrow \tilde{n}_i(\tilde{r})$, v(t) – solid line, x(t) – dashed line, y(t) – dotted line, $\tilde{r}_{\lim} = 3273.69$, A=0.001, B=H=P=Q=1, E=1000.

Let us consider now the situation related to anti-atom or if you want to anti-matter problem. With this aim we introduce in the Cauchy conditions the relations $x(0) = 0.99$, $y(0) = 0.01$, where x(t) $\leftrightarrow \tilde{n}_e(\tilde{r})$, y(t) $\leftrightarrow \tilde{n}_i(\tilde{r})$. Antimatter is defined as matter which is composed of the antiparticles of the corresponding particles of "ordinary" matter. In theory, a particle and its anti-particle (for example, proton and antiproton) have the same mass, but opposite electric charge. For example, a proton has positive charge while an antiproton has negative charge. A collision between any particle and its anti-particle partner leads to their mutual annihilation, giving rise to various proportions of intense photons (gamma rays), neutrinos, and sometimes less-massive particle-antiparticle pairs.

The corresponding Maple program looks as follows

```
dsolve[interactive]({

diff(t^2*diff(v(t), t), t) = A·t^2*(H
    *exp(B·v(t)/E) − Q*exp(−B·v(t)
    /P)),
−B·x(t)*diff(v(t), t) + E*diff(x(t),
    t) = 0,
B·y(t)*diff(v(t), t) + P*diff(y(t), t)
    = 0,
v(0) = 1, D(v)(0) = 0, y(0) = 0.01, x(0)
    = .99
});
```

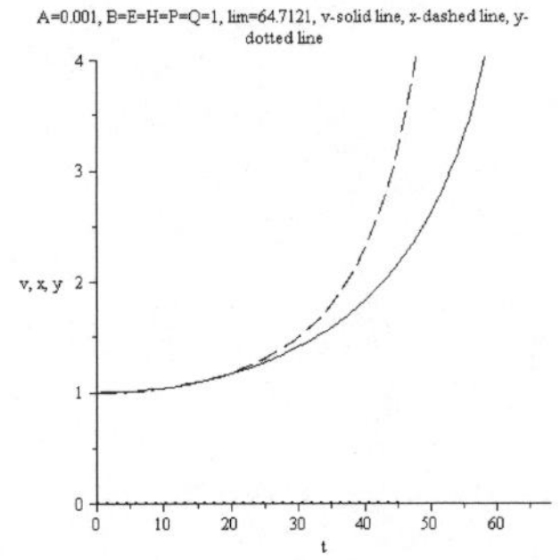

Fig. 7.6.7. Dependence v(t)$\leftrightarrow \tilde{\Psi}(\tilde{r})$, x(t)$\leftrightarrow \tilde{n}_e(\tilde{r})$, y(t)$\leftrightarrow \tilde{n}_i(\tilde{r})$, v(t) – solid line, x(t) – dashed line, y(t) – dotted line, $\tilde{r}_{\lim} = 64.721$, A=0.001, B=H=P=Q=1, E=1.

The following figures 7.6.8 – 7.6.11 correspond to the "anti-atom" appearance when $Q > H$ (H - $\tilde{n}_{e0} = \tilde{n}_{e,\tilde{\Psi}=0}$, Q - $\tilde{n}_{i0} = \tilde{n}_{i,\tilde{\Psi}=0}$), typical for the *neutron structure*. Really the typical problem exists: in neutron electric charge is distributed? The typical answers: a) negative inside, positive outside; b) neutral everywhere; c) positive inside, negative outside. No reason to discuss knowingly false answer b), but answers a) and c) has its supporters.

Authors [131] writes: "The neutron is electrically neutral, but its substructure consists of charged quarks so it may have an internal charge distribution. In fact it is known to have a negative mean square charge radius, the second moment of the radial charge density. In other words the neutron has a positive core and negative skin". A thorough study was undertaken by Gerald A. Miller, who came to the conclusion c), (see for example [132 – 137]. In [132] he writes: "A model-independent analysis of the infinite-momentum-frame charge density of partons in the transverse plane is presented for the nucleon. We find that the neutron parton charge density is negative at the center, so that the square of the transverse charge radius is positive, in contrast with many expectations".

Let us consider the examples of calculations in the frame of nonlocal physics for parameters A=0.001, B=E=H=P=1, with enlarging Q from 1 to 10^4 (figures 7.6.7 – 7.6.11).

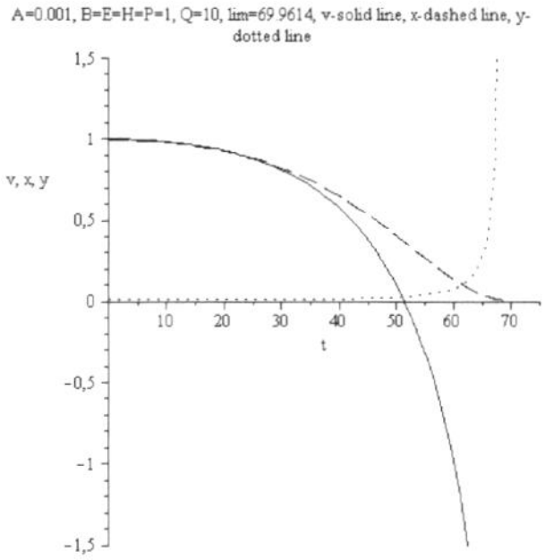

Fig. 7.6.8. Dependence $v(t) \leftrightarrow \widetilde{\Psi}(\widetilde{r})$, $x(t) \leftrightarrow \widetilde{n}_e(\widetilde{r})$, $y(t) \leftrightarrow \widetilde{n}_i(\widetilde{r})$, v(t) – solid line, x(t) – dashed line, y(t) – dotted line, $\widetilde{r}_{\lim} = 69.9614$, A=0.001, B=H=P=E=1, Q=10.

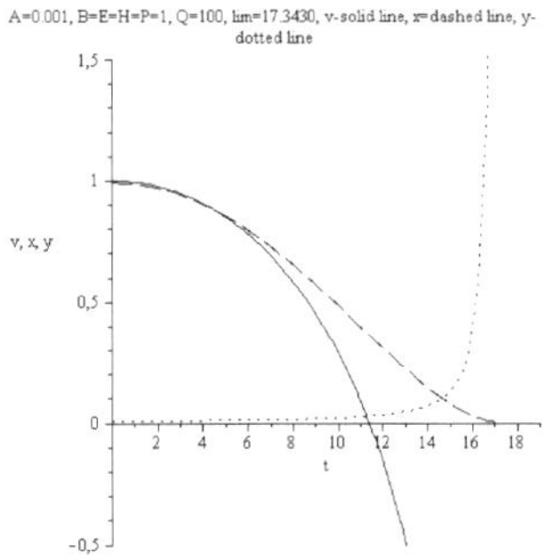

Fig. 7.6.9. Dependence $v(t) \leftrightarrow \widetilde{\Psi}(\widetilde{r})$, $x(t) \leftrightarrow \widetilde{n}_e(\widetilde{r})$, $y(t) \leftrightarrow \widetilde{n}_i(\widetilde{r})$, v(t) – solid line, x(t) – dashed line, y(t) – dotted line, $\widetilde{r}_{\lim} = 17.3430$, A=0.001, B=H=P=E=1, Q=100.

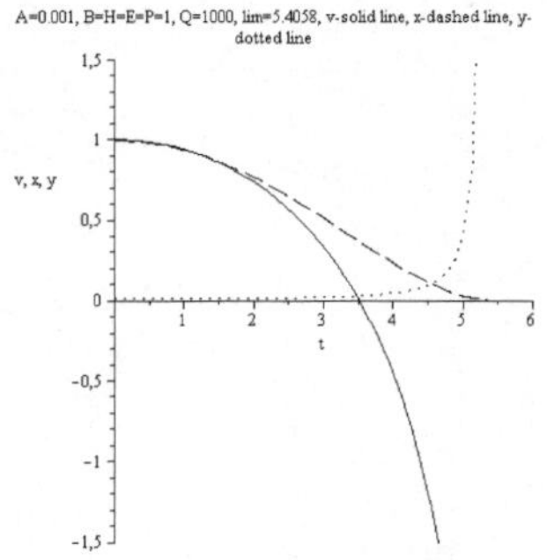

Fig. 7.6.10. Dependence $v(t) \leftrightarrow \tilde{\Psi}(\tilde{r})$, $x(t) \leftrightarrow \tilde{n}_e(\tilde{r})$, $y(t) \leftrightarrow \tilde{n}_i(\tilde{r})$, v(t) – solid line, x(t) – dashed line, y(t) – dotted line, $\tilde{r}_{\lim} = 5.4058$, A=0.001, B=H=P=E=1, Q=1000.

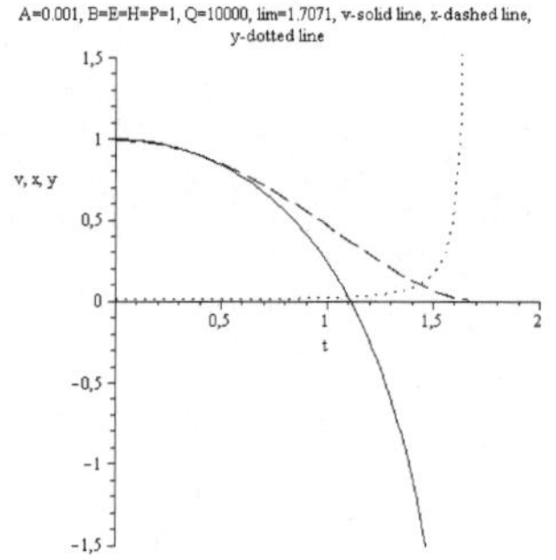

Fig. 7.6.11. Dependence $v(t) \leftrightarrow \tilde{\Psi}(\tilde{r})$, $x(t) \leftrightarrow \tilde{n}_e(\tilde{r})$, $y(t) \leftrightarrow \tilde{n}_i(\tilde{r})$, v(t) – solid line, x(t) – dashed line, y(t) – dotted line, $\tilde{r}_{\lim} = 1.7071$, A=0.001, B=H=P=Q=1, E=10000.

In this case:

1. The object has the negative nucleus and positive shell.
2. The object has no intermediate “empty” space.
3. The cross section of the object is diminishing with the Q grows.
4. The transport cross sections of the corresponding anti-particles are significantly less than for the ordinary matter (compare figures 7.6.2 – 7.6.6 and 7.6.7 – 7.6.11). This fact leads to discrepancy between concentration of particles and anti-particles.

Charge, parity, and time reversal symmetry is a fundamental symmetry of physical laws under the simultaneous transformations of charge conjugation (C), parity transformation (P) and time reversal (T). These results can lead to additional problems in the CPT theory (see also [138, 139]).

Conclusion

1. In the frame of restrictions of the Schrödinger model nonlocal physics leads to appearance of resonance curves using the Schrödinger terminology.
2. The results are obtained as a solution to the Cauchy problem. The area of the solution existence is determined automatically. This conclusion applies also to calculations of the structure of electron and proton.
3. Schrödinger equation (SE) has obvious shortcomings:
a. SE has phenomenological character.
b. SE does not contain dissipation in principle, because Schrödinger – Madelung theory has no independent energy equation. Then strictly speaking SE cannot be applied for investigation of dissipative systems including nanotechnology.
c. Schrödinger – Madelung theory cannot be applied to the self-consistent modeling "shell-nucleus". Schrödinger theory needs in additional principles like Pauli principle.
d. Schrödinger theory does not contain spin.
e. In many cases the appearance of quantum numbers has the artificial character as a result of truncation an infinite series and turning it into a polynomial. In this case, we have the effect of the appearance of nodes of a standing wave. A typical example is a rubber cord tied at one end to a wall as a demonstration of the superposition of the incident and reflected waves.

I agree with Schrödinger that appearance of jumps is only a mathematical effect of phenomenological theory like appearance of the infinitely thin shock wave in aerodynamics.

7.7. Nonlocal physics and biophysics.

In this Item 7.7 I intend to discuss the connection between nonlocal physics and biophysics. Moreover I'm convinced that nonlocal physics is the single natural bridge between theoretical physics and biophysics. From this position it is interesting the Schrödinger opinion about this problem. His position is concentrated in lections in Trinity College delivered in Dublin in February, 1943, [140]. A feature of the lectures was the intention of the lecturer to clarify the primary ideas (associated with biology and with physics), to physicists and biologists.

Namely: how can physics and chemistry explain the phenomena in space and time that occur inside a living organism? The preliminary answer given by Schrödinger can be formulated as follows: the apparent inability of modern physics and chemistry to explain such phenomena does not give reason to doubt that they can be explained by these sciences in future. A chromosome is a deoxyribonucleic acid (DNA) molecule with part or all of the genetic material (genome) of an organism. Schrödinger talks about the location of the chromosome as stable inherited "properties" or "attributes". In reality these “attributes” are certain material structures (genes), differences in which lead to modifications of certain properties of the whole organism.

As you know, the gene (from the ancient Greek γένος-genus) - structural and functional unit of heredity of living organisms. Initially, the term "gene" appeared as a theoretical unit of transmission of discrete hereditary information. A gene is a section of DNA that specifies the sequence of a particular polypeptide or functional RNA. Gene size is determined in two completely independent ways. One is based on genetic data (crossbreeding experiments), the other on cytological data (direct microscopic observation).

The first method is quite simple. By establishing the location of various features (large scale) within a particular chromosome (say, in the fly Drosophila), determining the size of the gene is reduced to dividing the length of this chromosome by the number of features. The characteristic size of the gene is a cube with a side of 300 Å. Gene is a very stable formation. As a result, selection fails because small, continuous differences are not inherited. They are obviously not due to the structure of the hereditary substance, they are accidental.

Hugo de Vries (1848 – 1935), the Dutchman, came to believe that new species do not arise by the gradual accumulation of continuous fluctuating changes, as the Darwinists believed, but by the sudden appearance of abrupt changes that transform one species into another. The appearance of these sudden changes, transforming one species into another, de Vries called mutation. A long search for a species that would possess these mutational changes remained fruitless until de Vries found near Hilversum near Amsterdam (1886) a large number of biennial wild plants from the species of plants (Oenothera lamarckiana). Plants of this species their behavior is fully consistent with the views of de Vries on the process of evolution [141].

In other words, in the offspring of even perfectly pure lines, a very small number of individuals appear — say, two or three in tens of thousands — with small but abrupt changes. The expression discontinuous in this case does not mean that the changes are very significant, but only the fact of discontinuity, since there are no intermediate forms between the unmodified individuals and the few modified. According to Schrödinger, the physics of mutation resembles quantum theory - there is also no intermediate steps between the two adjacent energy levels of the atom. A physicist would be inclined to call de Vries ' mutation theory figuratively the quantum theory of biology.

Here there is a contradiction in Schrodinger's views. On the one hand, he denies the existence of jumps in quantum theory without an intermediate process (the theory of resonances, see section 7.6), and on the other hand, he is forced to use the terminology of the Copenhagen school of physics. Schrödinger is fully aware of the inconsistency of this position and writes that for small-scale systems, most characteristics change intermittently. They are "quantized" in exactly the same way as energy. Therefore, if a number of atomic nuclei, including orbital electrons, are close to each other and form a "system", they are already able to take not all the arbitrary configurations that we can imagine.

Their own nature leaves them to choose from a numerous but intermittent series of "states." We usually call these states as energy levels, because energy is a very important characteristic. And further: "I accept the interpretation which is usually given in popular books, and which is satisfactory also for our purpose, but I myself always condemn those who fix a convenient error. The true picture is much more complex, as it involves much more characteristics than just energy." In fact, it is more correct to imagine the state as a certain configuration of all particles. The transition from one configuration to another is a quantum leap. If the second configuration corresponds to a large energy (higher level), then for the transition of the system to this level, it must receive energy from the outside, which is not less than the energy difference corresponding to these states. At a lower level, the system can go spontaneously, emitting excess energy in the form of radiation.

The origin of mutations really owes "quantum jumps" in the gene molecule. Mutations are inherited just as well. It is necessary only in Darwin's theory to replace its "small random changes" with mutations (just as in quantum theory "quantum transition" replaces "continuous change of energy"). In all other respects, only very small changes were necessary in Darwin's theory. Mutation can be caused by exposure to x-rays on the gene. It is essential that the mutation is not the accumulated result of successive irradiation in small doses that would enhance one another. Mutation is a single phenomenon that occurs in the chromosome under the influence of x-rays, exceeding a certain threshold. The lower limit of the number of ionization or accompanying processes (excitations) in live tissue is obtained by multiplying the number of ionization in air by the ratio of their densities. Thus, the phenomenon that causes a single mutation is ionization (or some other process) that occurs within a certain "critical" volume of the germ cell. Max Delbrück (1906 – 1981, Nobel prize in physiology or medicine, 1969) estimated this volume as 10 average atomic distances taken in a cube; this volume thus contains only about 1,000 atoms. The simplest interpretation of this result is that there is a sufficient probability of occurrence of this mutation, if ionization (or excitation) occurs no further than at a distance of about 10 atoms from a certain place in the chromosome.

There is another point of view. There is a danger of increasing mutational pressure on the future of humanity due to increased background radiation, especially after the development and testing of nuclear weapons and the use of more chemicals in everyday life. There is no genetically harmless dose of radiation. The question arises: how can we reconcile, from the point of view of statistical physics, the fact that the gene structure seems to include only a relatively small number of atoms (about 1000, and perhaps much less) and yet shows a very regular activity and such constancy as borders on a miracle. Schrödinger gives an example of this surprising position.

Several members of the Habsburg dynasty had a special lower lip shape ("Habsburg lip"). The inheritance of this trait has been studied very carefully, and the results published by the Imperial Academy in Vienna. The trait turned out to be a real Mendelian allele in relation to the normal lip. Looking closely at portraits of family members who lived in the sixteenth and nineteenth centuries, we can confidently say that the material gene structure responsible for this abnormal trait was passed down from generation to generation over the centuries and reproduced exactly in each of the few cell divisions that occurred during this period. Moreover, the number of atoms contained in the corresponding gene structure should probably be of the same order as in the cases tested with x-rays. All this time, the gene was at a temperature of about 36° C. How do you know that it has remained unchanged for centuries, despite the tendency of thermal motion to disrupt the order in the structure? Schrödinger then uses the language and terminology of thermodynamics.

What, then, is the precious something contained in our food that protects us from death? That's easy to answer. Every process, phenomenon, event (call it what you will), in short, everything that happens in Nature, means an increase in entropy in the part of the Universe where it takes place. And a living organism continuously increases its entropy, or else produces positive entropy, and thus approaches the dangerous state of maximum entropy, which is death. He can escape this state, that is, remain alive, only by constantly extracting from his environment a negative entropy, which is something very positive, as we shall presently see. Negative entropy is what an organism feeds on. Or, to put it less paradoxically, what is essential in metabolism is that the organism manages to free itself of all the entropy it is forced to produce while it is alive.

The unfolding of events in the life cycle of the organism reveals a remarkable regularity unmatched by anything we encounter in inanimate objects. The organism is controlled by a highly well-ordered group of atoms, which make up only a very small part of the total mass of each cell. Moreover, from our point of view of the mechanism of mutations, we conclude that the movement of only a few atoms within the group of "governing atoms" of the germ cell is sufficient to cause a very definite change in the hereditary characteristics of a large scale. When approaching the temperature of absolute zero molecular disorder ceases to affect physical phenomena. This was found in the study of chemical reactions in wide temperature ranges and the subsequent extrapolation of the results to a virtually unattainable temperature equal to absolute zero. This result is a thermodynamic theorem of Walter Nernst, which is called the third principle of thermodynamics (the first-the law of conservation of energy, the second — the law of evolution of entropy).

What is the temperature in each case is almost equivalent to zero? Now, Schrodinger writes, one should not think that it must always be a very low temperature. Indeed, Nernst's discovery was prompted by the fact that even at room temperature entropy plays a surprisingly minor role in many chemical reactions. Quantum uncertainty is of no fundamental importance for biological processes. Schrödinger explains the stability of the gene by the aperiodic crystal effect. A molecule that has the correct periodic arrangement of its constituent particles is a crystal. He calls this formation an aperiodic crystal or solid, and hypothesizes that a gene, or perhaps an entire chromosomal strand, is an aperiodic solid.

What is the reason for Schrödinger's dual position, the attraction of equilibrium thermodynamics and the ideas of discrete description in the form of discrete quantum jumps, which Schrödinger himself considered a relic of the old Copenhagen quantum theory. The fact is that the gene necessarily leads to the appearance of quantum solitons. But the wave packets in Schrodinger's theory are blurred! This undoubted fact does not allow us to connect Schrödinger's quantum mechanics with the discrete gene in quantum Biophysics.

From this point of view, it is interesting to study the theoretical studies of the outstanding
scientist Joseph Abramovich Rapoport (March 14, 1912, — December 31, 1990, Moscow). He was a Soviet geneticist who discovered chemical mutagenesis. In particular he was corresponding member of the USSR Academy of Sciences (since 1979), Winner of the Lenin prize (1984), Hero of Socialist Labor (1990).

Joseph Rapoport graduated from the biology faculty of Leningrad State University, where, after defending his thesis, he took a course in genetics. This was followed by postgraduate studies in the genetic laboratory of the Institute of experimental biology of the USSR Academy of Sciences, headed by biologist Nikolai Konstantinovich Koltsov.

Postgraduate studies were completed in 1938, and the thesis for the title of candidate of biological sciences was defended at the Institute of genetics of the USSR Academy of Sciences.
During the Second World War, Joseph Rapoport went from platoon commander to chief of staff of the 184-th guards regiment 62nd guards rifle division, was seriously wounded twice, lost his left eye. May 5, 1943 defended his doctoral dissertation, while on treatment after one of the wounds. The doctorate itself was written before the war, and its defense was scheduled for the end of June 1941, but postponed due to conscription. For courage and ingenuity shown on the battlefields of the guard Rapoport was awarded two orders of the Red Banner, the order of the Patriotic War of the first degree, the order of Suvorov of the third degree, the American order "Legion of Honor". He was three times presented for the title Hero of the Soviet Union.

After the war, Joseph Rapoport continued research in the field of genetics at the Institute of Cytology, histology and embryology of the USSR Academy of Sciences. The main scientific achievement Rapoport was the discovery of chemicals that had strong mutagenic properties, and conduct appropriate experiments on fruit flies, confirming the initial guesses and insights of a scientist, which later resulted in the independent section of genetics, known as chemical mutagenesis.

At the "August session of Agricultural Academy" in 1948, Joseph Rapoport, being a supporter of genetics, opposed the views of academician T. D. Lysenko. In 1949, for disagreeing with the decisions of this session and "failure to recognize mistakes" Rappaport was expelled from the CPSU(b).

The defeat of genetics and subsequent punitive measures against its adherents, consisting primarily in the collapse of scientific schools and forced retraining of scientists did not pass by Joseph Rapoport: from 1949 to 1957, he worked as an employee of the expeditions of the Oil and geological ministries, dealing with paleontology and stratigraphy.

In 1957, Rapoport returned to research in the field of genetics: at the Institute of chemical physics of the USSR Academy of Sciences, together with a group of scientists, he is searching for chemical mutagens, analyzing their properties in comparison with radiation mutagens. In 1962, the Nobel Committee informed the Soviet authorities about the nomination of Rapoport (together with Charlotte Auerbach) for the Nobel Prize for the discovery of chemical mutagenesis.

In 1965, at the suggestion of academician N. N. Semenov in the same Institute of chemical physics begins the creation of a Department of chemical genetics consisting of four laboratories. This allowed expanding research in a number of areas of theoretical and experimental genetics, but the main topic remained the study of hereditary and non-hereditary variability. Since the early 1960s, the implementation of the results in agricultural breeding has unfolded. In the early 1970s, Joseph Rapoport was awarded the order of the Red Banner of Labor; in 1979 he was elected a corresponding member of the USSR Academy of Sciences in the Department of biology.

In 1984 he was awarded the Lenin prize. By the decree of the President of the USSR of October 16, 1990 Joseph Rapoport was awarded the title of Hero of Socialist Labor with the wording "for a special contribution to the preservation and development of genetics and breeding, training of highly qualified scientific personnel".

His doctoral dissertation was published in the form of a monograph entitled "Microgenetics", which also contained theoretical biophysics. The main thesis was a new thermodynamic interpretation of genetics as a zero-entropy system for living systems. In other words, the thermodynamics of the genome was considered as an independent law of thermodynamics.

The state of the discrete micro-genetic apparatus is able to maintain stationarity in conditions where it is impossible for other molecular bodies. Genetic bodies are credited with the ability to maintain a remarkable ordering and existence in the temperature range of $T = 300K \pm (25^{\circ}C)$ and resist their destruction, while nucleic acids under the same conditions are marked by a significant amount of entropy. The zero state is the most probable condition for the deployment of the internal field of the elementary body. Zero condition automatically determines a zero entropy genetic structure. A system cannot enter a state with energy less than zero energy without changing the structure of the system. Genetic nucleotides cannot go into a state below themselves, otherwise they will turn into a chemical structure, so nucleotides are at zero.

In the micro-genetic material of almost all living forms there is the same extremely rigid standard of composition of the ensemble of amino acids and nucleotides. This limited set of structural members remains almost unchanged throughout the long history of the living. Zero entropy, exists only in the triplets and nucleotides within genes. Free nucleotides and triplets can not create a gene structure without the participation of the matrix, although this occasionally occurs in a spontaneous order.

This theoretical model has caused a sharply negative attitude of theoretical physicists (including academician Igor E. Tamm). The book was withdrawn and years later was restored to drafts and republished.

It is interesting to add that as long as the virus is in the extracellular environment or in the process of infecting the cell, it exists as an independent particle. Viral particles (virions) consist of two or three components: genetic material in the form of DNA or RNA; a protein shell that protects these molecules, and, in some cases, additional lipid shells. Viruses are obligate parasites, since they are not able to reproduce outside the cell. Outside the cell, viral particles do not show signs of life and behave like particles of biopolymers. In other words virus is a complex of organic molecules that interact with living organisms. Viruses have genetic material, but are devoid of cellular structure.

Most viruses vary in diameter from 20 nm to 250–400 nm; the largest, however, measure about 500 nm in diameter and are about 700–1,000 nm in length. Only the largest and most complex viruses can be seen under the light microscope at the highest resolution. The diameter of an atom ranges from about 0.1 to 0.5 nanometers (1×10^{-10} m to 5×10^{-10} m). An atom is a million times smaller than the thickest human hair and in a thousand times smaller than the typical virus diameter. Nevertheless the transport processes in media containing the virus objects can be considered in the frame nonlocal physical kinetics.

As we can see, I. A. Rapoport was fully aware that it is impossible for quantum biophysics to use Schrödinger's quantum mechanics without radical transformation. This "protest" he transformed into the “fourth” law of thermodynamics.

I can only note that quantum solitons are a common, "routine" object of nonlocal physics. Nonlocal physics is the bridge between theoretical Physics and theoretical Biophysics.

CHAPTER 8. NON-LOCAL PHYSICS IN THE THEORY OF GRAVITATIONAL WAVES AND THE MATTER MOVEMENT IN BLACK HOLES

The theory of the matter movement in black holes (BH) in the frame of non – local quantum hydrodynamics (NLQHD) is considered. The theory corresponds to the limit case when the matter density tends to infinity when the theory of General Relativity is not applicable in principle. From calculations follow that NLQHD equations for the black holes have the solutions limited in space. The domain of the solution existence is limited by the event horizon where gravity tends to infinity. It was shown: 1) internal perturbations in BH lead to the appearance of the packets of the gravitational waves. 2) The width of the wave packet is inversely proportional to the magnitude of internal energy. 3) Increasing of the internal energy leads to the transformation of the mode of anti-gravity into the attraction regime. 4) A strong mutual influence of the gravitational, anti-gravitational and electromagnetic fields exists. The velocity of gravitational waves is more than the speed of light. The numerical calculations of the Cauchy problem are delivered. The domain of the solution existence is limited by the event horizon where gravity tends to infinity. The simple analytical particular cases and numerical calculations are delivered.

Keywords: Black Holes, Transport processes in Black Holes, Velocity of gravitational waves, Microscopic and macroscopic Black Holes, Explosive maximon instability, transformations of gravitation and anti-gravitation regimes, The theory of traveling waves

8.1. Introduction to Chapter 8

The first ideas about the existence of cosmic objects which gravitation is be so big that the escape velocity would be faster than the speed of light, were formulated in 1783 by English geologist named John Michell. In 1796, Pierre-Simon Laplace promoted the same idea in his book "Exposition du système du Monde". In 1916 Albert Einstein introduced an explanation of gravity called general relativity. According to the general theory of relativity, a black hole is a region of space from which nothing, including light, can escape. It is the result of "the denting of spacetime" caused by a very compact mass.

In 1930, Subrahmanyan Chandrasekhar [142, 143] predicted that stars heavier than the Sun could collapse when they ran out of hydrogen or other nuclear fuels to burn and die. In 1967, John Wheeler gave black holes the name "black hole" (BH) for the first time, [144]. Astronomers have identified numerous stellar black hole candidates, and have also found evidence of super massive black holes at the center of every galaxy.

In 1970, Stephen Hawking and Roger Penrose proved that black holes must exist (see for example [145]). Around a black hole there is an undetectable surface which marks the point of no return, called an event horizon. It is called "black" because it absorbs all the light that hits it, reflecting nothing, just like a perfect black body in thermodynamics. Black holes possess a temperature (and therefore the internal energy) and emit Hawking radiation through slow dissipation by anti-protons. This temperature is on the order of billionths of a kelvin for black holes of stellar mass, making it essentially impossible to observe. BH could be also electrically charged.

Let us investigate the possibilities delivering by the unified generalized quantum hydrodynamics [20, 146] for investigation of these problems. From position of non – local quantum hydrodynamics (NLQHD) the mentioned theory has two limit cases connected with the density ρ evolution:

1. The density $\rho \to \infty$. From the physical point of view this case corresponds to the matter motion in the Black Hole regime.

2. The density $\rho \to 0$. From the physical point of view this case corresponds to the motion in the Big Bang regime.

Newtonian gravity propagates with the infinite speed. This conclusion is connected only with the description in the frame of local physics. Usual affirmation - general relativity (GR) reduces to Newtonian gravity in the weak-field, low-velocity limit. In literature you can find criticism of this affirmation because the conservation of angular momentum is implicit in the assumptions on which GR rests. Finite propagation speeds and conservation of angular momentum are incompatible in GR. Therefore, GR was forced to claim that gravity is not a force that propagates in any classical sense, and that aberration does not apply.

But here I do not intend to join to this widely discussed topic using only unified non-local model.

8.2. Main transport equations.

Strict consideration leads to the following system of the generalized hydrodynamic equations (GHE) [20] written in the generalized Euler form: continuity equation for species α

$$\frac{\partial}{\partial t}\left\{\rho_\alpha-\tau_\alpha\left[\frac{\partial\rho_\alpha}{\partial t}+\frac{\partial}{\partial\mathbf{r}}\cdot(\rho_\alpha\mathbf{v}_0)\right]\right\}+\frac{\partial}{\partial\mathbf{r}}\cdot\left\{\rho_\alpha\mathbf{v}_0-\tau_\alpha\left[\frac{\partial}{\partial t}(\rho_\alpha\mathbf{v}_0)+\frac{\partial}{\partial\mathbf{r}}\cdot(\rho_\alpha\mathbf{v}_0\mathbf{v}_0)+\overset{\leftrightarrow}{\mathrm{I}}\cdot\frac{\partial p_\alpha}{\partial\mathbf{r}}\right.\right.$$
$$\left.\left.-\rho_\alpha\mathbf{F}_\alpha^{(1)}-\frac{q_\alpha}{m_\alpha}\rho_\alpha\mathbf{v}_0\times\mathbf{B}\right]\right\}=R_\alpha,$$

(8.2.1)

and continuity equation for mixture

$$\frac{\partial}{\partial t}\left\{\rho-\sum_\alpha\tau_\alpha\left[\frac{\partial\rho_\alpha}{\partial t}+\frac{\partial}{\partial\mathbf{r}}\cdot(\rho_\alpha\mathbf{v}_0)\right]\right\}+\frac{\partial}{\partial\mathbf{r}}\cdot\left\{\rho\mathbf{v}_0-\sum_\alpha\tau_\alpha\left[\frac{\partial}{\partial t}(\rho_\alpha\mathbf{v}_0)+\frac{\partial}{\partial\mathbf{r}}\cdot(\rho_\alpha\mathbf{v}_0\mathbf{v}_0)\right.\right.$$
$$\left.\left.+\overset{\leftrightarrow}{\mathrm{I}}\cdot\frac{\partial p_\alpha}{\partial\mathbf{r}}-\rho_\alpha\mathbf{F}_\alpha^{(1)}-\frac{q_\alpha}{m_\alpha}\rho_\alpha\mathbf{v}_0\times\mathbf{B}\right]\right\}=0.$$

(8.2.2)

Momentum equation for species

$$\frac{\partial}{\partial t}\left\{\rho_\alpha\mathbf{v}_0-\tau_\alpha\left[\frac{\partial}{\partial t}(\rho_\alpha\mathbf{v}_0)+\frac{\partial}{\partial\mathbf{r}}\cdot\rho_\alpha\mathbf{v}_0\mathbf{v}_0+\frac{\partial p_\alpha}{\partial\mathbf{r}}-\rho_\alpha\mathbf{F}_\alpha^{(1)}\right.\right.$$
$$\left.\left.-\frac{q_\alpha}{m_\alpha}\rho_\alpha\mathbf{v}_0\times\mathbf{B}\right]\right\}-\mathbf{F}_\alpha^{(1)}\left[\rho_\alpha-\tau_\alpha\left(\frac{\partial\rho_\alpha}{\partial t}+\frac{\partial}{\partial\mathbf{r}}(\rho_\alpha\mathbf{v}_0)\right)\right]-$$
$$-\frac{q_\alpha}{m_\alpha}\left\{\rho_\alpha\mathbf{v}_0-\tau_\alpha\left[\frac{\partial}{\partial t}(\rho_\alpha\mathbf{v}_0)+\frac{\partial}{\partial\mathbf{r}}\cdot\rho_\alpha\mathbf{v}_0\mathbf{v}_0+\frac{\partial p_\alpha}{\partial\mathbf{r}}-\rho_\alpha\mathbf{F}_\alpha^{(1)}\right.\right.$$
$$\left.\left.-\frac{q_\alpha}{m_\alpha}\rho_\alpha\mathbf{v}_0\times\mathbf{B}\right]\right\}\times\mathbf{B}+\frac{\partial}{\partial\mathbf{r}}\cdot\left\{\rho_\alpha\mathbf{v}_0\mathbf{v}_0+p_\alpha\overset{\leftrightarrow}{\mathrm{I}}-\tau_\alpha\left[\frac{\partial}{\partial t}\left(\rho_\alpha\mathbf{v}_0\mathbf{v}_0\right.\right.\right. \qquad (8.2.3)$$
$$\left.+p_\alpha\overset{\leftrightarrow}{\mathrm{I}}\right)+\frac{\partial}{\partial\mathbf{r}}\cdot\rho_\alpha(\mathbf{v}_0\mathbf{v}_0)\mathbf{v}_0+2\overset{\leftrightarrow}{\mathrm{I}}\left(\frac{\partial}{\partial\mathbf{r}}\cdot(p_\alpha\mathbf{v}_0)\right)+\frac{\partial}{\partial\mathbf{r}}\cdot\left(\overset{\leftrightarrow}{\mathrm{I}}p_\alpha\mathbf{v}_0\right)$$
$$\left.\left.-\mathbf{F}_\alpha^{(1)}\rho_\alpha\mathbf{v}_0-\rho_\alpha\mathbf{v}_0\mathbf{F}_\alpha^{(1)}-\frac{q_\alpha}{m_\alpha}\rho_\alpha[\mathbf{v}_0\times\mathbf{B}]\mathbf{v}_0-\frac{q_\alpha}{m_\alpha}\rho_\alpha\mathbf{v}_0[\mathbf{v}_0\times\mathbf{B}]\right]\right\}$$
$$=\int m_\alpha\mathbf{v}_\alpha J_\alpha^{st,el}d\mathbf{v}_\alpha+\int m_\alpha\mathbf{v}_\alpha J_\alpha^{st,inel}d\mathbf{v}_\alpha.$$

Generalized moment equation for mixture

$$
\begin{aligned}
&\frac{\partial}{\partial t}\left\{\rho\mathbf{v}_0-\sum_\alpha\tau_\alpha\left[\frac{\partial}{\partial t}(\rho_\alpha\mathbf{v}_0)+\frac{\partial}{\partial\mathbf{r}}\cdot\rho_\alpha\mathbf{v}_0\mathbf{v}_0+\frac{\partial p_\alpha}{\partial\mathbf{r}}-\rho_\alpha\mathbf{F}_\alpha^{(1)}\right.\right.\\
&\left.\left.-\frac{q_\alpha}{m_\alpha}\rho_\alpha\mathbf{v}_0\times\mathbf{B}\right]\right\}-\sum_\alpha\mathbf{F}_\alpha^{(1)}\left[\rho_\alpha-\tau_\alpha\left(\frac{\partial\rho_\alpha}{\partial t}+\frac{\partial}{\partial\mathbf{r}}(\rho_\alpha\mathbf{v}_0)\right)\right]\\
&-\sum_\alpha\frac{q_\alpha}{m_\alpha}\left\{\rho_\alpha\mathbf{v}_0-\tau_\alpha^{(0)}\left[\frac{\partial}{\partial t}(\rho_\alpha\mathbf{v}_0)+\frac{\partial}{\partial\mathbf{r}}\cdot\rho_\alpha\mathbf{v}_0\mathbf{v}_0+\frac{\partial p_\alpha}{\partial\mathbf{r}}-\rho_\alpha\mathbf{F}_\alpha^{(1)}\right.\right.\\
&\left.\left.-\frac{q_\alpha}{m_\alpha}\rho_\alpha\mathbf{v}_0\times\mathbf{B}\right]\right\}\times\mathbf{B}+\frac{\partial}{\partial\mathbf{r}}\cdot\left\{\rho\mathbf{v}_0\mathbf{v}_0+p\tilde{\mathrm{I}}-\sum_\alpha\tau_\alpha\left[\frac{\partial}{\partial t}(\rho_\alpha\mathbf{v}_0\mathbf{v}_0\right.\right.\\
&+p_\alpha\tilde{\mathrm{I}})+\frac{\partial}{\partial\mathbf{r}}\cdot\rho_\alpha(\mathbf{v}_0\mathbf{v}_0)\mathbf{v}_0+2\tilde{\mathrm{I}}\left(\frac{\partial}{\partial\mathbf{r}}\cdot(p_\alpha\mathbf{v}_0)\right)+\frac{\partial}{\partial\mathbf{r}}\cdot(\tilde{\mathrm{I}}p_\alpha\mathbf{v}_0)\\
&\left.\left.-\mathbf{F}_\alpha^{(1)}\rho_\alpha\mathbf{v}_0-\rho_\alpha\mathbf{v}_0\mathbf{F}_\alpha^{(1)}-\frac{q_\alpha}{m_\alpha}\rho_\alpha[\mathbf{v}_0\times\mathbf{B}]\mathbf{v}_0-\frac{q_\alpha}{m_\alpha}\rho_\alpha\mathbf{v}_0[\mathbf{v}_0\times\mathbf{B}]\right]\right\}=0
\end{aligned}
\tag{8.2.4}
$$

Energy equation for component

$$
\begin{aligned}
&\frac{\partial}{\partial t}\left\{\frac{\rho_\alpha v_0^2}{2}+\frac{3}{2}p_\alpha+\varepsilon_\alpha n_\alpha-\tau_\alpha\left[\frac{\partial}{\partial t}\left(\frac{\rho_\alpha v_0^2}{2}+\frac{3}{2}p_\alpha+\varepsilon_\alpha n_\alpha\right)\right.\right.\\
&\left.\left.+\frac{\partial}{\partial\mathbf{r}}\cdot\left(\frac{1}{2}\rho_\alpha v_0^2\mathbf{v}_0+\frac{5}{2}p_\alpha\mathbf{v}_0+\varepsilon_\alpha n_\alpha\mathbf{v}_0\right)-\mathbf{F}_\alpha^{(1)}\cdot\rho_\alpha\mathbf{v}_0\right]\right\}\\
&+\frac{\partial}{\partial\mathbf{r}}\cdot\left\{\frac{1}{2}\rho_\alpha v_0^2\mathbf{v}_0+\frac{5}{2}p_\alpha\mathbf{v}_0+\varepsilon_\alpha n_\alpha\mathbf{v}_0-\tau_\alpha\left[\frac{\partial}{\partial t}\left(\frac{1}{2}\rho_\alpha v_0^2\mathbf{v}_0\right.\right.\right.\\
&\left.+\frac{5}{2}p_\alpha\mathbf{v}_0+\varepsilon_\alpha n_\alpha\mathbf{v}_0\right)+\frac{\partial}{\partial\mathbf{r}}\cdot\left(\frac{1}{2}\rho_\alpha v_0^2\mathbf{v}_0\mathbf{v}_0+\frac{7}{2}p_\alpha\mathbf{v}_0\mathbf{v}_0+\frac{1}{2}p_\alpha v_0^2\tilde{\mathrm{I}}\right.\\
&\left.+\frac{5}{2}\frac{p_\alpha^2}{\rho_\alpha}\tilde{\mathrm{I}}+\varepsilon_\alpha n_\alpha\mathbf{v}_0\mathbf{v}_0+\varepsilon_\alpha\frac{p_\alpha}{m_\alpha}\tilde{\mathrm{I}}\right)-\rho_\alpha\mathbf{F}_\alpha^{(1)}\cdot\mathbf{v}_0\mathbf{v}_0-p_\alpha\mathbf{F}_\alpha^{(1)}\cdot\tilde{\mathrm{I}}\\
&-\frac{1}{2}\rho_\alpha v_0^2\mathbf{F}_\alpha^{(1)}-\frac{3}{2}\mathbf{F}_\alpha^{(1)}p_\alpha-\frac{\rho_\alpha v_0^2}{2}\frac{q_\alpha}{m_\alpha}[\mathbf{v}_0\times\mathbf{B}]-\frac{5}{2}p_\alpha\frac{q_\alpha}{m_\alpha}[\mathbf{v}_0\times\mathbf{B}]\\
&\left.\left.-\varepsilon_\alpha n_\alpha\frac{q_\alpha}{m_\alpha}[\mathbf{v}_0\times\mathbf{B}]-\varepsilon_\alpha n_\alpha\mathbf{F}_\alpha^{(1)}\right]\right\}\\
&-\left\{\rho_\alpha\mathbf{F}_\alpha^{(1)}\cdot\mathbf{v}_0-\tau_\alpha\left[\mathbf{F}_\alpha^{(1)}\cdot\left(\frac{\partial}{\partial t}(\rho_\alpha\mathbf{v}_0)+\frac{\partial}{\partial\mathbf{r}}\cdot\rho_\alpha\mathbf{v}_0\mathbf{v}_0+\frac{\partial}{\partial\mathbf{r}}\cdot p_\alpha\tilde{\mathrm{I}}-\rho_\alpha\mathbf{F}_\alpha^{(1)}-q_\alpha n_\alpha[\mathbf{v}_0\times\mathbf{B}]\right)\right]\right\}\\
&=\int\left(\frac{m_\alpha v_\alpha^2}{2}+\varepsilon_\alpha\right)J_\alpha^{st,el}d\mathbf{v}_\alpha+\int\left(\frac{m_\alpha v_\alpha^2}{2}+\varepsilon_\alpha\right)J_\alpha^{st,inel}d\mathbf{v}_\alpha.
\end{aligned}
\tag{8.2.5}
$$

and after summation the generalized energy equation for mixture

$$
\frac{\partial}{\partial t}\left\{\frac{\rho v_0^2}{2}+\frac{3}{2}p+\sum_\alpha \varepsilon_\alpha n_\alpha-\sum_\alpha \tau_\alpha\left[\frac{\partial}{\partial t}\left(\frac{\rho_\alpha v_0^2}{2}+\frac{3}{2}p_\alpha+\varepsilon_\alpha n_\alpha\right)\right.\right.
$$

$$
\left.\left.+\frac{\partial}{\partial \mathbf{r}}\cdot\left(\frac{1}{2}\rho_\alpha v_0^2\mathbf{v}_0+\frac{5}{2}p_\alpha\mathbf{v}_0+\varepsilon_\alpha n_\alpha\mathbf{v}_0\right)-\mathbf{F}_\alpha^{(1)}\cdot\rho_\alpha\mathbf{v}_0\right]\right\}
$$

$$
+\frac{\partial}{\partial \mathbf{r}}\cdot\left\{\frac{1}{2}\rho v_0^2\mathbf{v}_0+\frac{5}{2}p\mathbf{v}_0+\mathbf{v}_0\sum_\alpha\varepsilon_\alpha n_\alpha-\sum_\alpha\tau_\alpha\left[\frac{\partial}{\partial t}\left(\frac{1}{2}\rho_\alpha v_0^2\mathbf{v}_0\right.\right.\right.
$$

$$
\left.+\frac{5}{2}p_\alpha\mathbf{v}_0+\varepsilon_\alpha n_\alpha\mathbf{v}_0\right)+\frac{\partial}{\partial \mathbf{r}}\cdot\left(\frac{1}{2}\rho_\alpha v_0^2\mathbf{v}_0\mathbf{v}_0+\frac{7}{2}p_\alpha\mathbf{v}_0\mathbf{v}_0+\frac{1}{2}p_\alpha v_0^2\vec{\mathrm{I}}\right.
$$

$$
\left.+\frac{5}{2}\frac{p_\alpha^2}{\rho_\alpha}\vec{\mathrm{I}}+\varepsilon_\alpha n_\alpha\mathbf{v}_0\mathbf{v}_0+\varepsilon_\alpha\frac{p_\alpha}{m_\alpha}\vec{\mathrm{I}}\right)-\rho_\alpha\mathbf{F}_\alpha^{(1)}\cdot\mathbf{v}_0\mathbf{v}_0-p_\alpha\mathbf{F}_\alpha^{(1)}\cdot\vec{\mathrm{I}}
$$

$$
-\frac{1}{2}\rho_\alpha v_0^2\mathbf{F}_\alpha^{(1)}-\frac{3}{2}\mathbf{F}_\alpha^{(1)}p_\alpha-\frac{\rho_\alpha v_0^2}{2}\frac{q_\alpha}{m_\alpha}[\mathbf{v}_0\times\mathbf{B}]-\frac{5}{2}p_\alpha\frac{q_\alpha}{m_\alpha}[\mathbf{v}_0\times\mathbf{B}]
$$

$$
\left.\left.-\varepsilon_\alpha n_\alpha\frac{q_\alpha}{m_\alpha}[\mathbf{v}_0\times\mathbf{B}]-\varepsilon_\alpha n_\alpha\mathbf{F}_\alpha^{(1)}\right]\right\}-\mathbf{v}_0\cdot\sum_\alpha\rho_\alpha\mathbf{F}_\alpha^{(1)}
$$

$$
+\sum_\alpha\tau_\alpha\mathbf{F}_\alpha^{(1)}\cdot\left[\frac{\partial}{\partial t}(\rho_\alpha\mathbf{v}_0)+\frac{\partial}{\partial \mathbf{r}}\cdot\rho_\alpha\mathbf{v}_0\mathbf{v}_0+\frac{\partial}{\partial \mathbf{r}}\cdot p_\alpha\vec{\mathrm{I}}-\rho_\alpha\mathbf{F}_\alpha^{(1)}-q_\alpha n_\alpha[\mathbf{v}_0\times\mathbf{B}]\right]=0.
$$

(8.2.6)

Here $\mathbf{F}_\alpha^{(1)}$ are the forces of the non-magnetic origin acting on the mass unit, $\mathbf{B}$ - magnetic induction, $\vec{\mathrm{I}}$ - unit tensor, q_α - charge of the α-component particle, p_α - static pressure for α-component, ε_α - internal energy for the particles of α- component, $\mathbf{v}_0$ - hydrodynamic velocity for mixture. For calculations in the self-consistent electro-magnetic field the system of non-local Maxwell equations should be added.

In the following item we intend to consider the 1D transport processes in the spherical one species Black Holes (BH) after perturbations on the BH surface.

The nonlocal 1D hydrodynamic equations (8.2.2), (8.2.4), (8.2.6) take the form:

continuity equation (non-stationary spherically symmetric case)

$$
\frac{\partial}{\partial t}\left\{\rho-\tau\left[\frac{\partial\rho}{\partial t}+\frac{1}{r^2}\frac{\partial(r^2\rho v_{0r})}{\partial r}\right]\right\}+\frac{1}{r^2}\frac{\partial}{\partial r}\left\{r^2\left\{\rho v_{0r}-\tau\left[\frac{\partial}{\partial t}(\rho v_{0r})+\frac{1}{r^2}\frac{\partial(r^2\rho v_{0r}^2)}{\partial r}-F_r\right]\right\}\right\} \quad (8.2.7)
$$

$$
-\frac{1}{r^2}\frac{\partial}{\partial r}\left(\tau r^2\frac{\partial p}{\partial r}\right)=0,
$$

where τ is a non-locality parameter.

Momentum equation in the non-stationary spherically symmetric case is

$$\frac{\partial}{\partial t}\left\{\rho v_{0r}-\tau\left[\frac{\partial}{\partial t}(\rho v_{0r})+\frac{1}{r^2}\frac{\partial(r^2\rho v_{0r}^2)}{\partial r}+\frac{\partial p}{\partial r}-F_r\right]\right\}-\left[F_r-\tau g_r\left(\frac{\partial\rho}{\partial t}+\frac{1}{r^2}\frac{\partial(r^2\rho v_{0r})}{\partial r}\right)\right]$$
$$+\frac{1}{r^2}\frac{\partial}{\partial r}\left\{r^2\left\{\rho v_{0r}^2-\tau\left[\frac{\partial}{\partial t}(\rho v_{0r}^2)+\frac{1}{r^2}\frac{\partial(r^2\rho v_{0r}^3)}{\partial r}-2F_r v_{0r}\right]\right\}\right\}$$
$$+\frac{\partial p}{\partial r}-\frac{\partial}{\partial r}\left(\tau\frac{\partial p}{\partial t}\right)-2\frac{\partial}{\partial r}\left(\frac{\tau}{r^2}\frac{\partial(r^2 p v_{0r})}{\partial r}\right)-\frac{1}{r^2}\frac{\partial}{\partial r}\left(\tau r^2\frac{\partial(p v_{0r})}{\partial r}\right)=0. \qquad (8.2.8)$$

The energy equation

$$\frac{\partial}{\partial t}\left\{\frac{1}{2}\rho v_{0r}^2+\frac{3}{2}p-\tau\left[\frac{\partial}{\partial t}\left(\frac{1}{2}\rho v_{0r}^2+\frac{3}{2}p\right)+\frac{1}{r^2}\frac{\partial}{\partial r}\left(r^2 v_{0r}\left(\frac{1}{2}\rho v_{0r}^2+\frac{5}{2}p\right)\right)-F_r v_{0r}\right]\right\}$$
$$+\frac{1}{r^2}\frac{\partial}{\partial r}\left\{r^2\left\{\left(\frac{1}{2}\rho v_{0r}^2+\frac{5}{2}p\right)v_{0r}-\tau\left[\frac{\partial}{\partial t}\left(\left(\frac{1}{2}\rho v_{0r}^2+\frac{5}{2}p\right)v_{0r}\right)+\frac{1}{r^2}\frac{\partial}{\partial r}\left(r^2\left(\frac{1}{2}\rho v_{0r}^2+\frac{7}{2}p\right)v_{0r}^2\right)\right.\right.\right.$$
$$\left.\left.\left.-F_r v_{0r}^2-\left(\frac{1}{2}\rho v_{0r}^2+\frac{3}{2}p\right)g_r\right]\right\}\right\}-\left\{F_r v_{0r}-\tau\left[g_r\left(\frac{\partial}{\partial t}(\rho v_{or})+\frac{1}{r^2}\frac{\partial}{\partial r}(r^2\rho v_{0r}^2)+\frac{\partial p}{\partial r}-F_r\right)\right]\right\}$$
$$-\frac{1}{r^2}\frac{\partial}{\partial r}\left(\tau r^2\frac{\partial}{\partial r}\left(\frac{1}{2}p v_{0r}^2+\frac{5}{2}\frac{p^2}{\rho}\right)\right)+\frac{1}{r^2}\frac{\partial}{\partial r}(r^2\tau p g_r)=0. \qquad (8.2.9)$$

We consider the limit case of the one species system in which the density $\rho\to\infty$. From the physical point of view this case corresponds to the matter motion in the Black Hole regime. Let us introduce now the main mentioned before assumption leading to the theory of motion inside the black holes: the density $\rho\to\infty$. In deriving the basic system of equations, we should take into account two facts:

1. The density can tend to infinity by the arbitrary law.
2. The ratio of pressure to density defines the internal energy of the mass unit $E=p/\rho$ and should be considered as a dependent variable by $\rho\to\infty$.

As result we have the following system of equations (see also Appendix 1):

(continuity equation)

$$\frac{\partial}{\partial t}\left\{\tau\left[\frac{1}{r^2}\frac{\partial(r^2 v_{0r})}{\partial r}\right]\right\}-\frac{1}{r^2}\frac{\partial}{\partial r}\left\{r^2\left\{v_{0r}-\tau\left[\frac{\partial v_{0r}}{\partial t}+\frac{1}{r^2}\frac{\partial(r^2 v_{0r}^2)}{\partial r}-g_r\right]\right\}\right\}+\frac{1}{r^2}\frac{\partial}{\partial r}\left(\tau r^2\frac{\partial E}{\partial r}\right)=0, \qquad (8.2.10)$$

(momentum equation)

$$\frac{\partial}{\partial t}\left\{v_{0r}-\tau\left[\frac{\partial}{\partial t}(v_{0r})+\frac{1}{r^2}\frac{\partial\left(r^2v_{0r}^2\right)}{\partial r}+\frac{\partial E}{\partial r}-g_r\right]\right\}-\left[g_r-\tau g_r\left(\frac{1}{r^2}\frac{\partial\left(r^2v_{0r}\right)}{\partial r}\right)\right]$$

$$+\frac{1}{r^2}\frac{\partial}{\partial r}\left\{r^2\left\{v_{0r}^2-\tau\left[\frac{\partial}{\partial t}\left(v_{0r}^2\right)+\frac{1}{r^2}\frac{\partial\left(r^2v_{0r}^3\right)}{\partial r}-2g_rv_{0r}\right]\right\}\right\}$$

$$+\frac{\partial E}{\partial r}-\frac{\partial}{\partial r}\left(\tau\frac{\partial E}{\partial t}\right)-2\frac{\partial}{\partial r}\left(\frac{\tau}{r^2}\frac{\partial\left(r^2Ev_{0r}\right)}{\partial r}\right)-\frac{1}{r^2}\frac{\partial}{\partial r}\left(\tau r^2\frac{\partial\left(Ev_{0r}\right)}{\partial r}\right)=0. \quad (8.2.11)$$

(energy equation)

$$\frac{\partial}{\partial t}\left\{\frac{1}{2}v_{0r}^2+\frac{3}{2}E-\tau\left[\frac{\partial}{\partial t}\left(\frac{1}{2}v_{0r}^2+\frac{3}{2}E\right)+\frac{1}{r^2}\frac{\partial}{\partial r}\left(r^2v_{0r}\left(\frac{1}{2}v_{0r}^2+\frac{5}{2}E\right)\right)-g_rv_{0r}\right]\right\}+$$

$$+\frac{1}{r^2}\frac{\partial}{\partial r}\left\{r^2\left\{\left(\frac{1}{2}v_{0r}^2+\frac{5}{2}E\right)v_{0r}-\tau\left[\frac{\partial}{\partial t}\left(\left(\frac{1}{2}v_{0r}^2+\frac{5}{2}E\right)v_{0r}\right)+\frac{1}{r^2}\frac{\partial}{\partial r}\left(r^2\left(\frac{1}{2}v_{0r}^2+\frac{7}{2}E\right)v_{0r}^2\right)-\right.\right.\right.$$

$$\left.\left.\left.-g_rv_{0r}^2-\left(\frac{1}{2}v_{0r}^2+\frac{3}{2}E\right)g_r\right]\right\}\right\}-g_r\left\{v_{0r}-\tau\left[\frac{\partial v_{0r}}{\partial t}+\frac{1}{r^2}\frac{\partial}{\partial r}\left(r^2v_{0r}^2\right)+\frac{\partial E}{\partial r}-g_r\right]\right\}-$$

$$-\frac{1}{r^2}\frac{\partial}{\partial r}\left(\tau r^2\frac{\partial}{\partial r}\left(\frac{1}{2}Ev_{0r}^2+\frac{5}{2}E^2\right)\right)+\frac{1}{r^2}\frac{\partial}{\partial r}\left(r^2\tau Eg_r\right)=0. \quad (8.2.12)$$

The transfer to the stationary case leads to the result:
(continuity equation)

$$\frac{\partial}{\partial r}\left\{r^2\left[v_{0r}-\tau\left(\frac{1}{r^2}\frac{\partial\left(r^2v_{0r}^2\right)}{\partial r}-g_r\right)\right]\right\}-\frac{\partial}{\partial r}\left(\tau r^2\frac{\partial E}{\partial r}\right)=0, \quad (8.2.13)$$

(momentum equation)

$$\frac{\partial E}{\partial r}-g_r+\tau g_r\left(\frac{1}{r^2}\frac{\partial\left(r^2v_{0r}\right)}{\partial r}\right)+\frac{1}{r^2}\frac{\partial}{\partial r}\left\{r^2\left[v_{0r}^2-\tau\left(\frac{1}{r^2}\frac{\partial\left(r^2v_{0r}^3\right)}{\partial r}-2g_rv_{0r}\right)\right]\right\}$$

$$-2\frac{\partial}{\partial r}\left(\frac{\tau}{r^2}\frac{\partial\left(r^2Ev_{0r}\right)}{\partial r}\right)-\frac{1}{r^2}\frac{\partial}{\partial r}\left(\tau r^2\frac{\partial\left(Ev_{0r}\right)}{\partial r}\right)=0 \quad (8.2.14)$$

(energy equation)

$$\frac{1}{r^2}\frac{\partial}{\partial r}\left\{r^2\left\{\left(v_{0r}^2+5E\right)v_{0r}-\tau\left[\frac{1}{r^2}\frac{\partial}{\partial r}\left(r^2\left(v_{0r}^2+7E\right)v_{0r}^2\right)-2g_rv_{0r}^2-\left(v_{0r}^2+3E\right)g_r\right]\right\}\right\}$$

$$-2g_r\left\{v_{0r}-\tau\left[\frac{1}{r^2}\frac{\partial}{\partial r}\left(r^2v_{0r}^2\right)+\frac{\partial E}{\partial r}-g_r\right]\right\}-\frac{1}{r^2}\frac{\partial}{\partial r}\left(\tau r^2\frac{\partial}{\partial r}\left(Ev_{0r}^2+5E^2\right)\right)$$

$$+\frac{2}{r^2}\frac{\partial}{\partial r}\left(r^2\tau Eg_r\right)=0 \quad (8.2.15)$$

8.3. Transformations of nonlocal transport equations

The nonlocal continuity equation can be immediately integrated

$$v_{0r}-\tau\left(\frac{1}{r^2}\frac{\partial\left(r^2v_{0r}^2\right)}{\partial r}+\frac{\partial E}{\partial r}-g_r\right)=0. \tag{8.3.1}$$

From (8.3.1) follows the relation

$$\frac{\partial\left(r^2v_{0r}^2\right)}{\partial r}=\frac{1}{\tau}v_{0r}r^2-r^2\left(\frac{\partial E}{\partial r}-g_r\right) \tag{8.3.2}$$

which is used in the following transformations of momentum and energy equations. Obvious question - what equations correspond to the local physical description ($\tau=0$)? From (8.3.1) we find $v_{0r}=0$, from momentum equation one obtains the transparent force relation

$$\frac{\partial E}{\partial r}-g_r=0 \tag{8.3.3}$$

and energy equation (8.2.15) is satisfied identically. Then the local description of transport processes in BH leads to the unacceptable physical picture.

As the result we have the system of equations for unknown values: $E,\ v_{0r},\ g_r$:

1. $\tau\neq const$

$$v_{0r}-\tau\left(\frac{1}{r^2}\frac{\partial\left(r^2v_{0r}^2\right)}{\partial r}+\frac{\partial E}{\partial r}-g_r\right)=0, \tag{8.3.4}$$

$$\begin{gathered}r^2\left[\frac{\partial E}{\partial r}-g_r\right]+\frac{\partial}{\partial r}\left\{r^2v_{0r}^2\right\}-\frac{\partial}{\partial r}\left\{\tau\frac{\partial\left(r^2v_{0r}^3\right)}{\partial r}\right\}+3\tau g_r\frac{\partial}{\partial r}\left\{r^2v_{0r}\right\}+2v_{0r}r^2\frac{\partial}{\partial r}\left\{\tau g_r\right\}-\\-3r^2\frac{\partial}{\partial r}\left(\tau\frac{\partial\left(Ev_{0r}\right)}{\partial r}\right)-4r\frac{\partial}{\partial r}\left(\tau Ev_{0r}\right)+4\tau Ev_{0r}-2r\tau\frac{\partial\left(Ev_{0r}\right)}{\partial r}=0,\end{gathered} \tag{8.3.5}$$

$$\begin{gathered}\frac{\partial}{\partial r}\left\{r^2\left[\left(v_{0r}^2+5E\right)v_{0r}\right]\right\}-2r^2v_{0r}g_r-\\-\frac{\partial}{\partial r}\left\{\tau\left[r^2\frac{\partial}{\partial r}\left(\left(v_{0r}^2+8E\right)v_{0r}^2\right)+2r\left(v_{0r}^2+7E\right)v_{0r}^2-3r^2g_rv_{0r}^2-5r^2Eg_r+10r^2E\frac{\partial E}{\partial r}\right]\right\}\\+2g_r\tau\left(\frac{\partial}{\partial r}\left(r^2v_{0r}^2\right)+r^2\frac{\partial E}{\partial r}-r^2g_r\right)=0\end{gathered} \tag{8.3.6}$$

2. For the case $\tau=const$ we obtain the system

$$v_{0r} - \tau\left(\frac{1}{r^2}\frac{\partial\left(r^2 v_{0r}^2\right)}{\partial r} + \frac{\partial E}{\partial r} - g_r\right) = 0\,,$$

$$\begin{aligned} & r^2\left[\frac{\partial E}{\partial r} - g_r\right] + \frac{\partial}{\partial r}\left\{r^2 v_{0r}^2\right\} - \tau\frac{\partial^2\left(r^2 v_{0r}^3\right)}{\partial r^2} + 3\tau g_r\frac{\partial}{\partial r}\left\{r^2 v_{0r}\right\} + 2v_{0r} r^2 \tau\frac{\partial g_r}{\partial r} - \\ & -3r^2\tau\frac{\partial^2\left(E v_{0r}\right)}{\partial r^2} + 4\tau E v_{0r} - 6r\tau\frac{\partial\left(E v_{0r}\right)}{\partial r} = 0, \end{aligned} \quad (8.3.7)$$

$$\begin{aligned} & \frac{\partial}{\partial r}\left\{r^2\left[\left(v_{0r}^2 + 5E\right)v_{0r}\right]\right\} - 2r^2 v_{0r} g_r - \\ & -\tau\frac{\partial}{\partial r}\left[r^2\frac{\partial}{\partial r}\left(\left(v_{0r}^2 + 8E\right)v_{0r}^2\right) + 2r\left(v_{0r}^2 + 7E\right)v_{0r}^2 - 3r^2 g_r v_{0r}^2 - 5r^2 E g_r + 10r^2 E\frac{\partial E}{\partial r}\right] \\ & + 2g_r\tau\left(\frac{\partial}{\partial r}\left(r^2 v_{0r}^2\right) + r^2\frac{\partial E}{\partial r} - r^2 g_r\right) = 0 \end{aligned} \quad (8.3.8)$$

We use (8.3.2) for the transformation of the moment equation (8.3.7). We have

$$\begin{aligned} & 3r^2\frac{\partial^2\left(E v_{0r}\right)}{\partial r^2} + \frac{\partial^2\left(r^2 v_{0r}^3\right)}{\partial r^2} - 3g_r\frac{\partial}{\partial r}\left\{r^2 v_{0r}\right\} - 2v_{0r} r^2\frac{\partial g_r}{\partial r} - \\ & -4E v_{0r} + 6r\frac{\partial\left(E v_{0r}\right)}{\partial r} - \frac{1}{\tau}\frac{\partial}{\partial r}\left\{r^2 v_{0r}^2\right\} - r^2\frac{1}{\tau}\left[\frac{\partial E}{\partial r} - g_r\right] = 0, \end{aligned} \quad (8.3.9)$$

or

$$\begin{aligned} & 3r^2\frac{\partial^2\left(E v_{0r}\right)}{\partial r^2} + \frac{\partial^2\left(r^2 v_{0r}^3\right)}{\partial r^2} - 3g_r\frac{\partial}{\partial r}\left\{r^2 v_{0r}\right\} - 2v_{0r} r^2\frac{\partial g_r}{\partial r} - \\ & -4E v_{0r} + 6r\frac{\partial\left(E v_{0r}\right)}{\partial r} - \frac{1}{\tau}\frac{\partial}{\partial r}\left\{r^2 v_{0r}^2\right\} + \frac{1}{\tau}\frac{\partial\left(r^2 v_{0r}^2\right)}{\partial r} - \frac{1}{\tau^2} v_{0r} r^2 = 0, \end{aligned} \quad (8.3.10)$$

or

$$3r^2\frac{\partial^2\left(E v_{0r}\right)}{\partial r^2} + \frac{\partial^2\left(r^2 v_{0r}^3\right)}{\partial r^2} - 3g_r\frac{\partial}{\partial r}\left\{r^2 v_{0r}\right\} - 2v_{0r} r^2\frac{\partial g_r}{\partial r} - 4E v_{0r} + 6r\frac{\partial\left(E v_{0r}\right)}{\partial r} - \frac{1}{\tau^2} v_{0r} r^2 = 0$$

(8.3.11)

Transform analogically the energy equation (8.3.8). We find

$$\begin{aligned} & \frac{\partial}{\partial r}\left\{r^2\left[\left(v_{0r}^2 + 5E\right)v_{0r}\right]\right\} - \\ & -\tau\frac{\partial}{\partial r}\left[r^2\frac{\partial}{\partial r}\left(\left(v_{0r}^2 + 8E\right)v_{0r}^2\right) + 2r\left(v_{0r}^2 + 7E\right)v_{0r}^2 - 3r^2 g_r v_{0r}^2 - 5r^2 E g_r + 10r^2 E\frac{\partial E}{\partial r}\right] \\ & + 2g_r\tau\left(\frac{\partial}{\partial r}\left(r^2 v_{0r}^2\right) + r^2\left(\frac{\partial E}{\partial r} - g_r\right)\right) - 2r^2 v_{0r} g_r = 0 \end{aligned} \quad (8.3.12)$$

and using (8.3.2) we reach

$$\frac{\partial}{\partial r}\left\{r^2\left[\left(v_{0r}^2+5E\right)v_{0r}\right]\right\}-$$
$$-\tau\frac{\partial}{\partial r}\left[r^2\frac{\partial}{\partial r}\left(\left(v_{0r}^2+8E\right)v_{0r}^2\right)+2r\left(v_{0r}^2+7E\right)v_{0r}^2-3r^2g_rv_{0r}^2-5r^2Eg_r+10r^2E\frac{\partial E}{\partial r}\right]=0. \qquad (8.3.13)$$

This energy equation can be integrated

$$r^2\left(v_{0r}^2+5E\right)v_{0r}-$$
$$-\tau\left[r^2\frac{\partial}{\partial r}\left(\left(v_{0r}^2+8E\right)v_{0r}^2\right)+2r\left(v_{0r}^2+7E\right)v_{0r}^2-3r^2g_rv_{0r}^2-5r^2Eg_r+10r^2E\frac{\partial E}{\partial r}\right]+C=0. \qquad (8.3.14)$$

The constant C can be found using the condition for $r=0$. As a result we have $C=0$, then

$$\left(v_{0r}^2+5E\right)v_{0r}-$$
$$-\tau\left[\frac{\partial}{\partial r}\left(\left(v_{0r}^2+8E\right)v_{0r}^2\right)+\frac{2}{r}\left(v_{0r}^2+7E\right)v_{0r}^2-3g_rv_{0r}^2-5Eg_r+10E\frac{\partial E}{\partial r}\right]=0. \qquad (8.3.15)$$

The system of equations (8.3.1), (8.3.11) and (8.3.15) can be numerically integrated using for example the Maple possibilities.

8.4. Results of the mathematical modeling.

Let us formulate the mathematical problem:

1. We consider the limit case of the one species system in which the density $\rho\to\infty$. From the physical point of view this case corresponds to the matter motion in the Black Hole regime.
2. We intend to find the energy E, velocity v_{0r} and gravitational acceleration g_r in the vicinity of BH after appearing the speed and energy perturbations on the spherical BH surface.
3. The investigation of the Black Hole configuration in the spherical coordinate system leads to the appearance of the singular point at the origin $r=0$. The numeric problem of the transport processes description in the vicinity of this singular point is fully adequate to the analogue situation in the classic theory of the point explosion in the gas dynamics (see for example [147 - 154]). As usual with the aim to avoid the non-physical influence of the singularity $r=0$, the Lagrangian coordinates system is introduced and an additional area in

the vicinity $r=0$ where the Sedov's self-similar solution is fulfilled [148]. But we investigate the system evolution after appearance the perturbations on the spherical surface. As a result we have no problems with the mentioned singularity. The appearance of two boundaries for the equation solution corresponds to two event horizons.

In other words we intend to consider the BH evolution under influence of the perturbations of the Cauchy conditions. Therefore we reach the following system of equations (8.3.1), (8.3.7) and (8.3.15) written in the dimensionless form using the scales (dimensionless quantities marked with tilde)

$$[r_0],\ [u_0],\ [E_0],\ [t_0]=\frac{r_0}{u_0},\ [g_r]=\frac{u_0^2}{r_0}. \tag{8.4.1}$$

$$\tilde{v}_{0r}-\tilde{\tau}\left(\frac{1}{\tilde{r}^2}\frac{\partial(\tilde{r}^2\tilde{v}_{0r}^2)}{\partial\tilde{r}}+\frac{\partial\tilde{E}}{\partial\tilde{r}}-\tilde{g}_r\right)=0, \tag{8.4.2}$$

$$\begin{aligned}&\tilde{r}^2\left[\frac{\partial\tilde{E}}{\partial\tilde{r}}-\tilde{g}_r\right]+\frac{\partial}{\partial\tilde{r}}\left\{\tilde{r}^2\tilde{v}_{0r}^2\right\}-\tilde{\tau}\frac{\partial^2(\tilde{r}^2\tilde{v}_{0r}^3)}{\partial\tilde{r}^2}+3\tilde{\tau}\tilde{g}_r\frac{\partial}{\partial\tilde{r}}\left\{\tilde{r}^2\tilde{v}_{0r}\right\}+2\tilde{v}_{0r}\tilde{r}^2\tilde{\tau}\frac{\partial\tilde{g}_r}{\partial\tilde{r}}-\\&-3\tilde{r}^2\tilde{\tau}\frac{\partial^2(\tilde{E}\tilde{v}_{0r})}{\partial\tilde{r}^2}+4\tilde{\tau}\tilde{E}\tilde{v}_{0r}-6\tilde{r}\tilde{\tau}\frac{\partial(\tilde{E}\tilde{v}_{0r})}{\partial\tilde{r}}=0,\end{aligned} \tag{8.4.3}$$

$$\begin{aligned}&(\tilde{v}_{0r}^2+5\tilde{E})\tilde{v}_{0r}-\\&-\tilde{\tau}\left[\frac{\partial}{\partial\tilde{r}}\left((\tilde{v}_{0r}^2+8\tilde{E})\tilde{v}_{0r}^2\right)+\frac{2}{\tilde{r}}(\tilde{v}_{0r}^2+7\tilde{E})\tilde{v}_{0r}^2-3\tilde{g}_r\tilde{v}_{0r}^2-5\tilde{E}\tilde{g}_r+10\tilde{E}\frac{\partial\tilde{E}}{\partial\tilde{r}}\right]=0.\end{aligned} \tag{8.4.4}$$

Now we are ready to display the results of the mathematical modeling realized with the help of Maple (the versions Maple 9 or more can be used). The system (8.4.2) - (8.4.4) have the great possibilities of mathematical modeling as result of changing of five Cauchy conditions and parameter $\tilde{\tau}$ describing the character features of physical system.

Maple program contains Maple's notations – for example the expression $D(\tilde{v}_{0r})(1)=1$ means in the usual notations $(\partial\tilde{v}_{0r}/\partial\tilde{r})(1)=1$, independent variable t responds to $\tilde{r}$. The following Maple notations on figures are used: v- velocity $\tilde{v}_{0r}$, g - self-consistent gravitational acceleration $\tilde{g}$, and E- the energy $\tilde{E}$, T - $\tilde{\tau}$. Explanations placed under all following figures. The results of the calculations are presented in figures 8.4.1 - 8.4.19. The information required is contained in the figures and in figure captions. We use for all calculations reflected on figures 8.4.1 - 8.4.11 the Cauchy conditions

$$v_{0r}(1)=1,\ \tilde{E}(1)=1,\ D(\tilde{v}_{0r})(1)=1,\ D(\tilde{E})(1)=1,\ \tilde{g}(1)=1, \tag{8.4.5}$$

which of course can be changed; parameter $\widetilde{\tau}$ varies widely. As a rule we use the following lines: $\widetilde{v}_{0r}$ - solid line, $\widetilde{E}$ - dashed line, $\widetilde{g}$ - dotted line.

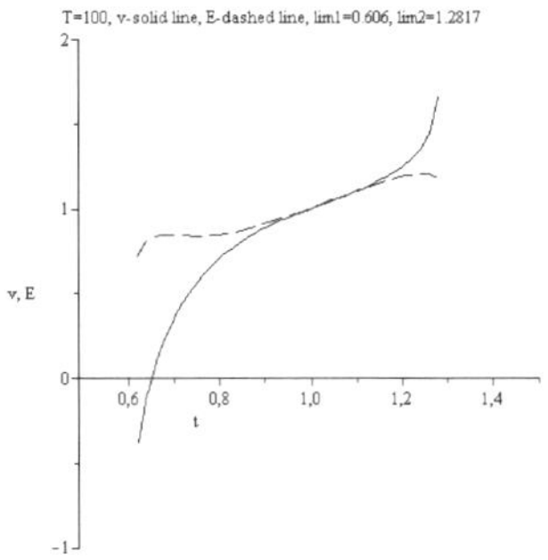

Fig. 8.4.1. Evolution of $\widetilde{v}(\widetilde{r})$, $\widetilde{E}(\widetilde{r})$; $\widetilde{\tau} = 100$.

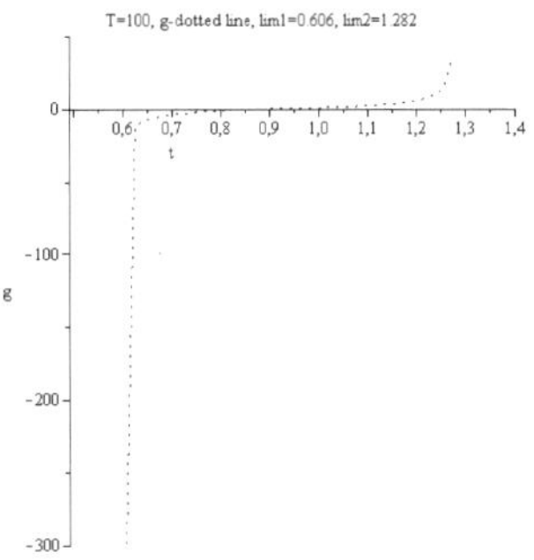

Fig. 8.4.2. Evolution of $\widetilde{g}(\widetilde{r})$; $\widetilde{\tau} = 100$.

As we see from figures 8.4.1 and 8.4.2 the left boundary of the solution existence is 0.606; the right boundary of the solution existence is 1.282 and the width of the perturbation zone is $\Delta\widetilde{r} = 0.676$.

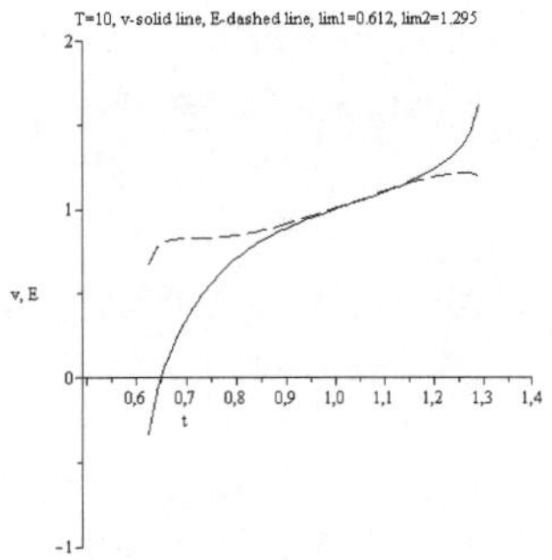

Fig. 8.4.3. Evolution of $\tilde{v}(\tilde{r})$, $\tilde{E}(\tilde{r})$; $\tilde{\tau}=10$.

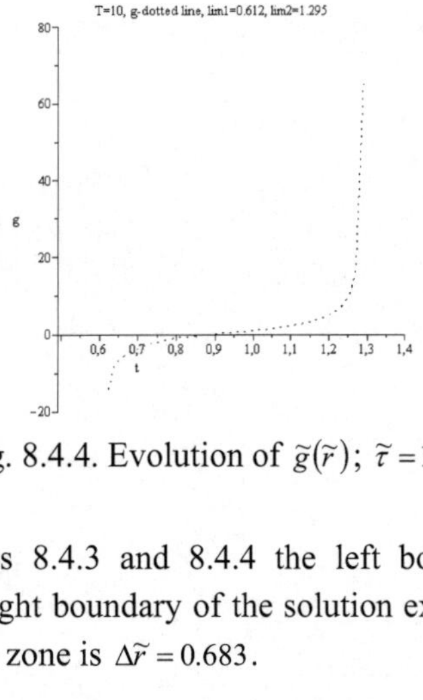

Fig. 8.4.4. Evolution of $\tilde{g}(\tilde{r})$; $\tilde{\tau}=10$.

As we see from figures 8.4.3 and 8.4.4 the left boundary of the solution existence is 0.612; the right boundary of the solution existence is 1.295 and the width of the perturbation zone is $\Delta\tilde{r}=0.683$.

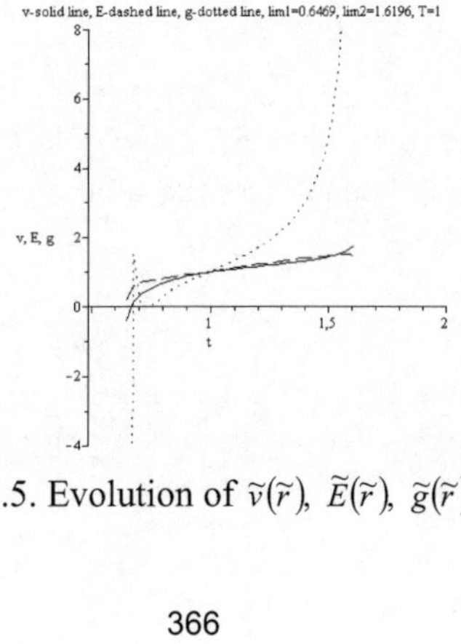

Fig. 8.4.5. Evolution of $\tilde{v}(\tilde{r})$, $\tilde{E}(\tilde{r})$, $\tilde{g}(\tilde{r})$; $\tilde{\tau}=1$.

From figure 8.4.5 follows that the left boundary of the solution existence is 0.647; the right boundary of the solution existence is 1.620 and the width of the perturbation zone is $\Delta\tilde{r} = 0.973$.

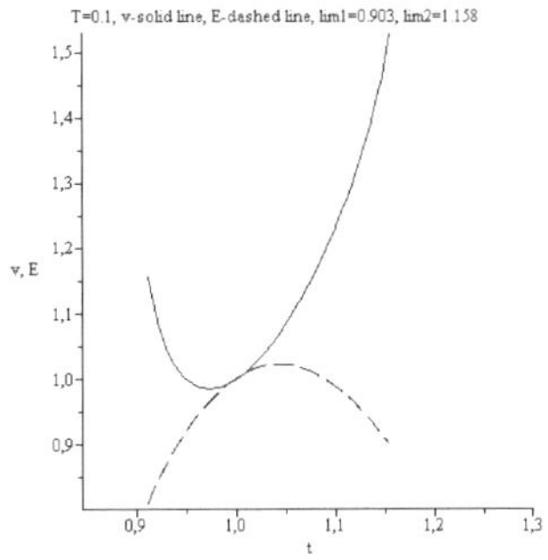

Fig. 8.4.6. Evolution of $\tilde{v}(\tilde{r})$, $\tilde{E}(\tilde{r})$; $\tilde{\tau} = 0.1$.

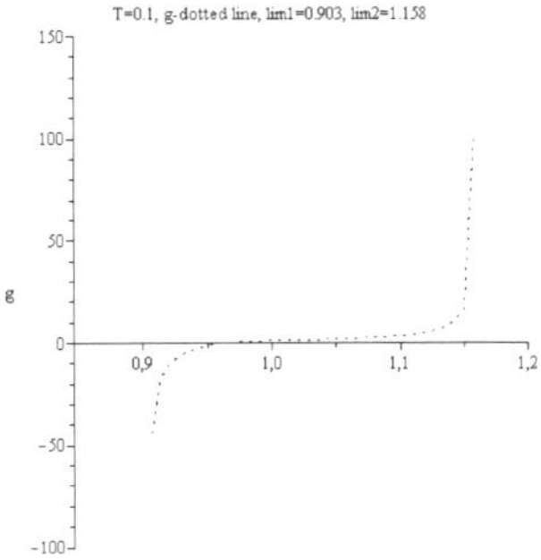

Fig. 8.4.7. Evolution of $\tilde{g}(\tilde{r})$; $\tilde{\tau} = 0{,}1$.

As we see from figures 8.4.6 and 8.4.7 the left boundary of the solution existence is 0.903; the right boundary of the solution existence is 1.158 and the width of the perturbation zone is $\Delta\tilde{r} = 0.255$.

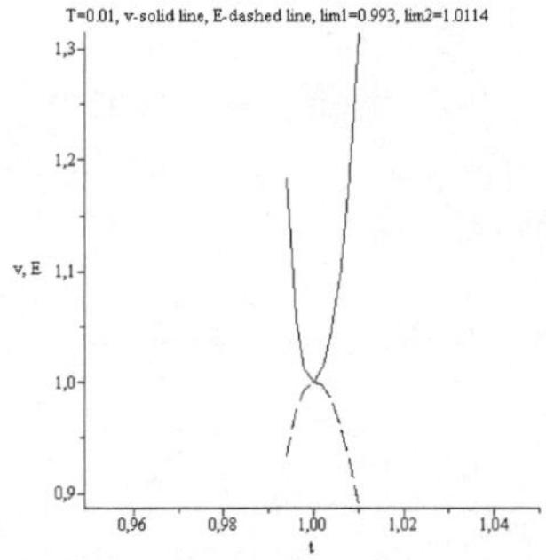

Fig. 8.4.8. Evolution of $\tilde{v}(\tilde{r})$, $\tilde{E}(\tilde{r})$; $\tilde{\tau} = 0.01$.

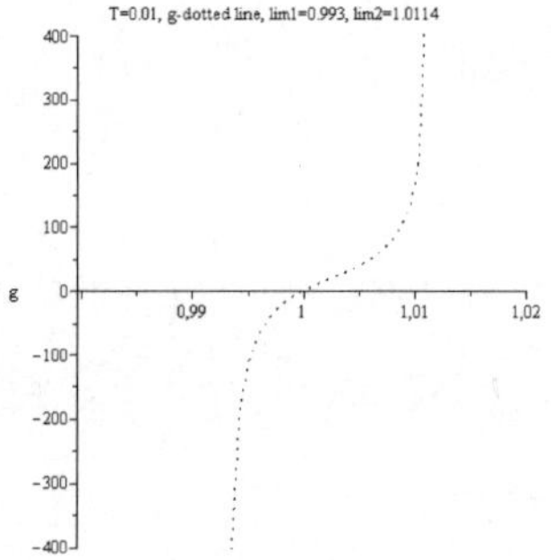

Fig. 8.4.9. Evolution of $\tilde{g}(\tilde{r})$; $\tilde{\tau} = 0.01$.

From figures 8.4.8 and 8.4.9 follow that the left boundary of the solution existence is 0.993; the right boundary of the solution existence is 1.011 and the width of the perturbation zone is $\Delta\tilde{r} = 0.0184$.

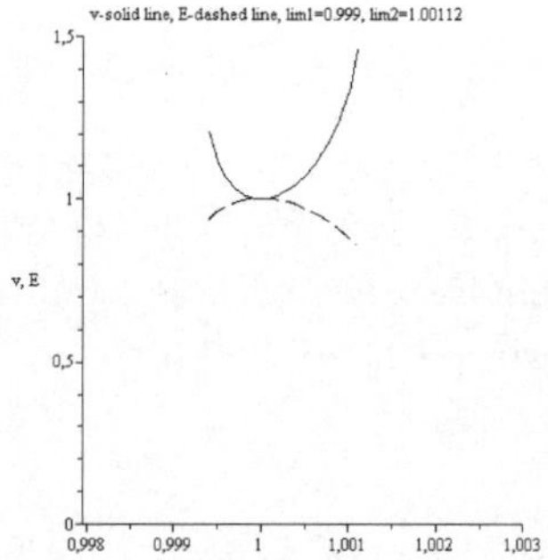

Fig. 8.4.10. Evolution of $\tilde{v}(\tilde{r})$, $\tilde{E}(\tilde{r})$; $\tilde{\tau} = 0.001$.

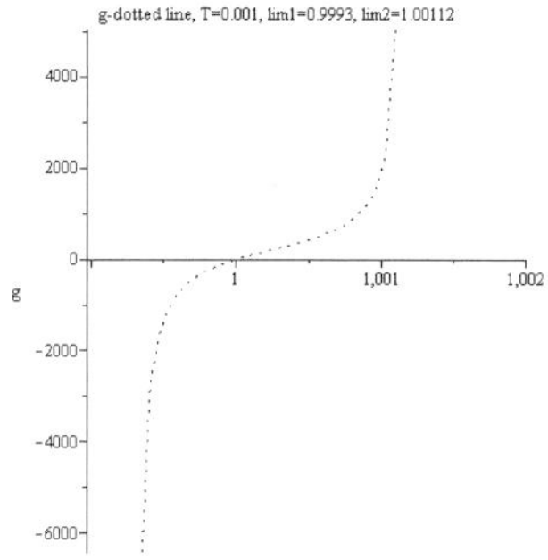

Fig. 8.4.11. Evolution of $\tilde{g}(\tilde{r})$; $\tilde{\tau} = 0.001$.

From figures 8.4.10 and 8.4.11 follow that the left boundary of the solution existence is 0.9993; the right boundary of the solution existence is 1.00112 and the width of the perturbation zone is $\Delta\tilde{r} = 0.00182$.

We use for the following calculations reflected on figures 8.4.12, 8.4.13 the Cauchy conditions

$$v_{0r}(1) = 1,\ \tilde{E}(1) = 1,\ D(\tilde{v}_{0r})(1) = -1,\ D(\tilde{E})(1) = -1,\ \tilde{g}(1) = 1, \qquad (8.4.6)$$

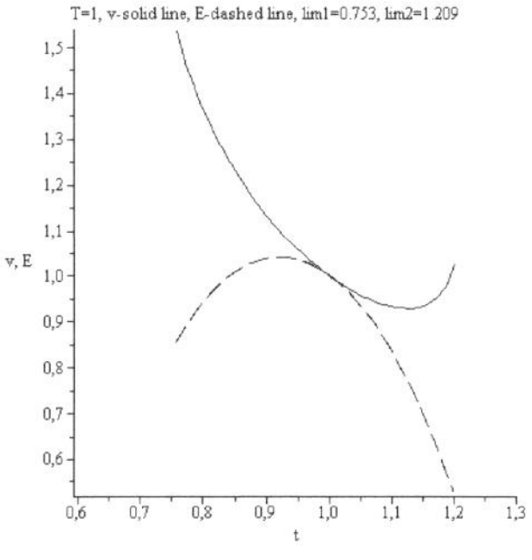

Fig. 8.4.12. Evolution of $\tilde{g}(\tilde{r})$; $\tilde{\tau} = 1$.

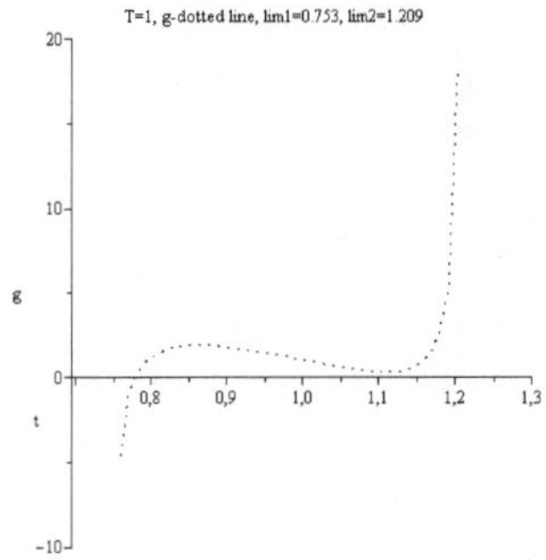

Fig. 8.4.13. Evolution of $\tilde{g}(\tilde{r})$; $\tilde{\tau}=1$.

From figures 8.4.12 and 8.4.13 follow that the left boundary of the solution existence is 0.753; the right boundary of the solution existence is 1.209 and the width of the perturbation zone is $\Delta\tilde{r}=0.456$. Compare now the results of the calculations shown in figures 8.4.5 and 8.4.12, 8.4.13, corresponding to the same value of the parameter τ but the opposite gradient values.

We see:

1. The width of the solution existence for the negative gradients in the Cauchy conditions diminished practically in two times.
2. The general features of the $\tilde{g}(\tilde{r})$ distribution remain the same.
3. The decrease in the nonlocal parameter $\tilde{\tau}$ (if $\tilde{\tau}<1$) leads to decreasing the width of the solution existence.

Let us investigate now the behavior of BH in the case of the very large $\tilde{\tau}$-parameters. For example this case can correspond to BH of small radii (see figures 8.4.14 - 8.4.16).

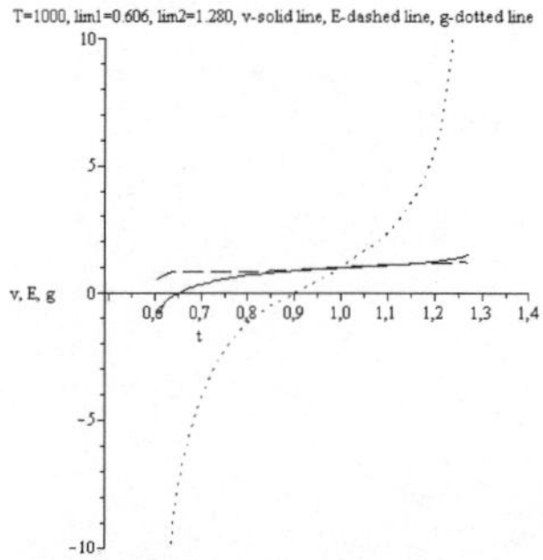

Fig. 8.4.14. Evolution of $\tilde{v}(\tilde{r})$, $\tilde{E}(\tilde{r})$, $\tilde{g}(\tilde{r})$; $\tilde{\tau}=1000$, Cauchy conditions (8.4.5).

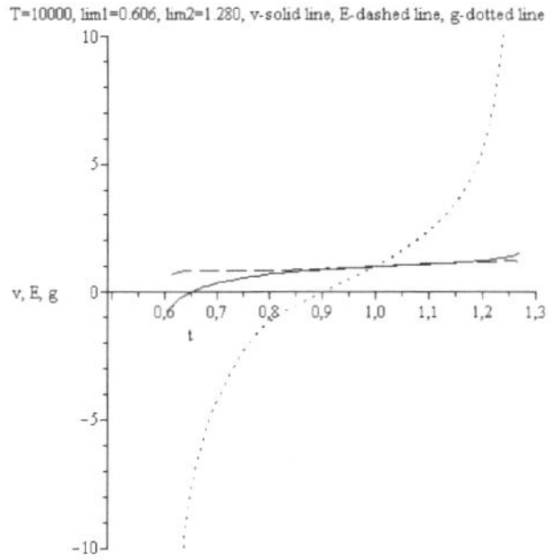

Fig.8.4.15. Evolution of $\widetilde{v}(\widetilde{r})$, $\widetilde{E}(\widetilde{r})$, $\widetilde{g}(\widetilde{r})$; $\widetilde{\tau}=10000$, Cauchy conditions (8.4.5).

From figures 8.4.2, 7.4.3, 8.4.14 and 8.4.15 follow that increasing dimensionless parameter $\widetilde{\tau}$ leads to the same limit distribution of the BH characteristics. For the negative gradients in the Cauchy conditions (4.6) we have the similar picture inside BH, see Figs. 8.4.12, 8.4.13 and 8.4.16.

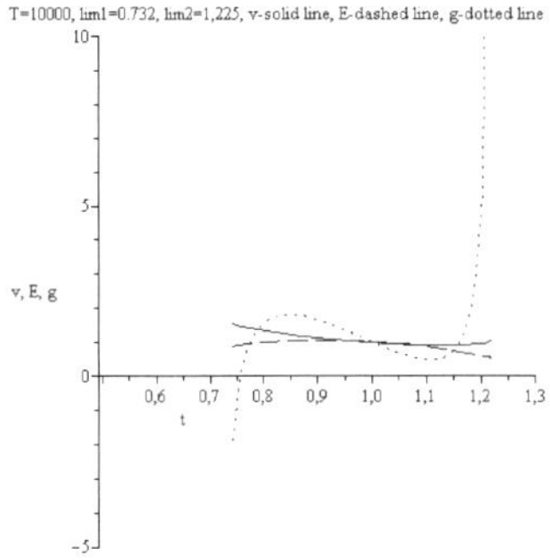

Fig. 8.4.16. Evolution of $\widetilde{v}(\widetilde{r})$, $\widetilde{E}(\widetilde{r})$, $\widetilde{g}(\widetilde{r})$; $\widetilde{\tau}=10000$, Cauchy conditions (8.4.6).

From figures 8.4.1 - 8.4.16 follow that the solutions exist in the finite domains of space. Let us deliver more details concerning the solution behavior near the boundaries of the perturbation zone. Compare for example the results of the calculations shown in figure 8.4.13 near the left and right boundaries. We find for the left boundary

$\widetilde{\tau}=0.753251,\ \widetilde{E}=0.8423862,\ \widetilde{v}=1.5889098,\ \widetilde{g}=-73937.719,\ \widetilde{\tau}_{\lim 1}=0.75325;$

for right boundary

$\tilde{\tau} = 1.20882243,\ \tilde{E} = 0.4900765,\ \tilde{v} = 1.2080964,\ \tilde{g} = 1265827699,\ \tilde{\tau}_{\lim 2} = 1.2088225$

$\tilde{\tau} = 1.20882244,\ \tilde{E} = 0.4900749,\ \tilde{v} = 1.207204,\ \tilde{g} = 183021.2718.$

The Maple program writes "cannot evaluate the solution further right $\lim 2 = 1.2088225$, probably singularity". Near the mentioned boundaries $\tilde{g} \to \pm\infty$ in spite of the finite values of energy $\tilde{E}$ and velocity $\tilde{v}$.

8.5. Multi-scale modeling and nonlocal physics. Maximon instabilities.

The concept of a massive body, whose gravitational attraction is so great that the velocity needed to overcome the gravity (the escape velocity) equals or exceeds the speed of light, was first proposed in 1784 by John Michell in a letter that he sent to the Royal society. The letter included a calculation, which indicated that for a radius of 500 solar radii and density of the Sun the escape velocity at its surface would equal the speed of light. Thus, the light will not be able to leave this body, and it will be invisible. Michelle suggested that in space there can be many such inaccessible to observation objects. In 1796, Laplace included a discussion of this idea in his work "Exposition du Systeme du Monde". These ideas have the very simple mathematical support in the frame of local physics.

According to the Newton's law the gravitational between two point-like bodies is directly proportional to the product of their masses (M and m) and inversely proportional to the distance r between them. In a Newtonian gravitational field for a particle at rest at infinity the law of conservation of energy is written as

$$-\frac{GMm}{r} + \frac{mv^2}{2} = 0, \qquad (8.5.1)$$

where G is the gravitational constant - an empirical physical constant involved in the calculation of gravitational effects in the Newton's law of universal gravitation and in the Einstein variant of general theory of relativity (GR). Its measured value is approximately $G = 6.674 \cdot 10^{-11} m^3 kg^{-1} s^{-2}$. From (8.5.1) follows the well known relation

$$r = \frac{2GM}{v^2}, \qquad (8.5.2)$$

which is transforming for $v = c$ in relation known even to Michell

$$r_g = \frac{2GM}{c^2}. \qquad (8.5.3)$$

The BH has a "horizon," which radius is $r = r_g$ defining the event horizon or Schwarzschild radius. It means there is a region from which you can't escape. But if you stay outside of the horizon, you can avoid getting sucked in. In other words, if the Universe mass tends to infinity the horizon radii also tends to infinity and from position of local physics (including GR) all Universe transforms into BH [155, 156].

As you see we investigate the limit case $M \to \infty$ which can not be considered in local physics including GR. Conclusions:

1. Limit case $\rho \to \infty$ does not lead to singularities in nonlocal description of the limit BH_∞.
2. The corresponding BH_∞ can form a stable structure of a finite size. In the definite sense we obtain the space quantization.
3. The perturbations on the BH_∞ surface do not destroy this object in the considered above calculations.
4. If dimensionless parameter $\tilde{\tau} \to \infty$ (for example for the very small radii) the BH_∞ structure tends to the limit reasonable structure.

Now we intend demonstrate how the multi-scale problems can be solved in nonlocal description. Two time limits exist in physics: τ_U - time of the visible Universe existence ($\sim 4.35 \cdot 10^{17} s$) and the Planck time τ_P ($\sim 5.39 \cdot 10^{-44} s$). The following definitions are used:

Planck length $l_P = \sqrt{\frac{\hbar G}{c^3}}$, Planck mass $m_P = \sqrt{\frac{\hbar c}{G}}$, Planck time $\tau_P = \frac{l_P}{c} = \frac{\hbar}{m_P c^2} = \sqrt{\frac{\hbar G}{c^5}}$, $G = 6.6739 \cdot 10^{-8} cm^3 / (g \cdot s^2)$, $c = 2.99 \cdot 10^{10} cm/s$. Let us calculate now the dimensional nonlocal time

$$\tau = \tilde{\tau} t_0 \tag{8.5.4}$$

for the before considered cases.

1. $t_0 = \tau_U$.

Let $\tilde{\tau} = 0.001$, then $\tau = 4.35 \cdot 10^{14} s$. It is reasonable to believe that it should be $\tilde{\tau} << \tilde{\tau}_U = 1$ in spite the existing reasonable numerical solutions for the larger $\tilde{\tau}$, referring to invisible part of the Universe. Interesting to notice, that the theories exist suggesting that our own Universe may be the interior of a black hole existing inside another Universe [157].

2. $t_0 = \tau_P$; $\tau = \tilde{\tau}\tau_P$. In this case $\tilde{E} = E / E_0 = E / E_P = E / (k_B T_P) = \sqrt{\frac{G}{\hbar c^5}} E$.

Let $\widetilde{\tau} = 0.001$, then $\tau = 5.39 \cdot 10^{-47} s$. It is reasonable to believe that it should be $\widetilde{\tau} \geq \widetilde{\tau}_P = 1$ in spite the existing reasonable numerical solutions for the smaller $\widetilde{\tau}$. Then for the scale $t_0 = \tau_P$ ($\widetilde{\tau} \geq 1$) the area begins of the maximon particles.

In 1966, Markov had suggested the existence of elementary particles with extremely large mass (maximón). Heavier particles, which the de-Broglie wavelength is less than their gravitational radius, may be quantum black holes. Since all known quantum particles have only certain possible values of the mass, it seems that quantum black holes should also have a discrete spectrum of well-defined masses. In [158] a theory is considered in which a 'maximon' (a particle of maximum mass in the mass spectrum of 'elementary particles') determines the numerical value of a 'minimon' (a particle of minimum, though nonzero, mass).

If $\tau = \widetilde{\tau}\tau_P$, as we see from the calculations presented in the figures (8.4.1) - (8.4.5), (8.4.14), (8.4.15) that the solutions exist in the same finite domains of space with the same distribution of the energy $\widetilde{E}$ and velocity $\widetilde{v}$. This investigation supports the maximon theory from nonlocal positions.

But what can be said about the maximon stability? Let us consider now the following calculations (see figures 8.5.1 - 8.5.4) from this point of view. We use the Cauchy conditions $v_{0r}(1) = 1$, $\widetilde{E}(1) = 1$, $D(\widetilde{v}_{0r})(1) = 1$, $\widetilde{g}(1) = 1$ with the variations of $D(\widetilde{E})(1)$.

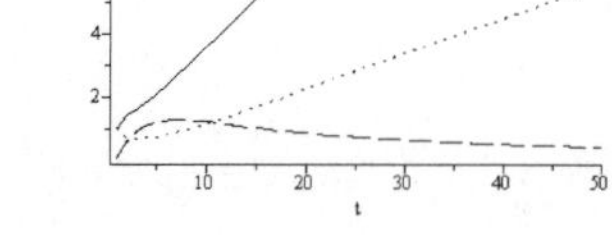

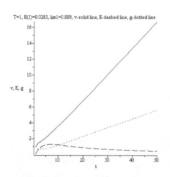

Fig. 8.5.1. Evolution of $\widetilde{v}(\widetilde{r})$, $\widetilde{E}(\widetilde{r})$, $\widetilde{g}(\widetilde{r})$; $\widetilde{\tau} = 1$, $\widetilde{E}(1) = 0.0285$.

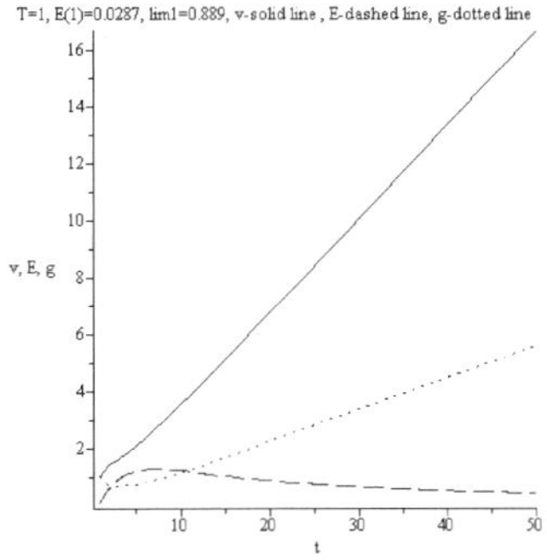

Fig. 8.5.2. Evolution of $\widetilde{v}(\widetilde{r})$, $\widetilde{E}(\widetilde{r})$, $\widetilde{g}(\widetilde{r})$; $\widetilde{\tau}=1$, $\widetilde{E}(1)=0.0287$.

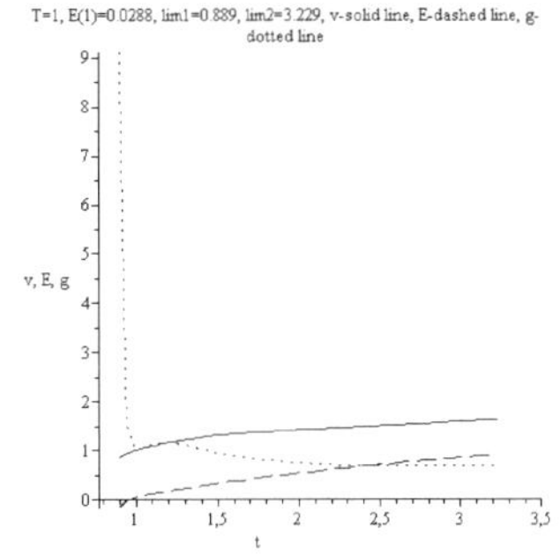

Fig. 8.5.3. Evolution of $\widetilde{v}(\widetilde{r})$, $\widetilde{E}(\widetilde{r})$, $\widetilde{g}(\widetilde{r})$; $\widetilde{\tau}=1$, $\widetilde{E}(1)=0.0288$.

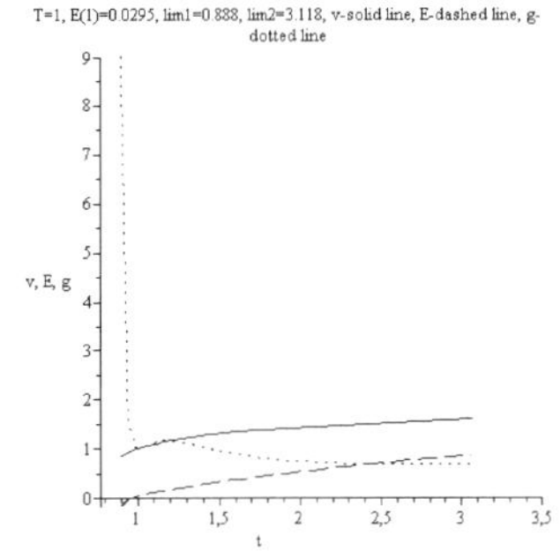

Fig. 8.5.4. Evolution of $\widetilde{v}(\widetilde{r})$, $\widetilde{E}(\widetilde{r})$, $\widetilde{g}(\widetilde{r})$; $\widetilde{\tau}=1$, $\widetilde{E}(1)=0.0295$.

From figures 8.5.1 - 8.5.4 follow that decreasing of $\widetilde{E}(1)$ to the values less than 0.0288 leads to the maximon explosion because the quantum pressure no longer holds this microscopic BH. This process can be realized under the influence of the external action as a result of collisions with the high energy particles in spite of the existence of anti-gravitational forces.

Let us consider now the situation when the derivatives in the Cauchy conditions have the opposite signs (Figures 8.5.5 - 8.5.8). Namely

$D(\widetilde{v}_{0r})(1) = -1,\ D(\widetilde{E})(1) = 1,\ \widetilde{g}(1) = 1,\ v_{0r}(1) = 1,\ \widetilde{E}(1) = 6.96,\ \widetilde{\tau} = 1.$ (Fig. 8.5.5)

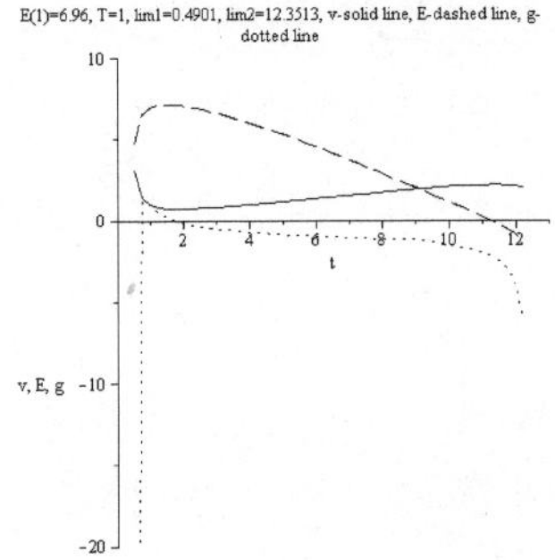

Fig. 8.5.5. Evolution of $\widetilde{v}(\widetilde{r}),\ \widetilde{E}(\widetilde{r}),\ \widetilde{g}(\widetilde{r});\ \widetilde{\tau} = 1,\ \widetilde{E}(1) = 6.96$.

$D(\widetilde{v}_{0r})(1) = -1,\ D(\widetilde{E})(1) = 1,\ \widetilde{g}(1) = 1,\ v_{0r}(1) = 1,\ \widetilde{E}(1) = 6.97,\ \widetilde{\tau} = 1.$ (Fig. 7.5.6)

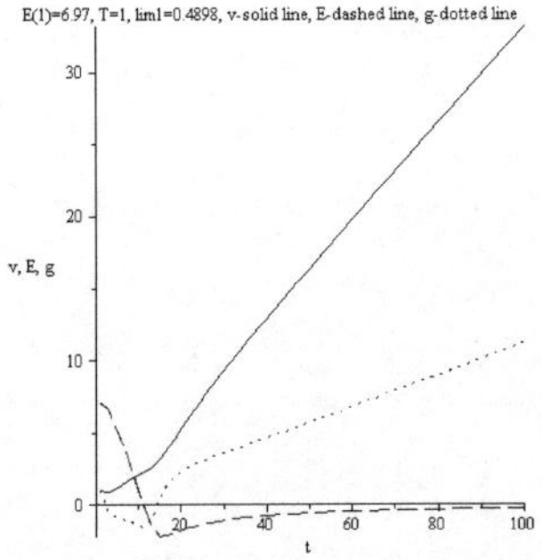

Fig. 8.5.6. Evolution of $\widetilde{v}(\widetilde{r}),\ \widetilde{E}(\widetilde{r}),\ \widetilde{g}(\widetilde{r});\ \widetilde{\tau} = 1,\ \widetilde{E}(1) = 6.97$.

$D(\widetilde{v}_{0r})(1) = 1,\ D(\widetilde{E})(1) = -1,\ \widetilde{g}(1) = 1,\ v_{0r}(1) = 1,\ \widetilde{E}(1) = 0.333,\ \widetilde{\tau} = 1.$ (Fig. 7.5.7)

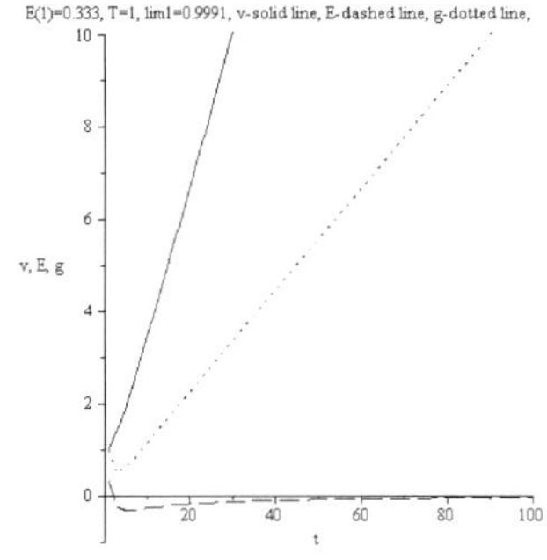

Fig. 8.5.7. Evolution of $\tilde{v}(\tilde{r})$, $\tilde{E}(\tilde{r})$, $\tilde{g}(\tilde{r})$; $\tilde{\tau}=1$, $\tilde{E}(1)=0.333$.

$D(\tilde{v}_{0r})(1)=1$, $D(\tilde{E})(1)=-1$, $\tilde{g}(1)=1$, $v_{0r}(1)=1$, $\tilde{E}(1)=0.334$, $\tilde{\tau}=1$. (Fig. 8.5.8)

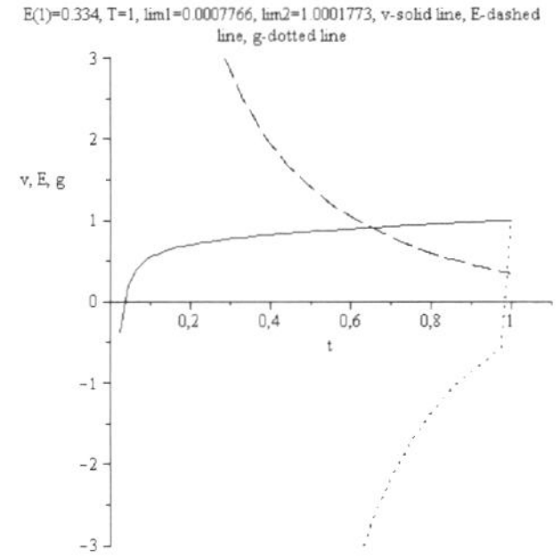

Fig. 8.5.8. Evolution of $\tilde{v}(\tilde{r})$, $\tilde{E}(\tilde{r})$, $\tilde{g}(\tilde{r})$; $\tilde{\tau}=1$, $\tilde{E}(1)=0.334$.

As we see the situation when the derivatives in the Cauchy conditions have the opposite signs also can lead to the explosive maximon instability (Figures 8.5.6, 8.5.7). Figures 8.5.1 - 8.5.8 contain the nearest results to the explosion boundary. Interesting to notice that the Cauchy conditions with the negative gradients for $\tilde{v}_{0r}$ and $\tilde{E}$ on the surface do not lead to the explosion regime. The explosive instability forms a natural limit to the existence conditions of maximons.

The maximon mass is equal to the Planck mass $m_P = 1.2209\cdot 10^{19} GeV/c^2 = 2.176\cdot 10^{-5} g$. The energy corresponding to the rest mass of maximon is $5\cdot 10^{28} eV$. LHC in CERN has the planned maximum energy per beam $7\cdot 10^{12} eV$. The TNT equivalent is a convention for expressing energy released in an explosion. Then the maximon explosion corresponds to 1912 kg in TNT equivalent.

8.6. Oscillations of Black Holes as a source of the gravitational waves

Usually at least two major types of black holes are involved into consideration: a) Stellar Mass Black Holes which are formed when dying stars run out of nuclear fuel in their centers. The result is a massive supernova explosion, leaving a black hole behind where the star once existed. b) Super-massive Black Holes are the largest type of black hole, up to billions of solar masses. It could be suppose that super-massive black holes grow over billions of years by the constant accretion of huge plumes of gases and other matter.

A dying star goes to the energetically more economical oscillating mode of operation (like the global Sun oscillations). No surprise that X-ray light coming from black holes often exhibit rhythmic pulses, referred to as quasi-periodic oscillations or QPOs, usually occurring at multiple frequencies [159, 160]. From the power density spectra follow, that quasi-periodic oscillations are seen at a few Hz and also occasionally at hundreds of Hz for stellar black holes. For super-massive black holes, the time-scale of the oscillations ranges from hours to weeks. The various explanations of QPOs remain controversial and the conclusions reached from their study remain provisional.

Let us apply the nonlocal physics to the investigation of the wave processes in the spherical black holes. The following problems are interesting for us:

1. Is it possible to tie the oscillation processes in BH with the birth of gravitational waves?
2. Can gravity waves form the wave packets?
3. Is it possible to obtain the continuous transformation of the gravitational force of attraction into so called the "event horizon" that marks the point of no return as a result of the self-consistent solution of nonlocal hydrodynamic equations?

All the mentioned above questions have the positive answer. Then we intend to follow the creation of the theory of the transport processes in the field where the classical GR theory is not applicable.

However, it is worth noting that the concepts of a non-rotating (or Schwarzschild) black hole, the basic properties of such a black hole as a static solution to Einstein phenomenological equations in a spherically symmetric and vacuum space-time are discussed in [161]. The research area is increasing steadily as gravitational detectors become more and more sensitive, and as detectors of new generation are becoming operative [162].

In following we intend to investigate the possibility of the travelling wave's appearance as a result of the transport processes in BH. For solution of these problems we suppose:

1. One species object has spherical symmetry,
2. We use the condition

$$\upsilon_p = const \tag{8.6.1}$$

for periodic BH's pulsation.

Let us write down the basic nonlocal hydrodynamic equations in the limit $\rho \to \infty$.

(The continuity equation)

$$\frac{\partial}{\partial t}\left\{\tau\left[\frac{1}{r^2}\frac{\partial\left(r^2 v_{0r}\right)}{\partial r}\right]\right\} - \frac{1}{r^2}\frac{\partial}{\partial r}\left\{r^2\left\{v_{0r} - \tau\left[\frac{\partial v_{0r}}{\partial t} + \frac{1}{r^2}\frac{\partial\left(r^2 v_{0r}^2\right)}{\partial r} - g_r\right]\right\}\right\} + \frac{1}{r^2}\frac{\partial}{\partial r}\left(\tau r^2\frac{\partial E}{\partial r}\right) = 0 \tag{8.6.2}$$

(Momentum equation)

$$\frac{\partial}{\partial t}\left\{v_{0r} - \tau\left[\frac{\partial}{\partial t}\left(v_{0r}\right) + \frac{1}{r^2}\frac{\partial\left(r^2 v_{0r}^2\right)}{\partial r} + \frac{\partial E}{\partial r} - g_r\right]\right\} - \left[g_r - \tau g_r\left(\frac{1}{r^2}\frac{\partial\left(r^2 v_{0r}\right)}{\partial r}\right)\right]$$

$$+\frac{1}{r^2}\frac{\partial}{\partial r}\left\{r^2\left\{v_{0r}^2 - \tau\left[\frac{\partial}{\partial t}\left(v_{0r}^2\right) + \frac{1}{r^2}\frac{\partial\left(r^2 v_{0r}^3\right)}{\partial r} - 2g_r v_{0r}\right]\right\}\right\} +$$

$$+\frac{\partial E}{\partial r} - \frac{\partial}{\partial r}\left(\tau\frac{\partial E}{\partial t}\right) - 2\frac{\partial}{\partial r}\left(\frac{\tau}{r^2}\frac{\partial\left(r^2 E v_{0r}\right)}{\partial r}\right) - \frac{1}{r^2}\frac{\partial}{\partial r}\left(\tau r^2\frac{\partial\left(E v_{0r}\right)}{\partial r}\right) = 0. \tag{8.6.3}$$

(Energy equation)

$$\frac{\partial}{\partial t}\left[v_{0r}^2 + 3E + 2\frac{\varepsilon}{m}\right] - \tau\frac{\partial}{\partial t}\left[\frac{\partial}{\partial t}\left(v_{0r}^2 + 3E + 2\frac{\varepsilon}{m}\right) - 2g_r v_{0r}\right] -$$

$$-\tau\frac{\partial}{\partial t}\left[\frac{1}{r^2}\frac{\partial}{\partial r}\left(r^2 v_{0r}\left(v_{0r}^2 + 5E + 2\frac{\varepsilon}{m}\right)\right)\right] + \frac{1}{r^2}\frac{\partial}{\partial r}\left[r^2\left(v_{0r}^2 + 5E + 2\frac{\varepsilon}{m}\right)v_{0r}\right] -$$

$$-\tau\frac{1}{r^2}\frac{\partial}{\partial r}\left\{r^2\left[\frac{\partial}{\partial t}\left(\left(v_{0r}^2 + 5E + 2\frac{\varepsilon}{m}\right)v_{0r}\right) - 2g_r v_{0r}^2 - \left(v_{0r}^2 + 3E\right)g_r\right]\right\} -$$

$$-\tau\frac{1}{r^2}\frac{\partial^2}{\partial r^2}\left(r^2\left(v_{0r}^4 + 7Ev_{0r}^2 + 2\frac{\varepsilon}{m}v_{0r}^2 + 2\frac{\varepsilon}{m}E\right)\right) -$$

$$-2g_r\left\{v_{0r} - \tau\left[\frac{\partial v_{0r}}{\partial t} + \frac{1}{r^2}\frac{\partial}{\partial r}\left(r^2 v_{0r}^2\right) + \frac{\partial E}{\partial r} - g_r\right]\right\} - \tag{8.6.4}$$

$$-\frac{1}{r^2}\frac{\partial}{\partial r}\left(\tau r^2\frac{\partial}{\partial r}\left(Ev_{0r}^2 + 5E^2\right)\right) + \frac{2}{r^2}\frac{\partial}{\partial r}\left(r^2\tau E g_r\right) = 0,.$$

where the following notations are introduced: v_{0r} is the radial component of the hydrodynamic velocity, g_r is the radial gravitational acceleration, ε/m is the internal energy for the mass unit, E is the thermal energy for the mass unit.

We apply the dimensionless form of non-local equations (8.6.1) – (8.6.4) using the scales ρ_0, u_0, $r_0 = u_0 t_0$, , $p_0 = \rho_0 u_0^2$ and condition $\widetilde{C} = C/u_0 = 1$. Let us introduce the frequency of oscillations

$$\frac{v_r}{r} = \upsilon_p , \tag{8.6.5}$$

and the additional conditions written in the dimensionless form

$$\widetilde{\tau} = const, \; \widetilde{\upsilon}_p = const . \tag{8.6.6}$$

Obviously the condition $\widetilde{\upsilon}_p = const$ corresponds to the Hubble regime. Let us introduce now new variable

$$\xi = r - Ct , \tag{8.6.7}$$

where *C* is phase velocity of the travelling wave. We intend to find the solutions of equations (8.6.2) - (8.6.4) in the form of travelling waves, depending on ξ and satisfying the conditions (8.6.6).

We find the following system of the dimensionless equations:

(continuity equation)

$$\begin{aligned} &\widetilde{\tau}\widetilde{v}_{0r}\frac{\partial^2 \widetilde{E}}{\partial \widetilde{\xi}^2} - 4\widetilde{\tau}\widetilde{v}_{0r}\frac{\partial^2 \widetilde{v}_{0r}}{\partial \widetilde{\xi}^2} + 2\widetilde{\tau}\frac{\partial \widetilde{E}}{\partial \widetilde{\xi}}\frac{\partial \widetilde{v}_{0r}}{\partial \widetilde{\xi}} + \\ &+ 3\widetilde{\tau}\widetilde{v}_{0r}\frac{\partial}{\partial \widetilde{\xi}}\left(\widetilde{v}_{0r}\frac{\partial \widetilde{v}_{0r}}{\partial \widetilde{\xi}}\right) - \widetilde{\tau}\widetilde{v}_{0r}\frac{\partial \widetilde{g}_r}{\partial \widetilde{\xi}} - \\ &- 3\widetilde{v}_{0r}\frac{\partial \widetilde{v}_{0r}}{\partial \widetilde{\xi}} + 2\widetilde{\tau}\frac{\partial \widetilde{v}_{0r}}{\partial \widetilde{\xi}}\left(-\frac{\partial \widetilde{v}_{0r}}{\partial \widetilde{\xi}} + 3\widetilde{v}_{0r}\frac{\partial \widetilde{v}_{0r}}{\partial \widetilde{\xi}} - \widetilde{g}_r\right) = 0, \end{aligned} \tag{8.6.8}$$

(motion equation)

$$\begin{aligned} &4\widetilde{v}_{0r}\frac{\partial \widetilde{v}_{0r}}{\partial \widetilde{\xi}} - \frac{\partial \widetilde{v}_{0r}}{\partial \widetilde{\xi}} + \widetilde{\tau}\frac{\partial}{\partial \widetilde{\xi}}\left[4\widetilde{v}_r\frac{\partial \widetilde{v}_{0r}}{\partial \widetilde{\xi}} - \frac{\partial \widetilde{v}_{0r}}{\partial \widetilde{\xi}} + \frac{\partial \widetilde{E}}{\partial \widetilde{\xi}} - \widetilde{g}_r\right] - \left[\widetilde{g}_r - 3\widetilde{\tau}\widetilde{g}_r\frac{\partial \widetilde{v}_{0r}}{\partial \widetilde{\xi}}\right] + \\ &+ \widetilde{\tau}\frac{\partial}{\partial \widetilde{\xi}}\left[2\widetilde{v}_{0r}\frac{\partial \widetilde{v}_{0r}}{\partial \widetilde{\xi}} - 5\widetilde{v}_r^2\frac{\partial \widetilde{v}_{0r}}{\partial \widetilde{\xi}} + 2\widetilde{g}_r\widetilde{v}_{0r}\right] + 2\widetilde{\tau}\frac{\partial \widetilde{v}_{0r}}{\partial \widetilde{\xi}}\left[2\frac{\partial \widetilde{v}_{0r}}{\partial \widetilde{\xi}} - 5\widetilde{v}_{0r}\frac{\partial \widetilde{v}_{0r}}{\partial \widetilde{\xi}} + 2\widetilde{g}_r\right] + \\ &+ \frac{\partial \widetilde{E}}{\partial \widetilde{\xi}} + \widetilde{\tau}\frac{\partial^2 E}{\partial \widetilde{\xi}^2} - 3\widetilde{\tau}\frac{\partial^2\left(\widetilde{E}\widetilde{v}_{0r}\right)}{\partial \widetilde{\xi}^2} - 4\widetilde{\tau}\frac{\partial}{\partial \widetilde{\xi}}\left(\widetilde{E}\frac{\partial \widetilde{v}_{0r}}{\partial \widetilde{\xi}}\right) - \widetilde{\tau}\frac{2}{\widetilde{v}_{0r}}\frac{\partial\left(\widetilde{E}\widetilde{v}_{0r}\right)}{\partial \widetilde{\xi}}\frac{\partial \widetilde{v}_{0r}}{\partial \widetilde{\xi}} = 0, \end{aligned} \tag{8.6.9}$$

(energy equation)

$$
-\frac{\partial}{\partial\tilde{\xi}}\left[\tilde{v}_{0r}^{2}\left(\tilde{v}_{0r}^{2}+3\tilde{E}+2\frac{\tilde{\varepsilon}}{\tilde{m}}\right)\right]-\tau\frac{\partial^{2}}{\partial\tilde{\xi}^{2}}\left(\tilde{v}_{0r}^{2}\left(\tilde{v}_{0r}^{2}+3\tilde{E}+2\frac{\tilde{\varepsilon}}{\tilde{m}}\right)\right)-2\tilde{\tau}\frac{\partial}{\partial\tilde{\xi}}\left[\tilde{g}_{r}\tilde{v}_{r}^{3}\right]+
$$

$$
+\tilde{\tau}\frac{\partial^{2}}{\partial\tilde{\xi}^{2}}\left(\tilde{v}_{0r}^{3}\left(\tilde{v}_{0r}^{2}+5\tilde{E}+2\frac{\tilde{\varepsilon}}{\tilde{m}}\right)\right)+\frac{\partial}{\partial\tilde{\xi}}\left[\tilde{v}_{0r}^{3}\left(\tilde{v}_{0r}^{2}+5\tilde{E}+2\frac{\tilde{\varepsilon}}{\tilde{m}}\right)\right]+
$$

$$
+\tau\tilde{v}_{0r}^{2}\frac{\partial^{2}}{\partial\tilde{\xi}^{2}}\left(\left(\tilde{v}_{0r}^{2}+5\tilde{E}+2\frac{\tilde{\varepsilon}}{\tilde{m}}\right)\tilde{v}_{0r}\right)+\tilde{\tau}\tilde{v}_{0r}^{2}\frac{\partial}{\partial\tilde{\xi}}\left[2\tilde{g}_{r}\tilde{v}_{0r}^{2}+\left(\tilde{v}_{0r}^{2}+3\tilde{E}\right)\tilde{g}_{r}\right]+ \tag{8.6.10}
$$

$$
+2\tilde{\tau}\tilde{v}_{0r}\frac{\partial\tilde{v}_{0r}}{\partial\tilde{\xi}}\frac{\partial}{\partial\tilde{\xi}}\left(\left(\tilde{v}_{0r}^{2}+5\tilde{E}+2\frac{\tilde{\varepsilon}}{\tilde{m}}\right)\tilde{v}_{0r}\right)+2\tilde{\tau}\tilde{v}_{0r}\left[2\tilde{g}_{r}\tilde{v}_{0r}^{2}+\left(\tilde{v}_{0r}^{2}+3\tilde{E}\right)\tilde{g}_{r}\right]\frac{\partial\tilde{v}_{0r}}{\partial\tilde{\xi}}-
$$

$$
-\tau\frac{\partial^{2}}{\partial\tilde{\xi}^{2}}\left(\tilde{v}_{0r}^{6}+7\tilde{E}\tilde{v}_{0r}^{4}+2\frac{\tilde{\varepsilon}}{\tilde{m}}\tilde{v}_{0r}^{4}+2\frac{\tilde{\varepsilon}}{\tilde{m}}\tilde{E}\tilde{v}_{0r}^{2}\right)-
$$

$$
-2\tilde{g}_{r}\tilde{v}_{0r}^{3}+2\tilde{g}_{r}\tilde{v}_{0r}^{2}\tilde{\tau}\left[-\frac{\partial\tilde{v}_{0r}}{\partial\tilde{\xi}}+4\tilde{v}_{0r}\frac{\partial\tilde{v}_{0r}}{\partial\tilde{\xi}}+\frac{\partial\tilde{E}}{\partial\tilde{\xi}}-\tilde{g}_{r}\right]-
$$

$$
-\tilde{\tau}\frac{\partial}{\partial\tilde{\xi}}\left(\tilde{v}_{0r}^{2}\frac{\partial}{\partial\tilde{\xi}}\left(\tilde{E}\tilde{v}_{0r}^{2}+5\tilde{E}^{2}\right)\right)+2\tilde{\tau}\frac{\partial}{\partial\tilde{\xi}}\left(\tilde{v}_{0r}^{2}\tilde{E}\tilde{g}_{r}\right)=0.
$$

This system of equations after transformations takes the form:

CONTINUITY EQUATION

$$
\tilde{\tau}\tilde{v}_{0r}\frac{\partial^{2}\tilde{E}}{\partial\tilde{\xi}^{2}}-\tilde{\tau}\tilde{v}_{0r}\frac{\partial^{2}\tilde{v}_{0r}}{\partial\tilde{\xi}^{2}}\left(4-3\tilde{v}_{0r}\right)+\tilde{\tau}\left(\frac{\partial\tilde{v}_{0r}}{\partial\tilde{\xi}}\right)^{2}\left(9\tilde{v}_{0r}-2\right)-\tilde{\tau}\tilde{v}_{0r}\frac{\partial\tilde{g}_{r}}{\partial\tilde{\xi}}
$$

$$
-3\tilde{v}_{0r}\frac{\partial\tilde{v}_{0r}}{\partial\tilde{\xi}}+2\tilde{\tau}\frac{\partial\tilde{v}_{0r}}{\partial\tilde{\xi}}\left(\frac{\partial\tilde{E}}{\partial\tilde{\xi}}-\tilde{g}_{r}\right)=0, \tag{8.6.11}
$$

MOMENTUM EQUATION

$$
4\tilde{v}_{0r}\frac{\partial\tilde{v}_{0r}}{\partial\tilde{\xi}}-\frac{\partial\tilde{v}_{0r}}{\partial\tilde{\xi}}+\tilde{\tau}\frac{\partial}{\partial\tilde{\xi}}\left[6\tilde{v}_{r}\frac{\partial\tilde{v}_{0r}}{\partial\tilde{\xi}}-\frac{\partial\tilde{v}_{0r}}{\partial\tilde{\xi}}+\frac{\partial\tilde{E}}{\partial\tilde{\xi}}-\tilde{g}_{r}-5\tilde{v}_{0r}^{2}\frac{\partial\tilde{v}_{0r}}{\partial\tilde{\xi}}+2\tilde{g}_{r}\tilde{v}_{0r}\right]
$$

$$
-\left[\tilde{g}_{r}-3\tilde{\tau}\tilde{g}_{r}\frac{\partial\tilde{v}_{0r}}{\partial\tilde{\xi}}\right]+2\tilde{\tau}\frac{\partial\tilde{v}_{0r}}{\partial\tilde{\xi}}\left[2\frac{\partial\tilde{v}_{0r}}{\partial\tilde{\xi}}-5\tilde{v}_{0r}\frac{\partial\tilde{v}_{0r}}{\partial\tilde{\xi}}+2\tilde{g}_{r}\right] \tag{8.6.12}
$$

$$
+\frac{\partial\tilde{E}}{\partial\tilde{\xi}}+\tilde{\tau}\frac{\partial^{2}E}{\partial\tilde{\xi}^{2}}-7\tilde{\tau}\tilde{E}\frac{\partial^{2}\tilde{v}_{0r}}{\partial\tilde{\xi}^{2}}-12\tilde{\tau}\frac{\partial\tilde{v}_{0r}}{\partial\tilde{\xi}}\frac{\partial\tilde{E}}{\partial\tilde{\xi}}-3\tilde{\tau}\tilde{v}_{0r}\frac{\partial^{2}\tilde{E}}{\partial\tilde{\xi}^{2}}-\tilde{\tau}\frac{2}{\tilde{v}_{0r}}\tilde{E}\left(\frac{\partial\tilde{v}_{0r}}{\partial\tilde{\xi}}\right)^{2}=0,
$$

ENERGY EQUATION

$$
\frac{\partial}{\partial\tilde{\xi}}\left[\tilde{v}_{0r}^{3}\left(\tilde{v}_{0r}^{2}+5\tilde{E}+2\frac{\tilde{\varepsilon}}{\tilde{m}}\right)\right]-\frac{\partial}{\partial\tilde{\xi}}\left[\tilde{v}_{0r}^{2}\left(\tilde{v}_{0r}^{2}+3\tilde{E}+2\frac{\tilde{\varepsilon}}{\tilde{m}}\right)\right]-2\tilde{g}_{r}\tilde{v}_{0r}^{3}
$$

$$
-\tau\frac{\partial^{2}}{\partial\tilde{\xi}^{2}}\left(\tilde{v}_{0r}^{2}\left(\tilde{v}_{0r}^{2}+3\tilde{E}+2\frac{\tilde{\varepsilon}}{\tilde{m}}\right)\right)+\tilde{\tau}\frac{\partial^{2}}{\partial\tilde{\xi}^{2}}\left(\tilde{v}_{0r}^{3}\left(\tilde{v}_{0r}^{2}+5\tilde{E}+2\frac{\tilde{\varepsilon}}{\tilde{m}}\right)\right)
$$

$$
-\tau\frac{\partial^{2}}{\partial\tilde{\xi}^{2}}\left(\tilde{v}_{0r}^{6}+7\tilde{E}\tilde{v}_{0r}^{4}+2\frac{\tilde{\varepsilon}}{\tilde{m}}\tilde{v}_{0r}^{4}+2\frac{\tilde{\varepsilon}}{\tilde{m}}\tilde{E}\tilde{v}_{0r}^{2}\right)+\tau\tilde{v}_{0r}^{2}\frac{\partial^{2}}{\partial\tilde{\xi}^{2}}\left(\left(\tilde{v}_{0r}^{2}+5\tilde{E}+2\frac{\tilde{\varepsilon}}{\tilde{m}}\right)\tilde{v}_{0r}\right)
$$

$$
-\tilde{\tau}\tilde{v}_{0r}^{2}\frac{\partial^{2}}{\partial\tilde{\xi}^{2}}\left(\tilde{E}\tilde{v}_{0r}^{2}+5\tilde{E}^{2}\right)+2\tilde{\tau}\frac{\partial}{\partial\tilde{\xi}}\left(\tilde{v}_{0r}^{2}\tilde{E}\tilde{g}_{r}-\tilde{g}_{r}\tilde{v}_{0r}^{3}\right)+3\tilde{\tau}\tilde{v}_{0r}^{2}\frac{\partial}{\partial\tilde{\xi}}\left[\tilde{g}_{r}\tilde{v}_{0r}^{2}+\tilde{E}\tilde{g}_{r}\right]
$$

$$+2\tilde{\tau}\tilde{v}_{0r}\frac{\partial\tilde{v}_{0r}}{\partial\tilde{\xi}}\frac{\partial}{\partial\tilde{\xi}}\left(\tilde{v}_{0r}^3+5\tilde{E}\tilde{v}_{0r}+2\frac{\tilde{\varepsilon}}{\tilde{m}}\tilde{v}_{0r}\right)-2\tilde{\tau}\tilde{v}_{0r}\frac{\partial\tilde{v}_{0r}}{\partial\tilde{\xi}}\frac{\partial}{\partial\tilde{\xi}}\left(\tilde{E}\tilde{v}_{0r}^2+5\tilde{E}^2\right)$$

$$+\tilde{\tau}\tilde{v}_{0r}\tilde{g}_r\left[14\tilde{v}_{0r}^2+6\tilde{E}\right]\frac{\partial\tilde{v}_{0r}}{\partial\tilde{\xi}}-2\tilde{\tau}\tilde{v}_{0r}^2\tilde{g}_r\left[\frac{\partial\tilde{v}_{0r}}{\partial\tilde{\xi}}-\frac{\partial\tilde{E}}{\partial\tilde{\xi}}+\tilde{g}_r\right]=0. \quad (8.6.13)$$

Now we are ready to display the results of the mathematical modeling realized with the help of Maple (the versions Maple 9 or more can be used). The system (8.6.11) - (8.6.13) have the great possibilities of mathematical modeling as result of changing of five Cauchy conditions and parameters $\tilde{\tau}$ and $\tilde{\varepsilon}/\tilde{m}$ describing the character features of physical system. The internal energy $\tilde{\varepsilon}/\tilde{m}$ contains the energy of the chemical origin and so called the BH spin. If BH can be presented as a rotating ball, then the corresponding part of the internal energy $(\tilde{\varepsilon}/\tilde{m})_{rot}=1/5$.

Maple program contains Maple's notations – for example the expression $D(\tilde{v}_{0r})(0)=1$ means in the usual notations $(\partial\tilde{v}_{0r}/\partial\tilde{r})(0)=1$, independent variable t responds to $\tilde{\xi}$. The following Maple notations on figures are used: v- velocity $\tilde{v}_{0r}$, g - self-consistent gravitational acceleration $\tilde{g}_r$, and E- the energy $\tilde{E}$, $\mathrm{T}\leftrightarrow\tilde{\tau}$, $Q\leftrightarrow\tilde{\varepsilon}/\tilde{m}$. Explanations placed under all following figures. The results of the calculations are presented in figures 8.6.1 - 8.6.11. The information required is contained in the figures and in figure captions. We use for all calculations reflected on figures 8.6.1 - 8.6.9 the Cauchy conditions

$$v_{0r}(0)=1,\ \tilde{E}(0)=1,\ D(\tilde{v}_{0r})(0)=1,\ D(\tilde{E})(0)=1,\ \tilde{g}_r(0)=0, \quad (8.6.14)$$

which of course can be changed; parameter $\tilde{\tau}$ varies widely. As a rule we use the following lines: $\tilde{v}_{0r}$ - solid line, $\tilde{E}$ - dashed line, $\tilde{g}_r$ - dotted line.

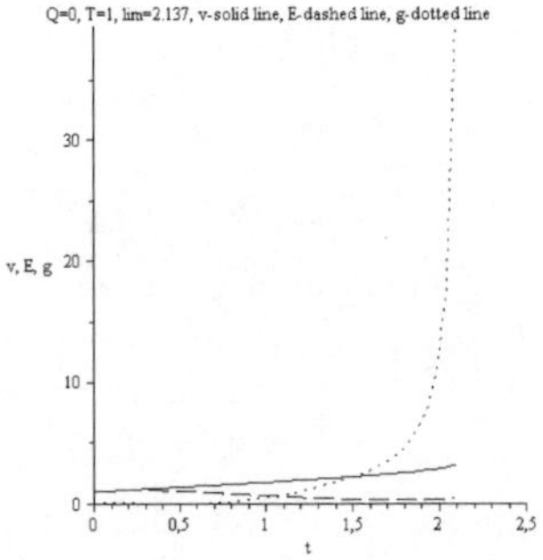

Fig. 8.6.1. Evolution of $\tilde{v}_{0r}(\tilde{r})$, $\tilde{E}(\tilde{r})$, $\tilde{g}_r(\tilde{r})$; $\tilde{\tau}=1$, $\tilde{\varepsilon}/\tilde{m}=0$, $\tilde{\tau}=1$, $\lim\tilde{\xi}=2.137$.

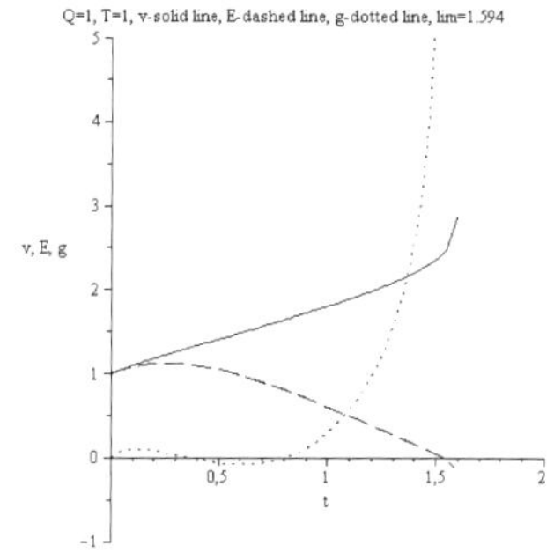

Fig. 8.6.2. Evolution of $\widetilde{v}_{0r}(\widetilde{r})$, $\widetilde{E}(\widetilde{r})$, $\widetilde{g}_r(\widetilde{r})$; $\widetilde{\tau}=1$, $\widetilde{\varepsilon}/\widetilde{m}=1$, $\widetilde{\tau}=1$, $\lim\widetilde{\xi}=1.594$.

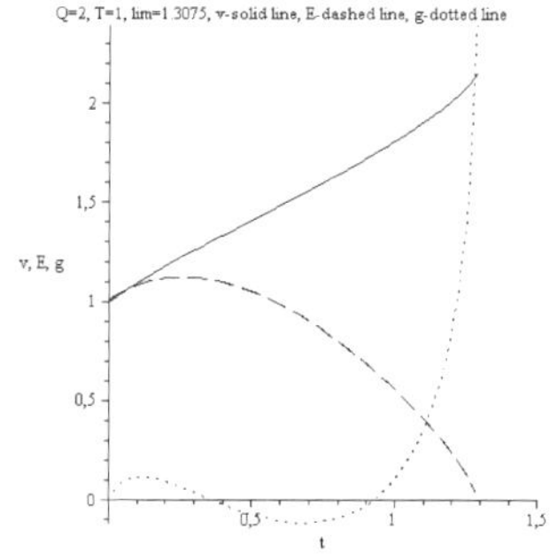

Fig. 8.6.3. Evolution of $\widetilde{v}_{0r}(\widetilde{r})$, $\widetilde{E}(\widetilde{r})$, $\widetilde{g}_r(\widetilde{r})$; $\widetilde{\tau}=1$, $\widetilde{\varepsilon}/\widetilde{m}=2$, $\widetilde{\tau}=1$, $\lim\widetilde{\xi}=1.3075$.

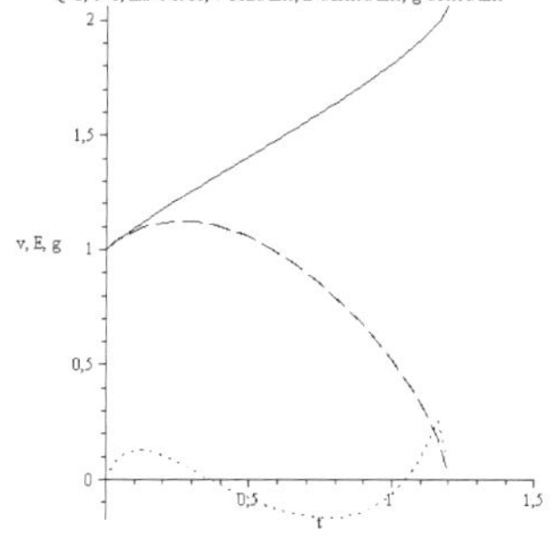

Fig. 8.6.4. Evolution of $\widetilde{v}_{0r}(\widetilde{r})$, $\widetilde{E}(\widetilde{r})$, $\widetilde{g}_r(\widetilde{r})$; $\widetilde{\tau}=1$, $\widetilde{\varepsilon}/\widetilde{m}=3$, $\widetilde{\tau}=1$, $\lim\widetilde{\xi}=1.1986$.

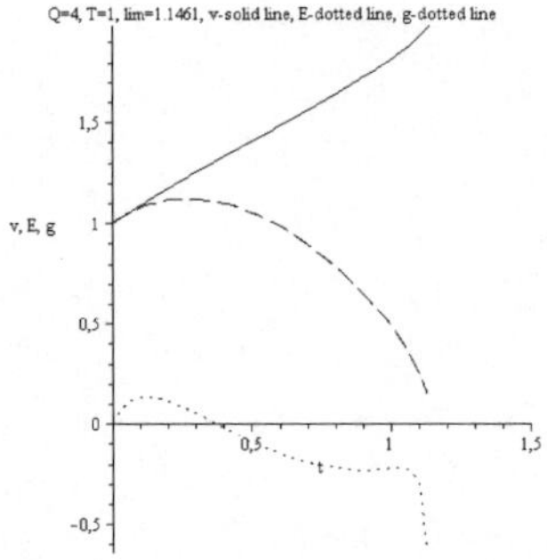

Fig. 8.6.5. Evolution of $\widetilde{v}_{0r}(\widetilde{r})$, $\widetilde{E}(\widetilde{r})$, $\widetilde{g}_r(\widetilde{r})$; $\widetilde{\tau}=1$, $\widetilde{\varepsilon}/\widetilde{m}=4$, $\widetilde{\tau}=1$, $\lim\widetilde{\xi}=1.1461$.

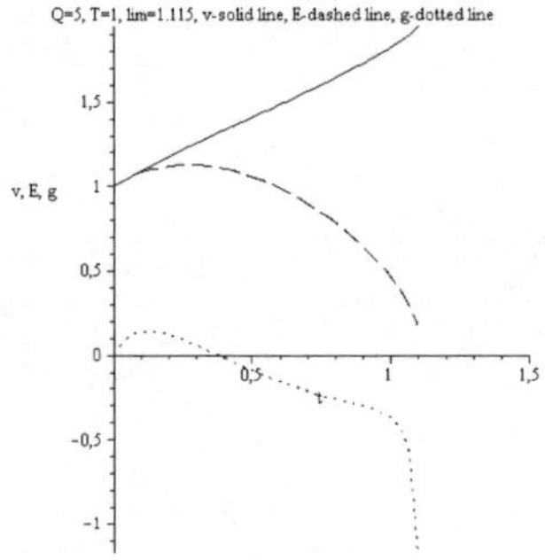

Fig. 8.6.6. Evolution of $\widetilde{v}_{0r}(\widetilde{r})$, $\widetilde{E}(\widetilde{r})$, $\widetilde{g}_r(\widetilde{r})$; $\widetilde{\tau}=1$, $\widetilde{\varepsilon}/\widetilde{m}=5$, $\widetilde{\tau}=1$, $\lim\widetilde{\xi}=1.115$.

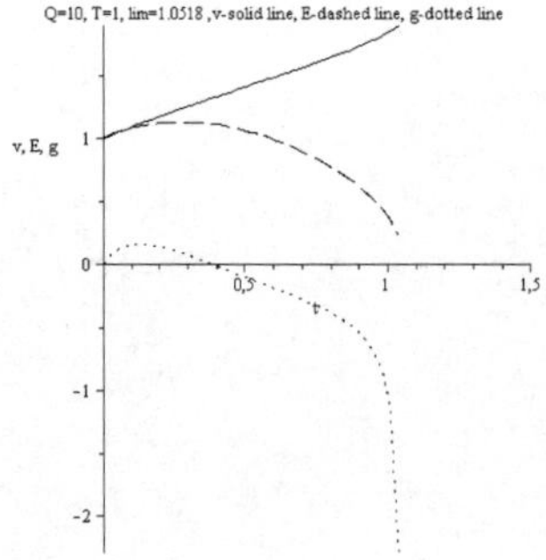

Fig. 8.6.7. Evolution of $\widetilde{v}_{0r}(\widetilde{r})$, $\widetilde{E}(\widetilde{r})$, $\widetilde{g}_r(\widetilde{r})$; $\widetilde{\tau}=1$, $\widetilde{\varepsilon}/\widetilde{m}=10$, $\widetilde{\tau}=1$, $\lim\widetilde{\xi}=1.0518$.

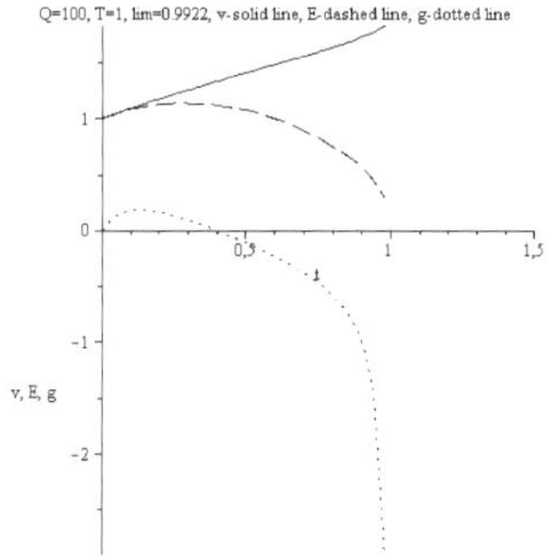

Fig. 8.6.8. Evolution of $\tilde{v}_{0r}(\tilde{r})$, $\tilde{E}(\tilde{r})$, $\tilde{g}_r(\tilde{r})$; $\tilde{\tau}=1$, $\tilde{\varepsilon}/\tilde{m}=100$, $\tilde{\tau}=1$, $\lim\tilde{\xi}=0.9922$.

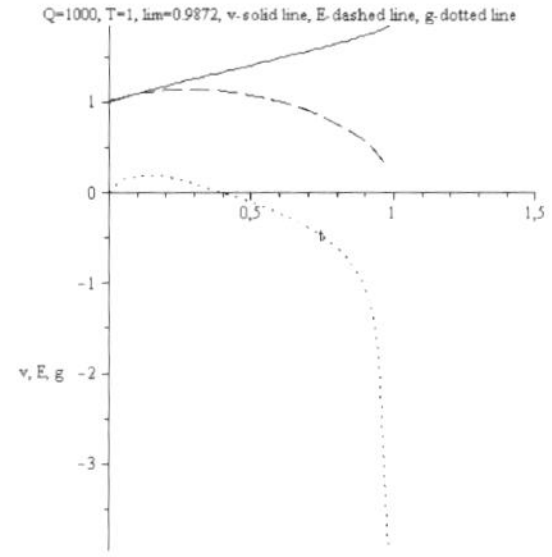

Fig. 8.6.9. Evolution of $\tilde{v}_{0r}(\tilde{r})$, $\tilde{E}(\tilde{r})$, $\tilde{g}_r(\tilde{r})$; $\tilde{\tau}=1$, $\tilde{\varepsilon}/\tilde{m}=1000$, $\tilde{\tau}=1$, $\lim\tilde{\xi}=0.9872$.

Cauchy conditions which were used for calculations reflected in Fig. 8.6.10:

$$v_{0r}(0)=0.001,\ \tilde{E}(0)=1,\ D(\tilde{v}_{0r})(0)=1,\ D(\tilde{E})(0)=1,\ \tilde{g}_r(0)=0, \quad (8.6.15)$$

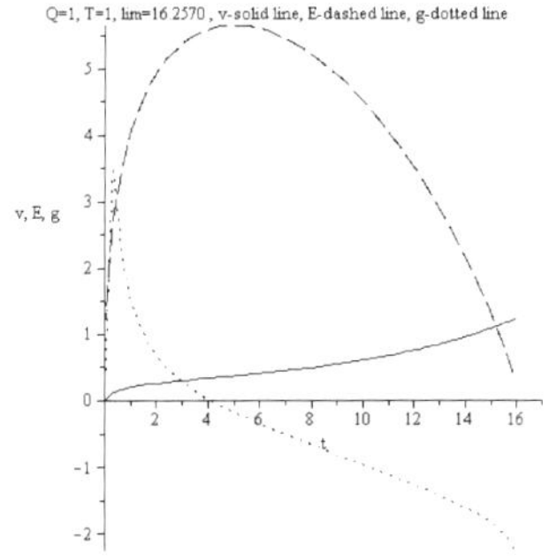

Fig. 8.6.10. Evolution of $\tilde{v}_{0r}(\tilde{r})$, $\tilde{E}(\tilde{r})$, $\tilde{g}_r(\tilde{r})$; $\tilde{\tau}=1$, $\tilde{\varepsilon}/\tilde{m}=1$, $\tilde{\tau}=1$, $\lim\tilde{\xi}=16.2570$.

Cauchy conditions which were used for calculations reflected in Fig. 8.6.11:
$v_{0r}(0)=1,\ \tilde{E}(0)=100,\ D(\tilde{v}_{0r})(0)=100,\ D(\tilde{E})(0)=1,\ \tilde{g}_r(0)=0$, (8.6.16)

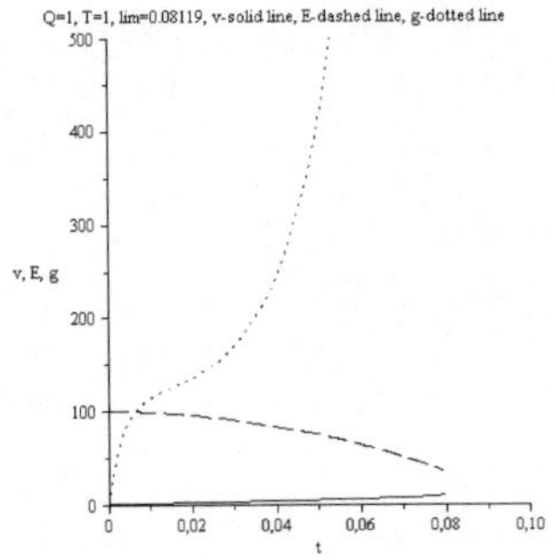

Fig. 8.6.11. Evolution of $\tilde{v}_{0r}(\tilde{r}),\ \tilde{E}(\tilde{r}),\ \tilde{g}_r(\tilde{r})$; $\tilde{\tau}=1,\ \tilde{\varepsilon}/\tilde{m}=1,\ \tilde{\tau}=1,\ \lim\tilde{\xi}=0.08119$.

The following figures 8.6.12, 8.6.13 and 8.6.14 reflect the difference between so called "cold" BH $E(0)<<1$ and "hot" BH $E(0)>>1$

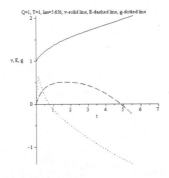

Fig. 8.6.12. Evolution of $\tilde{v}_{0r}(\tilde{r}),\ \tilde{E}(\tilde{r}),\ \tilde{g}_r(\tilde{r})$; $\tilde{\tau}=1,\ \tilde{\varepsilon}/\tilde{m}=1,\ \tilde{\tau}=1,\ \lim\tilde{\xi}=5.656$.
$v_{0r}(0)=1,\ \tilde{E}(0)=0.001,\ D(\tilde{v}_{0r})(0)=1,\ D(\tilde{E})(0)=1,\ \tilde{g}_r(0)=0$

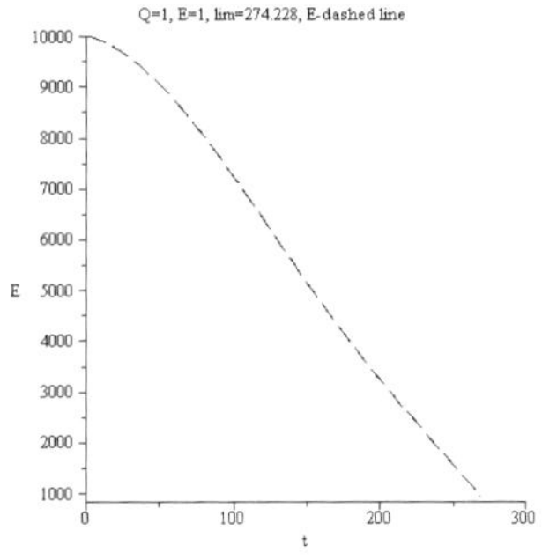

Fig. 8.6.13. Evolution of $\widetilde{E}(\widetilde{r})$; $\widetilde{\tau}=1$, $\widetilde{\varepsilon}/\widetilde{m}=1$, $\widetilde{\tau}=1$, $\lim\widetilde{\xi}=274.228$.
$v_{0r}(0)=1,\ \widetilde{E}(0)=10000,\ D(\widetilde{v}_{0r})(0)=1,\ D(\widetilde{E})(0)=1,\ \widetilde{g}_r(0)=0$

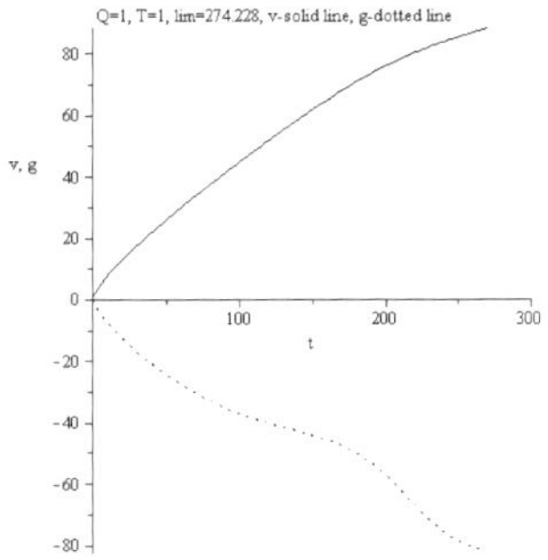

Fig. 8.6.14. Evolution of $\widetilde{v}_{0r}(\widetilde{r}),\widetilde{g}_r(\widetilde{r})$; $\widetilde{\tau}=1$, $\widetilde{\varepsilon}/\widetilde{m}=1$, $\widetilde{\tau}=1$, $\lim\widetilde{\xi}=274.228$.
$v_{0r}(0)=1,\ \widetilde{E}(0)=10000,\ D(\widetilde{v}_{0r})(0)=1,\ D(\widetilde{E})(0)=1,\ \widetilde{g}_r(0)=0$

From the equations 8.6.11 - 8.6.13 and the calculations (Figures 8.6.1 - 8.6.11) follow:

1. Internal perturbations in BH lead to the appearance of the packets of the gravitational waves.

2. The transport nonlocal equations do not contain the oscillation frequency in the explicit form in the case of the constant frequency υ_p.

3. The width of the wave packet is inversely proportional to the magnitude of internal energy $\widetilde{\varepsilon}/\widetilde{m}$ (figures 8.6.1 - 8.6.9).

4. Increasing $\tilde{\varepsilon}/\tilde{m}$ parameter leads to the transformation of the mode of anti-gravity (and therefore the event horizon) into the attraction regime (figures 8.6.1 -8.6.9). The critical $\tilde{\varepsilon}/\tilde{m}$ value is equal ~3 (see Fig. 8.6.4).
5. There is a strong influence of Cauchy conditions on the BH evolution (see also figures 8.6.10, 8.6.11).

8.7. Transport processes in the charged BH

Let us consider now the wave transport processes in the electrical charged Black Holes. Taking in view this aim we transform the system of equations (8.6.11) - (8.6.13). The non-stationary 1D nonlocal Gauss equation in spherical coordinate system can be written [20] as

$$i\frac{1}{r^2}\frac{\partial}{\partial r}\left(r^2\varepsilon\hat{g}_{r\varphi}\right)=4\pi e\left[n-\tau\left(\frac{\partial n}{\partial t}+\frac{1}{r^2}\frac{\partial\left(r^2 n v_{0r}\right)}{\partial r}\right)\right], \tag{8.7.1}$$

where $\hat{g}_{r\varphi}$ is radial component of the electric field intensity vector, n is the number density, e is the absolute electron charge, $i=\mp 1$ for the positive and negative charges of BH correspondingly. In the limit case $\rho\to\infty$ we find ($n=\lim\limits_{M,m\to\infty} M/m$)

$$i\frac{1}{r^2}\frac{\partial}{\partial r}\left(r^2\varepsilon\varepsilon_0\frac{\hat{g}_{r\varphi}}{e\tau n}\right)=\frac{1}{\tau}-\frac{1}{r^2}\frac{\partial\left(r^2 v_{0r}\right)}{\partial r}. \tag{8.7.2}$$

We introduce the acceleration

$$\frac{1}{\tau^2}\frac{\varepsilon_0\varepsilon\hat{g}_{r\varphi}}{en}=g_{r\varphi}, \tag{8.7.3}$$

then

$$\hat{g}_{r\varphi}=\tau^2\frac{en}{\varepsilon\varepsilon_0}g_{r\varphi} \tag{8.7.4}$$

and the electrical induction is

$$D_r=\varepsilon_0\varepsilon\hat{g}_{r\varphi}. \tag{8.7.5}$$

Let us transform the equation (8.7.2) using (8.7.4), (8.7.5)

$$i\frac{1}{r^2}\frac{\partial}{\partial r}\left(r^2\tau g_{r\varphi}\right)=\frac{1}{\tau}-\frac{1}{r^2}\frac{\partial\left(r^2 v_{0r}\right)}{\partial r}, \tag{8.7.6}$$

$$i\frac{1}{r^2}\frac{\partial}{\partial r}\left(r^2 D_r\frac{1}{e\tau n}\right)=\frac{1}{\tau}-\frac{1}{r^2}\frac{\partial\left(r^2 v_{0r}\right)}{\partial r}. \tag{8.7.7}$$

Applying the condition $\frac{v_{0r}}{r}=\upsilon_p=const$ we have

$$i\frac{\partial}{\partial r}\left(v_{0r}^2\tau g_{r\varphi}\right)=v_{0r}^2\left[\frac{1}{\tau}-3\frac{\partial v_{0r}}{\partial r}\right], \tag{8.7.8}$$

and in the dimensionless form

$$i\frac{\partial}{\partial\tilde{\xi}}\left(\tilde{v}_{0r}^2\tilde{\tau}\tilde{g}_{r\varphi}\right)=\tilde{v}_{0r}^2\left[\frac{1}{\tilde{\tau}}-3\frac{\partial\tilde{v}_{0r}}{\partial\tilde{\xi}}\right],\ i=\pm 1. \tag{8.7.9}$$

The current density is

$$j(\xi)=env_{0r}(\xi), \tag{8.7.10}$$

and the changing (in space and time) electric field

$$\frac{\partial}{\partial t}D_r(\xi)=\frac{\partial}{\partial t}\varepsilon\varepsilon_0\hat{g}_{r\varphi}=\frac{\partial}{\partial t}(\tau^2 eng_{r\varphi})=-\tau^2 enC\frac{\partial}{\partial\xi}g_{r\varphi}. \tag{8.7.11}$$

Following the Maxwell equation

$$rot\mathbf{H}'(\xi)=\mathbf{j}(\xi)+\frac{\partial}{\partial t}\mathbf{D}(\xi) \tag{8.7.12}$$

in the local spherical coordinate system (r,ϑ,ψ) one obtains

$$\left[rot\mathbf{H}'(\xi)\right]_{\vartheta,\psi}=env_{0r}(\xi)-\tilde{\tau}^2 enC\frac{\partial}{\partial\xi}g_{r\varphi} \tag{8.7.13}$$

or in the dimensionless form:

$$\left[rot\tilde{\mathbf{H}}'(\tilde{\xi})\right]_{\vartheta,\psi}=\tilde{v}_{0r}(\xi)-\tilde{\tau}^2\frac{\partial}{\partial\tilde{\xi}}\tilde{g}_{r\varphi}. \tag{8.7.14}$$

and finally

$$\left[rot\mathbf{E}'\right]_{\vartheta,\psi}=C\left[\frac{\partial\mathbf{B}'}{\partial\xi}\right]_{\vartheta,\psi}, \tag{8.7.15}$$

$$\left[rot\tilde{\mathbf{E}}'\right]_{\vartheta,\psi}=\left[\frac{\partial\tilde{\mathbf{B}}'}{\partial\tilde{\xi}}\right]_{\vartheta,\psi}. \tag{8.7.16}$$

Now we are ready to combine the full system of equations for the charged BH adding to (8.7.9) the following nonlocal continuity, momentum and energy equations:

CONTINUITY EQUATION

$$\begin{aligned}&\tilde{\tau}\tilde{v}_{0r}\frac{\partial^2\tilde{E}}{\partial\tilde{\xi}^2}-\tilde{\tau}\tilde{v}_{0r}\frac{\partial^2\tilde{v}_{0r}}{\partial\tilde{\xi}^2}(4-3\tilde{v}_{0r})+\tilde{\tau}\left(\frac{\partial\tilde{v}_{0r}}{\partial\tilde{\xi}}\right)^2(9\tilde{v}_{0r}-2)-\tilde{\tau}\tilde{v}_{0r}\frac{\partial}{\partial\tilde{\xi}}\left(\tilde{g}_r+i\tilde{g}_{r\varphi}\right)\\&-3\tilde{v}_{0r}\frac{\partial\tilde{v}_{0r}}{\partial\tilde{\xi}}+2\tilde{\tau}\frac{\partial\tilde{v}_{0r}}{\partial\tilde{\xi}}\left(\frac{\partial\tilde{E}}{\partial\tilde{\xi}}-\tilde{g}_r-i\tilde{g}_{r\varphi}\right)=0,\end{aligned} \tag{8.7.17}$$

MOMENTUM EQUATION

$$\begin{aligned}&4\tilde{v}_{0r}\frac{\partial\tilde{v}_{0r}}{\partial\tilde{\xi}}-\frac{\partial\tilde{v}_{0r}}{\partial\tilde{\xi}}+\tilde{\tau}\frac{\partial}{\partial\tilde{\xi}}\left[6\tilde{v}_r\frac{\partial\tilde{v}_{0r}}{\partial\tilde{\xi}}-\frac{\partial\tilde{v}_{0r}}{\partial\tilde{\xi}}+\frac{\partial\tilde{E}}{\partial\tilde{\xi}}-\tilde{g}_r-i\tilde{g}_{r\varphi}-5\tilde{v}_{0r}^2\frac{\partial\tilde{v}_{0r}}{\partial\tilde{\xi}}+2(\tilde{g}_r+i\tilde{g}_{r\varphi})\tilde{v}_{0r}\right]\\&-\left(\tilde{g}_r+i\tilde{g}_{r\varphi}\right)\left[1-3\tilde{\tau}\frac{\partial\tilde{v}_{0r}}{\partial\tilde{\xi}}\right]+2\tilde{\tau}\frac{\partial\tilde{v}_{0r}}{\partial\tilde{\xi}}\left[2\frac{\partial\tilde{v}_{0r}}{\partial\tilde{\xi}}-5\tilde{v}_{0r}\frac{\partial\tilde{v}_{0r}}{\partial\tilde{\xi}}+2(\tilde{g}_r+i\tilde{g}_{r\varphi})\right]\\&+\frac{\partial\tilde{E}}{\partial\tilde{\xi}}+\tilde{\tau}\frac{\partial^2 E}{\partial\tilde{\xi}^2}-7\tilde{\tau}\tilde{E}\frac{\partial^2\tilde{v}_{0r}}{\partial\tilde{\xi}^2}-12\tilde{\tau}\frac{\partial\tilde{v}_{0r}}{\partial\tilde{\xi}}\frac{\partial\tilde{E}}{\partial\tilde{\xi}}-3\tilde{\tau}\tilde{v}_{0r}\frac{\partial^2\tilde{E}}{\partial\tilde{\xi}^2}-\tilde{\tau}\frac{2}{\tilde{v}_{0r}}\tilde{E}\left(\frac{\partial\tilde{v}_{0r}}{\partial\tilde{\xi}}\right)^2=0,\end{aligned} \tag{8.7.18}$$

$$\frac{\partial}{\partial\tilde{\xi}}\left[\tilde{v}_{0r}^{3}\left(\tilde{v}_{0r}^{2}+5\tilde{E}+2\frac{\tilde{\varepsilon}}{\tilde{m}}\right)\right]-\frac{\partial}{\partial\tilde{\xi}}\left[\tilde{v}_{0r}^{2}\left(\tilde{v}_{0r}^{2}+3\tilde{E}+2\frac{\tilde{\varepsilon}}{\tilde{m}}\right)\right]-2(\tilde{g}_r+i\tilde{g}_{r\varphi})\tilde{v}_{0r}^{3}$$
$$-\tau\frac{\partial^2}{\partial\tilde{\xi}^2}\left(\tilde{v}_{0r}^{2}\left(\tilde{v}_{0r}^{2}+3\tilde{E}+2\frac{\tilde{\varepsilon}}{\tilde{m}}\right)\right)+\tilde{\tau}\frac{\partial^2}{\partial\tilde{\xi}^2}\left(\tilde{v}_{0r}^{3}\left(\tilde{v}_{0r}^{2}+5\tilde{E}+2\frac{\tilde{\varepsilon}}{\tilde{m}}\right)\right)$$
$$-\tau\frac{\partial^2}{\partial\tilde{\xi}^2}\left(\tilde{v}_{0r}^{6}+7\tilde{E}\tilde{v}_{0r}^{4}+2\frac{\tilde{\varepsilon}}{\tilde{m}}\tilde{v}_{0r}^{4}+2\frac{\tilde{\varepsilon}}{\tilde{m}}\tilde{E}\tilde{v}_{0r}^{2}\right)+\tau\tilde{v}_{0r}^{2}\frac{\partial^2}{\partial\tilde{\xi}^2}\left(\left(\tilde{v}_{0r}^{2}+5\tilde{E}+2\frac{\tilde{\varepsilon}}{\tilde{m}}\right)\tilde{v}_{0r}\right)$$
$$-\tilde{\tau}\tilde{v}_{0r}^{2}\frac{\partial^2}{\partial\tilde{\xi}^2}\left(\tilde{E}\tilde{v}_{0r}^{2}+5\tilde{E}^2\right)+2\tilde{\tau}\frac{\partial}{\partial\tilde{\xi}}\left[\tilde{v}_{0r}^{2}(\tilde{g}_r+i\tilde{g}_{r\varphi})(\tilde{E}-\tilde{v}_{0r})\right]+3\tilde{\tau}\tilde{v}_{0r}^{2}\frac{\partial}{\partial\tilde{\xi}}\left[(\tilde{g}_r+i\tilde{g}_{r\varphi})(\tilde{v}_{0r}^{2}+\tilde{E})\right]$$
$$+2\tilde{\tau}\tilde{v}_{0r}\frac{\partial\tilde{v}_{0r}}{\partial\tilde{\xi}}\frac{\partial}{\partial\tilde{\xi}}\left(\tilde{v}_{0r}^{3}+5\tilde{E}\tilde{v}_{0r}+2\frac{\tilde{\varepsilon}}{\tilde{m}}\tilde{v}_{0r}\right)-2\tilde{\tau}\tilde{v}_{0r}\frac{\partial\tilde{v}_{0r}}{\partial\tilde{\xi}}\frac{\partial}{\partial\tilde{\xi}}\left(\tilde{E}\tilde{v}_{0r}^{2}+5\tilde{E}^2\right)$$
$$+\tilde{\tau}\tilde{v}_{0r}(\tilde{g}_r+i\tilde{g}_{r\varphi})\left[14\tilde{v}_{0r}^{2}+6\tilde{E}\right]\frac{\partial\tilde{v}_{0r}}{\partial\tilde{\xi}}-2\tilde{\tau}\tilde{v}_{0r}^{2}(\tilde{g}_r+i\tilde{g}_{r\varphi})\left[\frac{\partial\tilde{v}_{0r}}{\partial\tilde{\xi}}-\frac{\partial\tilde{E}}{\partial\tilde{\xi}}+\tilde{g}_r+i\tilde{g}_{r\varphi}\right]=0. \quad (8.7.19)$$

As before we have the Cauchy problem with unknown variables $\tilde{v}_{0r}$, $\tilde{E}$ and two accelerations $\tilde{g}_r$ and $\tilde{g}_{r\varphi}$ connected with the gravitational or anti-gravitational forces and electric field correspondingly. Cauchy conditions are $\tilde{v}_{0r}(0)$, $\tilde{E}(0)$, $D(\tilde{v}_{0r})(0)$, $D(\tilde{E})(0)$, $\tilde{g}_r(0)$, $\tilde{g}_{r\varphi}(0)$ and three parameters i, $\frac{\tilde{\varepsilon}}{\tilde{m}}$, $\tilde{\tau}$ should be formulated. Let us demonstrate now the results of calculations using as before the Maple notifications. It is reasonable to remind Maple's notations – for example the expression $D(\tilde{v}_{0r})(0)=1$ means in the usual notations $(\partial\tilde{v}_{0r}/\partial\tilde{r})(0)=1$, independent variable t responds to $\tilde{\xi}$. The following Maple notations on figures are used: v- velocity $\tilde{v}_{0r}$, g - self-consistent gravitational acceleration $\tilde{g}_r$, h - the self-consistent acceleration $\tilde{g}_{r\varphi}$ originated by electric field, s is the resultant acceleration $\tilde{s}_r(\tilde{r})$ and E- the energy $\tilde{E}$, $\mathrm{T}\leftrightarrow\tilde{\tau}$, $Q\leftrightarrow\tilde{\varepsilon}/\tilde{m}$. Explanations placed under all following figures. The results of the calculations are presented in figures 8.7.1 - 8.7.18. The information required is contained in the figures and in figure captions. We use for all calculations reflected on figures 8.7.1 - 8.7.6 ($i=-1$) the Cauchy conditions

$$v_{0r}(0)=1,\ \tilde{E}(0)=1,\ D(\tilde{v}_{0r})(0)=1,\ D(\tilde{E})(0)=1,\ \tilde{g}_r(0)=0,\ \tilde{g}_{r\varphi}(0)=0, \quad (8.7.20)$$

The type of lines used is indicated in all figures.

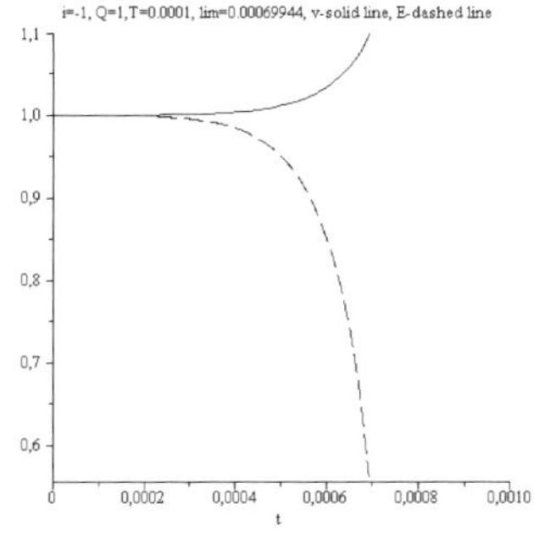

Fig. 8.7.1. Evolution of $\widetilde{v}_{0r}(\widetilde{r}), \widetilde{E}(\widetilde{r})$; $\widetilde{\varepsilon}/\widetilde{m}=1$, $\widetilde{\tau}=0.0001$, $\lim\widetilde{\xi}=0.00069944$

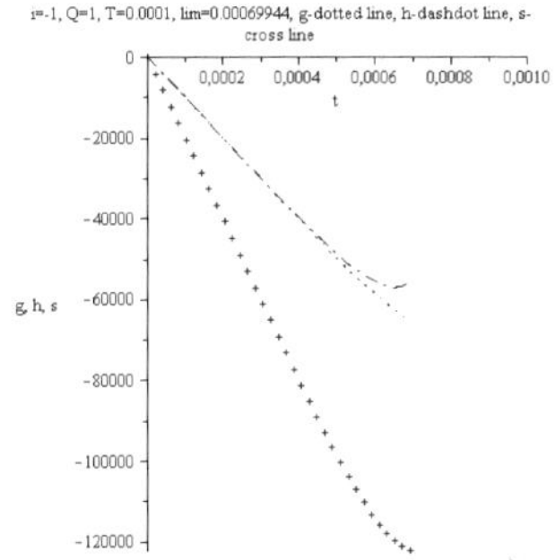

Fig. 8.7.2. Evolution of $\widetilde{g}_r(r)$, $\widetilde{g}_{r\varphi}(\widetilde{r})$, $\widetilde{s}_r(\widetilde{r})$; $\widetilde{\varepsilon}/\widetilde{m}=1$, $\widetilde{\tau}=0.0001$, $\lim\widetilde{\xi}=0.00069944$

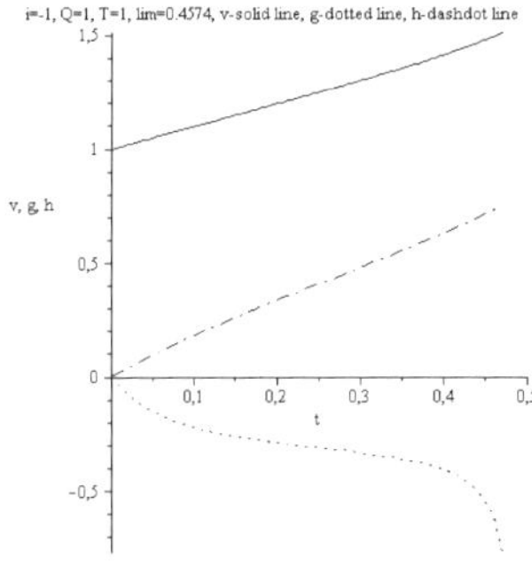

Fig. 8.7.3. Evolution of $\widetilde{v}_{0r}(\widetilde{r})$, $\widetilde{g}_r(\widetilde{r})$, $\widetilde{g}_{r\varphi}(\widetilde{r})$; $\widetilde{\tau}=1$, $\widetilde{\varepsilon}/\widetilde{m}=1$, $\lim\widetilde{\xi}=0.4574$.

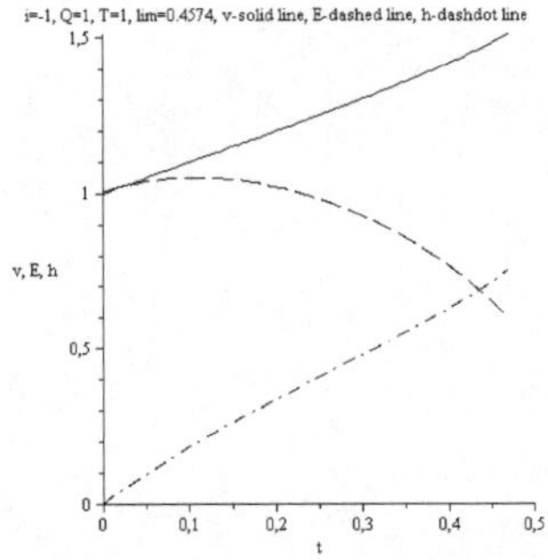

Fig. 8.7.4. Evolution of $\tilde{v}_{0r}(\tilde{r}), \tilde{E}(\tilde{r}), \tilde{g}_{r\varphi}(\tilde{r})$; $\tilde{\tau}=1$, $\tilde{\varepsilon}/\tilde{m}=1$, $\lim\tilde{\xi}=0.4574$.

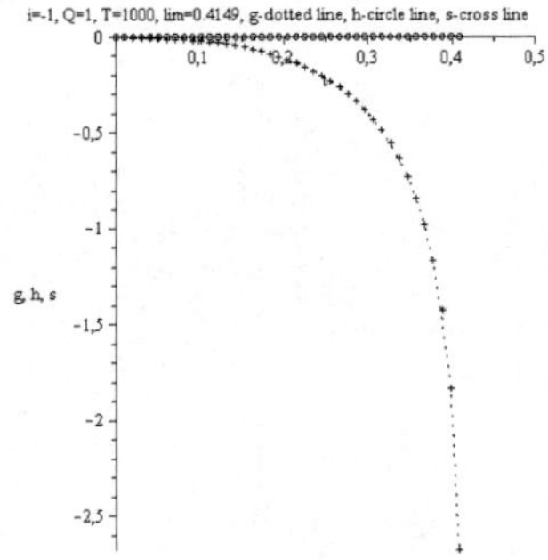

Fig. 8.7.5. Evolution of $\tilde{g}_r(r), \tilde{g}_{r\varphi}(\tilde{r}), \tilde{s}_r(\tilde{r})$; $\tilde{\varepsilon}/\tilde{m}=1$, $\tilde{\tau}=1000$, $\lim\tilde{\xi}=0.4149$.

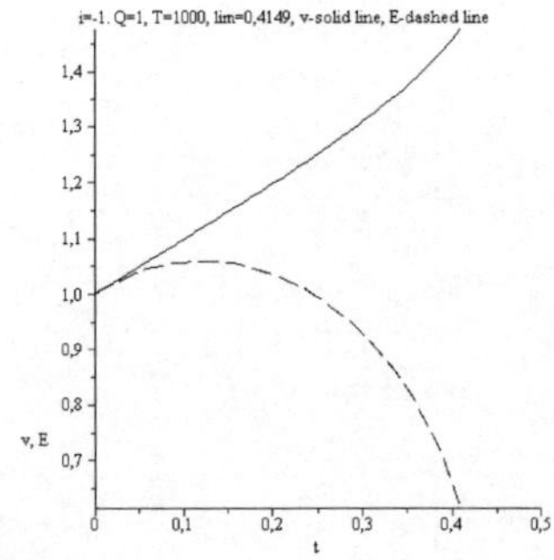

Fig. 8.7.6. Evolution of $\tilde{v}_{0r}(\tilde{r}), \tilde{E}(\tilde{r})$; $\tilde{\tau}=1000$, $\tilde{\varepsilon}/\tilde{m}=1$, $\lim\tilde{\xi}=0.4149$.

All calculations reflected on figures 8.7.7 - 8.7.14 correspond to ($i=1$) and the Cauchy conditions (7.7.20).

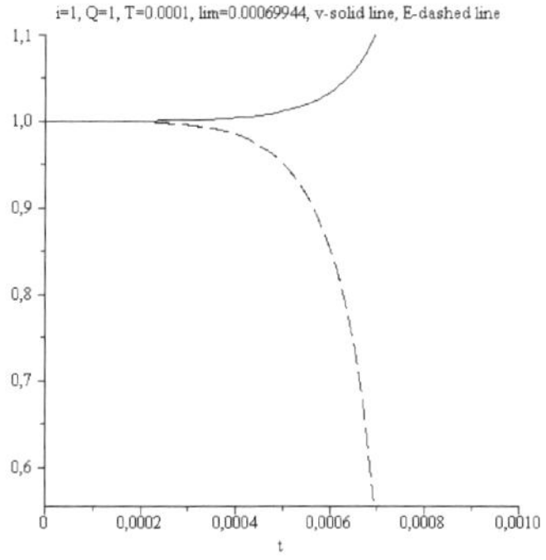

Fig. 8.7.7. Evolution of $\tilde{v}_{0r}(\tilde{r}), \tilde{E}(\tilde{r})$; $\tilde{\tau}=0.0001$, $\tilde{\varepsilon}/\tilde{m}=1$, $\lim\tilde{\xi}=0.00069944$

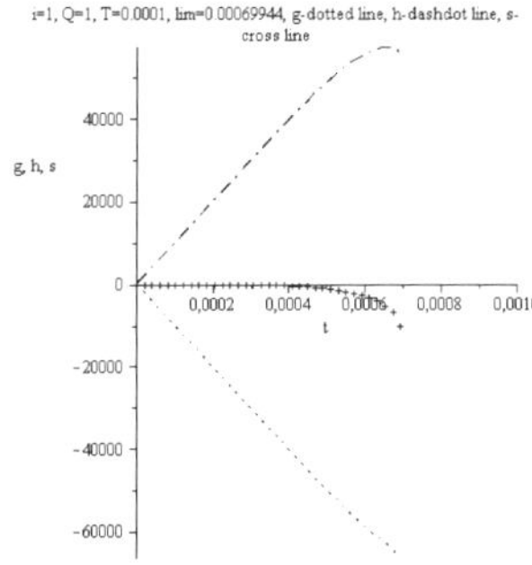

Fig. 8.7.8. Evolution of $\tilde{g}_r(r)$, $\tilde{g}_{r\varphi}(\tilde{r})$, $\tilde{s}_r(\tilde{r})$; $\tilde{\varepsilon}/\tilde{m}=1$, $\tilde{\tau}=0.0001$, $\lim\tilde{\xi}=0.00069944$

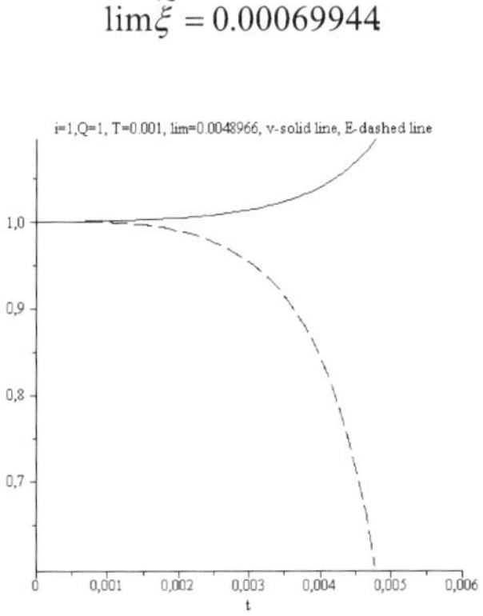

Fig. 8.7.9. Evolution of $\tilde{v}_{0r}(\tilde{r}), \tilde{E}(\tilde{r})$; $\tilde{\tau}=0.001$, $\tilde{\varepsilon}/\tilde{m}=1$, $\lim\tilde{\xi}=0.0048966$

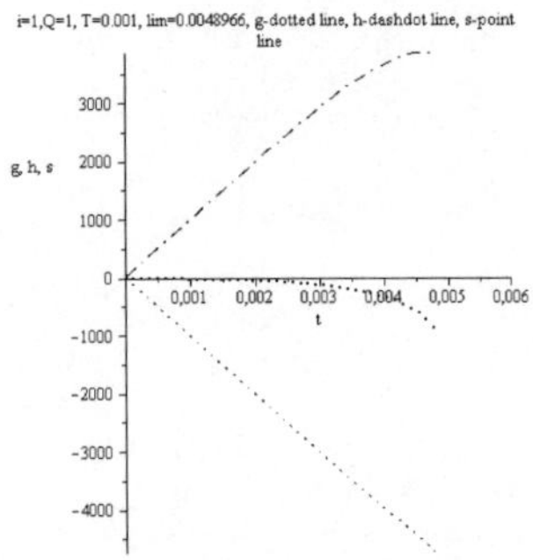

Fig. 8.7.10. Evolution of $\tilde{g}_r(r)$, $\tilde{g}_{r\varphi}(\tilde{r})$, $\tilde{s}_r(\tilde{r})$; $\tilde{\varepsilon}/\tilde{m}=1$, $\tilde{\tau}=0.001$, $\lim\tilde{\xi}=0.0048966$

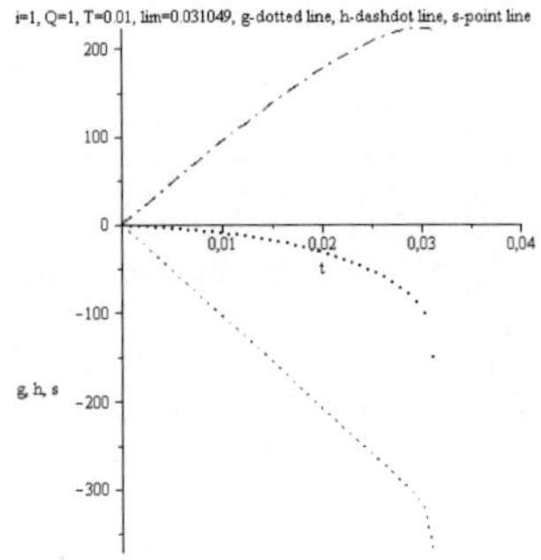

Fig. 8.7.11. Evolution of $\tilde{g}_r(r)$, $\tilde{g}_{r\varphi}(\tilde{r})$, $\tilde{s}_r(\tilde{r})$; $\tilde{\varepsilon}/\tilde{m}=1$, $\tilde{\tau}=0.01$, $\lim\tilde{\xi}=0.031049$.

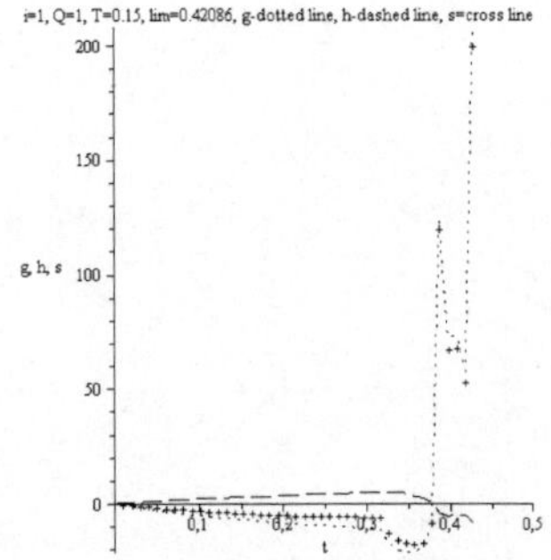

Fig. 8.7.12. Evolution of $\tilde{g}_r(r)$, $\tilde{g}_{r\varphi}(\tilde{r})$, $\tilde{s}_r(\tilde{r})$; $\tilde{\varepsilon}/\tilde{m}=1$, $\tilde{\tau}=0.15$, $\lim\tilde{\xi}=0.42086$.

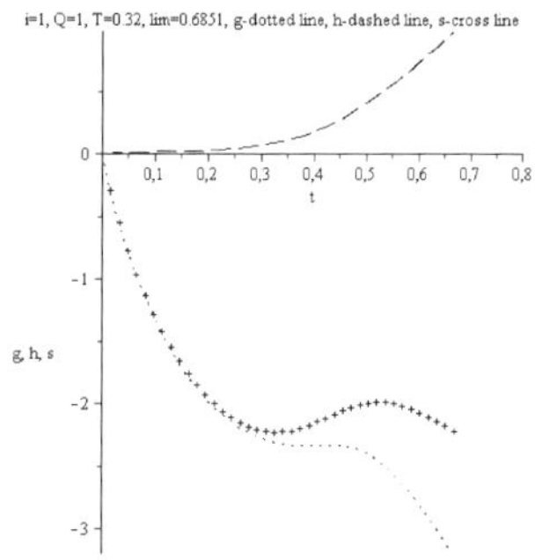

Fig. 8.7.13. Evolution of $\tilde{g}_r(r)$, $\tilde{g}_{r\varphi}(\tilde{r})$, $\tilde{s}_r(\tilde{r})$; $\tilde{\varepsilon}/\tilde{m}=1$, $\tilde{\tau}=0.32$, $\lim\tilde{\xi}=0.6851$.

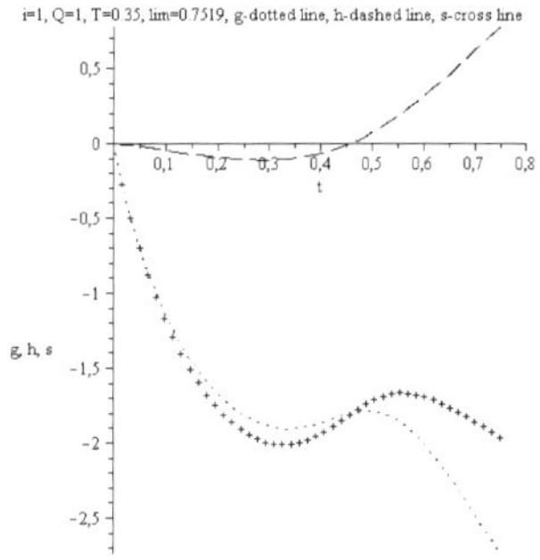

Fig. 8.7.14. Evolution of $\tilde{g}_r(r)$, $\tilde{g}_{r\varphi}(\tilde{r})$, $\tilde{s}_r(\tilde{r})$; $\tilde{\varepsilon}/\tilde{m}=1$, $\tilde{\tau}=0.35$, $\lim\tilde{\xi}=0.7519$.

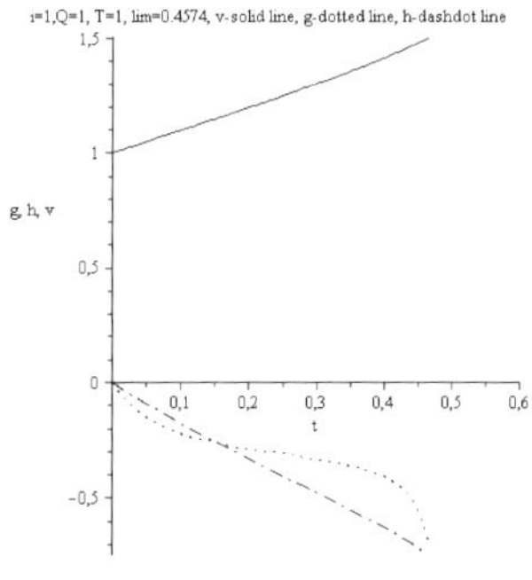

Fig. 8.7.15. Evolution of $\tilde{g}_r(r)$, $\tilde{g}_{r\varphi}(\tilde{r})$, $\tilde{v}_{0r}(\tilde{r})$; $\tilde{\varepsilon}/\tilde{m}=1$, $\tilde{\tau}=1$, $\lim\tilde{\xi}=0.4574$.

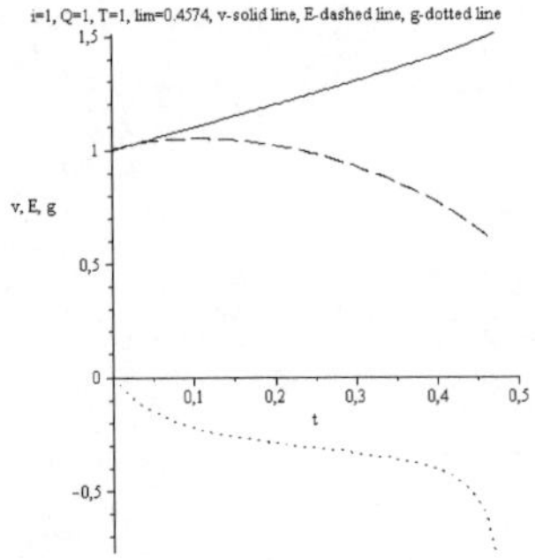

Fig. 8.7.16. Evolution of $\tilde{v}_{0r}(\tilde{r})$, $\tilde{E}(\tilde{r})$, $\tilde{g}_r(\tilde{r})$; $\tilde{\varepsilon}/\tilde{m}=1$, $\tilde{\tau}=1$, $\lim\tilde{\xi}=0.4574$.

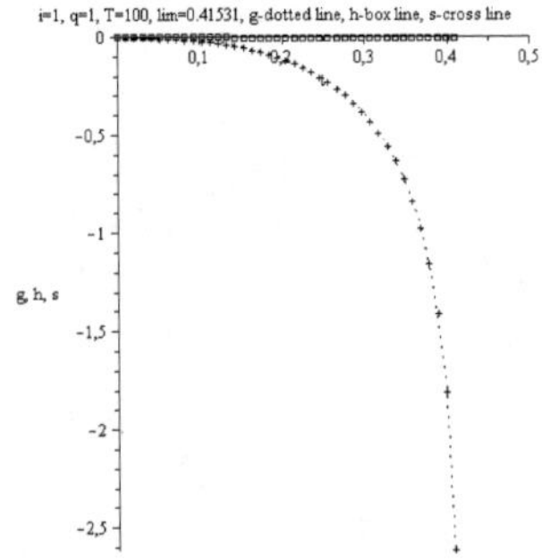

Fig. 8.7.17. Evolution of $\tilde{g}_r(r)$, $\tilde{g}_{r\varphi}(\tilde{r})$, $\tilde{s}_r(\tilde{r})$; $\tilde{\varepsilon}/\tilde{m}=1$, $\tilde{\tau}=100$, $\lim\tilde{\xi}=0.41531$.

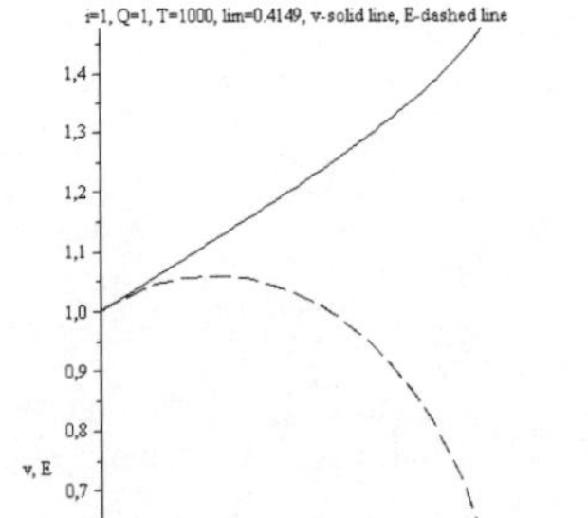

Fig. 8.7.18. Evolution of $\tilde{v}_{0r}(\tilde{r})$, $\tilde{E}(\tilde{r})$; $\tilde{\varepsilon}/\tilde{m}=1$, $\tilde{\tau}=1000$, $\lim\tilde{\xi}=0.4149$.

Conclusion and discussion:

1. The appearance of a charge in BH can lead to the absolutely different behavior of the acceleration curves (compare for example figures 8.6.2, 8.7.3 and 8.7.10 - 8.7.15) including the disappearance of the total gravitational, anti-gravitational and electric fields inside the wave packet.
2. The calculations are performed when the $\tilde{\tau}$ - nonlocal parameter is changed to seven orders of magnitude (see for example figures 8.7.7, 8.7.8 and 8.7.18). Diminishing $\tilde{\tau}$ leads to diminishing of the bunch character size.
3. The usual direction of the field strength lines for positive and negative charges is typical only for small nonlocal parameters $\tilde{\tau}$ (see figures 8.7.2, 8.7.8 and 8.7.15, 8.7.17). Moreover the directions of the field strength lines for positive and negative charges may experience changes in the bunch (see figure 8.7.14).
4. The Nobel Prize for Physics was awarded to the Ligo team that has spotted three instances of gravitational waves coming from black holes merging, the first of which was announced in February 2016. Recently, the team has spotted the gravitational waves from the merging of neutron stars for the first time. The team was also able to detect electromagnetic radiation coming from the event and gamma ray bursts given off just seconds later, (see also [162, 163])..
5. From our calculations follow that the very strong mutual influence of the gravitational, anti-gravitational and electromagnetic fields exists for the wave bunches originated by charged BH, (figures 8.7.2, 8.7.5, 8.7.10 - 8.7.17). Appearance of electromagnetic radiation (ER) and gamma ray bursts coming from the event later than the gravitation part (GP) of the bunch means that the gravitational waves (GW) have the velocity more than the speed of light (see the velocity distribution in the wave bunch, figures 8.7.1 - 8.7.17). The difference between the times of arriving for GP and ER defines the time parameter of nonlocality τ. The real velocity of GW depends on physical conditions originating these waves.
6. The regimes exist when the accelerations originated by the electric and gravitational fields compensate each other in large part (see figures 8.7.10 - 8.7.14). Then the nonlocal physics explains the appearance gravitational waves convoying electromagnetic bursts.

8.8. Propagation of Plane Traveling Waves in Black Channel

Let us apply generalized quantum hydrodynamic equations (8.2.1) – (8.2.5) for investigation of the traveling wave propagation inside the black hole using non-stationary 1D Cartesian description. It means that consideration corresponds so to speak to "the black channel".

Call attention to the fact that equations (8.2.1) – (8.2.6) contain two forces of gravitational origin, $\mathbf{F}$ the force acting on the unit volume of the space and $\mathbf{g}$ - the force acting on the unit mass. As r sult we have from equations (8.2.1) – (8.2.6):

(continuity equation)

$$\frac{\partial}{\partial t}\left\{\rho-\tau\left[\frac{\partial \rho}{\partial t}+\frac{\partial}{\partial \mathbf{r}}\cdot(\rho \mathbf{v}_0)\right]\right\}+\frac{\partial}{\partial \mathbf{r}}\cdot\left\{\rho \mathbf{v}_0-\tau\left[\frac{\partial}{\partial t}(\rho \mathbf{v}_0)+\frac{\partial}{\partial \mathbf{r}}\cdot(\rho \mathbf{v}_0 \mathbf{v}_0)+\ddot{\mathrm{I}}\cdot\frac{\partial p}{\partial \mathbf{r}}-\mathbf{F}\right]\right\}=0, \tag{8.8.1}$$

(continuity equation, 1D case)

$$\frac{\partial}{\partial t}\left\{\rho-\tau\left[\frac{\partial \rho}{\partial t}+\frac{\partial}{\partial x}(\rho v_0)\right]\right\}+\frac{\partial}{\partial x}\left\{\rho v_0-\tau\left[\frac{\partial}{\partial t}(\rho v_0)+\frac{\partial}{\partial x}(\rho v_0^2)+\frac{\partial p}{\partial x}-F\right]\right\}=0, \tag{8.8.2}$$

(momentum equation)

$$\frac{\partial}{\partial t}\left\{\rho \mathbf{v}_0-\tau\left[\frac{\partial}{\partial t}(\rho \mathbf{v}_0)+\frac{\partial}{\partial \mathbf{r}}\cdot\rho \mathbf{v}_0 \mathbf{v}_0+\frac{\partial p}{\partial \mathbf{r}}-\mathbf{F}\right]\right\}-\mathbf{g}\left[\rho-\tau\left(\frac{\partial \rho}{\partial t}+\frac{\partial}{\partial \mathbf{r}}(\rho \mathbf{v}_0)\right)\right]$$
$$+\frac{\partial}{\partial \mathbf{r}}\cdot\left\{\rho \mathbf{v}_0 \mathbf{v}_0+p\ddot{\mathrm{I}}-\tau\left[\begin{array}{l}\frac{\partial}{\partial t}(\rho \mathbf{v}_0 \mathbf{v}_0+p\ddot{\mathrm{I}})+\frac{\partial}{\partial \mathbf{r}}\cdot\rho(\mathbf{v}_0 \mathbf{v}_0)\mathbf{v}_0+2\ddot{\mathrm{I}}\left(\frac{\partial}{\partial \mathbf{r}}\cdot(p\mathbf{v}_0)\right)\\+\frac{\partial}{\partial \mathbf{r}}\cdot(\ddot{\mathrm{I}}p\mathbf{v}_0)-\mathbf{F}\mathbf{v}_0-\mathbf{v}_0\mathbf{F}\end{array}\right]\right\}=0, \tag{8.8.3}$$

(momentum equation, 1D case)

$$\frac{\partial}{\partial t}\left\{\rho v_0-\tau\left[\frac{\partial}{\partial t}(\rho v_0)+\frac{\partial}{\partial x}(\rho v_0^2)+\frac{\partial p}{\partial x}-F\right]\right\}$$
$$-g\left[\rho-\tau\left(\frac{\partial \rho}{\partial t}+\frac{\partial}{\partial x}(\rho v_0)\right)\right]$$
$$+\frac{\partial}{\partial x}\left\{\rho v_0^2+p-\tau\left[\frac{\partial}{\partial t}(\rho v_0^2+p)+\frac{\partial}{\partial x}(\rho v_0^3+3pv_0)-2Fv_0\right]\right\}=0, \tag{8.8.4}$$

(energy equation)

$$\frac{\partial}{\partial t}\left\{\frac{\rho v_0^2}{2}+\frac{3}{2}p-\tau\left[\frac{\partial}{\partial t}\left(\frac{\rho v_0^2}{2}+\frac{3}{2}p\right)+\frac{\partial}{\partial \mathbf{r}}\cdot\left(\frac{1}{2}\rho v_0^2\mathbf{v}_0+\frac{5}{2}p\mathbf{v}_0\right)-\mathbf{F}\cdot\mathbf{v}_0\right]\right\}$$
$$+\frac{\partial}{\partial \mathbf{r}}\cdot\left\{\frac{1}{2}\rho v_0^2\mathbf{v}_0+\frac{5}{2}p\mathbf{v}_0-\tau\left[\frac{\partial}{\partial t}\left(\frac{1}{2}\rho v_0^2\mathbf{v}_0+\frac{5}{2}p\mathbf{v}_0\right)\right.\right.$$
$$\left.\left.+\frac{\partial}{\partial \mathbf{r}}\cdot\left(\frac{1}{2}\rho v_0^2\mathbf{v}_0\mathbf{v}_0+\frac{7}{2}p\mathbf{v}_0\mathbf{v}_0+\frac{1}{2}pv_0^2\ddot{\mathbf{I}}+\frac{5}{2}\frac{p^2}{\rho}\ddot{\mathbf{I}}\right)-\mathbf{F}\cdot\mathbf{v}_0\mathbf{v}_0-p\mathbf{g}\cdot\ddot{\mathbf{I}}-\frac{1}{2}v_0^2\mathbf{F}-\frac{3}{2}\mathbf{g}p\right]\right\}$$
$$-\left\{\mathbf{F}\cdot\mathbf{v}_0-\tau\left[\mathbf{g}\cdot\left(\frac{\partial}{\partial t}(\rho\mathbf{v}_0)+\frac{\partial}{\partial \mathbf{r}}\cdot\rho\mathbf{v}_0\mathbf{v}_0+\frac{\partial}{\partial \mathbf{r}}\cdot p\ddot{\mathbf{I}}-\mathbf{F}\right)\right]\right\}=0$$

(8.8.5)

(energy equation, 1D case)

$$\frac{\partial}{\partial t}\left\{\rho v_0^2+3p-\tau\left[\frac{\partial}{\partial t}\left(\rho v_0^2+3p\right)+\frac{\partial}{\partial x}\left(\rho v_0^3+5pv_0\right)-2Fv_0\right]\right\}$$
$$+\frac{\partial}{\partial x}\left\{\rho v_0^3+5pv_0-\tau\left[\frac{\partial}{\partial t}\left(\rho v_0^3+5pv_0\right)+\frac{\partial}{\partial x}\left(\rho v_0^4+8pv_0^2\right)-2Fv_0^2-v_0^2F\right]\right\}$$
$$+5\frac{\partial}{\partial x}\left\{\tau\left(\frac{p}{\rho}F-\frac{\partial}{\partial x}\frac{p^2}{\rho}\right)\right\} \qquad (8.8.6)$$
$$-2\left\{Fv_0-\tau g\left(\frac{\partial}{\partial t}(\rho v_0)+\frac{\partial}{\partial x}\left(\rho v_0^2\right)+\frac{\partial p}{\partial x}-F\right)\right\}=0$$

Nonlinear evolution equations (8.8.1) - (8.8.6) contain forces $\mathbf{F}$, $\mathbf{g}$ acting on space and masses including cross-term (see for example the last line in equation (8.8.6)). The relation $\mathbf{F}=\rho\mathbf{g}$ comes into being only after the mass appearance as result of the Big Bang.

Let us introduce now the main mentioned before assumption leading to the theory of motion inside the black holes: the density $\rho\to\infty$. For the derivation of the basic system of equations we should take into account two facts:

1. The ensity can tend to infinity by the arbitrary law.

2. The ratio of pressure to density fines the internal energy of the mass unit $E=p/\rho$ and should be considered as a dependent variable by $\rho\to\infty$.

As result we have the following system of equations:

$$\frac{\partial}{\partial t}\left\{\tau\frac{\partial u}{\partial x}\right\}-\frac{\partial u}{\partial x}+\frac{\partial}{\partial x}\left\{\tau\left[\frac{\partial u}{\partial t}+2u\frac{\partial u}{\partial x}+\frac{\partial E}{\partial x}-g\right]\right\}=0, \tag{8.8.7}$$

$$\begin{aligned}&\frac{\partial}{\partial t}\left\{u-\tau\left[\frac{\partial u}{\partial t}+2u\frac{\partial u}{\partial x}+\frac{\partial E}{\partial x}-g\right]\right\}-g\left[1-\tau\frac{\partial u}{\partial x}\right]\\&+\frac{\partial}{\partial x}\left\{u^2+E-\tau\left[\frac{\partial}{\partial t}\left(u^2+E\right)+\frac{\partial}{\partial x}\left(u^3+3Eu\right)-2gu\right]\right\}=0,\end{aligned} \tag{8.8.8}$$

$$\begin{aligned}&\frac{\partial}{\partial t}\left\{u^2+3E-\tau\left[\frac{\partial}{\partial t}\left(u^2+3E\right)+\frac{\partial}{\partial x}\left(u^3+5Eu\right)-2gu\right]\right\}\\&+\frac{\partial}{\partial x}\left\{u^3+5Eu-\tau\left[\frac{\partial}{\partial t}\left(u^3+5Eu\right)+\frac{\partial}{\partial x}\left(u^4+8Eu^2\right)-3gu^2\right]\right\}\\&+5\frac{\partial}{\partial x}\left\{\tau E\left(g-2\frac{\partial E}{\partial x}\right)\right\}-2gu+2\tau g\left(\frac{\partial u}{\partial t}+2u\frac{\partial u}{\partial x}+\frac{\partial E}{\partial x}-g\right)=0.\end{aligned} \tag{8.8.9}$$

where u is the velocity component along the x direction. Let us introduce the coordinate system moving along the positive direction of x- axis in 1D space with velocity $C=u_0$ equal to phase velocity of considering object

$$\xi=x-Ct. \tag{8.8.10}$$

Taking into account the De Broglie relation we should wait that the group velocity u_g is equal $2u_0$. In moving coordinate system all dependent hydrodynamic values are function of (ξ,t). We investigate the possibility of the traveling wave formation. For this solution there is no explicit dependence on time for coordinate system moving with the phase velocity u_0. Write down the system of equations (8.8.7) - (8.8.9) in the moving coordinate system using the relation $\xi=x-ut$:

(continuity equation, 1D case)

$$\frac{\partial u}{\partial \xi}\quad\tau\left(\frac{\partial u}{\partial \xi}\right)^2-\frac{\partial}{\partial \xi}\left\{\tau\left[\frac{\partial E}{\partial \xi}-g\right]\right\}=0, \tag{8.8.11}$$

(momentum equation, 1D case)

$$\left(\frac{\partial E}{\partial \xi}-g\right)+3\tau g\frac{\partial u}{\partial \xi}-5\tau\frac{\partial u}{\partial \xi}\frac{\partial E}{\partial \xi}-3E\frac{\partial}{\partial \xi}\left\{\tau\frac{\partial u}{\partial \xi}\right\}=0, \tag{8.8.12}$$

(energy equation, 1D case)

$$2u\left(\frac{\partial E}{\partial \xi}-g\right)+5E\frac{\partial u}{\partial \xi}-10\,u\tau\frac{\partial u}{\partial \xi}\frac{\partial E}{\partial \xi}-6uE\frac{\partial}{\partial \xi}\left\{\tau\frac{\partial u}{\partial \xi}\right\}-11\,\tau E\left(\frac{\partial u}{\partial \xi}\right)^2$$

$$-10\frac{\partial}{\partial \xi}\left\{\tau E\frac{\partial E}{\partial \xi}\right\}+5\frac{\partial}{\partial \xi}\{\tau E g\}+6\tau g u\frac{\partial u}{\partial \xi}+2\tau g\left(\frac{\partial E}{\partial \xi}-g\right)=0,$$

(8.8.13)

Non-local equations are closed system of three differential equations with three dependent variables $u,\ E,\ g$. In this case *no needs* to use the additional Poisson equation leading to the Newton gravitational description.

If the non-locality parameter τ is equal to zero the mentioned system becomes unclosed.

Let us introduce the length scale ξ_0, the velocity scale u_0, time scale $\tau_0 = x_0/u_0$, and scales for the gravitation acceleration $g_0 = u_0/\tau_0 = u_0^2/x_0$ and for the internal energy of the mass unit $E_0 = u_0^2$. Using these scales one obtains

$$\frac{\partial \tilde{u}}{\partial \tilde{\xi}}-\tilde{\tau}\left(\frac{\partial \tilde{u}}{\partial \tilde{\xi}}\right)^2-\frac{\partial}{\partial \tilde{\xi}}\left\{\tilde{\tau}\left[\frac{\partial \tilde{E}}{\partial \tilde{\xi}}-\tilde{g}\right]\right\}=0, \tag{8.8.14}$$

$$\left(\frac{\partial \tilde{E}}{\partial \tilde{\xi}}-\tilde{g}\right)+3\tilde{\tau}\tilde{g}\frac{\partial \tilde{u}}{\partial \tilde{\xi}}-5\tilde{\tau}\frac{\partial \tilde{u}}{\partial \tilde{\xi}}\frac{\partial \tilde{E}}{\partial \tilde{\xi}}-3\tilde{E}\frac{\partial}{\partial \tilde{\xi}}\left\{\tilde{\tau}\frac{\partial \tilde{u}}{\partial \tilde{\xi}}\right\}=0, \tag{8.8.15}$$

$$2\tilde{u}\left(\frac{\partial \tilde{E}}{\partial \tilde{\xi}}-\tilde{g}\right)+5\tilde{E}\frac{\partial \tilde{u}}{\partial \tilde{\xi}}-10\,\tilde{u}\tilde{\tau}\frac{\partial \tilde{u}}{\partial \tilde{\xi}}\frac{\partial \tilde{E}}{\partial \tilde{\xi}}-6\tilde{u}\tilde{E}\frac{\partial}{\partial \tilde{\xi}}\left\{\tilde{\tau}\frac{\partial \tilde{u}}{\partial \tilde{\xi}}\right\}$$

$$-11\,\tilde{\tau}\tilde{E}\left(\frac{\partial \tilde{u}}{\partial \tilde{\xi}}\right)^2-10\frac{\partial}{\partial \tilde{\xi}}\left\{\tilde{\tau}\tilde{E}\frac{\partial \tilde{E}}{\partial \tilde{\xi}}\right\}+5\frac{\partial}{\partial \tilde{\xi}}\left(\tilde{\tau}\tilde{E}\tilde{g}\right)+6\tilde{\tau}\tilde{g}\tilde{u}\frac{\partial \tilde{u}}{\partial \tilde{\xi}} \tag{8.8.16}$$

$$+2\tilde{\tau}\tilde{g}\left(\frac{\partial \tilde{E}}{\partial \tilde{\xi}}-\tilde{g}\right)=0,$$

We need also an approximation for the non-local parameter $\tilde{\tau}$. Take this approximation in the form

$$\tilde{\tau} = H/\tilde{u}^2, \tag{8.8.17}$$

where H is dimensionless value. In the dimension form

$$\tau = u_0 x_0 \frac{H}{u^2}. \tag{8.8.18}$$

It means that the nonlocal parameter is proportional to the kinematic velocity and inversely with square of the velocity. Relation (8.8.18) resembles the Heisenberg relation "time – energy". Remark now that (as follow from the numerical calculations) the choice of the non-local parameter in this case has the small influence on the results of modeling.

8.9. Results of mathematical modeling

Now we are ready to display the results of the mathematical modeling realized with the help of Maple (the versions Maple 9 or higher can be used).

The system of equations (8.8.14) – (8.8.16) have the great possibilities of mathematical modeling as result of changing the parameter H five Cauchy conditions describing the character features of initial perturbations which lead to the traveling wave formation. Maple program contains Maple's notations – for example the expression $D(u)(0)=0$ means in the usual notations $\left(\partial\tilde{u}/\partial\tilde{\xi}\right)(0)=0$, independent variable t responds to $\tilde{\xi}$.

We begin with investigation of the problem of principle significance – is it possible after a perturbation (defined by Cauchy conditions) to obtain the traveling wave as result of the self-organization? With this aim let us consider the initial perturbations:

u(0)=1, E(0)=1, g(0)=1, D(u)(0)=0, D(E)(0)=1. (8.9.1)

The following Maple notations on figures are used: u- velocity $\tilde{u}$, E – energy $\tilde{E}$, and g – acceleration $\tilde{g}$. Explanations placed under all following figures. The mentioned calculations are displayed on figures 8.9.1 – 8.9.4.

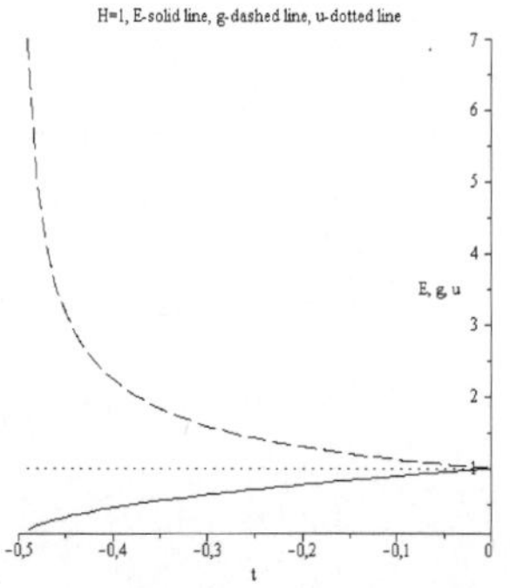

Figure 8.9.1. u – velocity $\tilde{u}$ (dotted line), $H=1$, E – energy $\tilde{E}$ (solid line), and g – acceleration $\tilde{g}$ (dashed line), area of event horizon (left).

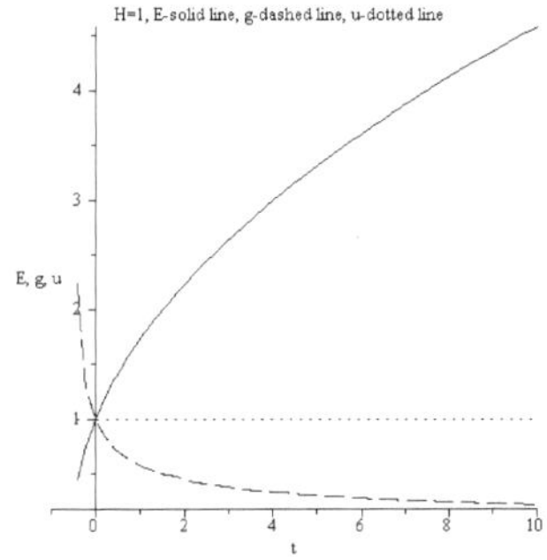

Figure 8.9.2. u – velocity $\tilde{u}$ (dotted line), $H = 1$, E – energy $\tilde{E}$ (solid line), and g – acceleration $\tilde{g}$ (dashed line) (right).

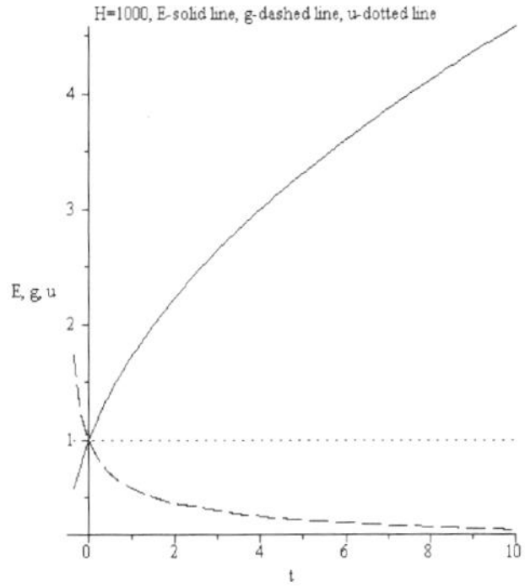

Figure 8.9.3. u – velocity $\tilde{u}$ (dotted line), $H = 1000$, E – energy $\tilde{E}$ (solid line), and g – acceleration $\tilde{g}$ (dashed line), area of event horizon (left).

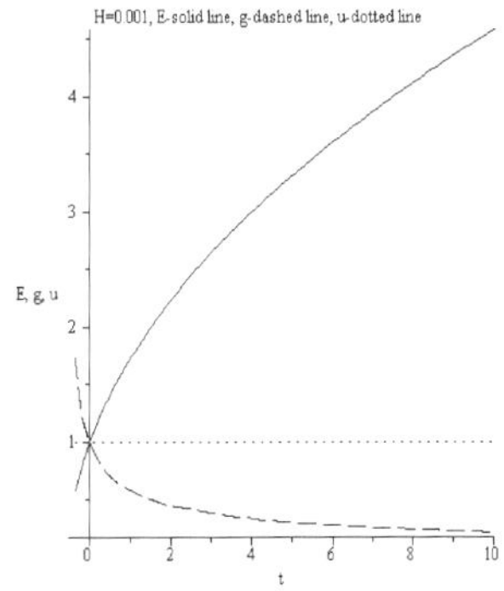

Figure 8.9.4. u – velocity $\tilde{u}$ (dotted line), $H = 0.001$, E – energy $\tilde{E}$ (solid line), and g – acceleration $\tilde{g}$ (dashed line) (right).

All calculations are realized using the conditions (7.9.1) but by the different value of the H parameter, namely $H = 0.001; 1; 1000$. Figure 8.9.1 reflects the evolution of the dependent values in the area of the event horizon in details.

In all calculations the boundary of the transition area of events is limited by the condition (obtained as the self-consistent result of calculations) $\tilde{\xi}_{\lim} > -0.5$

As follow from calculations (see figures 8.9.1 – 8.9.4) the variation of H-parameter has the weak influence on the numerical results. Let us show also the results obtained for $H = 0.0001$ (see figure 7.9.5) and the corresponding numerical results near singularity $\tilde{\xi}_{\lim} = -0.5$; namely: H=0.0001; $\tilde{\xi} = -0.4999999$; $\tilde{E} = 0.382 \cdot 10^{-3}$; $\tilde{g} = 2615.014$; $\tilde{u} = 1$.

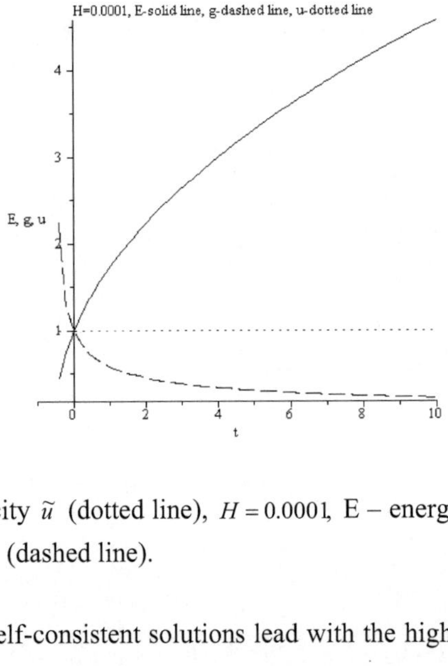

Figure 8.9.5. u – velocity $\tilde{u}$ (dotted line), $H = 0.0001$, E – energy $\tilde{E}$ (solid line), and g – acceleration $\tilde{g}$ (dashed line).

As we see the self-consistent solutions lead with the high accuracy to the relation

$$\tilde{u} = 1. \tag{8.9.2}$$

Let us use this condition for analytical transformations of the equations (8.8.14) – (8.8.16). We have correspondingly

$$\frac{\partial}{\partial \tilde{\xi}} \left\{ \tilde{\tau} \left[\frac{\partial \tilde{E}}{\partial \tilde{\xi}} - \tilde{g} \right] \right\} = 0, \tag{8.9.3}$$

$$\frac{\partial \tilde{E}}{\partial \tilde{\xi}} - \tilde{g} = 0, \tag{8.9.4}$$

$$2\frac{\partial}{\partial\tilde{\xi}}\left\{\tilde{\tau}\tilde{E}\frac{\partial\tilde{E}}{\partial\tilde{\xi}}\right\}-\frac{\partial}{\partial\tilde{\xi}}\left\{\tilde{\tau}\tilde{E}\tilde{g}\right\}=0. \quad (8.9.5)$$

From (8.9.4), (8.9.5) follow

$$\frac{\partial}{\partial\tilde{\xi}}\left(\tilde{\tau}\tilde{E}\frac{\partial\tilde{E}}{\partial\tilde{\xi}}\right)=0, \quad (8.9.6)$$

$$\tilde{\tau}\tilde{E}\frac{\partial\tilde{E}}{\partial\tilde{\xi}}=const \quad (8.9.7)$$

and for chosen $\tilde{\tau}$ approximation

$$\frac{\partial\tilde{E}^2}{\partial\tilde{\xi}}=C, \; \tilde{E}^2=C\tilde{\xi}+C_1, \quad (8.9.8)$$

$$\tilde{E}^2=\left[\frac{\partial\tilde{E}^2}{\partial\tilde{\xi}}\right]_{\tilde{\xi}=0}\tilde{\xi}+\tilde{E}^2(0). \quad (8.9.9)$$

It means that for large $\tilde{\xi}$

$$\tilde{E}\cong\sqrt{2\tilde{E}(0)\left[\frac{\partial\tilde{E}}{\partial\tilde{\xi}}\right]_{\tilde{\xi}=0}}\sqrt{\tilde{\xi}} \quad (8.9.10)$$

or in the dimensional form

$$E\cong\sqrt{2E(0)\left[\frac{\partial E}{\partial\xi}\right]_{\xi=0}}\sqrt{\xi} \quad (8.9.11)$$

where $\xi=x-ut$. Taking into account (8.9.4), (8.9.6) one obtains

$$\tilde{E}\tilde{g}=const=\tilde{E}(0)\tilde{g}(0) \quad (8.9.12)$$

$$\tilde{g}\cong\tilde{g}(0)\frac{\tilde{E}(0)}{\sqrt{\left[\frac{\partial\tilde{E}^2}{\partial\tilde{\xi}}\right]_{\tilde{\xi}=0}\tilde{\xi}+\tilde{E}^2(0)}}=\frac{\tilde{g}(0)}{\sqrt{1+\left[\frac{\partial\ln\tilde{E}^2}{\partial\tilde{\xi}}\right]_{\tilde{\xi}=0}\tilde{\xi}}} \quad (8.9.13)$$

and for large $\tilde{\xi}$

$$\tilde{g}\cong\tilde{g}(0)\sqrt{\frac{\tilde{E}(0)}{2\left[\frac{\partial\tilde{E}}{\partial\tilde{\xi}}\right]_{\tilde{\xi}=0}}}\frac{1}{\sqrt{\tilde{\xi}}}. \quad (8.9.14)$$

After the penetration through the frontier barrier the external matter is moving in the black channel in the form of the traveling wave. In this 1D Cartesian model the gravitational acceleration decreases as $\tilde{\xi}^{-0.5}$ with the rise of the $\tilde{\xi}$ - distance and, on the contrary, the internal energy of the mass unit increases as $\tilde{\xi}^{0.5}$.

The influence of the tidal force on the object in the black channel can be calculated using (8.9.13), (8.9.14). From (8.9.13) follows

$$d\widetilde{g} = -\left[\frac{\partial \widetilde{E}}{\partial \widetilde{\xi}}\right]_{\widetilde{\xi}=0} \widetilde{g}(0) \frac{\widetilde{E}^2(0)}{\left[\left[\frac{\partial \widetilde{E}^2}{\partial \widetilde{\xi}}\right]_{\widetilde{\xi}=0} \widetilde{\xi} + \widetilde{E}^2(0)\right]^{3/2}} d\widetilde{\xi} \,. \quad (8.9.15)$$

Relation (8.9.15) reflects the change Δg in the tidal force acting at the time moment t across the body element Δx. This change tends to infinity if the point of singularity

$$\widetilde{\xi}_s = -\left[\frac{\partial \ln \widetilde{E}^2}{\partial \widetilde{\xi}}\right]^{-1}_{\widetilde{\xi}=0} \quad (8.9.16)$$

which corresponds to the frontier barrier. For example for Cauchy conditions (8.9.1) $\widetilde{\xi}_s = -0.5$,

$$\Delta \widetilde{g} \cong -\frac{1}{\left[2\widetilde{\xi} + 1\right]^{3/2}} \Delta \widetilde{\xi} \quad (8.9.17)$$

In this case the change Δg in the tidal force acting at the time moment t across the body element Δx turns into infinity by $\widetilde{\xi} = -0.5$. In the following if

$$\left[\frac{\partial \widetilde{E}^2}{\partial \widetilde{\xi}}\right]_{\widetilde{\xi}=0} \widetilde{\xi} + \widetilde{E}^2(0) \neq 0 \quad (8.9.18)$$

the Δg change of the tidal force acting at the time moment t across the body element Δx has not the catastrophic character. As one can see during all investigation we needn't to use the theory Newtonian gravitation for solution of nonlinear non-local evolution equations (EE). In contrast with the local physics this approach in the frame of quantum non-local hydrodynamics leads to the closed mathematical description for the physical system under consideration.

If the density tends to infinity the matter evolution inside of "the black channel" (1D Cartesian model) is organizing in the form of the traveling waves.

Numerical modeling leads to appearance of the singularity on the left side of domain where the gravitational acceleration turns into infinity. This singularity corresponds to event horizon and the whole neighboring area of the strong gravitational variation can be named as the transition area of events, (see figure 8.9.1, 8.9.2).

All calculations are realized for the case $\xi = x - ut$, corresponding to the wave traveling along the positive direction of the x - axis. Obviously after the initial perturbations the analogical wave propagates in the opposite direction $(-\xi)$ after the sign change $x \to -x$, $u \to -u$. In the theory of Black Hole (BH) with the spherical symmetry it leads near the event horizon to the appearance of black body radiation which was predicted by Stephen Hawking. Hawking radiation reduces the mass and the energy of the black hole and is therefore also known as black hole evaporation. The structure of this radiation significantly depends on the topological features of BH.

Usually the appearance of the analogical picture in the left hand half-plane does not lead to information of the principal significance, but not for the case under consideration.

Really, after rotation the right half-plane picture by 180° two domains (see figures 1 and 2) create the joined domain with the width $\tilde{\xi} = 1$ and minimums for $\tilde{E}$ and $\tilde{g}$ in the centre of the infinite square well. On the whole the configuration reminds the known quantum mechanical problem of the particle evolution in a box with the infinite potential barriers of the gravitational origin. It is well known that the solution of the analogical problem in the Schrödinger quantum mechanics leads to the discrete energetic levels. Quantum calculations of oscillators in the arbitrary potential fields can be found in [19].

Finally some words concerning the following investigations. Is it possible to show the gravitation waves existence as an analytical result obtained in the frame of nonlocal physics? The following item answers this question.

8.10. Gravitational waves created by the Black Hole explosion. Analytical investigation.

The existence of the gravitational waves (GW) was proposed by Henri Poincaré in 1905. General theory of relativity (GTR, A. Einstein, 1916) leads to transport energy as gravitational radiation. GTR explains GW as an effect of disturbances in the curvature of spacetime, generated by accelerated masses; these disturbances propagate as waves outward from their source. Newton's law of universal gravitation as a part of local physics, does not provide for GW existence, since that law is predicated on the assumption that physical interactions propagate instantaneously, in other words at infinite speed. On 11 February 2016, the LIGO and VIRGO Scientific Collaboration announced they had made the first direct observation of the gravitational waves.

The gravitational waves originated from a pair of merging black holes [162, 163]. After the initial announcement the LIGO instruments detected two more confirmed, and one potential

gravitational wave events. In August 2017, the two LIGO instruments and the Virgo instrument observed a fourth gravitational wave from merging black holes, and a fifth gravitational wave from a binary neutron star merger. Several other gravitational wave detectors gravitational are planned or under construction.

In 2017, the Nobel Prize in Physics was awarded to Rainer Weiss, Kip Thorne and Barry Barish for their role in the direct detection of gravitational waves. The appearance of GW belongs to the extremely weak effect and we should wait the very significant (from the position of nonlocal physics) but very weak effect with the small time nonlocal parameter τ

Let us investigate the possibility of the gravitational waves (GV) appearance after the Black Hole (BH) explosion. We suppose:

1. The observer is placed at the very far distance from the BH and GV can be considered as a plane wave.
2. The internal structure of BH is not taken into account and the existence of BH is reflected only in initial conditions.

Then we can use the following system of the 1D non-stationary equations (see also (8.2.10) – (8.2.12)):

(continuity equation)

$$\frac{\partial}{\partial t}\left\{\tau\left[\frac{1}{r^2}\frac{\partial(r^2 v_{0r})}{\partial r}\right]\right\}-\frac{1}{r^2}\frac{\partial}{\partial r}\left\{r^2\left\{v_{0r}-\tau\left[\frac{\partial v_{0r}}{\partial t}+\frac{1}{r^2}\frac{\partial(r^2 v_{0r}^2)}{\partial r}-g_r\right]\right\}\right\}+\frac{1}{r^2}\frac{\partial}{\partial r}\left(\tau r^2\frac{\partial E}{\partial r}\right)=0, \tag{8.10.1}$$

(momentum equation)

$$\frac{\partial}{\partial t}\left\{v_{0r}-\tau\left[\frac{\partial}{\partial t}(v_{0r})+\frac{1}{r^2}\frac{\partial(r^2 v_{0r}^2)}{\partial r}+\frac{\partial E}{\partial r}-g_r\right]\right\}-\left[g_r-\tau g_r\left(\frac{1}{r^2}\frac{\partial(r^2 v_{0r})}{\partial r}\right)\right]$$

$$+\frac{1}{r^2}\frac{\partial}{\partial r}\left\{r^2\left\{v_{0r}^2-\tau\left[\frac{\partial}{\partial t}(v_{0r}^2)+\frac{1}{r^2}\frac{\partial(r^2 v_{0r}^3)}{\partial r}-2g_r v_{0r}\right]\right\}\right\}$$

$$+\frac{\partial E}{\partial r}-\frac{\partial}{\partial r}\left(\tau\frac{\partial E}{\partial t}\right)-2\frac{\partial}{\partial r}\left(\frac{\tau}{r^2}\frac{\partial(r^2 E v_{0r})}{\partial r}\right)-\frac{1}{r^2}\frac{\partial}{\partial r}\left(\tau r^2\frac{\partial(E v_{0r})}{\partial r}\right)=0. \tag{8.10.2}$$

(energy equation)

$$\frac{\partial}{\partial t}\left\{\frac{1}{2}v_{0r}^2+\frac{3}{2}E-\tau\left[\frac{\partial}{\partial t}\left(\frac{1}{2}v_{0r}^2+\frac{3}{2}E\right)+\frac{1}{r^2}\frac{\partial}{\partial r}\left(r^2 v_{0r}\left(\frac{1}{2}v_{0r}^2+\frac{5}{2}E\right)\right)-g_r v_{0r}\right]\right\}+$$

$$+\frac{1}{r^2}\frac{\partial}{\partial r}\left\{r^2\left\{\left(\frac{1}{2}v_{0r}^2+\frac{5}{2}E\right)v_{0r}-\tau\left[\frac{\partial}{\partial t}\left(\left(\frac{1}{2}v_{0r}^2+\frac{5}{2}E\right)v_{0r}\right)+\frac{1}{r^2}\frac{\partial}{\partial r}\left(r^2\left(\frac{1}{2}v_{0r}^2+\frac{7}{2}E\right)v_{0r}^2\right)-\right.\right.\right.$$

$$\left.\left.\left.-g_r v_{0r}^2-\left(\frac{1}{2}v_{0r}^2+\frac{3}{2}E\right)g_r\right]\right\}\right\}-g_r\left\{v_{0r}-\tau\left[\frac{\partial v_{0r}}{\partial t}+\frac{1}{r^2}\frac{\partial}{\partial r}(r^2 v_{0r}^2)+\frac{\partial E}{\partial r}-g_r\right]\right\}-$$

$$-\frac{1}{r^2}\frac{\partial}{\partial r}\left(\tau r^2\frac{\partial}{\partial r}\left(\frac{1}{2}E v_{0r}^2+\frac{5}{2}E^2\right)\right)+\frac{1}{r^2}\frac{\partial}{\partial r}\left(r^2\tau E g_r\right)=0. \tag{8.10.3}$$

In the local limit $(\tau \to 0)$ it follows from (8.10.1)

$$\frac{\partial}{\partial r}\left(r^2 v_{0r}\right)=0. \tag{8.10.4}$$

and

$$v_{0r}=\frac{const}{r^2}. \tag{8.10.5}$$

As we see we obtain from continuity equation in local limit:

1. No gravitational waves.
2. Non acceptable result if $r=0$, more over in local limit $r^2 v_{0r}=C_1$ for an arbitrary r; if $r=0$ $C_1=0 \to r^2 v_{0r}=0 \to v_{0r}=0$

Momentum equation leads to relation

$$\frac{\partial E}{\partial r}-g_r=0. \tag{8.10.6}$$

Energy equation leads to relation

$$E=E(r). \tag{8.10.7}$$

Conclusion: local physics can not be applied to investigation of GW. Nevertheless it should be noticed that (8.10.6) has the transparent physical sense – in the first approximation the gravitational acceleration is equal the $E(r)$ space derivation, where the internal energy $E(r)$ has the dimension of the squared velocity.

Let the independent variable r tends to infinity according to an arbitrary law. From equations (8.10.1) – (8.10.3) follow

(continuity equation)

$$\frac{\partial}{\partial t}\left\{\tau\left[\frac{\partial v_{0r}}{\partial r}\right]\right\}-\frac{\partial}{\partial r}\left\{v_{0r}-\tau\left[\frac{\partial v_{0r}}{\partial t}+\frac{\partial v_{0r}^2}{\partial r}-g_r+\frac{\partial}{\partial r}\left(\tau\frac{\partial E}{\partial r}\right)\right]\right\}=0 \tag{8.10.8}$$

(momentum equation)

$$\frac{\partial}{\partial t}\left\{v_{0r}-\tau\left[\frac{\partial v_{0r}}{\partial t}+\frac{\partial v_{0r}^2}{\partial r}+\frac{\partial E}{\partial r}-g_r\right]\right\}-g_r\left[1-\tau\frac{\partial v_{0r}}{\partial r}\right]+\frac{\partial}{\partial r}\left\{v_{0r}^2-\tau\left[\frac{\partial v_{0r}^2}{\partial t}+\frac{\partial v_{0r}^3}{\partial r}-2g_r v_{0r}\right]\right\}+$$

$$+\frac{\partial E}{\partial r}-\frac{\partial}{\partial r}\left(\tau\frac{\partial E}{\partial t}\right)-3\frac{\partial}{\partial r}\left(\tau\frac{\partial\left(E v_{0r}\right)}{\partial r}\right)=0. \tag{8.10.9}$$

(energy equation)

$$\frac{\partial}{\partial t}\left\{v_{0r}^2+3E-\tau\left[\frac{\partial}{\partial t}\left(v_{0r}^2+3E\right)+\frac{\partial}{\partial r}\left(v_{0r}\left(v_{0r}^2+5E\right)\right)-2g_r v_{0r}\right]\right\}+\frac{\partial}{\partial r}\left[\left(v_{0r}^2+5E\right)v_{0r}\right]$$

$$-\frac{\partial}{\partial r}\left\{\tau\left[\frac{\partial}{\partial t}\left(\left(v_{0r}^2+5E\right)v_{0r}\right)+\frac{\partial}{\partial r}\left(\left(v_{0r}^2+7E\right)v_{0r}^2\right)-2g_r v_{0r}^2-\left(v_{0r}^2+3E\right)g_r\right]\right\}-$$

$$-2g_r\left\{v_{0r}-\tau\left[\frac{\partial v_{0r}}{\partial t}+\frac{\partial v_{0r}^2}{\partial r}+\frac{\partial E}{\partial r}-g_r\right]\right\}-\frac{\partial}{\partial r}\left(\tau\frac{\partial}{\partial r}\left(Ev_{0r}^2+5E^2\right)\right)+2\frac{\partial}{\partial r}\left(\tau E g_r\right)=0.$$

(8.10.10)

In the following we suppose that nonlocal time parameter $\tau = const$. In this case we can integrate the continuity equation

$$\frac{\partial}{\partial t}\left\{\tau\left[\frac{\partial v_{0r}}{\partial r}\right]\right\}-\frac{\partial}{\partial r}\left\{v_{0r}-\tau\left[\frac{\partial v_{0r}}{\partial t}+\frac{\partial v_{0r}^2}{\partial r}-g_r+\frac{\partial}{\partial r}\left(\tau\frac{\partial E}{\partial r}\right)\right]\right\}=0 \qquad (8.10.11)$$

or

$$\frac{\partial}{\partial r}\left\{v_{0r}-\tau\left[\frac{\partial v_{0r}}{\partial t}+\frac{\partial v_{0r}^2}{\partial r}-g_r+\frac{\partial}{\partial r}\left(\tau\frac{\partial E}{\partial r}\right)\right]\right\}-\tau\frac{\partial}{\partial r}\frac{\partial v_{0r}}{\partial t}=0, \qquad (8.10.12)$$

or

$$v_{0r}=C+\tau\left[2\frac{\partial v_{0r}}{\partial t}+\frac{\partial v_{0r}^2}{\partial r}-g_r+\tau\frac{\partial^2 E}{\partial r^2}\right]. \qquad (8.10.13)$$

or

$$v_{0r}=C+v_r, \qquad (8.10.14)$$

where

$$v_r=\tau\left[2\frac{\partial v_{0r}}{\partial t}+\frac{\partial v_{0r}^2}{\partial r}-g_r+\tau\frac{\partial^2 E}{\partial r^2}\right] \qquad (8.10.15)$$

Relation (8.10.13) has the transparent physical sense, the wave velocity is the sum of the constant velocity C (most likely the speed of light) and the velocity fluctuation proportional to τ.

Let us consider now the moment equation (8.10.9). We omit the terms proportional to τ^2 (and less terms), but conserving the senior derivatives with small τ^1 parameter. We find

$$\frac{\partial}{\partial t}\left\{v_r-\tau\left[\frac{\partial v_r}{\partial t}+\frac{\partial v_r^2}{\partial r}+\frac{\partial E}{\partial t}-g_r\right]\right\}-g_r\left[1-\tau\frac{\partial v_r}{\partial r}\right]+\frac{\partial}{\partial r}\left\{v_r^2-\tau\left[\frac{\partial v_r^2}{\partial t}+\frac{\partial v_r^3}{\partial r}-2g_r v_r\right]\right\}+$$

$$+\frac{\partial E}{\partial r}-\frac{\partial}{\partial r}\left(\tau\frac{\partial E}{\partial t}\right)-3\frac{\partial}{\partial r}\left(\tau\frac{\partial(Ev_r)}{\partial r}\right)=0. \qquad (8.10.16)$$

$$\tau\frac{\partial^2 v_r}{\partial t^2}-g_r+\frac{\partial E}{\partial r}\left[E-\tau\frac{\partial E}{\partial t}\right]-3\tau\frac{\partial^2(Ev_r)}{\partial r^2}=0 \qquad (8.10.17)$$

or after dividing by τ

$$\frac{\partial^2 v_r}{\partial t^2}-\frac{g_r}{\tau}+\frac{\partial}{\partial r}\left[\frac{E}{\tau}-\frac{\partial E}{\partial t}\right]-3\frac{\partial^2(Ev_r)}{\partial r^2}=0 \qquad (8.10.18)$$

We suppose:

1. $\frac{\partial}{\partial r}\left[\frac{E}{\tau}-\frac{\partial E}{\partial t}\right]\cong 0$,

2. $\frac{\partial^2(Ev_r)}{\partial r^2}\cong \overline{E}\frac{\partial^2 v_r}{\partial r^2}$, where $\overline{E}$ is a mean value.

We obtain the hyperbolic equation which admits the analytical solution.

$$\frac{\partial^2 v_r}{\partial t^2}-3\overline{E}\frac{\partial^2 v_r}{\partial r^2}=\frac{g_r}{\tau} \qquad (8.10.19)$$

The general solution of a partial differential equation (8.10.19) in the domain of variable change

$-\infty<r<\infty$ is written as

$$v_r(r,t)=\frac{1}{2}\left[f\left(r+\sqrt{3\overline{E}}\,t\right)+f\left(r-\sqrt{3\overline{E}}\,t\right)\right]+\frac{1}{2\sqrt{3\overline{E}}}\int_{r-\sqrt{3\overline{E}}\,t}^{r+\sqrt{3\overline{E}}\,t}w(\xi)d\xi+$$
$$+\frac{1}{\tau 2\sqrt{3\overline{E}}}\int_0^t\int_{r-\sqrt{3\overline{E}}(t-\tau)}^{r+\sqrt{3\overline{E}}(t-\tau)}g_r(\xi,\tau)d\xi d\tau, \qquad (8.10.20)$$

where

$$v_r=f(r),\ \text{if}\ t=0, \qquad (8.10.21)$$

$$\frac{\partial v_r}{\partial t}=w(r),\ \text{if}\ t=0. \qquad (8.10.22)$$

For the better understanding the physical situation we suppose that

$$\frac{g_r}{\tau}=\frac{\overline{g}_r}{\overline{\tau}}=const. \qquad (8.10.23)$$

In this case

$$\frac{\partial^2 v_r}{\partial t^2}-3\overline{E}\frac{\partial^2 v_r}{\partial r^2}=\frac{\overline{g}_r}{\overline{\tau}}, \qquad (8.10.24)$$

which solution is

$$v_r(r,t)=f_1\left(\frac{r}{2}-\frac{t\sqrt{3E}}{2}\right)+f_2\left(t-\frac{r}{\sqrt{3E}}\right)+\frac{\overline{g}_r}{2\overline{\tau}}\frac{1}{\sqrt{3E}}\left(\frac{r}{2}-\frac{t\sqrt{3E}}{2}\right)\left(t-\frac{r}{\sqrt{3E}}\right). \qquad (8.10.25)$$

The validity of this solution can be easily proved by the substation (8.10.24). For example

$$\frac{\partial^2 v_r}{\partial r^2}=\frac{1}{4}\frac{\partial^2 f_1}{\partial \xi^2}+\frac{1}{3E}\frac{\partial^2 f_2}{\partial \eta^2}, \qquad (8.10.26)$$

$$\frac{\partial^2 v_r}{\partial t^2}=\frac{3E}{4}\frac{\partial^2 f_1}{\partial \xi^2}+\frac{\partial^2 f_2}{\partial \eta^2}+\frac{\overline{g}_r}{2\overline{\tau}}. \qquad (8.10.27)$$

where

$$\xi = \frac{r}{2} - \frac{t\sqrt{3E}}{2}, \quad (8.10.28)$$

$$\eta = t - \frac{r}{\sqrt{3E}} \quad (8.10.29)$$

Using variables ξ,η the solution of the PD-equation can be written in symmetric form

$$v_r(r,t) = f_1(\xi) + f_2(\eta) + \frac{\bar{g}_r}{2\bar{\tau}}\frac{1}{\sqrt{3E}}\xi\eta. \quad (8.10.30)$$

Let the observer be at some distance r_1 from the point of perturbation of the gravitational field. In this case

$$C_1 = \frac{r_1}{2} - \frac{{}^1t\sqrt{3E}}{2}, \; C_2 = {}^2t - \frac{r_1}{\sqrt{3E}}, \quad (8.10.31)$$

where ${}^1t$ and ${}^2t$ the corresponding time moments.

$$2C_1 + {}^1t\sqrt{3E} = {}^2t\sqrt{3E} - C_2\sqrt{3E} \quad (8.10.32)$$

or

$${}^2t - {}^1t = \frac{2C_1}{\sqrt{3E}} + C_2, \quad (8.10.33)$$

Then the observer should discover the gravitational bunch at the time interval which is equal to ${}^2t - {}^1t$.

Following the formulated approximation we find g_r. Really from (8.10.14) we obtain

$$g_r = 2\frac{\partial v_{0r}}{\partial t} + \frac{\partial (v_{0r}^2 + E)}{\partial r} - \frac{v_{0r}}{\tau} \cong -\frac{v_{0r}}{\tau}, \quad (8.10.34)$$

or

$$g_r = g_r^0 + g_r^{fl}, \quad (8.10.35)$$

where

$$g_r^0 = -\frac{C}{\bar{\tau}}, \quad (8.10.36)$$

$$g_r^{fl} = -\frac{v_r}{\bar{\tau}}$$

Using now (8.10.30) we find

$$g_r(r,t) = -\frac{f_1(\xi) + f_2(\eta) + C}{\bar{\tau}} - \frac{\bar{g}_r}{2\bar{\tau}^2}\frac{1}{\sqrt{3E}}\xi\eta. \quad (8.10.37)$$

Write down the energy equation (8.10.10) using the mentioned approximation

$$3\frac{\partial}{\partial t}\left[E - \tau\frac{\partial E}{\partial t}\right] + \frac{\partial}{\partial r}\{5Ev_{0r} + 3\tau E g_r\} - 2g_r v_{0r} - 5\tau\frac{\partial^2 E^2}{\partial r^2} + 2\tau\frac{\partial}{\partial r}(Eg_r) = 0. \quad (8.10.38)$$

or

$$\frac{\partial^2 E}{\partial t^2}=\frac{1}{\overline{\tau}}\frac{\partial E}{\partial t}+\frac{\partial}{\partial r}\left\{\frac{5}{3}E\frac{v_{0r}}{\overline{\tau}}+Eg_r\right\}-\frac{2}{3}g_r\frac{v_{0r}}{\overline{\tau}}-\frac{5}{3}\frac{\partial^2 E^2}{\partial r^2}+\frac{2}{3}\frac{\partial}{\partial r}(Eg_r) \qquad (8.10.39)$$

or (see (8.10.34))

$$\frac{\partial^2 E}{\partial t^2}=\frac{1}{\overline{\tau}}\frac{\partial E}{\partial t}+\frac{2}{3}g_r^2-\frac{5}{3}\frac{\partial^2 E^2}{\partial r^2} \qquad (8.10.40)$$

Taking into account the relation (8.10.37) it is possible to obtain the estimation

$$\frac{\partial^2 E}{\partial t^2}-\frac{1}{\overline{\tau}}\frac{\partial E}{\partial t}-\frac{2}{3}g_r^2=0. \qquad (8.10.41)$$

Obviously this equation also leads to the oscillating regime.

Conclusion:

1. In literature you can find different opinions about the GW velocity. It is shown by different authors (on the basement of the GRT) that both the phase velocity and group velocity of the gravitational waves can be greater or less than the speed of light. GRT does not lead to the transport equations and this problem (as it was shown) can be solved only be the methods of nonlocal physics. It is interesting to notice that in LIGO observations the electro-magnetic impulse came later than gravitational bunch.
2. Nonlocal physics is the effective theory of the GW investigation.
3. In comparison with the phenomenological GRT nonlocal physics (created from the first principles of physics) deliver the real transport equations in space and time for the gravitational field.

CHAPTER 9. TRANSPORT PROCESSES IN PHYSICAL VACUUM

Preliminary remarks to Chapter 9.

In monographs [19 - 22] reveals the following effects of the principal significance:

1. The birth of the Universe is convoying of appearance of the repulsion forces. In the existing terminology - we discover the “negative pressure” and “dark energy” in all cases. This fundamental result does not depend on the mechanism of external perturbations. In other words, the anti-gravity in the physical vacuum exists, if there is dissipation of energy or in the absence of dissipation at all.
2. Physical Vacuum (PV) is not a speculative object; it is a reality as “matter” and “fields”. In other words, the physical vacuum is "the third" physical reality along with matter and fields. In this case, it is natural to raise the question about the existence of the effect which is similar to the Hubble’s effect. As installing the appearance of this effect in the physical vacuum does not contradict the conclusions of non-local physics.
3. We investigated in the frame of non-local physics the connection between from the first glance different effects like Physical Vacuum and PV boxes, clear air turbulence (CAT), the Shawyer EM-drive (PV-engines), Special Theory of Relativity.
4. We intend to find the solutions of the transport equations defining the evolution the physical vacuum (PV). It means:

A) If the matter is absent, non-local evolution equations have nevertheless non-trivial solutions corresponding evolution of PV which description in time and 3D space on the level of quantum hydrodynamics demands only quantum pressure p, the self-consistent force $\mathbf{F}$ (acting on unit of the space volume) and velocity $\mathbf{v}_0$. The system of non local equations is written for the case when the usual matter is absent ($\rho = 0$), also radiation, gravitation (as well as other mass forces) and electromagnetic fields are absent. No reason to speak about special or general relativity in this situation, because these theories don’t work in the described conditions.

B) In all other cases we consider from the position of the nonlocal physics the interaction of Physical Vacuum with the external electromagnetic and gravitational fields taking into account the possible technical applications like EM-engine.

C) Formally speaking the Newtonian gravity propagates with the infinite speed. This conclusion is connected only with the description in the frame of local physics. Usual affirmation - general relativity (GR) reduces to Newtonian gravity in the weak-field, low-velocity limit. In literature you can find criticism of this affirmation because the conservation of angular momentum is implicit in the assumptions on which GR rests. Finite propagation speeds and conservation of angular momentum are incompatible in GR. Therefore, phenomenological GR was forced to claim that gravity is not a force that propagates in any classical sense. But here I do not intend to join to this widely discussed topic using only unified non-local model. The self-consistent description of PV with electromagnetic and gravitational fields originated by PV - is the topic other investigations. All results are obtained from the first principles of physics.

9.1. The burst of PV volume. Basic equations.

The following progress in cosmology, in understanding the origin and evolution of the Universe, will be based on projects like Planck, NASA WMAP (Wilkinson Microwave Anisotropy Probe) space mission and the BICEP2 (Background Imaging of Cosmic Extragalactic Polarization 2) experiment. In this case we can speak about (now speculative) models like the burst in domains filled by PV. These models are analogue of the Hubble boxes which are observed in reality.

In the mentioned case it is reasonable to use the spherical coordinate system; (see also Appendix 1). In the usual hydrodynamic notations we have continuity equation

$$\frac{\partial}{\partial t}\left\{\rho-\tau\left[\frac{\partial \rho}{\partial t}+\frac{\partial}{\partial \mathbf{r}}\cdot(\rho \mathbf{v}_0)\right]\right\}+\frac{\partial}{\partial \mathbf{r}}\cdot\left\{\rho \mathbf{v}_0-\tau\left[\frac{\partial}{\partial t}(\rho \mathbf{v}_0)+\frac{\partial}{\partial \mathbf{r}}\cdot(\rho \mathbf{v}_0 \mathbf{v}_0)+\ddot{\mathrm{I}}\cdot\frac{\partial p}{\partial \mathbf{r}}-\mathbf{F}\right]\right\}=0, \tag{9.1.1}$$

which in the non-stationary spherically symmetric case is written as

$$\frac{\partial}{\partial t}\left\{\rho-\tau\left[\frac{\partial \rho}{\partial t}+\frac{1}{r^2}\frac{\partial\left(r^2 \rho v_{0r}\right)}{\partial r}\right]\right\}+\frac{1}{r^2}\frac{\partial}{\partial r}\left\{r^2\left\{\rho v_{0r}-\tau\left[\frac{\partial}{\partial t}(\rho v_{0r})+\frac{1}{r^2}\frac{\partial\left(r^2 \rho v_{0r}^2\right)}{\partial r}-F_r\right]\right\}\right\}$$

$$-\frac{1}{r^2}\frac{\partial}{\partial r}\left(\tau r^2\frac{\partial p}{\partial r}\right)=0, \tag{9.1.2}$$

where τ is a non-locality parameter. The transfer to PV means the limit case $\rho \to 0$. As we see from continuity equation (9.1.2), we should introduce the mechanical characteristic of Physical Vacuum defining the interaction of PV with Matter.

These characteristics of PHYSICAL VACUUM (PV) are:

a) Pressure p of PV,

b) Force F_r acting on the volume unit of PV,

c) Hydrodynamic velocity v_{0r} of PV.

As a result we have from (9.1.2)

$$\frac{\partial}{\partial r}\left\{r^2\tau\left[\frac{\partial p}{\partial r}-F_r\right]\right\}=0, \tag{9.1.3}$$

In the analogical 1D case in the Cartesian coordinate system we have

$$\frac{\partial}{\partial x}\left[\tau\left(\frac{\partial p}{\partial x}-F_x\right)\right]=0 \tag{9.1.4}$$

(momentum equation)

$$\frac{\partial}{\partial t}\left\{\rho\mathbf{v}_0-\tau\left[\frac{\partial}{\partial t}(\rho\mathbf{v}_0)+\frac{\partial}{\partial\mathbf{r}}\cdot\rho\mathbf{v}_0\mathbf{v}_0+\frac{\partial p}{\partial\mathbf{r}}-\mathbf{F}\right]\right\}-\left[\mathbf{F}-\tau\mathbf{g}\left(\frac{\partial\rho}{\partial t}+\frac{\partial}{\partial\mathbf{r}}\cdot(\rho\mathbf{v}_0)\right)\right]$$
$$+\frac{\partial}{\partial\mathbf{r}}\cdot\left\{\rho\mathbf{v}_0\mathbf{v}_0+p\tilde{\mathbf{I}}-\tau\left[\begin{array}{l}\frac{\partial}{\partial t}\left(\rho\mathbf{v}_0\mathbf{v}_0+p\tilde{\mathbf{I}}\right)+\frac{\partial}{\partial\mathbf{r}}\cdot\rho(\mathbf{v}_0\mathbf{v}_0)\mathbf{v}_0+2\tilde{\mathbf{I}}\left(\frac{\partial}{\partial\mathbf{r}}\cdot(p\mathbf{v}_0)\right)\\+\frac{\partial}{\partial\mathbf{r}}\cdot\left(\tilde{\mathbf{I}}p\mathbf{v}_0\right)-\mathbf{F}\mathbf{v}_0-\mathbf{v}_0\mathbf{F}\end{array}\right]\right\}=0, \tag{9.1.5}$$

(momentum equation, 1D case)

$$\frac{\partial}{\partial t}\left\{\rho u-\tau\left[\frac{\partial}{\partial t}(\rho u)+\frac{\partial}{\partial x}(\rho u^2)+\frac{\partial p}{\partial x}-F\right]\right\}-\left[F-\tau g\left(\frac{\partial\rho}{\partial t}+\frac{\partial}{\partial x}(\rho u)\right)\right]+$$
$$+\frac{\partial}{\partial x}\left\{\rho u^2+p-\tau\left[\frac{\partial}{\partial t}(\rho u^2+p)+\frac{\partial}{\partial x}(\rho u^3+3pu)-2Fu\right]\right\}=0 \tag{9.1.6}$$

Momentum equation in the non-stationary spherically symmetric case is

$$\frac{\partial}{\partial t}\left\{\rho v_{0r}-\tau\left[\frac{\partial}{\partial t}(\rho v_{0r})+\frac{1}{r^2}\frac{\partial(r^2\rho v_{0r}^2)}{\partial r}+\frac{\partial p}{\partial r}-F_r\right]\right\}-\left[F_r-\tau g_r\left(\frac{\partial\rho}{\partial t}+\frac{1}{r^2}\frac{\partial(r^2\rho v_{0r})}{\partial r}\right)\right]$$
$$+\frac{1}{r^2}\frac{\partial}{\partial r}\left\{r^2\left\{\rho v_{0r}^2-\tau\left[\frac{\partial}{\partial t}(\rho v_{0r}^2)+\frac{1}{r^2}\frac{\partial(r^2\rho v_{0r}^3)}{\partial r}-2F_r v_{0r}\right]\right\}\right\}$$
$$+\frac{\partial p}{\partial r}-\frac{\partial}{\partial r}\left(\tau\frac{\partial p}{\partial t}\right)-2\frac{\partial}{\partial r}\left(\frac{\tau}{r^2}\frac{\partial(r^2 p v_{0r})}{\partial r}\right)-\frac{1}{r^2}\frac{\partial}{\partial r}\left(\tau r^2\frac{\partial(p v_{0r})}{\partial r}\right)=0. \tag{9.1.7}$$

$$-\frac{\partial}{\partial t}\left\{\tau\left[\frac{\partial p}{\partial r}-F\right]\right\}-\left[F_r-\tau g_r\left(\frac{\partial\rho}{\partial t}+\frac{1}{r^2}\frac{\partial(r^2\rho v_{0r})}{\partial r}\right)\right]+\frac{2}{r^2}\frac{\partial}{\partial r}\left[\tau r^2 F_r v_{0r}\right]$$
$$+\frac{\partial p}{\partial r}-\frac{\partial}{\partial r}\left(\tau\frac{\partial p}{\partial t}\right)-2\frac{\partial}{\partial r}\left(\frac{\tau}{r^2}\frac{\partial(r^2 p v_{0r})}{\partial r}\right)-\frac{1}{r^2}\frac{\partial}{\partial r}\left(\tau r^2\frac{\partial(p v_{0r})}{\partial r}\right)=0. \tag{9.1.8}$$

The second term contains the F_r fluctuation after the mass creation. The corresponding terms (proportional to g_r) are essential in the transition process at the birth of matter; these terms can be omitted in the limit $\rho \to 0$. Then for the PV case ($\rho \to 0$) one obtains

$$\frac{\partial p}{\partial r} - F_r - \frac{\partial}{\partial t}\left\{\tau\left[\frac{\partial p}{\partial r} - F_r\right]\right\} + \frac{2}{r^2}\frac{\partial}{\partial r}\left(\tau r^2 F_r v_{0r}\right) - \frac{\partial}{\partial r}\left(\tau\frac{\partial p}{\partial t}\right) - 2\frac{\partial}{\partial r}\left(\frac{\tau}{r^2}\frac{\partial\left(r^2 p v_{0r}\right)}{\partial r}\right)$$
$$-\frac{1}{r^2}\frac{\partial}{\partial r}\left(\tau r^2\frac{\partial\left(p v_{0r}\right)}{\partial r}\right) = 0, \qquad (9.1.9)$$

or

$$\frac{\partial p}{\partial r} - F_r - \frac{\partial}{\partial t}\left\{\tau\left[\frac{\partial p}{\partial r} - F_r\right]\right\} + \frac{2}{r^2}\frac{\partial}{\partial r}\left\{\tau r^2\left[F_r v_{0r} - \frac{\partial\left(p v_{0r}\right)}{\partial r}\right]\right\} - \frac{\partial}{\partial r}\left(\tau\frac{\partial p}{\partial t}\right) - 2\frac{\partial}{\partial r}\left(\frac{\tau}{r^2}\frac{\partial\left(r^2 p v_{0r}\right)}{\partial r}\right)$$
$$+\frac{2}{r^2}\frac{\partial}{\partial r}\left\{\tau r^2\frac{\partial\left(p v_{0r}\right)}{\partial r}\right\} - \frac{1}{r^2}\frac{\partial}{\partial r}\left(\tau r^2\frac{\partial\left(p v_{0r}\right)}{\partial r}\right) = 0, \qquad (9.1.10)$$

or

$$\frac{\partial p}{\partial r} - F_r - \frac{\partial}{\partial t}\left\{\tau\left[\frac{\partial p}{\partial r} - F_r\right]\right\} - \frac{2}{r^2}\frac{\partial}{\partial r}\left\{\tau r^2 v_{0r}\left[\frac{\partial p}{\partial r} - F_r\right]\right\}$$
$$-\frac{1}{r^2}\frac{\partial}{\partial r}\left\{\tau r^2 p\frac{\partial v_{0r}}{\partial r}\right\} - \frac{\partial}{\partial r}\left(\tau\frac{\partial p}{\partial t}\right) - 2\frac{\partial}{\partial r}\left(\frac{\tau}{r^2}\frac{\partial\left(r^2 p v_{0r}\right)}{\partial r}\right) + \frac{1}{r^2}\frac{\partial}{\partial r}\left(\tau r^2 v_{0r}\frac{\partial p}{\partial r}\right) = 0, \qquad (9.1.11)$$

or

$$\frac{\partial p}{\partial r} - F_r - \frac{\partial}{\partial t}\left\{\tau\left[\frac{\partial p}{\partial r} - F_r\right]\right\} - 2v_{0r}\frac{\partial}{\partial r}\left\{\tau\left[\frac{\partial p}{\partial r} - F_r\right]\right\} - \frac{4}{r}v_{0r}\tau\left[\frac{\partial p}{\partial r} - F_r\right] - 2\tau\left[\frac{\partial p}{\partial r} - F_r\right]\frac{\partial v_{0r}}{\partial r}$$
$$-\frac{1}{r^2}\frac{\partial}{\partial r}\left\{\tau r^2 p\frac{\partial v_{0r}}{\partial r}\right\} - \frac{\partial}{\partial r}\left(\tau\frac{\partial p}{\partial t}\right) - 2\frac{\partial}{\partial r}\left(\frac{\tau}{r^2}\frac{\partial\left(r^2 p v_{0r}\right)}{\partial r}\right) + \frac{1}{r^2}\frac{\partial}{\partial r}\left(\tau r^2 v_{0r}\frac{\partial p}{\partial r}\right) = 0, \qquad (9.1.12)$$

Let us remind that we have the following dependent variables in this variant of nonlocal theory of PV description - pressure p, the force F_r acting in the radial direction on the unit of PV volume and the radial hydrodynamic velocity v_{0r}.

The corresponding momentum equation in the Cartesian 1D case is written as

$$\frac{\partial p}{\partial x} - F_x - \frac{\partial}{\partial t}\left\{\tau\left[\frac{\partial p}{\partial x} - F_x\right]\right\} - 2u\frac{\partial}{\partial x}\left\{\tau\left[\frac{\partial p}{\partial x} - F_x\right]\right\} - 2\tau\left[\frac{\partial p}{\partial x} - F_x\right]\frac{\partial u}{\partial x}$$
$$-\frac{\partial}{\partial x}\left\{\tau p\frac{\partial u}{\partial x}\right\} - \frac{\partial}{\partial x}\left(\tau\frac{\partial p}{\partial t}\right) - 2\frac{\partial}{\partial x}\left(\tau\frac{\partial(pu)}{\partial x}\right) + \frac{\partial}{\partial x}\left(\tau u\frac{\partial p}{\partial x}\right) = 0, \qquad (9.1.13)$$

or

$$\frac{\partial p}{\partial x}-F_x-\frac{\partial}{\partial t}\left\{\tau\left[\frac{\partial p}{\partial x}-F_x\right]\right\}-2u\frac{\partial}{\partial x}\left\{\tau\left[\frac{\partial p}{\partial x}-F_x\right]\right\}-2\tau\left[\frac{\partial p}{\partial x}-F_x\right]\frac{\partial u}{\partial x}$$

$$-\frac{\partial}{\partial x}\left\{\tau\left[\frac{\partial p}{\partial t}+3p\frac{\partial u}{\partial x}+u\frac{\partial p}{\partial x}\right]\right\}=0, \qquad (9.1.14)$$

We have from (9.1.2)

$$r^2\tau\left[\frac{\partial p}{\partial r}-F_r\right]=C(t), \qquad (9.1.15)$$

From (9.1.15) follows $C(t)=0$, then

$$\frac{\partial p}{\partial r}-F_r=0 \qquad (9.1.16)$$

and from (9.1.12) we have

$$\frac{1}{r^2}\frac{\partial}{\partial r}\left\{\tau r^2 p\frac{\partial v_{0r}}{\partial r}\right\}+\frac{\partial}{\partial r}\left(\tau\frac{\partial p}{\partial t}\right)+2\frac{\partial}{\partial r}\left(\frac{\tau}{r^2}\frac{\partial\left(r^2 p v_{0r}\right)}{\partial r}\right)-\frac{1}{r^2}\frac{\partial}{\partial r}\left(\tau r^2 v_{0r}\frac{\partial p}{\partial r}\right)=0, \qquad (9.1.17)$$

or

$$\frac{\partial}{\partial r}\left\{\tau p\frac{\partial v_{0r}}{\partial r}\right\}+\frac{2}{r}\tau p\frac{\partial v_{0r}}{\partial r}+\frac{\partial}{\partial r}\left(\tau\frac{\partial p}{\partial t}\right)+2\frac{\partial}{\partial r}\left(\tau\frac{\partial\left(p v_{0r}\right)}{\partial r}\right)+4\frac{\partial}{\partial r}\left(\frac{1}{r}\tau p v_{0r}\right)-$$

$$-\frac{\partial}{\partial r}\left(\tau v_{0r}\frac{\partial p}{\partial r}\right)-\frac{2}{r}\tau v_{0r}\frac{\partial p}{\partial r}=0. \qquad (9.1.18)$$

Then in the non-stationary spherically symmetric case we have simplified momentum equation

$$\frac{\partial}{\partial r}\left\{3\tau p\frac{\partial v_{0r}}{\partial r}+\tau v_{0r}\frac{\partial p}{\partial r}+\frac{4}{r}\tau p v_{0r}+\tau\frac{\partial p}{\partial t}\right\}-\frac{2}{r}\tau\left[v_{0r}\frac{\partial p}{\partial r}-p\frac{\partial v_{0r}}{\partial r}\right]=0. \qquad (9.1.19)$$

Using (9.1.4) we have for 1D Cartesian case

$$\frac{\partial p}{\partial x}-F_x-\frac{\partial}{\partial t}\left\{\tau\left[\frac{\partial p}{\partial x}-F_x\right]\right\}-2\tau\left[\frac{\partial p}{\partial x}-F_x\right]\frac{\partial u}{\partial x}-\frac{\partial}{\partial x}\left\{\tau\left[\frac{\partial p}{\partial t}+3p\frac{\partial u}{\partial x}+u\frac{\partial p}{\partial x}\right]\right\}=0,$$

$$(9.1.20)$$

We can use also the simplest solution of equation (9.1.4)

$$\frac{\partial p}{\partial x}-F_x=0. \qquad (9.1.21)$$

Then in the analogical 1D case in the Cartesian coordinate system we have

$$\frac{\partial}{\partial x}\left\{\tau\left[\frac{\partial p}{\partial t}+3p\frac{\partial u}{\partial x}+u\frac{\partial p}{\partial x}\right]\right\}=0, \qquad (9.1.22)$$

or

$$\frac{\partial p}{\partial t}+3p\frac{\partial u}{\partial x}+u\frac{\partial p}{\partial x}=\frac{C(t)}{\tau}. \qquad (9.1.23)$$

Consider now the energy equation

$$
\begin{aligned}
&\frac{\partial}{\partial t}\left\{\frac{\rho v_0^2}{2}+\frac{3}{2}p-\tau\left[\frac{\partial}{\partial t}\left(\frac{\rho v_0^2}{2}+\frac{3}{2}p\right)+\frac{\partial}{\partial \mathbf{r}}\cdot\left(\frac{\rho v_0^2}{2}\mathbf{v}_0+\frac{5}{2}p\mathbf{v}_0\right)-\mathbf{F}\cdot\mathbf{v}_0\right]\right\}+\\
&+\frac{\partial}{\partial \mathbf{r}}\cdot\left\{\frac{\rho v_0^2}{2}\mathbf{v}_0+\frac{5}{2}p\mathbf{v}_0-\tau\left[\begin{array}{l}\frac{\partial}{\partial t}\left(\frac{\rho v_0^2}{2}\mathbf{v}_0+\frac{5}{2}p\mathbf{v}_0\right)+\\ +\frac{\partial}{\partial \mathbf{r}}\cdot\left(\frac{\rho v_0^2}{2}\mathbf{v}_0\mathbf{v}_0+\frac{7}{2}p\mathbf{v}_0\mathbf{v}_0+\frac{1}{2}pv_0^2\vec{\mathrm{I}}+\frac{5}{2}\frac{p^2}{\rho}\vec{\mathrm{I}}\right)-\\ -\mathbf{F}\cdot\mathbf{v}_0\mathbf{v}_0-p\mathbf{g}\cdot\vec{\mathrm{I}}-\frac{1}{2}v_0^2\mathbf{F}-\frac{3}{2}\mathbf{g}p\end{array}\right]\right\}-\\
&-\left\{\mathbf{F}\cdot\mathbf{v}_0-\tau\left[\mathbf{g}\cdot\left(\frac{\partial}{\partial t}(\rho\mathbf{v}_0)+\frac{\partial}{\partial \mathbf{r}}\cdot\rho\mathbf{v}_0\mathbf{v}_0+\frac{\partial}{\partial \mathbf{r}}\cdot p\vec{\mathrm{I}}-\mathbf{F}\right)\right]\right\}=0
\end{aligned}
\tag{9.1.24}
$$

Energy equation in the gravitational field (see also (2.1.20)):

$$
\begin{aligned}
&\frac{\partial}{\partial t}\left\{\frac{1}{2}\rho v_0^2+\varepsilon n+\frac{3}{2}p-\tau\left[\frac{\partial}{\partial t}\left(\frac{1}{2}\rho v_0^2+\varepsilon n+\frac{3}{2}p\right)+\frac{1}{r^2}\frac{\partial}{\partial r}\left(r^2v_{0r}\left(\frac{1}{2}\rho v_0^2+\varepsilon n+\frac{5}{2}p\right)\right)\right.\right.\\
&+\frac{1}{r\sin\theta}\frac{\partial}{\partial\varphi}\left(v_{0\varphi}\left(\frac{1}{2}\rho v_0^2+\varepsilon n+\frac{5}{2}p\right)\right)+\frac{1}{r\sin\theta}\frac{\partial}{\partial\theta}\left(\sin\theta v_{0\theta}\left(\frac{1}{2}\rho v_0^2+\varepsilon n+\frac{5}{2}p\right)\right)\\
&\left.\left.-\rho\left(g_rv_{0r}+g_\varphi v_{0\varphi}+g_\theta v_{0\theta}\right)\right]\right\}+\frac{1}{r^2}\frac{\partial}{\partial r}\left\{r^2\left\{\left(\frac{1}{2}\rho v_0^2+\varepsilon n+\frac{5}{2}p\right)v_{0r}-\tau\left[\frac{\partial}{\partial t}\left(\left(\frac{1}{2}\rho v_0^2+\varepsilon n+\frac{5}{2}p\right)v_{0r}\right)\right.\right.\right.\\
&+\frac{1}{r^2}\frac{\partial}{\partial r}\left(r^2\left(\frac{1}{2}\rho v_0^2+\varepsilon n+\frac{7}{2}p\right)v_{0r}^2\right)+\frac{1}{r\sin\theta}\frac{\partial}{\partial\varphi}\left(\left(\frac{1}{2}\rho v_0^2+\varepsilon n+\frac{7}{2}p\right)v_{0\varphi}v_{0r}\right)\\
&+\frac{1}{r\sin\theta}\frac{\partial}{\partial\theta}\left(\sin\theta\left(\frac{1}{2}\rho v_0^2+\varepsilon n+\frac{7}{2}p\right)v_{0\theta}v_{0r}\right)\\
&\left.\left.\left.-\rho\left(g_rv_{0r}+g_\varphi v_{0\varphi}+g_\theta v_{0\theta}\right)v_{0r}-\left(\frac{1}{2}\rho v_0^2+\varepsilon n+\frac{3}{2}p\right)g_r\right]\right\}\right\}+\frac{1}{r\sin\theta}\frac{\partial}{\partial\varphi}\left\{\left(\frac{1}{2}\rho v_0^2+\varepsilon n+\frac{5}{2}p\right)v_{0\varphi}\right.\\
&-\tau\left[\frac{\partial}{\partial t}\left(\left(\frac{1}{2}\rho v_0^2+\varepsilon n+\frac{5}{2}p\right)v_{0\varphi}\right)+\frac{1}{r^2}\frac{\partial}{\partial r}\left(r^2\left(\frac{1}{2}\rho v_0^2+\varepsilon n+\frac{7}{2}p\right)v_{0r}v_{0\varphi}\right)\right.\\
&+\frac{1}{r\sin\theta}\frac{\partial}{\partial\varphi}\left(\left(\frac{1}{2}\rho v_0^2+\varepsilon n+\frac{7}{2}p\right)v_{0\varphi}^2\right)+\frac{1}{r\sin\theta}\frac{\partial}{\partial\theta}\left(\sin\theta\left(\frac{1}{2}\rho v_0^2+\varepsilon n+\frac{7}{2}p\right)v_{0\theta}v_{0\varphi}\right)\\
&\left.\left.-\rho\left(g_rv_{0r}+g_\varphi v_{0\varphi}+g_\theta v_{0\theta}\right)v_{0\varphi}-\left(\frac{1}{2}\rho v_0^2+\varepsilon n+\frac{3}{2}p\right)g_\varphi\right]\right\}+\\
&+\frac{1}{r\sin\theta}\frac{\partial}{\partial\theta}\left\{\sin\theta\left\{\left(\frac{1}{2}\rho v_0^2+\varepsilon n+\frac{5}{2}p\right)v_{0\theta}-\tau\left[\frac{\partial}{\partial t}\left(\left(\frac{1}{2}\rho v_0^2+\varepsilon n+\frac{5}{2}p\right)v_{0\theta}\right)+\right.\right.\right.\\
&+\frac{1}{r^2}\frac{\partial}{\partial r}\left(r^2\left(\frac{1}{2}\rho v_0^2+\varepsilon n+\frac{7}{2}p\right)v_{0r}v_{0\theta}\right)+\frac{1}{r\sin\theta}\frac{\partial}{\partial\varphi}\left(\left(\frac{1}{2}\rho v_0^2+\varepsilon n+\frac{7}{2}p\right)v_{0\varphi}v_{0\theta}\right)+\\
&\left.\left.\left.+\frac{1}{r\sin\theta}\frac{\partial}{\partial\theta}\left(\sin\theta\left(\frac{1}{2}\rho v_0^2+\varepsilon n+\frac{7}{2}p\right)v_{0\theta}^2\right)-\rho\left(g_rv_{0r}+g_\varphi v_{0\varphi}+g_\theta v_{0\theta}\right)v_{0\theta}-\left(\frac{1}{2}\rho v_0^2+\varepsilon n+\frac{3}{2}p\right)g_\theta\right]\right\}\right\}
\end{aligned}
$$

$$-\left\{\rho\left(g_r v_{0r}+g_\varphi v_{0\varphi}+g_\theta v_{0\theta}\right)-\tau\left[g_r\left(\frac{\partial}{\partial t}(\rho v_{0r})+\frac{1}{r^2}\frac{\partial}{\partial r}\left(r^2\rho v_{0r}^2\right)+\frac{1}{r\sin\theta}\frac{\partial}{\partial\varphi}(\rho v_{0\varphi}v_{0r})+\right.\right.\right.$$

$$\left.+\frac{1}{r\sin\theta}\frac{\partial}{\partial\theta}(\rho v_{0\theta}v_{0r}\sin\theta)+\frac{\partial p}{\partial r}-\rho g_r\right)+$$

$$+g_\varphi\left(\frac{\partial}{\partial t}(\rho v_{0\varphi})+\frac{1}{r^2}\frac{\partial}{\partial r}\left(r^2\rho v_{0r}v_{0\varphi}\right)+\frac{1}{r\sin\theta}\frac{\partial}{\partial\varphi}\left(\rho v_{0\varphi}^2\right)+\frac{1}{r\sin\theta}\frac{\partial}{\partial\theta}(\rho v_{0\theta}v_{0\varphi}\sin\theta)\right.$$

$$\left.+\frac{1}{r\sin\theta}\frac{\partial p}{\partial\varphi}-\rho g_\varphi\right)+g_\theta\left(\frac{\partial}{\partial t}(\rho v_{0\theta})+\frac{1}{r^2}\frac{\partial}{\partial r}\left(r^2\rho v_{0r}v_{0\theta}\right)+\frac{1}{r\sin\theta}\frac{\partial}{\partial\varphi}(\rho v_{0\varphi}v_{0\theta})\right.$$

$$\left.\left.\left.+\frac{1}{r\sin\theta}\frac{\partial}{\partial\theta}\left(\rho v_{0\theta}^2\sin\theta\right)+\frac{1}{r}\frac{\partial p}{\partial\theta}-\rho g_\theta\right)\right]\right\}-\frac{1}{r^2}\frac{\partial}{\partial r}\left(\tau r^2\frac{\partial}{\partial r}\left(\frac{1}{2}pv_0^2+\varepsilon n v_0^2+\frac{5}{2}\frac{p^2}{\rho}\right)\right)$$

$$-\frac{1}{r^2\sin\theta}\frac{\partial}{\partial\theta}\left(\tau\sin\theta\frac{\partial}{\partial\theta}\left(\frac{1}{2}pv_0^2+\varepsilon n v_0^2+\frac{5}{2}\frac{p^2}{\rho}\right)\right)-\frac{1}{r^2\sin^2\theta}\frac{\partial}{\partial\varphi}\left(\tau\frac{\partial}{\partial\varphi}\left(\frac{1}{2}pv_0^2+\varepsilon n v_0^2+\frac{5}{2}\frac{p^2}{\rho}\right)\right)$$

$$+\frac{1}{r^2}\frac{\partial}{\partial r}\left(r^2\tau p g_r\right)+\frac{1}{r\sin\theta}\frac{\partial}{\partial\varphi}(\tau p g_\varphi)+\frac{1}{r\sin\theta}\frac{\partial}{\partial\theta}(\tau p g_\theta\sin\theta)=0, \qquad (9.1.25)$$

where ε is the internal energy, $v_0^2=v_{0r}^2+v_{0\varphi}^2+v_{0\theta}^2$.

Energy equation for the non-stationary 1D case in the spherical coordinate system has the form

$$\frac{\partial}{\partial t}\left\{\frac{1}{2}\rho v_{0r}^2+\varepsilon n+\frac{3}{2}p-\tau\left[\frac{\partial}{\partial t}\left(\frac{1}{2}\rho v_{0r}^2+\varepsilon n+\frac{3}{2}p\right)+\frac{1}{r^2}\frac{\partial}{\partial r}\left(r^2 v_{0r}\left(\frac{1}{2}\rho v_{0r}^2+\varepsilon n+\frac{5}{2}p\right)\right)-\rho g_r v_{0r}\right]\right\}$$

$$+\frac{1}{r^2}\frac{\partial}{\partial r}\left\{r^2\left\{\left(\frac{1}{2}\rho v_{0r}^2+\varepsilon n+\frac{5}{2}p\right)v_{0r}-\tau\left[\frac{\partial}{\partial t}\left(\left(\frac{1}{2}\rho v_{0r}^2+\varepsilon n+\frac{5}{2}p\right)v_{0r}\right)+\right.\right.\right.$$

$$\left.\left.\left.+\frac{1}{r^2}\frac{\partial}{\partial r}\left(r^2\left(\frac{1}{2}\rho v_{0r}^2+\varepsilon n+\frac{7}{2}p\right)v_{0r}^2\right)-\rho g_r v_{0r}^2-\left(\frac{1}{2}\rho v_{0r}^2+\varepsilon n+\frac{3}{2}p\right)g_r\right]\right\}\right\}-$$

$$-\left\{\rho g_r v_{0r}-\tau\left[g_r\left(\frac{\partial}{\partial t}(\rho v_{0r})+\frac{1}{r^2}\frac{\partial}{\partial r}\left(r^2\rho v_{0r}^2\right)+\frac{\partial p}{\partial r}-\rho g_r\right)\right]\right\}-$$

$$\frac{1}{r^2}\frac{\partial}{\partial r}\left(\tau r^2\frac{\partial}{\partial r}\left(\frac{1}{2}pv_{0r}^2+\varepsilon n v_0^2+\frac{5}{2}\frac{p^2}{\rho}\right)\right)+\frac{1}{r^2}\frac{\partial}{\partial r}\left(r^2\tau p g_r\right)=0, \qquad (9.1.26)$$

where ε is the internal energy which is omitted in the following energy equations. Omitting the internal energy we obtain energy equation in the gravitational field:

$$\frac{\partial}{\partial t}\left\{\frac{1}{2}\rho v_{0r}^2+\frac{3}{2}p-\tau\left[\frac{\partial}{\partial t}\left(\frac{1}{2}\rho v_{0r}^2+\frac{3}{2}p\right)+\frac{1}{r^2}\frac{\partial}{\partial r}\left(r^2 v_{0r}\left(\frac{1}{2}\rho v_{0r}^2+\frac{5}{2}p\right)\right)-\rho g_r v_{0r}\right]\right\}+$$

$$+\frac{1}{r^2}\frac{\partial}{\partial r}\left\{r^2\left\{\left(\frac{1}{2}\rho v_{0r}^2+\frac{5}{2}p\right)v_{0r}-\tau\left[\frac{\partial}{\partial t}\left(\left(\frac{1}{2}\rho v_{0r}^2+\frac{5}{2}p\right)v_{0r}\right)+\right.\right.\right.$$

$$\left.\left.\left.+\frac{1}{r^2}\frac{\partial}{\partial r}\left(r^2\left(\frac{1}{2}\rho v_{0r}^2+\frac{7}{2}p\right)v_{0r}^2\right)-\rho g_r v_{0r}^2-\left(\frac{1}{2}\rho v_{0r}^2+\frac{3}{2}p\right)g_r\right]\right\}\right\}-$$

$$-\left\{\rho g_r v_{0r}-\tau\left[g_r\left(\frac{\partial}{\partial t}(\rho v_{0r})+\frac{1}{r^2}\frac{\partial}{\partial r}\left(r^2\rho v_{0r}^2\right)+\frac{\partial p}{\partial r}-\rho g_r\right)\right]\right\}-$$

$$\frac{1}{r^2}\frac{\partial}{\partial r}\left(\tau r^2\frac{\partial}{\partial r}\left(\frac{1}{2}pv_{0r}^2+\frac{5}{2}\frac{p^2}{\rho}\right)\right)+\frac{1}{r^2}\frac{\partial}{\partial r}\left(r^2\tau p g_r\right)=0, \tag{9.1.27}$$

or

$$\frac{\partial}{\partial t}\left\{\rho v_{0r}^2+3p-\tau\left[\frac{\partial}{\partial t}\left(\rho v_{0r}^2+3p\right)+\frac{1}{r^2}\frac{\partial}{\partial r}\left(r^2 v_{0r}\left(\rho v_{0r}^2+5p\right)\right)-2F_r v_{0r}\right]\right\}$$

$$+\frac{1}{r^2}\frac{\partial}{\partial r}\left\{r^2\left\{\left(\rho v_{0r}^2+5p\right)v_{0r}-\tau\left[\begin{array}{l}\frac{\partial}{\partial t}\left(\left(\rho v_{0r}^2+5p\right)v_{0r}\right)+\frac{1}{r^2}\frac{\partial}{\partial r}\left(r^2\left(\rho v_{0r}^2+7p\right)v_{0r}^2\right)-\\-2F_r v_{0r}^2-\left(\rho v_{0r}^2+3p\right)g_r\end{array}\right]\right\}\right\}- \tag{9.1.28}$$

$$-2\left\{F_r v_{0r}-\tau g_r\left(\frac{\partial}{\partial t}(\rho v_{0r})+\frac{1}{r^2}\frac{\partial}{\partial r}\left(r^2\rho v_{0r}^2\right)+\frac{\partial p}{\partial r}-F_r\right)\right\}-\frac{1}{r^2}\frac{\partial}{\partial r}\left(\tau r^2\frac{\partial}{\partial r}\left(pv_{0r}^2+5\frac{p^2}{\rho}\right)\right)$$

$$+\frac{2}{r^2}\frac{\partial}{\partial r}\left(r^2\tau p\frac{F_r}{\rho}\right)=0.$$

Let us use the relation

$$\left(\rho v_{0r}^2+3p\right)g_r=F_r v_{0r}^2+3p\frac{F_r}{\rho}. \tag{9.1.29}$$

Then energy equation for the non-stationary 1D case in the spherical coordinate system is written as

$$\frac{\partial}{\partial t}\left\{\rho v_{0r}^2+3p-\tau\left[\frac{\partial}{\partial t}\left(\rho v_{0r}^2+3p\right)+\frac{1}{r^2}\frac{\partial}{\partial r}\left(r^2 v_{0r}\left(\rho v_{0r}^2+5p\right)\right)-2F_r v_{0r}\right]\right\}$$

$$+\frac{1}{r^2}\frac{\partial}{\partial r}\left\{r^2\left\{\left(\rho v_{0r}^2+5p\right)v_{0r}-\tau\left[\begin{array}{l}\frac{\partial}{\partial t}\left(\left(\rho v_{0r}^2+5p\right)v_{0r}\right)+\frac{1}{r^2}\frac{\partial}{\partial r}\left(r^2\left(\rho v_{0r}^2+7p\right)v_{0r}^2\right)-\\-2F_r v_{0r}^2-F_r v_{0r}^2-3p\frac{F_r}{\rho}\end{array}\right]\right\}\right\}- \tag{9.1.30}$$

$$-2\left\{F_r v_{0r}-\tau g_r\left(\frac{\partial}{\partial t}(\rho v_{0r})+\frac{1}{r^2}\frac{\partial}{\partial r}\left(r^2\rho v_{0r}^2\right)+\frac{\partial p}{\partial r}-F_r\right)\right\}-\frac{1}{r^2}\frac{\partial}{\partial r}\left(\tau r^2\frac{\partial}{\partial r}\left(pv_{0r}^2+5\frac{p^2}{\rho}\right)\right)$$

$$+\frac{2}{r^2}\frac{\partial}{\partial r}\left(r^2\tau p\frac{F_r}{\rho}\right)=0.$$

or

$$\frac{\partial}{\partial t}\left\{\rho v_{0r}^2+3p-\tau\left[\frac{\partial}{\partial t}\left(\rho v_{0r}^2+3p\right)+\frac{1}{r^2}\frac{\partial}{\partial r}\left(r^2 v_{0r}\left(\rho v_{0r}^2+5p\right)\right)-2F_r v_{0r}\right]\right\}$$

$$+\frac{1}{r^2}\frac{\partial}{\partial r}\left\{r^2\left\{\left(\rho v_{0r}^2+5p\right)v_{0r}-\tau\left[\frac{\partial}{\partial t}\left(\left(\rho v_{0r}^2+5p\right)v_{0r}\right)+\frac{1}{r^2}\frac{\partial}{\partial r}\left(r^2\left(\rho v_{0r}^2+7p\right)v_{0r}^2\right)-3F_r v_{0r}^2\right]\right\}\right\}-$$

$$-2\left\{F_r v_{0r}-\tau g_r\left(\frac{\partial}{\partial t}\left(\rho v_{0r}\right)+\frac{1}{r^2}\frac{\partial}{\partial r}\left(r^2\rho v_{0r}^2\right)+\frac{\partial p}{\partial r}-F_r\right)\right\}-\frac{1}{r^2}\frac{\partial}{\partial r}\left(\tau r^2\frac{\partial}{\partial r}\left(p v_{0r}^2+5\frac{p^2}{\rho}\right)\right)$$

$$+\frac{5}{r^2}\frac{\partial}{\partial r}\left(r^2\tau p\frac{F_r}{\rho}\right)=0. \qquad (9.1.31)$$

or

$$\frac{\partial}{\partial t}\left\{\rho v_{0r}^2+3p-\tau\left[\frac{\partial}{\partial t}\left(\rho v_{0r}^2+3p\right)+\frac{1}{r^2}\frac{\partial}{\partial r}\left(r^2 v_{0r}\left(\rho v_{0r}^2+5p\right)\right)-2F_r v_{0r}\right]\right\}+\frac{1}{r^2}\frac{\partial}{\partial r}\left\{r^2\left(\rho v_{0r}^2+5p\right)v_{0r}\right\}$$

$$-\frac{1}{r^2}\frac{\partial}{\partial r}\left\{r^2\left\{\tau\left[\frac{\partial}{\partial t}\left(\left(\rho v_{0r}^2+5p\right)v_{0r}\right)-3F_r v_{0r}^2\right]\right\}\right\}-\frac{1}{r^2}\frac{\partial}{\partial r}\left\{\tau\frac{\partial}{\partial r}\left(r^2\left(\rho v_{0r}^2+7p\right)v_{0r}^2\right)\right\}-$$

$$-2\left\{F_r v_{0r}-\tau g_r\left(\frac{\partial}{\partial t}\left(\rho v_{0r}\right)+\frac{1}{r^2}\frac{\partial}{\partial r}\left(r^2\rho v_{0r}^2\right)+\frac{\partial p}{\partial r}-F_r\right)\right\}-\frac{1}{r^2}\frac{\partial}{\partial r}\left(\tau r^2\frac{\partial}{\partial r}\left(p v_{0r}^2\right)\right)+ \qquad (9.1.32)$$

$$+\frac{5}{r^2}\frac{\partial}{\partial r}\left[\tau r^2\left(p\frac{F_r}{\rho}-\frac{\partial}{\partial r}\left(\frac{p^2}{\rho}\right)\right)\right]=0,$$

or using (9.1.16)

$$\frac{\partial}{\partial t}\left\{\rho v_{0r}^2+3p-\tau\left[\frac{\partial}{\partial t}\left(\rho v_{0r}^2+3p\right)+\frac{1}{r^2}\frac{\partial}{\partial r}\left(r^2 v_{0r}\left(\rho v_{0r}^2+5p\right)\right)-2F_r v_{0r}\right]\right\}+\frac{1}{r^2}\frac{\partial}{\partial r}\left\{r^2\left(\rho v_{0r}^2+5p\right)v_{0r}\right\}-$$

$$-\frac{1}{r^2}\frac{\partial}{\partial r}\left\{r^2\left\{\tau\left[\frac{\partial}{\partial t}\left(\left(\rho v_{0r}^2+5p\right)v_{0r}\right)-3F_r v_{0r}^2\right]\right\}\right\}-$$

$$-\frac{1}{r^2}\frac{\partial}{\partial r}\left\{\tau\frac{\partial}{\partial r}\left(r^2\left(\rho v_{0r}^2+7p\right)v_{0r}^2\right)\right\}-\frac{1}{r^2}\frac{\partial}{\partial r}\left(\tau r^2\frac{\partial}{\partial r}\left(p v_{0r}^2\right)\right)- \qquad (9.1.33)$$

$$-2\left\{F_r v_{0r}-\tau g_r\left(\frac{\partial}{\partial t}\left(\rho v_{0r}\right)+\frac{1}{r^2}\frac{\partial}{\partial r}\left(r^2\rho v_{0r}^2\right)+\frac{\partial p}{\partial r}-F_r\right)\right\}-\frac{5}{r^2}\frac{\partial}{\partial r}\left[\tau r^2 p\frac{\partial}{\partial r}\left(\frac{p}{\rho}\right)\right]=0.$$

The energy equation for the non-stationary 1D case in the Cartesian coordinate system is written as

$$\frac{\partial}{\partial t}\left\{\rho u^2+3p-\tau\left[\frac{\partial}{\partial t}\left(\rho u^2+3p\right)+\frac{\partial}{\partial x}\left(u\left(\rho u^2+5p\right)\right)-2F_x u\right]\right\}+$$

$$+\frac{\partial}{\partial x}\left\{\left(\rho u^2+5p\right)u-\tau\left[\frac{\partial}{\partial t}\left(\left(\rho u^2+5p\right)u\right)+\frac{\partial}{\partial x}\left(\left(\rho u^2+8p\right)u^2\right)-3F_x u^2\right]\right\}-$$

$$-2\left\{F_x u-\tau g_x\left(\frac{\partial}{\partial t}\left(\rho u\right)+\frac{\partial}{\partial x}\left(\rho u^2\right)+\frac{\partial p}{\partial x}-F_x\right)\right\}+5\frac{\partial}{\partial x}\left[\tau\left(\frac{p}{\rho}F_x-\frac{\partial}{\partial x}\frac{p^2}{\rho}\right)\right]=0. \qquad (9.1.34)$$

The transfer in the spherical coordinate system to the limit case $\rho \to 0$ leads to equation

$$\frac{\partial}{\partial t}\left\{3p-\tau\left[3\frac{\partial p}{\partial t}+\frac{5}{r^2}\frac{\partial}{\partial r}\left(r^2 v_{0r}p\right)-2F_r v_{0r}\right]\right\}+\frac{5}{r^2}\frac{\partial}{\partial r}\left\{r^2 p v_{0r}\right\}-$$
$$-\frac{1}{r^2}\frac{\partial}{\partial r}\left\{r^2\tau\left[5\frac{\partial}{\partial t}\left(p v_{0r}\right)-3F_r v_{0r}^2\right]\right\}-\frac{7}{r^2}\frac{\partial}{\partial r}\left\{\tau\frac{\partial}{\partial t}\left(r^2 p v_{0r}^2\right)\right\}-\frac{1}{r^2}\frac{\partial}{\partial r}\left(\tau r^2\frac{\partial}{\partial r}\left(p v_{0r}^2\right)\right)- \tag{9.1.35}$$
$$-2\left\{F_r v_{0r}-\tau g_r\left(\frac{\partial}{\partial t}\left(\rho v_{0r}\right)+\frac{1}{r^2}\frac{\partial}{\partial r}\left(r^2\rho v_{0r}^2\right)\right)\right\}-\frac{5}{r^2}\frac{\partial}{\partial r}\left[\tau r^2 p\frac{\partial}{\partial r}\left(\frac{p}{\rho}\right)\right]=0,$$

or

$$\frac{\partial}{\partial t}\left\{3p-\tau\left[3\frac{\partial p}{\partial t}+\frac{5}{r^2}\frac{\partial}{\partial r}\left(r^2 v_{0r}p\right)-2F_r v_{0r}\right]\right\}+\frac{5}{r^2}\frac{\partial}{\partial r}\left\{r^2 p v_{0r}\right\}-$$
$$-\frac{1}{r^2}\frac{\partial}{\partial r}\left\{r^2\tau\left[5\frac{\partial}{\partial t}\left(p v_{0r}\right)-3F_r v_{0r}^2\right]\right\}-\frac{7}{r^2}\frac{\partial}{\partial r}\left\{\tau\frac{\partial}{\partial t}\left(r^2 p v_{0r}^2\right)\right\}-\frac{1}{r^2}\frac{\partial}{\partial r}\left(\tau r^2\frac{\partial}{\partial r}\left(p v_{0r}^2\right)\right)- \tag{9.1.36}$$
$$-2\left\{F_r v_{0r}-\tau g_r\left(\frac{\partial}{\partial t}\left(\rho v_{0r}\right)+\frac{1}{r^2}\frac{\partial}{\partial r}\left(r^2\rho v_{0r}^2\right)\right)\right\}+A^{pert}=0,$$

where the perturbation for PV is introduced (like the appearance of the Higgs boson)

$$A^{pert}=\frac{5}{r^2}\frac{\partial}{\partial r}\left[\tau r^2\left(\frac{p}{\rho}F_r-\frac{\partial}{\partial r}\frac{p^2}{\rho}\right)\right] \tag{9.1.37}$$

or

$$A^{pert}=\frac{5}{r^2}\frac{\partial}{\partial r}\left[\tau r^2\left(\frac{p}{\rho}F_r-p\frac{\partial}{\partial r}\frac{p}{\rho}-\frac{p}{\rho}\frac{\partial p}{\partial r}\right)\right]=\frac{5}{r^2}\frac{\partial}{\partial r}\left\{\tau r^2 p\left[\frac{1}{\rho}\left(F_r-\frac{\partial p}{\partial r}\right)-\frac{\partial}{\partial r}\frac{p}{\rho}\right]\right\}= \tag{9.1.38}$$
$$=-\frac{5}{r^2}\frac{\partial}{\partial r}\left\{\tau r^2 p\frac{\partial}{\partial r}\frac{p}{\rho}\right\}.$$

As before the term (proportional to g_r and defining the perturbation of the velocity moment $F_r v_{0r}$) can be significant in the processes of the matter birth.

Let us transform now the stationary energy equation (9.1.35)

$$\frac{5}{r^2}\frac{\partial}{\partial r}\left[r^2 p v_{0r}\right]-\frac{7}{r^2}\frac{\partial}{\partial r}\left[\tau\frac{\partial}{\partial t}\left(r^2 p v_{0r}^2\right)\right]+\frac{3}{r^2}\frac{\partial}{\partial r}\left[\tau r^2 F_r v_{0r}^2\right]-\frac{1}{r^2}\frac{\partial}{\partial r}\left[\tau r^2\frac{\partial}{\partial r}\left(p v_{0r}^2\right)\right]- \tag{9.1.39}$$
$$-2\left\{F_r v_{0r}-\tau g_r\frac{1}{r^2}\frac{\partial}{\partial r}\left(r^2\rho v_{0r}^2\right)\right\}-\frac{5}{r^2}\frac{\partial}{\partial r}\left[\tau r^2 p\frac{\partial}{\partial r}\left(\frac{p}{\rho}\right)\right]=0,$$

or

$$\frac{5}{r^2}\frac{\partial}{\partial r}\left[r^2 p v_{0r}\right]-\frac{8}{r^2}\frac{\partial}{\partial r}\left[\tau\frac{\partial}{\partial t}\left(r^2 p v_{0r}^2\right)\right]+\frac{3}{r^2}\frac{\partial}{\partial r}\left[\tau r^2 F_r v_{0r}^2\right]+$$

$$+\frac{1}{r^2}\frac{\partial}{\partial r}\left[\tau\frac{\partial}{\partial t}\left(r^2 p v_{0r}^2\right)\right]-\frac{1}{r^2}\frac{\partial}{\partial r}\left[\tau r^2\frac{\partial}{\partial r}\left(p v_{0r}^2\right)\right] \tag{9.1.40}$$

$$-2\left\{F_r v_{0r}-\tau g_r\frac{1}{r^2}\frac{\partial}{\partial r}\left(r^2\rho v_{0r}^2\right)\right\}-\frac{5}{r^2}\frac{\partial}{\partial r}\left[\tau r^2 p\frac{\partial}{\partial r}\left(\frac{p}{\rho}\right)\right]=0,$$

or

$$\frac{5}{r^2}\frac{\partial}{\partial r}\left[r^2 p v_{0r}\right]-\frac{8}{r^2}\frac{\partial}{\partial r}\left[\tau\frac{\partial}{\partial t}\left(r^2 p v_{0r}^2\right)\right]+\frac{3}{r^2}\frac{\partial}{\partial r}\left\{r^2\tau F_r v_{0r}^2\right\}+\frac{2}{r^2}\frac{\partial}{\partial r}\left(\tau p v_{0r}^2 r\right)- \tag{9.1.41}$$

$$-2\left\{F_r v_{0r}-\tau g_r\frac{1}{r^2}\frac{\partial}{\partial r}\left(r^2\rho v_{0r}^2\right)\right\}-\frac{5}{r^2}\frac{\partial}{\partial r}\left(\tau r^2 p\frac{\partial}{\partial r}\left(\frac{p}{\rho}\right)\right)=0$$

Let us transform (9.1.41) for the stationary case using (9.1.16) and the condition $\tau = const$. We find

$$5p\frac{\partial v_{0r}}{\partial r}+3v_{0r}\frac{\partial p}{\partial r}+\frac{10}{r}p v_{0r}-\tau\frac{\partial}{\partial r}\left[16 p v_{0r}\frac{\partial v_{0r}}{\partial r}+5v_{0r}^2\frac{\partial p}{\partial r}-5pg_r\right]+$$

$$-\frac{14}{r^2}\tau p v_{0r}^2-20\frac{1}{r}\tau v_{0r}^2\frac{\partial p}{\partial r}-\frac{60}{r}\tau p v_{0r}\frac{\partial v_{0r}}{\partial r}+\frac{10}{r}\tau p g_r+$$

$$+4\tau v_{0r}\frac{\partial p}{\partial r}\frac{\partial v_{0r}}{\partial r}-\frac{5}{r^2}\frac{\partial}{\partial r}\left[\tau r^2\frac{\partial}{\partial r}\frac{p^2}{\rho}\right]=0 \tag{9.1.42}$$

The energy equation for the non-stationary 1D case in the Cartesian coordinate system is written (see also (9.1.34) as

$$\frac{\partial}{\partial t}\left\{\rho u^2+3p-\tau\left[\frac{\partial}{\partial t}\left(\rho u^2+3p\right)+\frac{\partial}{\partial x}\left(\rho u^3+5pu\right)-2F_x u\right]\right\}+$$

$$+\frac{\partial}{\partial x}\left\{\rho u^3+5pu-\tau\left[\frac{\partial}{\partial t}\left(\rho u^3+5pu\right)+\frac{\partial}{\partial x}\left(\rho u^4+8pu^2\right)-3F_x u^2\right]\right\}- \tag{9.1.43}$$

$$-2\left\{F_x u-\tau g_x\left[\frac{\partial}{\partial t}(\rho u)+\frac{\partial}{\partial x}\left(\rho u^2\right)+\frac{\partial p}{\partial x}-F_x\right]\right\}+5\frac{\partial}{\partial x}\left\{\tau\left[\frac{p}{\rho}F_x-\frac{\partial}{\partial x}\frac{p^2}{\rho}\right]\right\}=0$$

In the PV limit ($\rho\to 0$) we find

$$\frac{\partial}{\partial t}\left\{3p-\tau\left[3\frac{\partial p}{\partial t}+5\frac{\partial}{\partial x}(up)-2F_x u\right]\right\}+$$

$$+\frac{\partial}{\partial x}\left\{5pu-\tau\left[5\frac{\partial}{\partial t}(pu)+8\frac{\partial}{\partial x}\left(pu^2\right)-3F_x u^2\right]\right\}-2\left\{F_x u\right\}+A^{pert}=0, \tag{9.1.44}$$

or

$$
\begin{aligned}
&3\frac{\partial p}{\partial t}+5p\frac{\partial u}{\partial x}+3u\frac{\partial p}{\partial x}+2u\left(\frac{\partial p}{\partial x}-F_x\right)- \\
&-\frac{\partial}{\partial t}\left\{\tau\left[3\frac{\partial p}{\partial t}+3u\frac{\partial p}{\partial x}+5p\frac{\partial u}{\partial x}+2u\left(\frac{\partial p}{\partial x}-F_x\right)\right]\right\}- \\
&-\frac{\partial}{\partial x}\left\{\tau\left[5\frac{\partial}{\partial t}(pu)+8\frac{\partial}{\partial x}\left(pu^2\right)-3F_xu^2\right]\right\}+A^{pert}=0,
\end{aligned}
\tag{9.1.45}
$$

or

$$
\begin{aligned}
&3\frac{\partial p}{\partial t}+5p\frac{\partial u}{\partial x}+3u\frac{\partial p}{\partial x}+2u\left(\frac{\partial p}{\partial x}-F_x\right)- \\
&-\frac{\partial}{\partial t}\left\{\tau\left[3\frac{\partial p}{\partial t}+3u\frac{\partial p}{\partial x}+5p\frac{\partial u}{\partial x}+2u\left(\frac{\partial p}{\partial x}-F_x\right)\right]\right\}- \\
&-\frac{\partial}{\partial x}\left\{\tau\left[5\frac{\partial}{\partial t}(pu)+16pu\frac{\partial u}{\partial x}+5u^2\frac{\partial p}{\partial x}+3u^2\left(\frac{\partial p}{\partial x}-F_x\right)\right]\right\}+A^{pert}=0
\end{aligned}
\tag{9.1.46}
$$

9.2. Evolution of the Universe including the Planck time.

From the observations follow that about 13.7 billion years ago all the matter in the Universe was concentrated into a single incredibly small object. This object began to enlarge rapidly in a hot explosion, and it is still expanding today. Evidence for the Big Bang includes:

1. All the galaxies are moving away from us.
2. The further away a galaxy is, the faster it is moving away.
3. A cosmic microwave background radiation or CMBR was detected. This is received from all parts of the Universe and is thought to be the heat left over from the original explosion.

Let us investigate the situation after the explosion of a spherical object from the position of nonlocal physics. We begin consideration with the quasi-stationary spherical PV object which placed (generally speaking) in the external radial gravitational field. There are two reasons for this:

1. This generalization is important (and will be further implied) in the theory of PV-engines (including the EM-Drive) working in the external gravitational field.
2. The birth of matter after the Big Bang leads to the need to take into account gravity.

The following conditions are fulfilled:

1. The physical picture corresponds to the 1D stationary situation.
2. Nonlocal parameter τ is constant.

3. The gravitational field is an arbitrary function of radius. It means that we have two kinds of forces - the self-consistent force F_r (acting on the unit of volume) and known dependence $g_r(r)$ (gravitational acceleration). Other unknown values - radial hydrodynamic velocity v_{0r} and PV pressure p connected with the force F_r.

We use the following system of equation (see Item 9.1):

continuity equation

$$F_r = \frac{\partial p}{\partial r}, \tag{9.2.1}$$

moment equation

$$\frac{\partial}{\partial r}\left[3p\frac{\partial v_{0r}}{\partial r} + v_{0r}\frac{\partial p}{\partial r} + \frac{4}{r}pv_{0r}\right] - \frac{2}{r}\left[v_{0r}\frac{\partial p}{\partial r} - p\frac{\partial v_{0r}}{\partial r}\right] = 0, \tag{9.2.2}$$

energy equation

$$\begin{aligned} & 5p\frac{\partial v_{0r}}{\partial r} + 3v_{0r}\frac{\partial p}{\partial r} + \frac{10}{r}pv_{0r} - \tau\frac{\partial}{\partial r}\left[16pv_{0r}\frac{\partial v_{0r}}{\partial r} + 5v_{0r}^2\frac{\partial p}{\partial r} - 5pg_r\right] + \\ & -\frac{14}{r^2}\tau pv_{0r}^2 - 20\frac{1}{r}\tau v_{0r}^2\frac{\partial p}{\partial r} - \frac{60}{r}\tau pv_{0r}\frac{\partial v_{0r}}{\partial r} + \frac{10}{r}\tau pg_r + \\ & + 4\tau v_{0r}\frac{\partial p}{\partial r}\frac{\partial v_{0r}}{\partial r} - \frac{5}{r^2}\frac{\partial}{\partial r}\left(\tau r^2\frac{\partial}{\partial r}\left(\frac{p^2}{\rho}\right)\right) = 0 \end{aligned} \tag{9.2.3}$$

The last term of the energy equation (9.2.3) corresponds as before to the external energy fluctuation and will be omitted. In other words we intend to consider the PV evolution under influence of the perturbations of the Cauchy conditions. Therefore we reach the following system of equation written in the dimensionless form using the scales

$$[r_0],\ [u_0],\ [p_0],\ [F] = \frac{p_0}{r_0},\ [t_0] = \frac{r_0}{u_0},\ r_0 = u_0 t_0,\ [g_r] = \frac{u_0^2}{r_0}.$$

$$\tilde{F}_r = \frac{\partial \tilde{p}}{\partial \tilde{r}}, \tag{9.2.4}$$

$$\frac{\partial}{\partial \tilde{r}}\left[3\tilde{p}\frac{\partial \tilde{v}_{0r}}{\partial \tilde{r}} + \tilde{v}_{0r}\frac{\partial \tilde{p}}{\partial \tilde{r}} + \frac{4}{\tilde{r}}\tilde{p}\tilde{v}_{0r}\right] - \frac{2}{\tilde{r}}\left[\tilde{v}_{0r}\frac{\partial \tilde{p}}{\partial \tilde{r}} - \tilde{p}\frac{\partial \tilde{v}_{0r}}{\partial \tilde{r}}\right] = 0, \tag{9.2.5}$$

$$\begin{aligned} & 5\tilde{p}\frac{\partial \tilde{v}_{0r}}{\partial \tilde{r}} + 3\tilde{v}_{0r}\frac{\partial \tilde{p}}{\partial \tilde{r}} + \frac{10}{\tilde{r}}\tilde{p}\tilde{v}_{0r} - \\ & -\tilde{\tau}\frac{\partial}{\partial \tilde{r}}\left\{16\tilde{p}\tilde{v}_{0r}\frac{\partial \tilde{v}_{0r}}{\partial \tilde{r}} + 5\tilde{v}_{0r}^2\frac{\partial \tilde{p}}{\partial \tilde{r}} - 5\tilde{p}\tilde{g}_r\right\} - \frac{20}{\tilde{r}}\tilde{\tau}\tilde{v}_{0r}^2\frac{\partial \tilde{p}}{\partial \tilde{r}} - \frac{60}{\tilde{r}}\tilde{\tau}\tilde{p}\tilde{v}_{0r}\frac{\partial \tilde{v}_{0r}}{\partial \tilde{r}} + \\ & + \frac{10}{\tilde{r}}\tilde{\tau}\tilde{p}\tilde{g}_r - \frac{14}{\tilde{r}^2}\tilde{\tau}\tilde{p}\tilde{v}_{0r}^2 + 4\tilde{\tau}\tilde{v}_{0r}\frac{\partial \tilde{p}}{\partial \tilde{r}}\frac{\partial \tilde{v}_{0r}}{\partial \tilde{r}} = 0. \end{aligned} \tag{9.2.6}$$

Let us introduce the approximation for the gravitational acceleration

$$\tilde{g}_r = \frac{\mathrm{G}}{\tilde{r}^2}. \tag{9.2.7}$$

In this case system of equations (9.2.4) – (9.2.6) contains two dimensionless parameters G, $\mathrm{T} \leftrightarrow \tilde{\tau}$ and need four Cauchy conditions. These conditions we write down for the external surface of the spherical object. Then we investigate the evolution of the surface perturbation on the following scenario of the PV behavior or in other words, the stability of the PV object.

In the theory of Big Bang the external gravitational field is absent. Let on the surface of a spherical PV object the perturbation appears of physical parameters *in the absence* of the external gravitation (G=0), namely

$$p(1) = 1,\ u(1) \leftrightarrow v_{0r}(1) = 1,\ D(p)(1) = 1,\ D(u)(1) = 1. \tag{9.2.8}$$

Figures (9.2.1) - (9.2.14) demonstrate the results of calculations for different τ. The information required is indicated in the figures and in figure captions including the boundaries of the solution existence.

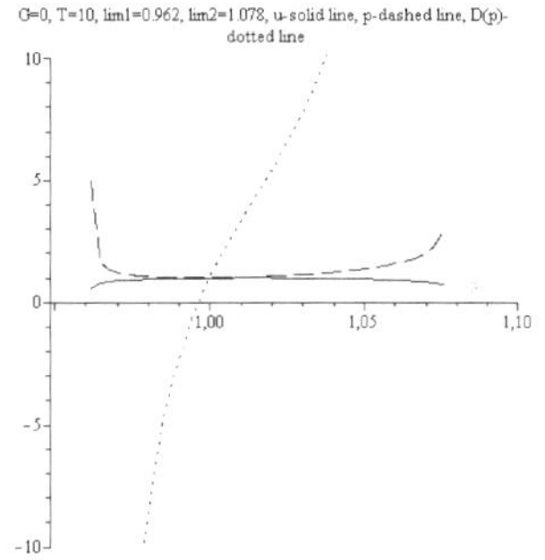

Fig. 9.2.1. Evolution of $\tilde{u}(\tilde{r})$, $\tilde{p}(\tilde{r})$, $\partial\tilde{p}(\tilde{r})/\partial\tilde{r} = F(\tilde{r})$; $\tilde{\tau} = 10$, $\mathrm{G} = 0$.

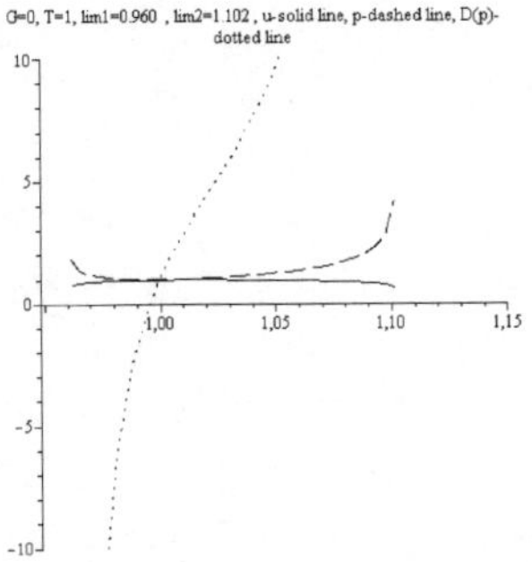

Fig. 9.2.2. Evolution of $\tilde{u}(\tilde{r})$, $\tilde{p}(\tilde{r})$, $\partial\tilde{p}(\tilde{r})/\partial\tilde{r}$; $\tilde{\tau}=1$, $G=0$.

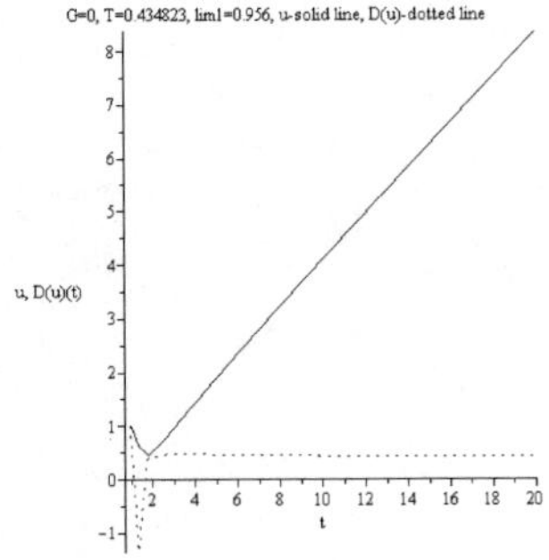

Fig. 9.2.3. Evolution of $\tilde{u}(\tilde{r})$, $\partial\tilde{u}(\tilde{r})/\partial\tilde{r}$; $\tilde{\tau}=0.434823$, $G=0$.

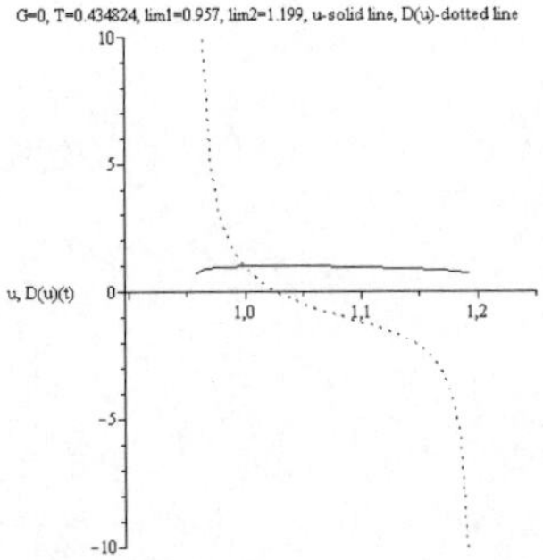

Fig. 9.2.4. Evolution of $\tilde{u}(\tilde{r})$, $\partial\tilde{u}(\tilde{r})/\partial\tilde{r}$; $\tilde{\tau}=0.434824$, $G=0$.

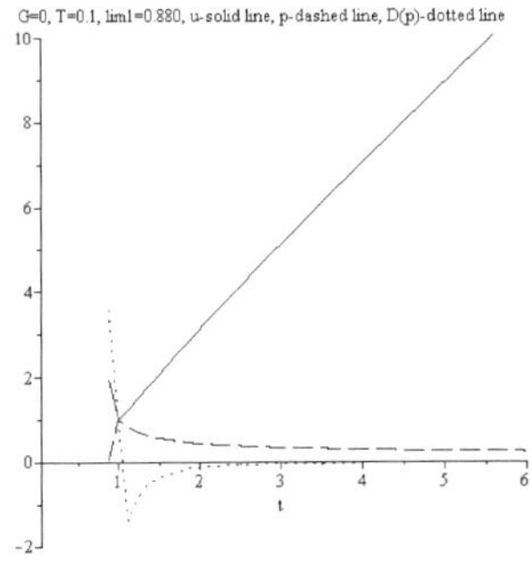

Fig. 9.2.5. Evolution of $\tilde{u}(\tilde{r})$, $\tilde{p}(\tilde{r})$, $\partial\tilde{p}(\tilde{r})/\partial\tilde{r}$; $\tilde{\tau} = 0.1$, $\mathrm{G} = 0$.

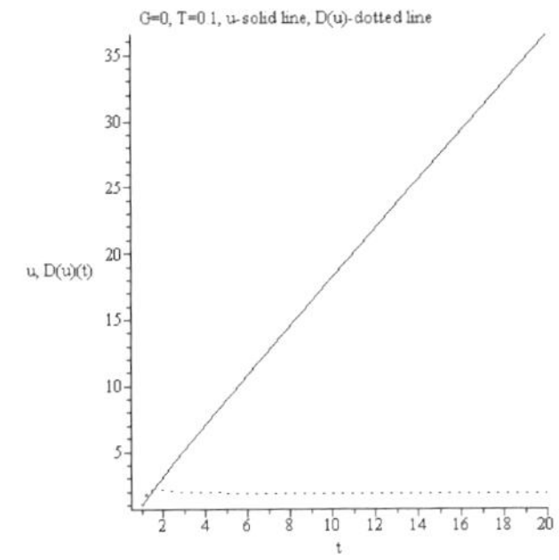

Fig. 9.2.6. Evolution of $\tilde{u}(\tilde{r})$, $\partial\tilde{u}(\tilde{r})/\partial\tilde{r}$; $\tilde{\tau} = 0.1$, $\mathrm{G} = 0$.

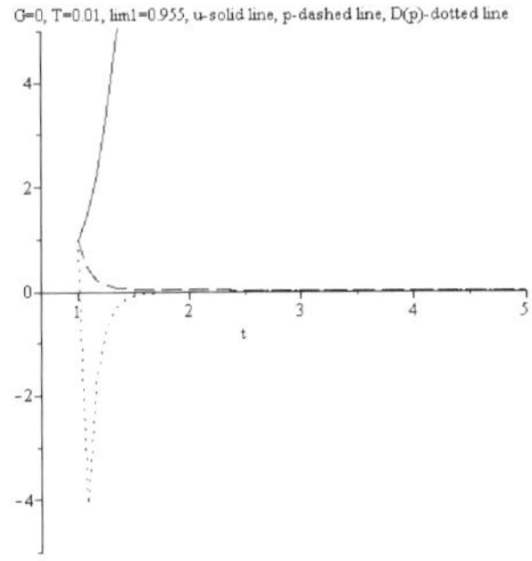

Fig. 9.2.7. Evolution of $\tilde{u}(\tilde{r})$, $\tilde{p}(\tilde{r})$, $F(\tilde{r})$; $\tilde{\tau} = 0.01$, $\mathrm{G} = 0$.

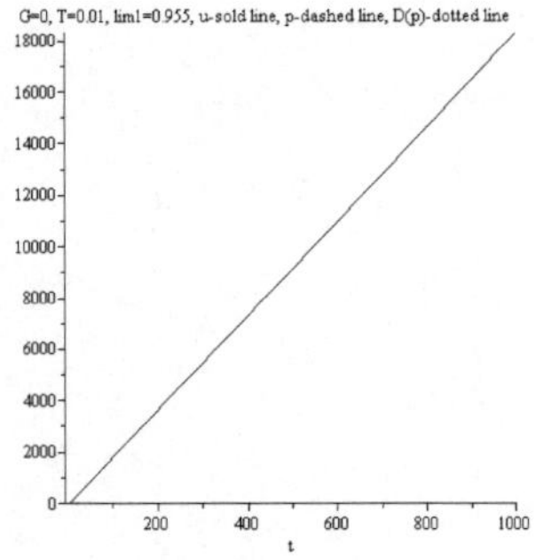

Fig. 9.2.8. Evolution of $\tilde{u}(\tilde{r})$; $\tilde{\tau} = 0.01$, $\mathrm{G} = 0$.

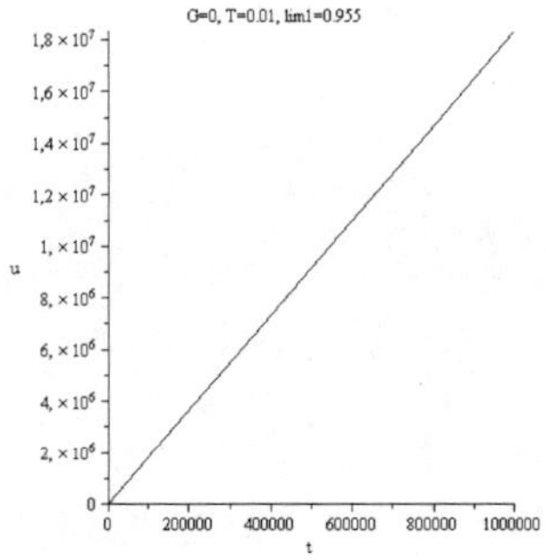

Fig. 9.2.9. Evolution of $\tilde{u}(\tilde{r})$; $\tilde{\tau} = 0.01$, $\mathrm{G} = 0$.

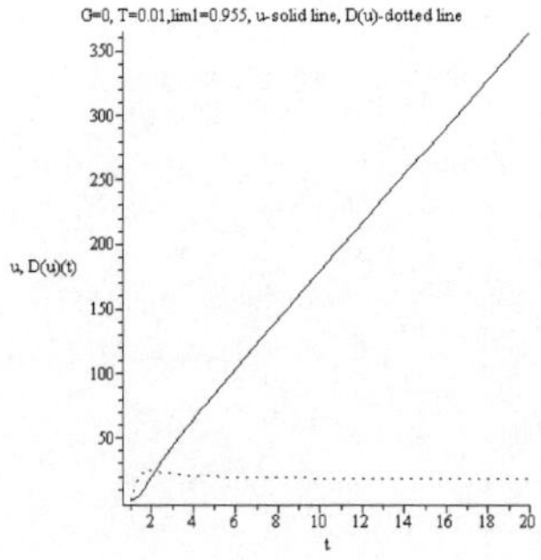

Fig. 9.2.10. Evolution of $\partial\tilde{u}(\tilde{r})/\partial\tilde{r}$; $\tilde{\tau} = 0.01$, $\mathrm{G} = 0$.

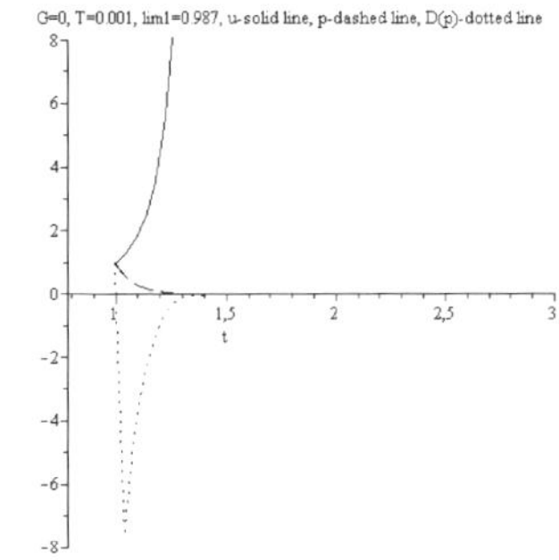

Fig. 9.2.11. Evolution of $\tilde{u}(\tilde{r})$, $\tilde{p}(\tilde{r})$, $\partial\tilde{p}(\tilde{r})/\partial\tilde{r}$; $\tilde{\tau} = 0.001$, $\mathrm{G} = 0$.

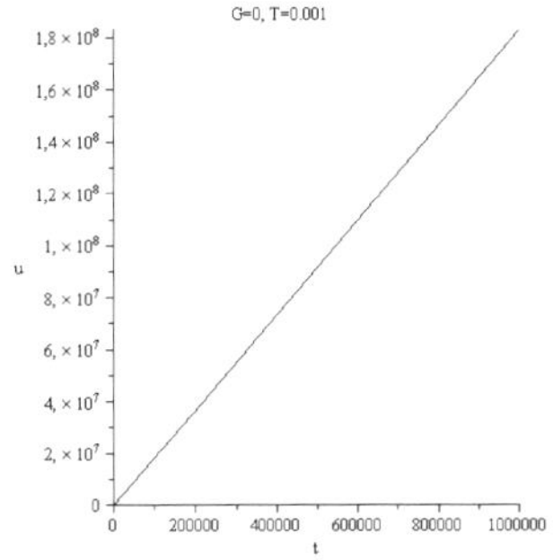

Fig. 9.2.12. Evolution of $\tilde{u}(\tilde{r})$; $\tilde{\tau} = 0.001$, $\mathrm{G} = 0$.

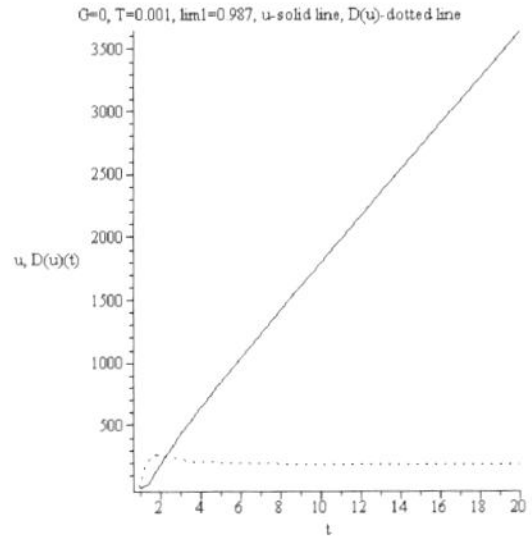

Fig. 9.2.13. Evolution of $\tilde{u}(\tilde{r})$, $\partial\tilde{u}(\tilde{r})/\partial\tilde{r}$; $\tilde{\tau} = 0.001$, $\mathrm{G} = 0$.

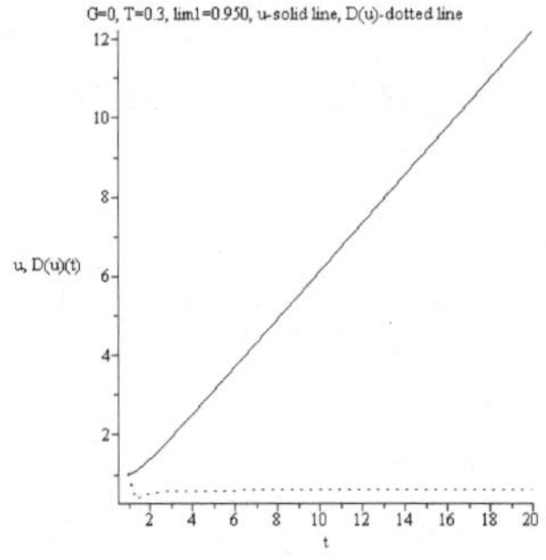

Fig. 9.2.14. Evolution of $\widetilde{u}(\widetilde{r})$, $\partial\widetilde{u}(\widetilde{r})/\partial\widetilde{r}$; $\widetilde{\tau} = 0.3$, $\mathrm{G} = 0$.

Conclusion:

1. The Universe evolution leads to the finite size of this system if the non-locality parameter $\widetilde{\tau} \sim 1$ (figures 9.2.1 - 9.2.3).
2. Nonlocal coefficient $\widetilde{\tau}$ plays the role of fundamental constant in the Universe. The critical $\widetilde{\tau}_{cr}$ exists when the infinite Universe transforms into the finite Universe (see figures 9.2.3 and 9.2.4). For this model $\widetilde{\tau}_{cr} = 0.4348235$.
3. If $\widetilde{\tau} \approx 0.1$ or less the Universe exists in the generalized Hubble regime (figures 9.2.6 -9.2.14).
4. If $\widetilde{\tau}$ is not too small the generalized Hubble regime contains the "regime with acceleration" when the Hubble coefficient $\mathrm{Hu}(\widetilde{r})$ is not constant and increasing with the distance $\widetilde{r}$. But with the $\widetilde{r}$ increasing the regime with acceleration transforms into classical Hubble regime with the constant Hu , $\widetilde{u}(\widetilde{r}) = \overline{\mathrm{Hu}}\widetilde{r}$, where $\overline{\mathrm{Hu}}$ is the dimensionless Hubble coefficient.

    This result should be verified by observations.
5. Varying $\widetilde{\tau}$ leads to the principally different the Universe evolution before achieving the Hubble regime. Look at figures 9.2.6, 9.2.10, 9.2.13 and 9.2.14. In the cases reflected in figures 9.2.6, 9.2.10, 9.2.13 we have our Universe with accelerations in the first stage of evolution. But the situation reflected in the figure 9.2.14 corresponds to the Universe with deceleration of the Universe expanding in the first stage of its evolution.
6. Diminishing of the nonlocal parameter $\widetilde{\tau}$ leads to the Hadamard effect - the smaller the parameter $\widetilde{\tau}$ the greater the rate of expansion (compare figures 9.2.6, 9.2.9, 9.2.10 and 9.2.12).

Let us estimate $\widetilde{\tau}$ for our Universe. The Hubble expression can be written in the dimensionless form

$$\frac{\tilde{u}}{\tilde{r}} = \overline{\mathrm{Hu}}, \qquad (9.2.9)$$

where the velocity scale u_0^i is the velocity of the initial radial perturbation and r_0^i is the radius of the initial object. It means that the dimensionless Hubble parameter can written as

$$\overline{\mathrm{Hu}} = \mathrm{Hu}\frac{r_0^i}{v_0^i}. \qquad (9.2.10)$$

The ratio r_0^i/u_0^i corresponds to the early times of the Universe evolution. For our time r_0^n/u_0^n can be estimated as the age of the Universe and within the ΛCDM model is about (4,354 ± 0,012)•$10^{17}s$. In this case

$$\frac{\tilde{u}}{\tilde{r}} = \overline{\mathrm{Hu}} = \mathrm{Hu}\frac{r_0^n}{u_0^n} \cong 2.169\cdot 10^{-18}\cdot 4.35\cdot 10^{17} = 0.943. \qquad (9.2.11)$$

Other estimates of the age of the Universe lead to much greater values of $\overline{\mathrm{Hu}}$ (and therefore to smaller values of the parameter $\tilde{\tau}$). Nevertheless we can formulate some conclusions using figures 9.2.5 - 9.2.7, 9.2.9, 9.2.10, 9.2.12 and 9.2.13:

1. We are living in the young Universe with varying $\overline{\mathrm{Hu}}$.
2. The origin of the Universe can not be considered as singular point. In other words it means that initial size of our Universe is not much less that the character size of the visible now Universe.
3. If the initial radius of the object tends to infinity, the physical picture is changing radically. This situation is investigated in the next Item.

9.3. Travelling waves in Physical Vacuum.

After the Big Bang and interaction of Physical Vacuum (PV) with the created matter the microwave background radiation should contain the traces of the travelling waves evolution. Let us look at the last measurements realized in the frame of the Planck programme. The temperature variations don't appear to behave the same on large scales as they do on small scales, and there are some particularly large features, such as a hefty cold spot, that were not predicted by basic inflation models.

From the position of the developed theory it is no surprise. Really, look at the Planck space observatory's map (Fig. 9.3.1) of the universe's cosmic microwave background. This map is in open Internet access (see for example SPACE.com Staff. Date: 21 March 2013 Time: 11:15 AM ET).

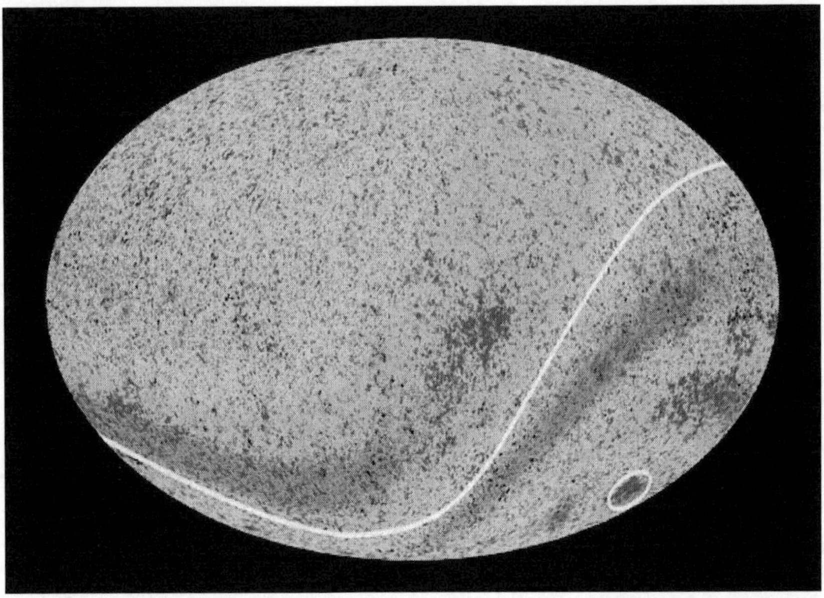

Fig. 9.3.1 Planck space observatory's map of the universe's cosmic microwave background

It was reported that cosmic microwave (CMW) is a snapshot of the oldest light in our Universe, imprinted on the sky when the Universe was just 380 000 years old. It shows tiny temperature fluctuations that correspond to regions of slightly different densities, representing the seeds of all future structure: the stars and galaxies of today.

From the position of the developed theory Planck's all-sky map contains the regular traces of traveling waves as the alternation of the "hot" (red) and "cold" (blue) strips. On figure 9.3,1 the Planck space observatory staff shows the "mysterious" hefty cold spot as the blue small area bounded by the white circle.

The radius of the "cold spot" subtends about 5°; it is centered at the galactic coordinate l_{II} = 207.8°, b_{II} = −56.3°. We remind that the galactic coordinates use the Sun as the origin. Galactic longitude (*l*) is measured with primary direction from the Sun to the center of the galaxy in the galactic plane, while the galactic latitude (*b*) measures the angle of the object above the galactic plane. It is, therefore, in the Southern Celestial Hemisphere in the direction of the constellation Eridanus.

From the position of the developed theory *it is the area reflecting the initial explosion of PV. In this case the center domain of the mentioned hefty cold spot should contain the smallest hot spot as the origin of the initial burst.*

I hope this fact will be established by astronomers after following more precise observations.

As we see on figure 9.3.1 after the PV explosion the following after Cold Spot wave fronts have the structure of the plane waves. Then we can use in investigations the system of equations (see Item 9.1)

(continuum equation)

$$\frac{\partial}{\partial x}\left[\tau\left(\frac{\partial p}{\partial x}-F_x\right)\right]=0, \tag{9.3.1}$$

(momentum equation)

$$\frac{\partial p}{\partial x}-F_x-\frac{\partial}{\partial t}\left\{\tau\left[\frac{\partial p}{\partial x}-F_x\right]\right\}-2\tau\left[\frac{\partial p}{\partial x}-F_x\right]\frac{\partial u}{\partial x}-\frac{\partial}{\partial x}\left\{\tau\left[\frac{\partial p}{\partial t}+3p\frac{\partial u}{\partial x}+u\frac{\partial p}{\partial x}\right]\right\}=0. \tag{9.3.2}$$

(energy equation, see also (9.1.44))

$$\begin{aligned}&3\frac{\partial p}{\partial t}+5p\frac{\partial u}{\partial x}+3u\frac{\partial p}{\partial x}+2u\left(\frac{\partial p}{\partial x}-F_x\right)-\\&-\frac{\partial}{\partial t}\left\{\tau\left[3\frac{\partial p}{\partial t}+3u\frac{\partial p}{\partial x}+5p\frac{\partial u}{\partial x}+2u\left(\frac{\partial p}{\partial x}-F_x\right)\right]\right\}-\\&-\frac{\partial}{\partial x}\left\{\tau\left[5\frac{\partial}{\partial t}(pu)+16pu\frac{\partial u}{\partial x}+5u^2\frac{\partial p}{\partial x}+3u^2\left(\frac{\partial p}{\partial x}-F_x\right)\right]\right\}+A^{pert}=0\end{aligned} \tag{9.3.3}$$

or

$$\begin{aligned}&3\frac{\partial p}{\partial t}+5p\frac{\partial u}{\partial x}+3u\frac{\partial p}{\partial x}+2u\left(\frac{\partial p}{\partial x}-F_x\right)-\\&-\frac{\partial}{\partial t}\left\{\tau\left[3\frac{\partial p}{\partial t}+3u\frac{\partial p}{\partial x}+5p\frac{\partial u}{\partial x}+2u\left(\frac{\partial p}{\partial x}-F_x\right)\right]\right\}-\\&-\frac{\partial}{\partial x}\left\{\tau\left[5\frac{\partial}{\partial t}(up)+11up\frac{\partial u}{\partial x}+5u\frac{\partial}{\partial x}(up)+3u^2\left(\frac{\partial p}{\partial x}-F_x\right)\right]\right\}+A^{pert}=0.\end{aligned} \tag{9.3.4}$$

Let us use (9.3.1) in the asymptotic form for the spherical wave of large radius of curvature, we find

$$\frac{\partial p}{\partial x}-F_x=0. \tag{9.3.5}$$

Then we have the system of equations (9.3.5) – (9.3.7) which can be applied for the beginning of the Universe evolution including the Plank time.

$$\frac{\partial}{\partial x}\left\{\tau\left[\frac{\partial p}{\partial t}+3p\frac{\partial u}{\partial x}+u\frac{\partial p}{\partial x}\right]\right\}=0, \tag{9.3.6}$$

$$3\frac{\partial p}{\partial t}+5p\frac{\partial u}{\partial x}+3u\frac{\partial p}{\partial x}-\frac{\partial}{\partial t}\left\{\tau\left[3\frac{\partial p}{\partial t}+3u\frac{\partial p}{\partial x}+5p\frac{\partial u}{\partial x}\right]\right\}-$$
$$-\frac{\partial}{\partial x}\left\{\tau\left[5\frac{\partial}{\partial t}(up)+11up\frac{\partial u}{\partial x}+5u\frac{\partial}{\partial x}(up)\right]\right\}+A^{pert}=0, \tag{9.3.7}$$

where

$$A^{pert}=5\frac{\partial}{\partial x}\left[\tau\left(\frac{p}{\rho}F_x-\frac{\partial}{\partial x}\frac{p^2}{\rho}\right)\right] \tag{9.3.8}$$

or using (9.3.5)

$$A^{pert}=5\frac{\partial}{\partial x}\left[\tau\left(\frac{p}{\rho}F_x-\frac{\partial}{\partial x}\frac{p^2}{\rho}\right)\right]=5\frac{\partial}{\partial x}\left[\tau\left(\frac{p}{\rho}F_x-\frac{p}{\rho}\frac{\partial p}{\partial x}-p\frac{\partial}{\partial x}\frac{p}{\rho}\right)\right]=-5\frac{\partial}{\partial x}\left[\tau p\frac{\partial}{\partial x}\frac{p}{\rho}\right]. \tag{9.3.9}$$

As we see equations (9.3.6) and (9.3.7) define the unknown variables $u(x,t), p(x,t)$ and relation (9.3.5) defines the F_x evolution.

Let us simplify consideration with the aim to obtain the most transparent result of the Universe evolution at the first time moment. Let us suppose:

1. The perturbation A^{pert} can be omitted.
2. Nonlocal parameter $\tau = const$
3. The time derivative of the logarithmic term can be omitted.

Namely, after dividing on the first line of equation (9.3.7) on $\left(3\frac{\partial p}{\partial t}+5p\frac{\partial u}{\partial x}+3u\frac{\partial p}{\partial x}\right)$ we obtain the term $-\tau\frac{\partial}{\partial t}\left\{\ln\left[3\frac{\partial p}{\partial t}+3u\frac{\partial p}{\partial x}+5p\frac{\partial u}{\partial x}\right]\right\}$. Then we have the energy equation

$$\frac{\partial}{\partial x}\left[5\frac{\partial}{\partial t}(up)+5u\frac{\partial}{\partial x}(up)+11up\frac{\partial u}{\partial x}\right]=0. \tag{9.3.10}$$

or

$$\frac{\partial}{\partial x}\left[5\frac{\partial}{\partial t}(up)+5u^2\frac{\partial p}{\partial x}+16up\frac{\partial u}{\partial x}\right]=0 \tag{9.3.11}$$

or

$$5\frac{\partial}{\partial t}\frac{\partial}{\partial x}(up)+\frac{\partial}{\partial x}\left[5u^2\frac{\partial p}{\partial x}+16up\frac{\partial u}{\partial x}\right]=0. \tag{9.3.12}$$

From equation (see (9.3.6))

$$\frac{\partial p}{\partial t}+3p\frac{\partial u}{\partial x}+u\frac{\partial p}{\partial x}=0, \tag{9.3.13}$$

we have

$$5\frac{\partial pu}{\partial x}=-10p\frac{\partial u}{\partial x}-5\frac{\partial p}{\partial t}. \tag{9.3.14}$$

After substitution (9.3.14) in (9.3.12) one obtains

$$-\frac{\partial}{\partial t}\left(5\frac{\partial p}{\partial t}+10p\frac{\partial u}{\partial x}\right)+\frac{\partial}{\partial x}\left[5u^2\frac{\partial p}{\partial x}+16up\frac{\partial u}{\partial x}\right]=0 \tag{9.3.15}$$

or

$$\frac{\partial^2 p}{\partial t^2}+\frac{\partial}{\partial t}\left[2p\frac{\partial u}{\partial x}\right]=\frac{\partial}{\partial x}\left[u^2\frac{\partial p}{\partial x}+\frac{16}{5}up\frac{\partial u}{\partial x}\right] \tag{9.3.16}$$

Let us use the Hubble law of the Universe expansion

$$u=\bar{u}(x,t)=Hx \tag{9.3.17}$$

From equations (9.3.16) and (9.3.17) follow

$$\frac{1}{H^2}\frac{\partial^2 p}{\partial t^2}+2\frac{1}{H}\frac{\partial p}{\partial t}=\frac{\partial}{\partial x}\left[x^2\frac{\partial p}{\partial x}+\frac{16}{5}px\right]. \tag{9.3.18}$$

Write down the equation (9.3.18) in the dimensionless forms using the scales

$$[x_0],\ [u_0],\ [p_0],\ [t_0]=\frac{1}{H}$$

and tilde for the dimensionless values. We find

$$\frac{\partial^2 \tilde{p}}{\partial \tilde{t}^2}+2\frac{\partial \tilde{p}}{\partial \tilde{t}}=\frac{\partial}{\partial \tilde{x}}\left[\tilde{x}^2\frac{\partial \tilde{p}}{\partial \tilde{x}}\right]+\frac{16}{5}\frac{\partial}{\partial \tilde{x}}[\tilde{x}\tilde{p}]. \tag{9.3.19}$$

For the numerical solution of this hyperbolic equation we should introduce the initial and boundary conditions. For example (Maple program)

$$> \frac{\partial}{\partial t}\frac{\partial}{\partial t}p(x,t)+2\frac{\partial}{\partial t}p(x,t)-\left(\frac{\partial}{\partial x}\left(x^2\frac{\partial}{\partial x}p(x,t)\right)\right)-\left(\frac{\partial}{\partial x}\left(xp(x,t)\right)\right)\frac{16}{5}=0$$

$$\frac{\partial^2}{\partial t^2}p(x,t)+2\left(\frac{\partial}{\partial t}p(x,t)\right)-\frac{26}{5}x\left(\frac{\partial}{\partial x}p(x,t)\right)-x^2\left(\frac{\partial^2}{\partial x^2}p(x,t)\right)-\frac{16}{5}p(x,t)=0$$

Enter the initial boundary conditions.

$$p(x, 0) = 1, p(0, t) = 0, D_1(p)(10, t)$$
$$= 0, D_2(p)(x, 0) = 10$$

Solve the equation.

> $s := pdsolve((\mathbf{31}), \{(\mathbf{32})\}, numeric):$

Plot the solution for select values of t.

> $p1 := s[plot](t = 0, color = black):$

> $p2 := s[plot]\left(t = \frac{1}{10}, color = black\right):$

> $p3 := s[plot]\left(t = \frac{1}{2}, color = black\right):$

> $p4 := s[plot](t = 1, color = black):$

> $p5 := s[plot](t = 2, color = black):$

> plots[

)

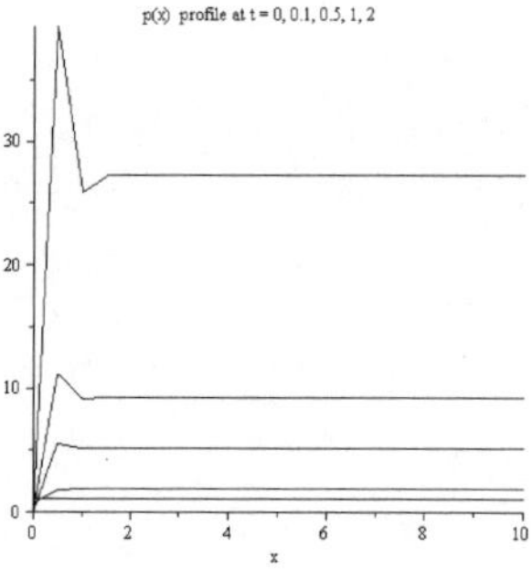

Figure 9.3.2. Profile $\tilde{p}(\tilde{x})$ at the time moments $\tilde{t} = 0$, 0.1, 0.5, 1, 2.

The arrangement of the curves from bottom to top corresponds to sequential increasing of the observation time after the explosion of the physical vacuum in the cold spot region. Compare now Figure 9.3.2 with strips positions on Figure 9.3.1. As we see the developed theory catches the main features of events during the Universe birth.

The corresponding approximate theory can be created in the spherical coordinate system.

We use the equations

$$F_r = \frac{\partial p}{\partial r}, \tag{9.3.20}$$

momentum equation in the non-stationary spherically symmetric case ($\tau - const$), which is written as

$$\frac{1}{r^2}\frac{\partial}{\partial r}\left\{r^2 p\frac{\partial v_{0r}}{\partial r}\right\}+\frac{\partial}{\partial r}\left(\frac{\partial p}{\partial t}\right)+2\frac{\partial}{\partial r}\left(\frac{1}{r^2}\frac{\partial\left(r^2 p v_{0r}\right)}{\partial r}\right)-\frac{1}{r^2}\frac{\partial}{\partial r}\left(r^2 v_{0r}\frac{\partial p}{\partial r}\right)=0, \quad (9.3.21)$$

or

$$\frac{\partial}{\partial r}\left\{p\frac{\partial v_{0r}}{\partial r}+\frac{\partial p}{\partial t}+\frac{4}{r}pv_{0r}-v_{0r}\frac{\partial p}{\partial r}+2p\frac{\partial v_{0r}}{\partial r}+2v_{0r}\frac{\partial p}{\partial r}\right\}+\frac{2}{r}p\frac{\partial v_{0r}}{\partial r}-\frac{2}{r}v_{0r}\frac{\partial p}{\partial r}=0 \quad (9.3.22)$$

or

$$2\left[v_{0r}\frac{\partial p}{\partial r}-p\frac{\partial v_{0r}}{\partial r}\right]-r\frac{\partial}{\partial r}\left[\frac{\partial p}{\partial t}+3p\frac{\partial v_{0r}}{\partial r}+v_{0r}\frac{\partial p}{\partial r}+\frac{4}{r}pv_{0r}\right]=0. \quad (9.3.23)$$

Transform now the energy equation (see also (9.1.36)) written here as follows

$$\begin{aligned}&\frac{\partial}{\partial t}\left\{3p-\tau\left[3\frac{\partial p}{\partial t}+\frac{5}{r^2}\frac{\partial}{\partial r}\left(r^2 v_{0r}p\right)-2F_r v_{0r}\right]\right\}+\frac{5}{r^2}\frac{\partial}{\partial r}\left\{r^2 p v_{0r}\right\}-\\&-\frac{1}{r^2}\frac{\partial}{\partial r}\left\{r^2\tau\left[5\frac{\partial}{\partial t}\left(pv_{0r}\right)-3F_r v_{0r}^2\right]\right\}-\frac{7}{r^2}\frac{\partial}{\partial r}\left\{\tau\frac{\partial}{\partial t}\left(r^2 p v_{0r}^2\right)\right\}-\frac{1}{r^2}\frac{\partial}{\partial r}\left(\tau r^2\frac{\partial}{\partial r}\left(pv_{0r}^2\right)\right)-\\&-2\left\{F_r v_{0r}-\tau g_r\left(\frac{\partial}{\partial t}\left(\rho v_{0r}\right)+\frac{1}{r^2}\frac{\partial}{\partial r}\left(r^2\rho v_{0r}^2\right)\right)\right\}+A^{pert}=0,\end{aligned} \quad (9.3.24)$$

where

$$\begin{aligned}A^{pert}&=\frac{5}{r^2}\frac{\partial}{\partial r}\left[\tau r^2\left(\frac{p}{\rho}F_r-p\frac{\partial}{\partial r}\frac{p}{\rho}-\frac{p}{\rho}\frac{\partial p}{\partial r}\right)\right]=\frac{5}{r^2}\frac{\partial}{\partial r}\left\{\tau r^2 p\left[\frac{1}{\rho}\left(F_r-\frac{\partial p}{\partial r}\right)-\frac{\partial}{\partial r}\frac{p}{\rho}\right]\right\}=\\&=-\frac{5}{r^2}\frac{\partial}{\partial r}\left\{\tau r^2 p\frac{\partial}{\partial r}\frac{p}{\rho}\right\}.\end{aligned} \quad (9.3.25)$$

We find

$$\begin{aligned}&3\frac{\partial p}{\partial t}+5\frac{\partial}{\partial r}\left\{pv_{0r}\right\}+\frac{10}{r}pv_{0r}-\frac{\partial}{\partial t}\left\{\tau\left[3\frac{\partial p}{\partial t}+5\frac{\partial}{\partial r}\left(v_{0r}p\right)+\frac{10}{r}v_{0r}p-2F_r v_{0r}\right]\right\}-\\&-\frac{\partial}{\partial r}\left\{\tau\left[5\frac{\partial}{\partial t}\left(pv_{0r}\right)-3F_r v_{0r}^2\right]\right\}-\frac{2}{r}\tau\left[5\frac{\partial}{\partial t}\left(pv_{0r}\right)-3F_r v_{0r}^2\right]-\\&-\frac{1}{r^2}\frac{\partial}{\partial r}\left\{\tau r^2\left[8\frac{\partial}{\partial r}\left(pv_{0r}^2\right)+\frac{14}{r}pv_{0r}^2\right]\right\}-\\&-2\left\{F_r v_{0r}-\tau g_r\left(\frac{\partial}{\partial t}\left(\rho v_{0r}\right)+\frac{1}{r^2}\frac{\partial}{\partial r}\left(r^2\rho v_{0r}^2\right)\right)\right\}+A^{pert}=0,\end{aligned} \quad (9.3.26)$$

Let us introduce an analogue the Hubble boxes which can be named as the PV box. Following this analogue we suppose:

A. The process of PV evolution after Big Bang is an implicit function of t.

B. Velocity v_{0r} is written as

$$v_{0r} = A(r)r. \tag{9.3.27}$$

From Item A follows that time dependence exists in the form

$$\frac{\partial}{\partial t} = \frac{\partial}{\partial r}\frac{\partial r}{\partial t} = v_{0r}\frac{\partial}{\partial r}. \tag{9.3.28}$$

Then we have from momentum equation (9.3.23)

$$2\tau\frac{\partial p}{\partial r}v_{0r} - 2p\frac{\partial}{\partial r}(\tau v_{0r}) - r\frac{\partial}{\partial r}\left\{\tau\left[3p\frac{\partial v_{0r}}{\partial r} + 2v_{0r}\frac{\partial p}{\partial r} + \frac{4}{r}pv_{0r}\right]\right\} = 0 \tag{9.3.29}$$

and from energy equation (9.3.26) follows

$$\begin{aligned}
&3v_{0r}\frac{\partial p}{\partial r} + 5\frac{\partial}{\partial r}\{pv_{0r}\} + \frac{10}{r}pv_{0r} - v_{0r}\frac{\partial}{\partial r}\left\{\tau\left[3v_{0r}\frac{\partial p}{\partial r} + 5\frac{\partial}{\partial r}(v_{0r}p) + \frac{10}{r}v_{0r}p - 2F_r v_{0r}\right]\right\} - \\
&-\frac{\partial}{\partial r}\left\{\tau\left[5v_{0r}\frac{\partial}{\partial r}(pv_{0r}) - 3F_r v_{0r}^2\right]\right\} - \frac{2}{r}\tau\left[5v_{0r}\frac{\partial}{\partial r}(pv_{0r}) - 3F_r v_{0r}^2\right] - \\
&-\frac{1}{r^2}\frac{\partial}{\partial r}\left\{\tau r^2\left[8\frac{\partial}{\partial r}(pv_{0r}^2) + \frac{14}{r}pv_{0r}^2\right]\right\} - \\
&-2\left\{F_r v_{0r} - \tau g_r\left(\frac{\partial}{\partial t}(\rho v_{0r}) + \frac{1}{r^2}\frac{\partial}{\partial r}(r^2\rho v_{0r}^2)\right)\right\} + A^{pert} = 0,
\end{aligned} \tag{9.3.30}$$

or

$$\begin{aligned}
&6v_{0r}\frac{\partial p}{\partial r} + 5p\frac{\partial v_{0r}}{\partial r} + \frac{10}{r}pv_{0r} - v_{0r}\frac{\partial}{\partial r}\left\{\tau\left[6v_{0r}\frac{\partial p}{\partial r} + 5p\frac{\partial v_{0r}}{\partial r} + \frac{10}{r}v_{0r}p\right]\right\} - \\
&-\frac{1}{r^2}\frac{\partial}{\partial r}\left\{\tau r^2\left[2v_{0r}\frac{\partial}{\partial r}(pv_{0r}) - 2pv_{0r}\frac{\partial v_{0r}}{\partial r} + 5v_{0r}p\frac{\partial v_{0r}}{\partial r}\right]\right\} - \\
&-\frac{1}{r^2}\frac{\partial}{\partial r}\left\{\tau r^2\left[8v_{0r}\frac{\partial}{\partial r}(pv_{0r}) + 8pv_{0r}\frac{\partial v_{0r}}{\partial r} + \frac{14}{r}pv_{0r}^2\right]\right\} + A^{pert} = 0
\end{aligned} \tag{9.3.31}$$

or

$$\begin{aligned}
&6v_{0r}\frac{\partial p}{\partial r} + 5p\frac{\partial v_{0r}}{\partial r} + \frac{10}{r}pv_{0r} - v_{0r}\frac{\partial}{\partial r}\left\{\tau\left[6v_{0r}\frac{\partial p}{\partial r} + 5p\frac{\partial v_{0r}}{\partial r} + \frac{10}{r}v_{0r}p\right]\right\} - \\
&-\frac{1}{r^2}\frac{\partial}{\partial r}\left\{\tau r^2\left[10v_{0r}\frac{\partial}{\partial r}(pv_{0r}) + 11pv_{0r}\frac{\partial v_{0r}}{\partial r} + \frac{14}{r}pv_{0r}^2\right]\right\} + A^{pert} = 0
\end{aligned} \tag{9.3.32}$$

Write down the system of equations in the dimensionless forms using the scales

$$[x_0],\ [u_0],\ [p_0],\ [F] = \frac{p_0}{x_0},\ [t_0] = \frac{x_0}{u_0},\ \rho_0,\ x_0 = u_0 t_0,\ p_0 = \rho_0 u_0^2.$$

and tilde for the dimensionless values. Then we have the following system (SYSTEM PV) of the dimensionless equation defining the PV evolution in the PV box:

$$\frac{\partial \tilde{p}}{\partial \tilde{r}} = \tilde{F}_r, \tag{9.3.33}$$

$$2\tilde{\tau}\tilde{v}_{0r}\frac{\partial \tilde{p}}{\partial \tilde{r}} - 2\tilde{p}\frac{\partial \tilde{\tau}\tilde{v}_{0r}}{\partial \tilde{r}} - \tilde{r}\frac{\partial}{\partial \tilde{r}}\left\{\tilde{\tau}\left[\tilde{v}_{0r}\frac{\partial \tilde{p}}{\partial \tilde{r}} + 3\tilde{p}\frac{\partial \tilde{v}_{0r}}{\partial \tilde{r}} + \frac{4}{\tilde{r}}\tilde{p}\tilde{v}_{0r}\right]\right\} = 0, \tag{9.3.34}$$

$$6\tilde{v}_{0r}\frac{\partial \tilde{p}}{\partial \tilde{r}} + 5\tilde{p}\frac{\partial \tilde{v}_{0r}}{\partial \tilde{r}} + \frac{10}{\tilde{r}}\tilde{p}\tilde{v}_{0r} - \tilde{v}_{0r}\frac{\partial}{\partial \tilde{r}}\left\{\tilde{\tau}\left[6\tilde{v}_{0r}\frac{\partial \tilde{p}}{\partial \tilde{r}} + 5\tilde{p}\frac{\partial \tilde{v}_{0r}}{\partial \tilde{r}} + \frac{10}{\tilde{r}}\tilde{v}_{0r}\tilde{p}\right]\right\}$$

$$-\frac{1}{\tilde{r}^2}\frac{\partial}{\partial \tilde{r}}\left\{\tilde{r}^2\tilde{\tau}\left[10\tilde{v}_{0r}\frac{\partial}{\partial \tilde{r}}(\tilde{p}\tilde{v}_{0r}) + 11\tilde{p}\tilde{v}_{0r}\frac{\partial \tilde{v}_{0r}}{\partial \tilde{r}} + \frac{14}{\tilde{r}}\tilde{p}\tilde{v}_{0r}^2\right]\right\} + \tilde{A}^{pert}(\tilde{r}). \tag{9.3.35}$$

Three ordinary differential equations (9.3.33) – (9.3.35) define three dependent variables $\tilde{F}_r$, $\tilde{v}_{0r}$ and $\tilde{p}$. The energy equation includes in the last term the external perturbation. In principal, there are no difficulties to organize the mathematical modeling using this system of equations.

Is it possible to speak about existence of PV boxes and moreover about the practical interaction between known fields and physical vacuum? The last events (which can be discussed further) leads to the conclusion that we can't exclude this possibility, [22].

It would be interesting to reveal the basic features which could be discovered. With this aim let us use the item B (9.3.33) in the form $\tilde{v}_{0r} = \tilde{A}(\tilde{r})\tilde{r}$. This relation should be introduced in the mentioned SYSTEM PV of equations; as a result we obtain the following dependent variables: $\tilde{F}_r(\tilde{r})$, $\tilde{p}(\tilde{r})$ and $\tilde{A}(\tilde{r})$.

Let us consider the more general case of relation (9.3.27) written as

$$\tilde{v}_{0r} = \tilde{A}\tilde{r}^n, \tag{9.3.36}$$

where $\tilde{A}$ is const. If $n = 1$ the space $v_{0r}(\tilde{r})$ evolution is an analogue of the Hubble expansion, $n > 1$ corresponds to the other types of the Universe expansion. Substituting (9.3.36) in (9.3.34) we find

$$2\left[\tilde{r}^n\frac{\partial \tilde{p}}{\partial \tilde{r}} - \tilde{p}n\tilde{r}^{n-1}\right] - \tilde{r}\frac{\partial}{\partial \tilde{r}}\left\{\left[\tilde{r}^n\frac{\partial \tilde{p}}{\partial \tilde{r}} + 3\tilde{p}n\tilde{r}^{n-1} + 4\tilde{p}\tilde{r}^{n-1}\right]\right\} = 0 \tag{9.3.37}$$

if $\tau = const$.

After transformation of the equation (9.3.37) one obtains

$$2\tilde{r}^{-1}\frac{\partial \tilde{p}}{\partial \tilde{r}} - 2\tilde{p}n\tilde{r}^{-2} - \frac{\partial^2 \tilde{p}}{\partial \tilde{r}^2} - 4n\tilde{r}^{-1}\frac{\partial \tilde{p}}{\partial \tilde{r}} - 3np(n-1)\tilde{r}^{-2} - 4\tilde{r}^{-1}\frac{\partial \tilde{p}}{\partial \tilde{r}} - 4\tilde{r}^{-2}\tilde{p}(n-1) = 0 \tag{9.3.38}$$

or

$$\tilde{r}^2\frac{\partial^2\tilde{p}}{\partial\tilde{r}^2}+4n\tilde{r}\frac{\partial\tilde{p}}{\partial\tilde{r}}+3n\tilde{p}(n-1)+2\tilde{r}\frac{\partial\tilde{p}}{\partial\tilde{r}}+2\tilde{p}[2(n-1)+n]=0 \tag{9.3.39}$$

or

$$\tilde{r}^2\frac{\partial^2\tilde{p}}{\partial\tilde{r}^2}+2(2n+1)\tilde{r}\frac{\partial\tilde{p}}{\partial\tilde{r}}+\left(3n^2+3n-4\right)\tilde{p}=0\,. \tag{9.3.40}$$

Hubble regime corresponds to $n=1$

$$\tilde{r}^2\frac{\partial^2\tilde{p}}{\partial\tilde{r}^2}+6\tilde{r}\frac{\partial\tilde{p}}{\partial\tilde{r}}+2\tilde{p}=0\,. \tag{9.3.41}$$

Equation (9.3.41) belongs to Euler type of the ordinary differential equations; in the general case Euler equation and its solution are written as

$$\tilde{r}^2\frac{\partial^2\tilde{p}}{\partial\tilde{r}^2}+a\tilde{r}\frac{\partial\tilde{p}}{\partial\tilde{r}}+b\tilde{p}=0\,, \tag{9.3.42}$$

$$\tilde{p}=|\tilde{r}|^{\frac{1-a}{2}}\left(C_1|\tilde{r}|^{\mu}+C_2|\tilde{r}|^{-\mu}\right),\qquad \text{if } (1-a)^2>4b\,, \tag{9.3.43}$$

$$\tilde{p}=|\tilde{r}|^{\frac{1-a}{2}}\left(C_1+C_2\ln|\tilde{r}|\right),\qquad \text{if } (1-a)^2=4b\,, \tag{9.3.44}$$

$$\tilde{p}=|\tilde{r}|^{\frac{1-a}{2}}\left(C_1\sin(\mu\ln|\tilde{r}|)+C_2\cos(\mu\ln|\tilde{r}|)\right),\ \text{if } (1-a)^2<4b\,, \tag{9.3.45}$$

where

$$\mu=\frac{1}{2}\left[(1-a)^2-4b\right]^{\frac{1}{2}}. \tag{9.3.46}$$

In the considered case we find

$$a=2(2n+1)\,,\ b=3n^2+3n-4\,,\ \mu=\frac{1}{2}\sqrt{4n^2-4n+17}\,,\ \frac{1-a}{2}=-\frac{4n+1}{2}. \tag{9.3.47}$$

$$(1-a)^2=16n^2+8n+1\,, \tag{9.3.48}$$

$$4b=12n^2+12n-16\,. \tag{9.3.49}$$

Obviously for the equation (9.3.40) the situation (9.3.43) is realized, because for all n we have

$$16n^2+8n+1>12n^2+12n-16$$

or

$$4n^2-4n+17>0\,. \tag{9.3.50}$$

Then after Big Bang in regime $\tilde{v}_{0r}=\tilde{A}\tilde{r}^n$ the following Universe evolution is realized

$$\tilde{p}=\tilde{r}^{-\frac{4n+1}{2}}\left(C_1\tilde{r}^{\frac{\sqrt{4n^2-4n+17}}{2}}+C_2\tilde{r}^{-\frac{\sqrt{4n^2-4n+17}}{2}}\right). \tag{9.3.51}$$

Limit cases:

1. If $n=0$, then $\tilde{v}_{0r}=const$, and

$$\tilde{p}=\tilde{r}^{-\frac{1}{2}}\left(C_1\tilde{r}^{\frac{\sqrt{17}}{2}}+C_2\tilde{r}^{-\frac{\sqrt{17}}{2}}\right), \tag{9.3.52}$$

In this mode, the energy of the explosion increases with the distance from the center of the explosion.

2. If $n=1$ (Hubble regime)

$$\widetilde{p}=\widetilde{r}^{-\frac{5}{2}}(C_1\widetilde{r}^{\frac{\sqrt{17}}{2}}+C_2\widetilde{r}^{-\frac{\sqrt{17}}{2}}), \tag{9.3.53}$$

or

$$p=C_1r^{-0.438}+C_2r^{-4,561}. \tag{9.3.54}$$

In this mode, the energy of the explosion decreases with the distance from the center of the explosion

3. If $n\to\infty$

$$\widetilde{p}=C_1\widetilde{r}^{-n}+C_2\widetilde{r}^{-3n}. \tag{9.3.55}$$

In this mode, the energy of the explosion decreases with increasing distance from the center of the explosion. In other words the explosion energy is damping $\widetilde{p}\to 0$ if $\widetilde{r}\to\infty$ without oscillations.

4. The boundary n for the mode changing can be found from the algebraic equation

$$4n+1=\sqrt{4n^2-4n+17}, \tag{9.3.56}$$

we have $n_1=-1.758,\ n_2=0.758$.

In this particular case we have the following chain of calculations: momentum equation becomes an independent equation; solution $\widetilde{p}(\widetilde{r})$ of this equation defines the force $\widetilde{F}_r(\widetilde{r})$ from equation (9.3.33) and $\widetilde{A}^{pert}(\widetilde{r})$ from the energy equation (9.3.35). It's important that the formulated above conclusions do not depend on nonlocal parameter if this parameter is constant.

9.4. PV evolution in the external radial gravitational field.

Let us consider now the PV evolution placed in the external gravitational field. Let us return for this aim to the following system of equations (see Item 9.2) written in the dimensionless form using the scales

$$[r_0],\ [u_0],\ [p_0],\ [F]=\frac{p_0}{r_0},\ [t_0]=\frac{r_0}{u_0},\ r_0=u_0t_0,\ [g_r]=\frac{u_0^2}{r_0}.$$

$$\widetilde{F}_r=\frac{\partial\widetilde{p}}{\partial\widetilde{r}}, \tag{9.4.1}$$

$$\frac{\partial}{\partial\widetilde{r}}\left[3\widetilde{p}\frac{\partial\widetilde{v}_{0r}}{\partial\widetilde{r}}+\widetilde{v}_{0r}\frac{\partial\widetilde{p}}{\partial\widetilde{r}}+\frac{4}{\widetilde{r}}\widetilde{p}\widetilde{v}_{0r}\right]-\frac{2}{\widetilde{r}}\left[\widetilde{v}_{0r}\frac{\partial\widetilde{p}}{\partial\widetilde{r}}-\widetilde{p}\frac{\partial\widetilde{v}_{0r}}{\partial\widetilde{r}}\right]=0, \tag{9.4.2}$$

$$5\tilde{p}\frac{\partial\tilde{v}_{0r}}{\partial\tilde{r}}+3\tilde{v}_{0r}\frac{\partial\tilde{p}}{\partial\tilde{r}}+\frac{10}{\tilde{r}}\tilde{p}\tilde{v}_{0r}-$$
$$-\tilde{\tau}\frac{\partial}{\partial\tilde{r}}\left\{5\tilde{v}_{0r}^{2}\frac{\partial\tilde{p}}{\partial\tilde{r}}+16\tilde{p}\tilde{v}_{0r}\frac{\partial\tilde{v}_{0r}}{\partial\tilde{r}}-5\tilde{p}\tilde{g}_{r}\right\}-\frac{20}{\tilde{r}}\tilde{\tau}\tilde{v}_{0r}^{2}\frac{\partial\tilde{p}}{\partial\tilde{r}}-\frac{60}{\tilde{r}}\tilde{\tau}\tilde{p}\tilde{v}_{0r}\frac{\partial\tilde{v}_{0r}}{\partial\tilde{r}}+$$
$$+\frac{10}{\tilde{r}}\tilde{\tau}\tilde{p}\tilde{g}_{r}-\frac{14}{\tilde{r}^{2}}\tilde{\tau}\tilde{p}\tilde{v}_{0r}^{2}+4\tilde{\tau}\tilde{v}_{0r}\frac{\partial\tilde{p}}{\partial\tilde{r}}\frac{\partial\tilde{v}_{0r}}{\partial\tilde{r}}=0. \qquad (9.4.3)$$

Let us introduce the approximation

$$\tilde{g}_{r}=\frac{\mathrm{G}}{\tilde{r}^{2}}. \qquad (9.4.4)$$

In this case system of equations (9.4.1) – (9.4.4) contains two dimensionless parameters G, $\mathrm{T}\leftrightarrow\tilde{\tau}$ and need four Cauchy conditions. These conditions we write down for the external surface of the spherical object. Then we investigate the evolution of the surface perturbation on the following scenario of the PV behavior.

In the theory of Big Bang the external gravitational field is absent. Let on the surface of a spherical PV object appears the perturbation of physical parameters, namely

$$p(1)=1,\ u(1)\leftrightarrow v_{0r}(1)=1,\ D(p)(1)=1,\ D(u)(1)=1. \qquad (9.4.5)$$

Figures (9.4.1) - (9.4.11) demonstrate the results of calculations for different τ. The information required is indicated in the figures and in figure captions including the boundaries of the solution existence. The following figures 9.4.1 - 9.4.3 contain the analogues results but for $\mathrm{G}=1$.

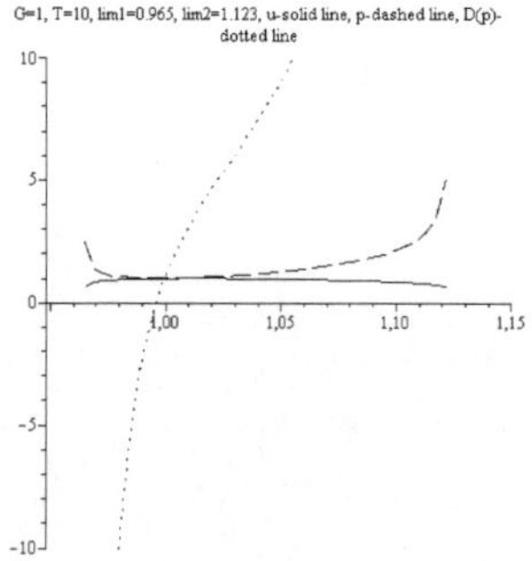

Fig. 9.4.1. Evolution of $\tilde{u}(\tilde{r})$, $\tilde{p}(\tilde{r})$, $\partial\tilde{p}(\tilde{r})/\partial\tilde{r}$; $\tilde{\tau}=10$, $\mathrm{G}=1$.

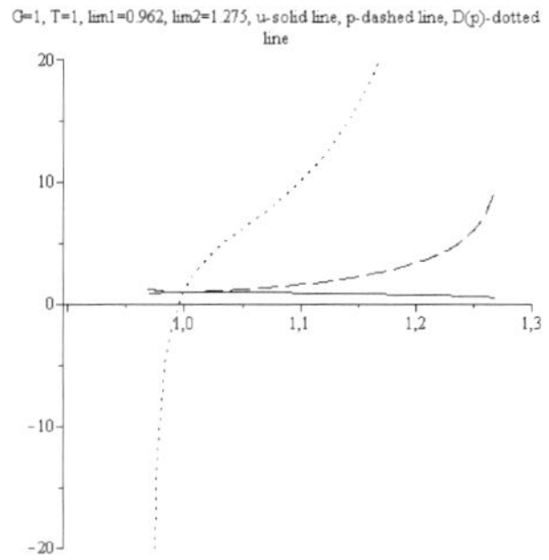

Fig. 9.4.2. Evolution of $\tilde{u}(\tilde{r})$, $\tilde{p}(\tilde{r})$, $\partial\tilde{p}(\tilde{r})/\partial\tilde{r}$; $\tilde{\tau} = 1$, $\mathrm{G} = 1$.

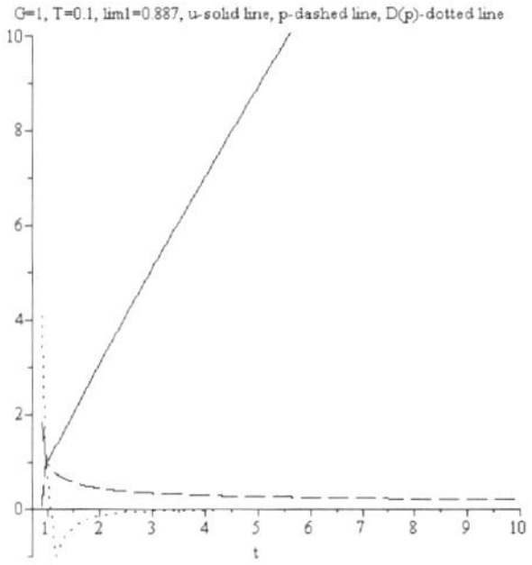

Fig. 9.4.3. Evolution of $\tilde{u}(\tilde{r})$, $\tilde{p}(\tilde{r})$, $\partial\tilde{p}(\tilde{r})/\partial\tilde{r}$; $\tilde{\tau} = 0.1$, $\mathrm{G} = 1$.

Figures 9.4.4 and 9.4.5 correspond to strong gravitational fields (G=1000).

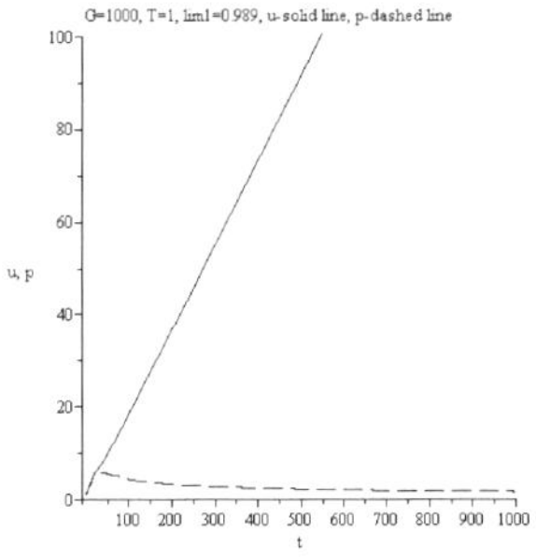

Fig. 9.4.4. Evolution of $\tilde{u}(\tilde{r})$, $\tilde{p}(\tilde{r})$; $\tilde{\tau} = 1$, $\mathrm{G} = 1000$.

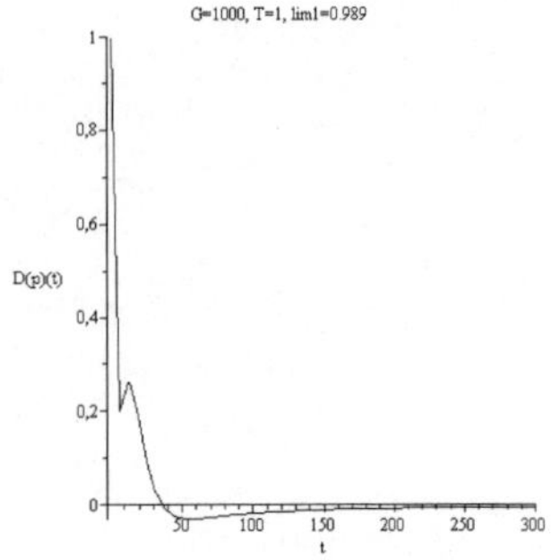

Fig. 9.4.5. Evolution of $\widetilde{F}(\widetilde{r}) = \partial\widetilde{p}(\widetilde{r})/\partial\widetilde{r}$; $\widetilde{\tau} = 1$, $\mathrm{G} = 1000$.

The figures 9.4.6 and 9.4.7 reflect the result of modeling for the gravitational field of forces opposite direction.

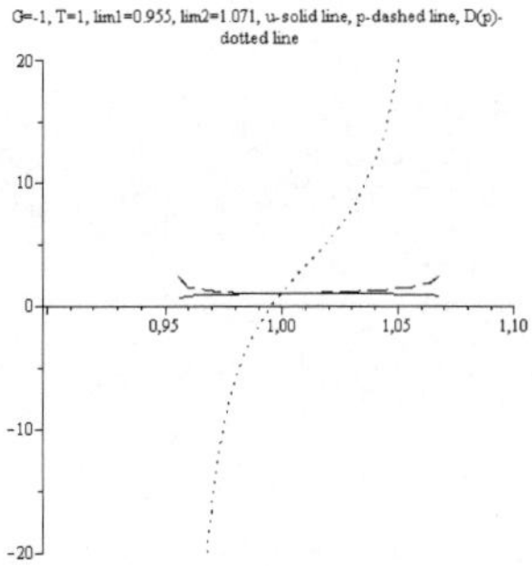

Fig. 9.4.6. Evolution of $\widetilde{u}(\widetilde{r})$, $\widetilde{p}(\widetilde{r})$, $\partial\widetilde{p}(\widetilde{r})/\partial\widetilde{r}$; $\widetilde{\tau} = 1$, $\mathrm{G} = -1$.

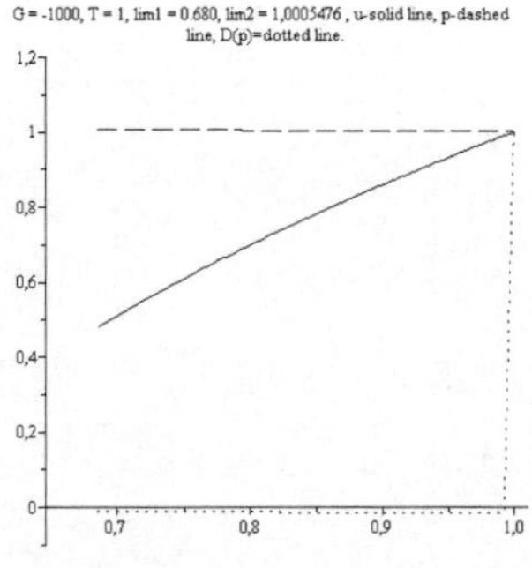

Fig. 9.4.7. Evolution of $\widetilde{u}(\widetilde{r})$, $\widetilde{p}(\widetilde{r})$, $\partial\widetilde{p}(\widetilde{r})/\partial\widetilde{r}$; $\widetilde{\tau} = 1$, $\mathrm{G} = -1000$.

The last figures 9.4.8 - 9.4.10 show the influence of the negative gradients, namely

$$p(1)=1,\ u(1)\leftrightarrow v_{0r}(1)=1,\ D(p)(1)=-1,\ D(u)(1)=-1. \qquad (9.4.6)$$

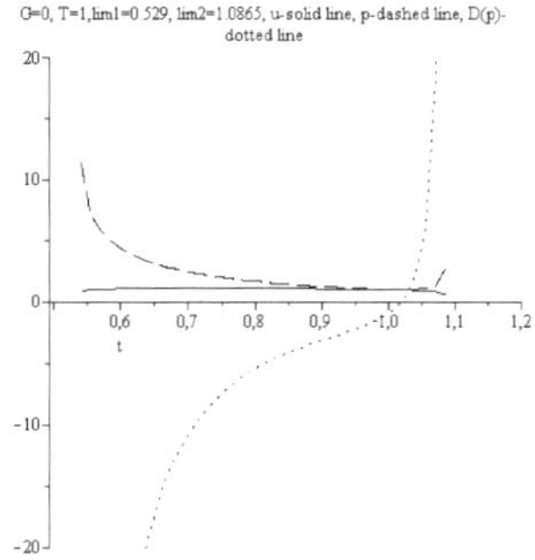

Fig. 9.4.8. Evolution of $\tilde{u}(\tilde{r})$, $\tilde{p}(\tilde{r})$, $\partial\tilde{p}(\tilde{r})/\partial\tilde{r}$; $\tilde{\tau}=1$, G = 0.

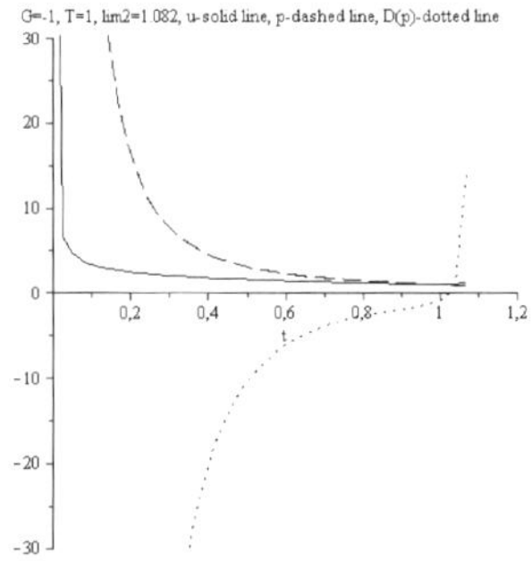

Fig. 9.4.10. Evolution of $\tilde{u}(\tilde{r})$, $\tilde{p}(\tilde{r})$, $\partial\tilde{p}(\tilde{r})/\partial\tilde{r}$; $\tilde{\tau}=1$, G = −1.

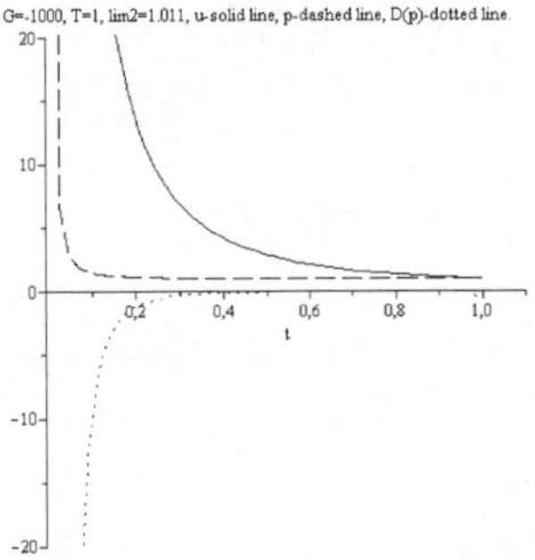

Fig. 9.4.11. Evolution of $\tilde{u}(\tilde{r}),\ \tilde{p}(\tilde{r}),\ \partial\tilde{p}(\tilde{r})/\partial\tilde{r}$; $\tilde{\tau}=1$, $\mathrm{G}=-1000$.

As we see from figures 9.4.1 - 9.4.3 diminishing of parameter τ leads to the significant reconstruction of the integral curves - typical effect of the theory differential equations with the small parameter in front of the senior derivatives. The other important effect - in many cases the perturbation on the surface leads to the PV-object reconstruction only in a narrow domain near the mentioned surface.

9.5. Semi-analytic solutions in the nonlocal theory with gravitation

Let us write down the system of equations (9.1.16), (9.1.19) and (9.1.42) for the limit case of the large radius. We find

$$\tilde{F}_r = \frac{\partial\tilde{p}}{\partial\tilde{r}}, \tag{9.5.1}$$

$$\frac{\partial}{\partial\tilde{r}}\left[3\tilde{p}\frac{\partial\tilde{v}_{0r}}{\partial\tilde{r}}+\tilde{v}_{0r}\frac{\partial\tilde{p}}{\partial\tilde{r}}\right]=0, \tag{9.5.2}$$

$$5\tilde{p}\frac{\partial\tilde{v}_{0r}}{\partial\tilde{r}}+3\tilde{v}_{0r}\frac{\partial\tilde{p}}{\partial\tilde{r}}-\tilde{\tau}\frac{\partial}{\partial\tilde{r}}\left\{5\tilde{v}_{0r}^{2}\frac{\partial\tilde{p}}{\partial\tilde{r}}+16\tilde{p}\tilde{v}_{0r}\frac{\partial\tilde{v}_{0r}}{\partial\tilde{r}}-5\tilde{p}\tilde{g}_r\right\}+4\tilde{\tau}\tilde{v}_{0r}\frac{\partial\tilde{p}}{\partial\tilde{r}}\frac{\partial\tilde{v}_{0r}}{\partial\tilde{r}}=0. \tag{9.5.3}$$

After integration of (9.5.2) we find

$$3\tilde{p}\frac{\partial\tilde{v}_{0r}}{\partial\tilde{r}}+\tilde{v}_{0r}\frac{\partial\tilde{p}}{\partial\tilde{r}}=0 \tag{9.5.4}$$

or

$$\tilde{v}_{0r}^{3}\tilde{p}=C. \tag{9.5.5}$$

Using (9.5.4) we have from (9.5.3)

$$2\frac{\partial}{\partial\tilde{r}}(\tilde{p}\tilde{v}_{0r})-\tilde{\tau}\frac{\partial}{\partial\tilde{r}}\left\{\tilde{p}\tilde{v}_{0r}\frac{\partial\tilde{v}_{0r}}{\partial\tilde{r}}-5\tilde{p}\tilde{g}_r\right\}+4\tilde{\tau}\tilde{v}_{0r}\frac{\partial\tilde{p}}{\partial\tilde{r}}\frac{\partial\tilde{v}_{0r}}{\partial\tilde{r}}=0. \tag{9.5.6}$$

The application of the analytic solution (9.5.5) obtains

$$2\frac{\partial}{\partial \tilde{r}}\frac{1}{\tilde{v}_{0r}^{2}}-\tilde{\tau}\frac{\partial}{\partial \tilde{r}}\left\{\frac{1}{\tilde{v}_{0r}^{2}}\frac{\partial \tilde{v}_{0r}}{\partial \tilde{r}}-5\frac{1}{\tilde{v}_{0r}^{3}}\tilde{g}_{r}\right\}+4\tilde{\tau}\tilde{v}_{0r}\frac{\partial \tilde{v}_{0r}}{\partial \tilde{r}}\frac{\partial}{\partial \tilde{r}}\frac{1}{\tilde{v}_{0r}^{3}}=0. \tag{9.5.7}$$

or

$$\tilde{\tau}\tilde{v}_{0r}^{2}\frac{\partial^{2}\tilde{v}_{0r}}{\partial \tilde{r}^{2}}+\left(4\tilde{v}_{0r}+15\tilde{\tau}\tilde{g}_{r}+10\tilde{\tau}\tilde{v}_{0r}\left(\frac{\partial \tilde{v}_{0r}}{\partial \tilde{r}}\right)\right)\frac{\partial \tilde{v}_{0r}}{\partial \tilde{r}}-5\tilde{\tau}\tilde{v}_{0r}\frac{\partial \tilde{g}_{r}}{\partial \tilde{r}}=0. \tag{9.5.8}$$

Let us use the dependence $\tilde{g}(\tilde{r})$ in the form

$$\tilde{g}(\tilde{r})=\frac{G}{\tilde{r}^{2}}. \tag{9.5.9}$$

In this case

$$\tilde{\tau}\tilde{v}_{0r}^{2}\frac{\partial^{2}\tilde{v}_{0r}}{\partial \tilde{r}^{2}}+\left(4\tilde{v}_{0r}+10\tilde{\tau}\tilde{v}_{0r}\left(\frac{\partial \tilde{v}_{0r}}{\partial \tilde{r}}\right)-15\tilde{\tau}\frac{G}{\tilde{r}^{2}}\right)\frac{\partial \tilde{v}_{0r}}{\partial \tilde{r}}-10\tilde{\tau}\tilde{v}_{0r}\frac{G}{\tilde{r}^{3}}=0. \tag{9.5.10}$$

The ordinary differential equation (9.5.10) can be easily integrated by numerical way. Let us show some corresponding results using for example the Cauchy conditions

$$\tilde{v}_{0r}(1)=1,\ \frac{\partial \tilde{v}_{0r}}{\partial \tilde{r}}(1)=1. \tag{9.5.11}$$

Figures 9.5.1 - 9.5.11 reflect the result of numerical calculations as the Maple application.

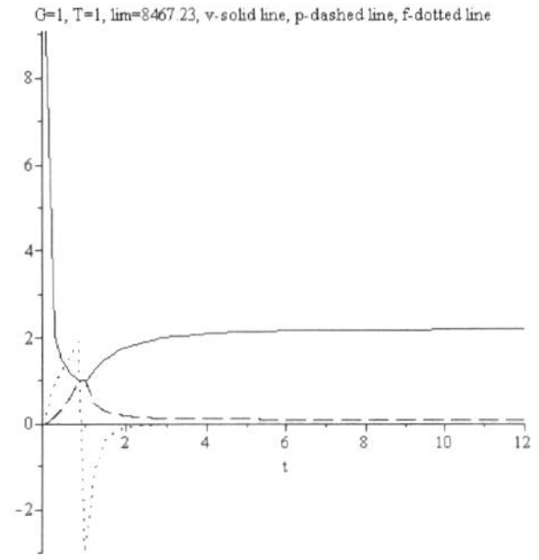

Fig. 9.5.1. Dependence $\tilde{v}(\tilde{r})$, $\tilde{p}(\tilde{r})$, $\tilde{F}(\tilde{r})$, $G=1$, $\tilde{\tau}=1$.

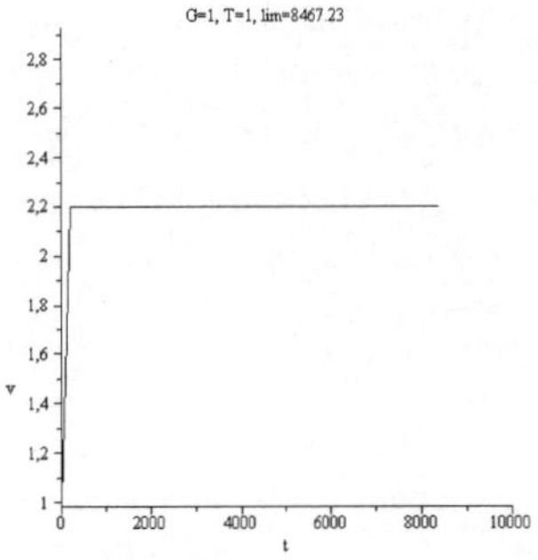

Fig. 9.5.2. Dependence $\tilde{v}(\tilde{r})$, $G=1$, $\tilde{\tau}=1$.

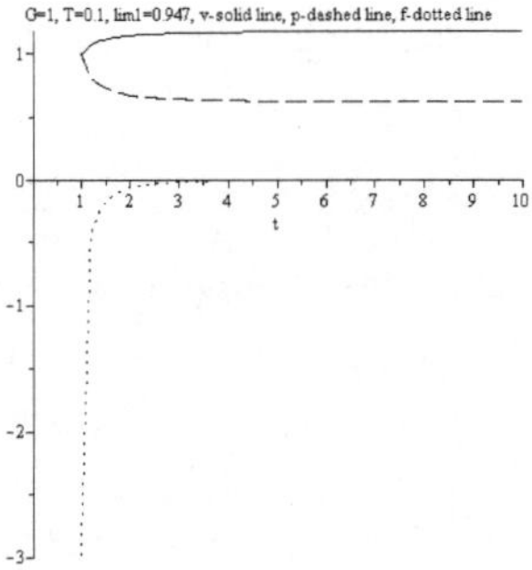

Fig. 9.5.3. Dependence $\tilde{v}(\tilde{r})$, $\tilde{p}(\tilde{r})$, $\tilde{F}(\tilde{r})$, $G=1$, $\tilde{\tau}=0.1$.

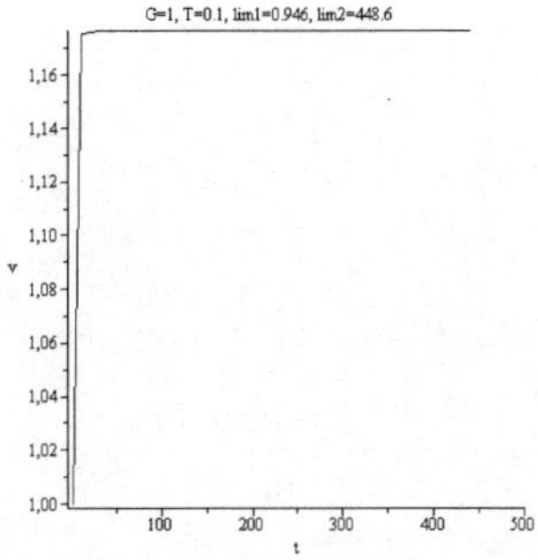

Fig. 9.5.4. Dependence $\tilde{v}(\tilde{r})$, $G=1$, $\tilde{\tau}=0.1$.

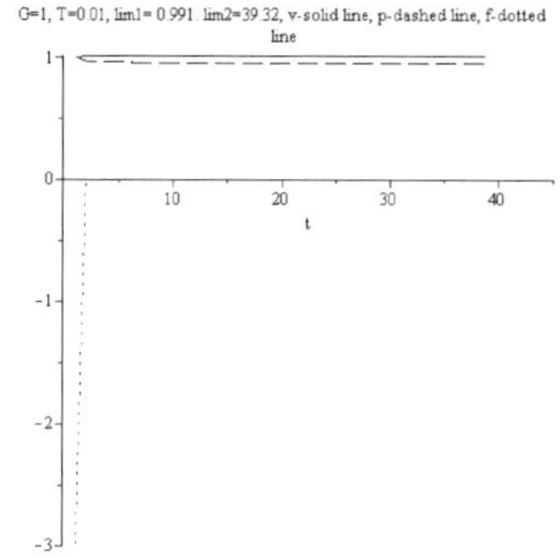

Fig.9.5.5. Dependence $\widetilde{v}(\widetilde{r})$, $\widetilde{p}(\widetilde{r})$, $\widetilde{F}(\widetilde{r})$, $G=1$, $\widetilde{\tau}=0.1$.

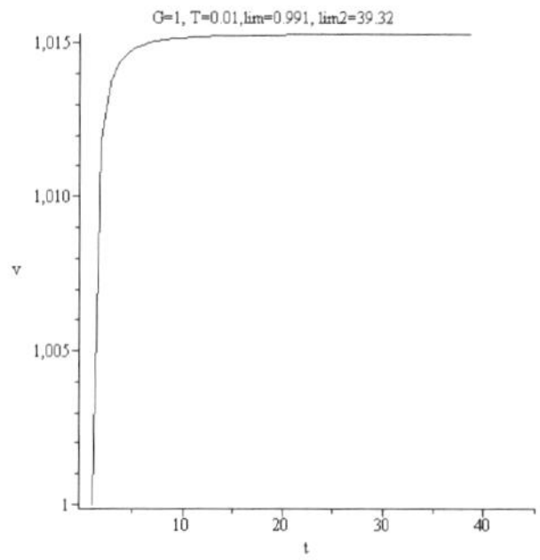

Fig. 9.5.6. Dependence $\widetilde{v}(\widetilde{r})$, $G=1$, $\widetilde{\tau}=0.01$.

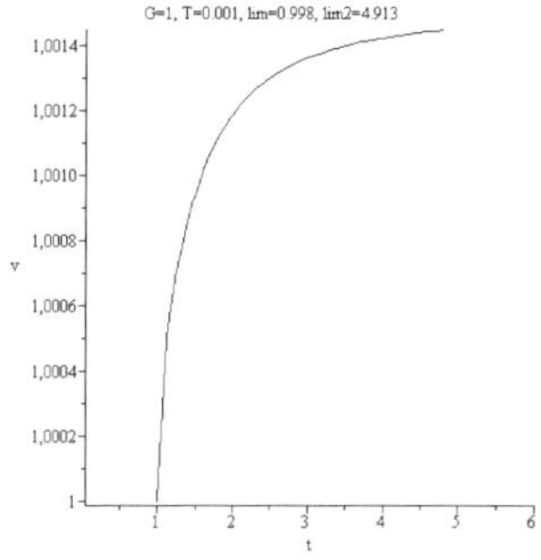

Fig. 9.5.7. Dependence $\widetilde{v}(\widetilde{r})$, $G=1$, $\widetilde{\tau}=0.001$.

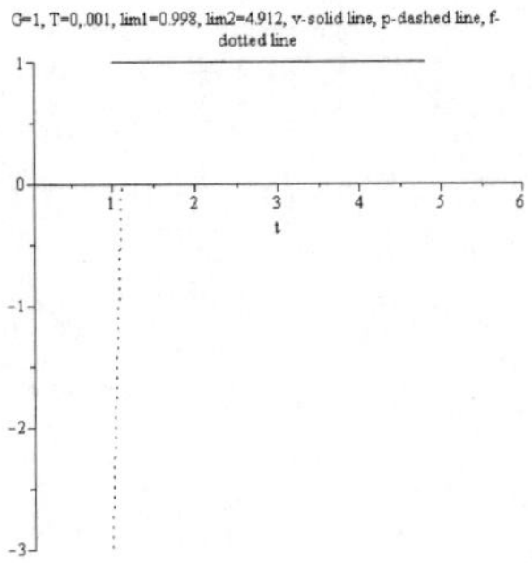

Fig. 9.5.8. Dependence $\tilde{v}(\tilde{r})$, $\tilde{p}(\tilde{r})$, $\tilde{F}(\tilde{r})$, $G = 1$, $\tilde{\tau} = 0.001$.

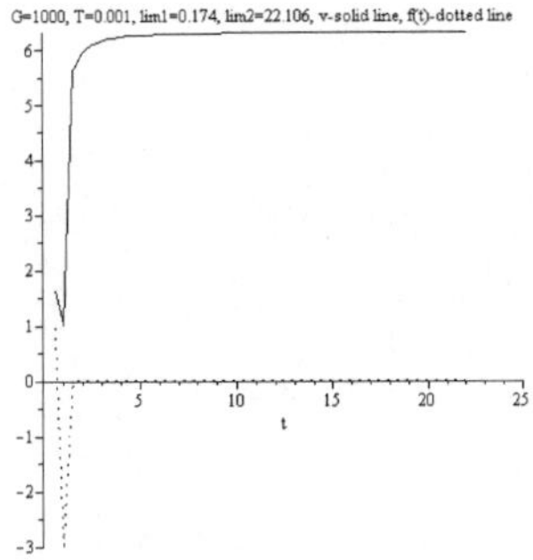

Fig. 9.5.9. Dependence $\tilde{v}(\tilde{r})$, $\tilde{F}(\tilde{r})$, $G = 1000$, $\tilde{\tau} = 0.001$.

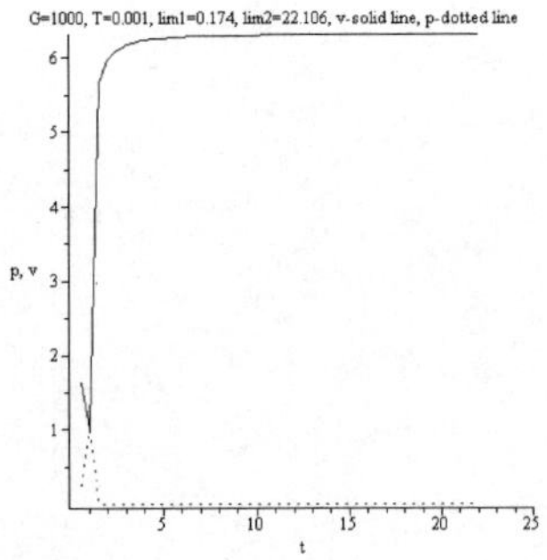

Fig. 9.5.10. Dependence $\tilde{v}(\tilde{r})$, $\tilde{p}(\tilde{r})$, $G = 1000$, $\tilde{\tau} = 0.001$.

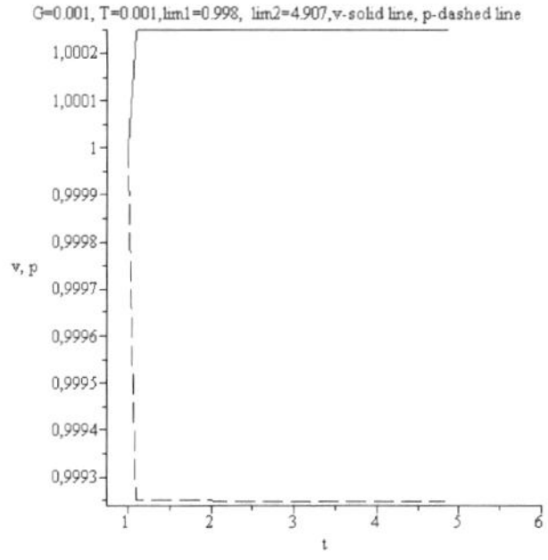

Fig. 9.5.11. Dependence $\tilde{v}(\tilde{r})$, $\tilde{p}(\tilde{r})$, $G = 1000$, $\tilde{\tau} = 0.001$.

If the external gravitational field does not exist we have from (9.5.10)

$$\tilde{\tau}\tilde{v}_{0r}^2 \frac{\partial^2 \tilde{v}_{0r}}{\partial \tilde{r}^2} + \left(4\tilde{v}_{0r} + 10\tilde{\tau}\tilde{v}_{0r}\left(\frac{\partial \tilde{v}_{0r}}{\partial \tilde{r}}\right)\right)\frac{\partial \tilde{v}_{0r}}{\partial \tilde{r}} = 0. \qquad (9.5.12)$$

Apart of the particular solution $\tilde{v}_{0r} = const$ this equation has the general analytical solution via W-Lambert function which leads to unique solution of the equation in the considered conditions. But simpler to use the numerical methods. The following figures 9.5.12 and 9.5.13 reflect the calculations for different $\tilde{\tau}$.

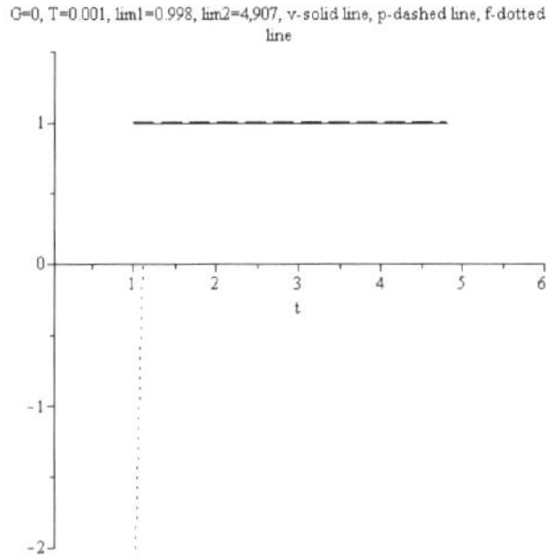

Fig. 9.5.12. Dependence $\tilde{v}(\tilde{r})$, $\tilde{p}(\tilde{r})$, $\tilde{F}(\tilde{r})$, $G = 0$, $\tilde{\tau} = 0.001$.

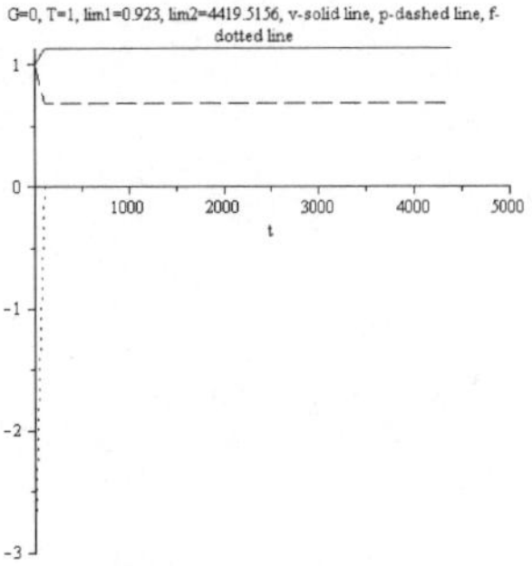

Fig. 9.5.13. Dependence $\tilde{v}(\tilde{r})$, $\tilde{p}(\tilde{r})$, $\tilde{F}(\tilde{r})$, $G = 0$, $\tilde{\tau} = 1$.

Conclusion:

1. Known dependence $\tilde{v}(\tilde{r})$ realizes immediately the calculation $\tilde{p}(\tilde{r})$ using (9.5.5) and $\tilde{F}_r$ using (9.5.1).
2. All mentioned calculations lead to so to speak "volume quantization" - the solutions exist only in the finite domain of space.
3. The linear size of these domains is diminishing with the $\tilde{\tau}$ diminishing. The figure captions include the boundaries of the solution existence. It means that the nonlocal theory leads to the explosion of object which size is significantly less than the size of the visible Universe.

9.6. To the theory of PV-engines

Let us discuss now from the position of the developed theory the situation with the so called "EM Drive". This (hypothetical) engine was invented by British scientist Roger Shawyer in 1999 [164, 165]. The principal scheme of this EM Drive can be shown as follows (Fig. 9.6.1):

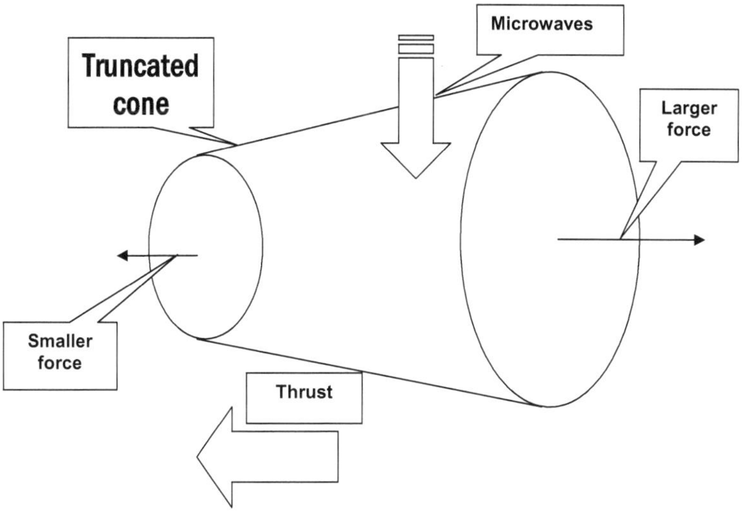

Fig. 9.6.1. Principal scheme of EM Drive.

Shawyer's testing was done on a torsion balance using air bearings ([166], see also [167, 168]). He observed rotation of the complete apparatus with all electronics and power supplies on-board. He discovered that the thrust (close to 5600 times) larger (Q-factor) than expected from pure classical radiation thrust. Q-factor can be defined by different way but in the general case Q ~ (maximum energy stored / power loss). Independent tests were carried out in China by Yang et al [166, 167] who tested the EMDrive on a force-feedback thrust stand and achieved up to 720 mN of thrust with 1000 W microwave power with even higher Q factors compared to Shawyer.

The typical parameters of following White's experiments [169, 170] are as follows. The RF resonance test article is a copper frustum with an inner diameter of 27.9 cm on the big end, an inner diameter of 15.9 cm on the small end, and an axial length of 22.9 cm. The vacuum test campaign consisted of a forward thrust phase and reverse thrust phase at less than 8×10^{-6} torr vacuum with power scans at 40, 60, and 80W. The test campaign included a null thrust test effort to identify any mundane sources of impulsive thrust; however, none were identified. Thrust data from forward, reverse, and null suggested that the system was consistently performing with a thrust-to-power ratio of 1.2 ± 0.1mN/kW.

The test article contains a 5.4-cm-thick disk of polyethylene with an outer diameter of 15.6 cm that is mounted to the inside face of the smaller diameter end of the frustum. A 13.5-mm-diam loop antenna drives the system in the TM212 mode at 1937 MHz. Because there are no analytical solutions for the resonant modes of a truncated cone, the use of the term TM212 describes a mode with two nodes in the axial direction and four nodes in the azimuthal direction. A small whip antenna provides feedback to the phase-locked loop (PLL) system. The steady-state displacement from the calibration force is used to calibrate any force applied to the torsion pendulum by a device under pendulum.

The usual comment for the thrust appearance in this construction sounds as follows. The EM Drive uses electromagnetic waves as “fuel”, creating thrust by bouncing microwave photons back and forth inside a cone-shaped closed metal cavity. In other words, electricity converts into microwaves within the cavity that push against the inside of the device, causing the thruster to accelerate in the opposite direction.

Obviously this explanation has no attitude to reality. The nozzle of this “jet engine” is closed by a round plate. It means that the formulated explanation leads to the contradiction with the Newton's Third Law, which states, "To each action there's an equal and opposite reaction," and many physicists say the EM Drive categorically violates that law. From the position of classical mechanics this corresponds to the attempt of Baron Münchhausen to pull itself out of the swamp by his own hair. In order for a thruster to gain momentum in a certain direction, it has to expel some kind of propellant or exhaust in the opposite direction. But the EM Drive knows nothing about the law of conservation of momentum, which Newton derived from his Third Law.

Since its invention, the EM Drive was tested many times and reveals “anomalous thrust signals”. Putting it mildly, we can say - if EM Drive indeed produces thrust we should find the corresponding explanation for this effect.

In this case I should define my position in connection with the mentioned problem:

1. Appearance of thrust in the systems like EM Drive does not contradict the conclusions following from nonlocal physics.
2. The emergence of the thrust is due to the interaction of radiation with physical vacuum.
3. It is impossible to provide an explanation of the effect using methods of local physics.

4. Then no reason to discuss other theoretical models originated by local physics.
5. We do not intend to go into details of the experiment organization including the possible experimental errors. For us it is interesting only the correspondence between theoretical and experimental data in basic experiments.
6. Here we indicated only some main stages of the vast experimental researches.
7. In reality EM Drive is only one from possible realizations of PV-engines, engines using the energy of physical vacuum.

Let us consider now the process of excitation of physical vacuum by radiation. It is known that the first experiments demonstrating the direct light pressure on a surface (including gases) were realized by P.N. Lebedev [171]. Then when light impinges on the surface of a liquid, part of the light is reflected (with the reflection coefficient χ) and the remaining fraction is transmitted. The new experiments show for the first time that the liquid surface bends inward, meaning that the light is pushing on the fluid in agreement with the Abraham momentum p_A of light. The corresponding equation for the photon momentum in a dielectric with refractive index n is:

$$p_A = \frac{h\nu}{nc} \quad , \tag{9.6.1}$$

where h is the Plank constant, ν is the frequency of the light and c is the speed of light in vacuum. Light pressure can be found by the formula

$$p_r = \frac{\Phi_r}{c}(\chi + 1), \tag{9.6.2}$$

where Φ_r is the density of radiation energy flux falling on a surface, for the mirror surface $\chi = 1$. For the state close to thermodynamic equilibrium we have

$$p_r = \frac{u}{3}, \tag{9.6.3}$$

where u is the energy density.

As before we consider the limit case $\rho \to 0$ corresponding to transfer to Physical Vacuum in 1D case. For our aims is sufficient to use the plane model (for example this case correspond the spherical wave front of the large radius). Then for the flat case $r \to \infty$ we have the following system (SYSTEM PV) of the dimensionless equations defining the PV evolution (see also (9.1.4), (9.1.14) and (9.1.45))

(continuum equation)

$$\frac{\partial \tilde{p}}{\partial \tilde{x}} = \tilde{F}_x, \tag{9.6.4}$$

(momentum equation)

$$\frac{\partial p}{\partial x}-F-\frac{\partial}{\partial t}\left\{\tau\left[\frac{\partial p}{\partial x}-F\right]\right\}-2\tau\left[\frac{\partial p}{\partial x}-F\right]\frac{\partial u}{\partial x}-\frac{\partial}{\partial x}\left\{\tau\left[\frac{\partial p}{\partial t}+3p\frac{\partial u}{\partial x}+u\frac{\partial p}{\partial x}\right]\right\}=0. \tag{9.6.5}$$

After using (9.6.4) one obtains

$$\frac{\partial}{\partial x}\left\{\tau\left[\frac{\partial p}{\partial t}+3p\frac{\partial u}{\partial x}+u\frac{\partial p}{\partial x}\right]\right\}=0. \tag{9.6.6}$$

or

$$\frac{\partial p}{\partial t}+3p\frac{\partial u}{\partial x}+u\frac{\partial p}{\partial x}=0; \tag{9.6.7}$$

(energy equation, see also (9.1.45))

$$\begin{aligned}&3\frac{\partial p}{\partial t}+5p\frac{\partial u}{\partial x}+3u\frac{\partial p}{\partial x}+2u\left(\frac{\partial p}{\partial x}-F_x\right)-\\&-\frac{\partial}{\partial t}\left\{\tau\left[3\frac{\partial p}{\partial t}+3u\frac{\partial p}{\partial x}+5p\frac{\partial u}{\partial x}+2u\left(\frac{\partial p}{\partial x}-F_x\right)\right]\right\}-\\&-\frac{\partial}{\partial x}\left\{\tau\left[5\frac{\partial}{\partial t}(pu)+16pu\frac{\partial u}{\partial x}+5u^2\frac{\partial p}{\partial x}+3u^2\left(\frac{\partial p}{\partial x}-F_x\right)\right]\right\}+A^{pert}=0\end{aligned} \tag{9.6.8}$$

Using (9.6.4) we reach

$$\begin{aligned}&3\frac{\partial p}{\partial t}+3u\frac{\partial p}{\partial x}+5p\frac{\partial u}{\partial x}-\frac{\partial}{\partial t}\left\{\tau\left[3\frac{\partial p}{\partial t}+3u\frac{\partial p}{\partial x}+5p\frac{\partial u}{\partial x}\right]\right\}\\&-\frac{\partial}{\partial x}\left\{\tau\left[5\frac{\partial}{\partial t}(pu)+5u\frac{\partial}{\partial x}(pu)+11pu\frac{\partial u}{\partial x}\right]\right\}+A^{pert}=0.\end{aligned} \tag{9.6.9}$$

Let us use (9.6.7) for the transforming of (9.6.9). We have

$$-4p\frac{\partial u}{\partial x}+4\frac{\partial}{\partial t}\left\{\tau p\frac{\partial u}{\partial x}\right\}-\frac{\partial}{\partial x}\left\{\tau\left[5p\frac{\partial u}{\partial t}+pu\frac{\partial u}{\partial x}\right]\right\}=0. \tag{9.6.10}$$

If $\tau=const$ we find

$$4p\frac{\partial u}{\partial x}-4\tau\frac{\partial}{\partial t}\left\{p\frac{\partial u}{\partial x}\right\}+\tau\frac{\partial}{\partial x}\left\{5p\frac{\partial u}{\partial t}+pu\frac{\partial u}{\partial x}\right\}=0 \tag{9.6.11}$$

or

$$4p\frac{\partial u}{\partial x}-4\tau\frac{\partial u}{\partial x}\frac{\partial p}{\partial t}+\tau p\frac{\partial}{\partial x}\left\{\frac{\partial u}{\partial t}\right\}+5\tau\frac{\partial u}{\partial t}\frac{\partial p}{\partial x}+\tau pu\frac{\partial}{\partial x}\left\{\frac{\partial u}{\partial x}\right\}+\tau\frac{\partial u}{\partial x}\frac{\partial}{\partial x}\{pu\}=0. \tag{9.6.12}$$

After dividing on pu one obtains

$$\begin{aligned}&4\frac{1}{u}\frac{\partial u}{\partial x}-4\tau\frac{1}{pu}\frac{\partial u}{\partial x}\frac{\partial p}{\partial t}+\\&+\tau\frac{1}{u}\frac{\partial}{\partial x}\left\{\frac{\partial u}{\partial t}\right\}+5\tau\frac{1}{pu}\frac{\partial u}{\partial t}\frac{\partial p}{\partial x}+\tau\frac{\partial}{\partial x}\left\{\frac{\partial u}{\partial x}\right\}+\tau\frac{\partial u}{\partial x}\frac{1}{pu}\frac{\partial}{\partial x}\{pu\}=0.\end{aligned} \tag{9.6.13}$$

or

$$4\frac{\partial \ln u}{\partial x}-4\tau\frac{\partial \ln u}{\partial x}\frac{\partial \ln p}{\partial t}+5\tau\frac{\partial \ln u}{\partial t}\frac{\partial \ln p}{\partial x}+\tau\frac{\partial u}{\partial x}\frac{\partial}{\partial x}\ln\{pu\}+$$
$$+\tau\frac{1}{u}\frac{\partial}{\partial x}\left\{\frac{\partial u}{\partial t}\right\}+\tau\frac{\partial}{\partial x}\left\{\frac{\partial u}{\partial x}\right\}=0. \qquad (9.6.14)$$

Omitting the small logarithmic terms we reach

$$\frac{1}{u}\frac{\partial}{\partial x}\left\{\frac{\partial u}{\partial t}\right\}+\frac{\partial}{\partial x}\left\{\frac{\partial u}{\partial x}\right\}=0. \qquad (9.6.15)$$

Write down this equation in the dimensionless form introducing the scales, $[x]=L$, $[t]=T$, $[u]=\frac{L}{T}=a$. We have

$$\tilde{u}\frac{\partial^2\tilde{u}}{\partial\tilde{x}^2}+\frac{\partial^2\tilde{u}}{\partial\tilde{x}\partial\tilde{t}}=0. \qquad (9.6.16)$$

Equation (9.6.16) has the following particular solutions

1. $\tilde{u}=const$, and a periodic solutions as travelling wave
2. $\tilde{u}=f(\tilde{z})=f(\tilde{\omega}\tilde{t}\pm\tilde{k}\tilde{x})$. (9.6.17)

Really after differentiating (9.6.17) and substitution in (9.6.16) we have,

$$f(\tilde{z})f_z''(\tilde{z})\tilde{k}^2\pm f_z''(\tilde{z})\tilde{\omega}\tilde{k}=0. \qquad (9.6.18)$$

Obviously the relation (9.6.17) can be satisfied if

$$f_z''(\tilde{z})=0, \qquad (9.6.19)$$

or

$$\tilde{u}(\tilde{x},\tilde{t})=\tilde{u}(\tilde{z})=C_1\tilde{z}+C_2=C_1(\tilde{\omega}\tilde{t}\pm\tilde{k}\tilde{x})+C_2. \qquad (9.6.20)$$

As we see

1. The PV flow from the EM Drive has the character of travelling wave.
2. The flow velocity has no restrictions.
3. The obtained result does not depend on the nonlocal parameter in the first approximation.

Taking into account the previous result, let us consider the PV evolution as an implicit function of t. From (9.6.9) (see also (9.3.35)) follows

$$6\tilde{v}_{0x}\frac{\partial\tilde{p}}{\partial\tilde{x}}+5\tilde{p}\frac{\partial\tilde{v}_{0x}}{\partial\tilde{x}}-\tilde{v}_{0r}\frac{\partial}{\partial\tilde{x}}\left\{\tilde{\tau}\left[6\tilde{v}_{0x}\frac{\partial\tilde{p}}{\partial\tilde{x}}+5\tilde{p}\frac{\partial\tilde{v}_{0x}}{\partial\tilde{x}}\right]\right\}$$
$$-\frac{\partial}{\partial\tilde{x}}\left\{\tilde{\tau}\left[10\tilde{v}_{0x}\frac{\partial}{\partial\tilde{x}}(\tilde{p}\tilde{v}_{0x})+11\tilde{p}\tilde{v}_{0x}\frac{\partial\tilde{v}_{0r}}{\partial\tilde{x}}\right]\right\}+5\frac{\partial}{\partial\tilde{r}}\left[\tilde{\tau}\left(\frac{\tilde{p}}{\tilde{\rho}}\tilde{F}_x-\frac{\partial}{\partial\tilde{r}}\frac{\tilde{p}^2}{\tilde{\rho}}\right)\right]=0. \qquad (9.6.21)$$

Therefore we can introduce in system of equations (9.6.4), (9.6.7) and (9.6.21) an external dimensionless pressure $\tilde{A}^{ex}$. We investigate here the case $\tilde{A}^{ex}=const$. Generally speaking $\tilde{A}^{ex}$ is a function of coordinates and time and should be calculated independently with the help of the Maxwell equations.

As a result (if the mass perturbation can be omitted) we have the "system A":

$$\frac{\partial \tilde{p}}{\partial \tilde{x}} = \tilde{F}_x, \tag{9.6.21}$$

$$3\left(\tilde{p} + \tilde{A}^{ex}\right)\frac{\partial \tilde{u}}{\partial \tilde{x}} + \tilde{u}\,\frac{\partial}{\partial \tilde{x}}\left(\tilde{p} + \tilde{A}^{ex}\right) = 0, \tag{9.6.22}$$

$$\begin{gathered} 6\tilde{v}_{0x}\frac{\partial \tilde{p}}{\partial \tilde{x}} + 5\left(\tilde{p} + \tilde{A}^{ex}\right)\frac{\partial \tilde{v}_{0x}}{\partial \tilde{x}} - \tilde{v}_{0x}\tilde{\tau}\frac{\partial}{\partial \tilde{x}}\left[6\tilde{v}_{0x}\frac{\partial \tilde{p}}{\partial \tilde{x}} + 5\left(\tilde{p} + \tilde{A}^{ex}\right)\frac{\partial \tilde{v}_{0x}}{\partial \tilde{x}}\right] \\ -\tilde{\tau}\frac{\partial}{\partial \tilde{x}}\left[10\tilde{v}_{0x}\frac{\partial}{\partial \tilde{x}}\left(\left(\tilde{p} + \tilde{A}^{ex}\right)\tilde{v}_{0x}\right) + 11\left(\tilde{p} + \tilde{A}^{ex}\right)\tilde{v}_{0x}\frac{\partial \tilde{v}_{0x}}{\partial \tilde{x}}\right] = 0. \end{gathered} \tag{9.6.23}$$

Now we are ready to display the results of the mathematical modeling realized with the help of Maple (the versions Maple 9 or more can be used). The system A of equations (9.6.21) – (9.6.23) has the great possibilities of mathematical modeling as result of changing of four Cauchy conditions and parameters $\tilde{\tau}$ and $\tilde{A}^{ex}$ describing the character features of physical system.

Maple program contains Maple's notations – for example the expression $D(\tilde{v}_{0x})(0) = 0$ means in the usual notations $(\partial \tilde{v}_{0x} / \partial \tilde{x})(0) = 0$, independent variable t responds to $\tilde{x}$. The following Maple notations on figures are used: u- velocity $\tilde{v}_{0x}$, p - pressure $\tilde{p}$, and f- the self consistent force $\tilde{F}$, A - $\tilde{A}^{ex}$. Explanations placed under all following figures. The results of the calculations are presented in figures 9.6.2 - 9.6.25. The information required is contained in the figures and in figure captions. We use for all calculations the Cauchy conditions

$$\tilde{v}_{0x}(0) = 1,\ \tilde{p}(0) = 1,\ D(\tilde{v}_{0x})(0) = 1,\ D(\tilde{p})(0) = 1 \rightarrow f(0) = 1,$$

which of course can be changed; parameter $\tilde{A}$ varies widely. As a rule we use the following lines: $\tilde{v}_{0x}$ - solid line, $\tilde{p}$ - dashed line, $\tilde{F}$ - dotted line.

Remarks:

1. If $D(\tilde{v}_{0x})(0) = 0,\ D(\tilde{p})(0) = 0$ and $\tilde{A}^{ex} = const$, we have only trivial solutions $\tilde{v}_{0x} = const,\ \tilde{p} = const$. Conditions $D(\tilde{v}_{0x})(0) \neq 0,\ D(\tilde{p})(0) \neq 0$ deliver the appearance of non trivial solutions even if the mass perturbation $A^{pert} = 0$.
2. The figures 9.6.2 - 9.6.4 are constructed for the case when the external field is absent. The left boundary of the solution existence (lim1) is indicated.
3. The following figures 9.6.5 - 9.6.17 are constructed for conditions $\tilde{v}_{0x}(0) = 1,\ \tilde{p}(0) = 1,\ D(\tilde{v}_{0x})(0) = 1,\ D(\tilde{p})(0) = 1$ but for the parameter $\tilde{A}^{ex}$ changing in the interval $(10,\ 10^4)$. Captions like lim1 reflect the domain of the solution existence.

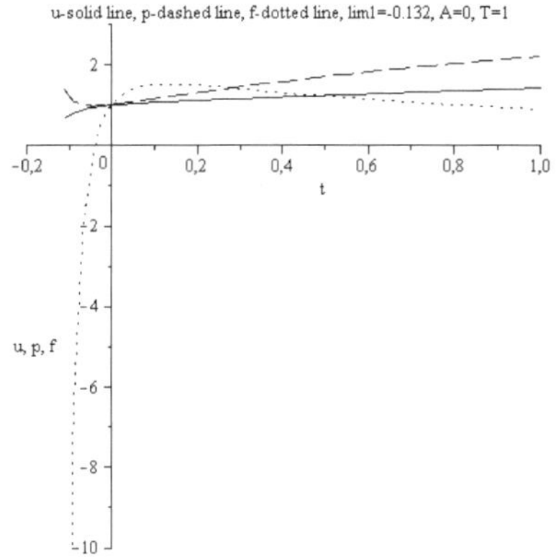

Fig. 9.6.2. Evolution of $\widetilde{v}_{0x}(\widetilde{x}),\ \widetilde{p}(\widetilde{x}),\ \widetilde{F}(\widetilde{x});\ \widetilde{A}^{ex}=0,\ \widetilde{\tau}=1.$

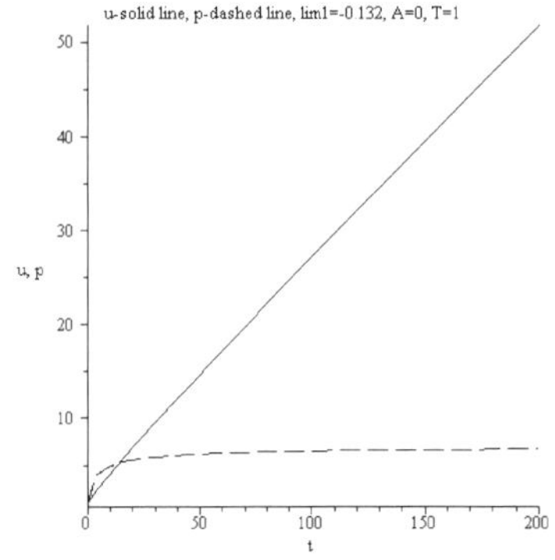

Fig.9.6.3. Evolution of $\widetilde{v}_{0x}(\widetilde{x}),\ \widetilde{p}(\widetilde{x});\widetilde{A}^{ex}=0,\ \widetilde{\tau}=1.$

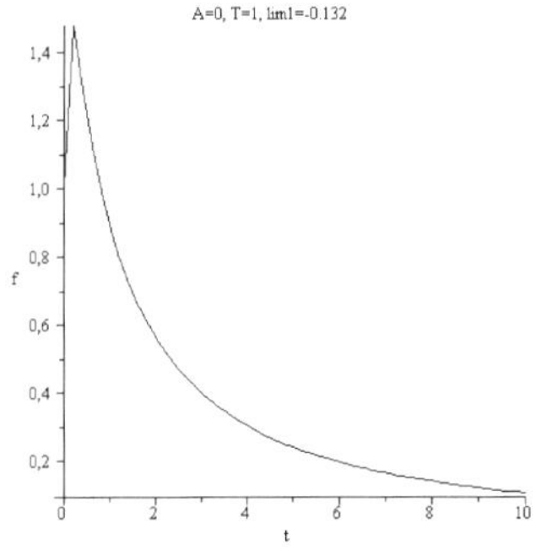

Fig. 9.6.4. Evolution of $\widetilde{F}(\widetilde{x});\widetilde{A}^{ex}=0,\ \widetilde{\tau}=1.$

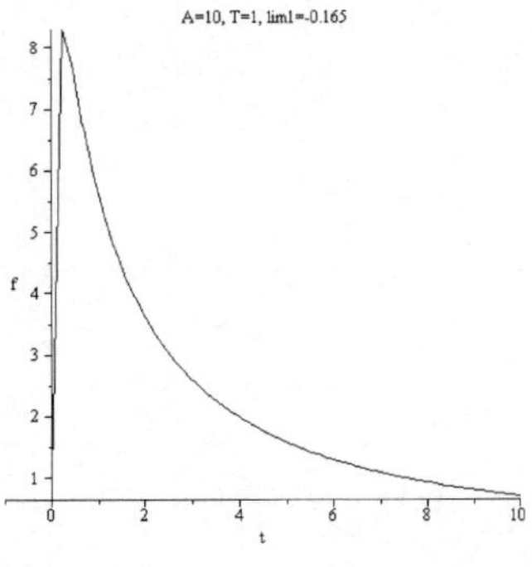

Fig. 9.6.5. Evolution of $\widetilde{F}(\widetilde{x})$; $\widetilde{A}^{ex}=10$, $\widetilde{\tau}=1$.

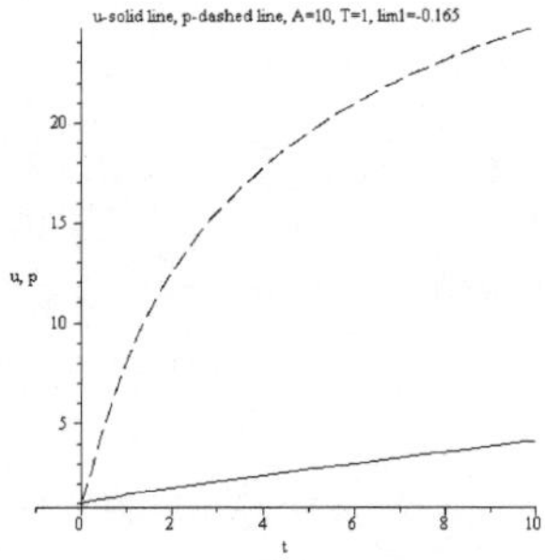

Fig. 9.6.6. Evolution of $\widetilde{v}_{0x}(\widetilde{x})$, $\widetilde{p}(\widetilde{x})$; $\widetilde{A}^{ex}=10$, $\widetilde{\tau}=1$.

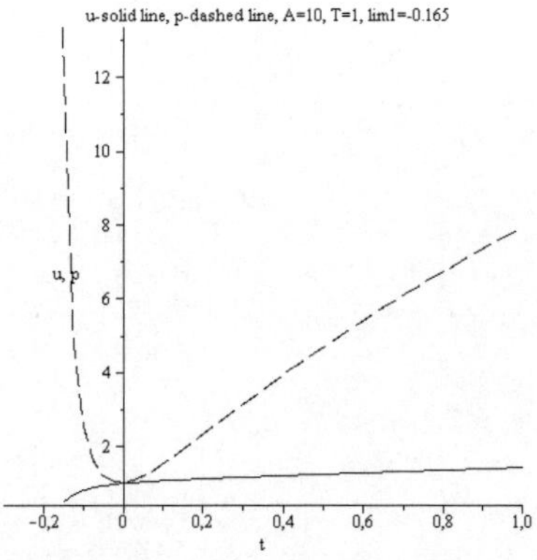

Fig. 9.6.7. Evolution of $\widetilde{v}_{0x}(\widetilde{x})$, $\widetilde{p}(\widetilde{x})$; $\widetilde{A}^{ex}=10$, $\widetilde{\tau}=1$.

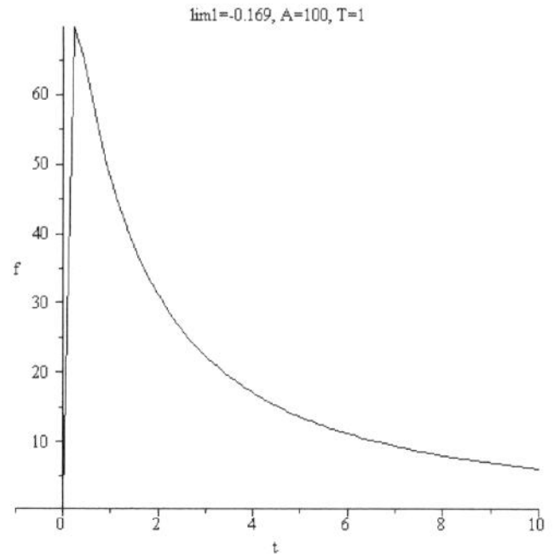

Fig. 9.6.8. Evolution of $\widetilde{F}(\widetilde{x})$; $\widetilde{A}^{ex}=100$, $\widetilde{\tau}=1$.

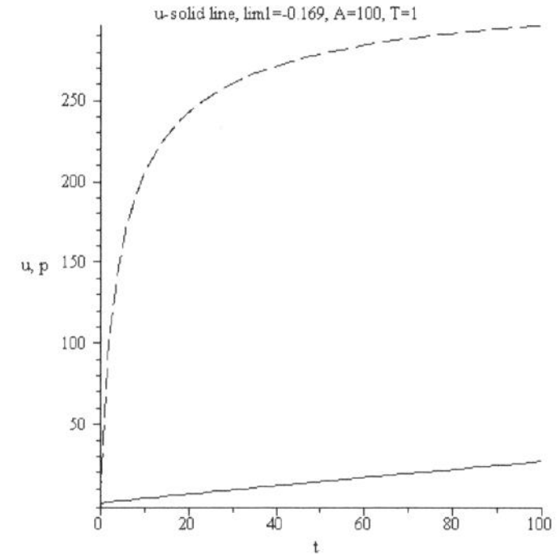

Fig. 9.6.9. Evolution of $\widetilde{v}_{0x}(\widetilde{x})$, $\widetilde{p}(\widetilde{x})$; $\widetilde{A}^{ex}=100$, $\widetilde{\tau}=1$.

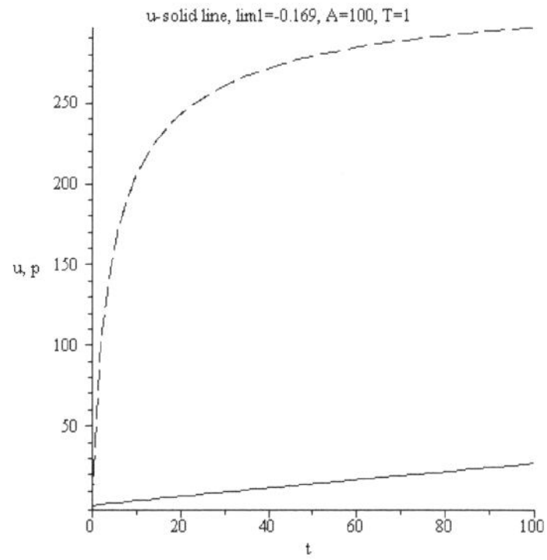

Fig. 9.6.10. Evolution of $\widetilde{v}_{0x}(\widetilde{x})$, $\widetilde{p}(\widetilde{x})$; $\widetilde{A}^{ex}=100$, $\widetilde{\tau}=1$.

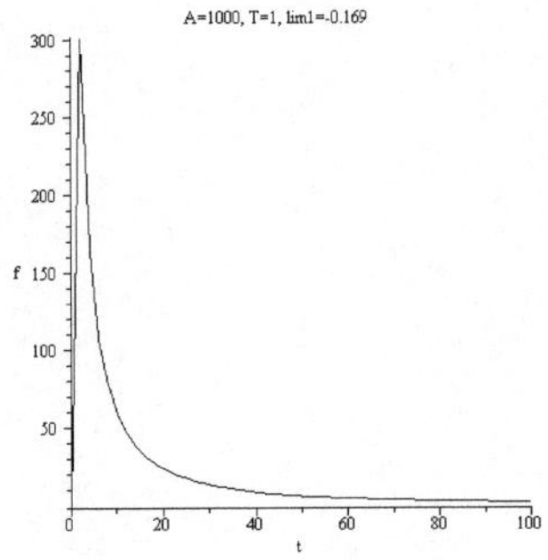

Fig. 9.6.11. Evolution of $\widetilde{F}(\widetilde{x})$; $\widetilde{A}^{ex} = 1000$, $\widetilde{\tau} = 1$.

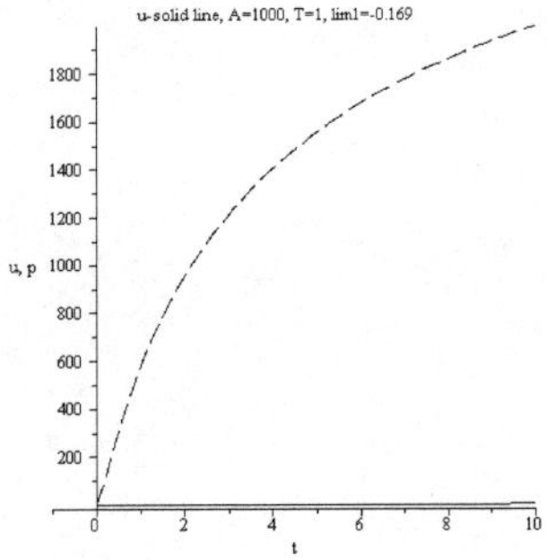

Fig. 9.6.12. Evolution of $\widetilde{v}_{0x}(\widetilde{x})$, $\widetilde{p}(\widetilde{x})$; $\widetilde{A}^{ex} = 1000$, $\widetilde{\tau} = 1$.

Figures 9.6.13 - 9.6.15 reflect the calculations for the $\widetilde{x}$ intervals (-0.5 - 2), (0 - 10), (0 - 100) correspondingly

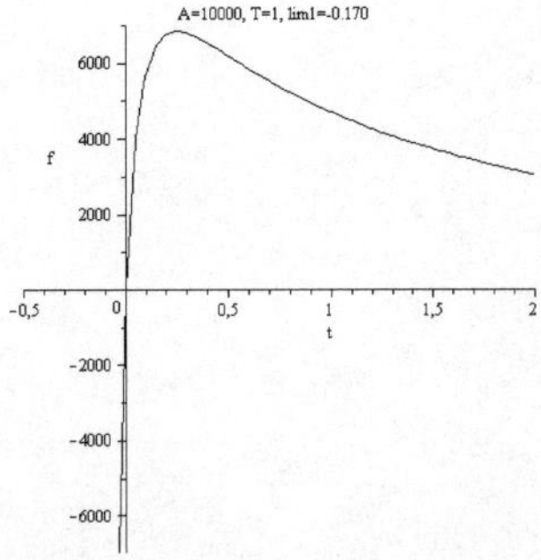

Fig. 9.6.13. Evolution of $\widetilde{F}(\widetilde{x})$; $\widetilde{A}^{ex} = 10^4$, $\widetilde{\tau} = 1$.

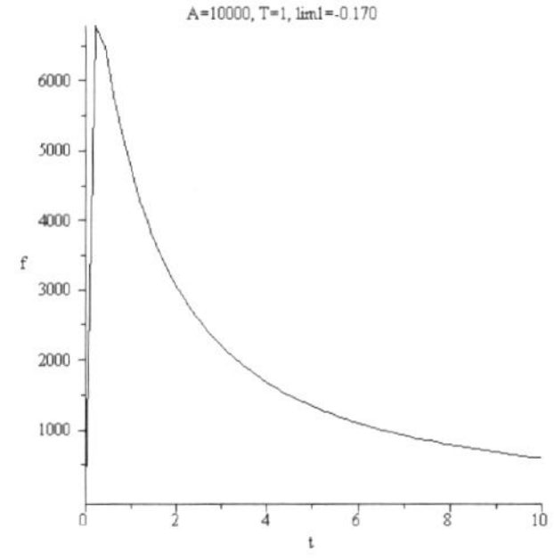

Fig. 9.6.14. Evolution of $\widetilde{F}(\widetilde{x})$; $\widetilde{A}^{ex} = 10^4$, $\widetilde{\tau} = 1$.

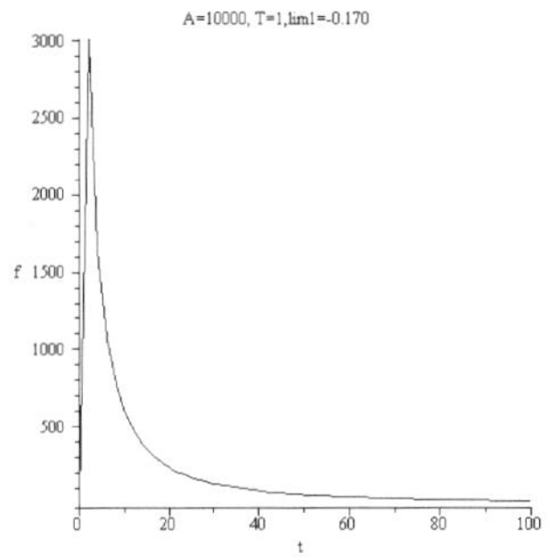

Fig. 9.6.15. Evolution of $\widetilde{F}(\widetilde{x})$; $\widetilde{A}^{ex} = 10^4$, $\widetilde{\tau} = 1$.

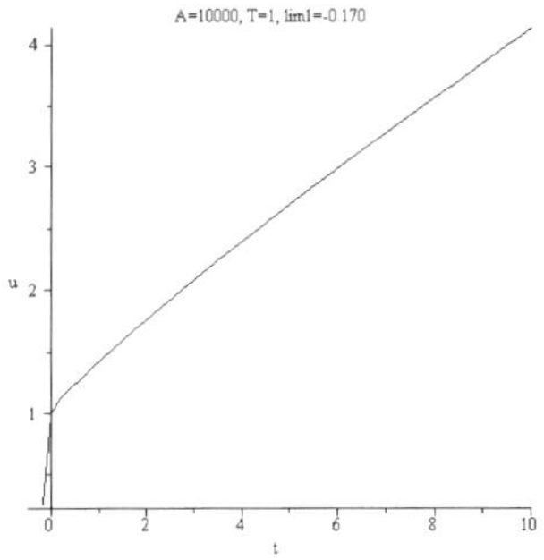

Fig. 9.6.16. Evolution of $\widetilde{v}_{0x}(\widetilde{x})$; $\widetilde{A}^{ex} = 10^4$, $\widetilde{\tau} = 1$.

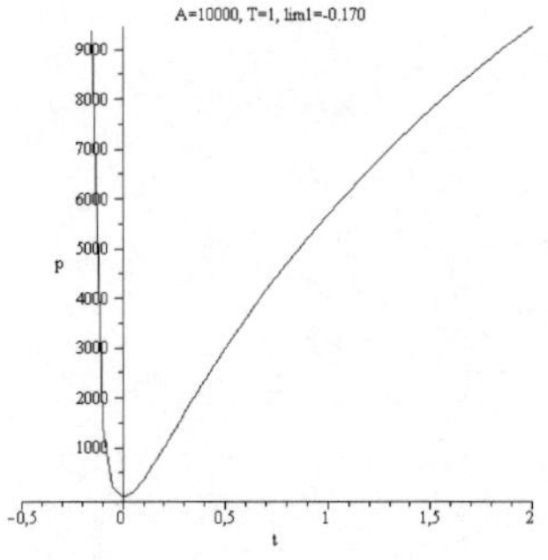

Fig. 9.6.17. Evolution of $\widetilde{p}(\widetilde{x})$; $\widetilde{A}^{ex} = 10^4$, $\widetilde{\tau} = 1$.

Important to notice that for all cases reflected in figures 9.6.2 -9.6.17 we have the physical modes with a predominance of so called "anti-gravity"; but a narrow domain with usual gravitation is also presented.

The following figures 9.6.18 - 9.6.25 reflect the hypothetical situation when $\widetilde{A} < 0$.

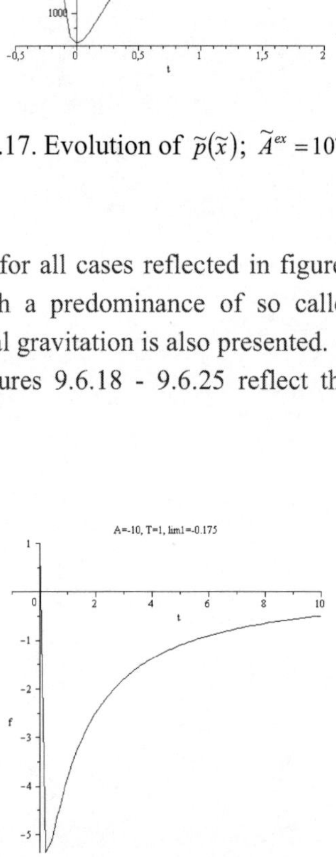

Fig. 9.6.18. Evolution of $\widetilde{F}(\widetilde{x})$; $\widetilde{A}^{ex} = -10$, $\widetilde{\tau} = 1$.

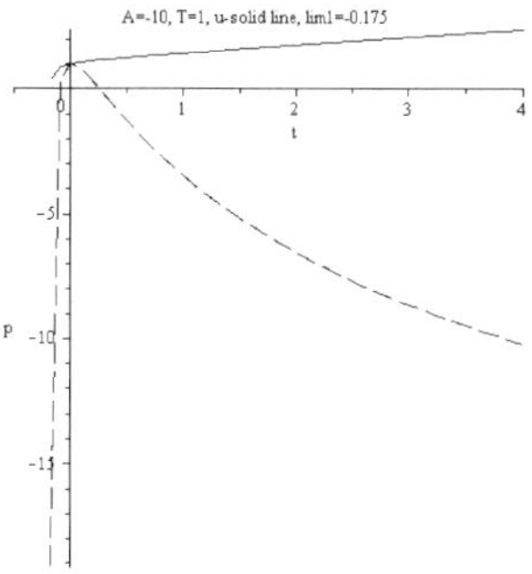

Fig. 9.6.19. Evolution of $\widetilde{u}(\widetilde{x})$, $\widetilde{p}(\widetilde{x})$; $\widetilde{A}^{ex} = -10$, $\widetilde{\tau} = 1$.

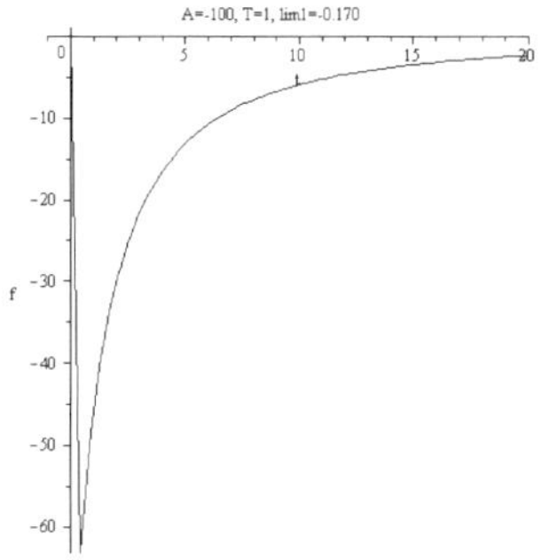

Fig. 9.6.20. Evolution of $\widetilde{F}(\widetilde{x})$; $\widetilde{A}^{ex} = -100$, $\widetilde{\tau} = 1$.

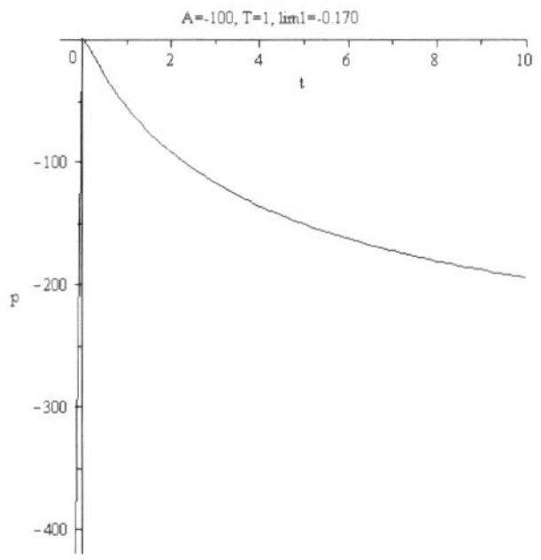

Fig. 9.6.21. Evolution of $\widetilde{p}(\widetilde{x})$; $\widetilde{A}^{ex} = -100$, $\widetilde{\tau} = 1$.

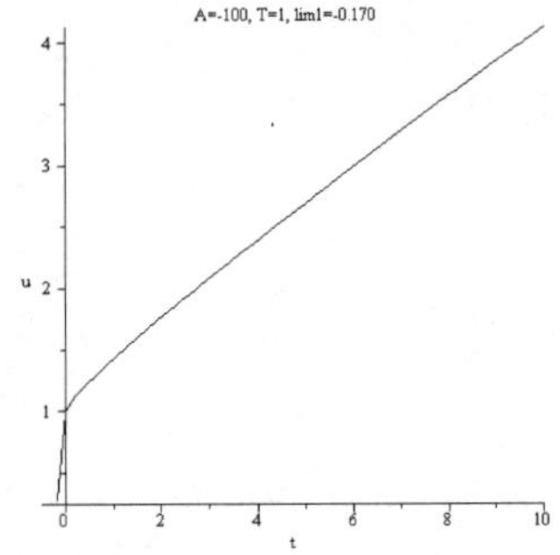

Fig. 9.6.22. Evolution of $\tilde{v}_{0x}(\tilde{x})$; $\tilde{A}^{ex} = -100$, $\tilde{\tau} = 1$.

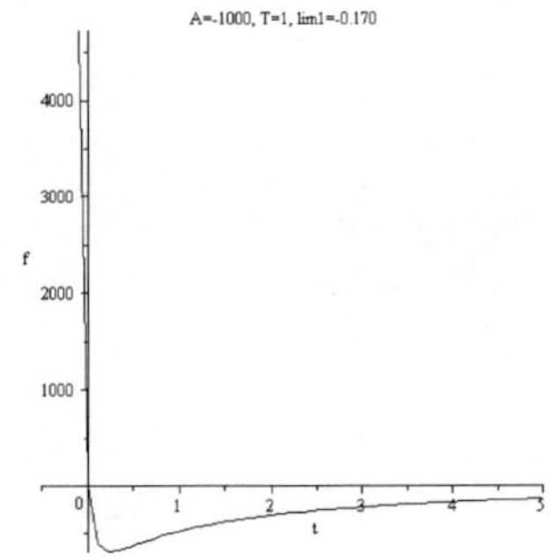

Fig. 9.6.23. Evolution of $\tilde{F}(\tilde{x})$; $\tilde{A}^{ex} = -1000$, $\tilde{\tau} = 1$.

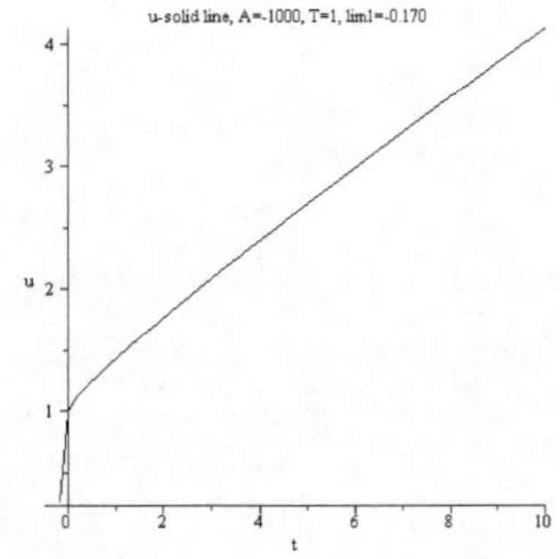

Fig. 9.6.24. Evolution of $\tilde{v}_{0x}(\tilde{x})$; $\tilde{A}^{ex} = -1000$, $\tilde{\tau} = 1$.

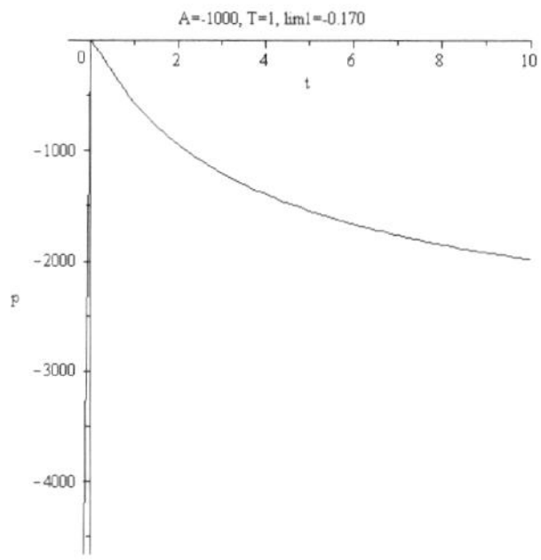

Fig. 9.6.25. Evolution of $\tilde{p}(\tilde{x})$; $\tilde{A}^{ex} = -1000$, $\tilde{\tau} = 1$.

9.7. EM Drive in the external gravitational field.

The calculations presented on figures 9.6.2 - 9.6.25 give a general idea of the physical system filled by radiation and PV. But radiation occupies only a part of the considered system diminishing with the grows of the distance $\tilde{x}$ Let us reflect this fact introducing the approximation

$$\tilde{A}^{ex} = \frac{\tilde{B}}{1+\tilde{x}^n} . \qquad (9.7.1)$$

As a result (if the mass perturbation can be omitted) we have the SYSTEM B:

$$\frac{\partial}{\partial \tilde{x}}\left(\tilde{p} + \tilde{A}^{ex}\right) = \tilde{F}, \qquad (9.7.2)$$

$$3\left(\tilde{p} + \tilde{A}^{ex}\right)\frac{\partial \tilde{u}}{\partial \tilde{x}} + \tilde{u}\frac{\partial}{\partial \tilde{x}}\left(\tilde{p} + \tilde{A}^{ex}\right) = 0, \qquad (9.7.3)$$

$$4\left(\tilde{p} + \tilde{A}^{ex}\right)\frac{\partial \tilde{u}}{\partial \tilde{x}} + \tau\frac{\partial}{\partial \tilde{x}}\left[16\,\tilde{u}\left(\tilde{p} + \tilde{A}^{ex}\right)\frac{\partial \tilde{u}}{\partial \tilde{x}} + 5\tilde{u}^2\frac{\partial}{\partial \tilde{x}}\left(\tilde{p} + \tilde{A}^{ex}\right) - 5\left(\tilde{p} + \tilde{A}^{ex}\right)\tilde{g}\right] - 4\tilde{u}\,\tilde{\tau}\frac{\partial \tilde{u}}{\partial \tilde{x}}\frac{\partial}{\partial \tilde{x}}\left(\tilde{p} + \tilde{A}^{ex}\right) = 0. \qquad (9.7.4)$$

The following figures 9.7.1 – 9.7.4 show the result of modeling for approximation (9.7.1) for different $\tilde{B}$ and n without the gravitation influence.

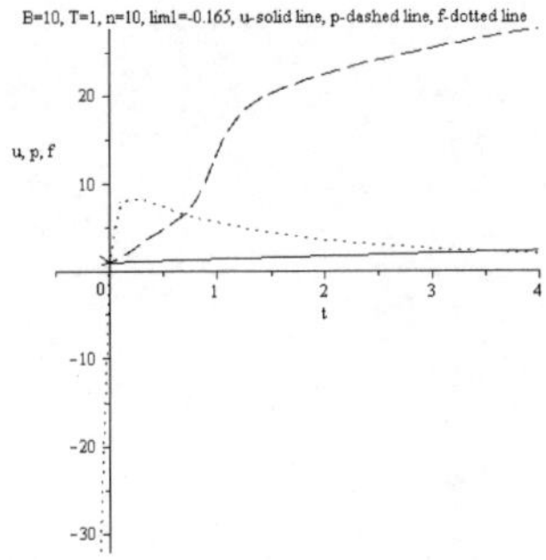

Fig. 9.7.1. Evolution of $\tilde{v}_{0x}(\tilde{x})$, $\tilde{p}(\tilde{x})$, $\tilde{F}(\tilde{x})$; $\tilde{B}=10$, $n=10$, $\tilde{\tau}=1$.

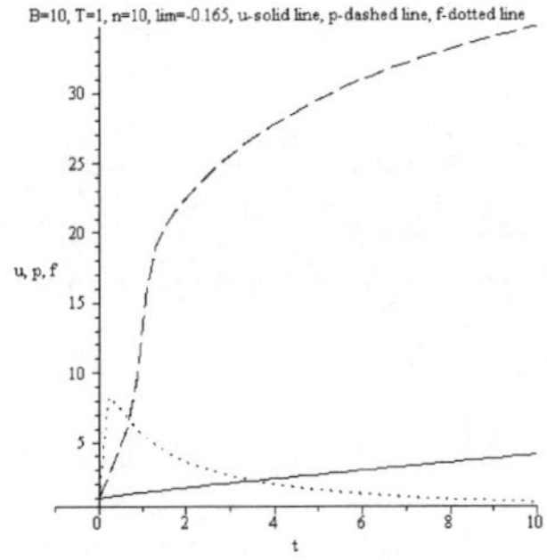

Fig. 9.7.2. Evolution of $\tilde{v}_{0x}(\tilde{x})$, $\tilde{p}(\tilde{x})$, $\tilde{F}(\tilde{x})$; $\tilde{B}=10$, $n=10$, $\tilde{\tau}=1$.

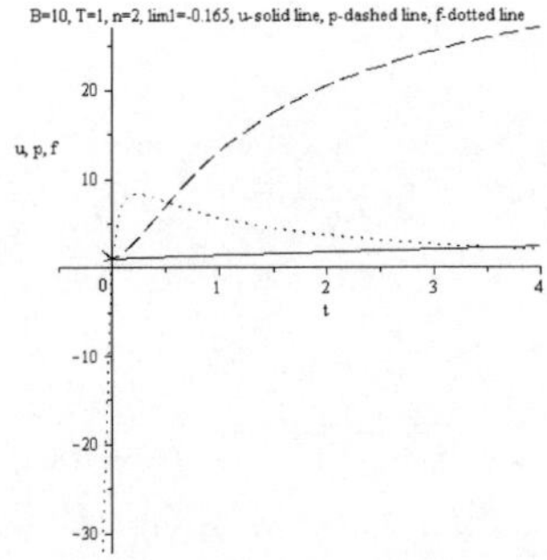

Fig. 9.7.3. Evolution of $\tilde{v}_{0x}(\tilde{x})$, $\tilde{p}(\tilde{x})$, $\tilde{F}(\tilde{x})$; $\tilde{B}=10$, $n=2$, $\tilde{\tau}=1$.

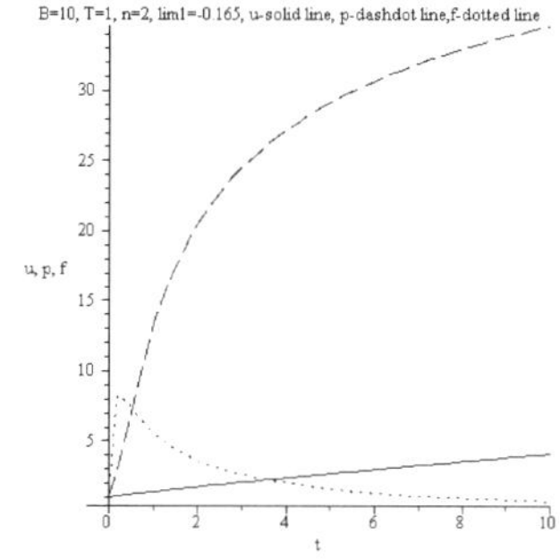

Fig. 9.7.4. Evolution of $\tilde{v}_{0x}(\tilde{x})$, $\tilde{p}(\tilde{x})$, $\tilde{F}(\tilde{x})$; $\tilde{B} = 10$, $n = 2$, $\tilde{\tau} = 1$.

Compare now the curves shown in the figures 9.6.2 - 9.6.7 and 9.7.1 - 9.7.4. As we see the general features of the $\tilde{v}_{0x}(\tilde{x})$, $\tilde{p}(\tilde{x})$, $\tilde{F}(\tilde{x})$ evolution remain the same. The greatest changes correspond to the pressure of the physical vacuum. The greatest influence on the results of the calculations provides the initial Cauchy conditions.

The main result consists in the affirmation that the physical system "works" in regime of anti-gravitation. It is well-known that the Van der Waals equation of state leads to the force curves shown in Figure 9.7.5.

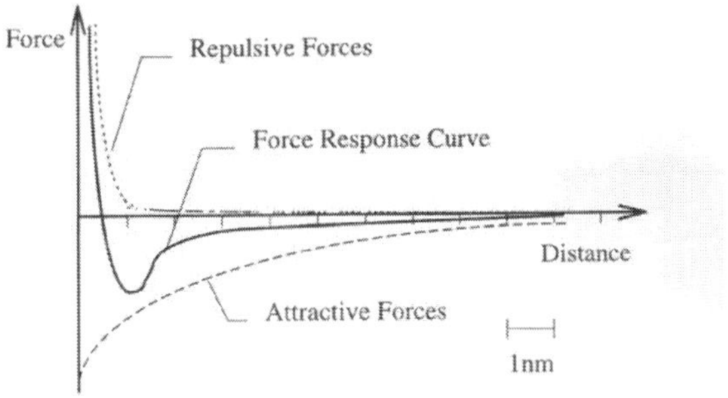

Fig. 9.7.5. The typical van der Waals curves.

Compare now the curves of Figures 9.7.5 and 9.7.2. We have the opposite behavior of curves - curves of attraction and repulsion are reversed. It is direct consequence of nonlocal physics.

Interesting to notice, that we return to the Van der Waals curves as a result of diminishing of PV pressure by an artificial way (compare figures 9.7.5 and 9.6.23).

There are the experimental works (see for example [172]) confirming that at larger distances and between macroscopic condensed media the retardation effects can be revealed. Although these long-range forces exist within all matter, only attractive interactions have so far been measured between material bodies [172 - 175]. In [175] is shown experimentally that, in accord with theoretical prediction [176 - 178], the sign of the force can be changed from attractive to repulsive by suitable choice of interacting materials immersed in a fluid. The mentioned theoretical predictions (as well as qualitative considerations in [179]) have phenomenological character and do not lead to transport PV equations in principal. From this point of view it is interesting for us the experimental results for EM Drive reflected in the Internet site http://www.masinaelectrica.com/emdrive-independent-test/. These experiments have the very important feature – EM Drive was placed in the vertical position. As a result it was revealed the direct influence of gravitation on the emdrive thrust. The experimenter had rather modest equipment and no surprise that he did not observe the horizontal thrust which leads to ~ mN/kW. But he discovered the more thrust for the vertical emdrive position depending on the orientation emdrive in the vertical plane (~0.2 - 1.4 grammas).

The following figures 9.7.6 – 9.7.10 show the result of modeling for approximation (9.6.1) for different $\widetilde{B}$ and n with the Cauchy conditions: $p(0)=1,\ u(0)=1,\ D(p)(0)=1,\ D(u)(0)=1$. The possible gravitational influence is taken into account.

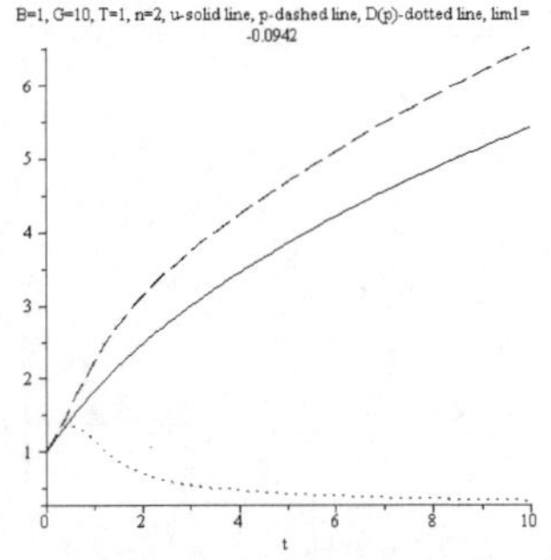

Fig. 9.7.6. Evolution of $\widetilde{u}(\widetilde{x})$, $\widetilde{p}(\widetilde{x})$, $\partial\widetilde{p}(\widetilde{x})/\partial\widetilde{x}$; $\widetilde{B}=1$, $\widetilde{\tau}=1$, $\widetilde{g}_x=10$, $n=2$.

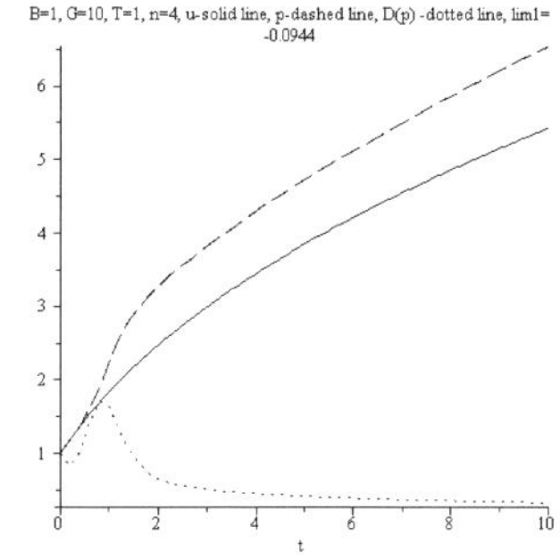

Fig. 9.7.7. Evolution of $\tilde{u}(\tilde{x})$, $\tilde{p}(\tilde{x})$, $\partial\tilde{p}(\tilde{x})/\partial\tilde{x}$; $\tilde{B}=1$, $\tilde{\tau}=1$, $\tilde{g}_x=10$, $n=4$.

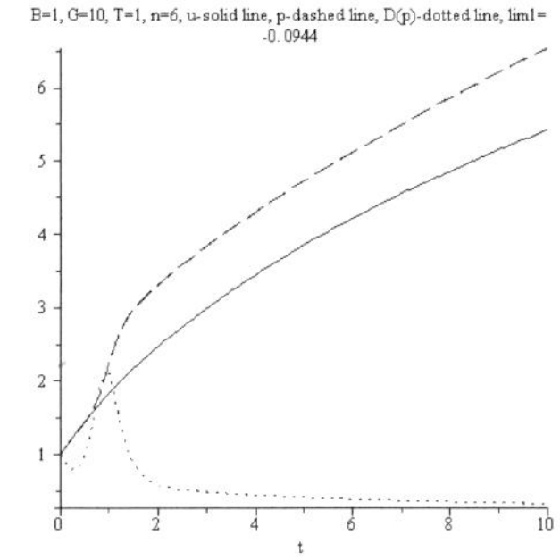

Fig. 9.7.8. Evolution of $\tilde{u}(\tilde{x})$, $\tilde{p}(\tilde{x})$, $\partial\tilde{p}(\tilde{x})/\partial\tilde{x}$; $\tilde{B}=1$, $\tilde{\tau}=1$, $\tilde{g}_x=10$, $n=6$.

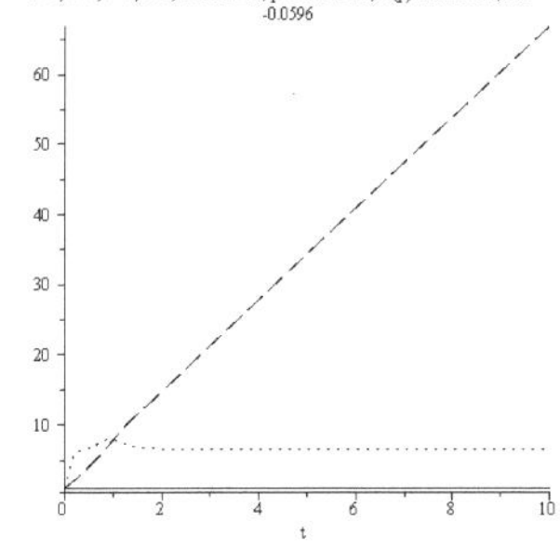

Fig. 9.7.9. Evolution of $\tilde{u}(\tilde{x})$, $\tilde{p}(\tilde{x})$, $\partial\tilde{p}(\tilde{x})/\partial\tilde{x}$; $\tilde{B}=1$, $\tilde{\tau}=1$, $\tilde{g}_x=0$, $n=6$.

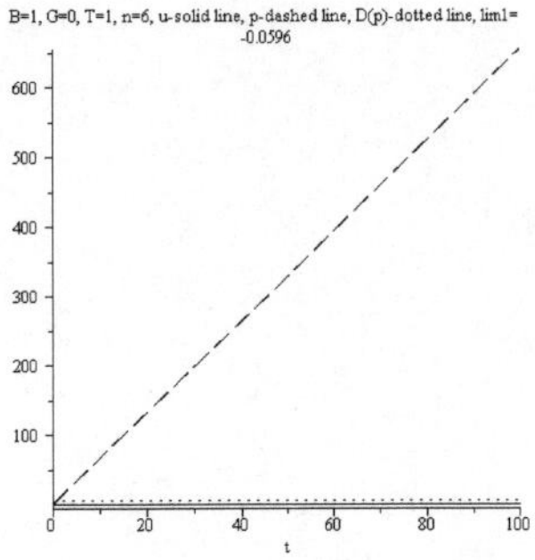

Fig. 9.7.10. Evolution of $\tilde{u}(\tilde{x})$, $\tilde{p}(\tilde{x})$, $\partial\tilde{p}(\tilde{x})/\partial\tilde{x}$; $\tilde{B}=1$, $\tilde{\tau}=1$, $\tilde{g}_x=0$, $n=6$.

The following figures 9.7.11, 9.7.12 show the result of modeling for different constant $\tilde{A}$ with the Cauchy conditions: $p(0)=1$, $u(0)=1$, $D(p)(0)=-1$, $D(u)(0)=-1$.

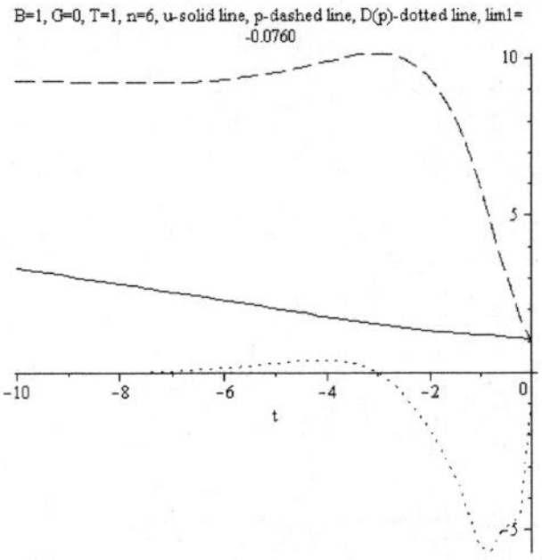

Fig. 9.7.11. Evolution of $\tilde{u}(\tilde{x})$, $\tilde{p}(\tilde{x})$, $\partial\tilde{p}(\tilde{x})/\partial\tilde{x}$; $\tilde{B}=1$, $\tilde{\tau}=1$, $\tilde{g}_x=0$, $n=6$.

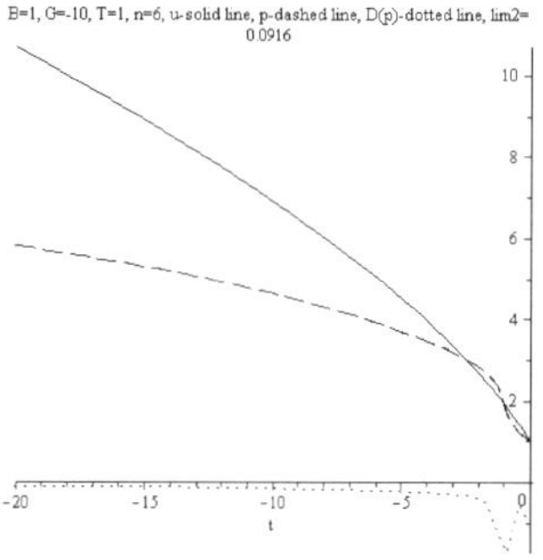

Fig. 9.7.12. Evolution of $\tilde{u}(\tilde{x})$, $\tilde{p}(\tilde{x})$, $\partial\tilde{p}(\tilde{x})/\partial\tilde{x}$; $\tilde{B}=1$, $\tilde{\tau}=1$, $\tilde{g}_x=-10$, $n=6$.

Compare now the curves reflecting the influence of the external gravitational field on the PV evolution; for example the curves shown in the figures 9.7.1 – 9.7.4 and 9.7.6 - 9.7.12. As we see the general features of the $\tilde{u}(\tilde{x})$, $\tilde{p}(\tilde{x})$, $\partial\tilde{p}/\partial\tilde{x}$ evolution demonstrate the different style of behavior.

We often read phrases like "quantum fluctuations create intermolecular forces that pervade macroscopic bodies" without concrete calculations of quantum fluctuations in the quantum hydrodynamic equations in reality. Is it possible using this terminology to indicate explicit fluctuations in the nonlocal theory of PV?

It is possible. Really, for example, let us return to 1D dimensional equations:

(continuity equation, 1D case)

$$\frac{\partial}{\partial x}\left\{\tau\left[\frac{\partial p}{\partial x}-F\right]\right\}=0, \tag{9.7.5}$$

(momentum equation, 1D case)

$$\begin{aligned}&\frac{\partial p}{\partial x}-F-\frac{\partial}{\partial t}\left\{\tau\left[\frac{\partial p}{\partial x}-F\right]\right\}-2\tau\left(\frac{\partial p}{\partial x}-F\right)\frac{\partial u}{\partial x}\\&-\frac{\partial}{\partial x}\left\{\tau\left[\frac{\partial p}{\partial t}+u\frac{\partial p}{\partial x}+3p\frac{\partial u}{\partial x}\right]\right\}=0,\end{aligned} \tag{9.7.6}$$

(energy equation, 1D case)

$$
\begin{aligned}
&3\frac{\partial p}{\partial t}+3u\frac{\partial p}{\partial x}+5p\frac{\partial u}{\partial x}+2u\left(\frac{\partial p}{\partial x}-F\right)\\
&-\frac{\partial}{\partial t}\left\{\tau\left[3\frac{\partial p}{\partial t}+3u\frac{\partial p}{\partial x}+5p\frac{\partial u}{\partial x}+2u\left(\frac{\partial p}{\partial x}-F\right)\right]\right\}\\
&-\frac{\partial}{\partial x}\left\{\tau\left[5\frac{\partial}{\partial t}(pu)+5u\frac{\partial}{\partial x}(pu)+11up\frac{\partial u}{\partial x}\right]\right\}\\
&-6\tau\left(\frac{\partial p}{\partial x}-F\right)u\frac{\partial u}{\partial x}+A^{pert}=0,
\end{aligned}
\tag{9.7.7}
$$

$$
A^{pert}=5\tau\left(F-\frac{\partial p}{\partial x}\right)\frac{\partial}{\partial x}\left[\frac{p}{\rho}\right]-5\frac{\partial}{\partial x}\left[\tau p\frac{\partial}{\partial x}\frac{p}{\rho}\right].
\tag{9.7.8}
$$

For the case under consideration all terms proportional to τ should be considered as quantum fluctuations containing PV flashes and the mass perturbation A^{pert}.

Remind the basic conclusions following in particular from the results of mathematical modeling:

1. The calculations are realized in the vast diapason of parameter changing and Cauchy conditions.
2. In considered case (if the external pressure input is positive or equal to zero) the front of the physical vacuum waves convoying of appearance of the repulsion forces. In the existing bad terminology - we discover the “negative pressure” and “dark energy” in all cases. This fundamental result does not depend on the mechanism of external perturbations. In other words, the “anti-gravity” (better to say, the repulsion forces) in the physical vacuum exists, if there is dissipation of energy, supply of energy or in the absence of dissipation at all.
3. If the external influence leads to diminishing the PV pressure we obtain the curves of the van der Waals type.

We have the following model EM thrust:

1. Electromagnetic waves create pressure acting on physical vacuum.
2. Appearing the PV flat waves create the repulsion forces. If the considered physical system creates PV boxes, it can lead firstly to the force of attraction and then repulsion demonstrating the effects like “anti-gravitation”, characteristic for so called “dark energy”. The point $\tilde{r}=\tilde{r}_{cr}$ exists where a mode of attraction is changed to repulsion mode. In this case a delay time should exist after the RF power is initiated.
3. The returning in the volume the repulsion mode is damping by the RF mode. As a result we obtain the outgoing flow of physical vacuum leading to the thrust

effect. Practically we have no restrictions for the velocity for the outgoing vacuum flow.

4. This type of engine better to name as a Physical Vacuum Engine (PV Engine). If this effect exists, it is certainly a revolution in physics and technology.

5. In collider LHC $\sigma_{tot}(pp)=10^{-25}cm^2$; taking into account the bunching effect $\sigma_{tot}^{bunch}\sim 10^{-21}cm^2$, [180]. This value is much less of the cross section of encountered particles which could lead to the dangerous anti-gravitation effect. But the mentioned particle collision can create -

a) Waves in the physical vacuum which correspond to the wake waves in colliders, [181].

b) Explosion of the PV bubbles in regime of Hadamard instabilities, [21].

Some general remarks:

1. The birth of the universe is convoying of appearance of the repulsion forces. In the existing terminology - we discover the "negative pressure" and "dark energy" in all cases. This fundamental result does not depend on the mechanism of external perturbations. In other words, the anti-gravity in the physical vacuum exists, if there is dissipation of energy or in the absence of dissipation at all.

2. Physical Vacuum is not a speculative object; it is a reality as "matter" and "fields". In other words, the physical vacuum is "the third" physical reality along with matter and fields. In this case, it is natural to raise the question about the existence of the effect which is similar to the Hubble's effect. As installed the appearance of this effect in the physical vacuum does not contradict the conclusions of non-local physics.

3. The birth of the PV boxes in Universe is convoying of appearance of the critical PV box dimension when a mode of attraction is changed to repulsion mode. In this case we can speak about models like the burst in domains filled by PV. These models are analogue of the Hubble boxes which are observed in reality. In principal the PV burst can be discovered in the collider experiments.

4. But in comparison with the Hubble expansion we need an evidence of the analogical PV expansion and the corresponding experimental data (from collider experiments for example). The excitation of the PV waves is the extremely important problem of the advanced technology.

9.8. Some general remarks and conclusion

In monographs [18-22] the evolution of Physical Vacuum (PV) in Planck epoch and wave effects in PV are considered in the frame of nonlocal physics. It should be underlined that the nonlocal transport equations obtained from the first principles of physics.

In principal we needn't to use the theory Newtonian gravitation or the Maxwell equations in explicit forms for solution of nonlinear non-local evolution equations. In contrast with the local physics this approach in the frame of quantum non-local hydrodynamics leads to the closed mathematical description for the physical system under consideration. If the matter is absent, non-local evolution equations have nevertheless non-trivial solutions corresponding evolution of PV which description in time and 3D space on the level of quantum hydrodynamics demands only quantum pressure p, the self-consistent force $\mathbf{F}$ (acting on unit of the space volume) and velocity $\mathbf{v}_0$.

Moreover, it could be said that we are living in physical vacuum in its form remaining after PV burst (Big Bang) and creation of fields and matter in the following PV evolution. Remind the basic conclusions following in particular from the results of mathematical modeling:

1. Nonlocal hydrodynamics contains also the limit cases for the density $\rho \to \infty$ (black hole) and $\rho \to 0$ (physical vacuum including Big Bang theory).
2. Processes in PV-engine can be considered for the case $\rho \neq 0$ as well. The initial Cauchy conditions provide the greatest influence on the results of the calculations.
3. The main result consists in the affirmation that the physical system "works" in regimes of attraction and repulsion. It is direct consequence of nonlocal physics.
4. Appearance of the initial gradients and the external gravitational field leads to moving of the PV-engine as a whole system, which has no attitude to the usual jet propulsion. If the initial gradients and gravitational force have the opposite directions, the space PV evolution is closed in the finite space domain.
5. The calculations are realized in the vast diapason of parameter changing and Cauchy conditions. In considered cases we find the strong influence of the external gravitational and electromagnetic fields on PV evolution and therefore on the PV Engine. If this effect can be independently confirmed, it is certainly a revolution in physics and technology.
6. The PV evolution near the massive objects (like stars) strongly depends on the force of the external gravitation.

CHAPTER 10. THE NONLOCAL THEORY OF LEVITATION

In this chapter we revisit the levitation phenomenon using the generalized Boltzmann kinetics theory which can represent the non-local physics of this levitation phenomenon. This approach can identify the conditions when the levitation can take place under the influence of correlated electromagnetic and gravitational fields. The sufficient mathematical conditions of levitation are obtained. It means that the regime of levitation could be realized from the position of the non-local hydrodynamics.

Keywords: Foundations of the theory of transport processes, Basements of non-local physics, Generalized hydrodynamic Alexeev equations, Levitation, Searl effect generator

10.1. Introduction to Chapter10.

The phenomenon of levitation has attracted attention from philosophers and scientists in the past and now. How can levitation be possible? What power or agent accomplishes it? The most obvious explanation - the possession of a word of mystical power - is not interesting here for us. In spite of the tremendous recent advances, notably in power electronics, magnetic materials, on the application of electromagnetic suspension and levitation techniques to advanced ground transportation, physics of levitations needs in following significant investigations. In this paper we revisit the levitation phenomenon using the generalized Bolzmann kinetics theory [18 – 22] which can represent the non-local physics of this levitation phenomenon.

The investigations of the levitation stability have a long history and are considered in details in [182 – 186]. As usual the problem review begins with the citation of the Earnshaw paper [182]. Earnshaw's theorem depends on a mathematical property of the $1/r$ type energy potential valid for magnetostatic and electrostatic events and gravitation. At any point where there is force balance is equal to zero, the equilibrium is unstable because there can be no local minimum in the potential energy. There must be some loopholes though, because magnets above superconductors and the magnet configuration do stably levitate including frogs [186] and toys like levitron (spinning magnet tops), flying globe and so on [187, 188]. It means that diamagnetic material can stabilize the levitation of permanent magnets. It is well known that the potential energy density of the magnetic field can be written as

$$w_m = -\mathbf{M} \cdot \mathbf{B} \tag{10.1.1}$$

where $\mathbf{B}$ is magnetic induction, $\mathbf{M}$ is magnetization. Using the phenomenological relation

$$\mathbf{M} = \chi \mathbf{H}, \tag{10.1.2}$$

where χ is magnetic susceptibility, we have for the unit volume of a magnetic material

$$w_m = -\frac{\chi}{\mu \mu_0} B^2 \tag{10.1.3}$$

The force acting on the unit volume of a levitating object is

$$\mathbf{F} = \frac{\chi}{\mu_0 \mu} \mathrm{grad} B^2, \tag{10.1.4}$$

if the phenomenological parameters are constant. Diamagnets (for which $\chi < 0$) are repelled by magnetic fields and attracted to field minima. As a result, diamagnets can satisfy the stability conditions [187 – 189] and the following conditions are exceptions to Earnshaw's theorem:

a) Diamagnetism occurs in materials which have a relative permeability less than one. The result is that eddy currents are induced in a diamagnetic material, it will repel magnetic flux.

b) The Meissner effect which occurs in superconductors. Superconductors have zero internal resistance. As such induced currents tend to persist, and as a result the magnetic field they cause will persist as well.

c) As result of oscillations, when an alternating current is passed through an electromagnet, it behaves like a diamagnetic material.

d) Rotation: employed by the Levitron, it uses gyroscopic motion to overcome levitation instability.

e) Feedback can be used in conjunction with electromagnets to dynamically adjust magnetic flux in order to maintain levitation.

The main shortcoming of the Earnshaw theory consists in application of principles of local physics to the non-equilibrium non-local statistical systems.

The aim of this Chapter consists in application of the non-local physics methods to the effect of levitation. We intend to answer two questions:

1) Is it possible to formulate the sufficient conditions of levitation from the position of the unified non-local theory of transport processes (UNTT) (see, also [189])?

2) Is it possible to speak about the mutual influence of electromagnetic field and gravitation in the frame of UNTT?

10.2. Basic equations

Non-local hydrodynamic equations have the form [18 - 22]:
(continuity equation for a mixture)

$$\frac{\partial}{\partial t}\left\{\rho-\sum_\alpha \tau_\alpha\left[\frac{\partial\rho_\alpha}{\partial t}+\frac{\partial}{\partial \mathbf{r}}\cdot(\rho_\alpha\mathbf{v}_0)\right]\right\}$$
$$+\frac{\partial}{\partial \mathbf{r}}\cdot\left\{\rho\mathbf{v}_0-\sum_\alpha \tau_\alpha\left[\frac{\partial}{\partial t}(\rho_\alpha\mathbf{v}_0)+\frac{\partial}{\partial \mathbf{r}}\cdot(\rho_\alpha\mathbf{v}_0\mathbf{v}_0)+\vec{\mathrm{I}}\cdot\frac{\partial p_\alpha}{\partial \mathbf{r}}\right.\right. \tag{10.2.1}$$
$$\left.\left.-\rho_\alpha\mathbf{F}_\alpha^{(1)}-\frac{q_\alpha}{m_\alpha}\rho_\alpha\mathbf{v}_0\times\mathbf{B}\right]\right\}=0,$$

(motion equation)

$$\frac{\partial}{\partial t}\left\{\rho\mathbf{v}_0-\sum_\alpha\tau_\alpha\left[\frac{\partial}{\partial t}(\rho_\alpha\mathbf{v}_0)+\frac{\partial}{\partial \mathbf{r}}\cdot\rho_\alpha\mathbf{v}_0\mathbf{v}_0+\frac{\partial p_\alpha}{\partial \mathbf{r}}-\rho_\alpha\mathbf{F}_\alpha^{(1)}\right.\right.$$
$$\left.\left.-\frac{q_\alpha}{m_\alpha}\rho_\alpha\mathbf{v}_0\times\mathbf{B}\right]\right\}-\sum_\alpha\mathbf{F}_\alpha^{(1)}\left[\rho_\alpha-\tau_\alpha\left(\frac{\partial\rho_\alpha}{\partial t}+\frac{\partial}{\partial \mathbf{r}}\cdot(\rho_\alpha\mathbf{v}_0)\right)\right]$$
$$-\sum_\alpha\frac{q_\alpha}{m_\alpha}\left\{\rho_\alpha\mathbf{v}_0-\tau_\alpha\left[\frac{\partial}{\partial t}(\rho_\alpha\mathbf{v}_0)+\frac{\partial}{\partial \mathbf{r}}\cdot\rho_\alpha\mathbf{v}_0\mathbf{v}_0+\frac{\partial p_\alpha}{\partial \mathbf{r}}-\rho_\alpha\mathbf{F}_\alpha^{(1)}\right.\right.$$
$$\left.\left.-\frac{q_\alpha}{m_\alpha}\rho_\alpha\mathbf{v}_0\times\mathbf{B}\right]\right\}\times\mathbf{B}+\frac{\partial}{\partial \mathbf{r}}\cdot\left\{\rho\mathbf{v}_0\mathbf{v}_0+p\vec{\mathrm{I}}-\sum_\alpha\tau_\alpha\left[\frac{\partial}{\partial t}(\rho_\alpha\mathbf{v}_0\mathbf{v}_0\right.\right. \tag{10.2.2}$$
$$+p_\alpha\vec{\mathrm{I}})+\frac{\partial}{\partial \mathbf{r}}\cdot\rho_\alpha(\mathbf{v}_0\mathbf{v}_0)\mathbf{v}_0+2\vec{\mathrm{I}}\left(\frac{\partial}{\partial \mathbf{r}}\cdot(p_\alpha\mathbf{v}_0)\right)+\frac{\partial}{\partial \mathbf{r}}\cdot\left(\vec{\mathrm{I}}p_\alpha\mathbf{v}_0\right)$$
$$\left.\left.-\mathbf{F}_\alpha^{(1)}\rho_\alpha\mathbf{v}_0-\rho_\alpha\mathbf{v}_0\mathbf{F}_\alpha^{(1)}-\frac{q_\alpha}{m_\alpha}\rho_\alpha[\mathbf{v}_0\times\mathbf{B}]\mathbf{v}_0-\frac{q_\alpha}{m_\alpha}\rho_\alpha\mathbf{v}_0[\mathbf{v}_0\times\mathbf{B}]\right]\right\}=0$$

(energy equation)

$$
\frac{\partial}{\partial t}\left\{\frac{\rho v_0^2}{2}+\frac{3}{2}p+\sum_\alpha \varepsilon_\alpha n_\alpha-\sum_\alpha \tau_\alpha\left[\frac{\partial}{\partial t}\left(\frac{\rho_\alpha v_0^2}{2}+\frac{3}{2}p_\alpha+\varepsilon_\alpha n_\alpha\right)\right.\right.
$$

$$
\left.\left.+\frac{\partial}{\partial \mathbf{r}}\cdot\left(\frac{1}{2}\rho_\alpha v_0^2\mathbf{v}_0+\frac{5}{2}p_\alpha\mathbf{v}_0+\varepsilon_\alpha n_\alpha\mathbf{v}_0\right)-\mathbf{F}_\alpha^{(1)}\cdot\rho_\alpha\mathbf{v}_0\right]\right\}
$$

$$
+\frac{\partial}{\partial \mathbf{r}}\cdot\left\{\frac{1}{2}\rho v_0^2\mathbf{v}_0+\frac{5}{2}p\mathbf{v}_0+\mathbf{v}_0\sum_\alpha\varepsilon_\alpha n_\alpha-\sum_\alpha\tau_\alpha\left[\frac{\partial}{\partial t}\left(\frac{1}{2}\rho_\alpha v_0^2\mathbf{v}_0\right.\right.\right.
$$

$$
\left.+\frac{5}{2}p_\alpha\mathbf{v}_0+\varepsilon_\alpha n_\alpha\mathbf{v}_0\right)+\frac{\partial}{\partial \mathbf{r}}\cdot\left(\frac{1}{2}\rho_\alpha v_0^2\mathbf{v}_0\mathbf{v}_0+\frac{7}{2}p_\alpha\mathbf{v}_0\mathbf{v}_0+\frac{1}{2}p_\alpha v_0^2\ddot{\mathrm{I}}\right.
$$

$$
\left.+\frac{5}{2}\frac{p_\alpha^2}{\rho_\alpha}\ddot{\mathrm{I}}+\varepsilon_\alpha n_\alpha\mathbf{v}_0\mathbf{v}_0+\varepsilon_\alpha\frac{p_\alpha}{m_\alpha}\ddot{\mathrm{I}}\right)-\rho_\alpha\mathbf{F}_\alpha^{(1)}\cdot\mathbf{v}_0\mathbf{v}_0-p_\alpha\mathbf{F}_\alpha^{(1)}\cdot\ddot{\mathrm{I}}
$$

$$
-\frac{1}{2}\rho_\alpha v_0^2\mathbf{F}_\alpha^{(1)}-\frac{3}{2}\mathbf{F}_\alpha^{(1)}p_\alpha-\frac{\rho_\alpha v_0^2}{2}\frac{q_\alpha}{m_\alpha}[\mathbf{v}_0\times\mathbf{B}]-\frac{5}{2}p_\alpha\frac{q_\alpha}{m_\alpha}[\mathbf{v}_0\times\mathbf{B}]
$$

$$
\left.\left.-\varepsilon_\alpha n_\alpha\frac{q_\alpha}{m_\alpha}[\mathbf{v}_0\times\mathbf{B}]-\varepsilon_\alpha n_\alpha\mathbf{F}_\alpha^{(1)}\right]\right\}-\mathbf{v}_0\cdot\sum_\alpha\rho_\alpha\mathbf{F}_\alpha^{(1)}
$$

$$
+\sum_\alpha\tau_\alpha\mathbf{F}_\alpha^{(1)}\cdot\left[\frac{\partial}{\partial t}(\rho_\alpha\mathbf{v}_0)+\frac{\partial}{\partial \mathbf{r}}\cdot\rho_\alpha\mathbf{v}_0\mathbf{v}_0+\frac{\partial}{\partial \mathbf{r}}\cdot p_\alpha\ddot{\mathrm{I}}-\rho_\alpha\mathbf{F}_\alpha^{(1)}-q_\alpha n_\alpha[\mathbf{v}_0\times\mathbf{B}]\right]=0. \qquad (10.2.3)
$$

where $\mathbf{v}_0$ is the hydrodynamic velocity in the coordinate system at rest, ρ_α is the density of α - species, p is the pressure, $\ddot{\mathrm{I}}$ - unit tensore, $\mathbf{F}_\alpha^{(1)}$ is the force of the non-nonmagnetic origin acting on the unit of mass, ε_α is the internal energy of a particle of the α - species, τ is non-local parameter.

Important remarks:

1. Equations (10.2.1) – (10.2.3) should be considered as local approximation of non-local equations (NLE) written in the hydrodynamic form. NLE include quantum hydrodynamics of Schrödinger – Madelung as a deep particular case [18-22] and can be applied in the frame of the unified theory from the atom scale to the Universe evolution.
2. The basic system contains the cross terms for the forces of the mass and electro- magneto-dynamic origin. It means that the fluctuation of the gravitational field leads to the electro- magneto dynamical fluctuations and verse versa.

Sufficient conditions of levitation can be obtained from Eqs. (10.2.1) – (10.2.3) after equalizing all terms containing forces to zero.

Namely:

from the continuity equation

$$
\frac{\partial}{\partial \mathbf{r}}\cdot\left\{\sum_\alpha\tau_\alpha\left[\rho_\alpha\mathbf{F}_\alpha^{(1)}+\frac{q_\alpha}{m_\alpha}\rho_\alpha\mathbf{v}_0\times\mathbf{B}\right]\right\}=0, \qquad (10.2.4)
$$

from the motion equation follows

$$\frac{\partial}{\partial t}\left\{\sum_\alpha \tau_\alpha\left[\rho_\alpha \mathbf{F}_\alpha^{(1)}+\frac{q_\alpha}{m_\alpha}\rho_\alpha \mathbf{v}_0\times\mathbf{B}\right]\right\}-\sum_\alpha \mathbf{F}_\alpha^{(1)}\left[\rho_\alpha-\tau_\alpha\left(\frac{\partial\rho_\alpha}{\partial t}+\frac{\partial}{\partial \mathbf{r}}\cdot(\rho_\alpha\mathbf{v}_0)\right)\right]$$
$$-\sum_\alpha\frac{q_\alpha}{m_\alpha}\left\{\tau_\alpha\left[\rho_\alpha \mathbf{F}_\alpha^{(1)}+\frac{q_\alpha}{m_\alpha}\rho_\alpha\mathbf{v}_0\times\mathbf{B}\right]\right\}\times\mathbf{B} \tag{10.2.5}$$
$$+\frac{\partial}{\partial \mathbf{r}}\cdot\left\{\sum_\alpha\tau_\alpha\left[\mathbf{F}_\alpha^{(1)}\rho_\alpha\mathbf{v}_0+\rho_\alpha\mathbf{v}_0\mathbf{F}_\alpha^{(1)}+\frac{q_\alpha}{m_\alpha}\rho_\alpha[\mathbf{v}_0\times\mathbf{B}]\mathbf{v}_0+\frac{q_\alpha}{m_\alpha}\rho_\alpha\mathbf{v}_0[\mathbf{v}_0\times\mathbf{B}]\right]\right\}=0,$$

from the energy equation

$$\frac{\partial}{\partial t}\sum_\alpha\tau_\alpha\left(\rho_\alpha\mathbf{F}_\alpha^{(1)}\cdot\mathbf{v}_0\right)$$
$$+\frac{\partial}{\partial \mathbf{r}}\cdot\left\{\sum_\alpha\tau_\alpha\left[\rho_\alpha\mathbf{F}_\alpha^{(1)}\cdot\mathbf{v}_0\mathbf{v}_0+p_\alpha\mathbf{F}_\alpha^{(1)}\cdot\vec{\mathrm{I}}+\frac{1}{2}\rho_\alpha v_0^2\mathbf{F}_\alpha^{(1)}+\frac{3}{2}\mathbf{F}_\alpha^{(1)}p_\alpha+\frac{\rho_\alpha v_0^2}{2}\frac{q_\alpha}{m_\alpha}[\mathbf{v}_0\times\mathbf{B}]\right.\right.$$
$$\left.\left.+\frac{5}{2}p_\alpha\frac{q_\alpha}{m_\alpha}[\mathbf{v}_0\times\mathbf{B}]+\varepsilon_\alpha n_\alpha\frac{q_\alpha}{m_\alpha}[\mathbf{v}_0\times\mathbf{B}]+\varepsilon_\alpha n_\alpha\mathbf{F}_\alpha^{(1)}\right]\right\}$$
$$-\mathbf{v}_0\cdot\sum_\alpha\rho_\alpha\mathbf{F}_\alpha^{(1)}+\sum_\alpha\tau_\alpha\mathbf{F}_\alpha^{(1)}\cdot\left[\frac{\partial}{\partial t}(\rho_\alpha\mathbf{v}_0)+\frac{\partial}{\partial \mathbf{r}}\cdot\rho_\alpha\mathbf{v}_0\mathbf{v}_0+\frac{\partial}{\partial \mathbf{r}}\cdot p_\alpha\vec{\mathrm{I}}-\rho_\alpha\mathbf{F}_\alpha^{(1)}-q_\alpha n_\alpha[\mathbf{v}_0\times\mathbf{B}]\right]=0.$$
$$\tag{10.2.6}$$

We introduce the notations

$$\mathbf{L}_\alpha=\tau_\alpha\left[\rho_\alpha\mathbf{F}_\alpha^{(1)}+\frac{q_\alpha}{m_\alpha}\rho_\alpha\mathbf{v}_0\times\mathbf{B}\right], \tag{10.2.7}$$

$$\mathbf{L}=\sum_\alpha\tau_\alpha\left[\rho_\alpha\mathbf{F}_\alpha^{(1)}+\frac{q_\alpha}{m_\alpha}\rho_\alpha\mathbf{v}_0\times\mathbf{B}\right]. \tag{10.2.8}$$

Then

$$\mathbf{L}=\sum_\alpha\mathbf{L}_\alpha\,. \tag{10.2.9}$$

From Eq. (10.2.4) we have

$$\mathbf{L}=\mathbf{L}(t),\ \text{or}\ \mathbf{L}=\mathbf{const}, \tag{10.2.10}$$

and rewrite now Eq. (10.2.5), which contains the density fluctuation [18]

$$\rho_\alpha^{fl}=\tau_\alpha^{(0)}\left(\frac{\partial\rho_\alpha}{\partial t}+\frac{\partial}{\partial \mathbf{r}}\cdot(\rho_\alpha\mathbf{v}_0)\right). \tag{10.2.11}$$

We have

$$\frac{\partial}{\partial t}\mathbf{L}(t)-\sum_\alpha \mathbf{F}_\alpha^{(1)}\rho_\alpha^a-\sum_\alpha \frac{q_\alpha}{m_\alpha}\mathbf{L}_\alpha(t)\times\mathbf{B}$$
$$+\mathbf{v}_0\left\{\frac{\partial}{\partial \mathbf{r}}\cdot\sum_\alpha \tau_\alpha\left[\mathbf{F}_\alpha^{(1)}\rho_\alpha+\frac{q_\alpha}{m_\alpha}\rho_\alpha[\mathbf{v}_0\times\mathbf{B}]\right]\right\}+\left(\sum_\alpha \tau_\alpha\left[\mathbf{F}_\alpha^{(1)}\rho_\alpha+\frac{q_\alpha}{m_\alpha}\rho_\alpha[\mathbf{v}_0\times\mathbf{B}]\right]\cdot\frac{\partial}{\partial \mathbf{r}}\right)\mathbf{v}_0$$
$$+\sum_\alpha \tau_\alpha\left[\rho_\alpha\mathbf{F}_\alpha^{(1)}+\frac{q_\alpha}{m_\alpha}\rho_\alpha[\mathbf{v}_0\times\mathbf{B}]\right]\frac{\partial}{\partial \mathbf{r}}\cdot\mathbf{v}_0+\left(\mathbf{v}_0\cdot\frac{\partial}{\partial \mathbf{r}}\right)\left\{\sum_\alpha \tau_\alpha\left[\rho_\alpha\mathbf{F}_\alpha^{(1)}+\frac{q_\alpha}{m_\alpha}\rho_\alpha[\mathbf{v}_0\times\mathbf{B}]\right]\right\}=0,$$
(10.2.12)

where
$$\rho_\alpha^a=\rho_\alpha-\rho_\alpha^{fl}. \qquad (10.2.13)$$
Using also (10.2.8), we find
$$\sum_\alpha \mathbf{F}_\alpha^{(1)}\rho_\alpha^a=\frac{\partial}{\partial t}\mathbf{L}(t)-\sum_\alpha \frac{q_\alpha}{m_\alpha}\mathbf{L}_\alpha(t)\times\mathbf{B}+\left(\mathbf{L}(t)\cdot\frac{\partial}{\partial \mathbf{r}}\right)\mathbf{v}_0+\mathbf{L}(t)\left(\frac{\partial}{\partial \mathbf{r}}\cdot\mathbf{v}_0\right)+\left(\mathbf{v}_0\cdot\frac{\partial}{\partial \mathbf{r}}\right)\mathbf{L}(t).$$
(10.2.14)

The vector product in Eq. (10.2.14) can be transformed as
$$\mathbf{L}_\alpha(t)\times\mathbf{B}=\tau_\alpha\rho_\alpha\mathbf{F}_\alpha^{(1)}\times\mathbf{B}-\tau_\alpha q_\alpha n_\alpha\left[\mathbf{v}_0B^2-\mathbf{B}(\mathbf{v}_0\cdot\mathbf{B})\right], \qquad (10.2.15)$$
where $q_\alpha n_\alpha$ is the charge of α-species in the unit volume.

Taking into account the relations (10.2.7), (10.2.11) - (10.2.13), we can realize the analogical transformation of the energy condition (10.2.6):
$$\mathbf{v}_0\cdot\sum_\alpha \mathbf{F}_\alpha^{(1)}\rho_\alpha^a=\frac{\partial}{\partial t}\sum_\alpha \tau_\alpha\left(\rho_\alpha\mathbf{F}_\alpha^{(1)}\cdot\mathbf{v}_0\right)+\sum_\alpha \tau_\alpha\mathbf{F}_\alpha^{(1)}\cdot\left[\rho_\alpha\frac{\partial\mathbf{v}_0}{\partial t}+\rho_\alpha\left(\mathbf{v}_0\cdot\frac{\partial}{\partial \mathbf{r}}\right)\mathbf{v}_0+\frac{\partial}{\partial \mathbf{r}}\cdot p_\alpha\vec{\mathrm{I}}\right]$$
$$+\frac{\partial}{\partial \mathbf{r}}\cdot\left\{\sum_\alpha \tau_\alpha\left[\begin{array}{l}\rho_\alpha\mathbf{F}_\alpha^{(1)}\cdot\mathbf{v}_0\mathbf{v}_0+p_\alpha\mathbf{F}_\alpha^{(1)}\cdot\vec{\mathrm{I}}+\frac{1}{2}\rho_\alpha v_0^2\mathbf{F}_\alpha^{(1)}+\frac{3}{2}\mathbf{F}_\alpha^{(1)}p_\alpha\\ +\frac{\rho_\alpha v_0^2}{2}\frac{q_\alpha}{m_\alpha}[\mathbf{v}_0\times\mathbf{B}]+\frac{5}{2}p_\alpha\frac{q_\alpha}{m_\alpha}[\mathbf{v}_0\times\mathbf{B}]\end{array}\right]\right\}$$
$$+\frac{\partial}{\partial \mathbf{r}}\cdot\sum_\alpha \varepsilon_\alpha n_\alpha\mathbf{L}_\alpha-\sum_\alpha \tau_\alpha\mathbf{F}_\alpha^{(1)}\cdot\mathbf{L}_\alpha$$
(10.2.16)

Equations (10.2.7), (10.2.14) and (10.2.16) define the system of the sufficient conditions for levitation.

The choice of the non-local parameter needs in the special consideration [18 - 22]. The system of equations (10.2.1) – (10.2.3) converts in the system of quantum hydrodynamic equations by the suitable choice of the non-local parameter τ. The relation between τ and kinetic energy is used in quantum hydrodynamics
$$\tau=H_\tau/mu^2, \qquad (10.2.17)$$

where u is the particle velocity, H_τ is the coefficient of proportionality which reflects the state of the physical system. In the simplest case H_τ is equal to the Plank constant $\hbar$ and the corresponding relation (10.2.16) correlates with the Heisenberg inequality. From the first glance the approximation (10.2.16) is distinguished radically from the kinetic relation known from the theory of the rarefied gases

$$\tau = \Pi \upsilon\rho \Big/ p, \tag{10.2.18}$$

which is used for the calculation of the non-local parameter in the macroscopic hydrodynamic case (υ is the kinematic viscosity). But it is not a case. In quantum approximation the value $\upsilon^{qu} = \hbar/m$ has the dimension $[cm^2/s]$ and can be called as quantum viscosity, for the electron species $\upsilon^{qu} = \hbar/m_e = 1.1577$ cm^2/s. If we take into account that the value $p/\rho \sim \overline{V^2}$, then the interrelation of (10.2.17) and (10.2.18) becomes obvious.

Conclusion:

Levitation control contains two self-consistent blocks:

1. Definition of the hydrodynamic parameters of the physical system, which are defined as a goal of evolution. The corresponding system of equations is (continuity equation for a mixture)

$$\frac{\partial}{\partial t}\left\{\rho - \sum_\alpha \tau_\alpha \left[\frac{\partial \rho_\alpha}{\partial t} + \frac{\partial}{\partial \mathbf{r}}\cdot(\rho_\alpha \mathbf{v}_0)\right]\right\} + \frac{\partial}{\partial \mathbf{r}}\cdot\left\{\rho\mathbf{v}_0 - \sum_\alpha \tau_\alpha \left[\frac{\partial}{\partial t}(\rho_\alpha \mathbf{v}_0) + \frac{\partial}{\partial \mathbf{r}}\cdot(\rho_\alpha \mathbf{v}_0\mathbf{v}_0) + \vec{\mathrm{I}}\cdot\frac{\partial p_\alpha}{\partial \mathbf{r}}\right]\right\} = 0, \tag{10.2.19}$$

(motion equation)

$$\frac{\partial}{\partial t}\left\{\rho\mathbf{v}_0 - \sum_\alpha \tau_\alpha \left[\frac{\partial}{\partial t}(\rho_\alpha \mathbf{v}_0) + \frac{\partial}{\partial \mathbf{r}}\cdot \rho_\alpha \mathbf{v}_0\mathbf{v}_0 + \frac{\partial p_\alpha}{\partial \mathbf{r}}\right]\right\} + \frac{\partial}{\partial \mathbf{r}}\cdot\left\{\rho\mathbf{v}_0\mathbf{v}_0 + p\vec{\mathrm{I}} - \sum_\alpha \tau_\alpha \left[\begin{aligned}&\frac{\partial}{\partial t}\left(\rho_\alpha\mathbf{v}_0\mathbf{v}_0 + p_\alpha\vec{\mathrm{I}}\right) + \frac{\partial}{\partial \mathbf{r}}\cdot\rho_\alpha(\mathbf{v}_0\mathbf{v}_0)\mathbf{v}_0 + \\ &+2\vec{\mathrm{I}}\left(\frac{\partial}{\partial \mathbf{r}}\cdot(p_\alpha\mathbf{v}_0)\right) + \frac{\partial}{\partial \mathbf{r}}\cdot\left(\vec{\mathrm{I}}p_\alpha\mathbf{v}_0\right)\end{aligned}\right]\right\} = 0, \tag{10.2.20}$$

(energy equation)

$$\frac{\partial}{\partial t}\left\{\rho v_0^2+3p+2\sum_\alpha\varepsilon_\alpha n_\alpha-\sum_\alpha\tau_\alpha\left[\frac{\partial}{\partial t}\left(\rho_\alpha v_0^2+3p_\alpha+2\varepsilon_\alpha n_\alpha\right)\right.\right.$$

$$\left.\left.+\frac{\partial}{\partial\mathbf{r}}\cdot\left(\rho_\alpha v_0^2\mathbf{v}_0+5p_\alpha\mathbf{v}_0+2\varepsilon_\alpha n_\alpha\mathbf{v}_0\right)\right]\right\}+$$

$$+\frac{\partial}{\partial\mathbf{r}}\cdot\left\{\rho v_0^2\mathbf{v}_0+5p\mathbf{v}_0+2\mathbf{v}_0\sum_\alpha\varepsilon_\alpha n_\alpha-\sum_\alpha\tau_\alpha\left[\frac{\partial}{\partial t}\left(\rho_\alpha v_0^2\mathbf{v}_0+\right.\right.\right. \tag{10.2.21}$$

$$\left.+5p_\alpha\mathbf{v}_0+2\varepsilon_\alpha n_\alpha\mathbf{v}_0\right)+\frac{\partial}{\partial\mathbf{r}}\cdot\left(\rho_\alpha v_0^2\mathbf{v}_0\mathbf{v}_0+7p_\alpha\mathbf{v}_0\mathbf{v}_0+p_\alpha v_0^2\ddot{\mathrm{I}}+\right.$$

$$\left.\left.\left.+5\frac{p_\alpha^2}{\rho_\alpha}\ddot{\mathrm{I}}+2\varepsilon_\alpha n_\alpha\mathbf{v}_0\mathbf{v}_0+2\varepsilon_\alpha\frac{p_\alpha}{m_\alpha}\ddot{\mathrm{I}}\right)\right]\right\}=0,$$

where $\mathbf{v}_0$ is the hydrodynamic velocity in the coordinate system at rest, ρ_α is the density of α - species, p is the pressure, $\ddot{\mathrm{I}}$ - unit tensore, ε_α is the internal energy of a particle of the α - species, τ is non-local parameter.

2. Definition of the self-consistent force parameters of the physical system, which supporting the levitation and providing remote control over the flight. The corresponding system of conditions is

$$\frac{\partial}{\partial\mathbf{r}}\cdot\left\{\sum_\alpha\tau_\alpha\left[\rho_\alpha\mathbf{F}_\alpha^{(1)}+\frac{q_\alpha}{m_\alpha}\rho_\alpha\mathbf{v}_0\times\mathbf{B}\right]\right\}=0, \tag{10.2.22}$$

$$\frac{\partial}{\partial t}\left\{\sum_\alpha\tau_\alpha\left[\rho_\alpha\mathbf{F}_\alpha^{(1)}+\frac{q_\alpha}{m_\alpha}\rho_\alpha\mathbf{v}_0\times\mathbf{B}\right]\right\}-\sum_\alpha\mathbf{F}_\alpha^{(1)}\left[\rho_\alpha-\tau_\alpha\left(\frac{\partial\rho_\alpha}{\partial t}+\frac{\partial}{\partial\mathbf{r}}\cdot(\rho_\alpha\mathbf{v}_0)\right)\right]$$

$$-\sum_\alpha\frac{q_\alpha}{m_\alpha}\left\{\tau_\alpha\left[\rho_\alpha\mathbf{F}_\alpha^{(1)}+\frac{q_\alpha}{m_\alpha}\rho_\alpha\mathbf{v}_0\times\mathbf{B}\right]\right\}\times\mathbf{B} \tag{10.2.23}$$

$$+\frac{\partial}{\partial\mathbf{r}}\cdot\left\{\sum_\alpha\tau_\alpha\left[\mathbf{F}_\alpha^{(1)}\rho_\alpha\mathbf{v}_0+\rho_\alpha\mathbf{v}_0\mathbf{F}_\alpha^{(1)}+\frac{q_\alpha}{m_\alpha}\rho_\alpha[\mathbf{v}_0\times\mathbf{B}]\mathbf{v}_0+\frac{q_\alpha}{m_\alpha}\rho_\alpha\mathbf{v}_0[\mathbf{v}_0\times\mathbf{B}]\right]\right\}=0,$$

$$\frac{\partial}{\partial t}\sum_\alpha\tau_\alpha\left(\rho_\alpha\mathbf{F}_\alpha^{(1)}\cdot\mathbf{v}_0\right)$$

$$+\frac{\partial}{\partial\mathbf{r}}\cdot\left\{\sum_\alpha\tau_\alpha\left[\rho_\alpha\mathbf{F}_\alpha^{(1)}\cdot\mathbf{v}_0\mathbf{v}_0+p_\alpha\mathbf{F}_\alpha^{(1)}\cdot\ddot{\mathrm{I}}+\frac{1}{2}\rho_\alpha v_0^2\mathbf{F}_\alpha^{(1)}+\frac{3}{2}\mathbf{F}_\alpha^{(1)}p_\alpha+\frac{\rho_\alpha v_0^2}{2}\frac{q_\alpha}{m_\alpha}[\mathbf{v}_0\times\mathbf{B}]\right.\right.$$

$$\left.\left.+\frac{5}{2}p_\alpha\frac{q_\alpha}{m_\alpha}[\mathbf{v}_0\times\mathbf{B}]+\varepsilon_\alpha n_\alpha\frac{q_\alpha}{m_\alpha}[\mathbf{v}_0\times\mathbf{B}]+\varepsilon_\alpha n_\alpha\mathbf{F}_\alpha^{(1)}\right]\right\}$$

$$-\mathbf{v}_0\cdot\sum_\alpha\rho_\alpha\mathbf{F}_\alpha^{(1)}+\sum_\alpha\tau_\alpha\mathbf{F}_\alpha^{(1)}\cdot\left[\frac{\partial}{\partial t}(\rho_\alpha\mathbf{v}_0)+\frac{\partial}{\partial\mathbf{r}}\cdot\rho_\alpha\mathbf{v}_0\mathbf{v}_0+\frac{\partial}{\partial\mathbf{r}}\cdot p_\alpha\ddot{\mathrm{I}}-\rho_\alpha\mathbf{F}_\alpha^{(1)}-q_\alpha n_\alpha[\mathbf{v}_0\times\mathbf{B}]\right]=0.$$

(10.2.24)

In particular

$$\rho_\alpha \mathbf{F}_\alpha^{(1)} = q_\alpha n_\alpha \mathbf{E} + \mathbf{g}\rho_\alpha . \quad (10.2.25)$$

The hydrodynamic values corresponding (10.2.22) – (10.2.25) are taken from the solution the system (10.2.19) – (10.2.21).

10.3. Some particular cases of the levitation conditions.

Let us consider now the physical sense of the sufficient condition of levitation. With this aim we begin with the simplest case where the stationary physical system is in rest, ($\mathbf{v}_0 = 0$). In the stationary case from the continuum condition (10.2.4)

$$\frac{\partial}{\partial \mathbf{r}} \cdot \left\{ \sum_\alpha \tau_\alpha \rho_\alpha \mathbf{F}_\alpha^{(1)} = 0, \right. \quad (10.3.1)$$

the motion condition (10.2.5) follows

$$\sum_\alpha \left\{ \rho_\alpha \mathbf{F}_\alpha^{(1)} + \frac{q_\alpha}{m_\alpha} \tau_\alpha \left[\rho_\alpha \mathbf{F}_\alpha^{(1)} \times \mathbf{B} \right] \right\} = 0, \quad (10.3.2)$$

and from the energy condition (10.2.6)

$$\frac{\partial}{\partial \mathbf{r}} \cdot \left\{ \sum_\alpha \tau_\alpha \left[p_\alpha \mathbf{F}_\alpha^{(1)} \cdot \vec{\mathrm{I}} + \frac{3}{2} \mathbf{F}_\alpha^{(1)} p_\alpha + \varepsilon_\alpha n_\alpha \mathbf{F}_\alpha^{(1)} \right] \right\} + \sum_\alpha \tau_\alpha \mathbf{F}_\alpha^{(1)} \cdot \left[\frac{\partial}{\partial \mathbf{r}} \cdot p_\alpha \vec{\mathrm{I}} - \rho_\alpha \mathbf{F}_\alpha^{(1)} \right] = 0. \quad (10.3.3)$$

or

$$\frac{\partial}{\partial \mathbf{r}} \cdot \left\{ \sum_\alpha \tau_\alpha \mathbf{F}_\alpha^{(1)} \left[\frac{5}{2} p_\alpha + \varepsilon_\alpha n_\alpha \right] \right\} + \sum_\alpha \tau_\alpha \mathbf{F}_\alpha^{(1)} \cdot \left[\frac{\partial}{\partial \mathbf{r}} \cdot p_\alpha \vec{\mathrm{I}} - \rho_\alpha \mathbf{F}_\alpha^{(1)} \right] = 0. \quad (10.3.4)$$

where ρ_α is the density of α - species, p is the pressure, $\vec{\mathrm{I}}$ - unit tensore, $\mathbf{F}_\alpha^{(1)}$ is the force of the non-nonmagnetic origin acting on the unit of mass, ε_α is the internal energy of a particle of the α - species, τ is non-local parameter and

$$m_\alpha \mathbf{F}_\alpha^{(1)} = q_\alpha \mathbf{E} + \mathbf{g} m_\alpha , \quad (10.3.5)$$

or

$$\rho_\alpha \mathbf{F}_\alpha^{(1)} = q_\alpha n_\alpha \mathbf{E} + \mathbf{g}\rho_\alpha . \quad (10.3.6)$$

Using (10.3.5) and (10.3.6) we obtain from (10.3.2)

$$\sum_\alpha \left\{ q_\alpha n_\alpha \mathbf{E} + \mathbf{g}\rho_\alpha + \frac{q_\alpha}{m_\alpha} \tau_\alpha \left[(q_\alpha n_\alpha \mathbf{E} + \mathbf{g}\rho_\alpha) \times \mathbf{B} \right] \right\} = 0, \quad (10.3.7)$$

We notice, that $\frac{q_\alpha}{m_\alpha} \tau_\alpha B$ is dimensionless value. Let us transform (10.3.7), we have

$$Q\mathbf{E} + \rho \mathbf{g} + \sum_\alpha \left\{ \frac{q_\alpha}{m_\alpha} \tau_\alpha \left[(q_\alpha n_\alpha \mathbf{E} + \mathbf{g}\rho_\alpha) \times \mathbf{B} \right] \right\} = 0 , \quad (10.3.8)$$

where

$$Q = \sum_\alpha q_\alpha n_\alpha = \sum_\alpha Q_\alpha \tag{10.3.9}$$

is the total charge of the unit volume and

$$\rho = \sum_\alpha \rho_\alpha \tag{10.3.10}$$

is the total density. We find from (10.3.8)

$$Q\mathbf{E} + \rho\mathbf{g} + \sum_\alpha \left\{ \frac{q_\alpha}{m_\alpha} \tau_\alpha^{(0)} [q_\alpha n_\alpha \mathbf{E} \times \mathbf{B}] \right\} + \sum_\alpha \left\{ \frac{q_\alpha}{m_\alpha} \tau_\alpha^{(0)} \rho_\alpha [\mathbf{g} \times \mathbf{B}] \right\} = 0 . \tag{10.3.11}$$

The Poynting vector represents the particular case of an energy flux vector for electromagnetic energy; in Poynting's original paper [190] the Poynting vector is defined as $\mathbf{S} = \mathbf{E} \times \mathbf{H}$ where bold letters represent $\mathbf{E}$ is (the electric field vector) and; $\mathbf{H}$ (the magnetic field vector). The Poynting vector is denoted by us as $\mathbf{S}_P$.

$$\mathbf{S}_P = \mathbf{E} \times \mathbf{B} . \tag{10.3.12}$$

Let us introduce the Alexeev vector

$$\mathbf{S}_A = \mathbf{g} \times \mathbf{B} . \tag{10.3.13}$$

We find

$$Q\mathbf{E} + \rho\mathbf{g} + \mathbf{S}_P \sum_\alpha \left\{ \frac{q_\alpha}{m_\alpha} \tau_\alpha Q_\alpha \right\} + \mathbf{S}_A \sum_\alpha \left\{ \frac{q_\alpha}{m_\alpha} \tau_\alpha \rho_\alpha \right\} = 0 \tag{10.3.14}$$

or

$$Q\mathbf{E} + \rho\mathbf{g} + \mathbf{S}_P \sum_\alpha \left\{ \tau_\alpha \left[\frac{q_\alpha}{m_\alpha} \right]^2 \rho_\alpha \right\} + \mathbf{S}_A \sum_\alpha \tau_\alpha Q_\alpha = 0 . \tag{10.3.15}$$

This relation is covering both types of energy and the conversion of one into the other. In local physics $(\tau_\alpha = 0)$ the existence of levitating of the rest body leads to trivial affirmations

$$\mathbf{E} = 0, \ \mathbf{g} = 0 . \tag{10.3.16}$$

It is known that the Umov–Poynting vector discovered by Nikolay Umov in 1874 describes energy flux in liquid and elastic media in a completely generalized view.

From the first glance the relation (10.3.15) is known generalization of Umov-Poynting theorem which in local physics written as

$$\frac{\partial}{\partial t}(u_e + u_m) + \frac{\partial}{\partial \mathbf{r}} \cdot (\mathbf{S}_P + \mathbf{S}_m) = 0 , \tag{10.3.17}$$

(where $\mathbf{S}_m$ is the mechanical energy density in the system) contains other types of energy as well, e.g., mechanical energy. BUT IT IS NOT THE CASE.

Really this relation does not contain the cross effects delivering transformation of the electromagnetic field in gravitation field and vice versa.

Let us consider now the non-stationary case, non-stationary motion condition now is written as follows

$$\frac{\partial}{\partial t}\left\{\sum_\alpha \tau_\alpha \rho_\alpha \mathbf{F}_\alpha^{(1)}\right\}-\sum_\alpha \mathbf{F}_\alpha^{(1)}\left[\rho_\alpha-\tau_\alpha\left(\frac{\partial \rho_\alpha}{\partial t}\right)\right]-\sum_\alpha \frac{q_\alpha}{m_\alpha}\tau_\alpha\left[\rho_\alpha \mathbf{F}_\alpha^{(1)}\times\mathbf{B}\right]=0, \qquad (10.3.18)$$

or (see (10.3.5) and (10.3.6))

$$\sum_\alpha\left\{\frac{\partial}{\partial t}\left[\tau_\alpha\left(q_\alpha n_\alpha \mathbf{E}+\mathbf{g}\rho_\alpha\right)\right]-\left(\frac{q_\alpha}{m_\alpha}\mathbf{E}+\mathbf{g}\right)\left[\rho_\alpha-\tau_\alpha\left(\frac{\partial \rho_\alpha}{\partial t}\right)\right]-\frac{q_\alpha}{m_\alpha}\tau_\alpha\left[\left(q_\alpha n_\alpha \mathbf{E}+\mathbf{g}\rho_\alpha\right)\times\mathbf{B}\right]\right\}=0,$$

$$(10.3.19)$$

or

$$\frac{\partial}{\partial t}\left\{\sum_\alpha \tau_\alpha\left[Q_\alpha \mathbf{E}+\mathbf{g}\rho_\alpha\right]\right\}+\sum_\alpha\left[\frac{q_\alpha}{m_\alpha}\mathbf{E}+\mathbf{g}\right]\tau_\alpha\left(\frac{\partial \rho_\alpha}{\partial t}\right)=$$

$$=\mathbf{S}_P\sum_\alpha \tau_\alpha\left[\frac{q_\alpha}{m_\alpha}\right]^2\rho_\alpha+\mathbf{S}_A\sum_\alpha \tau_\alpha Q_\alpha+Q\mathbf{E}+\rho\mathbf{g}, \qquad (10.3.20)$$

Let us transform the non-local energy equation (10.2.3) written in the general case. It is the law of the energy conservation in the nonlocal physics. This equation can be written in the form

$$\frac{\partial}{\partial t}\left\{\rho v_0^2+3p+2\sum_\alpha \varepsilon_\alpha n_\alpha-\sum_\alpha \tau_\alpha\left[\frac{\partial}{\partial t}\left(\rho_\alpha v_0^2+3p_\alpha+2\varepsilon_\alpha n_\alpha\right)\right.\right.$$

$$\left.\left.+\frac{\partial}{\partial \mathbf{r}}\cdot\left(\rho_\alpha v_0^2\mathbf{v}_0+5p_\alpha\mathbf{v}_0+2\varepsilon_\alpha n_\alpha\mathbf{v}_0\right)-2\mathbf{F}_\alpha^{(1)}\cdot\rho_\alpha\mathbf{v}_0\right]\right\}$$

$$+\frac{\partial}{\partial \mathbf{r}}\cdot\left\{\rho v_0^2\mathbf{v}_0+5p\mathbf{v}_0+2\mathbf{v}_0\sum_\alpha \varepsilon_\alpha n_\alpha-\sum_\alpha \tau_\alpha\left[\frac{\partial}{\partial t}\left(\rho_\alpha v_0^2\mathbf{v}_0\right.\right.\right.$$

$$\left.+5p_\alpha\mathbf{v}_0+2\varepsilon_\alpha n_\alpha\mathbf{v}_0\right)+\frac{\partial}{\partial \mathbf{r}}\cdot\left(\rho_\alpha v_0^2\mathbf{v}_0\mathbf{v}_0+7p_\alpha\mathbf{v}_0\mathbf{v}_0+p_\alpha v_0^2\overleftrightarrow{\mathbf{I}}\right.$$

$$\left.+5\frac{p_\alpha^2}{\rho_\alpha}\overleftrightarrow{\mathbf{I}}+2\varepsilon_\alpha n_\alpha\mathbf{v}_0\mathbf{v}_0+2\varepsilon_\alpha\frac{p_\alpha}{m_\alpha}\overleftrightarrow{\mathbf{I}}\right)-2\rho_\alpha\mathbf{F}_\alpha^{(1)}\cdot\mathbf{v}_0\mathbf{v}_0-2p_\alpha\mathbf{F}_\alpha^{(1)}\cdot\overleftrightarrow{\mathbf{I}}$$

$$-\rho_\alpha v_0^2\mathbf{F}_\alpha^{(1)}-3\mathbf{F}_\alpha^{(1)}p_\alpha-\rho_\alpha v_0^2\frac{q_\alpha}{m_\alpha}\left[\mathbf{v}_0\times\mathbf{B}\right]-5p_\alpha\frac{q_\alpha}{m_\alpha}\left[\mathbf{v}_0\times\mathbf{B}\right]$$

$$\left.\left.-2\varepsilon_\alpha n_\alpha\frac{q_\alpha}{m_\alpha}\left[\mathbf{v}_0\times\mathbf{B}\right]-2\varepsilon_\alpha n_\alpha\mathbf{F}_\alpha^{(1)}\right]\right\}-2\mathbf{v}_0\cdot\sum_\alpha \rho_\alpha\mathbf{F}_\alpha^{(1)}$$

$$+2\sum_\alpha \tau_\alpha\mathbf{F}_\alpha^{(1)}\cdot\left[\frac{\partial}{\partial t}\left(\rho_\alpha\mathbf{v}_0\right)+\frac{\partial}{\partial \mathbf{r}}\cdot\rho_\alpha\mathbf{v}_0\mathbf{v}_0+\frac{\partial}{\partial \mathbf{r}}\cdot p_\alpha\overleftrightarrow{\mathbf{I}}-\rho_\alpha\mathbf{F}_\alpha^{(1)}-q_\alpha n_\alpha\left[\mathbf{v}_0\times\mathbf{B}\right]\right]=0. \qquad (10.3.21)$$

or

$$
\begin{aligned}
&\frac{\partial}{\partial t}\Bigg\{\rho v_0^2+3p+2\sum_\alpha \varepsilon_\alpha n_\alpha-\sum_\alpha \tau_\alpha\Bigg[\frac{\partial}{\partial t}\left(\rho_\alpha v_0^2+3p_\alpha+2\varepsilon_\alpha n_\alpha\right)\\
&+\frac{\partial}{\partial \mathbf{r}}\cdot\left(\rho_\alpha v_0^2\mathbf{v}_0+5p_\alpha\mathbf{v}_0+2\varepsilon_\alpha n_\alpha\mathbf{v}_0\right)-2[Q_\alpha\mathbf{E}+\mathbf{g}\rho_\alpha]\cdot\mathbf{v}_0\Bigg]\Bigg\}\\
&+\frac{\partial}{\partial \mathbf{r}}\cdot\Bigg\{\rho v_0^2\mathbf{v}_0+5p\mathbf{v}_0+2\mathbf{v}_0\sum_\alpha \varepsilon_\alpha n_\alpha-\sum_\alpha \tau_\alpha\Bigg[\frac{\partial}{\partial t}\Big(\rho_\alpha v_0^2\mathbf{v}_0\\
&+5p_\alpha\mathbf{v}_0+2\varepsilon_\alpha n_\alpha\mathbf{v}_0\Big)+\frac{\partial}{\partial \mathbf{r}}\cdot\Big(\rho_\alpha v_0^2\mathbf{v}_0\mathbf{v}_0+7p_\alpha\mathbf{v}_0\mathbf{v}_0+p_\alpha v_0^2\ddot{\mathbf{I}}\\
&+5\frac{p_\alpha^2}{\rho_\alpha}\ddot{\mathbf{I}}+2\varepsilon_\alpha n_\alpha\mathbf{v}_0\mathbf{v}_0+2\varepsilon_\alpha\frac{p_\alpha}{m_\alpha}\ddot{\mathbf{I}}\Big)-2[Q_\alpha\mathbf{E}+\mathbf{g}\rho_\alpha]\cdot\mathbf{v}_0\mathbf{v}_0-2\frac{p_\alpha}{\rho_\alpha}[Q_\alpha\mathbf{E}+\mathbf{g}\rho_\alpha]\cdot\ddot{\mathbf{I}}\\
&-[Q_\alpha\mathbf{E}+\mathbf{g}\rho_\alpha]v_0^2-3\frac{p_\alpha}{\rho_\alpha}[Q_\alpha\mathbf{E}+\mathbf{g}\rho_\alpha]-\rho_\alpha v_0^2\frac{q_\alpha}{m_\alpha}[\mathbf{v}_0\times\mathbf{B}]-5p_\alpha\frac{q_\alpha}{m_\alpha}[\mathbf{v}_0\times\mathbf{B}]\\
&-2\varepsilon_\alpha n_\alpha\frac{q_\alpha}{m_\alpha}[\mathbf{v}_0\times\mathbf{B}]-2\frac{\varepsilon_\alpha}{m_\alpha}[Q_\alpha\mathbf{E}+\mathbf{g}\rho_\alpha]\Bigg]\Bigg\}-2\mathbf{v}_0\cdot\sum_\alpha[Q_\alpha\mathbf{E}+\mathbf{g}\rho_\alpha]\\
&+2\sum_\alpha\tau_\alpha\frac{1}{\rho_\alpha}[Q_\alpha\mathbf{E}+\mathbf{g}\rho_\alpha]\cdot\left[\frac{\partial}{\partial t}(\rho_\alpha\mathbf{v}_0)+\frac{\partial}{\partial \mathbf{r}}\cdot\rho_\alpha\mathbf{v}_0\mathbf{v}_0+\frac{\partial}{\partial \mathbf{r}}\cdot p_\alpha\ddot{\mathbf{I}}\right]-\\
&-2\sum_\alpha\tau_\alpha\frac{1}{\rho_\alpha}[Q_\alpha\mathbf{E}+\mathbf{g}\rho_\alpha]\cdot[Q_\alpha\mathbf{E}+\mathbf{g}\rho_\alpha]-2\sum_\alpha\tau_\alpha\left[\frac{q_\alpha}{m_\alpha}\right]^2\rho_\alpha\mathbf{E}\cdot[\mathbf{v}_0\times\mathbf{B}]-\\
&-2\sum_\alpha\tau_\alpha Q_\alpha\mathbf{g}\cdot[\mathbf{v}_0\times\mathbf{B}]=0.
\end{aligned}
\tag{10.3.22}
$$

or

$$
\begin{aligned}
&\frac{\partial}{\partial t}\left\{\rho v_0^2+3p+2\sum_\alpha \varepsilon_\alpha n_\alpha-\sum_\alpha \tau_\alpha\left[\frac{\partial}{\partial t}\left(\rho_\alpha v_0^2+3p_\alpha+2\varepsilon_\alpha n_\alpha\right)\right.\right.\\
&\left.\left.+\frac{\partial}{\partial \mathbf{r}}\cdot\left(\rho_\alpha v_0^2\mathbf{v}_0+5p_\alpha\mathbf{v}_0+2\varepsilon_\alpha n_\alpha\mathbf{v}_0\right)-2[Q_\alpha\mathbf{E}+\mathbf{g}\rho_\alpha]\cdot\mathbf{v}_0\right]\right\}\\
&+\frac{\partial}{\partial \mathbf{r}}\cdot\left\{\rho v_0^2\mathbf{v}_0+5p\mathbf{v}_0+2\mathbf{v}_0\sum_\alpha \varepsilon_\alpha n_\alpha-\sum_\alpha \tau_\alpha\left[\frac{\partial}{\partial t}\left(\rho_\alpha v_0^2\mathbf{v}_0\right.\right.\right.\\
&\left.+5p_\alpha\mathbf{v}_0+2\varepsilon_\alpha n_\alpha\mathbf{v}_0\right)+\frac{\partial}{\partial \mathbf{r}}\cdot\left(\rho_\alpha v_0^2\mathbf{v}_0\mathbf{v}_0+7p_\alpha\mathbf{v}_0\mathbf{v}_0+p_\alpha v_0^2\overleftrightarrow{\mathbf{I}}\right.\\
&\left.+5\frac{p_\alpha^2}{\rho_\alpha}\overleftrightarrow{\mathbf{I}}+2\varepsilon_\alpha n_\alpha\mathbf{v}_0\mathbf{v}_0+2\varepsilon_\alpha\frac{p_\alpha}{m_\alpha}\overleftrightarrow{\mathbf{I}}\right)-2[Q_\alpha\mathbf{E}+\mathbf{g}\rho_\alpha]\cdot\mathbf{v}_0\mathbf{v}_0-2\frac{p_\alpha}{\rho_\alpha}[Q_\alpha\mathbf{E}+\mathbf{g}\rho_\alpha]\cdot\overleftrightarrow{\mathbf{I}}\\
&-[Q_\alpha\mathbf{E}+\mathbf{g}\rho_\alpha]v_0^2-3\frac{p_\alpha}{\rho_\alpha}[Q_\alpha\mathbf{E}+\mathbf{g}\rho_\alpha]-\rho_\alpha v_0^2\frac{q_\alpha}{m_\alpha}[\mathbf{v}_0\times\mathbf{B}]-5p_\alpha\frac{q_\alpha}{m_\alpha}[\mathbf{v}_0\times\mathbf{B}]\\
&\left.\left.-2\varepsilon_\alpha n_\alpha\frac{q_\alpha}{m_\alpha}[\mathbf{v}_0\times\mathbf{B}]-2\frac{\varepsilon_\alpha}{m_\alpha}[Q_\alpha\mathbf{E}+\mathbf{g}\rho_\alpha]\right]\right\}-2\mathbf{v}_0\cdot\sum_\alpha[Q_\alpha\mathbf{E}+\mathbf{g}\rho_\alpha]\\
&+2\sum_\alpha\tau_\alpha\frac{1}{\rho_\alpha}[Q_\alpha\mathbf{E}+\mathbf{g}\rho_\alpha]\cdot\left[\frac{\partial}{\partial t}\left(\rho_\alpha\mathbf{v}_0\right)+\frac{\partial}{\partial \mathbf{r}}\cdot\rho_\alpha\mathbf{v}_0\mathbf{v}_0+\frac{\partial}{\partial \mathbf{r}}\cdot p_\alpha\overleftrightarrow{\mathbf{I}}\right]-\\
&-2\sum_\alpha\tau_\alpha\frac{1}{\rho_\alpha}[Q_\alpha\mathbf{E}+\mathbf{g}\rho_\alpha]\cdot[Q_\alpha\mathbf{E}+\mathbf{g}\rho_\alpha]-2\sum_\alpha\tau_\alpha\left[\frac{q_\alpha}{m_\alpha}\right]^2\rho_\alpha\mathbf{E}\cdot[\mathbf{v}_0\times\mathbf{B}]-\\
&-2\sum_\alpha\tau_\alpha Q_\alpha\mathbf{g}\cdot[\mathbf{v}_0\times\mathbf{B}]=0.
\end{aligned}
\tag{10.3.23}
$$

The mixed product is written as

$$\mathbf{E}\cdot[\mathbf{v}_0\times\mathbf{B}]=[\mathbf{v}_0\times\mathbf{B}]\cdot\mathbf{E}=-[\mathbf{E}\times\mathbf{B}]\cdot\mathbf{v}_0=-\mathbf{S}_P\cdot\mathbf{v}_0, \tag{10.3.24}$$

$$\mathbf{g}\cdot[\mathbf{v}_0\times\mathbf{B}]=[\mathbf{v}_0\times\mathbf{B}]\cdot\mathbf{g}=-[\mathbf{g}\times\mathbf{B}]\cdot\mathbf{v}_0=-\mathbf{S}_A\cdot\mathbf{v}_0. \tag{10.3.25}$$

Then

$$\frac{\partial}{\partial t}\left\{\rho v_0^2+3p+2\sum_\alpha \varepsilon_\alpha n_\alpha-\sum_\alpha \tau_\alpha\left[\frac{\partial}{\partial t}\left(\rho_\alpha v_0^2+3p_\alpha+2\varepsilon_\alpha n_\alpha\right)\right.\right.$$

$$\left.\left.+\frac{\partial}{\partial \mathbf{r}}\cdot\left(\rho_\alpha v_0^2\mathbf{v}_0+5p_\alpha\mathbf{v}_0+2\varepsilon_\alpha n_\alpha\mathbf{v}_0\right)-2\left[Q_\alpha\mathbf{E}+\mathbf{g}\rho_\alpha\right]\cdot\mathbf{v}_0\right]\right\}$$

$$+\frac{\partial}{\partial \mathbf{r}}\cdot\left\{\rho v_0^2\mathbf{v}_0+5p\mathbf{v}_0+2\mathbf{v}_0\sum_\alpha \varepsilon_\alpha n_\alpha-\sum_\alpha \tau_\alpha\left[\frac{\partial}{\partial t}\left(\rho_\alpha v_0^2\mathbf{v}_0\right.\right.\right.$$

$$\left.+5p_\alpha\mathbf{v}_0+2\varepsilon_\alpha n_\alpha\mathbf{v}_0\right)+\frac{\partial}{\partial \mathbf{r}}\cdot\left(\rho_\alpha v_0^2\mathbf{v}_0\mathbf{v}_0+7p_\alpha\mathbf{v}_0\mathbf{v}_0+p_\alpha v_0^2\vec{\mathrm{I}}\right.$$

$$\left.+5\frac{p_\alpha^2}{\rho_\alpha}\vec{\mathrm{I}}+2\varepsilon_\alpha n_\alpha\mathbf{v}_0\mathbf{v}_0+2\varepsilon_\alpha\frac{p_\alpha}{m_\alpha}\vec{\mathrm{I}}\right)-2\left[Q_\alpha\mathbf{E}+\mathbf{g}\rho_\alpha\right]\cdot\mathbf{v}_0\mathbf{v}_0-2\frac{p_\alpha}{\rho_\alpha}\left[Q_\alpha\mathbf{E}+\mathbf{g}\rho_\alpha\right]\cdot\vec{\mathrm{I}}$$

$$-\left[Q_\alpha\mathbf{E}+\mathbf{g}\rho_\alpha\right]v_0^2-3\frac{p_\alpha}{\rho_\alpha}\left[Q_\alpha\mathbf{E}+\mathbf{g}\rho_\alpha\right]-\rho_\alpha v_0^2\frac{q_\alpha}{m_\alpha}\left[\mathbf{v}_0\times\mathbf{B}\right]-5p_\alpha\frac{q_\alpha}{m_\alpha}\left[\mathbf{v}_0\times\mathbf{B}\right]$$

$$\left.\left.-2\varepsilon_\alpha n_\alpha\frac{q_\alpha}{m_\alpha}\left[\mathbf{v}_0\times\mathbf{B}\right]-2\frac{\varepsilon_\alpha}{m_\alpha}\left[Q_\alpha\mathbf{E}+\mathbf{g}\rho_\alpha\right]\right]\right\}-2\mathbf{v}_0\cdot\sum_\alpha\left[Q_\alpha\mathbf{E}+\mathbf{g}\rho_\alpha\right]$$

$$+2\sum_\alpha \tau_\alpha\frac{1}{\rho_\alpha}\left[Q_\alpha\mathbf{E}+\mathbf{g}\rho_\alpha\right]\cdot\left[\frac{\partial}{\partial t}\left(\rho_\alpha\mathbf{v}_0\right)+\frac{\partial}{\partial \mathbf{r}}\cdot\rho_\alpha\mathbf{v}_0\mathbf{v}_0+\frac{\partial}{\partial \mathbf{r}}\cdot p_\alpha\vec{\mathrm{I}}\right]-$$

$$-2\sum_\alpha \tau_\alpha\frac{1}{\rho_\alpha}\left[Q_\alpha\mathbf{E}+\mathbf{g}\rho_\alpha\right]^2+2\sum_\alpha \tau_\alpha\left[\frac{q_\alpha}{m_\alpha}\right]^2\rho_\alpha\mathbf{S}_P\cdot\mathbf{v}_0+2\sum_\alpha \tau_\alpha Q_\alpha\mathbf{S}_A\cdot\mathbf{v}_0=0.$$

(10.3.26)

Write down the system of the sufficient levitation conditions for the quasi-stationary case neglecting dissipation and the space derivatives in Eq. (10.2.14). We find

$$\sum_\alpha \mathbf{F}_\alpha^{(1)}\rho_\alpha^a=-\sum_\alpha\frac{q_\alpha}{m_\alpha}\mathbf{L}_\alpha(t)\times\mathbf{B}. \tag{10.3.27}$$

or

$$\sum_\alpha \mathbf{F}_\alpha^{(1)}\rho_\alpha^a=\mathbf{B}\times\sum_\alpha \tau_\alpha\frac{q_\alpha}{m_\alpha}\left[\rho_\alpha\mathbf{F}_\alpha^{(1)}+\frac{q_\alpha}{m_\alpha}\rho_\alpha\mathbf{v}_0\times\mathbf{B}\right]. \tag{10.3.28}$$

Introducing the current density

$$\mathbf{j}_\alpha=\tau_\alpha q_\alpha n_\alpha\mathbf{v}_0, \tag{10.3.29}$$

one obtains

$$\sum_\alpha \mathbf{F}_\alpha^{(1)}\rho_\alpha^a=\mathbf{B}\times\sum_\alpha \tau_\alpha q_\alpha n_\alpha\mathbf{F}_\alpha^{(1)}+\mathbf{B}\times\sum_\alpha\frac{q_\alpha}{m_\alpha}\left[\mathbf{j}_\alpha\times\mathbf{B}\right]. \tag{10.3.30}$$

The right-hand-side of Eq. (10.3.30) contains the cross terms for the forces of the mass and electro- magneto-dynamic origin. The last term in Eq. (10.3.30) can be written also in the form

$$\mathbf{B}\times\sum_{\alpha}\frac{q_\alpha}{m_\alpha}[\mathbf{j}_\alpha\times\mathbf{B}]=\sum_{\alpha}\rho_\alpha\tau_\alpha\left[\frac{q_\alpha}{m_\alpha}\right]^2\{\mathbf{v}_0B^2-\mathbf{B}(\mathbf{v}_0\cdot\mathbf{B})\}. \tag{10.3.31}$$

Taking into account (10.2.17), (10.2.18) it is naturally to suppose that

$$k_B T\tau_\alpha \geq \hbar, \tag{10.3.32}$$

Introduce now

$$\tau_\alpha = A\frac{\hbar}{k_B T}, \tag{10.3.33}$$

where A is a parameter which leads to appearance the effective temperature T_{eff}. Other approximations can be used, for example

$$\tau_\alpha = \frac{\hbar}{k_B T_{\alpha,eff}}. \tag{10.3.34}$$

Let us consider now the particular case when $\mathbf{v}_0 = 0$. In equations (10.2.7), (10.2.14) and (10.2.16) we conserve the terms up to the τ_α order. From Eq. (10.2.14) follows

$$\sum_{\alpha}\mathbf{F}_\alpha^{(1)}\rho_\alpha^a=\frac{\partial}{\partial t}\mathbf{L}(t)-\sum_{\alpha}\frac{q_\alpha}{m_\alpha}\mathbf{L}_\alpha(t)\times\mathbf{B}, \tag{10.3.35}$$

where now

$$\mathbf{L}_\alpha(t)=\tau_\alpha\rho_\alpha\mathbf{F}_\alpha^{(1)}, \tag{10.3.36}$$

$$\mathbf{L}(t)=\sum_{\alpha}\tau_\alpha\rho_\alpha\mathbf{F}_\alpha^{(1)}. \tag{10.3.37}$$

Then

$$\sum_{\alpha}\mathbf{F}_\alpha^{(1)}\rho_\alpha^a=\frac{\partial}{\partial t}\sum_{\alpha}\tau_\alpha^{(0)}\rho_\alpha^a\mathbf{F}_\alpha^{(1)}-\sum_{\alpha}q_\alpha n_\alpha^a\tau_\alpha\mathbf{F}_\alpha^{(1)}\times\mathbf{B}. \tag{10.3.38}$$

Introduce the explicit expression for the mass force

$$\mathbf{F}_\alpha^{(1)}=\mathbf{g}+\frac{q_\alpha}{m_\alpha}\mathbf{E} \tag{10.3.39}$$

in Eq. (10.3.30)

$$\sum_{\alpha}\mathbf{F}_\alpha^{(1)}\rho_\alpha^a=\frac{\partial}{\partial t}\sum_{\alpha}\tau_\alpha\rho_\alpha^a\left(\mathbf{g}+\frac{q_\alpha}{m_\alpha}\mathbf{E}\right)-\sum_{\alpha}q_\alpha n_\alpha^a\tau_\alpha\left(\mathbf{g}+\frac{q_\alpha}{m_\alpha}\mathbf{E}\right)\times\mathbf{B}, \tag{10.3.40}$$

where $n_\alpha^a=\rho_\alpha^a/m_\alpha$. From Eq. (10.3.40) follows

$$\sum_{\alpha}\mathbf{F}_\alpha^{(1)}\rho_\alpha^a=\frac{\partial}{\partial t}\sum_{\alpha}\tau_\alpha\rho_\alpha^a\mathbf{g}+\frac{\partial}{\partial t}\left[\mathbf{E}\sum_{\alpha}\tau_\alpha n_\alpha^a q_\alpha\right]-\mathbf{g}\times\mathbf{B}\sum_{\alpha}q_\alpha n_\alpha^a\tau_\alpha^{(0)}-\mathbf{E}\times\mathbf{B}\sum_{\alpha}\left(\frac{q_\alpha}{m_\alpha}\right)^2\rho_\alpha^a\tau_\alpha. \tag{10.3.41}$$

Let us introduce in Eq. (10.3.41) the Umov – Pointing vector $\mathbf{S}_P$ and Alexeev vector $\mathbf{S}_A$ in the forms (10.3.12) and (10.3.13). In this case

$$\sum_{\alpha}\mathbf{F}_\alpha^{(1)}\rho_\alpha^a=\frac{\partial}{\partial t}\left(\sum_{\alpha}\tau_\alpha\rho_\alpha^a\mathbf{g}\right)+\frac{\partial}{\partial t}\left[\mathbf{E}\sum_{\alpha}\tau_\alpha n_\alpha^a q_\alpha\right]-\mathbf{S}_A\sum_{\alpha}q_\alpha n_\alpha^a\tau_\alpha-\mathbf{S}_P\sum_{\alpha}\left(\frac{q_\alpha}{m_\alpha}\right)^2\rho_\alpha^a\tau_\alpha. \tag{10.3.42}$$

For the approximation (10.3.33) one obtains

$$\sum_\alpha \mathbf{F}_\alpha^{(1)} \rho_\alpha^a = A \frac{\hbar}{k_B}\left[\frac{\partial}{\partial t}\left(\frac{\rho^a}{T}\mathbf{g}\right)+\frac{\partial}{\partial t}\left(\mathbf{E}\frac{Q^a}{T}\right)-\mathbf{S}_A\frac{Q^a}{T}-\mathbf{S}_P\frac{1}{T}\sum_\alpha\left(\frac{q_\alpha}{m_\alpha}\right)^2\rho_\alpha^a\right], \qquad (10.3.43)$$

where the average charge density is introduced

$$Q^a = \sum_\alpha q_\alpha n_\alpha^a . \qquad (10.3.44)$$

The analogical transformations of the energy condition (10.2.16) can be realized for this particular case when $\mathbf{v}_0^a = 0$. Namely

$$-\sum_\alpha \tau_\alpha \rho_\alpha^a \mathbf{F}_\alpha^{(1)} \cdot \sum_\alpha \mathbf{F}_\alpha^{(1)} \rho_\alpha^a = \sum_\alpha \tau_\alpha \mathbf{F}_\alpha^{(1)} \cdot \left[\frac{\partial}{\partial \mathbf{r}} \cdot p_\alpha^a \vec{\mathrm{I}}\right] + \frac{\partial}{\partial \mathbf{r}} \cdot \left\{\sum_\alpha \tau_\alpha \left[p_\alpha^a \mathbf{F}_\alpha^{(1)} \cdot \vec{\mathrm{I}} + \frac{3}{2}\mathbf{F}_\alpha^{(1)} p_\alpha^a\right]\right\}$$
$$+\frac{\partial}{\partial \mathbf{r}} \cdot \sum_\alpha \varepsilon_\alpha n_\alpha^a \tau_\alpha \mathbf{F}_\alpha^{(1)}. \qquad (10.3.45)$$

For the approximation (10.3.33) we find from Eq. (10.3.45)

$$\frac{\partial}{\partial \mathbf{r}} \cdot \sum_\alpha \left[\frac{5}{2} p_\alpha^a + \varepsilon_\alpha n_\alpha^a\right] \mathbf{F}_\alpha^{(1)} - \sum_\alpha \left(\frac{5}{2} p_\alpha^a + \varepsilon_\alpha n_\alpha^a\right) \mathbf{F}_\alpha^{(1)} \cdot \frac{\partial \ln T}{\partial \mathbf{r}}$$
$$= -\left[\sum_\alpha \rho_\alpha^a \mathbf{F}_\alpha^{(1)}\right]^2 - \sum_\alpha \mathbf{F}_\alpha^{(1)} \cdot \frac{\partial p_\alpha^a}{\partial \mathbf{r}}. \qquad (10.3.46)$$

Eq. (10.3.46) should be considered as a relation defining the energy consumption needed for the levitation.

From (10.3.38) follows a relation

$$\sum_\alpha \mathbf{F}_\alpha^{(1)} \rho_\alpha^a = \mathbf{g}\rho^a + \mathbf{E}\sum \frac{q_\alpha}{m_\alpha}\rho_\alpha^a = \mathbf{g}\rho^a + \mathbf{E}\sum_\alpha q_\alpha n_\alpha^a = \mathbf{g}\rho^a + \mathbf{E}Q^a, \qquad (10.3.47)$$

which can be used for the transformation of Eq. (10.3.46). For a tentative estimate we can omit the derivatives of the logarithmic terms and the time derivatives for a quasi-neutral media. As a result from (10.3.46)

$$\frac{\partial}{\partial \mathbf{r}} \cdot \left\{\mathbf{g}\sum_\alpha\left[\frac{5}{2}p_\alpha^a + \varepsilon_\alpha n_\alpha^a\right]\right\} + \frac{\partial}{\partial \mathbf{r}} \cdot \left\{\mathbf{E}\sum_\alpha \frac{q_\alpha}{m_\alpha}\left[\frac{5}{2}p_\alpha^a + \varepsilon_\alpha n_\alpha^a\right]\right\}$$
$$= -\left[\rho^a \mathbf{g} + \mathbf{E}Q^a\right]^2 - \mathbf{g} \cdot \frac{\partial p^a}{\partial \mathbf{r}} - \mathbf{E} \cdot \sum_\alpha \frac{q_\alpha}{m_\alpha}\frac{\partial p_\alpha^a}{\partial \mathbf{r}}. \qquad (10.3.48)$$

For a quasi-neutral media

$$Q^a = 0, \qquad (10.3.49)$$

then

$$\frac{\partial}{\partial \mathbf{r}} \cdot \left[\mathbf{g}\left(\frac{5}{2}p^a + \Xi\right)\right] + \frac{\partial}{\partial \mathbf{r}} \cdot \left\{\mathbf{E}\sum_\alpha \frac{q_\alpha}{m_\alpha}\left[\frac{5}{2}p_\alpha^a + \Xi_\alpha\right]\right\}$$
$$= -\left[\rho^a \mathbf{g}\right]^2 - \mathbf{E} \cdot \sum_\alpha \frac{q_\alpha}{m_\alpha}\frac{\partial p_\alpha^a}{\partial \mathbf{r}} - \mathbf{g} \cdot \frac{\partial p^a}{\partial \mathbf{r}}, \qquad (10.3.50)$$

where

$$\Xi = \sum_\alpha \varepsilon_\alpha n_\alpha^a \,, \; \Xi_\alpha = \varepsilon_\alpha n_\alpha^a \,. \tag{10.3.51}$$

Let us obtain a tentative estimate from for the quasi-stationary case in a quasi-neutral media. From (10.3.42) for the case under consideration we have

$$\sum_\alpha \mathbf{F}_\alpha^{(1)} \rho_\alpha^a = -\mathbf{S}_A \sum_\alpha q_\alpha n_\alpha^a \tau_\alpha - \mathbf{S}_P \sum_\alpha \left(\frac{q_\alpha}{m_\alpha} \right)^2 \rho_\alpha^a \tau_\alpha \,. \tag{10.3.52}$$

From (10.3.47), (10.3.52) we find

$$\rho^a \mathbf{g} = -\mathbf{S}_A \sum_\alpha q_\alpha n_\alpha^a \tau_\alpha - \mathbf{S}_P \sum_\alpha \left(\frac{q_\alpha}{m_\alpha} \right)^2 \rho_\alpha^a \tau_\alpha \,, \tag{10.3.53}$$

or

$$\rho^a \mathbf{g} = -A \frac{\hbar}{k_B} \mathbf{S}_P \frac{1}{T} \sum_\alpha \left(\frac{q_\alpha}{m_\alpha} \right)^2 \rho_\alpha^a \tag{10.3.54}$$

in the case of (10.3.33) approximation. Relation leads in SI to the estimate

$$\rho^a \mathbf{g} \cong -A \frac{\mathbf{S}_P}{T} \cdot 2.138 \cdot 10^{-19} n_e^a \tag{10.3.55}$$

or

$$\rho^a \mathbf{g} \cong 2.138 \cdot 10^{-19} \frac{A}{T} [\mathbf{B} \times \mathbf{E}] n_e^a \,. \tag{10.3.56}$$

The following Table 10.1 lists known examples of number densities at 1 atm and 20 °C, unless otherwise noted.

Table 10.1. Molecular number densities

Molecular number density and related parameters of some materials

Material		Number density (*n*)	Density (ρ)
	Units	(10^{27} m^{-3}) or (10^{21} cm^{-3})	(10^3 kg/m^3) or (g/cm^3)
dry air		0.02504	1.2041×10^{-3}
water		33.3679	0.99820
diamond		176.2	3.513

Let us use now (10.1.4) and the obvious phenomenological condition of the force balance we have

$$\mathbf{F} = \frac{\chi}{\mu_0 \mu} \mathrm{grad} B^2 = \rho g \hat{\mathbf{e}}_z \,, \tag{10.3.57}$$

where ρ is the mass density of the material to be levitated and $\hat{\mathbf{e}}_z$ is the unit vector in the vertical direction, magnetic susceptibility χ is negative for diamagnetic materials. In the frame of the phenomenological description of the magnetic and gravitational field we have

$$w = w_m + w_g = -\frac{\chi}{\mu\mu_0} B^2 + \rho g z \,. \tag{10.3.58}$$

A necessary condition for stability is

$$\int_S \mathbf{F} \cdot d\mathbf{s} < 0 \,, \tag{10.3.59}$$

where S is any small closed surface surrounding the equilibrium point. It leads to the condition

$$\operatorname{div} \mathbf{F} < 0 \,. \tag{10.3.60}$$

This relation leads to the stability condition

$$\Delta w = \text{divgrad } w = \text{divgrad } w_m = -\frac{\chi}{\mu\mu_0} \Delta B^2 = -\text{div}\mathbf{F} > 0 \,, \tag{10.3.61}$$

if $\chi < 0$ (diamagnetic materials) and $\Delta B^2 > 0$. The corresponding stability investigation from the phenomenological point of view was realized in [182 - 186].

From the relation (10.3.56) follows ($\mu \sim 1$)

$$\rho g = 2 \frac{\chi}{\mu_0} B \frac{\partial B}{\partial z} \tag{10.3.62}$$

and from (10.3.51)

$$\rho^a \mathbf{g} = -\mathbf{S}_P \tau \sum_\alpha \left(\frac{q_\alpha}{m_\alpha} \right)^2 \rho_\alpha^a \,, \tag{10.3.63}$$

if the non-local parameter does not depend on the sort of species α. After equalizing the right-hand-sides of relations (10.3.61) and (10.3.62) one obtains

$$\tau^{(0)} \mu_0 E \frac{q_e}{2m_e} q_e n_e^a = \chi \frac{\partial B}{\partial z} \,, \tag{10.3.64}$$

because

$$\sum_\alpha \left(\frac{q_\alpha}{m_\alpha} \right)^2 \rho_\alpha^a \cong \left(\frac{q_i}{m_i} \right)^2 \rho^a + \left(\frac{q_e}{m_e} \right)^2 \rho_e^a = \frac{q_i^2}{m_i} n_i^a + \frac{q_e^2}{m_e} n_e^a \cong \left(\frac{q_e}{m_e} \right)^2 \rho_e^a \,. \tag{10.3.65}$$

Let us introduce the character length l_m

$$l_m = \mu_0 \frac{q_e^2}{2m_e} \,, \tag{10.3.66}$$

hence from (10.3.63), (10.3.65)

$$l_m E n_e^a = -|\chi| \frac{1}{\tau} \frac{\partial B}{\partial z} \,. \tag{10.3.67}$$

Introduce the electromotive force (EMF) for a particle

$$\mathrm{E}_{ind} = l_m E \,, \tag{10.3.68}$$

and for n_e^a particles

$$\mathrm{E}_{ind,n} = l_m E n_e^a \,. \tag{10.3.69}$$

Hence from (10.3.66), (10.3.68) we find

$$\mathrm{E}_{ind,n} = -\frac{|\chi|}{\tau}\frac{\partial B}{\partial z} \,. \tag{10.3.70}$$

Formally Eq. (10.3.69) can be written in the form of Faraday's law of induction, the most widespread version of this law states that the induced electromotive force in any closed circuit is equal to the rate of change of the magnetic flux through the circuit:

$$\mathrm{E}_{ind} = -\frac{\partial \Phi_B}{\partial t} \,, \tag{10.3.71}$$

where Φ_B is the magnetic flux. This version of Faraday's law strictly holds only when the closed circuit is a loop of infinitely thin wire and is invalid in some other circumstances. Nevertheless formally

$$\mathrm{E}_{ind,n} = -|\chi|\frac{1}{\tau}\frac{\partial B}{\partial t}\frac{\partial t}{\partial z} \,, \tag{10.3.72}$$

or

$$\mathrm{E}_{ind,n} = -|\chi|\frac{1}{\tau}\frac{\partial B}{\partial t}\frac{1}{v_m} \,. \tag{10.3.73}$$

After introduction of the character counter square

$$S_m = \frac{|\chi|}{\tau v_m n_e^a} \,, \tag{10.3.74}$$

we reach the relation in the form of Faraday's law

$$\mathrm{E}_{ind} = -\frac{\partial \Phi_B}{\partial t} \,. \tag{10.3.75}$$

The following conclusions of the principal significance can be done:

1. The levitation effects are the direct consequence of the non-local equations (10.2.1) – (10.2.3).
2. The sufficient conditions of levitation are the particular case of Eqs. (10.2.1) – (10.2.3).
3. The strict theory of levitation can be constructed only in the frame of non-local physics.

4. Fluctuations of the gravitational field lead to the electro- magneto dynamical fluctuations and verse versa. This fact can effect on the work of electronic devices during the evolution of the wave atmospheric fronts.
5. Levitation effects are connected not only with the electro-magnetic energy flux $\mathbf{S}_P$, but also with the cross flux $\mathbf{S}_A$.
6. Usual local conditions of levitation are the deep particular cases of the non-local theory.

Let us consider now the problems of stability of levitating objects. We revisit the levitation phenomenon using the nonlocal physical description of this levitation phenomenon. This approach can identify the conditions when the levitation can take place under the influence of correlated electromagnetic and gravitational fields. The sufficient mathematical conditions of levitation are used. It means that the regime of levitation could be realized from the position of the non-local hydrodynamics. The stability of the spherical levitating objects is investigated. The appearance of the strong radial fluctuations leads to the destruction of the levitation regime. Then we intend apply the non-local physics methods (obtained in the frame of the unified non-local theory of transport processes (UNT)) to the effect of levitation. We intend to answer two questions:
1) Is it possible using the sufficient conditions of levitation to obtain the stable levitating object?
2) Is it possible to speak about the destruction of the radial stability of the levitating spherical object as a result of the strong radial fluctuations?

10.4. Spherical levitating object

Let us construct the theory of levitating objects in the frame of UNT. This theory leads to the two systems of the hydrodynamic equations:
1. The first one does not contain the forces at all. This situation can be realized if the second item takes place.
2. All sufficient conditions (10.2.7), (10.2.14) and (10.2.16) which define the physical system levitation are fulfilled. This second system uses the hydrodynamic values $\rho_\alpha, \mathbf{v}_0, p_\alpha$ (obtained from the first system) for defining of the electro-magnetic field configuration.

This splitting of description leads to the significant simplification of the numerical calculations. Let us write down the nonlocal hydrodynamic equations in the spherical coordinate system corresponding to the Item 1.

As an example we write Eq. (10.2.1) for the case (see Appendix 1)

$$\frac{\partial}{\partial t}\left\{\rho-\tau\left[\frac{\partial \rho}{\partial t}+\frac{1}{r^2}\frac{\partial\left(r^2\rho v_{0r}\right)}{\partial r}+\frac{1}{r\sin\theta}\frac{\partial\left(\rho v_{0\varphi}\right)}{\partial\varphi}+\frac{1}{r\sin\theta}\frac{\partial\left(\rho v_{0\theta}\sin\theta\right)}{\partial\theta}\right]\right\}$$

$$+\frac{1}{r^2}\frac{\partial}{\partial r}\left\{r^2\left\{\rho v_{0r}-\tau\left[\frac{\partial}{\partial t}\left(\rho v_{0r}\right)+\frac{1}{r^2}\frac{\partial\left(r^2\rho v_{0r}^2\right)}{\partial r}+\frac{1}{r\sin\theta}\frac{\partial\left(\rho v_{0\varphi}v_{0r}\right)}{\partial\varphi}\right.\right.\right.$$

$$\left.\left.\left.+\frac{1}{r\sin\theta}\frac{\partial\left(\rho v_{0\theta}v_{0r}\sin\theta\right)}{\partial\theta}-\rho g_r\right]\right\}\right\}+\frac{1}{r\sin\theta}\frac{\partial}{\partial\varphi}\left\{\rho v_{0\varphi}-\tau\left[\frac{\partial}{\partial t}\left(\rho v_{0\varphi}\right)+\frac{1}{r^2}\frac{\partial\left(r^2\rho v_{0r}v_{0\varphi}\right)}{\partial r}\right.\right.$$

$$\left.\left.+\frac{1}{r\sin\theta}\frac{\partial\left(\rho v_{0\varphi}^2\right)}{\partial\varphi}+\frac{1}{r\sin\theta}\frac{\partial\left(\rho v_{0\theta}v_{0\varphi}\sin\theta\right)}{\partial\theta}-\rho g_\varphi\right]\right\}+\frac{1}{r\sin\theta}\frac{\partial}{\partial\theta}\left\{\sin\theta\left\{\rho v_{0\theta}-\tau\left[\frac{\partial}{\partial t}\left(\rho v_{0\theta}\right)\right.\right.\right.$$

$$\left.\left.\left.+\frac{1}{r^2}\frac{\partial\left(r^2\rho v_{0r}v_{0\theta}\right)}{\partial r}+\frac{1}{r\sin\theta}\frac{\partial\left(\rho v_{0\varphi}v_{0\theta}\right)}{\partial\varphi}+\frac{1}{r\sin\theta}\frac{\partial\left(\rho v_{0\theta}^2\sin\theta\right)}{\partial\theta}-\rho g_\theta\right]\right\}\right\}$$

$$-\frac{1}{r^2}\frac{\partial}{\partial r}\left(\tau r^2\frac{\partial p}{\partial r}\right)-\frac{1}{r^2\sin\theta}\frac{\partial}{\partial\theta}\left(\tau\sin\theta\frac{\partial p}{\partial\theta}\right)-\frac{1}{r^2\sin^2\theta}\frac{\partial}{\partial\varphi}\left(\tau\frac{\partial p}{\partial\varphi}\right)=0. \quad (10.4.1)$$

The full system of equations for the multi-component species (containing also particles with the internal energies) in the spherical coordinate system can be found in [19 - 22]. Here we write the simplified system of equations for the one component physical system with the azimuthally φ - symmetry.

Continuity equation

$$\frac{\partial}{\partial t}\left\{\rho-\tau\left[\frac{\partial \rho}{\partial t}+\frac{1}{r^2}\frac{\partial\left(r^2\rho v_{0r}\right)}{\partial r}+\frac{1}{r\sin\theta}\frac{\partial\left(\rho v_{0\theta}\sin\theta\right)}{\partial\theta}\right]\right\}$$

$$+\frac{1}{r^2}\frac{\partial}{\partial r}\left\{r^2\left\{\rho v_{0r}-\tau\left[\frac{\partial}{\partial t}\left(\rho v_{0r}\right)+\frac{1}{r^2}\frac{\partial\left(r^2\rho v_{0r}^2\right)}{\partial r}+\frac{1}{r\sin\theta}\frac{\partial\left(\rho v_{0\theta}v_{0r}\sin\theta\right)}{\partial\theta}\right]\right\}\right\}$$

$$+\frac{1}{r\sin\theta}\frac{\partial}{\partial\theta}\left\{\sin\theta\left\{\rho v_{0\theta}-\tau\left[\frac{\partial}{\partial t}\left(\rho v_{0\theta}\right)+\frac{1}{r^2}\frac{\partial\left(r^2\rho v_{0r}v_{0\theta}\right)}{\partial r}+\frac{1}{r\sin\theta}\frac{\partial\left(\rho v_{0\theta}^2\sin\theta\right)}{\partial\theta}\right]\right\}\right\}$$

$$-\frac{1}{r^2}\frac{\partial}{\partial r}\left(\tau r^2\frac{\partial p}{\partial r}\right)-\frac{1}{r^2\sin\theta}\frac{\partial}{\partial\theta}\left(\tau\sin\theta\frac{\partial p}{\partial\theta}\right)=0. \quad (10.4.2)$$

Momentum equation (radial r - component)

$$\frac{\partial}{\partial t}\left\{\rho v_{0r}-\tau\left[\frac{\partial}{\partial t}\left(\rho v_{0r}\right)+\frac{1}{r^2}\frac{\partial\left(r^2\rho v_{0r}^2\right)}{\partial r}+\frac{1}{r\sin\theta}\frac{\partial\left(\rho v_{0\theta}v_{0r}\sin\theta\right)}{\partial\theta}+\frac{\partial p}{\partial r}\right]\right\}$$

$$+\frac{1}{r^2}\frac{\partial}{\partial r}\left\{r^2\left\{\rho v_{0r}^2-\tau\left[\frac{\partial}{\partial t}\left(\rho v_{0r}^2\right)+\frac{1}{r^2}\frac{\partial\left(r^2\rho v_{0r}^3\right)}{\partial r}+\frac{1}{r\sin\theta}\frac{\partial\left(\rho v_{0\theta}v_{0r}^2\sin\theta\right)}{\partial\theta}\right]\right\}\right\}$$

$$+\frac{1}{r\sin\theta}\frac{\partial}{\partial\theta}\left\{\sin\theta\left\{\rho v_{0\theta}v_{0r}-\tau\left[\frac{\partial}{\partial t}\left(\rho v_{0\theta}v_{0r}\right)+\frac{1}{r^2}\frac{\partial\left(r^2\rho v_{0\theta}v_{0r}^2\right)}{\partial r}++\frac{1}{r\sin\theta}\frac{\partial\left(\rho v_{0\theta}^2v_{0r}\sin\theta\right)}{\partial\theta}\right]\right\}\right\}$$

$$+\frac{\partial p}{\partial r}-\frac{\partial}{\partial r}\left(\tau\frac{\partial p}{\partial t}\right)-2\frac{\partial}{\partial r}\left(\tau\left(\frac{1}{r^2}\frac{\partial\left(r^2 p v_{0r}\right)}{\partial r}+\frac{1}{r\sin\theta}\frac{\partial\left(p v_{0\theta}\sin\theta\right)}{\partial\theta}\right)\right)$$

$$-\frac{1}{r^2}\frac{\partial}{\partial r}\left(\tau r^2\frac{\partial\left(p v_{0r}\right)}{\partial r}\right)-\frac{1}{r^2\sin\theta}\frac{\partial}{\partial\theta}\left(\tau\sin\theta\frac{\partial\left(p v_{0r}\right)}{\partial\theta}\right)=0. \qquad (10.4.3)$$

Momentum equation (angle θ- component)

$$\frac{\partial}{\partial t}\left\{\rho v_{0\theta}-\tau\left[\frac{\partial}{\partial t}\left(\rho v_{0\theta}\right)+\frac{1}{r^2}\frac{\partial\left(r^2\rho v_{0r}v_{0\theta}\right)}{\partial r}+\frac{1}{r\sin\theta}\frac{\partial\left(\rho v_{0\theta}^2\sin\theta\right)}{\partial\theta}+\frac{1}{r}\frac{\partial p}{\partial\theta}\right]\right\}$$

$$+\frac{1}{r^2}\frac{\partial}{\partial r}\left\{r^2\left\{\rho v_{0r}v_{0\theta}-\tau\left[\frac{\partial}{\partial t}\left(\rho v_{0r}v_{0\theta}\right)+\frac{1}{r^2}\frac{\partial\left(r^2\rho v_{0r}^2 v_{0\theta}\right)}{\partial r}+\frac{1}{r\sin\theta}\frac{\partial\left(\rho v_{0\theta}^2 v_{or}\sin\theta\right)}{\partial\theta}\right]\right\}\right\}$$

$$+\frac{1}{r\sin\theta}\frac{\partial}{\partial\theta}\left\{\sin\theta\left\{\rho v_{0\theta}^2-\tau\left[\frac{\partial}{\partial t}\left(\rho v_{0\theta}^2\right)+\frac{1}{r^2}\frac{\partial\left(r^2\rho v_{0r}v_{0\theta}^2\right)}{\partial r}\right.\right.\right.$$

$$\left.\left.\left.+\frac{1}{r\sin\theta}\frac{\partial\left(\rho v_{0\theta}^3\sin\theta\right)}{\partial\theta}\right]\right\}\right\}+\frac{1}{r}\frac{\partial p}{\partial\theta}-\frac{1}{r}\frac{\partial}{\partial\theta}\left(\tau\frac{\partial p}{\partial t}\right)$$

$$-\frac{2}{r}\frac{\partial}{\partial\theta}\left(\tau\left(\frac{1}{r^2}\frac{\partial\left(r^2 p v_{0r}\right)}{\partial r}+\frac{1}{r\sin\theta}\frac{\partial\left(p v_{0\theta}\sin\theta\right)}{\partial\theta}\right)\right)$$

$$-\frac{1}{r^2}\frac{\partial}{\partial r}\left(\tau r^2\frac{\partial\left(p v_{0\theta}\right)}{\partial r}\right)-\frac{1}{r^2\sin\theta}\frac{\partial}{\partial\theta}\left(\tau\sin\theta\frac{\partial\left(p v_{0\theta}\right)}{\partial\theta}\right)=0. \qquad (10.4.4)$$

Energy equation

$$\frac{\partial}{\partial t}\left\{\frac{1}{2}\rho v_0^2+\frac{3}{2}p\right\}$$

$$-\frac{\partial}{\partial t}\left\{\tau\left[\frac{\partial}{\partial t}\left(\frac{1}{2}\rho v_0^2+\frac{3}{2}p\right)+\frac{1}{r^2}\frac{\partial}{\partial r}\left(r^2 v_{0r}\left(\frac{1}{2}\rho v_0^2+\frac{5}{2}p\right)\right)+\frac{1}{r\sin\theta}\frac{\partial}{\partial\theta}\left(\sin\theta v_{0\theta}\left(\frac{1}{2}\rho v_0^2+\frac{5}{2}p\right)\right)\right]\right\}$$

$$+\frac{1}{r^2}\frac{\partial}{\partial r}\left\{r^2\left\{\left(\frac{1}{2}\rho v_0^2+\frac{5}{2}p\right)v_{0r}-\tau\left[\frac{\partial}{\partial t}\left(\left(\frac{1}{2}\rho v_0^2+\frac{5}{2}p\right)v_{0r}\right)+\frac{1}{r^2}\frac{\partial}{\partial r}\left(r^2\left(\frac{1}{2}\rho v_0^2+\frac{7}{2}p\right)v_{0r}^2\right)\right.\right.\right.$$

$$\left.\left.\left.+\frac{1}{r\sin\theta}\frac{\partial}{\partial\theta}\left(\sin\theta\left(\frac{1}{2}\rho v_0^2+\frac{7}{2}p\right)v_{0\theta}v_{0r}\right)\right]\right\}\right\}+\frac{1}{r\sin\theta}\frac{\partial}{\partial\theta}\left\{\sin\theta\left\{\left(\frac{1}{2}\rho v_0^2+\frac{5}{2}p\right)v_{0\theta}\right.\right.$$

$$-\tau\left[\frac{\partial}{\partial t}\left(\left(\frac{1}{2}\rho v_0^2+\frac{5}{2}p\right)v_{0\theta}\right)+\frac{1}{r^2}\frac{\partial}{\partial r}\left(r^2\left(\frac{1}{2}\rho v_0^2+\frac{7}{2}p\right)v_{0r}v_{0\theta}\right)\right.$$

$$\left.\left.\left.+\frac{1}{r\sin\theta}\frac{\partial}{\partial\theta}\left(\sin\theta\left(\frac{1}{2}\rho v_0^2+\frac{7}{2}p\right)v_{0\theta}^2\right)\right]\right\}\right\}-\frac{1}{r^2\sin\theta}\frac{\partial}{\partial\theta}\left(\tau\sin\theta\frac{\partial}{\partial\theta}\left(\frac{1}{2}p v_0^2+\frac{5}{2}\frac{p^2}{\rho}\right)\right)=0.$$

(10.4.5)

For the full spherical symmetry, when only r - dependence takes place we have:

Continuity equation

$$\frac{\partial}{\partial t}\left\{\rho-\tau\left[\frac{\partial\rho}{\partial t}+\frac{1}{r^2}\frac{\partial\left(r^2\rho v_{0r}\right)}{\partial r}\right]\right\}$$

$$+\frac{1}{r^2}\frac{\partial}{\partial r}\left\{r^2\left\{\rho v_{0r}-\tau\left[\frac{\partial}{\partial t}(\rho v_{0r})+\frac{1}{r^2}\frac{\partial\left(r^2\rho v_{0r}^2\right)}{\partial r}\right]\right\}\right\}-\frac{1}{r^2}\frac{\partial}{\partial r}\left(\tau r^2\frac{\partial p}{\partial r}\right)=0\,. \qquad (10.4.6)$$

Momentum equation

$$\frac{\partial}{\partial t}\left\{\rho v_{0r}-\tau\left[\frac{\partial}{\partial t}(\rho v_{0r})+\frac{1}{r^2}\frac{\partial\left(r^2\rho v_{0r}^2\right)}{\partial r}+\frac{\partial p}{\partial r}\right]\right\}+\frac{1}{r^2}\frac{\partial}{\partial r}\left\{r^2\left\{\rho v_{0r}^2-\tau\left[\frac{\partial}{\partial t}(\rho v_{0r}^2)+\frac{1}{r^2}\frac{\partial\left(r^2\rho v_{0r}^3\right)}{\partial r}\right]\right\}\right\}$$

$$+\frac{\partial p}{\partial r}-\frac{\partial}{\partial r}\left(\tau\frac{\partial p}{\partial t}\right)-2\frac{\partial}{\partial r}\left(\tau\frac{1}{r^2}\frac{\partial\left(r^2 p v_{0r}\right)}{\partial r}\right)-\frac{1}{r^2}\frac{\partial}{\partial r}\left(\tau r^2\frac{\partial(p v_{0r})}{\partial r}\right)=0\,. \qquad (10.4.7)$$

Energy equation

$$\frac{\partial}{\partial t}\left\{\frac{1}{2}\rho v_0^2+\frac{3}{2}p-\tau\left[\frac{\partial}{\partial t}\left(\frac{1}{2}\rho v_0^2+\frac{3}{2}p\right)+\frac{1}{r^2}\frac{\partial}{\partial r}\left(r^2 v_{0r}\left(\frac{1}{2}\rho v_0^2+\frac{5}{2}p\right)\right)\right]\right\}+$$

$$+\frac{1}{r^2}\frac{\partial}{\partial r}\left\{r^2\left(\frac{1}{2}\rho v_0^2+\frac{5}{2}p\right)v_{0r}-\tau\left[\frac{\partial}{\partial t}\left(\left(\frac{1}{2}\rho v_0^2+\frac{5}{2}p\right)v_{0r}\right)+\frac{1}{r^2}\frac{\partial}{\partial r}\left(r^2\left(\frac{1}{2}\rho v_0^2+\frac{7}{2}p\right)v_{0r}^2\right)\right]\right\}=0\,.$$

$$(10.4.8)$$

For the stationary case we find after some transformations:
continuity equation

$$r^2\rho v_{0r}-\tau\frac{\partial\left(r^2\rho v_{0r}^2\right)}{\partial r}-\tau r^2\frac{\partial p}{\partial r}=0\,, \qquad (10.4.9)$$

motion equation

$$\frac{\partial}{\partial r}\left\{\rho v_{0r}^2 r^2\right\}-\tau\frac{\partial^2}{\partial r^2}\left(r^2\rho v_{0r}^3\right)+r^2\frac{\partial p}{\partial r}-3\tau r^2\frac{\partial^2}{\partial r^2}(p v_{0r})-6\tau r\frac{\partial}{\partial r}(p v_{0r})+8\tau p v_{0r}=0\,, \quad (10.4.10)$$

energy equation

$$r^2\left(\rho v_0^2+5p\right)v_{0r}-\tau\frac{\partial}{\partial r}\left(r^2\left(\rho v_0^2+7p\right)v_{0r}^2\right)=0\,. \qquad (10.4.11)$$

Obviously continuity equation (10.4.6) and energy equation can be integrated once in the stationary case (see (10.4.10), (10.4.11)). For the following application of the numerical methods it is reasonable to continue the transformation of Eqs. (10.4.9) - (10.4.11). We find:
continuity equation

$$r\rho v_{0r}-2\tau\rho v_{0r}^2-2\tau r\rho v_{0r}\frac{\partial v_{0r}}{\partial r}-\tau r v_{0r}^2\frac{\partial\rho}{\partial r}-\tau r\frac{\partial p}{\partial r}=0\,, \qquad (10.4.12)$$

momentum equation

$$\tau^2 r^2 \frac{\partial^2}{\partial r^2}\left(\rho v_{0r}^3\right) + 4\tau^2 r \frac{\partial}{\partial r}\left(\rho v_{0r}^3\right) + 2\tau^2 \rho v_{0r}^3$$
$$+ 3\tau^2 r^2 \frac{\partial^2}{\partial r^2}\left(p v_{0r}\right) + 6\tau^2 r \frac{\partial}{\partial r}\left(p v_{0r}\right) - 8\tau^2 p v_{0r} - r^2 \rho v_{0r} = 0, \tag{10.4.13}$$

energy equation

$$r\left(\rho v_0^2 + 5p\right) - \tau r\left(14p + 4\rho v_0^2\right)\frac{\partial v_{0r}}{\partial r} - \tau r v_{0r}^3 \frac{\partial \rho}{\partial r} - 7\tau r v_{0r} \frac{\partial p}{\partial r} - 2\tau\left(\rho v_0^2 + 7p\right)v_{0r} = 0. \tag{10.4.14}$$

Equation (10.4.13) is obtained after adding the momentum equation (10.4.10) multiplied by the coefficient τ with the continuity equation (10.4.9). Let us introduce now the new dependent variables

$$y = \rho v_{0r}^3, \tag{10.4.15}$$

$$z = p v_{0r}. \tag{10.4.16}$$

We reach the system of equations which was used in the following numerical integrations:

continuity equation

$$ry - 2\tau y v_{0r} - 2\tau r y \frac{\partial v_{0r}}{\partial r} - \tau r v_{0r} \frac{\partial y}{\partial r} + 3\tau r y \frac{\partial v_{0r}}{\partial r} - \tau r v_{0r} \frac{\partial z}{\partial r} + \tau r z \frac{\partial v_{0r}}{\partial r} = 0, \tag{10.4.17}$$

momentum equation

$$\tau^2 r^2 \frac{\partial^2 y}{\partial r^2} + 4\tau^2 r \frac{\partial y}{\partial r} + 2\tau^2 y + 3\tau^2 r^2 \frac{\partial^2 z}{\partial r^2} + 6\tau^2 r \frac{\partial z}{\partial r} - 8\tau^2 z - r^2 \frac{y}{v_{0r}^2} = 0, \tag{10.4.18}$$

energy equation

$$r(y + 5z) - \tau r(7z + y)\frac{\partial v_{0r}}{\partial r} - \tau r v_{0r} \frac{\partial y}{\partial r} - 7\tau r v_{0r} \frac{\partial z}{\partial r} - 2\tau v_{0r}(y + 7z) = 0. \tag{10.4.19}$$

The system of equations (10.4.17) - (10.4.19) contains the dependent variables v_{0r}, y, z. We transform (10.4.17) - (10.4.19) to the dimensionless form using the scales of length L, velocity V, time τ, pressure P, mass density R. The dimensionless equations (10.4.17) - (10.4.19) have the form

continuity equation

$$\hat{r}\hat{z}\frac{\partial \hat{v}_{0r}}{\partial \hat{r}} - 2\hat{r}\hat{y}\frac{\partial \hat{v}_{0r}}{\partial \hat{r}} - \hat{r}\hat{v}_{0r}\frac{\partial \hat{y}}{\partial \hat{r}} + 3\hat{r}\hat{y}\frac{\partial \hat{v}_{0r}}{\partial \hat{r}} - \hat{r}\hat{v}_{0r}\frac{\partial \hat{z}}{\partial \hat{r}} + \hat{r}\hat{y} - 2\hat{y}\hat{v}_{0r} = 0, \tag{10.4.20}$$

momentum equation

$$\hat{r}^2 \frac{\partial^2 \hat{y}}{\partial \hat{r}^2} + 3\hat{r}^2 \frac{\partial^2 \hat{z}}{\partial \hat{r}^2} + 4\hat{r}\frac{\partial \hat{y}}{\partial \hat{r}} + 6\hat{r}\frac{\partial \hat{z}}{\partial \hat{r}} + 2\hat{y} - 8\hat{z} - \hat{r}^2 \frac{\hat{y}}{\hat{v}_{0r}^2} = 0, \tag{10.4.21}$$

energy equation

$$\hat{r}(7\hat{z} + \hat{y})\frac{\partial \hat{v}_{0r}}{\partial \hat{r}} + \hat{r}\hat{v}_{0r}\frac{\partial \hat{y}}{\partial \hat{r}} + 7\hat{r}\hat{v}_{0r}\frac{\partial \hat{z}}{\partial \hat{r}} + 2\hat{v}_{0r}(\hat{y} + 7\hat{z}) - \hat{r}(\hat{y} + 5\hat{z}) = 0. \tag{10.4.22}$$

$$\hat{y} = \hat{\rho}\hat{v}_{0r}^3, \tag{10.4.23}$$

$$\hat{z} = \hat{p}\hat{v}_{0r}. \tag{10.4.24}$$

10.5. About stability of levitating objects

We will use the following statement of the problem. The spherical levitating object is placed in the space. A perturbation takes place on the surface $(\hat{r} = 1)$ of this object. What can be said about stability of this object? This statement belongs to the class of Cauchy problems. If $\hat{v}_{0r}(1) = 0$, then the object is stable and Eqs. (10.4.20) - (10.4.22) are satisfied identically. Let us introduce the radial perturbations on the surface of the object. Now we are ready to display the results of the mathematical modeling realized with the help of Maple (the versions Maple 9 or more can be used). The system (10.4.20) - (10.4.22) have the great possibilities of mathematical modeling as result of changing of six Cauchy conditions describing the character features of physical system.

Maple program contains Maple's notations – for example the expression $D(\widetilde{v}_{0r})(1) = 1$ means in the usual notations $(\partial \widetilde{v}_{0r} / \partial \widetilde{r})(1) = 1$, independent variable t responds to $\widetilde{r}$. The following Maple notations on figures are used: v- velocity $\hat{v}_{0r}$, p - self-consistent pressure $\hat{p}$, and r- the density $\hat{\rho}$, T - $\widetilde{\tau} = 1$. Explanations placed under all following figures. The results of the calculations are presented in figures 10.5.1 - 10.5.16. We use the following lines: $\widetilde{v}_{0r}$ - solid line, $\hat{p}$ - dashed line, $\hat{\rho}$ - dotted line. The information required is contained in the figures and in figure captions. The Cauchy conditions are written under each figure, these conditions can be changed widely. The upper label contains information about the limits of the solution existence. Figures 10.5.4, 10.5.8, 10.5.12 and 10.5.16 contain the space evolution of the ratio $\hat{p}/\hat{\rho}$, which is proportional to the temperature near the object surface. The left and right boundaries of the solution existence are indicated as lim1 and lim2 correspondingly.

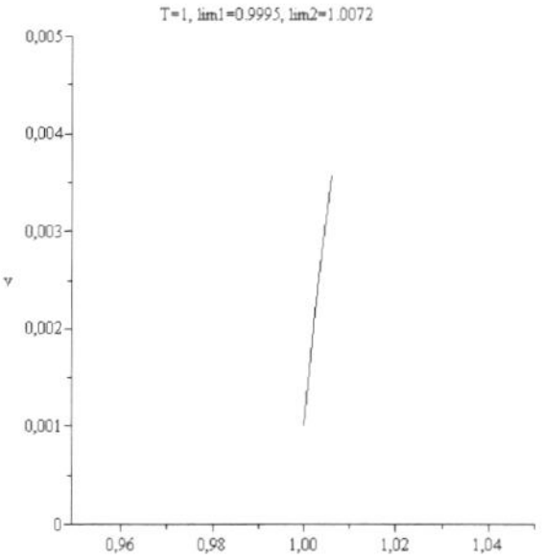

Fig. 10.5.1. Evolution of $\hat{v}_{0r}(\widetilde{r})$;

$v_{0r}(1) = 10^{-3}$, $\hat{y}(1) = 10^{-9}$, $\hat{z}(1) = 10^{-3}$, $D(\hat{v}_{0r})(1) = 1$, $D(\hat{y})(1) = 1$, $D(\hat{z})(1) = 1$, $\hat{p}(1) = 1$, $\hat{\rho}(1) = 1$.

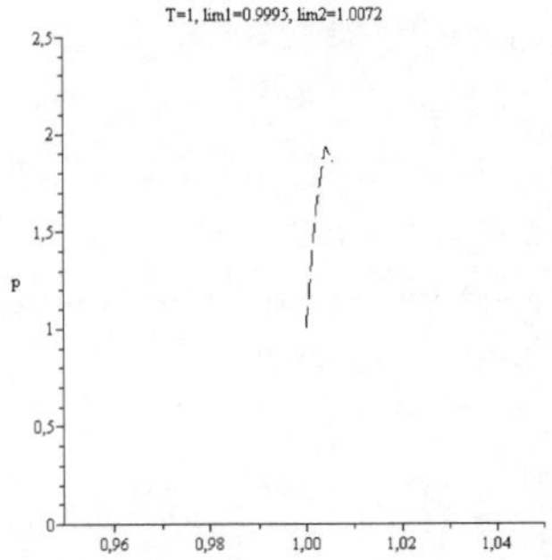

Fig. 10.5.2. Evolution of $\hat{p}(\widetilde{r})$;

$v_{0r}(1)=10^{-3},\ \hat{y}(1)=10^{-9},\ \hat{z}(1)=10^{-3},\ D(\hat{v}_{0r})(1)=1,\ D(\hat{y})(1)=1,\ D(\hat{z})(1)=1,\ \hat{p}(1)=1,\ \hat{\rho}(1)=1.$

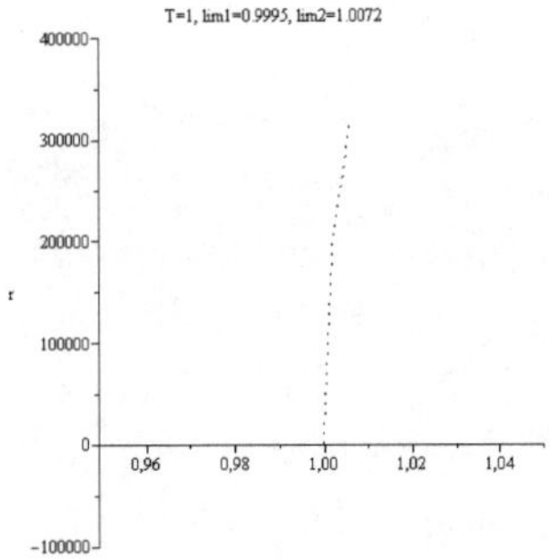

Fig. 10.5.3. Evolution of $\hat{\rho}(\widetilde{r})$;

$v_{0r}(1)=10^{-3},\ \hat{y}(1)=10^{-9},\ \hat{z}(1)=10^{-3},\ D(\hat{v}_{0r})(1)=1,\ D(\hat{y})(1)=1,\ D(\hat{z})(1)=1,\ \hat{p}(1)=1,\ \hat{\rho}(1)=1.$

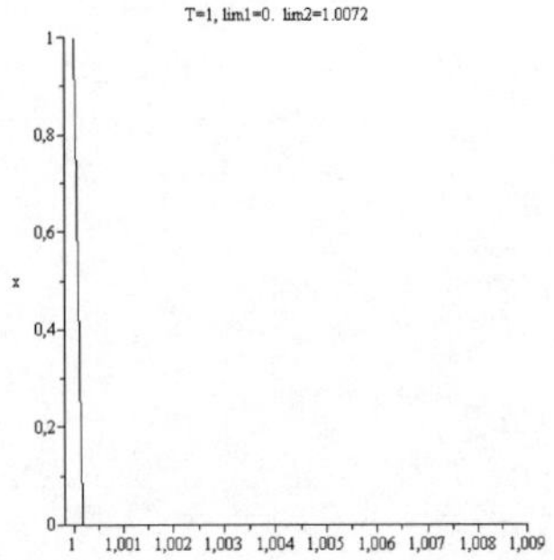

Fig. 10.5.4. Evolution of $\hat{p}(\hat{r})/\hat{\rho}(\widetilde{r})$

$v_{0r}(1)=10^{-3},\ \hat{y}(1)=10^{-9},\ \hat{z}(1)=10^{-3},\ D(\hat{v}_{0r})(1)=1,\ D(\hat{y})(1)=1,\ D(\hat{z})(1)=1,\ \hat{p}(1)=1,\ \hat{\rho}(1)=1.$

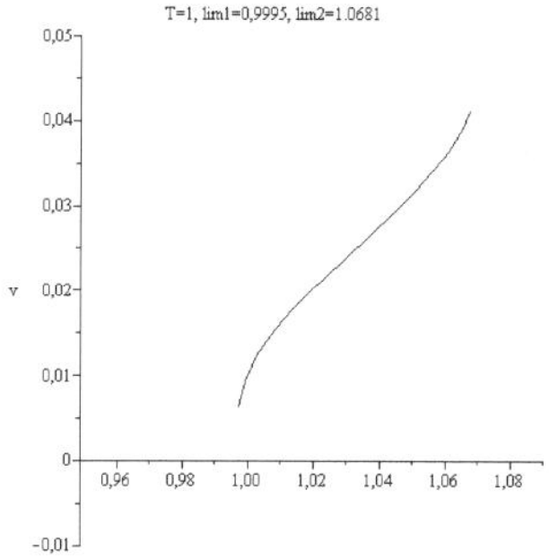

Fig. 10.5.5. Evolution of $\hat{v}_{0r}(\tilde{r})$;

$v_{0r}(1)=10^{-2},\ \hat{y}(1)=10^{-6},\ \hat{z}(1)=10^{-2},\ D(\hat{v}_{0r})(1)=1,\ D(\hat{y})(1)=1,\ D(\hat{z})(1)=1,\ \hat{p}(1)=1,\ \hat{\rho}(1)=1$

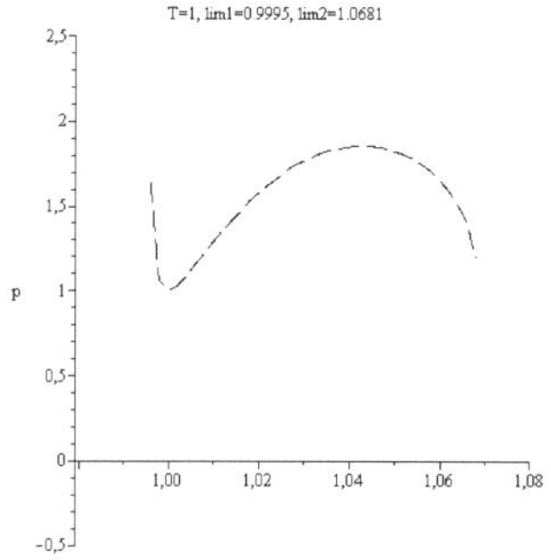

Fig.10.5.6. Evolution of $\hat{p}_{0r}(\tilde{r})$;

$v_{0r}(1)=10^{-2},\ \hat{y}(1)=10^{-6},\ \hat{z}(1)=10^{-2},\ D(\hat{v}_{0r})(1)=1,\ D(\hat{y})(1)=1,\ D(\hat{z})(1)=1,\ \hat{p}(1)=1,\ \hat{\rho}(1)=1$

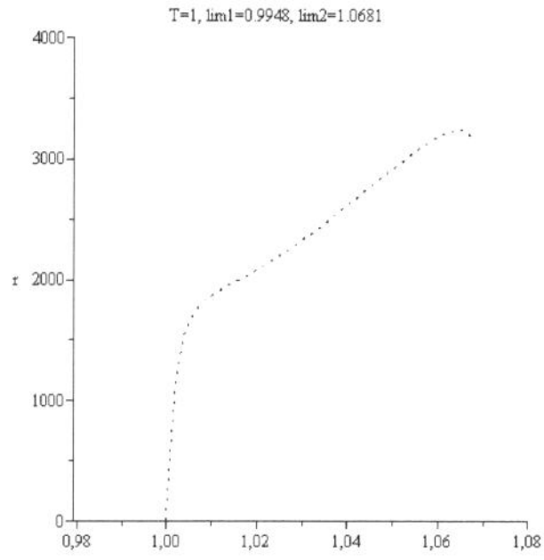

Fig. 10.5.7. Evolution of $\hat{\rho}(\tilde{r})$;

$v_{0r}(1)=10^{-2},\ \hat{y}(1)=10^{-6},\ \hat{z}(1)=10^{-2},\ D(\hat{v}_{0r})(1)=1,\ D(\hat{y})(1)=1,\ D(\hat{z})(1)=1,\ \hat{p}(1)=1,\ \hat{\rho}(1)=1$

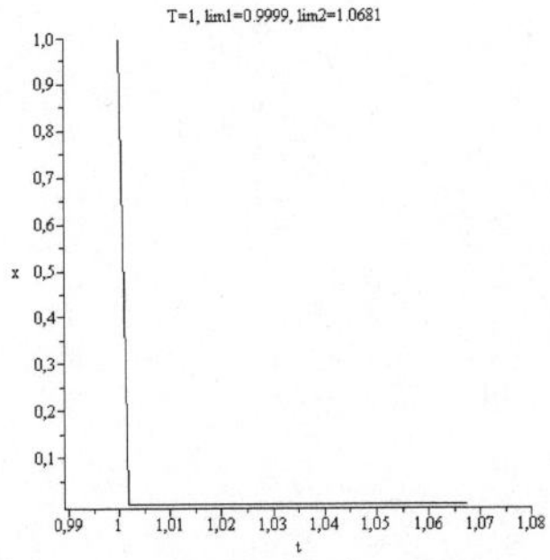

Fig. 10.5.8. Evolution of $\hat{p}(\hat{r})/\hat{\rho}(\tilde{r})$;

$v_{0r}(1)=10^{-2},\ \hat{y}(1)=10^{-6},\ \hat{z}(1)=10^{-2},\ D(\hat{v}_{0r})(1)=1,\ D(\hat{y})(1)=1,\ D(\hat{z})(1)=1,\ \hat{p}(1)=1,\ \hat{\rho}(1)=1$

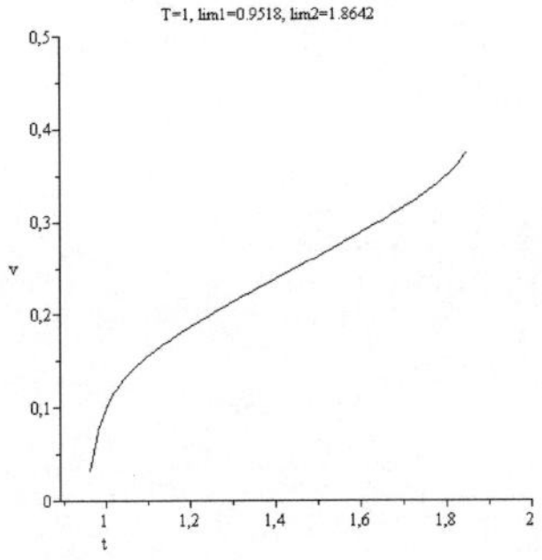

Fig. 10.5.9. Evolution of $\hat{v}_{0r}(\tilde{r})$;

$v_{0r}(1)=10^{-1},\ \hat{y}(1)=10^{-3},\ \hat{z}(1)=10^{-1},\ D(\hat{v}_{0r})(1)=1,\ D(\hat{y})(1)=1,\ D(\hat{z})(1)=1,\ \hat{p}(1)=1,\ \hat{\rho}(1)=1$

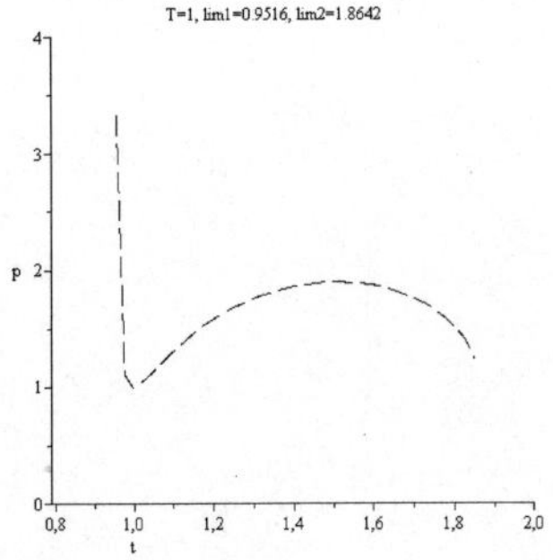

Fig. 10.5.10. Evolution of $\hat{p}(\tilde{r})$;

$v_{0r}(1)=10^{-1},\ \hat{y}(1)=10^{-3},\ \hat{z}(1)=10^{-1},\ D(\hat{v}_{0r})(1)=1,\ D(\hat{y})(1)=1,\ D(\hat{z})(1)=1,\ \hat{p}(1)=1,\ \hat{\rho}(1)=1$

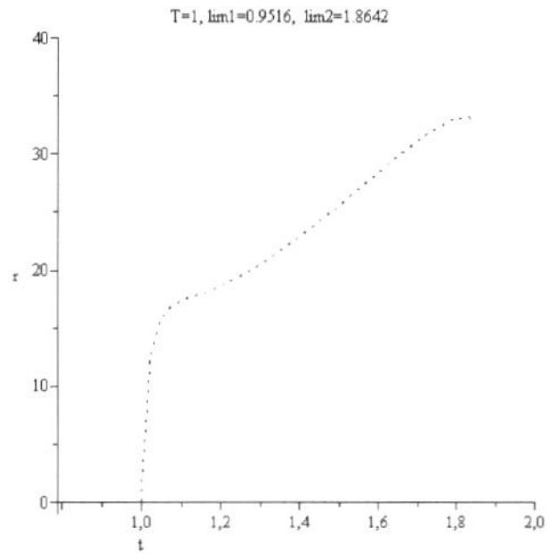

Fig. 10.5.11. Evolution of $\hat{\rho}(\tilde{r})$;

$v_{0r}(1)=10^{-1},\ \hat{y}(1)=10^{-3},\ \hat{z}(1)=10^{-1},\ D(\hat{v}_{0r})(1)=1,\ D(\hat{y})(1)=1,\ D(\hat{z})(1)=1,\ \hat{p}(1)=1,\ \hat{\rho}(1)=1$

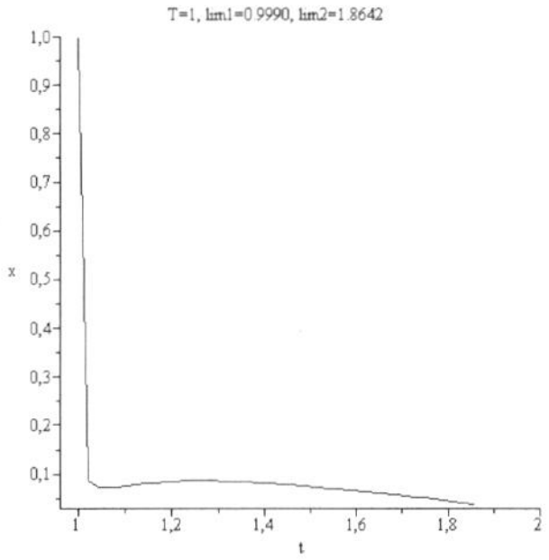

Fig. 10.5.12. Evolution of $\hat{p}(\hat{r})/\hat{\rho}(\tilde{r})$;

$v_{0r}(1)=10^{-1},\ \hat{y}(1)=10^{-3},\ \hat{z}(1)=10^{-1},\ D(\hat{v}_{0r})(1)=1,\ D(\hat{y})(1)=1,\ D(\hat{z})(1)=1,\ \hat{p}(1)=1,\ \hat{\rho}(1)=1$

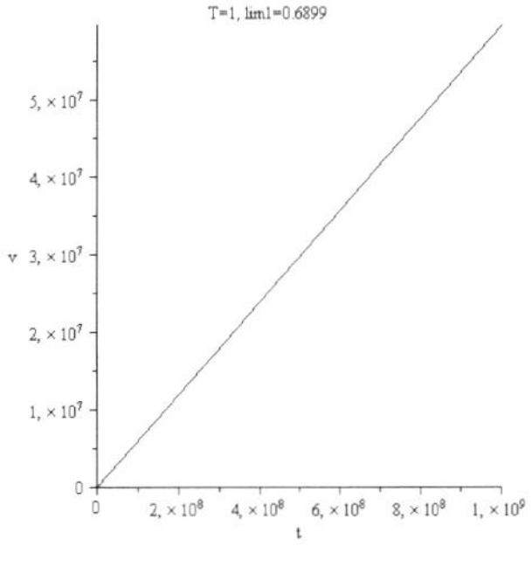

Fig. 10.5.13. Evolution of $\hat{v}_{0r}(\tilde{r})$;

$v_{0r}(1)=1,\ \hat{y}(1)=1,\ \hat{z}(1)=1,\ D(\hat{v}_{0r})(1)=1,\ D(\hat{y})(1)=1,\ D(\hat{z})(1)=1,\ \hat{p}(1)=1,\ \hat{\rho}(1)=1.$

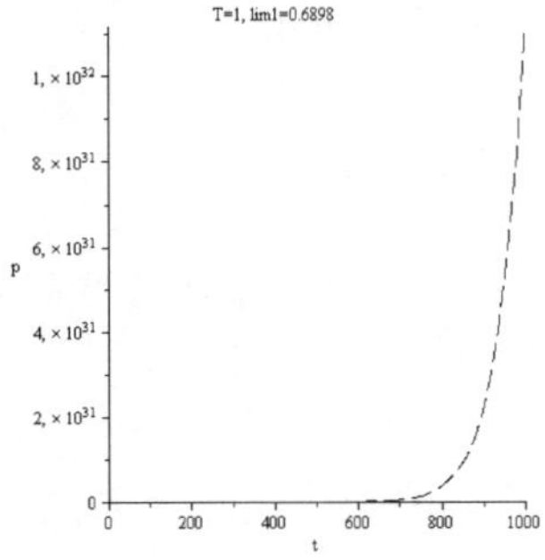

Fig. 10.5.14. Evolution of $\hat{p}(\tilde{r})$;

$v_{0r}(1)=1,\ \hat{y}(1)=1,\ \hat{z}(1)=1,\ D(\hat{v}_{0r})(1)=1,\ D(\hat{y})(1)=1,\ D(\hat{z})(1)=1,\ \hat{p}(1)=1,\ \hat{\rho}(1)=1$.

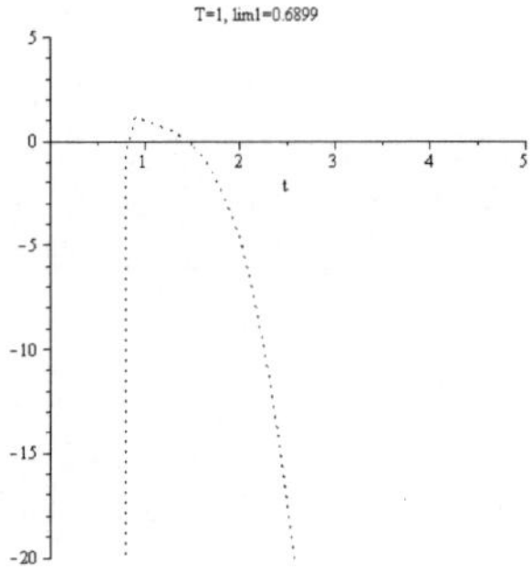

Fig. 10.5.15. Evolution of $\hat{\rho}(\tilde{r})$;

$v_{0r}(1)=1,\ \hat{y}(1)=1,\ \hat{z}(1)=1,\ D(\hat{v}_{0r})(1)=1,\ D(\hat{y})(1)=1,\ D(\hat{z})(1)=1,\ \hat{p}(1)=1,\ \hat{\rho}(1)=1$.

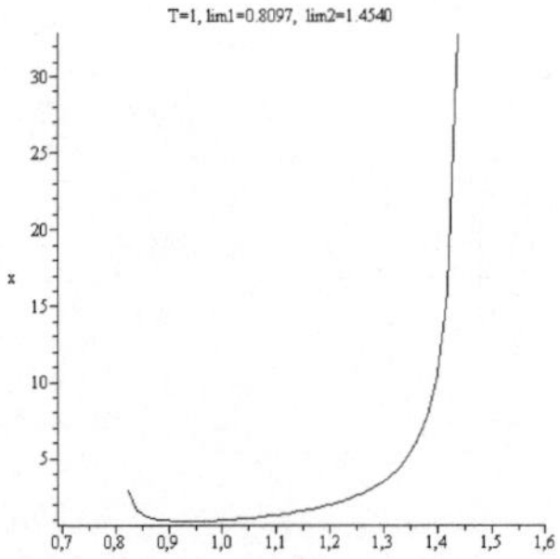

Fig. 10.5.16. Evolution of $\hat{p}(\hat{r})/\hat{\rho}(\tilde{r})$;

$v_{0r}(1)=1,\ \hat{y}(1)=1,\ \hat{z}(1)=1,\ D(\hat{v}_{0r})(1)=1,\ D(\hat{y})(1)=1,\ D(\hat{z})(1)=1,\ \hat{p}(1)=1,\ \hat{\rho}(1)=1$.

10.6. Necessary conditions for the stability

Let us consider now in details the second part of the problem which was formulated at the beginning of section 3. Namely we transform the general stability conditions (10.2.7), (10.2.14) and (10.2.16) for the simplest stationary case when $\mathbf{v}_0 = 0$. In other words we obtain the necessary conditions defining the configuration of the electro-magnetic field for the stable object. Then if $\mathbf{v}_0 = 0$ one obtains from (10.2.7), (10.2.14) and (10.2.16) correspondingly

$$\mathbf{L}_\alpha = \tau \rho_\alpha \mathbf{F}_\alpha^{(1)}, \tag{10.6.1}$$

$$\sum_\alpha \mathbf{F}_\alpha^{(1)} \rho_\alpha^a = -\tau \sum_\alpha q_\alpha n_\alpha \left[\mathbf{F}_\alpha^{(1)} \times \mathbf{B}\right], \tag{10.6.2}$$

$$\tau \frac{5}{2} \frac{\partial}{\partial \mathbf{r}} \cdot \sum_\alpha \left[\mathbf{F}_\alpha^{(1)} p_\alpha\right] + \frac{\partial}{\partial \mathbf{r}} \cdot \sum_\alpha \frac{1}{\rho_\alpha} \varepsilon_\alpha n_\alpha \mathbf{L}_\alpha - \sum_\alpha \mathbf{F}_\alpha^{(1)} \cdot \mathbf{L}_\alpha = 0, \tag{10.6.3}$$

where $\mathbf{F}_\alpha^{(1)}$ is a force of the non-magnetic origin acting on the mass unit of the particle α - species, $\varepsilon_\alpha n_\alpha$ - the internal energy of the particles α-species in the volume unit. If the force $\mathbf{F}_\alpha^{(1)}$ connected only with the electric field and gravitation we find

$$\mathbf{F}_\alpha^{(1)} = \mathbf{g} + \frac{q_\alpha}{m_\alpha} \mathbf{E}. \tag{10.6.4}$$

Equation (10.6.3) can be transformed using (10.6.1)

$$\frac{\partial}{\partial \mathbf{r}} \cdot \sum_\alpha \left[\mathbf{F}_\alpha^{(1)} \left(\frac{5}{2} p_\alpha + \rho_\alpha \frac{\varepsilon_\alpha}{m_\alpha}\right)\right] = \sum_\alpha \rho_\alpha \mathbf{F}_\alpha^{(1)} \cdot \mathbf{F}_\alpha^{(1)}. \tag{10.6.5}$$

Write down the final system of equations for the case under consideration

$$\sum_\alpha \rho_\alpha \mathbf{F}_\alpha^{(1)} = \tau \sum_\alpha \rho_\alpha \frac{q_\alpha}{m_\alpha} \left[\mathbf{B} \times \mathbf{F}_\alpha^{(1)}\right], \tag{10.6.6}$$

$$\frac{\partial}{\partial \mathbf{r}} \cdot \sum_\alpha \left[\mathbf{F}_\alpha^{(1)} \left(\frac{5}{2} p_\alpha + \rho_\alpha \frac{\varepsilon_\alpha}{m_\alpha}\right)\right] = \sum_\alpha \rho_\alpha \mathbf{F}_\alpha^{(1)} \cdot \mathbf{F}_\alpha^{(1)}, \tag{10.6.7}$$

$$\mathbf{F}_\alpha^{(1)} = \mathbf{g} + \frac{q_\alpha}{m_\alpha} \mathbf{E}. \tag{10.6.8}$$

If we intend to take into account only the electron component, then

$$\mathbf{F} = \tau \frac{e}{m_e} [\mathbf{F} \times \mathbf{B}], \tag{10.6.9}$$

$$\frac{5}{2} \frac{\partial}{\partial \mathbf{r}} \cdot \mathbf{F} p_e = \rho_e \mathbf{F} \cdot \mathbf{F}, \tag{10.6.10}$$

$$\mathbf{F} = \mathbf{g} - \frac{e}{m_e} \mathbf{E}, \tag{10.6.11}$$

where $e = 1.602176 \cdot 10^{-19}\text{C}$ is the absolute value of the electron charge, $\frac{e}{m_e} = 1.758819 \cdot 10^{11} \frac{C}{kg}$, $m_e = 9{,}109382 \cdot 10^{-31}\text{kg}$.

Two important conclusions:

1. Only Eq. (10.6.9) contains nonlocal parameter τ in the explicit form.

2. Relation (10.6.10) leads to the appearance two energy flux densities - Pointing flux and Alexeev flux denoted here correspondingly as

$$\mathbf{S}_P = [\mathbf{E} \times \mathbf{B}] \tag{10.6.12}$$

and

$$\mathbf{S}_A = [\mathbf{g} \times \mathbf{B}]. \tag{10.6.13}$$

As a result the relation (10.6.10) can be written as

$$\mathbf{g} - \frac{e}{m_e}\mathbf{E} = \tau\frac{e}{m_e}[\mathbf{g} \times \mathbf{B}] - \tau\left(\frac{e}{m_e}\right)^2 [\mathbf{E} \times \mathbf{B}], \tag{10.6.14}$$

or

$$\mathbf{g} - \frac{e}{m_e}\mathbf{E} = \tau\frac{e}{m_e}\mathbf{S}_A - \tau\left(\frac{e}{m_e}\right)^2 \mathbf{S}_P. \tag{10.6.15}$$

Here is a record of the system of equations in the cylindrical coordinate system

$$\frac{\partial}{\partial r}(rp_e g_r) + \frac{\partial}{\partial \theta}(p_e g_\theta) + \frac{\partial r p_e g_z}{\partial z} - \\ - \frac{e}{m_e}\left[\frac{\partial}{\partial r}(rp_e E_r) + \frac{\partial}{\partial \theta}(p_e E_\theta) + \frac{\partial r p_e E_z}{\partial z}\right] = \frac{2}{5} r\rho_e\left[g^2 + E^2 - 2gE\cos\chi\right], \tag{10.6.16}$$

$$[\mathbf{g}]_{r,\theta,z} - \frac{e}{m_e}[\mathbf{E}]_{r,\theta,z} = \tau\frac{e}{m_e} gB\sin\chi - \tau\left(\frac{e}{m_e}\right)^2 EB\sin\gamma, \tag{10.6.17}$$

where $\angle\chi = \angle(\mathbf{g},\mathbf{E})$; $\angle\gamma = \angle(\mathbf{B},\mathbf{E})$. As usual the angles between two vectors can be found using the dot product, for example

$$\cos\chi = \frac{\mathbf{g}\cdot\mathbf{E}}{gE}. \tag{10.6.18}$$

For the spherical coordinate system we have

$$\cos\chi = \cos\theta_g \cos\theta_E + \sin\theta_g \sin\theta_E \cos(\varphi_g - \varphi_E), \tag{10.6.19}$$

$$\frac{\partial}{\partial r}\left(r^2 p_e g_r \sin\theta\right) + \frac{\partial}{\partial \theta}(p_e g_\theta r\sin\theta) + \frac{\partial p_e g_\varphi r}{\partial \varphi} \\ - \frac{e}{m_e}\left[\frac{\partial}{\partial r}\left(r^2 p_e E_r \sin\theta\right) + \frac{\partial}{\partial \theta}(p_e E_\theta r\sin\theta) + \frac{\partial p_e E_\varphi r}{\partial \varphi}\right] = \frac{2}{5}\rho_e\left[g^2 + E^2 - 2gE\cos\chi\right]r^2\sin\theta \tag{10.6.20}$$

$$[\mathbf{g}]_{r,\theta,\varphi} - \frac{e}{m_e}[\mathbf{E}]_{r,\theta,\varphi} = \tau\frac{e}{m_e} gB\sin\chi - \tau\left(\frac{e}{m_e}\right)^2 EB\sin\gamma. \tag{10.6.21}$$

The discussed stability conditions should be fulfilled for all types of convertors including [186].

It is known from Internet so called flying "Searl discs". Descriptions of these flights sound fantastic. Less impressive but well-documented experiments were performed by V.V. Roschin and S.M. Godin [191], (see Figure 10.6.1). The first version of the Converter created by Roschin and Godin is made on the same principle as the Searle generator. Elements of the Converter construction [191] contain stator magnets, stator, rotating magnetic rollers, grid electrode and high voltage source; in [192] it is equal to 20 kV. Rollers rotate on a stator and there is a force directed on an axis of rotation.

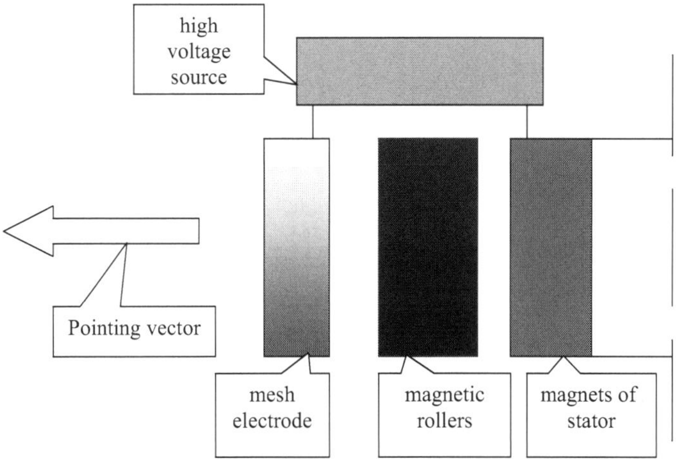

Fig. 10.6.1. Elements of the Converter construction.

They write [191]: "The installation was started by the promotion of the rotor with the help of an electric motor. Revolutions gradually increased as long as the ammeter included in the motor power circuit, did not start to show a zero value of the current consumed and the presence of reverse current. This corresponded to about 550 rpm, and the magnetic displacement sensor of the platform will begin to record the change in weight of the platform is already at 200rpm. ...

At a maximum output power of 7 kW, the weight change of the entire platform weighing 350 kg reaches 35% of the weight in a stationary state"...

The effect of changing the weight is reversible relative to the direction of rotation of the rotor, and has some hysteresis. When rotating clockwise, the critical mode occurs in the area of 550rpm and the thrust is created against the direction of the gravity vector, and when rotating anticlockwise, the critical mode occurs in the area of 600rpm and the thrust is created in the direction of the gravity vector."

Let us explain these phenomena from the position of nonlocal physics. To explain lifting force, let us consider (10.6.14) written in the form

$$\mathbf{F} = \tau \frac{e}{m_e}\left[\mathbf{S}_A - \frac{e}{m_e}\mathbf{S}_P\right]. \tag{10.6.22}$$

Obviously $\mathbf{F} = 0$, if

$$\mathbf{S}_A - \frac{e}{m_e}\mathbf{S}_P = 0. \tag{10.6.23}$$

In this case Eq. (10.6.10) satisfies identically. The sign in front of component of the magnetic induction $\mathbf{B}$ in the vector product $\mathbf{S}_P$ depends on the direction of rotation. Relation (10.6.23) has the transparent physical sense. As a result the forces of the electro-magnetic field delete the influence of gravitation.

Decompensate Pointing flux defines radial "magnetic walls" using the terminology [186]. Let us demonstrate the appearance of this effect using the considered simplest stability conditions but by the self-consistent way. In the spherical coordinate system Eq. (6.6.10) takes the form

$$\frac{5}{2}\frac{1}{r^2}\frac{\partial}{\partial r}\left(r^2 p F_r\right) = \rho F_r^2. \tag{10.6.24}$$

Equation (10.6.24) should be added to the system of Eqs. (10.6.20) - (10.6.22). Figures 10.6.2 - 10.6.7 show the typical "wall" obtained as a result of the self-consistent solution.

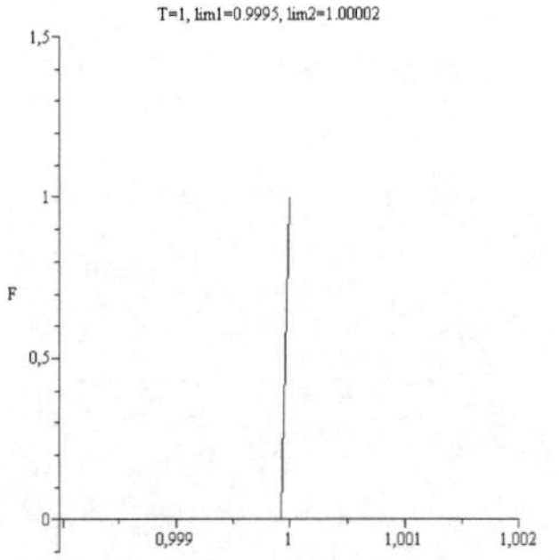

Fig. 10.6.2. Evolution of $\hat{F}_r(\hat{r})$;

$v_{0r}(1) = 10^{-3}$, $\hat{y}(1) = 10^{-9}$, $\hat{z}(1) = 10^{-3}$, $D(\hat{v}_{0r})(1) = 1$, $D(\hat{y})(1) = 1$, $D(\hat{z})(1) = 1$, $\hat{p}(1) = 1$, $\hat{\rho}(1) = 1$, $\hat{F}_r(1) = 1$

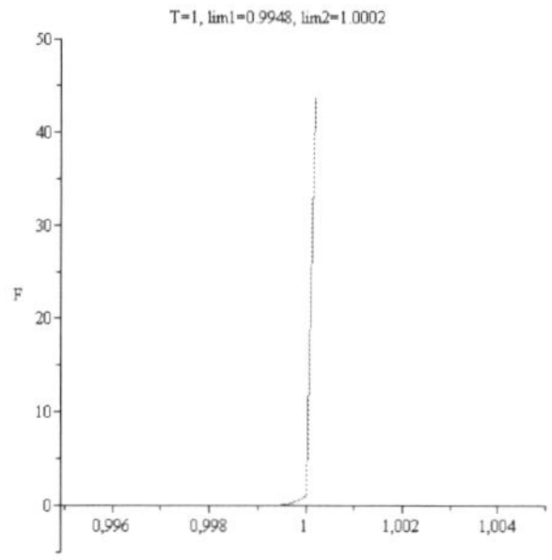

Fig. 10.6.3. Evolution of $\hat{F}_r(\hat{r})$; $\hat{F}_r(1)=1$,

$v_{0r}(1)=10^{-2}$, $\hat{y}(1)=10^{-6}$, $\hat{z}(1)=10^{-2}$, $D(\hat{v}_{0r})(1)=1$, $D(\hat{y})(1)=1$, $D(\hat{z})(1)=1$, $\hat{p}(1)=1$, $\hat{\rho}(1)=1$

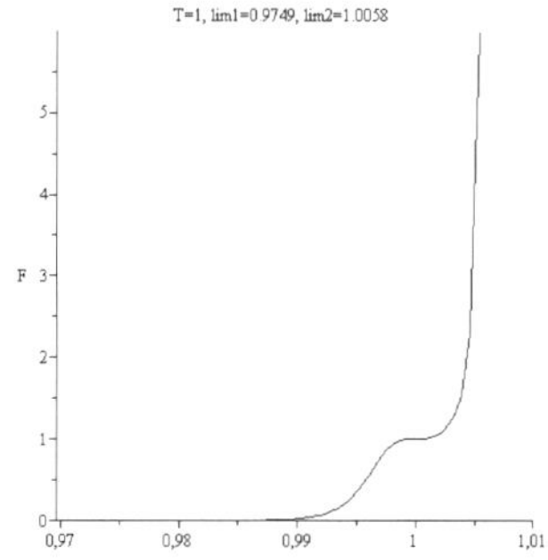

Fig. 10.6.4. Evolution of $\hat{F}_r(\hat{r})$;

$v_{0r}(1)=0.05$, $\hat{y}(1)=125\cdot10^{-6}$, $\hat{z}(1)=0.05$, $D(\hat{v}_{0r})(1)=1$, $D(\hat{y})(1)=1$, $D(\hat{z})(1)=1$, $\hat{p}(1)=1$, $\hat{\rho}(1)=1$

$\hat{F}_r(1)=1$

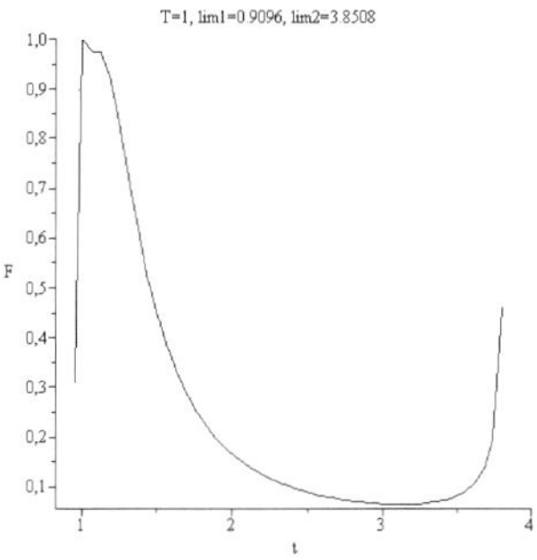

Fig. 10.6.5. Evolution of $\hat{F}_r(\hat{r})$; $\hat{F}_r(1)=1$,

$v_{0r}(1)=0.2$, $\hat{y}(1)=8\cdot10^{-3}$, $\hat{z}(1)=0.2$, $D(\hat{v}_{0r})(1)=1$, $D(\hat{y})(1)=1$, $D(\hat{z})(1)=1$, $\hat{p}(1)=1$, $\hat{\rho}(1)=1$

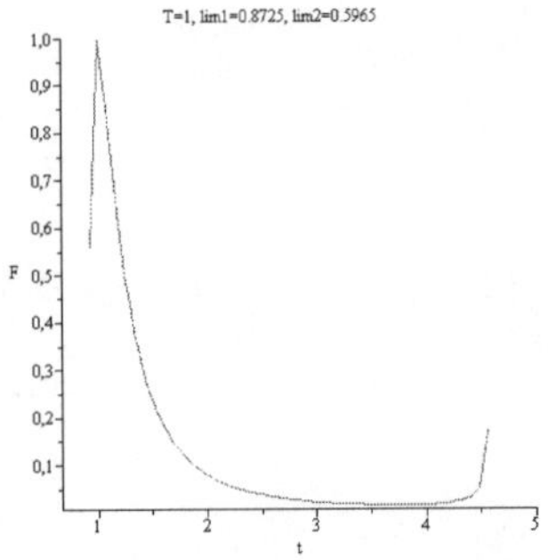

Fig. 10.6.6. Evolution of $\hat{F}_r(\hat{r})$;

$v_{0r}(1) = 0.3,\ \hat{y}(1) = 27 \cdot 10^{-3},\ \hat{z}(1) = 0.3,\ D(\hat{v}_{0r})(1) = 1,\ D(\hat{y})(1) = 1,\ D(\hat{z})(1) = 1,\ \hat{p}(1) = 1,\ \hat{\rho}(1) = 1$

$\hat{F}_r(1) = 1$

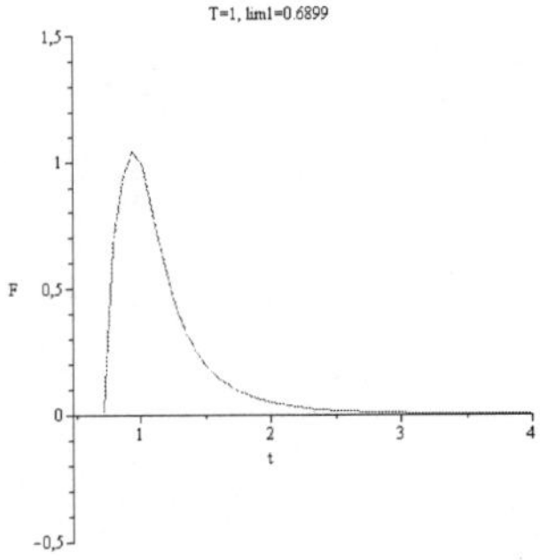

Fig. 10.6.7. Evolution of $\hat{F}_r(\hat{r})$;

$v_{0r}(1) = 1,\ \hat{y}(1) = 1,\ \hat{z}(1) = 1,\ D(\hat{v}_{0r})(1) = 1,\ D(\hat{y})(1) = 1,\ D(\hat{z})(1) = 1,\ \hat{p}(1) = 1,\ \hat{\rho}(1) = 1,\ \hat{F}_r(1) = 1$

The following conclusions of the principal significance can be done:

1. The levitating object remains in the stable state after the small radial perturbations, (figures 10.5.1 - 10.5.12).

2. The small radial perturbations lead to appearance of the layer of the finite width in the vicinity of sphere. This layer has a character feature - the smaller the disturbance, the greater the density of the layer (figures 10.5.3, 10.5.7, and 10.5.11). In the case of small perturbations this very thin layer has the extremely high density (see figure 10.5.3).

3. The small perturbations lead to appearance of the cold layer near the sphere (see figures 10.5.4, 10.5.8, 10.5.12 and 10.5.16). The perturbations lead also to

“the walls” of the electro-magnetic origin. These effects were observed in the real experiments [181].
4. Strong perturbations lead to the loss of stability and to the explosion of the object (figures 10.5.13 - 10.5.16).
5. The effect of the negative collective density takes place for the strong disturbances. This effect is known in the experimental physics [192 - 195]. For the levitation problem this effect needs in the additional investigation.
6. The necessary conditions of the levitation stability (see also Eqs. (10.6.6) - (10.6.11), (10.6.15)) lead to the influence of gravitation phenomena on electromagnetism and vice versa. The strict theory of levitation can be constructed only in the frame of non-local physics.

APPENDIX 1
General nonlocal equations in the hydrodynamic form

Strict consideration leads to the following system of the generalized hydrodynamic equations (GHE) [18-29] written in the generalized Euler form:

(Continuity equation for species α)

$$\frac{\partial}{\partial t}\left\{\rho_\alpha-\tau_\alpha\left[\frac{\partial\rho_\alpha}{\partial t}+\frac{\partial}{\partial\mathbf{r}}\cdot(\rho_\alpha\mathbf{v}_0)\right]\right\}$$
$$+\frac{\partial}{\partial\mathbf{r}}\cdot\left\{\rho_\alpha\mathbf{v}_0-\tau_\alpha\left[\frac{\partial}{\partial t}(\rho_\alpha\mathbf{v}_0)+\frac{\partial}{\partial\mathbf{r}}\cdot(\rho_\alpha\mathbf{v}_0\mathbf{v}_0)+\vec{\vec{\mathrm{I}}}\cdot\frac{\partial p_\alpha}{\partial\mathbf{r}}-\rho_\alpha\mathbf{F}_\alpha^{(1)}-\frac{q_\alpha}{m_\alpha}\rho_\alpha\mathbf{v}_0\times\mathbf{B}\right]\right\}=R_\alpha. \quad \text{(A.1.1)}$$

(Continuity equation for mixture)

$$\frac{\partial}{\partial t}\left\{\rho-\sum_\alpha\tau_\alpha\left[\frac{\partial\rho_\alpha}{\partial t}+\frac{\partial}{\partial\mathbf{r}}\cdot(\rho_\alpha\mathbf{v}_0)\right]\right\}+\frac{\partial}{\partial\mathbf{r}}\cdot\left\{\rho\mathbf{v}_0-\sum_\alpha\tau_\alpha\left[\frac{\partial}{\partial t}(\rho_\alpha\mathbf{v}_0)+\frac{\partial}{\partial\mathbf{r}}\cdot(\rho_\alpha\mathbf{v}_0\mathbf{v}_0)\right.\right.$$
$$\left.\left.+\vec{\vec{\mathrm{I}}}\cdot\frac{\partial p_\alpha}{\partial\mathbf{r}}-\rho_\alpha\mathbf{F}_\alpha^{(1)}-\frac{q_\alpha}{m_\alpha}\rho_\alpha\mathbf{v}_0\times\mathbf{B}\right]\right\}=0. \quad \text{(A.1.2)}$$

(Momentum equation for species α)

$$\frac{\partial}{\partial t}\left\{\rho_\alpha\mathbf{v}_0-\tau_\alpha\left[\frac{\partial}{\partial t}(\rho_\alpha\mathbf{v}_0)+\frac{\partial}{\partial\mathbf{r}}\cdot\rho_\alpha\mathbf{v}_0\mathbf{v}_0+\frac{\partial p_\alpha}{\partial\mathbf{r}}-\rho_\alpha\mathbf{F}_\alpha^{(1)}\right.\right.$$
$$\left.\left.-\frac{q_\alpha}{m_\alpha}\rho_\alpha\mathbf{v}_0\times\mathbf{B}\right]\right\}-\mathbf{F}_\alpha^{(1)}\left[\rho_\alpha-\tau_\alpha\left(\frac{\partial\rho_\alpha}{\partial t}+\frac{\partial}{\partial\mathbf{r}}(\rho_\alpha\mathbf{v}_0)\right)\right]$$
$$-\frac{q_\alpha}{m_\alpha}\left\{\rho_\alpha\mathbf{v}_0-\tau_\alpha\left[\frac{\partial}{\partial t}(\rho_\alpha\mathbf{v}_0)+\frac{\partial}{\partial\mathbf{r}}\cdot\rho_\alpha\mathbf{v}_0\mathbf{v}_0+\frac{\partial p_\alpha}{\partial\mathbf{r}}-\rho_\alpha\mathbf{F}_\alpha^{(1)}\right.\right.$$
$$\left.\left.-\frac{q_\alpha}{m_\alpha}\rho_\alpha\mathbf{v}_0\times\mathbf{B}\right]\right\}\times\mathbf{B}+\frac{\partial}{\partial\mathbf{r}}\cdot\left\{\rho_\alpha\mathbf{v}_0\mathbf{v}_0+p_\alpha\vec{\vec{\mathrm{I}}}-\tau_\alpha\left[\frac{\partial}{\partial t}(\rho_\alpha\mathbf{v}_0\mathbf{v}_0\right.\right. \quad \text{(A.1.3)}$$
$$\left.+p_\alpha\vec{\vec{\mathrm{I}}})+\frac{\partial}{\partial\mathbf{r}}\cdot\rho_\alpha(\mathbf{v}_0\mathbf{v}_0)\mathbf{v}_0+2\vec{\vec{\mathrm{I}}}\left(\frac{\partial}{\partial\mathbf{r}}\cdot(p_\alpha\mathbf{v}_0)\right)+\frac{\partial}{\partial\mathbf{r}}\cdot(\vec{\vec{\mathrm{I}}}p_\alpha\mathbf{v}_0)\right.$$
$$\left.\left.-\mathbf{F}_\alpha^{(1)}\rho_\alpha\mathbf{v}_0-\rho_\alpha\mathbf{v}_0\mathbf{F}_\alpha^{(1)}-\frac{q_\alpha}{m_\alpha}\rho_\alpha[\mathbf{v}_0\times\mathbf{B}]\mathbf{v}_0-\frac{q_\alpha}{m_\alpha}\rho_\alpha\mathbf{v}_0[\mathbf{v}_0\times\mathbf{B}]\right]\right\}$$
$$=\int m_\alpha\mathbf{v}_\alpha J_\alpha^{st,el}d\mathbf{v}_\alpha+\int m_\alpha\mathbf{v}_\alpha J_\alpha^{st,inel}d\mathbf{v}_\alpha.$$

(Momentum equation for mixture)

$$
\begin{aligned}
&\frac{\partial}{\partial t}\left\{\rho\mathbf{v}_0-\sum_\alpha\tau_\alpha\left[\frac{\partial}{\partial t}(\rho_\alpha\mathbf{v}_0)+\frac{\partial}{\partial\mathbf{r}}\cdot\rho_\alpha\mathbf{v}_0\mathbf{v}_0+\frac{\partial p_\alpha}{\partial\mathbf{r}}-\rho_\alpha\mathbf{F}_\alpha^{(1)}\right.\right.\\
&\left.\left.-\frac{q_\alpha}{m_\alpha}\rho_\alpha\mathbf{v}_0\times\mathbf{B}\right]\right\}-\sum_\alpha\mathbf{F}_\alpha^{(1)}\left[\rho_\alpha-\tau_\alpha\left(\frac{\partial\rho_\alpha}{\partial t}+\frac{\partial}{\partial\mathbf{r}}(\rho_\alpha\mathbf{v}_0)\right)\right]\\
&-\sum_\alpha\frac{q_\alpha}{m_\alpha}\left\{\rho_\alpha\mathbf{v}_0-\tau_\alpha\left[\frac{\partial}{\partial t}(\rho_\alpha\mathbf{v}_0)+\frac{\partial}{\partial\mathbf{r}}\cdot\rho_\alpha\mathbf{v}_0\mathbf{v}_0+\frac{\partial p_\alpha}{\partial\mathbf{r}}-\rho_\alpha\mathbf{F}_\alpha^{(1)}\right.\right.\\
&\left.\left.-\frac{q_\alpha}{m_\alpha}\rho_\alpha\mathbf{v}_0\times\mathbf{B}\right]\right\}\times\mathbf{B}+\frac{\partial}{\partial\mathbf{r}}\cdot\left\{\rho\mathbf{v}_0\mathbf{v}_0+p\ddot{\mathrm{I}}-\sum_\alpha\tau_\alpha\left[\frac{\partial}{\partial t}(\rho_\alpha\mathbf{v}_0\mathbf{v}_0\right.\right.\\
&+p_\alpha\ddot{\mathrm{I}})+\frac{\partial}{\partial\mathbf{r}}\cdot\rho_\alpha(\mathbf{v}_0\mathbf{v}_0)\mathbf{v}_0+2\ddot{\mathrm{I}}\left(\frac{\partial}{\partial\mathbf{r}}\cdot(p_\alpha\mathbf{v}_0)\right)+\frac{\partial}{\partial\mathbf{r}}\cdot\left(\ddot{\mathrm{I}}p_\alpha\mathbf{v}_0\right)\\
&\left.\left.-\mathbf{F}_\alpha^{(1)}\rho_\alpha\mathbf{v}_0-\rho_\alpha\mathbf{v}_0\mathbf{F}_\alpha^{(1)}-\frac{q_\alpha}{m_\alpha}\rho_\alpha[\mathbf{v}_0\times\mathbf{B}]\mathbf{v}_0-\frac{q_\alpha}{m_\alpha}\rho_\alpha\mathbf{v}_0[\mathbf{v}_0\times\mathbf{B}]\right]\right\}=0.
\end{aligned}
\tag{A.1.4}
$$

(Energy equation for α species)

$$
\begin{aligned}
&\frac{\partial}{\partial t}\left\{\frac{\rho_\alpha v_0^2}{2}+\frac{3}{2}p_\alpha+\varepsilon_\alpha n_\alpha-\tau_\alpha\left[\frac{\partial}{\partial t}\left(\frac{\rho_\alpha v_0^2}{2}+\frac{3}{2}p_\alpha+\varepsilon_\alpha n_\alpha\right)\right.\right.\\
&\left.\left.+\frac{\partial}{\partial\mathbf{r}}\cdot\left(\frac{1}{2}\rho_\alpha v_0^2\mathbf{v}_0+\frac{5}{2}p_\alpha\mathbf{v}_0+\varepsilon_\alpha n_\alpha\mathbf{v}_0\right)-\mathbf{F}_\alpha^{(1)}\cdot\rho_\alpha\mathbf{v}_0\right]\right\}\\
&+\frac{\partial}{\partial\mathbf{r}}\cdot\left\{\frac{1}{2}\rho_\alpha v_0^2\mathbf{v}_0+\frac{5}{2}p_\alpha\mathbf{v}_0+\varepsilon_\alpha n_\alpha\mathbf{v}_0-\tau_\alpha\left[\frac{\partial}{\partial t}\left(\frac{1}{2}\rho_\alpha v_0^2\mathbf{v}_0\right.\right.\right.\\
&\left.+\frac{5}{2}p_\alpha\mathbf{v}_0+\varepsilon_\alpha n_\alpha\mathbf{v}_0\right)+\frac{\partial}{\partial\mathbf{r}}\cdot\left(\frac{1}{2}\rho_\alpha v_0^2\mathbf{v}_0\mathbf{v}_0+\frac{7}{2}p_\alpha\mathbf{v}_0\mathbf{v}_0+\frac{1}{2}p_\alpha v_0^2\ddot{\mathrm{I}}\right.\\
&\left.+\frac{5}{2}\frac{p_\alpha^2}{\rho_\alpha}\ddot{\mathrm{I}}+\varepsilon_\alpha n_\alpha\mathbf{v}_0\mathbf{v}_0+\varepsilon_\alpha\frac{p_\alpha}{m_\alpha}\ddot{\mathrm{I}}\right)-\rho_\alpha\mathbf{F}_\alpha^{(1)}\cdot\mathbf{v}_0\mathbf{v}_0-p_\alpha\mathbf{F}_\alpha^{(1)}\cdot\ddot{\mathrm{I}}\\
&-\frac{1}{2}\rho_\alpha v_0^2\mathbf{F}_\alpha^{(1)}-\frac{3}{2}\mathbf{F}_\alpha^{(1)}p_\alpha-\frac{\rho_\alpha v_0^2}{2}\frac{q_\alpha}{m_\alpha}[\mathbf{v}_0\times\mathbf{B}]-\frac{5}{2}p_\alpha\frac{q_\alpha}{m_\alpha}[\mathbf{v}_0\times\mathbf{B}]\\
&\left.\left.-\varepsilon_\alpha n_\alpha\frac{q_\alpha}{m_\alpha}[\mathbf{v}_0\times\mathbf{B}]-\varepsilon_\alpha n_\alpha\mathbf{F}_\alpha^{(1)}\right]\right\}-\left\{\rho_\alpha\mathbf{F}_\alpha^{(1)}\cdot\mathbf{v}_0\right.\\
&\left.-\tau_\alpha\left[\mathbf{F}_\alpha^{(1)}\cdot\left(\frac{\partial}{\partial t}(\rho_\alpha\mathbf{v}_0)+\frac{\partial}{\partial\mathbf{r}}\cdot\rho_\alpha\mathbf{v}_0\mathbf{v}_0+\frac{\partial}{\partial\mathbf{r}}\cdot p_\alpha\ddot{\mathrm{I}}-\rho_\alpha\mathbf{F}_\alpha^{(1)}-q_\alpha n_\alpha[\mathbf{v}_0\times\mathbf{B}]\right)\right]\right\}\\
&=\int\left(\frac{m_\alpha v_\alpha^2}{2}+\varepsilon_\alpha\right)J_\alpha^{st,el}d\mathbf{v}_\alpha+\int\left(\frac{m_\alpha v_\alpha^2}{2}+\varepsilon_\alpha\right)J_\alpha^{st,inel}d\mathbf{v}_\alpha.
\end{aligned}
\tag{A.1.5}
$$

(Energy equation for mixture)

$$\frac{\partial}{\partial t}\left\{\frac{\rho v_0^2}{2}+\frac{3}{2}p+\sum_\alpha \varepsilon_\alpha n_\alpha-\sum_\alpha \tau_\alpha\left[\frac{\partial}{\partial t}\left(\frac{\rho_\alpha v_0^2}{2}+\frac{3}{2}p_\alpha+\varepsilon_\alpha n_\alpha\right)\right.\right.$$
$$\left.\left.+\frac{\partial}{\partial \mathbf{r}}\cdot\left(\frac{1}{2}\rho_\alpha v_0^2\mathbf{v}_0+\frac{5}{2}p_\alpha\mathbf{v}_0+\varepsilon_\alpha n_\alpha\mathbf{v}_0\right)-\mathbf{F}_\alpha^{(1)}\cdot\rho_\alpha\mathbf{v}_0\right]\right\}$$
$$+\frac{\partial}{\partial \mathbf{r}}\cdot\left\{\frac{1}{2}\rho v_0^2\mathbf{v}_0+\frac{5}{2}p\mathbf{v}_0+\mathbf{v}_0\sum_\alpha \varepsilon_\alpha n_\alpha-\sum_\alpha \tau_\alpha\left[\frac{\partial}{\partial t}\left(\frac{1}{2}\rho_\alpha v_0^2\mathbf{v}_0\right.\right.\right.$$
$$\left.+\frac{5}{2}p_\alpha\mathbf{v}_0+\varepsilon_\alpha n_\alpha\mathbf{v}_0\right)+\frac{\partial}{\partial \mathbf{r}}\cdot\left(\frac{1}{2}\rho_\alpha v_0^2\mathbf{v}_0\mathbf{v}_0+\frac{7}{2}p_\alpha\mathbf{v}_0\mathbf{v}_0+\frac{1}{2}p_\alpha v_0^2\ddot{I}\right.$$
$$\left.+\frac{5}{2}\frac{p_\alpha^2}{\rho_\alpha}\ddot{I}+\varepsilon_\alpha n_\alpha\mathbf{v}_0\mathbf{v}_0+\varepsilon_\alpha\frac{p_\alpha}{m_\alpha}\ddot{I}\right)-\rho_\alpha\mathbf{F}_\alpha^{(1)}\cdot\mathbf{v}_0\mathbf{v}_0-p_\alpha\mathbf{F}_\alpha^{(1)}\cdot\ddot{I}$$
$$-\frac{1}{2}\rho_\alpha v_0^2\mathbf{F}_\alpha^{(1)}-\frac{3}{2}\mathbf{F}_\alpha^{(1)}p_\alpha-\frac{\rho_\alpha v_0^2}{2}\frac{q_\alpha}{m_\alpha}[\mathbf{v}_0\times\mathbf{B}]-\frac{5}{2}p_\alpha\frac{q_\alpha}{m_\alpha}[\mathbf{v}_0\times\mathbf{B}]$$
$$\left.\left.-\varepsilon_\alpha n_\alpha\frac{q_\alpha}{m_\alpha}[\mathbf{v}_0\times\mathbf{B}]-\varepsilon_\alpha n_\alpha\mathbf{F}_\alpha^{(1)}\right]\right\}-\left\{\mathbf{v}_0\cdot\sum_\alpha\rho_\alpha\mathbf{F}_\alpha^{(1)}\right.$$
$$\left.-\sum_\alpha\tau_\alpha\left[\mathbf{F}_\alpha^{(1)}\cdot\left(\frac{\partial}{\partial t}(\rho_\alpha\mathbf{v}_0)+\frac{\partial}{\partial \mathbf{r}}\cdot\rho_\alpha\mathbf{v}_0\mathbf{v}_0+\frac{\partial}{\partial \mathbf{r}}\cdot p_\alpha\ddot{I}-\rho_\alpha\mathbf{F}_\alpha^{(1)}-q_\alpha n_\alpha[\mathbf{v}_0\times\mathbf{B}]\right)\right]\right\}=0. \quad \text{(A.1.6)}$$

Here $\mathbf{F}_\alpha^{(1)}$ are the forces of the non-magnetic origin acting on the mass unit of α-species ($\rho_\alpha\mathbf{F}_\alpha^{(1)}$ is a force of the α-kind acting on the unit of volume), $\mathbf{B}$ - magnetic induction, $\ddot{I}$ - unit tensor, q_α - charge of the α-component particle, p_α - static pressure for α-component, ε_α - internal energy for the particles of α-component, $\mathbf{v}_0$ - hydrodynamic velocity for mixture, τ_α - non-local parameter.

GHE can be applied to the physical systems from the Universe to atomic scales. All additional explanations will be done by delivering the results of modeling of corresponding physical systems with the special consideration of non-local parameters τ_α. Generally speaking to GHE should be added the system of generalized Maxwell equations (for example in the form of the generalized Poisson equation for electric potential) and gravitational equations (for example in the form of the generalized Poisson equation for gravitational potential).

REFERENCES

1. Boltzmann, L. 1872 Weitere Studien über das Wärmegleichgewicht unter Gasmolekulen.
Sitz. Ber. Kaiserl. Akad. Wiss. **66(2)** s.275.
2. Chapman S. On the Law of Distribution of Velocities and on the Theory of Viscosity and Thermal Conduction in a Non-uniform Simple Monoatomic Gas. *Phil. Trans. Roy. Soc.* **A216** p.279 (1916)
3. Chapman S. On the Theory of a Gas, part 2. A Composite Monoatomic Gas, Diffusion, Viscosity and Thermal Conduction. *Phil. Trans. Roy. Soc.* **A217** p.115 (1917)
4. Enskog D. The Kinetic Theory of Phenomena in Fairly Rare Gases. Upsala. (1917)
5. Enskog D. The Numerical Calculation of Phenomena in Fairly Rare Gases *Svensk. Vet. Akad. Arkiv. f. Math. Ast. och Fys.* **16** p.1 (1921)
6. Boltzmann L. Vorlesungen über Gastheorie. (Leipzig: *Verlag von Johann Barth*. Zweiter unveränderten Abdruck.2 Teile, (1912)
7. Ehrenfest P. *Otnositelnost', kvanty, statistika.* (Relativity, quantum, statistics.) (Moscow *Nauka* 1972)
8. Ehrenfest P. Collected scientific papers. Ed. by M. Klein. (*North-Holland Publ. Co.* Amsterdam 1979)
9. Maxwell J.C. Illustrations of the Dynamical Theory of Gases, I. On the Motion and Collisions of Perfectly Elastic Spheres; II. On the Process of Diffusion of Two or More Kinds of Moving Particles Among One Another; III. On the Collision of Perfectly Elastic Bodies of any Form. *Fhil. Mag.* **19**, p.19;20, p.21;20, p.33 (1860)
10. Landau L.D., Lifshitz E.M. *Gidrodinamika* (Kurs Teoreticheskoi Fiziki T 6) (Hydrodynamics Course of Theoretical Physics Vol 6) (Moscow *Nauka* 1988) [Translated into English (Oxford *Pergamon Press* 1990)]
11. Klimontovich Yu.L. Statisticheskaya Teoriya Otkrytykh Sistem (Statistical Theory of Open Systems) (Moscow: *Yanus-K*, 1995) [Translated into English (Dordrecht: *Kluwer Acad. Publ.*, 1995)]
12. Bogolyubov N.N. *Problemy Dinamicheskoi Teorii v Statisticheskoi Fizike* (Dynamic Theory Problems in Statistical Physics) (Moscow Leningrad *Gostekhizdat* 1946) [Translated into English *The Dynamical Theory in Statistical Physics* (*Delhi Hindustan Publ. Corp.* 1965)]

13. Born M., Green H.S. A General Kinetic Theory of Liquids 1. The molecular distribution function. Proc.Roy.Soc. **188** (1012) p.10 (1946)
14. Green H.S. The Molecular Theory of Fluids. (Amsterdam, 1952)
15. Kirkwood J.G. The Statistical Mechanical Theory of Transports Processes II.Transport in gases. *J.Chem.Phys*. **15** (1) p.72 (1947)
16. Yvon J. La Theorie Statistique des Fluide et l'Equation d'etat. (Paris, 1935)
17. Alekseev B.V. Matematicheskaya Kinetika Reagiruyushchikh Gazov (Mathematical Theory of Reacting Gases) (Moscow, *Nauka* 1982)
18. Alexeev B.V. Generalized Boltzmann Physical Kinetics. Elsevier Amsterdam, The Netherlands (2004) 368p.
19. Alexeev B.V. Unified Non-local Theory of Transport Processes, Elsevier Amsterdam, The Netherlands (2015) 644p.
20. Alexeev B.V. Unified Non-local Relativistic Theory of Transport Processes, Elsevier Amsterdam, The Netherlands (2016) 455p.
21. Alexeev B.V. Nonlocal Astrophysics. Dark Matter, Dark Energy, Physical Vacuum. Elsevier Amsterdam, The Netherlands (2017) 454p.
22. Alexeev B.V. Extremal States in Nonlocal Physics. Lambert Academic Publishing. 2018.
23. My lections on YouTube https://www.youtube.com/channel/UCAUbLXYSJLom9U1eqXizZtg
24. Alexeev B.V. The generalized Boltzmann equation, generalized hydrodynamic equations and their applications. *Phil. Trans. Roy. Soc. Lond.* **349** p.417-443. (1994)
25.Alexeev, B. V. The generalized Boltzmann equation. *Physica A*. **216.** 459-468. (1995)
26. Alekseev, B.V. Physical principles of the generalized Boltzmann kinetic theory of gases. *Physics-Uspekhi*, **170** (6) 601-629 (2000)
27. Alekseev, B.V. Physical principles of the generalized Boltzmann kinetic theory of ionized gases. *Physics-Uspekhi*, **173** (2) 139-167 (2003)
28. Alexeev, B.V. Generalized Quantum Hydrodynamics and Principles of Non-Local Physics, *J. Nanoelectron. Optoelectron.* **3**, 143 – 158 (2008)
29. Alexeev, B.V. Application of generalized quantum hydrodynamics in the theory of quantum soliton's evolution. *J. Nanoelectron. Optoelectron.* **3**, 316 – 328 (2008)
30. Alexeev, B.V. Generalized Theory of Landau Damping *J. Nanoelectron. Optoelectron.* **4**, 186 – 199 (2009)

31. Alexeev, B.V. Generalized Theory of Landau Damping in Collisional Media *J. Nanoelectron. Optoelectron.* **4**, 379 – 393 (2009)
32. Chapman S., Cowling T.G. The Mathematical Theory of Non-uniform Gases. (Cambridge: *At the University Press*, 1952)
33. Hirschfelder I.O., Curtiss Ch.F., Bird R.B. Molecular Theory of Gases and Liquids. (*John Wiley and sons*, inc. New York. Chapman and Hall, lim., London, 1954)
34. Uhlenbeck G. *Physics-Uspekhi* **103** (2) 275 (1971)
35. Kramers H.A. *Physica* **7** (4) 284 (1940)
36. Bell J.S. On the Einstein Podolsky Rosen paradox. *Physics*. V.1, 1964. P.195.
37. Madelung E. (1927). "Quantentheorie in hydrodynamischer Form". *Zeitschrift für physik.* V.40, 1927. P. 322–326.
38. Alekseev B.V. Hydrodynamic Equations in Kinetic Theory of Reacting Gases. *J. Comp. Math. and Math. Physics*. **27** pp.730-740 (1987)
39. Alekseev B.V. To the Theory of Generalized Boltzmann Equation. *High Temperature*. **31** (4) c.624-633 (1993)
40. Alexeev B.V. Generalized Boltzmann Physical Kinetics. *High Temperature* **35** (1) p. 125 (1997)
41. Prigogine I. Introduction to Thermodynamics of Irreversible Processes. (N.Y., London: *Wiley Interscience*, 2- nd edition.1962)
42. Nikolis G. Prigogine I. Self-organization in Nonequilibrium Systems. (N.Y.: *Wiley-Interscience Publication*, 1977)
43. Glasstone S, Laidler K J and Eyring H. The Theory of Rate Processes. The kinetics of chemical reactions, viscosity, diffusion and electrochemical phenomena. NY and London (1941)
44. Gulin A.V., Samarskii A.A. On some results and problems in the theory of stability of difference schemes. Matematicheskii sbornik, v. 99(141), N3, p. 299 - 321, 1976.
45. Krömer Herbert, Proposed Negative-Mass Microwave Amplifier, Phys. Rev. **109**, 1856 (1958). Published 1 March 1958.
46. Ryzhii V.I., Fiz. Tverd. Tela **11**, 2471 (1969) [Sov. Phys. Solid State **11**, 1995 (1969)].
47. Ryzhii V. I., Usp. Fiz. Nauk **175**, 205 (2005) [Phys. Usp. **48**, 191-198 (2005)]. Microwave-induced negative conductivity and zero-resistance states in two-dimensional electronic systems: history and current status **DOI:** https://doi.org/10.3367/UFNr.0175.200502k.0205

48. Monstein C., Wesley J.P. Observation of scalar longitudinal electrodynamic waves. Europhys. Lett., **59** (4), pp. 514–520 (2002)
49. Tesla N. System of electric lighting, No 454,622. Patented June 23, 1891.
50. Eidelman S. *et al.* (Particle Data Group), Phys. Lett. B **592**, 1 (2004) (URL: http://pdg.lbl.gov)
51. Einstein A. Quantentheorie des einatomigen idealen Gases. *Sitzungsberichte der Preussischen Akademie der Wissenschaften* (Berlin), Physikalisch-mathematische Klasse (in German) 261–267 (1924)
52. Einstein A. Quantentheorie des einatomigen idealen Gases, Zweite Abhandlung. *Sitzungsberichte der Preussischen Akademie der Wissenschaften* (Berlin), Physikalisch-mathematische Klasse (in German) 3–14. (1925) doi:10.1002/3527608958.ch28. ISBN 978-3-527-60895-9.53. Cherenkov Pavel A. Visible emission of clean liquids by action of γ radiation. *Doklady Akademii Nauk SSSR* **2**: 451 (1934).
54. Rubin V., Ford W. K., Jr. Rotation of the Andromeda Nebula from a spectroscopic survey of emission regions. *Astrophysical Journal* **159**: 379, 1970
55. Rubin V., Thonnard N., Ford W.K., Jr, Rotational properties of 21 Sc galaxies with a large range of luminosities and radii from NGC 4605 (R=4kpc) to UGC 2885 (R=122kpc). *Astrophysical Journal* **238**, 471, 1980.
56. Zwicky F., Die Rotverschiebung von extragalaktischen Nebeln, Helvetica Physica Acta, **6**: 110–127,1933, *Bibcode:1933AcHPh...6..110Z*
57. Zwicky F., On the Masses of Nebulae and of Clusters of Nebulae, Astrophysical Journal, **86**: 217, 1937, *Bibcode:1937ApJ....86..217Z, doi:10.1086/143864*
58. Bertone G.; Hooper, D.; Silk, J. (2005). "Particle dark matter: Evidence, candidates and constraints". Physics Reports. **405** (5–6): 279–390. arXiv:hep-ph/0404175. Bibcode:2005PhR...405..279B. doi:10.1016/j.physrep.2004.08.031
59. Jörg D.; et al. (2012). "A filament of dark matter between two clusters of galaxies". Nature. **487** (7406): 202–204. arXiv:1207.0809. Bibcode:2012Natur.487..202D. doi:10.1038/nature11224.
60. Collins G. W. (1978). "The Virial Theorem in Stellar Astrophysics". Pachart Press.
61. Rejkuba M.; Dubath, P.; Minniti, D.; Meylan, G. (2008). "Masses and M/L Ratios of Bright Globular Clusters in NGC 5128". Proceedings of the International Astronomical Union. **246**: 418–422. Bibcode:2008IAUS..246..418R. doi:10.1017/S1743921308016074.

62. Soldner J. G. V. (1804). "On the deflection of a light ray from its rectilinear motion, by the attraction of a celestial body at which it nearly passes by". Berliner Astronomisches Jahrbuch: 161–172.
63. Newton Isaac (1998). Opticks: or, a treatise of the reflexions, refractions, inflexions and colours of light. Also two treatises of the species and magnitude of curvilinear figures. Commentary by Nicholas Humez (Octavo ed.). Palo Alto, Calif.: Octavo. ISBN 1-891788-04-3. (Opticks was originally published in 1704).
64. Landau L.D. & Lifshitz E.M. Mechanics (Volume 1 of A Course of Theoretical Physics) Pergamon Press, 1969.
65. Dyson, F. W.; Eddington, A. S.; Davidson C. (1920). "A determination of the deflection of light by the Sun's gravitational field, from observations made at the total eclipse of 29 May 1919". Philosophical Transactions of the Royal Society. **220A**: 291–333. *Bibcode:1920RSPTA.220..291D. doi:10.1098/rsta.1920.0009.*
66. Stanley, Matthew (2003). "'An Expedition to Heal the Wounds of War': The 1919 Eclipse and Eddington as Quaker Adventurer". Isis. **94** (1): 57–89. *doi:10.1086/376099. PMID 12725104.*
67. Chernin A.D. Physics – Uspekhi, Dark energy and universal antigravitation, 51 (3), 267 – 300 (2008).
68. Gliner E.B. Sov. Phys. Dokl. 15, 559 (1970).
69. Walsh D.; Carswell R. F.; Weymann R. J. (31 May 1979). "0957 + 561 A, B: twin quasistellar objects or gravitational lens?". Nature. **279** (5712): 381–384. *Bibcode:1979Natur.279..381W. doi:10.1038/279381a0. PMID 16068158.*
70. Taylor A. N.; et al. (1998). "Gravitational Lens Magnification and the Mass of Abell 1689". The Astrophysical Journal. 501 (2): 539–553. arXiv:astro-ph/9801158. Bibcode:1998ApJ...501..539T. doi:10.1086/305827.
71. Wu X.; Chiueh T.; Fang L.; Xue Y. (1998). "A comparison of different cluster mass estimates: consistency or discrepancy?". Monthly Notices of the Royal Astronomical Society. 301 (3): 861–871. arXiv:astro-ph/9808179. Bibcode:1998MNRAS.301..861W. doi:10.1046/j.1365-8711.1998.02055.x.
72. Gradstein Felix M.; Ogg James G.; Smith, Alan G., eds. (2004). A Geological Time Scale 2004 (3rd ed.). Cambridge University Press: Cambridge University Press. p. 28. ISBN 9780521786737.
73. Leonardo Sagnotti; Giancarlo Scardia; Biagio Giaccio; Joseph C. Liddicoat; Sebastien Nomade; Paul R. Renne; Courtney J. Sprain (21 July 2014). "Extremely rapid directional change during Matuyama-Brunhes geomagnetic

polarity reversal". Geophys. J. Int. 199 (2): 1110–1124. Bibcode:2014GeoJI.199.1110S. doi:10.1093/gji/ggu287.
74. Jeffreys, H The Earth, Its Origin, History and Physical Constitution, Cambridge University Press, 1924.
75. Jeffreys, H. The relation of cohesion to Roche's limit. Monthly Notices of the Royal Astronomical Society, Vol.107, p. 260-272 (1947)
76. Buffett, Bruce A. (2010). "Tidal dissipation and the strength of the Earth's internal magnetic field". Nature. 468 (7326): 952–94. Bibcode:2010Natur.468..952B. doi:10.1038/nature09643. PMID 21164483.
77. Monnereau, Marc; Calvet, Marie; Margerin, Ludovic; Souriau, Annie (May 21, 2010). "Lopsided Growth of Earth's Inner Core". Science. 328 (5981): 1014–17. Bibcode:2010Sci...328.1014M. doi:10.1126/science.1186212. PMID 20395477.
78. Herndon, J.M. (1980). "The chemical composition of the interior shells of the Earth". Proc. R. Soc. Lond. A372 (1748): 149–54. Bibcode:1980RSPSA.372..149H. doi:10.1098/rspa.1980.0106. JSTOR 2398362.
79. Herndon, J.M. (2005). "Scientific basis of knowledge on Earth's composition" (PDF). Current Science. 88 (7): 1034–37.
80. Ozawa, H.; al., et (2011). "Phase Transition of FeO and Stratification in Earth's Outer Core". Science. 334 (6057): 792–94. Bibcode:2011Sci...334..792O. doi:10.1126/science.1208265. PMID 22076374.
81. A.M. Dziewonski, D.L. Anderson (1981). "Preliminary reference Earth model" (PDF). Physics of the Earth and Planetary Interiors. 25 (4): 297–356. Bibcode:1981PEPI...25..297D. doi:10.1016/0031-9201(81)90046-7. ISSN 0031-9201.
82. Hazlett, James S.; Monroe, Reed; Wicander, Richard (2006). Physical geology : exploring the earth (6. ed.). Belmont: Thomson. p. 346. ISBN 978-0-495-01148-4.
83. Bullen K.E. The earth's density. London. Chapman and Hall, 1975.
84. Michelson, Albert A.; Morley, Edward W. (1887). "On the Relative Motion of the Earth and the Luminiferous Ether". American Journal of Science. **34**: 333–345 (1887). doi:10.2475/ajs.s3-34.203.33
85. Lorentz H.A. Aether theories and aether models (1901 – 1902). Lectures on theoretical physics delivered at the University of Leyden, Volume 1. Edited by H.Bremecamp.

86. Logunov A.A., Loskutov Yu. M., Mestvirishvili M. A., Relativistic theory of gravitation and criticism of general relativity, TMF, 1987, Volume 73, Number 2, 163–186.
87. Laplace P. S,, Mechanique Celeste, English transl. reprinted by Chelsea Publ., (New York, 1966).
88. Пуанкаре А, О науке, (Наука, Москва, 1983).
89. Pauli Wolfgang, Wave Mechanics: Volume 5 of Pauli Lectures on Physics, Books on Physics, Dover Publications 2000, ISBN 978-0486414621
90. Kamerlingh Onnes, H., "Further experiments with liquid helium. G. On the electrical resistance of pure metals, etc. VI. On the sudden change in the rate at which the resistance of mercury disappears." *Comm. Phys. Lab. Univ. Leiden*; No. 124c, 1911.
91. Reynolds C.A., Serin B., Wright W.H. & Nesbitt L.B. Superconductivity of Isotopes of Mercury. *Phys. Rev.*, v. 78, p. 487-487, (1950).
92. Maxwell E., Isotope Effect in Superconductivity of Mercury. *Phys. Rev.*, v. 78, p. 477-477, (1950).
93. Fröhlich H., Theory of the Superconductive State. I. The Ground State at the Absolute Zero of Temperature. *Phys. Rev.*, v. 79, p. 845-856, (1950).
94. Hirsch J.E., Did Herbert Fröhlich Predict or Postdict the Isotope Effect in Superconductors? ArXiv:1108.3835v2 [cond-mat.supr-con] 18 Oct 2011.
95. Bardeen J., Cooper L.N., and Schrieffer J.R. Microscopic Theory of Superconductivity Phys. Rev. 106, 162–164 (1957).
96. Meissner, W.; Ochsenfeld, R. (1933). "Ein neuer Effekt bei Eintritt der Supraleitfähigkeit". Naturwissenschaften. **21** (44): 787–788. *Bibcode:1933NW.....21..787M. doi:10.1007/BF01504252.*
97. Debye, Peter (1912). "Zur Theorie der spezifischen Waerme". *Annalen der Physik* (in German). **39** (4): 789–839. *Bibcode:1912AnP...344..789D. doi:10.1002/andp.19123441404.*
98. Васильев Н.В. Парадоксы и проблемы Тунгусского метеорита // Известия высших учебных заведений. Физика. 1992. № 3.
99. Stenhoff M. Ball Lightning. An Unsolved Problem in Atmospheric Physics. New York: Kluwer/Plenum, 1999.
100. Grigor'ev A.I., Grigor'eva I.D., Shiriaeva S.O.. Observations of ball lightning and their analysis. In: Khimia Plasmy. Ed. B. M. Smirnov. Moscow: Energoatomizdat, 1993. P. 218 - 248 (in Russian).
101. Amirov A.Kh., Bychkov V.L., Strijev A.Yu.. Principles of Creating and Processing Data Bank: Meteorologic Applications Illustrated with Regard to

Ball Lightning Processing. Journ. of Meteorology. 1995, V.20, N. 197, P. 85 - 93.
102. Rayle W.D. Ball Lightning Characteristics. NASA Techn. Note –D –3188, 1966
103. McNally J.R., Jr. Preliminary Report on the Ball Lightning. Oak-Ridge Nat. Lab/ No 3938, May 1966.
104. Egely G.. Analysis of Hungarian Ball Lightning Observations. In: Progress in Ball Lightning Research. Ed. A. G. Keul. Proc. VIZOTUM, P. 22. The Vizotum Project, Salzburg, Austria, 1993.
105. Hubert P. Nouvelle Enquete sur la Foudre en Boule – Analyse et Discussion des Resultats. Rapport PH/SC/96001, Commisariat a l'Energy Atomique, Service d'Electronique Physique, Centre d'Etudes Nucleairs de Saclay, France, 1996.
106. Dijkhuis G.C. Statistics and Structure of Ball Lightning. Proc. 3d Intern. Symp. on Ball Lightning (ISBL'92), 1992, Los Angeles, USA.
107. Смирнов Б.М. Наблюдательные свойства шаровой молнии //Успехи физических наук. 1992. Т. 162, № 8. С. 43 - 81.
108. Стаханов И.П. Физическая природа шаровой молнии. — М.: Атомиздат, 1979.
109. Стаханов И.П. О физической природе шаровой молнии. — М.: Энергоатомиздат, 1985.
110. Brand W. Der Kugelblitz. - Hamburg: Henri Grand Verlag, 1923.
111. Roth, J. Reece, Ball lightning: what nature is trying to tell the plasma research community// Fusion Technology 1995; V. 27, P. 255-270.
112. Byturin V., Bocharov A., Klimov A.,et.al., Analysis of Non-Thermal Plasma Aerodynamics Effects, 44 AIAA Aerospace Sciences Meeting & Exhibit. AIAA 2006-1209, 9-12 January 2006, Reno, NV, 1. 2. th. p.8.
113. Klimov A.I., Int. Journ. Unconventional Electromagnetics and Plasmas (UEP), 2011, V.3, N. 1-2, P. 55.
114. Егоров А.И., Степанов С.И. Долгоживущие плазмоиды — аналоги шаровой молнии, возникающие во влажном воздухе // Журн. технической физики. 2002. Т. 72. № 12. С. 104.
115. Oreshko A.G. // Proc. XVIII Int. Conf. on Gas Discharge and Their Applications. Greifswald, 2010. P. 526.
116. Schrödinger E.. Quantisierung als Eigenwertproblem (Erste Mitteilung) // Annalen der Physik. Vol. 384 (79). P. 361—376. (1926)

117. Schrödinger E.. Quantisierung als Eigenwertproblem (Zweite Mitteilung) // Annalen der Physik. Vol. 384 (79). P. 489—527 (1926)
118. Schrödinger E.. Über das Verhältnis der Heisenberg-Born-Jordanschen Quantenmechanik zu der meinem // Annalen der Physik. Vol. 384 (79). P. 734—756 (1926)
119. Schrödinger E.. Quantisierung als Eigenwertproblem (Dritte Mitteilung) // Annalen der Physik. Vol. 385 (80). P. 437—490 (1926)
120. Schrödinger E.. Quantisierung als Eigenwertproblem (Vierte Mitteilung) // Annalen der Physik. Vol. 386 (81). P. 109—139 (1926)
121. Bhatnagar P.L., Gross E.P., Krook M.A. Model for Collision Processes in Gases. *Physical Review*, vol. 94, pp.511-525, (1954)
122. Holway L.H.. New statistical models for kinetic theory: methods of construction. *Physics of Fluids.* vol. 9, pp. 1658-1673. (1966) DOI: 10.1063/11.1761920
123. Shahov E.M. Generalization of the Krook kinetic equation. *Izvestiya Akademii Nauk SSSR. Mekhanika Zhidkosti I Gaza.* No.5, pp. 142-145 (in Russian) (1968). (English version: *Fluid Dynamics*, No.5, pp. 95-96. DOI: 10.1007/BF0109546)
124. Struchtrup H., The BGK model with velocity depending collision frequency. *Continuum Mechanics and Thermodynamics,* vol.9, no. 1, pp. 23-31, (1997) DOI: 10.1007/s001610050053
125. Cheng Y., Struchtrup H. Ellipsoidal statistical Bhatnagar-Gross-Krook model with velocity-dependent collision frequency. *Physics of Fluids,* vol. 17, pp. 127103. (2005) DOI: 1063/1.2140710
126. Brillouin L. La théorie des quanta et l'atome de Bohr. (Chapter 7), Blanchard, Paris, 1922.
127. Boltzmann L. Prinzipe der Mechanik. J.-A. Barth, Leipzig, 1897.
128. Bohr N., "On the Constitution of Atoms and Molecules," Philosophical Magazine, 26, 476 (1913)
129. Schrödinger E., "Are There Quantum Jumps?" British Journal for the Philosophy of Science, 3, 109 and 233 (1952).
130. Minev Z.K., Mundhada S.O., Shankar S., Reinhold P., Gutierrez-Jauregui R., Schoelkopf R.J., Mirrahimi M., Carmichael H.J., Devoret M.H.. To catch and reverse a quantum jump mid-flight. arXiv:1803.00545 [quant-ph]
131. Wietfeldt F.E., M. Huber, Black T.C., Kaiser H., Arif M., Jacobson D.L., and Werner S.A. Measuring the Neutron's Mean Square Charge Radius Using Neutron Interferometry. arXiv:nucl-ex/0509018 v1 14 Sep 2005

132. Miller G.A.. Charge densities of the neutron and proton. arXiv:0705.2409v3 [nucl-th] 19 Nov 2007.
133. Miller G.A., Arrington J.R. The neutron negative central charge density: an inclusive-exclusive connection, Phys. Rev. C78, 032201 (2008).
134. Miller G.A., Singular Charge Density at the Center of the Pion?, Phys. Rev. C 79, 055204 (2009).
135. Cloet I., Miller G.A., Piasetzsky E., Ron G., Neutron Properties in the Medium", I. Cloet, accepted PRL Phys. Rev. Lett.103, 082301 (2009) [arXiv:0903.1312 [nucl-th]
136. Rinehimer J.A., Miller G.A., Neutron Charge Density from Simple Pion Cloud Models, Phys. Rev. C 80, 025206 (2009).
137. Miller G.A., and Arrington J., "The Inclusive-Exclusive Connection and the Neutron Negative Central Charge Density," Int. J. Mod. Phys. E 18, 1809 (2009).
138. Miller G.A., Wagman M. Charge Symmetry Breaking and Parity Violating Electron-Proton Scattering, Phys. Rev. C 89, 065206 (2014), arXiv:1402.7169 [nucl-th]
139. Miller G.A., Charge Symmetry Breaking in Electromagnetic Nucleon Form Factors in Elastic Parity-Violating Electron-Nucleus Scattering," Phys. Rev. C91, 055503 (2015) [arXiv:1412.5515 [nucl-th]].
140. Schrödinger E. What is life? *The Physical Aspect of the Living Cell.* Lections in Trinity College delivered in Dublin in February, 1943. See also; Что такое жизнь? Москва: Государственное издательство иностранной литературы, 1947 - с.150.
141. *The Mutation Theory: Experiments and Observations on the Origin of Species in the Vegetable Kingdom* (German edition, 1900—1903), (English edition, 1910—1911).
142. Chandrasekhar, S. (1958) [first edition 1939]. An Introduction to the Study of Stellar Structure. New York: Dover. ISBN 0-486-60413-6.
143. Chandrasekhar, S. (2005) [first edition 1942]. Principles of Stellar Dynamics. New York: Dover. ISBN 0-486-44273-X.
144. Wheeler, John Archibald (2000). Exploring Black Holes: Introduction to General Relativity. Addison Wesley. ISBN 0-201-38423-X.
145. Hawking, S W, Gravitationally collapsed objects of very low mass, *Monthly Notices of the Royal Astronomical Society*, Vol. 152, 1971, p. 75.
146. Alexeev B.V. Application of the Non-Local Physics in the Theory of the Matter Movement in Black Hole // *J. Modern Physics*. V. 4. p. 42–49 (2013)

doi:10.4236/jmp.2013.47A1005. Published Online July 2013 (http://www.scirp.org/journal/jmp)
147. Shevelev Yu D, Andrushchenko V A, Murashkin I V, Numerical Solution of the Problem of the Theory of Point Explosion in Lagrangian Coordinates. Some New Results. *Mathematical Modeling*, v. 23, (2011), (in Russian).
148. Sedov L. I., the Movement of air in a strong explosion // DAN SSSR, 1946, vol. 52, No. 1, pp. 17–20.
149. Taylor G. The formation of a blast wave by a very intense explosion // Proc. Roy. Soc., London, 1950, A. 201, No. 1065, p.159-186.
150. Zeldovich Y. B., Raizer Yu. P. Physics of shock waves and the high-temperature gas dynamics phenomena. – M.: Nauka, 1963, 632c.
151. Kestenbaum, H. S., Roslyakov G. S., and L. A. Chudov L. A., A Point explosion. (Methods of calculation. The tables). –M.: Nauka, 1974, 255p.
152. Korobeinikov V. P. Problems in the theory of point explosion. – M.: Nauka, 1985, 400 p.
153. Kestenbaum, H. S., Turkish F. D., Chudov L.A., Shevelev Yu. D. Eulerian and Lagrangian methods for calculation of a point explosion in an inhomogeneous atmosphere. *Numerical methods in gas dynamics*. Second International Colloquium on the dynamics of explosion and reactive systems. Vol. 3. Novosibirsk, 19-23 Aug. 1969. – M.: pp. 85–97.
154. Shevelev Yu. D. Spatial problems of computational Aero-and hydrodynamics. – M.: Nauka, 1986, 368c.
155. Robert M. Wald. General relativity. — University of Chicago Press, 1984. — ISBN 978-0-226-87033-5.
156. Poplawski N. J., Radial motion into an Einstein - Rosen bridge, Physics Letters B, Vol. 687, Nos. 2-3 (2010) pp. 110–113.
157. McHardy I.M., Koerding E., Knigge C., et al., Active galactic nuclei as scaled-up Galactic black holes. Nature 444, 730 (2006) doi:10.1038/nature05389
158. Markov M.A. “Maximon” and “minimon” in the light of a possible formulation of the concept of an “elementary particle”, Pis'ma v Zhurnal Eksperimental'noi i Teoreticheskoi Fiziki (ISSN 0370-274X), vol. 45, Feb. 10, 1987, p. 115-117. In Russian.
159. Piotrovich, M.Y., Silant’ev, N.A., Gnedin, Y.N. et al. Magnetic fields and quasi-periodic oscillations of black hole radiation. Astrophys. Bull. (2011) 66: 320. https://doi.org/10.1134/S1990341311030047

160. Frolov, Valeri; Zelnikov, Andrei (2011). Introduction to Black Hole Physics. Oxford. p. 168. *ISBN 0-19-969229-7.*
161. Schutz B.F. Detection of gravitational waves in Proceedings of “Astrophysical sources of gravitational radiation”, J.A. Marck and J.P. Lasota Eds., Cambridge Univ. Press (1996)
162. Castelvecchi, Davide; Witze, Witze (11 February 2016). "Einstein's gravitational waves found at last". Nature News. doi:10.1038/nature.2016.19361. Retrieved 2016-02-11.
163. Abbott BP, et al. (LIGO Scientific Collaboration and Virgo Collaboration) (2016). "Observation of Gravitational Waves from a Binary Black Hole Merger". Physical Review Letters. **116** (6): 061102. arXiv:1602.03837. Bibcode:2016PhRvL.116f1102A. doi:10.1103/PhysRevLett.116.061102. PMID 26918975.
164. R.J. Shawyer, Microwave propulsion – progress in the EmDrive programme SPR Ltd UKIAC-08-C4.4.7, Glasgow, 2008.
165. Shawyer, Roger, "Second generation EmDrive propulsion applied to SSTO launcher and interstellar probe" (PDF). Acta Astronautica. 116: 166–174. (1 November 2015). doi:10.1016/j.actaastro.2015.07.002. (1 November 2015).
166. Juan Yang, et al., Prediction and Experimental Measurement of the Electromagnetic Thrust Generated by Microwave Thruster System, NWPU Xi'an China, Chinese Physical Society and IOP Publishing Ltd., 2013.
167. Yang, J.; Liu, X.-C.; Wang, Y.-G.; Tang, M.-J.; Luo, L.-T.; Jin, Y.-Z.; Ning, Z.-X. (February 2016). "Thrust Measurement of an Independent Microwave Thruster Propulsion Device with Three-Wire Torsion Pendulum Thrust Measurement System". Journal of Propulsion Technology (in Chinese). 37 (2): 362–371.
168. D. Brady, et al., Anomalous thrust production from an RF test device measured on a low thrust torsion pendulum. NASA USA IAA Joint Propulsion Conference, Cleveland, 2014.
169. H. White, P. March, W. Nehemiah, W. O'Neill, Eagleworks Laboratories: Advanced Propulsion Physics Research. NASA Technical Reports Server (NTRS) (Technical report). NASA. JSC-CN-25207 (5 December 2011).
170. H. White, P. March, J. Lawrence, J Vera, A. Sylvester, D. Brady and P. Bailey, Thrust from a Closed Radio-Frequency Cavity in Vacuum, NASA Johnson Space Center, Houston, Texas 77058 DOI: 10.2514/1.B36120, Journal of Propulsion and Power, Vol. 33, No. 4, July–August 2017, p. 830-841.

171. Lebedew P., Untersuchungen über die Druckkräfte des Lichtes, «Annalen der Physik», 1901, fasc. 4, Bd 6, S. 433—458. DOI: https://dx.doi.org/10.1002/andp.19013111102;
172. Munday, J.N.; Capasso, F.; Parsegian, V.A. (2009). "Measured long-range repulsive Casimir-Lifshitz forces". Nature. 457 (7226): 170–3. Bibcode:2009Natur.457..170M. doi:10.1038/nature07610. PMC 4169270. PMID 19129843.
173. Derjaguin, B. V., Abrikosova, I. I. & Lifshitz, E. M. Direct measurement of molecular attraction between solids separated by a narrow gap. Q. Rev. Chem. Soc. 10, 295–329 (1956)
174. van Blokland, P. H. G. M. & Overbeek, J. T. G. van der Waals forces between objects covered with a chrome layer. J. Chem. Soc. Faraday Trans. I 74, 2637–2651 (1978)
175. Lamoreaux, S. K. Demonstration of the Casimir force in the 0.6 to 6 μm range. Phys. Rev. Lett. 78, 5–8 (1997)
176. Casimir, H. B. G. On the attraction between two perfectly conducting plates. Proc. K. Ned. Akad. Wet. 51, 793–795 (1948)
177. Casimir, H. B. G. & Polder, D. The influence of retardation on the London-van der Waals forces. Phys. Rev. 73, 360–372 (1948)
178. Lifshitz, E. M. The theory of molecular attractive forces between solids. Sov. Phys. JETP 2, 73–83 (1956)
179. Harold White, Jerry Vera, Paul Bailey, Paul March, Tim Lawrence, Andre Sylvester, David Brady, Dynamics of the Vacuum and Casimir Analogs to the Hydrogen Atom. Journal of Modern Physics, Vol.6 No.9, August 2015, NASA Johnson Space Center, Houston, TX, USA.
180. Measurement of the total cross section from elastic scattering in pp collisions at ps = 7 TeV with the ATLAS detector. EUROPEAN ORGANISATION FOR NUCLEAR RESEARCH (CERN), CERN-PH-EP-2014-177 Submitted to: Nuclear Physics B. See also: arXiv:1408.5778v2 [hep-ex] 7 Nov 2014.
181. Alexeev B.V. To the nonlocal theory of waves in physical vacuum. Advances in Astrophysics, Vol. 3, No. 1, February 2018 https://dx.doi.org/10.22606/adap.2018.31001.
182. Earnshaw, S, On the nature of the molecular forces which regulate the constitution of the luminiferous ether, *Trans. Cambridge Phil. Soc.* 7, 97-112, 1842.

183. Berry, M.V. and Geim, A.K., “Of flying frogs and levitrons”, *Euro. J. Phys.*, **18**, 307–313 (1997) and http://wwwhfml. sci.kun.nl/hfml/levitate.html.
184. Geim, A.K., “Everyone’s Magnetism”, *Phys. Today*, **51** Sept., 36–39 (1998).
185. Geim, A. K, M. Simon, M.D., Boamfa, M.I. and Heflinger, O.L., “Magnet levitation at your fingertips”, *Nature*, **400**, 323–324 (1999).
186. Simon, M.D, Geim, A.K. “Diamagnetic levitation; Flying frogs and floating magnets”, *J. App. Phys.*, **87**, 6200–6204 (2000).
187. Berry, M.V. The LEVITRON and adiabatic trap for spins, *Proc. Roy Soc. Lond., A* (1996) 452, 1207-1220.
188. Harrigan, R.M., Levitation device, U.S. Patent $,382245, May 3, 1983.
189. Alexeev B.V., To the nonlocal theory of levitation. *International Journal of Astronomy, Astrophysics and Space Science* 2014; 1(5): 52-58. Published online January 20, 2015 (http://www.openscienceonline.com/journal/aass
190. *Poynting, J. H. "On the Transfer of Energy in the Electromagnetic Field".* Philosophical Transactions of the Royal Society of London, 1884, **175**: 343–361. *doi:10.1098/rstl.1884.0016.*
191. Рощин В.В., Годин С.М., Экспериментальное исследование физических эффектов в динамической магнитной системе. (Experimental investigation of physical effects in the dynamical magnetic system) Письма в ЖТФ, 2000, том 26, вып. 24, стр. 70-75.
192. Forward R.L., Negative Matter Propulsion, *Journal of Propulsion and Power*, Vol. 6, No., 1, 1990, pp. 28-37
193. Forward R.L., Propellantless Propulsion with Negative Matter Generated by Electric Charges, Joint Pripulsion Conference, July 14-17, 2013, San Jose, CA, 49th AIAA/ASME/SAE/ASEE Joint Propulsion Conference, AIAA 2013-3913, pp. 1-12.
194. Junginger J.E., and Popovic, Z.D., An experimental investigation of the influence of an electrostatic potential on electron mass as predicted by Weber’s force law, *Can. J. Phys.*, Vol. 82, 2004, pp. 731–735
195. Assis A.K.T., Changing the Inertial Mass of a Charged Particle, *Journal of the Physical Society of Japan,* Vol. 62, No. 5, 1993, pp. 1418-1422.

I want morebooks!

Buy your books fast and straightforward online - at one of world's fastest growing online book stores! Environmentally sound due to Print-on-Demand technologies.

Buy your books online at

www.morebooks.shop

Kaufen Sie Ihre Bücher schnell und unkompliziert online – auf einer der am schnellsten wachsenden Buchhandelsplattformen weltweit! Dank Print-On-Demand umwelt- und ressourcenschonend produzi ert.

Bücher schneller online kaufen

www.morebooks.shop

KS OmniScriptum Publishing
Brivibas gatve 197
LV-1039 Riga, Latvia
Telefax: +371 686 204 55

info@omniscriptum.com
www.omniscriptum.com

OMNIScriptum